Reveal the full potential in every student!

2 Explore and Develop

 LEARN

In the **Learn** section, students gain the foundational knowledge needed to actively work through upcoming Examples.

 EXAMPLES & CHECK

Students work through **Examples** related to the key concepts and engage in mathematical discourse.

Students complete a **Check** after several Examples as a quick formative assessment to help teachers adjust instruction as needed.

3 Reflect and Practice

 EXIT TICKET

The **Exit Ticket** gives students an opportunity to convey their understanding of the lesson concepts.

 PRACTICE

Students complete **Practice** exercises individually or collaboratively to solidify their understanding of lesson concepts and build proficiency with lesson skills.

D1308680

Reveal Math Key Areas of Focus

Reveal Algebra 1, Reveal Geometry, and *Reveal Algebra 2* (Reveal AGA) have a strong focus on rigor—especially the development of conceptual understanding—an emphasis on student mindset, and ongoing formative assessment feedback loops.

Rigor

Reveal AGA has been thoughtfully designed to incorporate a balance of the three elements of rigor: conceptual understanding, procedural skills and fluency, and application.

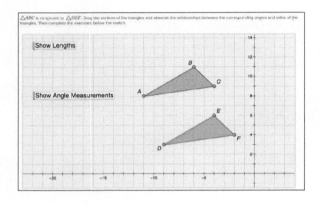

Conceptual Understanding

Explore activities give all students an opportunity to work collaboratively and discuss their thinking as they build conceptual understanding of new concepts. In the **Explore** activity to the left, students use **Web Sketchpad®** to build understanding of the relationships between corresponding sides and angles in congruent triangles.

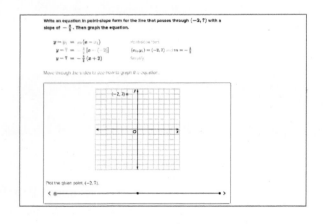

Procedural Skills and Fluency

Students use different strategies and tools to build procedural fluency. In the **Example** shown, students build proficiency with writing equations in point-slope form.

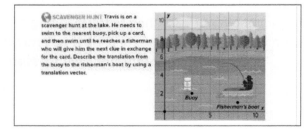

Application

Real-world examples and practice problems are opportunities for students to apply their learning to new situations. In the real-world example shown, students apply their understanding by solving a multi-step problem with translations.

Teacher Edition

Reveal GEOMETRY®

Volume 2

mheducation.com/prek-12

Copyright © 2020 McGraw-Hill Education

Cover: (t to b, l to r) Kenny McCartney/Moment Open/Getty Images; YinYang/E+/Getty Images;
nycshooter/Vetta/Getty Images; michaelgzc/E+/Getty Images

Send all inquiries to:
McGraw-Hill Education
8787 Orion Place
Columbus, OH 43240

ISBN: 978-0-07-662601-4 (*Interactive Student Edition*, Volume 1)
MHID: 0-07-662601-6 (*Interactive Student Edition*, Volume 1)
ISBN: 978-0-07-899749-5 (*Interactive Student Edition*, Volume 2)
MHID: 0-07-899749-6 (*Interactive Student Edition*, Volume 2)

ISBN: 978-0-07-899750-1 (*Reveal Geometry Teacher Edition*, Volume 1)
MHID: 0-07-899750-X (*Reveal Geometry Teacher Edition*, Volume 1)
ISBN: 978-0-07-899751-8 (*Reveal Geometry Teacher Edition*, Volume 2)
MHID: 0-07-899751-8 (*Reveal Geometry Teacher Edition*, Volume 2)

Printed in the United States of America.

6 7 8 9 10 WEB 27 26 25 24 23 22 21

Contents in Brief

Reveal Math Guiding Principles

Academic research and the science of learning provide the foundation for this powerful K–12 math program designed to help reveal the mathematician in every student.

Reveal Math is built on a solid foundation of **RESEARCH** that shaped the **PEDAGOGY** of the program.

Reveal Algebra 1, Reveal Geometry, and *Reveal Algebra 2* (Reveal AGA) used findings from research on teaching and learning mathematics to develop its instructional model. Based on analyses of research findings, these areas form the foundational structure of the program:

- Rigor
- Productive Struggle
- Formative Assessment
- Rich Tasks
- Mathematical Discourse
- Collaborative Learning

Instructional Model

1 Launch

 WARM UP

 LAUNCH THE LESSON

 EXPLORE

During the **Warm Up,** students complete exercises to activate prior knowledge and review prerequisite concepts and skills.

In **Launch the Lesson**, students view a real-world scenario and image to pique their interest in the lesson content. They are introduced to questions that they will be able to answer at the end of the lesson.

During the **Explore** activity, students work in partners or small groups to explore a rich mathematical problem related to the lesson content.

 INDIVIDUAL ACTIVITY

 GROUP ACTIVITY

 CLASS ACTIVITY

Student Mindset

Mindset Matters tips located in each module provide specific examples of how Reveal AGA content can be used to promote a growth mindset in all students. Another feature focused on promoting a growth mindset is **Ignite! Activities** developed by Dr. Raj Shah to spark student curiosity about why the math works. An **Ignite!** delivers problem sets that are flexible enough so that students with varying background knowledge can engage with the content and motivates them to ask questions, solve complex problems, and develop a can-do attitude toward math.

Teacher Edition Mindset Tip

Student Ignite! Activity

Formative Assessment

The key to reaching all learners is to adjust instruction based on each student's understanding. Reveal AGA offers powerful formative assessment tools that help teachers to efficiently and effectively differentiate instruction for all students.

Math Probes

Each module includes a **Cheryl Tobey Formative Assessment Math Probe** that is focused on addressing student misconceptions about key math topics. Students can complete these probes at the beginning, middle, or end of a module. The teacher support includes a list of recommended differentiated resources that teachers assign based on students' responses.

Example Checks

After multiple examples, a formative assessment **Check** that students complete on their own allows teachers to gauge students' understanding of the concept or skill presented. When students complete the Check online, the teacher receives resource recommendations which can be assigned to students.

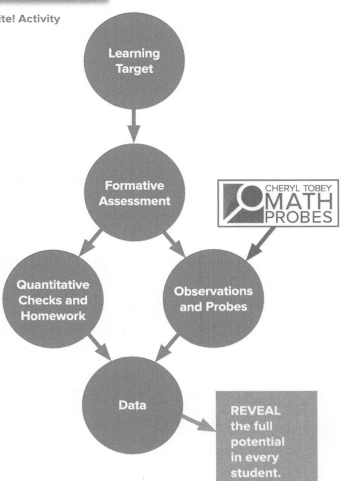

A Powerful Blended Learning Experience

The *Reveal Algebra 1, Reveal Geometry,* and *Reveal Algebra 2* (Reveal AGA) blended learning experience was designed to include purposeful print and digital components focused on sparking student curiosity and providing teachers with flexible implementation options.

Reveal AGA has been thoughtfully developed to provide a rich learning experience no matter where a district, school, or classroom falls on the digital spectrum. All of the instructional content can be projected or can be accessed via desktop, laptop, or tablet.

Lesson

1 Launch

👥 WARM UP	👥 LAUNCH THE LESSON	👥 EXPLORE

The **Warm Up** exercise can be projected on an interactive whiteboard.	**Launch the Lesson** can be projected or assigned to students to access on their own devices.	The **Explore** activity can be projected while students record their observations in the Interactive Student Edition or can be assigned for students to complete on individual devices.

Launch the Lesson

Explore

👤 INDIVIDUAL ACTIVITY	🖥️ INTERACTIVE PRESENTATION
👥 GROUP ACTIVITY	📖 PRINT INTERACTIVE STUDENT EDITION
👥 CLASS ACTIVITY	

2 Explore and Develop

LEARN

As students are introduced to the key lesson concepts, they can progress through the **Learn** by recording guided notes in their Interactive Student Edition or on their own devices.

EXAMPLES & CHECK

In their Interactive Student Edition or on an individual device, students work through one or more **Examples** related to key lesson concepts.

A **Check** follows several Examples in either the Interactive Student Edition or on each student device.

3 Reflect and Practice

EXIT TICKET

The **Exit Ticket** is projected or accessed via student devices to provide students with lesson closure and an opportunity to revisit the lesson concepts.

PRACTICE

Assign students **Practice** problems from their Interactive Student Edition or create a digital assignment for them to work on their device in class or at home to solidify lesson concepts.

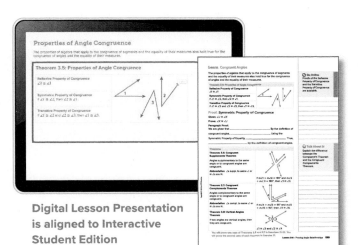

Digital Lesson Presentation is aligned to Interactive Student Edition

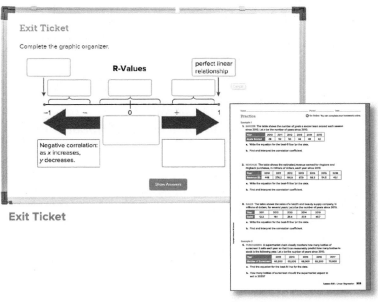

Exit Ticket

Practice

Supporting All Learners

The *Reveal Algebra 1, Reveal Geometry,* and *Reveal Algebra 2* (Reveal AGA) programs were designed so that all students have access to:

- rich tasks that promote productive struggle,
- opportunities to develop proficiency with the habits of mind and thinking strategies of mathematicians, and
- prompts to promote mathematical discourse and build academic language.

Resources for Differentiating Instruction

When needed, resources are available to differentiate math instruction for students who may need to see a concept in a different way, practice prerequisite skills, or are ready to extend their learning.

 Approaching Level Resources

- Remediation Activities
- Extra Examples

BL **Beyond Level Resources**

- Beyond Level Differentiated Activities
- Extension Activities

Resources for English Language Learners

Reveal AGA also includes student and teacher resources to support students who are simultaneously learning grade-level math and building their English proficiency. Appropriate, research-based language scaffolds are also provided to support students as they engage in rigorous mathematical tasks and discussions.

 English Language Learners

- Spanish Interactive Student Edition
- Spanish Personal Tutors
- Math Language-Building Activities
- Language Scaffolds
- *Think About It!* and *Talk About It!* Prompts
- Multilingual eGlossary
- Audio
- Graphic Organizers
- Web Sketchpad, Desmos, and eTools

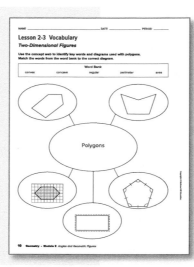

Developing Mathematical Thinking and Strategic Questioning

Reveal Algebra 1, Reveal Geometry, and *Reveal Algebra 2* (Reveal AGA) are comprised of high-quality math content designed to be accessible and relevant to each student. Throughout the program, students are presented with a variety of thoughtfully designed questioning strategies related to the content. Using these questions provides you with an additional, built-in type of formative assessment that can be used to modify instruction. They also strengthen students' ownership of mathematical content knowledge and daily use of the Standards for Mathematical Practice.

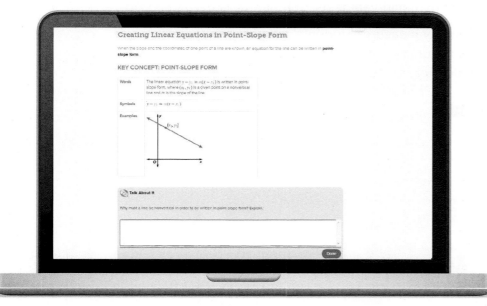

Key Concept Introduction followed by a Talk About It question to discuss with a classmate.

You will find these types of questioning strategies throughout Reveal AGA. The related Standard for Mathematical Practice for each is also indicated.

- **Talk About It** questions encourage students to engage in mathematical discourse with classmates (SMP3)

- **Alternate Method** shows students another way to solve a problem and asks them to compare and contrast the methods and solutions (SMP1)

- **Avoid a Common Error** shows students a problem similar to an example but with a flaw in reasoning, and students have to find and explain the error (SMP3)

- **State Your Assumptions** requires that student state the assumptions they made to solve a problem (SMP4)

- **Use a Source** asks students to find information using an external source, such as the Internet, and use it to pose or solve a problem (SMP5)

- **Think About It** questions help students make sense of mathematical problems (SMP1)

- **Concept Checks** prompt students to analyze how the Key Concepts of the lesson apply to various use cases (SMP3)

Reveal Student Readiness with Individualized Learning Tools

Reveal Algebra 1, Reveal Geometry, and *Reveal Algebra 2* (Reveal AGA) incorporate innovative, technology-based tools that are designed to extend the teacher's reach in the classroom to help address a wide range of knowledge gaps, set and align academic goals, and meet student individualized learning needs.

LEARNSMART®

Topic-Mastery

With embedded **LearnSmart,**® students have a built-in study partner for topic practice and review to prepare for multi-module or mid-year tests.

LearnSmart's revolutionary adaptive technology measures students' awareness of their own learning, time on topic, answer accuracy, and suggests alternative resources to support student learning, confidence, and topic mastery.

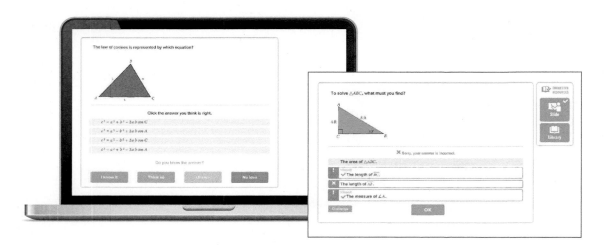

ALEKS®

Individualized Learning Pathways

Learners of all levels benefit from the use of **ALEKS'** adaptive, online math technology designed to pinpoint what each student knows, does not know, and most importantly, what each student is ready to learn.

When paired with Reveal AGA, **ALEKS** is a powerful tool designed to provide integrated instructionally actionable data enabling teachers to utilize Reveal AGA resources for individual students, groups, or the entire classroom.

Activity Report

Powerful Tools for Modeling Mathematics

Reveal Algebra 1, Reveal Geometry, and *Reveal Algebra 2* (Reveal AGA) have been designed with purposeful, embedded digital tools to increase student engagement and provide unique modeling opportunities.

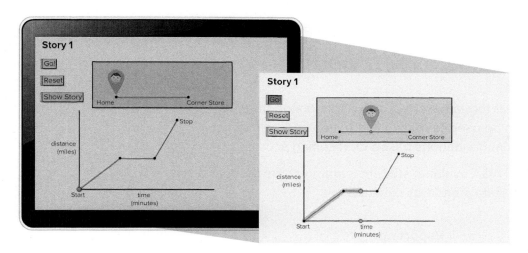

Web Sketchpad® Activities

The leading dynamic mathematics visualization software has now been integrated with **Web Sketchpad Activities** at point of use within Reveal AGA. Student exploration (and practice) using **Web Sketchpad** encourages problem solving and visualization of abstract math concepts.

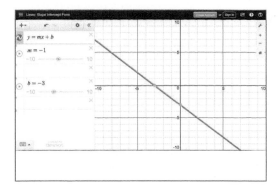

desmos

The powerful **Desmos** graphing calculator is available in Reveal AGA for students to explore, model, and apply math to the real-world.

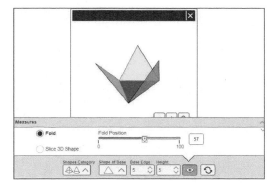

eTools

By using a wide variety of digital **eTools** embedded within Reveal AGA, students gain additional hands-on experience while they learn and teachers have the option to create problem-based learning opportunities.

Technology-Enhanced Items

Embedded within the digital lesson, technology-enhanced items—such as drag-and-drop, flashcard flips, or diagram completion—are strategically placed to give students the practice with common computer functions needed to master computer-based testing.

TYPE	SWIPE
DRAG & DROP	FLASHCARDS
eTOOLS	MULTI-SELECT
WATCH	EXPAND

Assessment Tools to Reveal Student Progress and Success

Reveal Algebra 1, Reveal Geometry, and *Reveal Algebra 2* (Reveal AGA) provide a comprehensive array of assessment tools, with both print and digital administration options, to measure student understanding and progress. The digital assessment tools include next-generation assessment items, such as multiple-response, selected-response, and technology-enhanced items.

Assessment Solutions

Reveal AGA provides embedded, regular formative checkpoints to monitor student learning and provide feedback that can be used to modify instruction and help direct student learning using reports and recommendations based on resulting scores.

Summative assessments built in Reveal AGA evaluate student learning at the module conclusion by comparing it against the state standards covered.

Formative Assessment Resources
- Cheryl Tobey Formative Assessment Math Probes
- Checks
- Exit Tickets
- Put It All Together

Summative Assessment Resources
- Module Tests
- Performance Tasks
- End-of-Course Tests
- LearnSmart

Reporting

Clear, instructionally actionable data is a click away with the Reveal AGA Reporting Dashboard.

Activity Report Real-time class and student reporting of activities completed by the class. Includes average score, submission rate, and skills covered for the class and each student.

- **Item Analysis Report** A detailed analysis of response rates and patterns, answers, and question types in a class snapshot or by student.

Standards Report Performance data by class or individual student are aggregated by standards, skills, or objectives linked to the related activities completed.

Or **Build Your Own** assessments focused on standards or objectives. Access to banks of questions, including those with tech-enhanced capabilities, enable a wide range of options to mirror high-stakes assessment formats.

Activity Report

Professional Development Support for Continuous Learning

McGraw-Hill Education supports lifelong learning and demonstrates commitment to teachers with a built-in professional learning environment designed for support during planning or extended learning opportunities.

What You Will Find

- Best-practice resources
- Implementation support
- Teaching Strategies
- Classroom Videos
- Math Misconception Videos
- Content and Pedagogy Videos
- Content Progression Information

Why Professional Development Is so Important

- Research-based understanding of student learning
- Improved student performance
- Evidence-based instructional best practices
- Collaborative content strategy planning
- Extended knowledge of program how-to's

Kevin Dodge/Blend Images/Getty Images

Reveal Math Expert Advisors

Cathy Seeley, Ed.D.

Austin, Texas

Mathematics educator, speaker, and writer, former Senior Fellow at the Charles A. Dana Center at The University of Texas at Austin, past President of NCTM, former Director of K-12 Mathematics for the State of Texas

Areas of expertise:
Mathematics Teaching, Equity, Assessment, STEM Learning, Informal Learning, Upside-Down Teaching, Productive Struggling, Mathematical Practices, Mathematical Habits of Mind, Family and Community Outreach, Mathematics Education Policy, Advocacy

"We want students to believe deeply that mathematics makes sense—in generating answers to problems, discussing their thinking and other students' thinking, and learning new material."

—Seeley, 2016, Making Sense of Math

Cheryl R. Tobey, M.Ed.

Gardiner, Maine

Senior Mathematics Associate at Education Development Center (EDC)

Areas of expertise:
Formative assessment and professional development for mathematics teachers; tools and strategies to uncovering misconceptions

"Misunderstandings and partial understandings develop as a normal part of learning mathematics. Our job as educators is to minimize the chances of students' harboring misconceptions by knowing the potential difficulties students are likely to encounter, using assessments to elicit misconceptions and implementing instruction designed to build new and accurate mathematical ideas."

—Tobey, et al 2007, 2009, 2010, 2013, 2104, Uncovering Student Thinking Series

Nevels Nevels, Ph.D.

Saint Louis, Missouri

PK-12 Mathematics Curriculum Coordinator for Hazelwood School District

Areas of expertise:
Mathematics Teacher Education; Student Agency & Identity; Socio-Cultural Perspective in Mathematics Learning

"A school building is one setting for learning mathematics. It is understood that all children should be expected to learn meaningful mathematics within its walls. Additionally, teachers should be expected to learn within the walls of this same building. More poignantly, I posit that if teachers are not learning mathematics in their school building, then it is not a school."

—Nevels, 2018

Raj Shah, Ph.D.

Columbus, Ohio

Founder of Math Plus Academy, a STEM enrichment program and founding member of The Global Math Project

Areas of expertise:
Sparking student curiosity, promoting productive struggle, and creating math experiences that kids love

"As teachers, it's imperative that we start every lesson by getting students to ask more questions because curiosity is the fuel that drives engagement, deeper learning and perseverance."

—Shah, 2017

Walter Secada, Ph.D.

Coral Gables, Florida

Professor of Teaching and Learning at the University of Miami

Areas of expertise:
Improving education for English language learners, equity in education, mathematics education, bilingual education, school restructuring, professional development of teachers, student engagement, Hispanic dropout and prevention, and reform

"The best lessons take place when teachers have thought about how their individual English language learners will respond not just to the mathematical content of that lesson, but also to its language demands and mathematical practices."

—Secada, 2018

Ryan Baker, Ph.D.

Philadelphia, Pennsylvania

Associate Professor and Director of Penn Center for Learning Analytics at the University of Pennsylvania

Areas of expertise:
Interactions between students and educational software; data mining and learning analytics to understand student learning

"The ultimate goal of the field of Artificial Intelligence in Education is not to promote artificial intelligence, but to promote education... systems that are designed intelligently, and that leverage teachers' intelligence. Modern online learning systems used at scale are leveraging human intelligence to improve their design, and they're bringing human beings into the decision-making loop and trying to inform them."

—Baker, 2016

Chris Dede, Ph.D.

Cambridge, Massachusetts

Timothy E. Wirth Professor in Learning Technologies at Harvard Graduate School of Education

Areas of expertise:
Provides leadership in educational innovation; educational improvements using technology

"People are very diverse in how they prefer to learn. Good instruction is like an ecosystem that has many niches for alternative types of learning: lectures, games, engaging video-based animations, readings, etc. Learners then can navigate to the niche that best fulfills their current needs."

—Dede, 2017

Dinah Zike, M.Ed.

Comfort, Texas

President of Dinah.com in San Antonio, Texas and Dinah Zike Academy

Areas of expertise:
Developing educational materials that include three-dimensional graphic organizers; interactive notebook activities for differentiation; and kinesthetic, cross-curricular manipulatives

"It is education's responsibility to meet the unique needs of students, and not the students' responsibility to meet education's need for uniformity."

—Zike, 2017, InRIGORating Math Notebooks

Reveal Everything Needed for Effective Instruction

Reveal Algebra 1, Reveal Geometry, and *Reveal Algebra 2* (Reveal AGA) provide both print and innovative, technology-based tools designed to address a wide range of classrooms. No matter whether you're in a 1:1 district, or have a classroom projector, Reveal AGA provides you with the resources you need for a rich learning experience.

Blended Classrooms

Focused on projection of the **Interactive Presentation**, students follow along, taking notes and working through problems in their Interactive Student Edition during class time. Also included in the Interactive Student Edition is a glossary, selected answers, and a reference sheet.

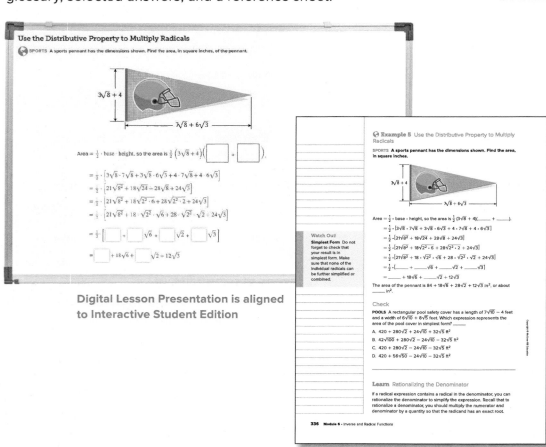

Digital Lesson Presentation is aligned to Interactive Student Edition

Andrey_Kuzmin/iStock/Getty Images / KLND

Digital Classrooms

Projection is a focal point for key areas of the course with students interacting with the lesson using their own devices. Each student can access teacher-assigned sections of the lessons for **Explore** activities, **Learn** sections, and **Examples**. Point of use videos, animations, as well as interactive content enable students to experience math in interesting and impactful ways.

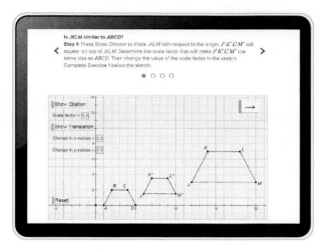

Web Sketchpad

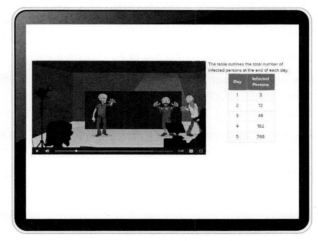

Desmos

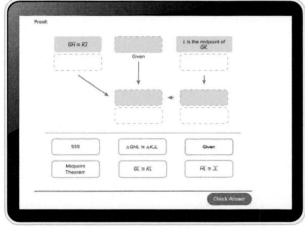

Drag-and-Drop

Video

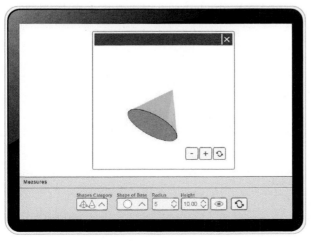

eTools

In Reveal AGA,
R is for—

- Research
- Rigor
- Relevant Connections

Are you...
READY to start?

Module 1
Tools of Geometry

Module 2
Angles and Geometric Figures

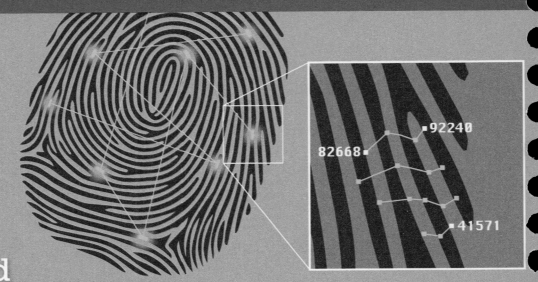

Module 3
Logical Arguments and Line Relationships

Module 4

Transformations and Symmetry

Module 5
Triangles and Congruence

Module 6
Relationships in Triangles

Module 7
Quadrilaterals

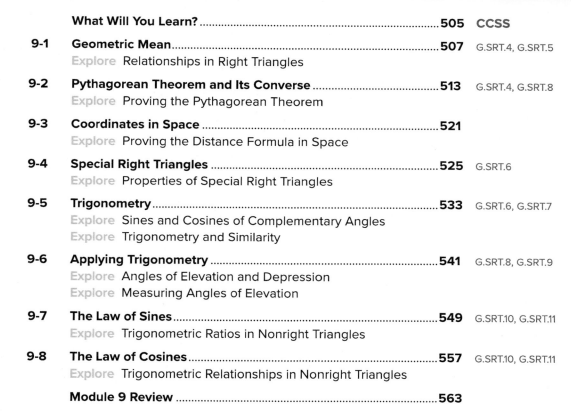

Module 9

Right Triangles and Trigonometry

Module 9
Right Triangles and Trigonometry

Module 10
Circles

Module 11
Measurement

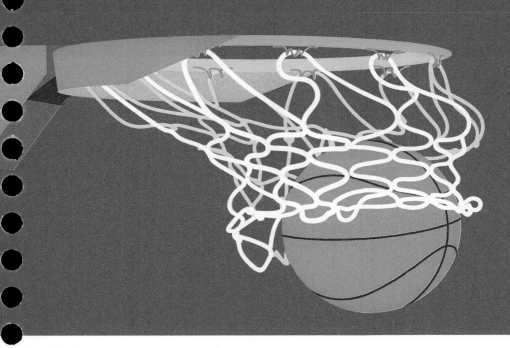

Module 12
Probability

Standards for Mathematical Content, Geometry

This correlation shows the alignment of *Reveal Geometry* to the Standards for Mathematical Content, Geometry, from the Common Core State Standards for Mathematics. Lessons in which the standard is the primary focus are indicated in **bold**.

Additional mathematics that students should learn in order to take advanced mathematical courses is indicated by (+).

Standard		Lesson(s)
Geometry		
Congruence G-CO		
G.CO.1	Experiment with transformations in the plane. Know precise definitions of angle, circle, perpendicular line, parallel line, and line segment, based on the undefined notions of point, line, distance along a line, and distance around a circular arc.	**1-2, 1-3, 1-4, 2-1, 2-2, 3-7, 10-1**
G.CO.2	Represent transformations in the plane using, e.g., transparencies and geometry software; describe transformations as functions that take points in the plane as inputs and give other points as outputs. Compare transformations that preserve distance and angle to those that do not (e.g., translation versus horizontal stretch).	**2-4, 8-1**
G.CO.3	Given a rectangle, parallelogram, trapezoid, or regular polygon, describe the rotations and reflections that carry it onto itself.	**4-6**
G.CO.4	Develop definitions of rotations, reflections, and translations in terms of angles, circles, perpendicular lines, parallel lines, and line segments.	**4-1, 4-2, 4-3,** 4-5, 4-6
G.CO.5	Given a geometric figure and a rotation, reflection, or translation, draw the transformed figure using, e.g., graph paper, tracing paper, or geometry software. Specify a sequence of transformations that will carry a given figure onto another.	**4-1, 4-2, 4-3, 4-4, 4-5, 4-6**
G.CO.6	Understand congruence in terms of rigid motions. Use geometric descriptions of rigid motions to transform figures and to predict the effect of a given rigid motion on a given figure; given two figures, use the definition of congruence in terms of rigid motions to decide if they are congruent.	**4-1, 4-2, 4-3, 4-4,** 4-6
G.CO.7	Use the definition of congruence in terms of rigid motions to show that two triangles are congruent if and only if corresponding pairs of sides and corresponding pairs of angles are congruent.	**5-2**
G.CO.8	Explain how the criteria for triangle congruence (ASA, SAS, and SSS) follow from the definition of congruence in terms of rigid motions.	**5-3, 5-4**
G.CO.9	Prove geometric theorems. Prove theorems about lines and angles.	**3-5, 3-6, 3-7, 3-9, 6-1,** 6-2
G.CO.10	Prove theorems about triangles.	**5-1, 5-4, 5-5, 5-6, 5-7, 6-1,** 6-2, 6-3, 6-4, 6-5, 6-6, 6-7, 8-5
G.CO.11	Prove theorems about parallelograms.	**7-2, 7-3, 7-4, 7-5**
G.CO.12	Make geometric constructions. Make formal geometric constructions with a variety of tools and methods (compass and straightedge, string, reflective devices, paper folding, dynamic geometric software, etc.).	**1-3, 1-7, 2-1, 2-2, 3-5, 3-9, 3-10, 4-1, 5-3, 5-4, 5-6, 6-1, 6-2, 6-3, 7-3, 7-4, 7-5, 8-5, 10-3, 10-5**
G.CO.13	Construct an equilateral triangle, a square, and a regular hexagon inscribed in a circle.	**10-3, 10-5**
Similarity, Right Triangles, and Trigonometry G-SRT		
G.SRT.1	Understand similarity in terms of similarity transformations. Verify experimentally the properties of dilations given by a center and a scale factor: **a.** A dilation takes a line not passing through the center of the dilation to a parallel line, and leaves a line passing through the center unchanged.	**8-1**
	b. The dilation of a line segment is longer or shorter in the ratio given by the scale factor.	**8-1**

★ Mathematical Modeling Standards

Standard		Lesson(s)
G.SRT.2	Given two figures, use the definition of similarity in terms of similarity transformations to decide if they are similar; explain using similarity transformations the meaning of similarity for triangles as the equality of all corresponding pairs of angles and the proportionality of all corresponding pairs of sides.	8-2, 8-3, 8-4
G.SRT.3	Use the properties of similarity transformations to establish the AA criterion for two triangles to be similar.	8-3
G.SRT.4	Prove theorems involving similarity. Prove theorems about triangles.	8-5, 8-6, 9-1, 9-2
G.SRT.5	Use congruence and similarity criteria for triangles to solve problems and to prove relationships in geometric figures.	5-2, 5-3, 5-4, 5-5, 5-6, 8-3, 8-4, 9-1
G.SRT.6	Define trigonometric ratios and solve problems involving right triangles. Understand that by similarity, side ratios in right triangles are properties of the angles in the triangle, leading to definitions of trigonometric ratios for acute angles.	9-4, 9-5
G.SRT.7	Explain and use the relationship between the sine and cosine of complementary angles.	9-5
G.SRT.8	Use trigonometric ratios and the Pythagorean Theorem to solve right triangles in applied problems.★	9-2, 9-5, 9-6
G.SRT.9	Apply trigonometry to general triangles. (+) Derive the formula $A = \frac{1}{2}\,ab \sin(C)$ for the area of a triangle by drawing an auxiliary line from a vertex perpendicular to the opposite side.	9-6
G.SRT.10	(+) Prove the Laws of Sines and Cosines and use them to solve problems.	9-7, 9-8
G.SRT.11	(+) Understand and apply the Law of Sines and the Law of Cosines to find unknown measurements in right and non-right triangles (e.g., surveying problems, resultant forces).	9-7, 9-8

Circles G-C

Standard		Lesson(s)
G.C.1	Understand and apply theorems about circles. Prove that all circles are similar.	10-1
G.C.2	Identify and describe relationships among inscribed angles, radii, and chords.	10-2, 10-3, 10-4, 10-5, 10-6
G.C.3	Construct the inscribed and circumscribed circles of a triangle, and prove properties of angles for a quadrilateral inscribed in a circle.	10-4
G.C.4	(+) Construct a tangent line from a point outside a given circle to the circle.	10-5
G.C.5	Find arc lengths and areas of sectors of circles. Derive using similarity the fact that the length of the arc intercepted by an angle is proportional to the radius, and define the radian measure of the angle as the constant of proportionality; derive the formula for the area of a sector.	10-2, 11-3

Expressing Geometric Properties with Equations G-GPE

Standard		Lesson(s)
G.GPE.1	Translate between the geometric description and the equation for a conic section. Derive the equation of a circle of given center and radius using the Pythagorean Theorem; complete the square to find the center and radius of a circle given by an equation.	10-7
G.GPE.2	Derive the equation of a parabola given a focus and directrix.	10-8
G.GPE.4	Use coordinates to prove simple geometric theorems algebraically.	5-7, 7-2, 7-3, 7-4, 7-5, 7-6, 10-7
G.GPE.5	Prove the slope criteria for parallel and perpendicular lines and use them to solve geometric problems (e.g., find the equation of a line parallel or perpendicular to a given line that passes through a given point).	3-8, Expand 8-4
G.GPE.6	Find the point on a directed line segment between two given points that partitions the segment in a given ratio.	1-5, 1-6, 1-7
G.GPE.7	Use coordinates to compute perimeters of polygons and areas of triangles and rectangles, e.g., using the distance formula.★	2-3

★ Mathematical Modeling Standards

Standard		Lesson(s)
Geometric Measurement and Dimension G-GMD		
G.GMD.1	Explain volume formulas and use them to solve problems. Give an informal argument for the formulas for the circumference of a circle, area of a circle, volume of a cylinder, pyramid, and cone.	**10-1, 11-3, 11-6, 11-7**
G.GMD.2	(+) Give an informal argument using Cavalieri's principle for the formulas for the volume of a sphere and other solid figures.	**11-6, 11-7**
G.GMD.3	Use volume formulas for cylinders, pyramids, cones, and spheres to solve problems.★	**2-5, 11-6, 11-7, 11-8**
G.GMD.4	Visualize relationships between two-dimensional and three-dimensional objects. Identify the shapes of two-dimensional cross-sections of three-dimensional objects, and identify three-dimensional objects generated by rotations of two-dimensional objects.	**11-5**
Modeling with Geometry G-MG		
G.MG.1	Apply geometric concepts in modeling situations. Use geometric shapes, their measures, and their properties to describe objects (e.g., modeling a tree trunk or a human torso as a cylinder).★	**1-2, 2-3, 2-5, 2-6, 7-1**
G.MG.2	Apply concepts of density based on area and volume in modeling situations (e.g., persons per square mile, BTUs per cubic foot).★	**11-9**
G.MG.3	Apply geometric methods to solve problems (e.g., designing an object or structure to satisfy physical constraints or minimize cost; working with typographic grid systems based on ratios).★	**3-10, 6-1, 6-2, 11-2, 11-4**
Statistics and Probability		
Conditional Probability and the Rules of Probability S-CP		
S.CP.1	Understand independence and conditional probability and use them to interpret data. Describe events as subsets of a sample space (the set of outcomes) using characteristics (or categories) of the outcomes, or as unions, intersections, or complements of other events ("or," "and," "not").	**12-2**
S.CP.2	Understand that two events A and B are independent if the probability of A and B occurring together is the product of their probabilities, and use this characterization to determine if they are independent.	**12-5**
S.CP.3	Understand the conditional probability of A given B as $\frac{P(A \text{ and } B)}{P(B)}$, and interpret independence of A and B as saying that the conditional probability of A given B is the same as the probability of A, and the conditional probability of B given A is the same as the probability of B.	**12-7**
S.CP.4	Construct and interpret two-way frequency tables of data when two categories are associated with each object being classified. Use the two-way table as a sample space to decide if events are independent and to approximate conditional probabilities.	**12-8**
S.CP.5	Recognize and explain the concepts of conditional probability and independence in everyday language and everyday situations.	**12-7**
S.CP.6	Use the rules of probability to compute probabilities of compound events in a uniform probability model. Find the conditional probability of A given B as the fraction of B's outcomes that also belong to A, and interpret the answer in terms of the model.	**12-8**
S.CP.7	Apply the Addition Rule, $P(A \text{ or } B) = P(A) + P(B) - P(A \text{ and } B)$, and interpret the answer in terms of the model.	**12-6**
S.CP.8	(+) Apply the general Multiplication Rule in a uniform probability model, $P(A \text{ and } B) = P(A)P(B\|A) = P(B)P(A\|B)$, and interpret the answer in terms of the model.	**12-5**
S.CP.9	(+) Use permutations and combinations to compute probabilities of compound events and solve problems.	**12-4**
Using Probability to Make Decisions S-MD		
S.MD.6	Use probability to evaluate outcomes of decisions. (+) Use probabilities to make fair decisions (e.g., drawing by lots, using a random number generator).	**12-3, Expand 12-3**
S.MD.7	(+) Analyze decisions and strategies using probability concepts (e.g., product testing, medical testing, pulling a hockey goalie at the end of a game).	**12-3**

★ Mathematical Modeling Standards

Standards for Mathematical Practice

This correlation shows the alignment of *Reveal Geometry* to the Standards for Mathematical Practice, from the Common Core State Standards.

Standard	Lesson(s)
1 Make sense of problems and persevere in solving them. Mathematically proficient students start by explaining to themselves the meaning of a problem and looking for entry points to its solution. They analyze givens, constraints, relationships, and goals. They make conjectures about the form and meaning of the solution and plan a solution pathway rather than simply jumping into a solution attempt. They consider analogous problems, and try special cases and simpler forms of the original problem in order to gain insight into its solution. They monitor and evaluate their progress and change course if necessary. Older students might, depending on the context of the problem, transform algebraic expressions or change the viewing window on their graphing calculator to get the information they need. Mathematically proficient students can explain correspondences between equations, verbal descriptions, tables, and graphs or draw diagrams of important features and relationships, graph data, and search for regularity or trends. Younger students might rely on using concrete objects or pictures to help conceptualize and solve a problem. Mathematically proficient students check their answers to problems using a different method, and they continually ask themselves, "Does this make sense?" They can understand the approaches of others to solving complex problems and identify correspondences between different approaches.	*Reveal Geometry* requires students to make sense of problems and persevere in solving them in Examples and Independent Practice throughout the program. Some specific lessons for review are: Lessons 1-4, 1-7, 2-3, 3-1, 3-7, 3-8, 3-10, 4-2, 5-3, 5-5, 5-7, 6-1, 6-3, 6-7, 7-1, 8-1, 8-6, 9-4, 10-2, 10-3, 10-4, 10-5, 10-7, 11-3, 11-4, 11-6, 12-5, 12-7
2 Reason abstractly and quantitatively. Mathematically proficient students make sense of quantities and their relationships in problem situations. They bring two complementary abilities to bear on problems involving quantitative relationships: the ability to *decontextualize*—to abstract a given situation and represent it symbolically and manipulate the representing symbols as if they have a life of their own, without necessarily attending to their referents—and the ability to *contextualize*, to pause as needed during the manipulation process in order to probe into the referents for the symbols involved. Quantitative reasoning entails habits of creating a coherent representation of the problem at hand; considering the units involved; attending to the meaning of quantities, not just how to compute them; and knowing and flexibly using different properties of operations and objects.	*Reveal Geometry* requires students to reason abstractly and quantitatively in Think About It features and H.O.T. problems throughout the program. Some specific lessons for review are: Lessons 1-3, 1-4, 2-3, 2-6, 2-7, 3-2, 3-9, 4-4, 5-3, 5-7, 6-1, 7-1, 7-3, 7-4, 7-5, 8-1, 8-5, 9-1, 10-2, 11-3, 12-8
3 Construct viable arguments and critique the reasoning of others. Mathematically proficient students understand and use stated assumptions, definitions, and previously established results in constructing arguments. They make conjectures and build a logical progression of statements to explore the truth of their conjectures. They are able to analyze situations by breaking them into cases, and can recognize and use counterexamples. They justify their conclusions, communicate them to others, and respond to the arguments of others. They reason inductively about data, making plausible arguments that take into account the context from which the data arose. Mathematically proficient students are also able to compare the effectiveness of two plausible arguments, distinguish correct logic or reasoning from that which is flawed, and—if there is a flaw in an argument—explain what it is. Elementary students can construct arguments using concrete referents such as objects, drawings, diagrams, and actions. Such arguments can make sense and be correct, even though they are not generalized or made formal until later grades. Later, students learn to determine domains to which an argument applies. Students at all grades can listen or read the arguments of others, decide whether they make sense, and ask useful questions to clarify or improve the arguments.	*Reveal Geometry* requires students to construct viable arguments and critique the reasoning of others in Talk About It features and Independent Practice throughout the program. Some specific lessons for review are: Lessons 1-1, 1-2, 1-5, 2-2, 2-8, 3-1, 3-5, 3-6, 3-8, 3-9, 3-10, 4-1, 4-4, 4-5, 5-1, 5-3, 5-5, 5-7, 6-1, 6-4, 6-5, 6-6, 7-2, 7-3, 7-4, 7-5, 7-6, 8-2, 8-3, 8-4, 8-6, 9-1, 9-2, 9-3, 9-4, 9-7, 9-8, 10-2, 10-4, 10-5, 10-6, 10-7, 11-2, 11-5, 11-7, 11-8, 12-2, 12-6

Standard	Lesson(s)
4 Model with mathematics. Mathematically proficient students can apply the mathematics they know to solve problems arising in everyday life, society, and the workplace. In early grades, this might be as simple as writing an addition equation to describe a situation. In middle grades, a student might apply proportional reasoning to plan a school event or analyze a problem in the community. By high school, a student might use geometry to solve a design problem or use a function to describe how one quantity of interest depends on another. Mathematically proficient students who can apply what they know are comfortable making assumptions and approximations to simplify a complicated situation, realizing that these may need revision later. They are able to identify important quantities in a practical situation and map their relationships using such tools as diagrams, two-way tables, graphs, flowcharts and formulas. They can analyze those relationships mathematically to draw conclusions. They routinely interpret their mathematical results in the context of the situation and reflect on whether the results make sense, possibly improving the model if it has not served its purpose.	*Reveal Geometry* requires students to model with mathematics collaborate and discuss mathematics in Examples and Independent Practice throughout the program. Some specific lessons for review are: Lessons 1-2, 1-6, 1-7, 2-1, 2-4, 2-5, 2-6, 3-3, 3-4, 3-6, 3-9, 3-10, 4-1, 4-4, 5-1, 5-4, 5-5, 6-2, 6-4, 6-5, 6-7, 7-2, 8-3, 9-1, 9-2, 9-3, 9-6, 10-1, 10-3, 10-6, 10-8, 11-1, 11-2, 11-4, 11-6, 11-7, 11-9, 12-2, 12-3, 12-5, 12-6, 12-7, 12-8
5 Use appropriate tools strategically. Mathematically proficient students consider the available tools when solving a mathematical problem. These tools might include pencil and paper, concrete models, a ruler, a protractor, a calculator, a spreadsheet, a computer algebra system, a statistical package, or dynamic geometry software. Proficient students are sufficiently familiar with tools appropriate for their grade or course to make sound decisions about when each of these tools might be helpful, recognizing both the insight to be gained and their limitations. For example, mathematically proficient high school students analyze graphs of functions and solutions generated using a graphing calculator. They detect possible errors by strategically using estimation and other mathematical knowledge. When making mathematical models, they know that technology can enable them to visualize the results of varying assumptions, explore consequences, and compare predictions with data. Mathematically proficient students at various grade levels are able to identify relevant external mathematical resources, such as digital content located on a website, and use them to pose or solve problems. They are able to use technological tools to explore and deepen their understanding of concepts.	*Reveal Geometry* requires students to use appropriate tools strategically in Explore activities throughout the program. Some specific lessons for review are: Lessons 1-2, 1-6, 2-4, 2-8, 3-1, 3-7, 3-8, 4-1, 4-3, 4-5, 4-6, 5-2, 5-4, 5-6, 6-2, 6-4, 6-6, 6-7, 7-2, 8-1, 8-2, 8-3, 8-5, 9-2, 9-5, 9-6, 9-7, 10-4, 10-8, 11-3, 11-9, 12-1, 12-3, 12-4
6 Attend to precision. Mathematically proficient students try to communicate precisely to others. They try to use clear definitions in discussion with others and in their own reasoning. They state the meaning of the symbols they choose, including using the equal sign consistently and appropriately. They are careful about specifying units of measure, and labeling axes to clarify the correspondence with quantities in a problem. They calculate accurately and efficiently, express numerical answers with a degree of precision appropriate for the problem context. In the elementary grades, students give carefully formulated explanations to each other. By the time they reach high school they have learned to examine claims and make explicit use of definitions.	*Reveal Geometry* requires students to attend to precision in Examples and Independent Practice throughout the program. Some specific lessons for review are: Lessons 1-1, 2-1, 2-6, 2-7, 2-8, 3-2, 3-3, 3-4, 3-5, 3-6, 3-7, 4-2, 4-3, 4-6, 5-2, 5-4, 5-6, 6-2, 6-5, 6-6, 7-3, 7-4, 7-5, 7-6, 8-1, 8-2, 8-4, 8-6, 9-1, 9-2, 9-3, 9-8, 10-1, 10-3, 10-7, 10-8, 11-1, 11-7, 11-8, 11-9

Standard	Lesson(s)
7 Look for and make use of structure. Mathematically proficient students look closely to discern a pattern or structure. Young students, for example, might notice that three and seven more is the same amount as seven and three more, or they may sort a collection of shapes according to how many sides the shapes have. Later, students will see 7 × 8 equals the well remembered 7 × 5 + 7 × 3, in preparation for learning about the distributive property. In the expression $x^2 + 9x + 14$, older students can see the 14 as 2 × 7 and the 9 as 2 + 7. They recognize the significance of an existing line in a geometric figure and can use the strategy of drawing an auxiliary line for solving problems. They also can step back for an overview and shift perspective. They can see complicated things, such as some algebraic expressions, as single objects or as being composed of several objects. For example, they can see $5 - 3(x - y)^2$ as 5 minus a positive number times a square and use that to realize that its value cannot be more than 5 for any real numbers x and y.	*Reveal Geometry* requires students to look for and make use of structure in Explore activities and H.O.T. problems throughout the program. Some specific lessons for review are: Lessons 1-5, 2-5, 3-2, 4-3, 4-6, 5-2, 5-6, 6-3, 7-1, 8-4, 9-5, 10-1, 10-6, 11-1, 11-2, 11-5, 11-6, 11-8
8 Look for and express regularity in repeated reasoning. Mathematically proficient students notice if calculations are repeated, and look both for general methods and for shortcuts. Upper elementary students might notice when dividing 25 by 11 that they are repeating the same calculations over and over again, and conclude they have a repeating decimal. By paying attention to the calculation of slope as they repeatedly check whether points are on the line through (1, 2) with slope 3, middle school students might abstract the equation $(y - 2)/(x - 1) = 3$. Noticing the regularity in the way terms cancel when expanding $(x - 1)(x + 1)$, $(x - 1)(x^2 + x + 1)$, and $(x - 1)(x^3 + x^2 + x + 1)$ might lead them to the general formula for the sum of a geometric series. As they work to solve a problem, mathematically proficient students maintain oversight of the process, while attending to the details. They continually evaluate the reasonableness of their intermediate results.	*Reveal Geometry* requires students to look for and express regularity in repeated reasoning in Concept Check and Think About It features and H.O.T. problems throughout the program. Some specific lessons for review are: Lessons 1-3, 2-2, 3-3, 3-4, 4-2, 5-1, 6-3, 7-6, 8-5, 9-4, 10-5, 11-4, 11-5, 12-4

Quadrilaterals

Module Goals

- Students prove theorems and solve problems about polygons and parallelograms.
- Students recognize and apply the properties of rectangles, rhombi, squares, kites, and trapezoids.
- Students determine whether quadrilaterals are parallelograms and whether parallelograms are rectangles.

Focus

Domain: Geometry

Standards for Mathematical Content:

G.CO.11 Prove theorems about parallelograms.

G.GPE.4 Use coordinates to prove simple geometric theorems algebraically.

Also addresses G.MG.1.

Standards for Mathematical Practice:

All Standards for Mathematical Practice will be used in this module.

✪ Be Sure to Cover

To completely cover G.CO.12, go online to assign the following constructions:

- Construct a Parallelogram (Lesson 7-3)
- Construct a Rectangle (Lesson 7-4)
- Construct a Rhombus (Lesson 7-5)
- Construct a Square (Lesson 7-5)

Coherence

Vertical Alignment

Previous
Students proved theorems about relationships in triangles.
G.CO.10, G.SRT.4

Now
Students prove theorems about parallelograms.
G.CO.11, G.GPE.4

Next
Students will use similarity criteria for triangles to solve problems and to prove relationships in geometric figures.
G.SRT.5

Rigor

The Three Pillars of Rigor

To help students meet standards, they need to illustrate their ability to use the three pillars of rigor. Students gain conceptual understanding as they move from the Explore to Learn sections within a lesson. Once they understand the concept, they practice procedural skills and fluency and apply their mathematical knowledge as they go through the Examples and Independent Practice.

| 1 CONCEPTUAL UNDERSTANDING | 2 FLUENCY | 3 APPLICATION |

EXPLORE 〉 LEARN 〉 EXAMPLE & PRACTICE

Suggested Pacing

Lessons	Standards	45-min classes	90-min classes
Module Pretest and Launch the Module Video		1	0.5
7-1 Angles of Polygons	G.MG.1	1	0.5
7-2 Parallelograms	G.CO.11, G.GPE.4	1	0.5
7-3 Tests for Parallelograms	G.CO.11, G.CO.12, G.GPE.4	1	0.5
7-4 Rectangles	G.CO.11, G.CO.12, G.GPE.4	1	0.5
7-5 Rhombi and Squares	G.CO.11, G.CO.12, G.GPE.4	1	0.5
7-6 Trapezoids and Kites	G.GPE.4	1	0.5
Put It All Together: Lessons 7-2 through 7-6		1	0.5
Module Review		1	0.5
Module Assessment		1	0.5
	Total Days	**10**	**5**

Formative Assessment Math Probe
Is It a Parallelogram?

Analyze the Probe

Review the probe prior to assigning it to your students.

In this probe, students will determine which figures are parallelograms and explain their choices.

Targeted Concepts Understand what information is sufficient or appropriate for a figure to represent a parallelogram.

Targeted Misconceptions

- Students may overgeneralize that any figure with parallel opposite sides is a parallelogram.
- Students may assume right angles where they are not labeled.
- Students may not know the properties of parallelograms, or they may not know the information needed to prove that figures are parallelograms.

Use the Probe after Lesson 7-3.

Answers: 1. no; 2. no; 3. yes; 4. no; 5. no; 6. no; 7. yes

Collect and Assess Student Answers

If the student selects these responses...	**Then** the student likely...
1. yes **6.** yes	believes that a parallelogram is any figure with parallel opposite sides.
2. yes **5.** yes	is assuming that the unlabeled angles are right angles. **Example:** With only two right angles given as in Item 5, the figure could also be:
3. no **4.** yes **7.** no	does not have a solid understanding of the properties of parallelograms and/or what information is needed to prove that a figure is a parallelogram.

Take Action

After the Probe Design a plan to address any possible misconceptions. You may wish to assign the following resources.

- **ALEKS** Parallelograms and Trapezoids
- Lesson 7-3, Learns, Examples 1–2

Revisit the probe at the end of the module to be sure that your students no longer carry these misconceptions.

The Ignite! activities, created by Dr. Raj Shah, cultivate curiosity and engage and challenge students. Use these open-ended, collaborative activities, located online in the module Launch section, to encourage your students to develop a growth mindset towards mathematics and problem solving. Use the teacher notes for implementation suggestions and support for encouraging productive struggle.

ⓔ Essential Question

At the end of this module, students should be able to answer the Essential Question.

What are the different types of quadrilaterals, and how can their characteristics be used to model real-world situations? Sample answer: Parallelograms, rectangles, rhombi, squares, trapezoids, and kites; You can use these quadrilaterals to model real-world objects, and then you can use what you know about the properties of these shapes to approximate the measures of the real-world objects.

What Will You Learn?

Prior to beginning this module, have your students rate their knowledge of each item listed. Then, at the end of the module, you will be reminded to have your students return to these pages to rate their knowledge again. They should see that their knowledge and skills have increased.

DINAH ZIKE FOLDABLES

Focus Students read about quadrilaterals.

Teach Throughout the module, have students take notes under the tabs of their Foldables while working through each lesson. They should include definitions, terms, and key concepts. Encourage students to record examples of each type of quadrilateral from a lesson on the back of their Foldable.

When to Use It Use the appropriate tabs as students cover each lesson in this module. Students should add to the vocabulary tab during each lesson.

Launch the Module

For this module, the Launch the Module video uses engineering to demonstrate the usefulness of quadrilaterals and their relationships. Students learn about the use of quadrilaterals for correct movement in engineering.

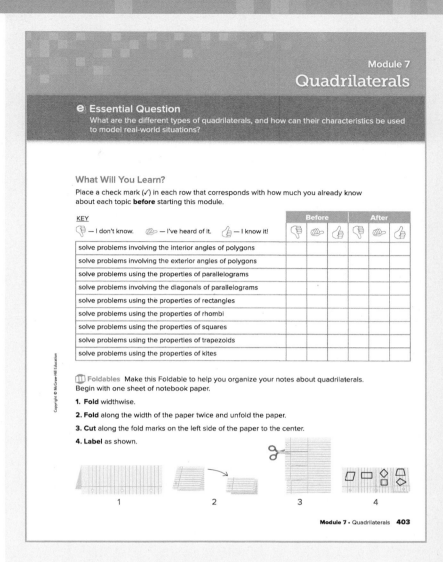

Interactive Presentation

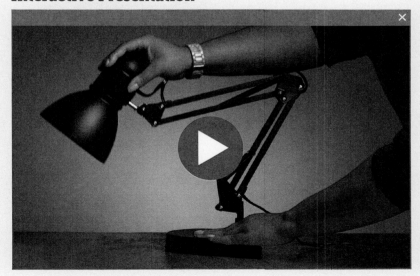

What Vocabulary Will You Learn?

Check the box next to each vocabulary term that you may already know.

- ☐ base angle of a trapezoid
- ☐ bases of a trapezoid
- ☐ diagonal
- ☐ isosceles trapezoid
- ☐ kite
- ☐ legs of a trapezoid
- ☐ midsegment of a trapezoid
- ☐ parallelogram
- ☐ rectangle
- ☐ rhombus
- ☐ square
- ☐ trapezoid

Are You Ready?

Complete the Quick Review to see if you are ready to start this module. Then complete the Quick Check.

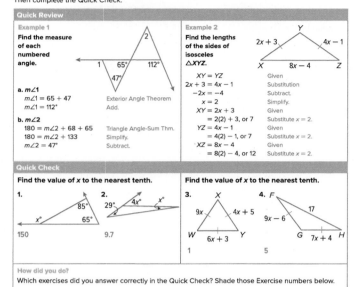

Quick Review

Example 1
Find the measure of each numbered angle.

a. $m\angle 1$
$m\angle 1 = 65 + 47$ Exterior Angle Theorem
$m\angle 1 = 112°$ Add.

b. $m\angle 2$
$180 = m\angle 2 + 68 + 65$ Triangle Angle-Sum Thm.
$180 = m\angle 2 + 133$ Simplify.
$m\angle 2 = 47°$ Subtract.

Example 2
Find the lengths of the sides of isosceles $\triangle XYZ$.

$XY = YZ$ Given
$2x + 3 = 4x - 1$ Substitution
$-2x = -4$ Subtract.
$x = 2$ Simplify.
$XY = 2x + 3$ Given
$\quad = 2(2) + 3$, or 7   Substitute $x = 2$.
$YZ = 4x - 1$ Given
$\quad = 4(2) - 1$, or 7   Substitute $x = 2$.
$XZ = 8x - 4$ Given
$\quad = 8(2) - 4$, or 12   Substitute $x = 2$.

Quick Check

Find the value of x to the nearest tenth.

1.

150

2.

9.7

Find the value of x to the nearest tenth.

3.

1

4.

5

How did you do?
Which exercises did you answer correctly in the Quick Check? Shade those Exercise numbers below.

① ② ③ ④

What Vocabulary Will You Learn?

ELL As you proceed through the module, introduce the key vocabulary by using the following routine.

Define A parallelogram is a quadrilateral with both pairs of opposite sides parallel.

Example

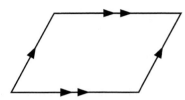

Ask How do you think the opposite sides are related? Opposite sides are congruent. How do you think the measures of the opposite angles are related? Opposite angles are congruent.

Are You Ready?

Students may need to review the following prerequisite skills to succeed in this module.

- reviewing polygons
- exploring angles formed by lines cut by a transversal
- exploring quadrilaterals
- understanding parallel and perpendicular lines

◎ ALEKS·

ALEKS is an adaptive, personalized learning environment that identifies precisely what each student knows and is ready to learn, ensuring student success at all levels.

You may want to use the **Parallelograms and Trapezoids** section to ensure student success in this module.

🧠 Mindset Matters

Collaborative Risk Taking

Some students may be averse to taking risks during math class, like sharing an idea, strategy, or solution. They may worry about their grades or scores on tests, or some might feel less confident solving math problems, especially in front of their peers.

How Can I Apply It?

Assign the **Practice** problems of each lesson and encourage students to take risks as they solve problems, try new paths, and discuss their strategies with their partner or group.

Angles of Polygons

Lesson 7-1 • Angles of Polygons **405a**

LESSON GOAL

Students prove theorems about the interior and exterior angles of polygons and use the theorems to solve problems.

1 LAUNCH

 Launch the lesson with a **Warm Up** and an introduction.

2 EXPLORE AND DEVELOP

 Explore: Angles of Polygons

 Develop:

Interior Angles of Polygons
- Find the Interior Angles Sum of a Polygon
- Interior Angle Measures of a Regular Polygon
- Identify the Polygon Given the Interior Angle Measure

Exterior Angles of Polygons
- Find Missing Values
- Find Exterior Angle Measures of a Polygon

 You may want your students to complete the **Checks** online.

3 REFLECT AND PRACTICE

 Exit Ticket

 Practice

DIFFERENTIATE

 View reports of student progress on the **Checks** after each example.

Resources	AL	OL	BL	ELL
Remediation: Two-Dimensional Figures	●	●		●
Extension: Central Angles of Regular Polygons		●	●	●

Language Development Handbook

Assign page 46 of the *Language Development Handbook* to help your students build mathematical language related to the interior and exterior angles of polygons.

ELL You can use the tips and suggestions on page T46 of the handbook to support students who are building English proficiency.

Suggested Pacing

90 min	0.5 day	
45 min		1 day

Focus

Domain: Geometry

Standards for Mathematical Content:

G.MG.1 Use geometric shapes, their measures, and their properties to describe objects (e.g., modeling a tree trunk or human torso as a cylinder).

Standards for Mathematical Practice:

1 Make sense of problems and persevere in solving them.

2 Reason abstractly and quantitatively.

7 Look for and make use of structure.

Coherence

Vertical Alignment

Previous
Students proved theorems about relationships in triangles.
G.CO.10, G.SRT.4

Now
Students prove theorems about the interior and exterior angles of polygons and use the theorems to solve problems.
G.MG.1

Next
Students will prove theorems and solve problems about the properties of parallelograms.
G.CO.11

Rigor

The Three Pillars of Rigor

1 CONCEPTUAL UNDERSTANDING	2 FLUENCY	3 APPLICATION

🏛 **Conceptual Bridge** In this lesson, students draw on their understanding of how geometric concepts can be applied to real-world objects. They apply their understanding of polygons to solve real-world problems.

Mathematical Background

If a convex polygon has n sides and S is the sum of the measures of its interior angles, then $S = 180(n - 2)$. This equation can be used to find the measure of each interior angle in a regular polygon or to find the number of sides in a polygon if the sum of the interior angle measures is known.

Interactive Presentation

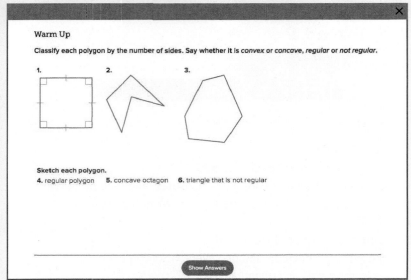

Warm Up

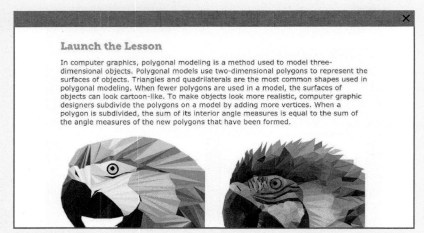

Launch the Lesson

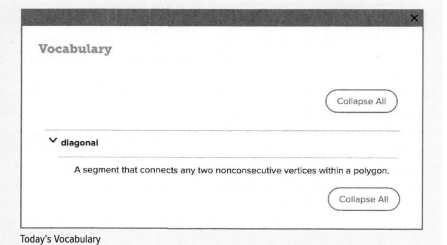

Today's Vocabulary

Warm Up

Prerequisite Skills

The Warm Up exercises address the following prerequisite skills for this lesson:

- classifying polygons
- drawing polygons from descriptions

Answers:

1. quadrilateral, convex, regular
2. pentagon, concave, not regular
3. hexagon, convex, not regular

4–6. Sample answers are shown.

4.   5.   6.

Launch the Lesson

MP Teaching the Mathematical Practices

> **4 Apply Mathematics** In this Launch the Lesson, students can see a real-world application of two-dimensional polygons.

Go Online to find additional teaching notes and questions to promote classroom discourse.

Today's Standards

Tell students that they will be addressing these content and practice standards in this lesson. You may wish to have a student volunteer read aloud *How can I meet these standards?* and *How can I use these practices?*, and connect these to the standards.

See the Interactive Presentation for I Can statements that align with the standards covered in this lesson.

Today's Vocabulary

Tell students that they will be using this vocabulary term in this lesson. You can expand the row if you wish to share the definition. Then, discuss the questions below with the class.

Explore Angles of Polygons

Objective
Students use dynamic geometry software and inductive reasoning to discover the Polygon Interior Angles Sum Theorem.

 Teaching the Mathematical Practices

> **2 Create Representations** Guide students to write an equation that models the situation in this Explore. Then use the equation to solve the problem.

Ideas for Use

Recommended Use Present the Inquiry Question, or have a student volunteer read it aloud. Have students work in pairs to complete the Explore activity on their devices. Pairs should discuss each of the questions. Monitor student progress during the activity. Upon completion of the Explore activity, have student volunteers share their responses to the Inquiry Question.

What if my students don't have devices? You may choose to project the activity on a whiteboard. A printable worksheet for each Explore is available online. You may choose to print the worksheet so that individuals or pairs of students can use it to record their observations.

Summary of the Activity
Students will complete guiding exercises throughout the Explore activity. Students construct a triangle and examine the sum of its angle measures using dynamic geometry software. Then, students construct a convex quadrilateral and one of its diagonals and determine the sum of its angle measures from the two triangles created by the diagonal. After this, students do the same with a pentagon and a hexagon. At each stage students record the number of sides of the polygon, the number of triangles formed by the diagonals, and the sum of the angle measures of the polygon. Then, students complete guiding exercises to determine a formula for the angle sum of the polygon based on the number of sides. Then, students will answer the Inquiry Question.

(continued on the next page)

Interactive Presentation

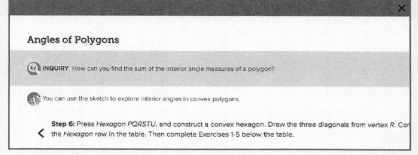

Angles of Polygons

 INQUIRY How can you find the sum of the interior angle measures of a polygon?

 You can use the sketch to explore interior angles in convex polygons.

Step 6: Press *Hexagon PQRSTU*, and construct a convex hexagon. Draw the three diagonals from vertex *R*. Co[m]... the *Hexagon* row in the table. Then complete Exercises 1-5 below the table.

Explore

WEB SKETCHPAD

Students use a sketch to explore the Polygon Interior Angles Sum Theorem.

TYPE

Students type answers to the guiding exercises and fill in the table.

Interactive Presentation

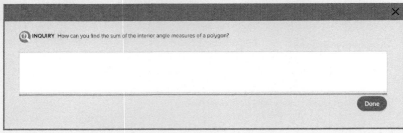

Explore

TYPE

Students respond to the Inquiry Question and can view a sample answer.

Explore Angles of Polygons (*continued*)

MP **Teaching the Mathematical Practices**

7 Look for a Pattern Help students to see the pattern in the explore.

Questions

Have students complete the Explore activity.

Ask:

- Would it make sense to draw both diagonals inside quadrilateral *DEFG* to measure the interior angles?   No; sample answer: Drawing both diagonals would create overlapping triangles and would duplicate measures.

- How do you find the sum of the interior angles in an octagon? Sample answer: There are 8 sides in an octagon, and we found that there are $n - 2$ diagonals, so there are 6 diagonals and 6 triangles in the octagon. Multiply $180° \cdot 6$ to find the sum of the interior angles, or 1080°.

@ **Inquiry**

How can you find the sum of the interior angle measures of a polygon? Sample answer: You can subtract two from the number of sides of the polygon, and then multiply the difference by 180°. You can also use diagonals to divide the polygon into triangles. Then you can multiply the number of triangles created by the diagonals by 180° to calculate the sum of the interior angle measures.

Go Online to find additional teaching notes and sample answers for the guiding exercises.

Learn Interior Angles of Polygons

Objective
Students prove and use the Polygon Interior Angles Sum Theorem.

 Teaching the Mathematical Practices

7 Use Structure Help students to explore the structure of the Polygon Interior Angles Sum Theorem in this Learn.

About the Key Concept

The Polygon Interior Angles Sum Theorem is an extension of the Triangle Angle-Sum Theorem. It takes a concept that is true for triangles, that all triangles have an angle sum of 180°, and extends it to a similar fact for all convex polygons. For all convex polygons, regular and irregular, the angle sum is $(n - 2) \cdot 180°$, where n is the number of sides of the polygon.

Example 1 Find the Interior Angles Sum of a Polygon

 Teaching the Mathematical Practices

6 Use Precision In this example, students should calculate accurately and efficiently and express numerical answers with a degree of precision appropriate to the problem context.

Questions for Mathematical Discourse

AL If not using the Polygon Interior Angles Sum Theorem, how else can you determine the sum of the interior angle measures in a polygon? Sample answer: Because every triangle has an angle sum of 180°, count the number of triangles in the polygon and multiply by 180. More specifically, extend as many segments as possible from one vertex of the polygon to every other vertex and count the number of triangles formed.

OL What are the steps needed to solve the equation?
$10x + 170 = 540$; $10x = 370$; $x = 37$

BL If a pentagon has two congruent angles and three angles measuring twice the two congruent angles, what is the measure of the two congruent angles? 67.5°

Go Online

- Find additional teaching notes.
- View performance reports of the Checks.
- Assign or present an Extra Example.

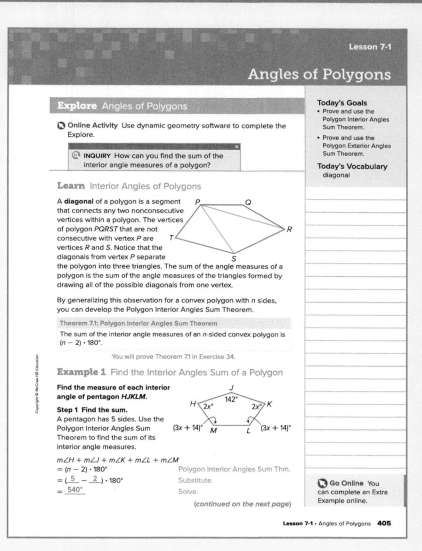

Interactive Presentation

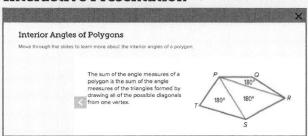

Learn

TAP

Students move through the slides to learn how to calculate the interior angles of a polygon.

1 CONCEPTUAL UNDERSTANDING **2 FLUENCY** | **3 APPLICATION**

Step 2 Find the value of x.
Use the sum of the interior angle measures to determine the value of x.

$2x + 2x + (3x + 14) + (3x + 14) + 142 = 540°$ Write an equation.
$x = \underline{37}$ Solve.

Step 3 Find the measure of each angle.
Use the value of x to find the measure of each angle.

$m\angle J = \underline{142°}$ $m\angle K = 2(\underline{37}.)$ or $\underline{74°}$ $m\angle L = [3(37) + 14]$ or $\underline{125°}$

$m\angle M = [3(37) + 14]$ or 125° $m\angle H = 2x° = 2(\underline{37}.)$ or $\underline{74°}$

Check
Find the measure of ∠E.

A. 108°

B. 120°

C. 122°

Ⓓ 126°

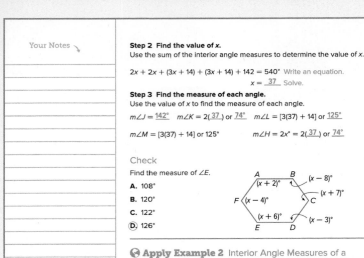

Apply Example 2 Interior Angle Measures of a Regular Polygon

FLOOR PLANS **Penny is building a house using a floor plan that she designed. What is the measure of ∠ABC?**

1 What is the task?
Describe the task in your own words. Then list any questions that you may have. How can you find answers to your questions?
Sample answer: I need to find the measure of ∠ABC. What is the relationship between the interior angle measures of the regular hexagon?

2 How will you approach the task? What have you learned that you can use to help you complete the task?
Sample answer: I will use the Polygon Interior Angle Sum
Theorem to find the sum of the measures of the interior angles
of the regular hexagon. Then, I will find the measure of ∠ABC
by dividing the sum by the total number of angles. I have learned
that the interior angles of a regular polygon are congruent.

🔵 **Go Online** You can complete an Extra Example online.

Interactive Presentation

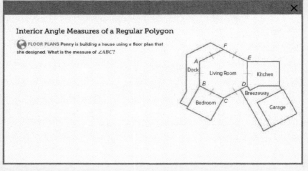

Apply Example 2

Students type to explain their solution process.

🌐 **Apply Example 2** Interior Angle Measures of a Regular Polygon

ⓂⓅ Teaching the Mathematical Practices

> **1 Make Sense of Problems and Persevere in Solving Them, 4 Model with Mathematics** Students will be presented with a task. They will first seek to understand the task, and then determine possible entry points to solving it. As students come up with their own strategies, they may propose mathematical models to aid them. As they work to solve the problem, encourage them to evaluate their model and/or progress, and change direction, if necessary.

Recommended Use
Have students work in pairs or small groups. You may wish to present the task, or have a volunteer read it aloud. Then allow students the time to make sure they understand the task, think of possible strategies, and work to solve the problem.

Encourage Productive Struggle
As students work, monitor their progress. Instead of instructing them on a particular strategy, encourage them to use their own strategies to solve the problem and to evaluate their progress along the way. They may or may not find that they need to change direction or try out several strategies.

Signs of Non-Productive Struggle
If students show signs of non-productive struggle, such as feeling overwhelmed, frustrated, or disengaged, intervene to encourage them to think of alternate approaches to the problem. Some sample questions are shown.

- What is the relationship between the interior angles of a regular polygon?
- How many interior angles does the plan for the living room have?

✏️ Write About It!
Have students share their responses with another pair/group of students or the entire class. Have them clearly state or describe the mathematical reasoning they can use to defend their solution.

DIFFERENTIATE

Enrichment Activity 🅐🅛 🅑🅛
Have students use a straightedge to construct an irregular polygon that has five or more sides. Have students use a protractor to measure and label half of the interior angles of the figure and all but one of the exterior angles of the remaining vertices. Instruct students to trade drawings with another student and measure and label the remaining interior and exterior angles without using a protractor. Students should then return the drawing to the owner. Answers can be checked by using a protractor.

Example 3 Identify the Polygon Given the Interior Angle Measure

 **Teaching the Mathematical Practices**

2 Attend to Quantities Point out that it is important to note the meaning of the quantities used in this problem.

Questions for Mathematical Discourse

AL What is the name for a polygon with 8 sides? an octagon

OL The measure of an interior angle of a regular polygon is 140°. How many sides does the polygon have? 9

BL The measure of an interior angle of a regular polygon rounds to 128.6°. How many sides does the polygon have? 7

Common Error

Students may incorrectly set up the equation to find the number of sides of the polygon. They may not understand that the given angle measure needs to be multiplied by the number of sides of the polygon. Guide them to correctly construct the equation.

DIFFERENTIATE

Enrichment Activity BL

Have students draw a concave polygon using pencil and paper. They should then measure the interior and exterior angles with a protractor. Ask them to determine whether the Polygon Interior Angles Sum Theorem and the Polygon Exterior Angles Sum Theorem hold true to their measurements. Ask questions about the lesson content to elicit short answers. "Is there a correlation between the interior angles of a polygon and the exterior angles of the same polygon?"

---

3 What is your solution?
Use your strategy to solve the problem.

Write the equation that you will use to find the sum of the interior angles of the regular hexagon.

$m\angle FAB + m\angle ABC + m\angle BCD + m\angle CDE + m\angle DEF + m\angle EFA = (n - 2) \cdot 180°$

The sum of the interior angles of the regular hexagon is ___720°___

$m\angle ABC =$ ___120°___

4 How can you know that your solution is reasonable?

Write About It! Write an argument that can be used to defend your solution.

Sample answer: 6(120) = 720°, which is the sum of the measures of the interior angles of the hexagon.

Check

PONDS Miguel has commissioned a pentagonal koi pond to be built in his backyard. He wants the pond to have a deck of equal width around it. The lengths of the interior deck sides are the same length, and the lengths of the exterior sides are the same.

The measure of the angle of the pond formed by two sides of the deck is ___108°___

Example 3 Identify the Polygon Given the Interior Angle Measure

The measure of an interior angle of a regular polygon is 144°. Find the number of sides in the polygon.

Let $n =$ the number of sides in the polygon. Because all angles of a regular polygon are congruent, the sum of the interior angle measures is 144n°. By the Polygon Interior Angles Sum Theorem, the sum of the interior angle measures can also be expressed as $(n - 2) \cdot 180°$.

$\underline{144}\, n° = (n - 2) \cdot 180°$ Write an equation.

$n = \underline{10}$ Solve.

The polygon has ___10___ sides, so it is a regular decagon.

Check

The measure of an interior angle of a regular polygon is 150°. Find the number of sides in the polygon.

The polygon has ___12___ sides.

 Go Online You can complete an Extra Example online.

Study Tip
Naming Polygons Remember, a polygon with n-sides is an n-gon, but several polygons have special names.

Number of Sides	Polygon
3	triangle
4	quadrilateral
5	pentagon
6	hexagon
7	heptagon
8	octagon
9	nonagon
10	decagon
11	hendecagon
12	dodecagon
n	n-gon

Interactive Presentation

Identify the Polygon Given the Interior Angle Measure

The measure of an interior angle of a regular polygon is 144°. Find the number of sides in the polygon.

Let $n =$ the number of sides in the polygon. Because all angles of a regular polygon are congruent, the sum of the interior angle measures is 144n°. By the Polygon Interior Angles Sum Theorem, the sum of the interior angle measures can also be expressed as $(n - 2) \cdot 180°$.

[   ] $n° = (n - 2) \cdot 180°$ Write an equation.

$n =$ [   ]   Solve.

The polygon has [   ] sides, so it is a regular decagon.

Check Answer

Example 3

TYPE

Students type to fill in parts of a solution.

CHECK

Students complete the Check online to determine whether they are ready to move on.

G.MG.1

Learn Exterior Angles of Polygons

Theorem 7.2 Polygon Exterior Angles Sum Theorem	
Words	The sum of the exterior angle measures of a convex polygon, one angle at each vertex, is 360°.
Example	$m\angle 1 + m\angle 2 + m\angle 3 + m\angle 4 + m\angle 5 + m\angle 6 = 360°$

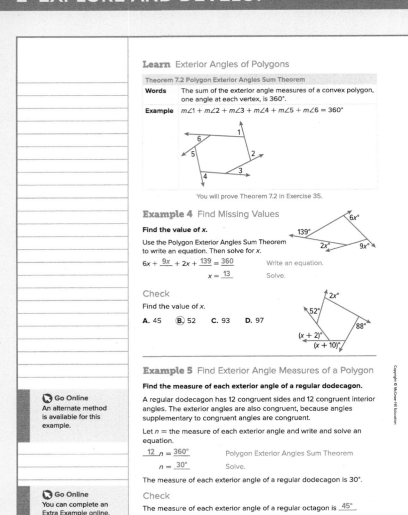

You will prove Theorem 7.2 in Exercise 35.

Example 4 Find Missing Values

Find the value of *x*.

Use the Polygon Exterior Angles Sum Theorem to write an equation. Then solve for *x*.

$6x + \underline{9x} + 2x + \underline{139} = 360$ Write an equation.

$x = \underline{13}$ Solve.

Check

Find the value of *x*.

A. 45   B. 52   C. 93   D. 97

Example 5 Find Exterior Angle Measures of a Polygon

Find the measure of each exterior angle of a regular dodecagon.

A regular dodecagon has 12 congruent sides and 12 congruent interior angles. The exterior angles are also congruent, because angles supplementary to congruent angles are congruent.

Let *n* = the measure of each exterior angle and write and solve an equation.

$\underline{12}\,n = \underline{360°}$ Polygon Exterior Angles Sum Theorem

$n = \underline{30°}$ Solve.

The measure of each exterior angle of a regular dodecagon is 30°.

Check

The measure of each exterior angle of a regular octagon is $\underline{45°}$.

 Go Online
An alternate method is available for this example.

 Go Online
You can complete an Extra Example online.

Interactive Presentation

Example 5

TAP

Students tap to see an alternate method.

CHECK

Students complete the Check online to determine whether they are ready to move on.

Learn Exterior Angles of Polygons

Objective
Students prove and use the Polygon Exterior Angles Sum Theorem.

MP Teaching the Mathematical Practices

7 Use Structure Help students to explore the structure of the Polygon Exterior Angles Sum Theorem in this Learn.

Example 4 Find Missing Values

Questions for Mathematical Discourse

AL What is the difference between interior and exterior angles? Sample answer: Interior angles are located inside the polygon. Exterior angles are formed between a side of a polygon and the extension of an adjacent side of the polygon.

OL How many angle measures will there be in the sum? Explain. 4; A quadrilateral has four angles.

BL What are the missing angle measures? 26°, 78°, 117°

Example 5 Find Exterior Angle Measures of a Polygon

Questions for Mathematical Discourse

AL What is the measure of each interior angle? 150°

OL What is the measure of each exterior angle of a regular pentagon? 72°

BL If you forget how to find the measure of an interior angle of a regular polygon, how can you use the sum of the exterior angles to help? Sample answer: Find the measure of an exterior angle and subtract the measure from 180° to find the measure of an interior angle.

Exit Ticket

Recommended Use
At the end of class, go online to display the Exit Ticket prompt and ask students to respond using a separate piece of paper. Have students hand you their responses as they leave the room.

Alternate Use
At the end of class, go online to display the Exit Ticket prompt and ask students to respond verbally or by using a mini-whiteboard. Have students hold up their whiteboards so that you can see all student responses. Tap to reveal the answer when most or all students have completed the Exit Ticket.

Practice and Homework

Suggested Assignments

Use the table below to select appropriate exercises.

DOK	Topic	Exercises
1, 2	exercises that mirror the examples	1–24
2	exercises that use a variety of skills from this lesson	25–33
2	exercises that extend concepts learned in this lesson to new contexts	34–40
3	exercises that emphasize higher-order and critical-thinking skills	41–45

ASSESS AND DIFFERENTIATE

📊 Use the data from the **Checks** to determine whether to provide resources for extension, remediation, or intervention.

IF students score 90% or more on the Checks, **OL** **BL**
THEN assign:

- Practice, Exercises 1–39 odd, 41–45
- Extension: Central Angles of Regular Polygons
- 🔲 **ALEKS**· Angles of Polygons

IF students score 66%–89% on the Checks, **AL** **OL**
THEN assign:

- Practice, Exercises 1–45 odd
- Remediation, Review Resources: Two-Dimensional Figures
- Personal Tutors
- Extra Examples 1–5
- 🔲 **ALEKS**· Introduction to Perimeter and Area

IF students score 65% or less on the Checks, **AL**
THEN assign:

- Practice, Exercises 1–23 odd
- Remediation, Review Resources: Two-Dimensional Figures
- *Quick Review Math Handbook*: Angles of Polygons
- 🔲 **ALEKS**· Introduction to Perimeter and Area

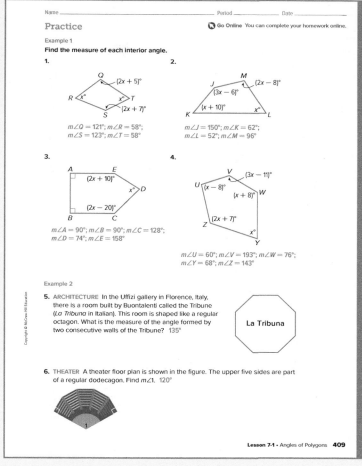

Name _____ Period _____ Date _____

Practice 🔵 Go Online You can complete your homework online.

Example 1
Find the measure of each interior angle.

1. $m\angle Q = 121°$; $m\angle R = 58°$; $m\angle S = 123°$; $m\angle T = 58°$

2. $m\angle J = 150°$; $m\angle K = 62°$; $m\angle L = 52°$; $m\angle M = 96°$

3. $m\angle A = 90°$; $m\angle B = 90°$; $m\angle C = 128°$; $m\angle D = 74°$; $m\angle E = 158°$

4. $m\angle U = 60°$; $m\angle V = 193°$; $m\angle W = 76°$; $m\angle Y = 68°$; $m\angle Z = 143°$

Example 2

5. ARCHITECTURE In the Uffizi gallery in Florence, Italy, there is a room built by Buontalenti called the Tribune (*La Tribuna* in Italian). This room is shaped like a regular octagon. What is the measure of the angle formed by two consecutive walls of the Tribune? 135°

6. THEATER A theater floor plan is shown in the figure. The upper five sides are part of a regular dodecagon. Find $m\angle 1$. 120°

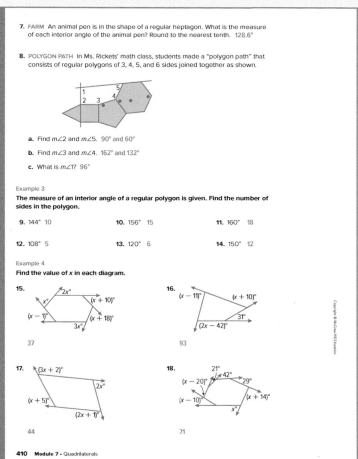

7. FARM An animal pen is in the shape of a regular heptagon. What is the measure of each interior angle of the animal pen? Round to the nearest tenth. 128.6°

8. POLYGON PATH In Ms. Rickets' math class, students made a "polygon path" that consists of regular polygons of 3, 4, 5, and 6 sides joined together as shown.

   a. Find $m\angle 2$ and $m\angle 5$. 90° and 60°

   b. Find $m\angle 3$ and $m\angle 4$. 162° and 132°

   c. What is $m\angle 1$? 96°

Example 3
The measure of an interior angle of a regular polygon is given. Find the number of sides in the polygon.

9. 144° 10   10. 156° 15   11. 160° 18

12. 108° 5   13. 120° 6   14. 150° 12

Example 4
Find the value of x in each diagram.

15. 37

16. 93

17. 44

18. 71

3 REFLECT AND PRACTICE

G.MG.1

1 CONCEPTUAL UNDERSTANDING 2 FLUENCY 3 APPLICATION

Name _____ Period _____ Date _____

Example 5
Find the measure of each exterior angle of each regular polygon.

19. pentagon 72°

20. 15-gon 24°

21. hexagon 60°

22. octagon 45°

23. nonagon 40°

24. 12-gon 30°

Mixed Exercises

Find the measures of an exterior angle and an interior angle given the number of sides of each regular polygon. Round to the nearest tenth, if necessary.

25. 7 51.4°; 128.6°

26. 13 27.7°; 152.3°

27. 14 25.7°; 154.3°

For Exercises 28 and 29, find the value of x.

28. A convex octagon has interior angles with measures $(x + 55)°$, $(3x + 20)°$, $4x°$, $(4x - 10)°$, $(6x - 55)°$, $(3x + 52)°$, $3x°$, and $(2x + 30)°$. 38

29. A convex hexagon has interior angles with measures $x°$, $(5x - 103)°$, $(2x + 60)°$, $(7x - 31)°$, $(6x - 6)°$, and $(9x - 100)°$. 30

For Exercises 30 and 31, find the measure of each interior angle in the given polygon.

30. A decagon in which the measures of the interior angles are $(x + 5)°$, $(x + 10)°$, $(x + 20)°$, $(x + 30)°$, $(x + 35)°$, $(x + 40)°$, $(x + 60)°$, $(x + 70)°$, $(x + 80)°$, and $(x + 90)°$. 105°; 110°; 120°; 130°; 135°; 140°; 160°; 170°; 180°; 190°

31. A polygon ABCDE in which the measures of the interior angles are $(6x)°$, $(4x + 13)°$, $(x + 9)°$, $(2x - 8)°$, and $(4x - 1)°$. 186°; 137°; 40°; 54°; 123°

32. Find the measure of each exterior angle of a regular 2x-gon. $\frac{180°}{x}$

33. Find the sum of the measures of the exterior angles of a convex 65-gon. 360°

34. PROOF Write a paragraph proof to prove the Polygon Interior Angles Sum Theorem. See margin.

35. PROOF Use algebra to prove the Polygon Exterior Angles Sum Theorem. See margin.

36. REASONING The measure of each interior angle of a regular polygon is 24 more than 38 times the measure of each exterior angle. Find the number of sides of the polygon. 90

Lesson 7-1 • Angles of Polygons **411**

37. ARCHAEOLOGY Archaeologists unearthed parts of two adjacent walls of an ancient castle. Before it was unearthed, they knew from ancient texts that the castle was shaped like a regular polygon, but nobody knew how many sides it had. Some said 6, others 8, and some even said 100. From the information in the figure, how many sides did the castle really have? 15

24°

38. DESIGN Ronella is designing boxes she will use to ship her jewelry. She wants to shape the box like a regular polygon. For the boxes to pack tightly, she decides to use a regular polygon in which the measure of its interior angles is half the measure of its exterior angles. What regular polygon should she use? equilateral triangle

39. CRYSTALLOGRAPHY Crystals are classified according to seven crystal systems. The basis of the classification is the shapes of the faces of the crystal. Turquoise belongs to the triclinic system. Each of the six faces of turquoise is in the shape of a quadrilateral. Find the sum of the measures of the interior angles of one such face. 360°

40. STRUCTURE If three of the interior angles of a convex hexagon each measure 140°, a fourth angle measures 84°, and the measure of the fifth angle is 3 times the measure of the sixth angle, find the measure of the sixth angle. 54°

Higher-Order Thinking Skills

41. FIND THE ERROR Marshawn says that the sum of the exterior angles of a decagon is greater than that of a heptagon because a decagon has more sides. Liang says that the sum of the exterior angles for both polygons is the same. Who is correct? Explain your reasoning. Liang; by the Polygon Exterior Angles Sum Theorem, the sum of the measures of any convex polygon is 360°.

42. WRITE Explain how triangles are related to the Polygon Interior Angles Sum Theorem. The Polygon Interior Angles Sum Theorem is derived from the pattern between the number of sides in a polygon and the number of triangles. The formula is the product of the sum of the measures of the angles in a triangle, 180°, and the number of triangles in the polygon.

43. CREATE Sketch a polygon and find the sum of its interior angles. How many sides does a polygon with twice this interior angles sum have? Justify your answer. See margin.

44. PERSEVERE Find the values of a, b, and c if QRSTVX is a regular hexagon. Justify your answer. See margin.

45. ANALYZE If two sides of a regular hexagon are extended to meet at a point in the exterior of the polygon, will the triangle formed be *sometimes*, *always*, or *never* be equilateral? Justify your argument. See margin.

412 Module 7 • Quadrilaterals

Answers

34. Given: A convex n-sided polygon.

Prove: The sum of the interior angles is $(n - 2) \cdot 180°$.

Proof: From a single vertex, draw line segments to each of the other vertices except adjacent vertices. These line segments form $n - 2$ triangles. The sum of the measures of the interior angles of a triangle is 180°, so the sum of the measures of the interior angles of the n-sided polygon is $(n - 2) \cdot 180°$, because there are $n - 2$ triangles.

35. Consider the sum of the measures of the exterior angles N for an n-gon.

N = sum of measures of linear pairs − sum of measures of interior angles
$$= 180n - 180(n - 2)$$
$$= 180n - 180n + 360$$
$$= 360$$

So, the sum of the exterior angle measures is 360° for any convex polygon.

43. 8; Sample answer: interior angles sum = $(5 - 2) \cdot 180$ or 540°. Twice this sum is 2(540) or 1080°. A polygon with this interior angles sum is the solution to $(n - 2) \cdot 180 = 1080$. So, $n = 8$.

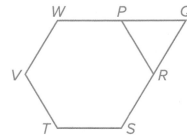

44. 30°, 90°, 60°; By the Polygon Interior Angles Sum Theorem, the sum of the interior angles is 720°. Because polygon QRSTVX is regular, there are 6 congruent angles. Each angle has a measure of 120°. So $m\angle XQR = 120°$ and $m\angle QRS = 120°$. Because polygon QRSTVX is regular, $XQ = QR$. By the Isosceles Triangle Theorem, $m\angle QXR = m\angle QRX$. The sum of the interior angle measures of a triangle is 180°, so $m\angle QXR + m\angle QRX + m\angle XQR = 180°$. By substitution, $a + a + 120 = 180$. So, $2a = 60$ and $a = 30$. $m\angle QRS = m\angle QRX + m\angle XRS$ by angle addition. By substitution, $120 = 30 + m\angle XRS$. From subtraction, $m\angle XRS = 90°$. So, $b = 90$. By SAS, $\triangle XVT \cong \triangle XQR$ and $\triangle XTS \cong \triangle XRS$. By angle addition, $m\angle VXQ = m\angle VXT + m\angle TXS + m\angle SXR + 30$. By substitution, $120 = 30 + m\angle TXS + m\angle SXR + 30$. So, $m\angle TXS + m\angle SXR = 60°$, and because $\angle TXS \cong \angle SXR$ by CPCTC, $m\angle TXS = m\angle SXR = 30°$. In $\triangle XTS$, $m\angle XTS + m\angle TSX + m\angle SXT = 180°$. By substitution, $90 + c + 30 = 180$, so $c = 60$.

45. Always; sample answer: By the Polygon Exterior Angles Sum Theorem, $m\angle QPR = 60°$ and $m\angle QRP = 60°$. Because the sum of the interior angle measures of a triangle is 180°, the measure of $\angle PQR = 180 - m\angle QPR - m\angle QRP = 180 - 60 - 60 = 60°$. So, $\triangle PQR$ is an equilateral triangle.

Parallelograms

LESSON GOAL

Students prove theorems about the properties of parallelograms and use the properties of parallelograms to solve problems.

1 LAUNCH

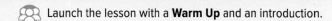 Launch the lesson with a **Warm Up** and an introduction.

2 EXPLORE AND DEVELOP

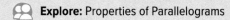 **Explore:** Properties of Parallelograms

Develop:

Parallelograms
- Use Properties of Parallelograms
- Proofs Using the Properties of Parallelograms

Diagonals of Parallelograms
- Use Properties of Parallelograms and Algebra
- Parallelograms and Coordinate Geometry

You may want your students to complete the **Checks** online.

3 REFLECT AND PRACTICE

Exit Ticket

Practice

DIFFERENTIATE

 View reports of student progress on the **Checks** after each example.

Resources	AL	OL	BL	ELL
Remediation: Parallel Lines and Transversals	●	●		●
Extension: Antiparallelograms		●	●	●

Language Development Handbook

Assign page 47 of the *Language Development Handbook* to help your students build mathematical language related to the properties of parallelograms.

ELL You can use the tips and suggestions on page T47 of the handbook to support students who are building English proficiency.

Suggested Pacing

| 90 min | 0.5 day |
| 45 min | 1 day |

Focus

Domain: Geometry
Standards for Mathematical Content:
G.CO.11 Prove theorems about parallelograms.
G.GPE.4 Use coordinates to prove simple geometric theorems algebraically.
Standards for Mathematical Practice:
3 Construct viable arguments and critique the reasoning of others.
4 Model with mathematics.
5 Use appropriate tools strategically.

Coherence

Vertical Alignment

Previous
Students proved theorems about the interior and exterior angles of polygons and used the theorems to solve problems.
G.MG.1

Now
Students prove theorems and solve problems about the properties of parallelograms.
G.CO.11, G.GPE.4

Next
Students will prove and use tests to determine whether quadrilaterals are parallelograms.
G.CO.11, G.GPE.4

Rigor

The Three Pillars of Rigor

1 CONCEPTUAL UNDERSTANDING	2 FLUENCY	3 APPLICATION

Conceptual Bridge In this lesson, students extend their understanding of the angles of polygons to prove theorems related to parallelograms. They build fluency and apply their understanding by solving real-world problems related to parallelograms.

Mathematical Background

A parallelogram is a quadrilateral with both pairs of opposite sides parallel and congruent. Opposite angles of a parallelogram are congruent. Finally, the diagonals of a parallelogram bisect each other, and each diagonal separates the parallelogram into two congruent triangles. These properties can be used to identify parallelograms.

Interactive Presentation

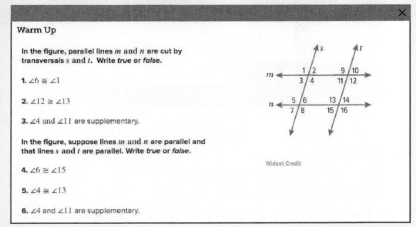

Warm Up

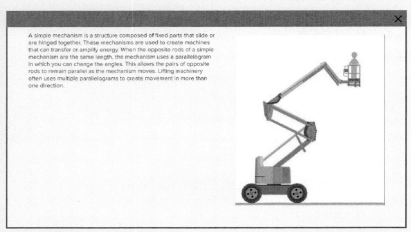

Launch the Lesson

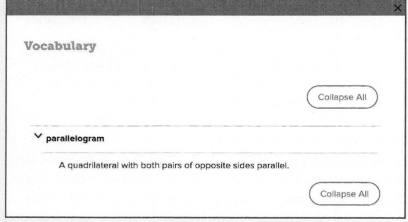

Today's Vocabulary

Warm Up

Prerequisite Skills

The Warm Up exercises address the following prerequisite skill for this lesson:

- identifying angle relationships formed by lines cut by a transversal

Answers:

1. false
2. true
3. false
4. true
5. true
6. true

Launch the Lesson

 Teaching the Mathematical Practices

4 Apply Mathematics In this Launch the Lesson, students can see a real-world application of parallelograms.

Go Online to find additional teaching notes and questions to promote classroom discourse.

Today's Standards

Tell students that they will be addressing these content and practice standards in this lesson. You may wish to have a student volunteer read aloud *How can I meet these standards?* and *How can I use these practices?*, and connect these to the standards.

See the Interactive Presentation for I Can statements that align with the standards covered in this lesson.

Today's Vocabulary

Tell students that they will be using this vocabulary term in this lesson. You can expand the row if you wish to share the definition. Then, discuss the questions below with the class.

Explore Properties of Parallelograms

Objective
Students use dynamic geometry software to analyze relationships in parallelograms and make conjectures about the properties of parallelograms.

 Teaching the Mathematical Practices

> **5 Use Mathematical Tools** Point out that to solve the problem in this Explore, students will need to use dynamic geometry software. Work with students to explore and deepen their understanding of relationships and properties of parallelograms.

Ideas for Use

Recommended Use Present the Inquiry Question, or have a student volunteer read it aloud. Have students work in pairs to complete the Explore activity on their devices. Pairs should discuss each of the questions. Monitor student progress during the activity. Upon completion of the Explore activity, have student volunteers share their responses to the Inquiry Question.

What if my students don't have devices? You may choose to project the activity on a whiteboard. A printable worksheet for each Explore is available online. You may choose to print the worksheet so that individuals or pairs of students can use it to record their observations.

Summary of the Activity

Students will complete guiding exercises throughout the Explore activity. Students construct a parallelogram and measure its sides, observing that the opposite sides are the same length. Students then measure the angles and observe that the opposite angles are the same measurement. Next, students construct the diagonals of the parallelogram and measure the length of each diagonal from a vertex to the intersection point of the diagonals. Students then observe that the two parts of each diagonal are the same. The students complete guiding exercises that lead them to write conjectures about these properties. Then, students will answer the Inquiry Question.

(continued on the next page)

Interactive Presentation

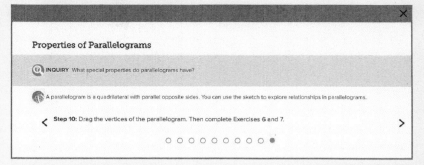

Properties of Parallelograms

INQUIRY What special properties do parallelograms have?

A parallelogram is a quadrilateral with parallel opposite sides. You can use the sketch to explore relationships in parallelograms.

Step 10: Drag the vertices of the parallelogram. Then complete Exercises 6 and 7.

Explore

WEB SKETCHPAD

Students use a sketch to explore the measures of parts of parallelograms.

G.CO.11

Interactive Presentation

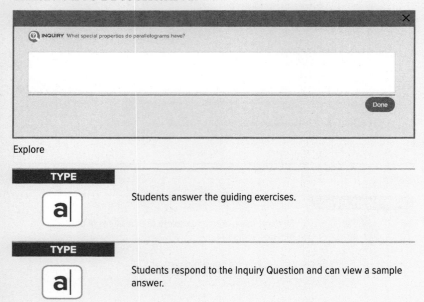

Explore

TYPE

Students answer the guiding exercises.

TYPE

Students respond to the Inquiry Question and can view a sample answer.

Explore Properties of Parallelograms *(continued)*

Teaching the Mathematical Practices

3 Construct Arguments In the Explore, students will use stated definitions and observed measurements to make a conjecture.

Questions

Have students complete the Explore activity.

Ask:

- Does the relationship that you described in Exercise **1** remain true as you move the vertices of parallelogram *ABCD*? If so, make a conjecture about the opposite sides of a parallelogram. Yes; sample answer: The opposite sides of a parallelogram are always congruent.

Inquiry

What special properties do parallelograms have? Sample answer: The opposite sides and angles of a parallelogram are congruent. The diagonals of a parallelogram bisect each other.

Go Online to find additional teaching notes and sample answers for the guiding exercises.

1 CONCEPTUAL UNDERSTANDING | **2 FLUENCY** | 3 APPLICATION

Learn Parallelograms

Objective
Students prove and use theorems about the properties of parallelograms.

 Teaching the Mathematical Practices

7 Use Structure Help students to explore the structure of parallelograms in this Learn.

What Students Are Learning

Parallelograms are interesting figures because with limited requirements in the definition (opposite parallel sides) you can prove many useful facts about the figure (opposite congruent sides and angles, supplementary adjacent angles, diagonals bisect each other).

Example 1 Use Properties of Parallelograms

 Teaching the Mathematical Practices

2 Create Representations Encourage students to write an equation that models the situation. Then use the equation to solve the problem.

Questions for Mathematical Discourse

AL How do we know that $\overline{CD} \cong \overline{AB}$? Sample answer: Because *ABDC* is a parallelogram, we know that opposite sides are congruent.

OL How do you know if two angles are *consecutive*? Sample answer: Consecutive angles in a polygon share a segment as one of the sides.

BL What is *AC*? Explain. *AC* = 1.5 ft; sample answer: Because opposite sides are congruent, they have the same measure.

🅖 Go Online

- Find additional teaching notes.
- View performance reports of the Checks.
- Assign or present an Extra Example.

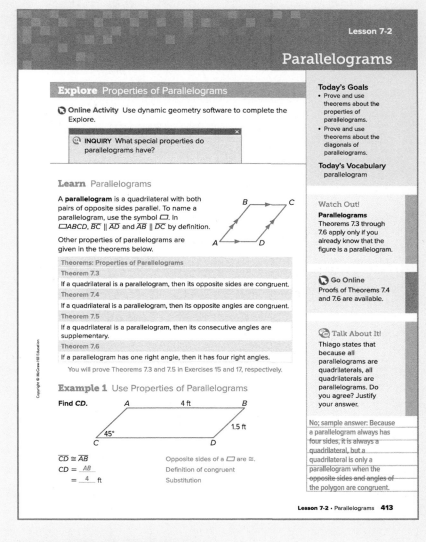

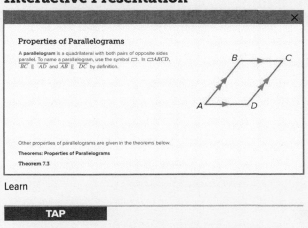

Interactive Presentation

Properties of Parallelograms

A **parallelogram** is a quadrilateral with both pairs of opposite sides parallel. To name a parallelogram, use the symbol ▱. In ▱*ABCD*, $\overline{BC} \parallel \overline{AD}$ and $\overline{AB} \parallel \overline{DC}$ by definition.

Other properties of parallelograms are given in the theorems below.

Theorems: Properties of Parallelograms

Theorem 7.3

Learn

TAP

Students tap to see a Study Tip.

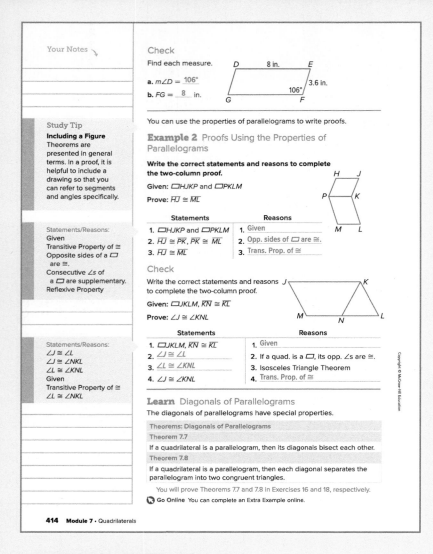

Check

Find each measure.

a. $m\angle D =$ __106°__

b. $FG =$ __8__ in.

You can use the properties of parallelograms to write proofs.

Example 2 Proofs Using the Properties of Parallelograms

Write the correct statements and reasons to complete the two-column proof.

Given: ▱HJKP and ▱PKLM

Prove: $\overline{HJ} \cong \overline{ML}$

Statements	Reasons
1. ▱HJKP and ▱PKLM	1. Given
2. $\overline{HJ} \cong \overline{PK}, \overline{PK} \cong \overline{ML}$	2. Opp. sides of ▱ are ≅.
3. $\overline{HJ} \cong \overline{ML}$	3. Trans. Prop. of ≅

Check

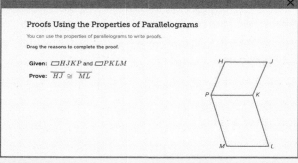

Write the correct statements and reasons to complete the two-column proof.

Given: ▱JKLM, $\overline{KN} \cong \overline{KL}$

Prove: $\angle J \cong \angle KNL$

Statements	Reasons
1. ▱JKLM, $\overline{KN} \cong \overline{KL}$	1. Given
2. $\angle J \cong \angle L$	2. If a quad. is a ▱, its opp. ∠s are ≅.
3. $\angle L \cong \angle KNL$	3. Isosceles Triangle Theorem
4. $\angle J \cong \angle KNL$	4. Trans. Prop. of ≅

Learn Diagonals of Parallelograms

The diagonals of parallelograms have special properties.

Theorems: Diagonals of Parallelograms

Theorem 7.7

If a quadrilateral is a parallelogram, then its diagonals bisect each other.

Theorem 7.8

If a quadrilateral is a parallelogram, then each diagonal separates the parallelogram into two congruent triangles.

You will prove Theorems 7.7 and 7.8 in Exercises 16 and 18, respectively.

🖥 **Go Online** You can complete an Extra Example online.

414 Module 7 · Quadrilaterals

Your Notes ↘

Study Tip
Including a Figure
Theorems are presented in general terms. In a proof, it is helpful to include a drawing so that you can refer to segments and angles specifically.

Statements/Reasons:
Given
Transitive Property of ≅
Opposite sides of a ▱ are ≅.
Consecutive ∠s of a ▱ are supplementary.
Reflexive Property

Statements/Reasons:
$\angle J \cong \angle L$
$\angle J \cong \angle NKL$
$\angle L \cong \angle KNL$
Given
Transitive Property of ≅
$\angle L \cong \angle NKL$

Interactive Presentation

Proofs Using the Properties of Parallelograms

You can use the properties of parallelograms to write proofs.

Drag the reasons to complete the proof.

Given: ▱HJKP and ▱PKLM

Prove: $\overline{HJ} \cong \overline{ML}$

Example 2

DRAG

Students drag reasons to complete the proof.

CHECK

Students complete the Check online to determine whether they are ready to move on.

Example 2 Proofs Using the Properties of Parallelograms

 Teaching the Mathematical Practices

3 Construct Arguments In this example, students will use stated assumptions, definitions, and previously established results to complete the given proof.

Questions for Mathematical Discourse

AL What relationships does $\overline{HJ}$ have with other parts of ▱HJKP? Sample answer: $\overline{HJ}$ is opposite $\overline{PK}$, so $\overline{HJ} \cong \overline{PK}$.

OL Which theorem helps you prove segments that are sides of a parallelogram congruent to other segments? Theorem 7.3

BL Is it possible to prove any of the angles of ▱HJKP congruent to any of the angles of ▱PKLM? Explain. No; sample answer: None of the angles are shared between the two parallelograms and there is no other information about the angles given.

DIFFERENTIATE

Reteaching Activity **AL**
Have students plot $P(-4, -3)$, $L(-1, 2)$, and $S(5, 1)$ on a coordinate plane. Have them locate and plot a fourth point T that will create a parallelogram. They should prove that the figure is a parallelogram by using the slopes and definition in this lesson. The ordered pair for the fourth point is $(2, -4)$. Then have students check that the opposite sides are congruent using the Distance Formula, and that the opposite angles are congruent using a protractor.

Learn Diagonals of Parallelograms

Objective
Students prove and use theorems about the diagonals of parallelograms.

MP **Teaching the Mathematical Practices**

7 Use Structure Help students to explore the structure of diagonals of parallelograms in this Learn.

Common Misconception
Once students learn facts about parallelograms, they may forget which facts come from theorems proved using the definition and which facts come directly from the definition. Encourage students to state which definition or fact they are using and to be precise in their usage of these facts and definitions.

1 CONCEPTUAL UNDERSTANDING | **2 FLUENCY** | 3 APPLICATION

Example 3 Use Properties of Parallelograms and Algebra

 Teaching the Mathematical Practices

> **2 Create Representations** Guide students to write an equation that models the situation in this example. Then use the equation to solve the problem.

Questions for Mathematical Discourse

AL What are the diagonals of *ABCD*? $\overline{AC}$ and $\overline{BD}$

OL What is $m\angle ADC$? 124°

BL How many pairs of congruent triangles are formed by the diagonals of the parallelogram? 4

Common Error

Students may think that the angles in the problem are congruent when they are supplementary. Remind them to examine how the angles are located related to each other and then ask them what kind of relationship that type of location has in parallelograms.

Example 4 Parallelograms and Coordinate Geometry

 Teaching the Mathematical Practices

> **4 Apply Mathematics** In this example, students apply what they have learned about properties of parallelograms to solving a real-world problem.

Questions for Mathematical Discourse

AL What are the diagonals of the parallelogram? $\overline{AD}$ and $\overline{BC}$

OL What fact about parallelograms can you use to help you calculate the perimeter of the parallelogram? Sample answer: Opposite sides of a parallelogram are congruent.

BL What are the lengths of the other two sides of the flap? Both sides measure 8.6 centimeters.

Example 3 Use Properties of Parallelograms and Algebra

Find the values of *x* and *z* in ▱*ABCD*.
$m\angle ADC = 4x°$ and $m\angle DAB = (2x - 6)°$.

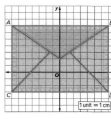

Part A Find the value of *x*.

$180 = m\angle ADC + m\angle DAB$		Consec. ∠s in a ▱ are supplementary.
$180 = \underline{\;4x\;} + \underline{(2x-6)}$		Substitution
$x = \underline{\;31\;}$		Solve.

Part B Find the value of *z*.

$\overline{AE} \cong \overline{CE}$		Diagonals of a ▱ bisect each other.
$AE = CE$		Definition of congruent
$3z - 4 = \underline{\;z+5\;}$		Substitution
$z = \underline{\;4.5\;}$		Solve.

 Example 4 Parallelograms and Coordinate Geometry

SCRAPBOOKING Tomas is making envelopes to sell with handmade cards. He uses a different style of paper to create the flap of the envelope, and he edges the envelopes with washi tape. The envelopes are parallelograms, and the edges of the flaps lie along the diagonals of the parallelograms. Find the area of the flap and the perimeter of the envelope.

1 unit = 1 cm

Problem-Solving Tip

Make a Plan To find the area of the paper needed for the envelope flap, you need to calculate the point of intersection of the diagonals of the envelope. Before solving for the area, analyze the information you are given, develop a plan, and determine the theorems you will need to apply.

Part A Find the amount of paper needed to create the flap.

You can approximate the area of the flap with a triangle, so the area is $A = \frac{1}{2}bh$.

Step 1 Find the height.

To find the height, determine the coordinates of the intersection of the diagonals of the envelope, which has vertices at $A(-7, 7)$, $B(7, 7)$, $C(-7, -3)$, and $D(7, -3)$. Because the diagonals of a parallelogram bisect each other, the intersection point is the midpoint of $\overline{AD}$ and $\overline{BC}$. Find the midpoint of $\overline{AD}$.

$$\left(\frac{x_1 + x_2}{2}, \frac{y_1 + y_2}{2}\right) = \left(\frac{-7 + 7}{2}, \frac{7 + (-3)}{2}\right) \quad \text{Midpoint Formula}$$
$$= (0, 2) \quad \text{Simplify.}$$

(continued on the next page)

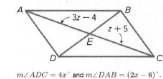 Go Online You can complete an Extra Example online.

Interactive Presentation

Use Properties of Parallelograms and Algebra

Find the values of *x* and *z* in ▱*ABCD*.

$m\angle ADC = 4x°$ and $m\angle DAB = (2x - 6)°$.

Example 3

TAP

Students tap to fill in parts of the solution and select correct answers.

The height is the difference in the *y*-coordinates of the intersection of the diagonals and the vertices of the top edge of the envelope.

$h = 7 - 2$ or $\underline{5}$ cm

Step 2 Find the base.

The base of the flap is the length of the top edge of the envelope. You can count the units to determine the base.

$b = \underline{14}$ cm

Step 3 Find the area of the flap.

$A = \frac{1}{2}bh$ Area of a triangle

$= \frac{1}{2}(\underline{14})(\underline{5})$ Substitute.

$= \underline{35}$ cm²   Solve.

Part B Find the length of washi tape needed to create the border.

Step 1 Find the length.

The length of the envelope is the same as the base of the triangle determined above.

$\ell = \underline{14}$ cm

Step 2 Find the width.

The width of the envelope is the distance between the top edge and the bottom edge of the envelope.

$w = 7 - (-3) = 10$ cm

Step 3 Find the perimeter.

Because the envelope is a parallelogram, opposite sides are congruent. So, the perimeter is given by $P = 2\ell + 2w$.

$P = 2\ell + 2w$ Perimeter formula

$= 2(14) + 2(10)$ Substitute.

$= 48$ cm   Solve.

Check

QUILTING Jimena is making a quilt. Each block is a parallelogram made of a single piece of patterned fabric and is trimmed with a gray border. Find the area of the fabric used to make the block. Find the length of fabric used to make the border of the block. Round to the nearest tenth if necessary.

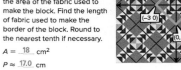

$A = \underline{18}$ cm²

$P \approx \underline{17.0}$ cm

 Go Online You can complete an Extra Example online.

> **💭 Think About It!**
>
> What assumptions did you make when calculating the area of the paper and the length of washi tape?
>
> Sample answer: I assumed that Tomas did not need any extra paper or tape to overlap the seams of the envelopes. I assumed that the envelopes were perfect parallelograms and that the edges of the flaps aligned perfectly with the diagonals. I also assumed that the flap was a triangle.

Common Error

Students may not recognize the rectangle as the parallelogram mentioned in the problem statement. They may also not recognize the edges of the flap as being part of the diagonals of that parallelogram. Guide them in reading the problem statement and examining the figure to see where the described objects are in the figure.

Exit Ticket

Recommended Use

At the end of class, go online to display the Exit Ticket prompt and ask students to respond using a separate piece of paper. Have students hand you their responses as they leave the room.

Alternate Use

At the end of class, go online to display the Exit Ticket prompt and ask students to respond verbally or by using a mini-whiteboard. Have students hold up their whiteboards so that you can see all student responses. Tap to reveal the answer when most or all students have completed the Exit Ticket.

Interactive Presentation

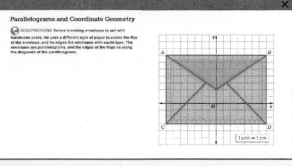

Example 4

TAP

Students tap to reveal steps in the solution.

CHECK

Students complete the Check online to determine whether they are ready to move on.

1 CONCEPTUAL UNDERSTANDING | **2 FLUENCY** | 3 APPLICATION

Practice and Homework

Suggested Assignments

Use the table below to select appropriate exercises.

DOK	Topic	Exercises
1, 2	exercises that mirror the examples	1–14
2	exercises that use a variety of skills from this lesson	15–24
2	exercises that extend concepts learned in this lesson to new contexts	25–26
3	exercises that emphasize higher-order and critical-thinking skills	27–31

ASSESS AND DIFFERENTIATE

📊 Use the data from the **Checks** to determine whether to provide resources for extension, remediation, or intervention.

IF students score 90% or more on the Checks, `BL`
THEN assign:

- Practice, Exercises 1–25 odd, 27–31
- Extension: Antiparallelograms
- 🅐 **ALEKS** Parallelograms and Trapezoids

IF students score 66%–89% on the Checks, `OL`
THEN assign:

- Practice, Exercises 1–31 odd
- Remediation, Review Resources: Parallel Lines and Transversals
- Personal Tutors
- Extra Examples 1–4
- 🅐 **ALEKS** Parallel Lines and Transversals

IF students score 65% or less on the Checks, `AL`
THEN assign:

- Practice, Exercises 1–13 odd
- Remediation, Review Resources: Parallel Lines and Transversals
- *Quick Review Math Handbook*: Parallelograms
- 🅐 **ALEKS** Parallel Lines and Transversals

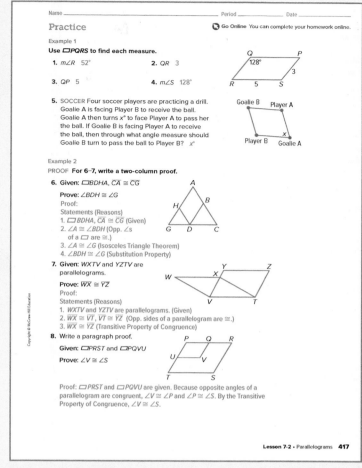

Name _____ Period _____ Date _____

Practice   🔄 Go Online You can complete your homework online.

Example 1

Use ▱PQRS to find each measure.

1. $m\angle R$ 52°
2. QR 3
3. QP 5
4. $m\angle S$ 128°

5. SOCCER Four soccer players are practicing a drill. Goalie A is facing Player B to receive the ball. Goalie A then turns $x°$ to face Player A to pass her the ball. If Goalie B is facing Player A to receive the ball, then through what angle measure should Goalie B turn to pass the ball to Player B? $x°$

Example 2

PROOF For 6–7, write a two-column proof.

6. Given: ▱BDHA, $\overline{CA} \cong \overline{CG}$
   Prove: $\angle BDH \cong \angle G$
   Proof:
   Statements (Reasons)
   1. ▱BDHA, $\overline{CA} \cong \overline{CG}$ (Given)
   2. $\angle A \cong \angle BDH$ (Opp. $\angle$s of a ▱ are $\cong$.)
   3. $\angle A \cong \angle G$ (Isosceles Triangle Theorem)
   4. $\angle BDH \cong \angle G$ (Substitution Property)

7. Given: WXTV and YZTV are parallelograms.
   Prove: $\overline{WX} \cong \overline{YZ}$
   Proof:
   Statements (Reasons)
   1. WXTV and YZTV are parallelograms. (Given)
   2. $\overline{WX} \cong \overline{VT}$, $\overline{VT} \cong \overline{YZ}$ (Opp. sides of a parallelogram are $\cong$.)
   3. $\overline{WX} \cong \overline{YZ}$ (Transitive Property of Congruence)

8. Write a paragraph proof.
   Given: ▱PRST and ▱PQVU
   Prove: $\angle V \cong \angle S$

   Proof: ▱PRST and ▱PQVU are given. Because opposite angles of a parallelogram are congruent, $\angle V \cong \angle P$ and $\angle P \cong \angle S$. By the Transitive Property of Congruence, $\angle V \cong \angle S$.

Lesson 7-2 • Parallelograms   **417**

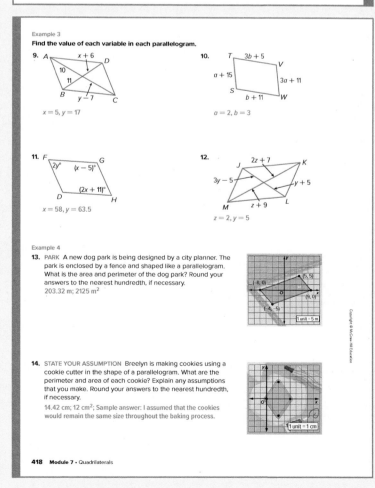

Example 3

Find the value of each variable in each parallelogram.

9.
   $x = 5, y = 17$

10.
   $a = 2, b = 3$

11.
   $x = 58, y = 63.5$

12.
   $z = 2, y = 5$

Example 4

13. PARK A new dog park is being designed by a city planner. The park is enclosed by a fence and shaped like a parallelogram. What is the area and perimeter of the dog park? Round your answers to the nearest hundredth, if necessary.
   203.32 m; 2125 m²

14. STATE YOUR ASSUMPTION Breelyn is making cookies using a cookie cutter in the shape of a parallelogram. What are the perimeter and area of each cookie? Explain any assumptions that you make. Round your answers to the nearest hundredth, if necessary.
   14.42 cm; 12 cm²; Sample answer: I assumed that the cookies would remain the same size throughout the baking process.

418 Module 7 • Quadrilaterals

1 CONCEPTUAL UNDERSTANDING	2 FLUENCY	3 APPLICATION

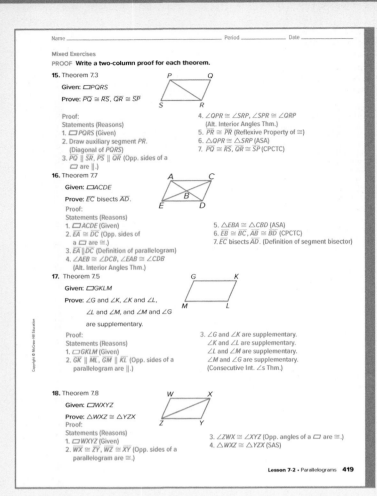

Name _____ Period _____ Date _____

Mixed Exercises

PROOF Write a two-column proof for each theorem.

15. Theorem 7.3

Given: ▱PQRS

Prove: $\overline{PQ} \cong \overline{RS}$, $\overline{QR} \cong \overline{SP}$

Proof:
Statements (Reasons)
1. ▱PQRS (Given)
2. Draw auxiliary segment PR. (Diagonal of PQRS)
3. $\overline{PQ} \parallel \overline{SR}$, $\overline{PS} \parallel \overline{QR}$ (Opp. sides of a ▱ are ∥.)
4. ∠QPR ≅ ∠SRP, ∠SPR ≅ ∠QRP (Alt. Interior Angles Thm.)
5. $\overline{PR} \cong \overline{PR}$ (Reflexive Property of ≅)
6. △QPR ≅ △SRP (ASA)
7. $\overline{PQ} \cong \overline{RS}$, $\overline{QR} \cong \overline{SP}$ (CPCTC)

16. Theorem 7.7

Given: ▱ACDE

Prove: $\overline{EC}$ bisects $\overline{AD}$.

Proof:
Statements (Reasons)
1. ▱ACDE (Given)
2. $\overline{EA} \cong \overline{DC}$ (Opp. sides of a ▱ are ≅.)
3. $\overline{EA} \parallel \overline{DC}$ (Definition of parallelogram)
4. ∠AEB ≅ ∠DCB, ∠EAB ≅ ∠CDB (Alt. Interior Angles Thm.)
5. △EBA ≅ △CBD (ASA)
6. $\overline{EB} \cong \overline{BD}$, $\overline{AB} \cong \overline{BD}$ (CPCTC)
7. $\overline{EC}$ bisects $\overline{AD}$. (Definition of segment bisector)

17. Theorem 7.5

Given: ▱GKLM

Prove: ∠G and ∠K, ∠K and ∠L, ∠L and ∠M, and ∠M and ∠G are supplementary.

Proof:
Statements (Reasons)
1. ▱GKLM (Given)
2. $\overline{GK} \parallel \overline{ML}$, $\overline{GM} \parallel \overline{KL}$ (Opp. sides of a parallelogram are ∥.)
3. ∠G and ∠K are supplementary. ∠K and ∠L are supplementary. ∠L and ∠M are supplementary. ∠M and ∠G are supplementary. (Consecutive Int. ∠s Thm.)

18. Theorem 7.8

Given: ▱WXYZ

Prove: △WXZ ≅ △YZX

Proof:
Statements (Reasons)
1. ▱WXYZ (Given)
2. $\overline{WX} \cong \overline{ZY}$, $\overline{WZ} \cong \overline{XY}$ (Opp. sides of a parallelogram are ≅.)
3. ∠ZWX ≅ ∠XYZ (Opp. angles of a ▱ are ≅.)
4. △WXZ ≅ △YZX (SAS)

Lesson 7-2 • Parallelograms **419**

Use ▱ABCD to find each measure or value.

19. x 3

20. y 6

21. m∠AFB 131°

22. m∠DAC 72°

23. m∠ACD 29°

24. m∠DAB 101°

25. REGULARITY Use the graph shown. See margin.

a. Use the Distance Formula to determine if the diagonals of JKLM bisect each other. Explain.

b. Determine whether the diagonals are congruent. Explain.

c. Use slopes to determine if the consecutive sides are perpendicular. Explain.

26. USE TOOLS Make a Venn diagram showing the relationship between squares, rectangles, and parallelograms. See margin.

🧠 Higher-Order Thinking Skills

27. PERSEVERE ABCD is a parallelogram with side lengths as indicated in the figure at the right. The perimeter of ABCD is 22. Find AB. 7

28. ANALYZE Explain why parallelograms are always quadrilaterals, but quadrilaterals are sometimes parallelograms. See margin.

29. WRITE Summarize the properties of the sides, angles, and diagonals of a parallelogram. See margin.

30. CREATE Provide an example to show that parallelograms are not always congruent if their corresponding sides are congruent.

Sample answer:

31. PERSEVERE Find m∠1 and m∠10 in the figure. Explain your reasoning. See margin.

Answers

25a. $JP = \sqrt{13}$, $LP = \sqrt{13}$, $MP = \sqrt{34}$, $KP = \sqrt{34}$; because $JP = LP$ and $MP = KP$, the diagonals bisect each other.

25b. No; $JP + LP \neq MP + KP$.

25c. No; sample answer: The slope of $\overline{JK} = 0$, and the slope of $\overline{JM} = 2$. The slopes are not negative reciprocals of each other, so the consecutive sides are not perpendicular.

26.

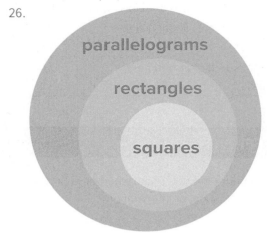

parallelograms

rectangles

squares

28. Sample answer: A parallelogram is a polygon with four sides in which the opposite sides and angles are congruent. Quadrilaterals are defined as four-sided polygons. Because a parallelogram always has four sides, it is always a quadrilateral. A quadrilateral is only a parallelogram when the opposite sides and angles of the polygon are congruent.

29. Sample answer: In a parallelogram, the opposite sides and angles are congruent. Two consecutive angles in a parallelogram are supplementary. If one angle of a parallelogram is right, then all the angles are right. The diagonals of a parallelogram bisect each other.

31. $m\angle 1 = 116°$, $m\angle 10 = 115°$; Sample answer: $m\angle 8 = 64°$ because alternate interior angles are congruent. ∠1 is supplementary to ∠8 because consecutive angles in a parallelogram are supplementary, so $m\angle 1 = 116°$. ∠10 is supplementary to the 65°-angle because consecutive angles in a parallelogram are supplementary, so $m\angle 10 = 180° - 65°$ or 115°.

Tests for Parallelograms

LESSON GOAL

Students prove and use the tests for parallelograms to determine whether quadrilaterals are parallelograms.

1 LAUNCH

 Launch the lesson with a **Warm Up** and an introduction.

2 EXPLORE AND DEVELOP

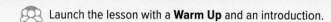 **Explore:** Constructing Parallelograms

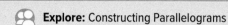 **Develop:**

Tests for Parallelograms
- Identify Parallelograms
- Use Parallelograms to Find Values
- Identify Parallelograms on the Coordinate Plane
- Parallelograms and Coordinate Proofs

 You may want your students to complete the **Checks** online.

3 REFLECT AND PRACTICE

 Exit Ticket

 Practice

 Formative Assessment Math Probe

DIFFERENTIATE

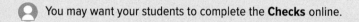 View reports of student progress on the **Checks** after each example.

Resources	AL	OL	BL	ELL
Remediation: Parallelograms	●	●		●
Extension: Proving that Quadrilaterals are Parallelograms		●	●	●

Language Development Handbook

Assign page 48 of the *Language Development Handbook* to help your students build mathematical language related to using the tests for parallelograms.

ELL You can use the tips and suggestions on page T48 of the handbook to support students who are building English proficiency.

Suggested Pacing

90 min	**0.5 day**
45 min	**1 day**

Focus

Domain: Geometry

Standards for Mathematical Content:

G.CO.11 Prove theorems about parallelograms.

G.GPE.4 Use coordinates to prove simple geometric theorems algebraically.

Standards for Mathematical Practice:

2 Reason abstractly and quantitatively.

3 Construct viable arguments and critique the reasoning of others.

6 Attend to precision.

Coherence

Vertical Alignment

Previous
Students proved theorems and solved problems about the properties of parallelograms.
G.CO.11, G.GPE.4

Now
Students prove and use tests to determine whether quadrilaterals are parallelograms.
G.CO.11, G.GPE.4

Next
Students will recognize the properties of rectangles and will use them to determine whether a parallelogram is a rectangle.
G.CO.11, G.GPE.4

Rigor

The Three Pillars of Rigor

1 CONCEPTUAL UNDERSTANDING	2 FLUENCY	3 APPLICATION

Conceptual Bridge In this lesson, students continue to extend their understanding of polygons to prove theorems related to parallelograms. They build fluency and apply their understanding by solving real-world problems related to parallelograms.

Mathematical Background

The properties of parallelograms can be used to determine if a quadrilateral is a parallelogram. If a quadrilateral is graphed on the coordinate plane, the Distance Formula and the Slope Formula can be used to determine if it is a parallelogram.

Interactive Presentation

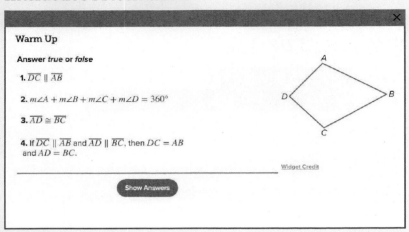

Warm Up

Answer *true* or *false*

1. $\overline{DC} \parallel \overline{AB}$

2. $m\angle A + m\angle B + m\angle C + m\angle D = 360°$

3. $\overline{AD} \cong \overline{BC}$

4. If $\overline{DC} \parallel \overline{AB}$ and $\overline{AD} \parallel \overline{BC}$, then $DC = AB$ and $AD = BC$.

Widget Credit

[Show Answers]

Warm Up

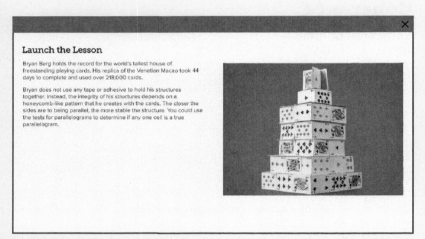

Launch the Lesson

Bryan Berg holds the record for the world's tallest house of freestanding playing cards. His replica of the Venetian Macao took 44 days to complete and used over 218,000 cards.

Bryan does not use any tape or adhesive to hold his structures together. Instead, the integrity of his structures depends on a honeycomb-like pattern that he creates with the cards. The closer the sides are to being parallel, the more stable the structure. You could use the tests for parallelograms to determine if any one cell is a true parallelogram.

Launch the Lesson

Warm Up

Prerequisite Skills

The Warm Up exercises address the following prerequisite skill for this lesson:

- applying facts about quadrilaterals and parallelograms

Answers:

1. false; not enough information

2. true

3. false; not enough information

4. true

Launch the Lesson

 **Teaching the Mathematical Practices**

4 Apply Mathematics In this Launch the Lesson, students can see a real-world application of tests for parallelograms.

Go Online to find additional teaching notes and questions to promote classroom discourse.

Today's Standards

Tell students that they will be addressing these content and practice standards in this lesson. You may wish to have a student volunteer read aloud *How can I meet these standards?* and *How can I use these practices?*, and connect these to the standards.

See the Interactive Presentation for I Can statements that align with the standards covered in this lesson.

Explore Constructing Parallelograms

Objective
Students use dynamic geometry software to construct parallelograms using the properties of parallelograms.

MP Teaching the Mathematical Practices

2 Different Properties Mathematically proficient students look for different ways to solve problems. Encourage students to use the different properties of parallelograms to construct parallelograms using different methods.

Ideas for Use

Recommended Use Present the Inquiry Question, or have a student volunteer read it aloud. Have students work in pairs to complete the Explore activity on their devices. Pairs should discuss each of the questions. Monitor student progress during the activity. Upon completion of the Explore activity, have student volunteers share their responses to the Inquiry Question.

What if my students don't have devices? You may choose to project the activity on a whiteboard. A printable worksheet for each Explore is available online. You may choose to print the worksheet so that individuals or pairs of students can use it to record their observations.

Summary of the Activity
Students will complete guiding exercises throughout the Explore activity. Students construct a parallelogram using dynamic geometry software. Then they complete guiding exercises to analyze their construction method and determine how they know their construction method works. They repeat this multiple times. Then, students will answer the Inquiry Question.

(continued on the next page)

Interactive Presentation

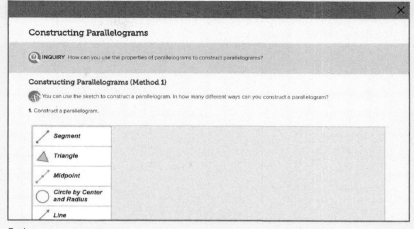

Explore

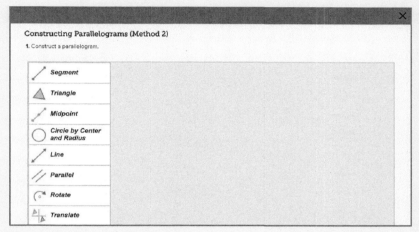

Explore

WEB SKETCHPAD

 Students will use a sketch to complete an activity in which they explore the construction of parallelograms.

G.CO.12

1 CONCEPTUAL UNDERSTANDING | 2 FLUENCY | 3 APPLICATION

Interactive Presentation

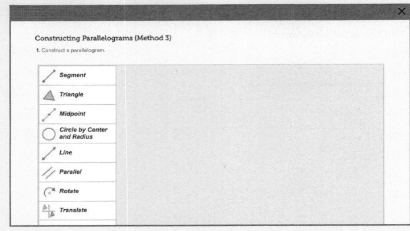

Explore

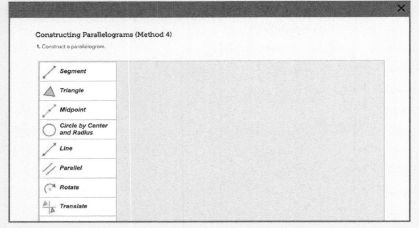

Explore

TYPE

Students respond to the Inquiry Question and can view a sample answer.

Explore Constructing Parallelograms (*continued*)

MP Teaching the Mathematical Practices

5 Use Mathematical Tools Point out that to solve the problem in this Explore, students will need to use dynamic geometry software. Work with students to explore and deepen their understanding of constructing parallelograms.

Questions

Have students complete the Explore activity.

Ask:
• Describe which properties of parallelograms you used to verify that your construction was a parallelogram. Sample answer: I used Theorem 7.7. If a quadrilateral is a parallelogram, then its diagonals bisect each other.

Inquiry

How can you use the properties of parallelograms to construct parallelograms? Sample answer: I used the properties of parallelograms to determine what constraints to place on my constructions. The theorems used to define parallelograms outline the properties that every parallelogram must have.

Go Online to find additional teaching notes and sample answers for the guiding exercises.

1 CONCEPTUAL UNDERSTANDING | **2 FLUENCY** | 3 APPLICATION

Learn Tests for Parallelograms

Objective
Students use the tests for parallelograms to determine whether quadrilaterals are parallelograms.

Teaching the Mathematical Practices

7 Use Structure Help students to explore the structure of conditions for parallelograms in this Learn to determine whether a quadrilateral is a parallelogram.

Important to Know
The first test of determining whether any mathematical object is of a particular type is the definition of that type. Sometimes, as with parallelograms, there are other tests. These are theorems where if an object has certain characteristics different from the definition, the proof of the theorem shows that the definition is true.

Common Misconception
Remind the students that a quadrilateral only needs to pass one of the five tests to be proven a parallelogram. All of the properties do not need to be proven.

Essential Question Follow-Up
Students learn properties and tests for parallelograms.
Ask:
Why is it important to know when a quadrilateral is a parallelogram in the real world? Sample answer: Parallelograms have many useful properties, and it is useful to know when an object has those properties.

Example 1 Identify Parallelograms

Teaching the Mathematical Practices

3 Justify Conclusions Mathematically proficient students can explain the conclusions drawn when solving a problem. This example asks students to justify their conclusions.

Questions for Mathematical Discourse

AL In a quadrilateral, what are opposite sides? sides that are not adjacent to each other

OL If the left side and the right side of the quadrilateral measure 10 centimeters, is the quadrilateral still a parallelogram? Explain. Yes; sample answer: Opposite sides are still congruent.

BL If you did not know the measures of the left and right sides of the quadrilateral, what else would you need to know about the top and bottom sides of the quadrilateral to know that the quadrilateral is a parallelogram? Sample answer: You would need to know that the top and bottom sides are also parallel.

Go Online
- Find additional teaching notes.
- View performance reports of the Checks.
- Assign or present an Extra Example.

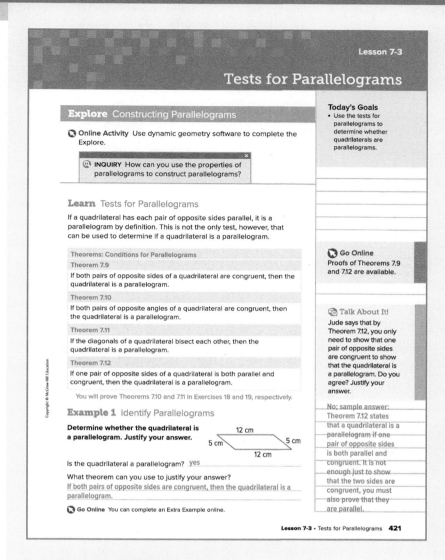

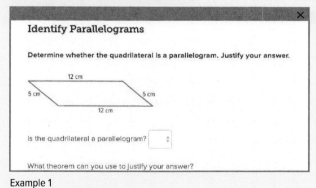

Interactive Presentation

Identify Parallelograms

Determine whether the quadrilateral is a parallelogram. Justify your answer.

Is the quadrilateral a parallelogram?

What theorem can you use to justify your answer?

Example 1

TAP

 Students tap to choose correct answers.

Your Notes

You can use the conditions of parallelograms to find missing values that make a quadrilateral a parallelogram.

Example 2 Use Parallelograms to Find Values

SCHOOL SUPPLIES The top of the eraser appears to be a parallelogram. Find the values of x and y so that the side of the eraser is a parallelogram.

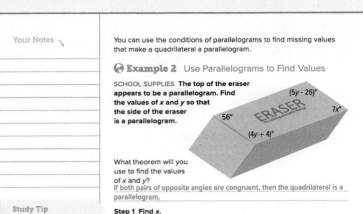

What theorem will you use to find the values of x and y?
If both pairs of opposite angles are congruent, then the quadrilateral is a parallelogram.

Study Tip
Parallelograms A quadrilateral needs to pass only one of the five tests to be proven a parallelogram. All of the properties of a parallelogram do not need to be proven.

Step 1 Find x.
Find x such that $7x = 56$.

$7x = 56$ Opp. angles of a ▱ are ≅.
$x = \underline{8}$ Solve.

Step 2 Find y.
Find y such that $4y + 4 = 5y - 26$.

$4y + 4 = 5y - 26$ Opp. angles of a ▱ are ≅.
$y = \underline{30}$ Solve.

So, when x is $\underline{8}$ and y is $\underline{30}$, the quadrilateral is a parallelogram.

Check

MOSAICS The mosaic pattern of the floor is made up of different tiles.

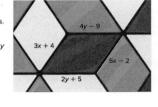

Part A
Find the values of x and y so that the tile is a parallelogram.

$x = \underline{3}$
$y = \underline{7}$

Part B
Select the theorem you used to find the values of x and y.
- **A.** If both pairs of opp. sides are ≅, then quad. is a ▱.
- **B.** If both pairs of opp. ∠s are ≅, then quad. is a ▱.
- **C.** If diag. bisect each other, then quad. is a ▱.
- **D.** If one pair of opp. sides is ≅ and ∥, then quad. is a ▱.

🔗 **Go Online** You can complete an Extra Example online.

🌐 Example 2 Use Parallelograms to Find Values

MP Teaching the Mathematical Practices

4 Apply Mathematics In this example, students apply what they have learned about properties of parallelograms to solving a real-world problem.

Questions for Mathematical Discourse

AL For the quadrilateral to be a parallelogram, what must be true about the angles? Opposite angles are congruent.

OL If the quadrilateral is a parallelogram, what is the measure of the bottom angle? 124°

BL What equation is true whether or not the quadrilateral is a parallelogram? $9y + 7x + 34 = 360$

DIFFERENTIATE

Reteaching Activity AL ELL
Intrapersonal Learners Have students choose a partner. Instruct one student to draw a parallelogram with enough information to use one of the tests. Then ask the partner to prove that the quadrilateral is a parallelogram. Next, switch roles and do the activity again.

Interactive Presentation

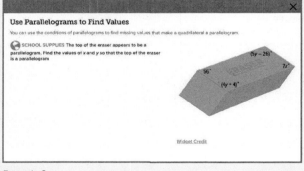

Use Parallelograms to Find Values

You can use the conditions of parallelograms to find missing values that make a quadrilateral a parallelogram.

🌐 SCHOOL SUPPLIES The top of the eraser appears to be a parallelogram. Find the values of x and y so that the top of the eraser is a parallelogram

Widget Credit

Example 2

EXPAND

Students can tap to see the solution to the exercise.

CHECK

Students complete the Check online to determine whether they are ready to move on.

1 CONCEPTUAL UNDERSTANDING   **2 FLUENCY**   3 APPLICATION

Example 3 Identify Parallelograms on the Coordinate Plane

MP Teaching the Mathematical Practices

2 Different Properties Mathematically proficient students look for different ways to solve problems. Encourage them to work through both ways to solve the problem and to choose the method that works best for them.

Questions for Mathematical Discourse

AL How are the diagonals of a parallelogram related? Sample answer: The diagonals bisect each other.

OL What property of a parallelogram involves a midpoint? Sample answer: The intersection point of the diagonals is the midpoint of the diagonals.

BL How would you change *FGHJ* to make it a parallelogram? Sample answer: Move *F* down one unit.

We can use the Distance, Slope, and Midpoint Formulas to determine whether a quadrilateral in the coordinate plane is a parallelogram.

Example 3 Identify Parallelograms on the Coordinate Plane

Determine whether quadrilateral *FGHJ* is a parallelogram. Justify your answer using the Midpoint Formula.

What theorem will you use to determine whether quadrilateral *FGHJ* is a parallelogram?
If the diagonals bisect each other, then the quadrilateral is a parallelogram.

Step 1 Calculate the midpoint of $\overline{GJ}$.

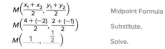

$M\left(\dfrac{x_1+x_2}{2}, \dfrac{y_1+y_2}{2}\right)$ Midpoint Formula

$M\left(\dfrac{4+(-2)}{2}, \dfrac{2+(-1)}{2}\right)$ Substitute.

$M\left(1, \dfrac{1}{2}\right)$ Solve.

Step 2 Calculate the midpoint of $\overline{FH}$.

$M\left(\dfrac{x_1+x_2}{2}, \dfrac{y_1+y_2}{2}\right)$ Midpoint Formula

$M\left(\dfrac{-2+4}{2}, \dfrac{4+(-2)}{2}\right)$ Substitute.

$M\left(1, 1\right)$ Solve.

Step 3 Determine whether *FGHJ* is a ▱.

If the diagonals of a quadrilateral bisect each other, then it is a parallelogram. The diagonals of a quadrilateral bisect each other if the midpoints coincide. Because the midpoints of diagonals $\overline{FH}$ and $\overline{GJ}$ do not have the same coordinates, quadrilateral *FGHJ* is not a parallelogram.

Check

Determine whether quadrilateral *ABCD* is a parallelogram. Justify your answer.

Yes; sample answer: I used the Distance Formula to find that both pairs of opposite sides are congruent.

Think About It!
Describe another method you could use to determine whether quadrilateral *FGHJ* is a parallelogram.

Sample answer: To determine whether quadrilateral *FGHJ* is a parallelogram, you could also use the Distance Formula. If both pairs of opposite sides are congruent and parallel, then *FGHJ* is a parallelogram.

Go Online You can complete an Extra Example online.

Interactive Presentation

Identify Parallelograms on the Coordinate Plane

We can use the Distance, Slope, and Midpoint Formulas to determine whether a quadrilateral in the coordinate plane is a parallelogram.

Determine whether quadrilateral *FGHJ* is a parallelogram. Justify your answer using the Midpoint Formula.

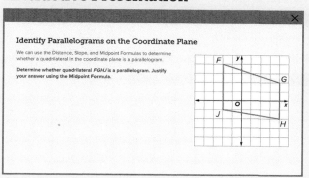

Example 3

TAP

Students tap to reveal steps in the solution and to select answers.

You can assign variable coordinates to the vertices of quadrilaterals. Then, you can use the Distance, Slope, and Midpoint Formulas to write coordinate proofs of theorems.

Example 4 Parallelograms and Coordinate Proofs

Write a coordinate proof for the following statement.
If one pair of opposite sides of a quadrilateral is both parallel and congruent, then the quadrilateral is a parallelogram.

Step 1 Position a quadrilateral on the coordinate plane.

Position quadrilateral *ABCD* on the coordinate plane such that $\overline{AB} \parallel \overline{DC}$ and $\overline{AB} \cong \overline{DC}$.

- Begin by placing the vertex *A* at the origin.
- Let $\overline{AB}$ have a length of *a* units. Then *B* has coordinates (*a*, 0).
- Because horizontal segments are parallel, position the endpoints of $\overline{DC}$ so that they have the same *y*-coordinate, *c*.
- So that the distance from *D* to *C* is also *a* units, let the *x*-coordinate of *D* be *b* and the *x*-coordinate of *C* be *b* + *a*.

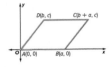

Step 2 Use your figure to write a proof.

Given: quadrilateral *ABCD*, $\overline{AB} \parallel \overline{DC}$, $\overline{AB} \cong \overline{DC}$

Prove: *ABCD* is a parallelogram.

Proof:
By definition, a quadrilateral is a parallelogram if opposite sides are parallel. We are given that $\overline{AB} \parallel \overline{DC}$, so we need to show that $\overline{AD} \parallel \overline{BC}$.

Use the Slope Formula.

slope of $\overline{AD} = \dfrac{c - 0}{b - 0} = \dfrac{c}{b}$ slope of $\overline{BC} = \dfrac{c - 0}{b + a - a} = \dfrac{c}{b}$

Because $\overline{AD}$ and $\overline{BC}$ have the same slope, $\overline{AD} \parallel \overline{BC}$. So, quadrilateral *ABCD* is a parallelogram because opposite sides are parallel.

Pause and Reflect

Did you struggle with anything in this lesson? If so, how did you deal with it?

> Record your observations here.

See students' observations.

 Go Online You can complete an Extra Example online.

 Go Online
You may want to complete the construction activities for this lesson.

424 Module 7 · Quadrilaterals

Interactive Presentation

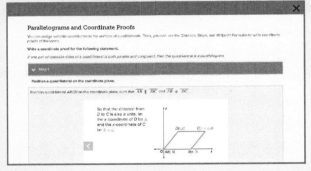

Example 4

Students tap to reveal parts of the solution.

CHECK

Students complete the Check online to determine whether they are ready to move on.

Example 4 Parallelograms and Coordinate Proofs

MP Teaching the Mathematical Practices

2 Create Representations Guide students to write an equation that models the situation in this example. Then use the equation to solve the problem.

Questions for Mathematical Discourse

AL In **Step 1**, why do you think we place a vertex at the origin? Sample answer: We know the coordinates of the origin.

OL In **Step 2**, how do we know to use *b* + *a* for the *x*-coordinate of vertex *C*? Sample answer: *AB* = *a* units, *AB* = *DC*, and *DC* is shifted right *b* units

BL If you were given the coordinates of the vertices of a quadrilateral, how could you use a coordinate proof to show that the quadrilateral is a parallelogram? Sample answer: Use slope to show that both pairs of opposite sides are parallel.

Common Error

Students may not remember that they can position part of a figure for a coordinate proof anywhere they want, so remind them that positioning one vertex at the origin and one side on the *x*-axis makes the proof easier.

DIFFERENTIATE

Enrichment Activity BL
Have students construct a parallelogram that lies within all four quadrants of a coordinate grid. Then have students draw the diagonals of the figure. Next, have students draw two dilations of the figure on the same coordinate grid using scale factors 0.5 and 2. Students should include the diagonals on the dilated figures. Have students journal about the relationship between the interior angles of all three figures and the diagonals of all three figures.

Exit Ticket

Recommended Use

At the end of class, go online to display the Exit Ticket prompt and ask students to respond using a separate piece of paper. Have students hand you their responses as they leave the room.

Alternate Use

At the end of class, go online to display the Exit Ticket prompt and ask students to respond verbally or by using a mini-whiteboard. Have students hold up their whiteboards so that you can see all student responses. Tap to reveal the answer when most or all students have completed the Exit Ticket.

Practice and Homework

Suggested Assignments

Use the table below to select appropriate exercises.

DOK	Topic	Exercises
1, 2	exercises that mirror the examples	1–17
2	exercises that use a variety of skills from this lesson	18–26
2	exercises that extend concepts learned in this lesson to new contexts	27–30
3	exercises that emphasize higher-order and critical-thinking skills	31–35

ASSESS AND DIFFERENTIATE

📊 Use the data from the **Checks** to determine whether to provide resources for extension, remediation, or intervention.

IF students score 90% or more on the Checks,   **BL**
THEN assign:

- Practice, Exercises 1–29 odd, 31–35
- Extension: Proving that Quadrilaterals are Parallelograms
- 🄰 **ALEKS** Parallelograms and Trapezoids

IF students score 66%–89% on the Checks,   **OL**
THEN assign:

- Practice, Exercises 1–35 odd
- Remediation, Review Resources: Parallelograms
- Personal Tutors
- Extra Examples 1–4
- 🄰 **ALEKS** Parallelograms and Trapezoids

IF students score 65% or less on the Checks,   **AL**
THEN assign:

- Practice, Exercises 1–17 odd
- Remediation, Review Resources: Parallelograms
- *Quick Review Math Handbook*: Tests for Parallelograms
- 🄰 **ALEKS** Parallelograms and Trapezoids

Answers

11. Yes; sample answer:

Use the Slope Formula.

$$m = \frac{y_2 - y_1}{x_2 - x_1}.$$

slope of $\overline{AD} = \frac{3 - 0}{-2 - (-3)} = \frac{3}{1} = 3$

slope of $\overline{BC} = \frac{2 - (-1)}{3 - 2} = \frac{3}{1} = 3$

slope of $\overline{AB} = \frac{2 - 3}{3 - (-2)} = -\frac{1}{5}$

slope of $\overline{CD} = \frac{-1 - 0}{2 - (-3)} = -\frac{1}{5}$

Because opposite sides have the same slope, $\overline{AB} \parallel \overline{CD}$ and $\overline{AD} \parallel \overline{BC}$. Therefore, *ABCD* is a parallelogram by definition.

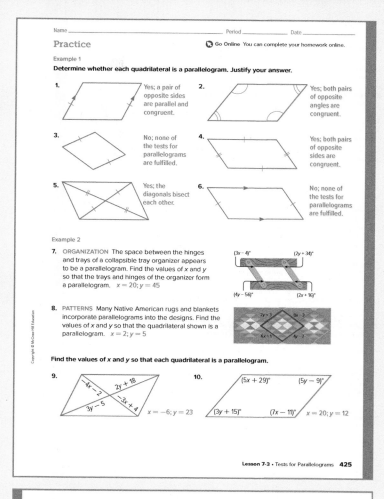

Name _____ Period _____ Date _____

Practice   🌐 **Go Online** You can complete your homework online.

Example 1

Determine whether each quadrilateral is a parallelogram. Justify your answer.

1. Yes; a pair of opposite sides are parallel and congruent.

2. Yes; both pairs of opposite angles are congruent.

3. No; none of the tests for parallelograms are fulfilled.

4. Yes; both pairs of opposite sides are congruent.

5. Yes; the diagonals bisect each other.

6. No; none of the tests for parallelograms are fulfilled.

Example 2

7. ORGANIZATION The space between the hinges and trays of a collapsible tray organizer appears to be a parallelogram. Find the values of *x* and *y* so that the trays and hinges of the organizer form a parallelogram. $x = 20; y = 45$

$(3x - 4)°$ $(2y + 34)°$ $(4y - 56)°$ $(2x + 16)°$

8. PATTERNS Many Native American rugs and blankets incorporate parallelograms into the designs. Find the values of *x* and *y* so that the quadrilateral shown is a parallelogram. $x = 2; y = 5$

$2y + 3$ $8x - 3$ $6x + 1$ $4y - 7$

Find the values of *x* and *y* so that each quadrilateral is a parallelogram.

9. $-4x - 2$ $2y + 18$ $3y - 5$ $-3x + 4$ $x = -6; y = 23$

10. $(5x + 29)°$ $(5y - 9)°$ $(3y + 15)°$ $(7x - 11)°$ $x = 20; y = 12$

Lesson 7-3 • Tests for Parallelograms   **425**

Example 3

11. Determine whether *ABCD* is a parallelogram. Justify your answer. See margin.

CONSTRUCT ARGUMENTS For Exercises 12–15, graph each quadrilateral with the given vertices. Determine whether the figure is a parallelogram. Justify your argument with the method indicated. 12–15. See margin for graphs.

12. *P*(0, 0), *Q*(3, 4), *S*(7, 4), *Y*(4, 0); Slope Formula
Yes; the slopes of $\overline{PY}$ and $\overline{QS}$ are equal and the slopes of $\overline{PQ}$ and $\overline{YS}$ are equal, so $\overline{PY} \parallel \overline{QS}$ and $\overline{PQ} \parallel \overline{YS}$. Therefore, the opposite sides are parallel.

13. *S*(−2, 1), *R*(1, 3), *T*(2, 0), *Z*(−1, −2); Distance and Slope Formulas
Yes; $SR = ZT$ and the slopes of $\overline{SR}$ and $\overline{ZT}$ are equal, so one pair of opposite sides is both parallel and congruent.

14. *W*(2, 5), *R*(3, 3), *Y*(−2, −3), *N*(−3, 1); Midpoint Formula
No; the midpoints of the diagonals are not the same point.

15. *W*(1, −4), *X*(−4, 2), *Y*(1, −1), and *Z*(−2, −3); Slope Formula
No; slope $\overline{XY} = -\frac{3}{5}$ and slope of $\overline{WZ} = -\frac{1}{3}$, so opposite sides are not parallel.

Example 4

16. PROOF Write a coordinate proof for the statement: *If both pairs of opposite sides of a quadrilateral are congruent, then the quadrilateral is a parallelogram.* See margin.

17. PROOF Write a coordinate proof for the statement: *If a parallelogram has one right angle, it has four right angles.* See Mod. 7 Answer Appendix.

Mixed Exercises

PROOF Write the specified type of proof for each theorem.

18. paragraph proof of Theorem 7.10
Given: $\angle K \cong \angle M$, $\angle N \cong \angle L$.
Prove: *KLMN* is a parallelogram.
See Mod. 7 Answer Appendix.

19. two-column proof of Theorem 7.11
Given: $\overline{PR}$ bisects $\overline{TQ}$.
$\overline{TQ}$ bisects $\overline{PR}$.
Prove: *PQRT* is a parallelogram.
See Mod. 7 Answer Appendix.

20. *ABCD* is a parallelogram with *A*(5, 4), *B*(−1, −2), and *C*(8, −2). Find one possible set of coordinates for *D*. Sample answer: *D*(14, 4)

426   Module 7 • Quadrilaterals

1 CONCEPTUAL UNDERSTANDING   **2 FLUENCY** | 3 APPLICATION

Name _____ Period _____ Date _____

21. STRUCTURE A parallelogram has vertices $R(-2, -1)$, $S(2, 1)$, and $T(0, -3)$. Find all possible coordinates for the fourth vertex. $(4, -1)$, $(0, 3)$, or $(-4, -5)$

22. If the slope of $\overline{PQ}$ is $\frac{2}{3}$ and the slope of $\overline{QR}$ is $-\frac{1}{2}$, find the slope of $\overline{SR}$ so that $PQRS$ is a parallelogram. $\frac{2}{3}$

23. If the slope of $\overline{AB}$ is $\frac{1}{2}$, the slope of $\overline{BC}$ is -4, and the slope of $\overline{CD}$ is $\frac{1}{2}$, find the slope of $\overline{DA}$ so that $ABCD$ is a parallelogram. -4

24. REASONING The pattern shown in the figure is to consist of congruent parallelograms. How can the designer be certain that the shapes are parallelograms? Sample answer: Confirm that both pairs of opposite angles are congruent.

25. Refer to parallelogram $ABCD$. If $AB = 8$ cm, what is the perimeter of the parallelogram? 28 cm

6 cm

26. PICTURE FRAME Aston is making a wooden picture frame in the shape of a parallelogram. He has two pieces of wood that are 3 feet long and two that are 4 feet long.

a. If he connects the pieces of wood at their ends to each other, in what order must he connect them to make a parallelogram? He must alternate the lengths 3, 4, 3, 4 or 4, 3, 4, 3.

b. How many different parallelograms could he make with these four lengths of wood? infinitely many

c. Explain something Aston might do to specify precisely the shape of the parallelogram. Sample answer: He could specify the length of one of the diagonals.

27. STATE YOUR ASSUMPTION When a coordinate plane is placed over the Harrisville town map, the four street lamps in the center are located as shown. Do the four lamps form the vertices of a parallelogram? Justify your reasoning. Explain any assumptions that you make regarding the coordinate plane and the map.
Yes; sample answer: The lengths of the opposite sides are congruent. When the coordinate plane is placed over the map, the street lamps align perfectly with the points on the grid.

28. USE TOOLS Explain how you can use Theorem 7.11 to construct a parallelogram. Then construct a parallelogram using your method. See Mod. 7 Answer Appendix.

Lesson 7-3 • Tests for Parallelograms **427**

29. BALANCING Nikia, Madison, Angela, and Shelby are balancing on an X-shaped floating object. To balance, they want to stand so they are at the vertices of a parallelogram. To achieve this, do all four of them have to be the same distance from the center of the object? Explain. No; sample answer: Madison and Angela have to be the same distance from the center and Nikia and Shelby have to be the same distance from the center, but Nikia and Shelby's distance from the center does not have to be equal to Madison and Angela's distance.

30. FORMATION Four jets are flying in formation. Three of the jets are shown in the graph. If the four jets are located at the vertices of a parallelogram, what are the three possible locations of the missing jet? $(1, 7)$, $(9, -1)$, or $(-7, -3)$

🌐 **Higher-Order Thinking Skills**

31. PROOF Write a coordinate proof to prove that the segments joining the midpoints of the sides of any quadrilateral form a parallelogram. See Mod. 7 Answer Appendix.

32. ANALYZE If two parallelograms have four congruent corresponding angles, are the parallelograms *sometimes*, *always*, or *never* congruent? Justify your argument.
Sometimes; sample answer: The two parallelograms could be congruent, but you can also make the parallelogram bigger or smaller without changing the angle measures by changing the side lengths.

33. WRITE Compare and contrast Theorem 7.9 and Theorem 7.3.
Sample answer: The theorems are converses of each other. The hypothesis of Theorem 7.3 is *a quadrilateral is a parallelogram*, and the hypothesis of Theorem 7.9 is *both pairs of opposite sides of a quadrilateral are congruent*. The conclusion of Theorem 7.3 is *opposite sides are congruent*, and the conclusion of Theorem 7.9 is *the quadrilateral is a parallelogram*.

34. PERSEVERE If $ABCD$ is a parallelogram and $\overline{AJ} \cong \overline{KC}$, show that quadrilateral $JBKD$ is a parallelogram.
See Mod. 7 Answer Appendix.

35. ANALYZE The diagonals of a parallelogram meet at the point $(0, 1)$. One vertex of the parallelogram is located at $(2, 4)$, and a second vertex is located at $(3, 1)$. Find the locations of the remaining vertices. $(-3, 1)$ and $(-2, -2)$

Answers

12.

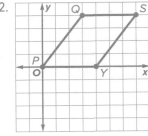

13.

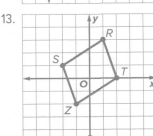

14.

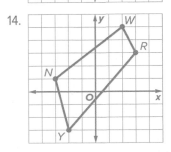

15.

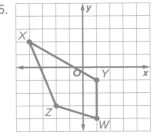

16. Given: $\overline{AB} \cong \overline{CD}$, $\overline{AD} \cong \overline{BC}$
Prove: $ABCD$ is a parallelogram.

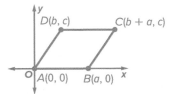

Proof:

slope of $\overline{AD} = \dfrac{c - 0}{b - 0} = \dfrac{c}{b}$

slope of $\overline{BC} = \dfrac{c - 0}{b + a - a} = \dfrac{c}{b}$

slope of $\overline{AB} = \dfrac{0 - 0}{a - 0} = 0$

slope of $\overline{CD} = \dfrac{0 - 0}{b + a - b} = 0$

Therefore, $\overline{AD} \parallel \overline{BC}$ and $\overline{AB} \parallel \overline{CD}$. So, $ABCD$ is a parallelogram by definition.

LESSON GOAL

Students recognize and apply the properties of rectangles and use them to determine whether a parallelogram is a rectangle.

1 LAUNCH

Launch the lesson with a **Warm Up** and an introduction.

2 EXPLORE AND DEVELOP

Explore: Properties of Rectangles

Develop:

Properties of Rectangles
- Use Properties of Rectangles
- Use Properties of Rectangles and Algebra

Proving that Parallelograms are Rectangles
- Prove Rectangular Relationships
- Identify Rectangles on the Coordinate Plane

You may want your students to complete the **Checks** online.

3 REFLECT AND PRACTICE

Exit Ticket

Practice

DIFFERENTIATE

 View reports of student progress on the **Checks** after each example.

Resources	AL	OL	BL	ELL
Remediation: Tests for Parallelograms	●	●		●
Extension: Constant Perimeter		●	●	●

Language Development Handbook

Assign page 49 of the *Language Development Handbook* to help your students build mathematical language related to the properties of rectangles.

ELL You can use the tips and suggestions on page T49 of the handbook to support students who are building English proficiency.

Suggested Pacing

90 min	0.5 day
45 min	1 day

Focus

Domain: Geometry

Standards for Mathematical Content:

G.CO.11 Prove theorems about parallelograms.

G.GPE.4 Use coordinates to prove simple geometric theorems algebraically.

Standards for Mathematical Practice:

2 Reason abstractly and quantitatively.

3 Construct viable arguments and critique the reasoning of others.

6 Attend to precision.

Coherence

Vertical Alignment

Previous
Students proved and used tests to determine whether quadrilaterals were parallelograms.
5.G.4, G.CO.11, G.GPE.4

Now
Students recognize and apply the properties of rectangles and use them to determine whether a parallelogram is a rectangle.
G.CO.11, G.GPE.4

Next
Students will recognize and apply the properties of rhombi and squares.
G.CO.11, G.GPE.4

Rigor

The Three Pillars of Rigor

1 CONCEPTUAL UNDERSTANDING	2 FLUENCY	3 APPLICATION

Conceptual Bridge In this lesson, students extend their understanding of parallelograms to prove theorems related to rectangles. They build fluency and apply their understanding by solving real-world problems related to rectangles.

Mathematical Background

A rectangle is a parallelogram with four right angles. If a quadrilateral is graphed on a coordinate plane, the Slope Formula can be used to determine whether consecutive sides are perpendicular. The Distance Formula can be used to calculate the measures of the diagonals. The diagonals of a rectangle are congruent.

Interactive Presentation

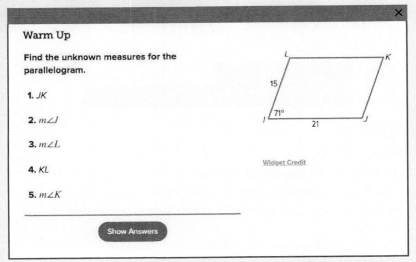

Warm Up

Find the unknown measures for the parallelogram.

1. *JK*

2. $m\angle J$

3. $m\angle L$

4. *KL*

5. $m\angle K$

Show Answers

Warm Up

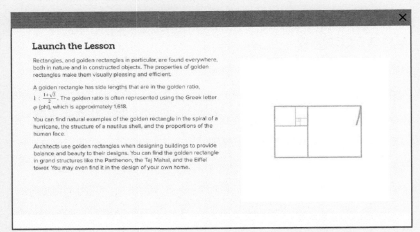

Launch the Lesson

Rectangles, and golden rectangles in particular, are found everywhere, both in nature and in constructed objects. The properties of golden rectangles make them visually pleasing and efficient.

A golden rectangle has side lengths that are in the golden ratio, $1 : \frac{1+\sqrt{5}}{2}$. The golden ratio is often represented using the Greek letter φ (phi), which is approximately 1.618.

You can find natural examples of the golden rectangle in the spiral of a hurricane, the structure of a nautilus shell, and the proportions of the human face.

Architects use golden rectangles when designing buildings to provide balance and beauty to their designs. You can find the golden rectangle in grand structures like the Parthenon, the Taj Mahal, and the Eiffel tower. You may even find it in the design of your own home.

Launch the Lesson

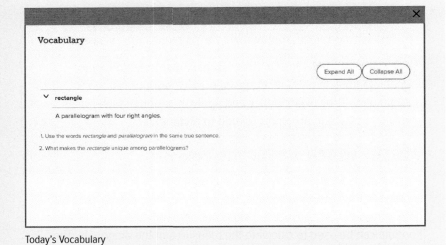

Vocabulary

Expand All   Collapse All

ˇ **rectangle**

A parallelogram with four right angles.

1. Use the words *rectangle* and *parallelogram* in the same true sentence.

2. What makes the *rectangle* unique among parallelograms?

Today's Vocabulary

Warm Up

Prerequisite Skills

The Warm Up exercises address the following prerequisite skill for this lesson:

- identifying measures of parts of parallelograms

Answers:

1. 15
2. 109°
3. 109°
4. 21
5. 71°

Launch the Lesson

MP **Teaching the Mathematical Practices**

4 Apply Mathematics In this Launch the Lesson, students can see a real-world application of rectangles.

Go Online to find additional teaching notes and questions to promote classroom discourse.

Today's Standards

Tell students that they will be addressing these content and practice standards in this lesson. You may wish to have a student volunteer read aloud *How can I meet these standards?* and *How can I use these practices?*, and connect these to the standards.

See the Interactive Presentation for I Can statements that align with the standards covered in this lesson.

Today's Vocabulary

Tell students that they will be using this vocabulary term in this lesson. You can expand the row if you wish to share the definition. Then, discuss the questions below with the class.

Explore Properties of Rectangles

Objective
Students use dynamic geometry software to explore the properties of rectangles.

Teaching the Mathematical Practices

6 Communicate Precisely Encourage students to routinely write or explain their solution methods. Point out that they should use clear definitions when they discuss their solutions with others.

Ideas for Use

Recommended Use Present the Inquiry Question, or have a student volunteer read it aloud. Have students work in pairs to complete the Explore activity on their devices. Pairs should discuss each of the questions. Monitor student progress during the activity. Upon completion of the Explore activity, have student volunteers share their responses to the Inquiry Question.

What if my students don't have devices? You may choose to project the activity on a whiteboard. A printable worksheet for each Explore is available online. You may choose to print the worksheet so that individuals or pairs of students can use it to record their observations.

Summary of the Activity

Students will complete guiding exercises throughout the Explore activity. Students are encouraged to move the vertices of a rectangle and observe what happens to the shape and side lengths of the rectangle. Students then complete guiding exercises leading them to conjecture that the opposite side lengths are congruent and all four angles are right angles. Then students show the diagonal measurements. They complete guiding exercises leading them to observe that the diagonals are congruent and bisect each other. Then, students will answer the Inquiry Question.

(continued on the next page)

Interactive Presentation

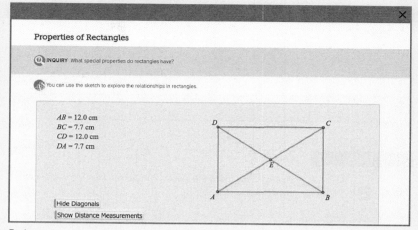

Explore

WEB SKETCHPAD

 Students use a sketch to complete an activity where they explore properties of rectangles.

Interactive Presentation

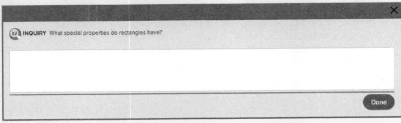

Explore

TYPE

Students respond to the Inquiry Question and can view a sample answer.

Explore Properties of Rectangles
(*continued*)

 Teaching the Mathematical Practices

3 Make Conjectures In the Explore, students will make conjectures and then build a logical progression of statements to validate the conjectures. Once students have made their conjectures, guide the students to validate them.

Questions
Have students complete the Explore activity.

Ask:
- What is the relationship between the lengths of the diagonals of a rectangle? Sample answer: The diagonals of a rectangle are congruent.

ⓠ Inquiry
What special properties do rectangles have? Sample answer: The two pairs of opposite sides of a rectangle are parallel and congruent. A rectangle has four congruent right angles. The diagonals of a rectangle bisect and are congruent.

 Go Online to find additional teaching notes and sample answers for the guiding exercises.

Learn Properties of Rectangles

Objective
Students recognize and apply the properties of rectangles.

 Teaching the Mathematical Practices

7 Use Structure Help students to explore the structure of rectangles in this Learn.

DIFFERENTIATE

Reteaching Activity AL ELL

Have students use two equal-length pieces of string, masking tape, and a smooth surface to mark off quadrilaterals. Secure the two pieces of string to the surface so that they intersect. Use the masking tape to form a quadrilateral by connecting the ends of the strings. Repeat several times, having the strings intersect at different points. Students should see that the quadrilateral is a rectangle only when the strings intersect at their midpoints.

Example 1 Use Properties of Rectangles

 Teaching the Mathematical Practices

3 Make Conjectures In this example, students will make conjectures and then build a logical progression of statements to validate the conjectures. Once students have made their conjectures, guide the students to validate them.

Questions for Mathematical Discourse

AL What kind of segment is $\overline{FC}$ in terms of the rectangle? It is a diagonal.

OL What do you know about the diagonals of a rectangle? Sample answer: They are congruent and bisect each other.

BL What kind of a triangle is $\triangle FGD$? isosceles

Go Online

- Find additional teaching notes.
- View performance reports of the Checks.
- Assign or present an Extra Example.

Interactive Presentation

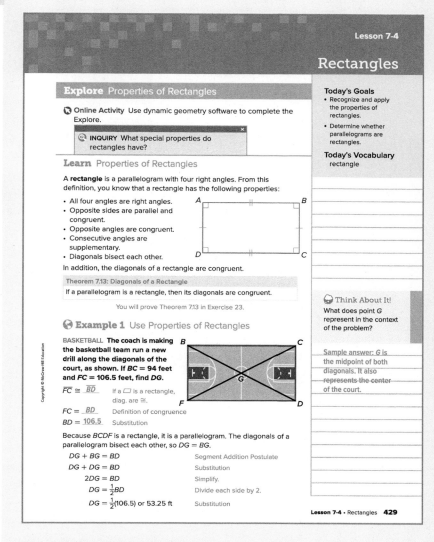

Example 1

TYPE

a|

Students type to answer the Think About It! question.

Your Notes

Check

FRAMING Jay is framing a barn door with an X-brace as shown. If $RT = 3\frac{9}{16}$, $QR = 7$ feet, and $m\angle RTS = 65°$, find each measure. If a measure is not a whole number, write it as a decimal.

$PS = \underline{7}$ ft $SQ = \underline{7.125}$ ft

$m\angle QTR = \underline{115°}$ $m\angle TQR = \underline{32.5°}$

Study Tip

Right Angles Recall from Theorem 7.6 that if a parallelogram has one right angle, then it has four right angles.

Think About It!

There are four congruent right triangles formed by the diagonals of a rectangle. How many pairs of congruent triangles are there in all?

_8_

Example 2 Use Properties of Rectangles and Algebra

Quadrilateral *ABCD* is a rectangle. If $m\angle BAC = 3x + 3$ and $m\angle ACB = 5x - 1$, find *x*.

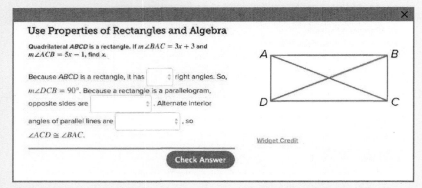

Because *ABCD* is a rectangle, it has ___four___ right angles. So, $m\angle DCB = 90°$. Because a rectangle is a parallelogram, opposite sides are ___parallel___. Alternate interior angles of parallel lines are ___congruent___, so $\angle ACD \cong \angle BAC$.

$m\angle ACD + m\angle ACB = 90°$ Angle Addition Postulate

$m\angle BAC + m\angle ACB = 90°$ Substitution

$\underline{3x + 3} + 5x - 1 = 90$ Substitution

$x = \underline{11}$ Solve.

Check

Quadrilateral *JKLM* is a rectangle.

Part A

If $MN = 3x + 1$ and $JL = 2x + 9$, find *MK*. Round to the nearest tenth if necessary.

$MK = \underline{12.5}$

Part B

If $m\angle JNK = (5x + 2)°$ and $m\angle JNM = (3x - 6)°$, find each measure.

$m\angle JNK = \underline{117°}$

$m\angle JNM = \underline{63°}$

 Go Online You can complete an Extra Example online.

Example 2 Use Properties of Rectangles and Algebra

Teaching the Mathematical Practices

2 Create Representations Guide students to write an equation that models the situation in this example. Then use the equation to solve the problem.

Questions for Mathematical Discourse

AL What are alternate interior angles? Sample answer: nonadjacent interior angles that lie on opposite sides of a transversal

OL Name one angle congruent to $\angle BDC$. Sample answers: $\angle ACD$; $\angle BAC$; $\angle ABD$

BL How many pairs of congruent triangles are formed by the diagonals of a rectangle? 8

Interactive Presentation

Use Properties of Rectangles and Algebra

Quadrilateral *ABCD* is a rectangle. If $m\angle BAC = 3x + 3$ and $m\angle ACB = 5x - 1$, find *x*.

Because *ABCD* is a rectangle, it has ⬍ right angles. So, $m\angle DCB = 90°$. Because a rectangle is a parallelogram, opposite sides are ⬍. Alternate interior angles of parallel lines are ⬍, so $\angle ACD \cong \angle BAC$.

Widget Credit

[Check Answer]

Example 2

TYPE

a|

Students type to answer the Think About It! question.

CHECK

Students complete the Check online to determine whether they are ready to move on.

1 CONCEPTUAL UNDERSTANDING | **2 FLUENCY** | 3 APPLICATION

Learn Prove that Parallelograms are Rectangles

Objective
Students determine whether a parallelogram is a rectangle by using the properties of a rectangle.

 Teaching the Mathematical Practices

> **7 Use Structure** Help students to explore the structure of diagonals of rectangles in this Learn.

Example 3 Prove Rectangular Relationships

 Teaching the Mathematical Practices

> **5 Use a Source** Guide students to find external information to answer the questions posed in the Use a Source feature.

Questions for Mathematical Discourse

AL What are the two parts of the hypothesis of Theorem 7.14? Sample answer: The figure is a parallelogram and the diagonals are congruent.

OL How do you know that this figure is a parallelogram? Sample answer: The pairs of opposite sides are congruent.

BL Why is it necessary to prove that the figure is a parallelogram? Sample answer: It is possible for a figure to have congruent diagonals without being a rectangle. If the figure is a parallelogram as well, the figure must be a rectangle.

DIFFERENTIATE

Enrichment Activity **BL**

Ask students to prove the statement *if a quadrilateral has four right angles, then it is a rectangle*. Ask the students the difference between the hypotheses in the definition of a rectangle and the hypothesis in this statement. Then ask them if the hypothesis that a quadrilateral is a parallelogram is necessary in the definition of a rectangle.

Learn Proving that Parallelograms are Rectangles

You have learned that if a parallelogram is a rectangle, then the diagonals of the parallelogram are congruent. The converse is also true.

> **Theorem 7.14: Diagonals of a Rectangle**
> If the diagonals of a parallelogram are congruent, then the parallelogram is a rectangle.

You will prove Theorem 7.14 in Exercise 24.

Example 3 Prove Rectangular Relationships

If $AB = 50$ feet, $BC = 20$ feet, $CD = 50$ feet, $AD = 20$ feet, $AC = 54$ feet, and $BD = 54$ feet, prove that quadrilateral $ABCD$ is a rectangle.

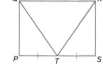

Because $AB = CD$, $BC = AD$, and $AC = BD$, $\overline{AB} \cong \overline{CD}$, $\overline{BC} \cong \overline{AD}$, and $\overline{AC} \cong \overline{BD}$. Because $\overline{AB} \cong \overline{CD}$ and $\overline{BC} \cong \overline{AD}$, $ABCD$ is a __parallelogram__. Because $\overline{AC}$ and $\overline{BD}$ are congruent diagonals, $ABCD$ is a __rectangle__.

Check

Complete the proof with the correct statements.

Given: $PQRS$ is a rectangle; $\overline{PT} \cong \overline{ST}$.

Prove: $\overline{QT} \cong \overline{RT}$

Proof:

Statements	Reasons
1. $PQRS$ is a rectangle; $\overline{PT} \cong \overline{ST}$	1. Given
2. $PQRS$ is a parallelogram.	2. Definition of rectangle
3. $\overline{RS} \cong \overline{QP}$	3. Opp. sides of a ▱ are ≅.
4. $\angle S$ and $\angle P$ are right angles.	4. Definition of rectangle
5. $\angle S \cong \angle P$	5. All right angles are congruent.
6. $\triangle RST \cong \triangle QPT$	6. SAS
7. $\overline{QT} \cong \overline{RT}$	7. CPCTC

 Go Online You can complete an Extra Example online.

Use a Source
In 1853, the New York State legislature enacted a law to set aside more than 750 acres of land in central Manhattan. This area is now known as Central Park, America's first major landscaped public park. Use available resources to find and use the dimensions of Central Park to prove that it is rectangular.

Sample answer: Central Park has two pairs of opposite sides that are congruent, with a length of 2.5 miles and a width of 0.5 miles. The four pairs of sides meet at 90° angles. Because opposite angles are congruent and adjacent angles are supplementary, we can prove that Central Park is rectangular.

Statements:
$\angle S$ and $\angle P$ are right $\angle$s.
$\overline{RS} \cong \overline{QP}$
$\overline{QT} \cong \overline{RT}$
$\triangle RST \cong \triangle QPT$

Lesson 7-4 · Rectangles **431**

Interactive Presentation

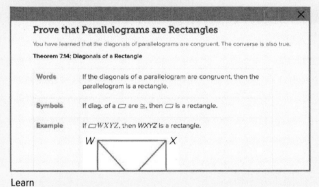

Learn

TAP

Students tap to select correct answers to complete the proof.

Study Tip

Rectangles and Parallelograms All rectangles are parallelograms, but all parallelograms are not necessarily rectangles.

Think About It!

Is there another way to show that GHJK is a rectangle? If yes, explain.

Sample answer: After finding that the opposite sides of GHJK are congruent, you can find the slope of each side and show that the slopes of adjacent sides are negative reciprocals, proving that all of the angles are right angles.

Go Online

You may want to complete the construction activities for this lesson.

You can also use the properties of rectangles to prove that a quadrilateral positioned on a coordinate plane is a rectangle given the coordinates of the vertices.

Example 4 Identify Rectangles on the Coordinate Plane

Quadrilateral *GHJK* has vertices *G*(−3, 0), *H*(3, 2), *J*(4, −1), and *K*(−2, −3). Determine whether *GHJK* is a rectangle by using the Distance Formula.

Step 1 Determine whether opposite sides are congruent.
Use the Distance Formula.

$GH = \sqrt{(-3-3)^2 + (0-2)^2}$ or $\sqrt{40}$

$HJ = \sqrt{(3-4)^2 + [2-(-1)]^2}$ or $\sqrt{10}$

$KJ = \sqrt{(-2-4)^2 + [-3-(-1)]^2}$ or $\sqrt{40}$

$GK = \sqrt{[-3-(-2)]^2 + [0-(-3)]^2}$ or $\sqrt{10}$

Because opposite sides of the quadrilateral have the same measure, they are congruent. So, quadrilateral *GHJK* is a parallelogram.

Step 2 Determine whether diagonals are congruent.
Use the Distance Formula.

$GJ = \sqrt{(-3-4)^2 + [0-(-1)]^2}$ or $\sqrt{50}$

$KH = \sqrt{(-2-3)^2 + (-3-2)^2}$ or $\sqrt{50}$

Because the diagonals have the same measure, they are congruent. So, ▱*GHJK* is a rectangle.

Check

A quadrilateral has vertices *A*(2, 6), *B*(3, 7), and *C*(6, 4). Which of the following points would make *ABCD* a rectangle?

A. *D*(5, 3)

B. *D*(5, 2)

C. *D*(4, 3)

D. *D*(6, 3)

Pause and Reflect

Did you struggle with anything in this lesson? If so, how did you deal with it?

 | See students' observations.

Go Online You can complete an Extra Example online.

Interactive Presentation

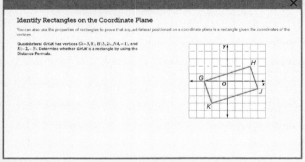

Example 4

TAP

Students tap to reveal steps in the solution.

CHECK

Students complete the Check online to determine whether they are ready to move on.

Example 4 Identify Rectangles on the Coordinate Plane

Teaching the Mathematical Practices

1 Understand the Approaches of Others Mathematically proficient students can explain the methods used to solve a problem. The Think About It! feature asks students to explain another solution to the problem.

Questions for Mathematical Discourse

AL What is the Distance Formula used to calculate? The distance between two points in the coordinate plane.

OL If each vertex of *GHJK* were translated up 6 units, could we use the new coordinates to show that it is a rectangle? Yes, because the distances would be the same.

BL What do the slopes of the quadrilateral tell us? Sample answer: The slopes of the opposite sides are the same, which means the opposite sides are parallel and the quadrilateral is a parallelogram. The adjacent sides have slopes that are negative reciprocals, so the adjacent sides are perpendicular and the angles formed are right angles.

Common Error

Students may forget that they need to prove that the quadrilateral is a parallelogram as well as prove the diagonals are congruent. Remind them that Theorem 7.14 requires both to be true for a quadrilateral to be a rectangle.

Exit Ticket

Recommended Use

At the end of class, go online to display the Exit Ticket prompt and ask students to respond using a separate piece of paper. Have students hand you their responses as they leave the room.

Alternate Use

At the end of class, go online to display the Exit Ticket prompt and ask students to respond verbally or by using a mini-whiteboard. Have students hold up their whiteboards so that you can see all student responses. Tap to reveal the answer when most or all students have completed the Exit Ticket.

Practice and Homework

Suggested Assignments

Use the table below to select appropriate exercises.

DOK	Topic	Exercises
1, 2	exercises that mirror the examples	1–22
2	exercises that use a variety of skills from this lesson	23–34
3	exercises that emphasize higher-order and critical-thinking skills	35–39

ASSESS AND DIFFERENTIATE

📊 Use the data from the **Checks** to determine whether to provide resources for extension, remediation, or intervention.

IF students score 90% or more on the Checks,   `OL` `BL`
THEN assign:

- Practice, Exercises 1–33 odd, 35–39
- Extension: Constant Perimeter
- 🅐 **ALEKS** Parallelograms and Trapezoids

IF students score 66%–89% on the Checks,   `AL` `OL`
THEN assign:

- Practice, Exercises 1–39 odd
- Remediation, Review Resources: Tests for Parallelograms
- Personal Tutors
- Extra Examples 1–4
- 🅐 **ALEKS** Parallelograms and Trapezoids

IF students score 65% or less on the Checks,   `AL`
THEN assign:

- Practice, Exercises 1–21 odd
- Remediation, Review Resources: Tests for Parallelograms
- *Quick Review Math Handbook*: Rectangles
- 🅐 **ALEKS** Parallelograms and Trapezoids

Answers

15. Proof
    Statements (Reasons)
    1. *ABCD* is a rectangle. (Given)
    2. *ABCD* is a parallelogram. (Def. of rectangle)
    3. $\overline{AD} \cong \overline{BC}$ (Opp. sides of a parallelogram are ≅.)
    4. $\overline{DC} \cong \overline{DC}$ (Reflexive Property of ≅)
    5. $\overline{AC} \cong \overline{BD}$ (Diag. of a rectangle are ≅.)
    6. $\triangle ADC \cong \triangle BCD$ (SSS)

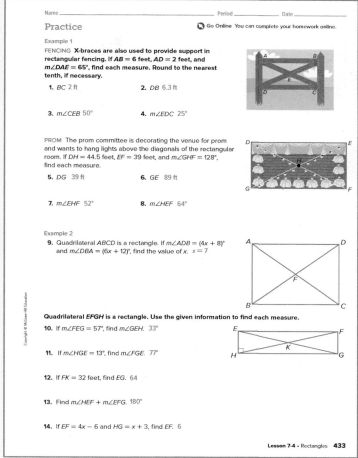

Practice

🔵 Go Online You can complete your homework online.

Example 1

FENCING **X-braces** are also used to provide support in rectangular fencing. If *AB* = 6 feet, *AD* = 2 feet, and *m∠DAE* = 65°, find each measure. Round to the nearest tenth, if necessary.

1. *BC* 2 ft
2. *DB* 6.3 ft
3. *m∠CEB* 50°
4. *m∠EDC* 25°

PROM The prom committee is decorating the venue for prom and wants to hang lights above the diagonals of the rectangular room. If *DH* = 44.5 feet, *EF* = 39 feet, and *m∠GHF* = 128°, find each measure.

5. *DG* 39 ft
6. *GE* 89 ft
7. *m∠EHF* 52°
8. *m∠HEF* 64°

Example 2

9. Quadrilateral *ABCD* is a rectangle. If *m∠ADB* = (4x + 8)° and *m∠DBA* = (6x + 12)°, find the value of x. x = 7

Quadrilateral *EFGH* is a rectangle. Use the given information to find each measure.

10. If *m∠FEG* = 57°, find *m∠GEH*. 33°
11. If *m∠HGE* = 13°, find *m∠FGE*. 77°
12. If *FK* = 32 feet, find *EG*. 64
13. Find *m∠HEF* + *m∠EFG*. 180°
14. If *EF* = 4x − 6 and *HG* = x + 3, find *EF*. 6

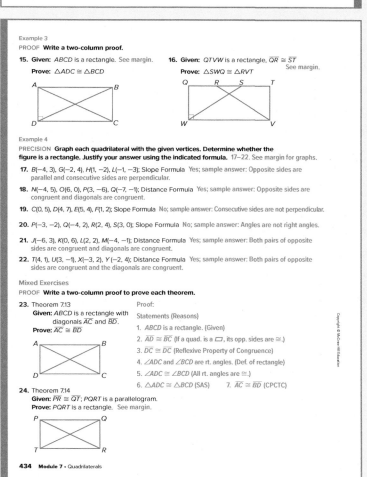

Example 3

PROOF Write a two-column proof.

15. Given: *ABCD* is a rectangle. See margin.
    Prove: $\triangle ADC \cong \triangle BCD$

16. Given: *QTVW* is a rectangle, $\overline{QR} \cong \overline{ST}$ See margin.
    Prove: $\triangle SWQ \cong \triangle RVT$

Example 4

PRECISION **Graph each quadrilateral with the given vertices. Determine whether the figure is a rectangle. Justify your answer using the indicated formula.** 17–22. See margin for graphs.

17. *B*(−4, 3), *G*(−2, 4), *H*(1, −2), *L*(−1, −3); Slope Formula Yes; sample answer: Opposite sides are parallel and consecutive sides are perpendicular.
18. *N*(−4, 5), *O*(6, 0), *P*(3, −6), *Q*(−7, −1); Distance Formula Yes; sample answer: Opposite sides are congruent and diagonals are congruent.
19. *C*(0, 5), *D*(4, 7), *E*(5, 4), *F*(1, 2); Slope Formula No; sample answer: Consecutive sides are not perpendicular.
20. *P*(−3, −2), *Q*(−4, 2), *R*(2, 4), *S*(3, 0); Slope Formula No; sample answer: Angles are not right angles.
21. *J*(−6, 3), *K*(0, 6), *L*(2, 2), *M*(−4, −1); Distance Formula Yes; sample answer: Both pairs of opposite sides are congruent and diagonals are congruent.
22. *T*(4, 1), *U*(3, −1), *X*(−3, 2), *Y*(−2, 4); Distance Formula Yes; sample answer: Both pairs of opposite sides are congruent and the diagonals are congruent.

Mixed Exercises

PROOF Write a two-column proof to prove each theorem.

23. Theorem 7.13
    Given: *ABCD* is a rectangle with diagonals $\overline{AC}$ and $\overline{BD}$.
    Prove: $\overline{AC} \cong \overline{BD}$

    Proof:
    Statements (Reasons)
    1. *ABCD* is a rectangle. (Given)
    2. $\overline{AD} \cong \overline{BC}$ (If a quad. is a ▱, its opp. sides are ≅.)
    3. $\overline{DC} \cong \overline{DC}$ (Reflexive Property of Congruence)
    4. ∠*ADC* and ∠*BCD* are rt. angles. (Def. of rectangle)
    5. ∠*ADC* ≅ ∠*BCD* (All rt. angles are ≅.)
    6. $\triangle ADC \cong \triangle BCD$ (SAS) 7. $\overline{AC} \cong \overline{BD}$ (CPCTC)

24. Theorem 7.14
    Given: $\overline{PR} \cong \overline{QT}$; *PQRT* is a parallelogram.
    Prove: *PQRT* is a rectangle. See margin.

Left worksheet page

Name _____ Period _____ Date _____

25. LANDSCAPING Huntington Park officials approved a rectangular plot of land for a Japanese Zen garden. Is it sufficient to know that opposite sides of the garden plot are congruent and parallel to determine that the garden plot is rectangular? Explain. No; sample answer: If you only know that opposite sides are congruent and parallel, then the most that you can conclude is that the plot is a parallelogram.

26. Name a property that is true for a rectangle and not always true for a parallelogram. A rectangle has four right angles and a parallelogram may not. The diagonals of a rectangle are congruent and those of a parallelogram may not be.

27. USE TOOLS Construct a rectangle using the construction for congruent segments and the construction for a line perpendicular to another line through a point on the line. Justify each step of the construction. See Mod. 7 Answer Appendix.

28. SIGNS The sign is attached to the front of Jackie's lemonade stand. Based on the dimensions given, can Jackie be sure that the sign is a rectangle? Explain your reasoning. No; sample answer: Both pairs of opposite sides are congruent, so the sign is a parallelogram, but no measure is given that can be used to prove that it is a rectangle.

For Exercises 29–30, refer to rectangle *WXYZ*.

29. If $XW = 3$ and $WZ = 4$, find YW. 5

30. If $ZY = 6$ and $XY = 8$, find WY. 10

31. FRAMES Jalen makes the rectangular frame shown. Jalen measures the distances BD and AC. How should these two distances compare if the frame is a rectangle? They should be equal.

32. BOOKSHELVES A bookshelf consists of two vertical planks with five horizontal shelves. Are each of the four sections for books rectangles? Explain. Yes; sample answer: Each of the four angles of each rectangle is created by a straight horizontal line and a straight vertical line, so each rectangle has four 90° angles.

33. REASONING A landscaper is marking off the corners of a rectangular plot of land. Three of the corners are in the place as shown. What are the coordinates of the fourth corner? (−6, 3)

Lesson 7-4 • Rectangles 435

34. STRUCTURE Veronica made the pattern shown out of 7 rectangles with four equal sides. The side length of each rectangle is written inside the rectangle.

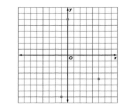

a. How many rectangles can be formed using the lines in this figure? 11

b. If Veronica wanted to extend her pattern by adding another rectangle with 4 equal sides to make a larger rectangle, what are the possible side lengths of rectangles that she can add? 8 and 13 units

🧠 Higher-Order Thinking Skills

35. PERSEVERE In rectangle *ABCD*, $m\angle EAB = (4x + 6)°$, $m\angle DEC = (10 − 11y)°$, and $m\angle EBC = 60°$. Find the values of x and y. $x = 6$; $y = −10$

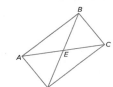

36. FIND THE ERROR Parker says that any two congruent acute triangles can be arranged to make a rectangle. Takeisha says that only two congruent right triangles can be arranged to make a rectangle. Who is correct? Explain your reasoning. Takeisha; sample answer: When two congruent triangles are arranged to form a quadrilateral, two of the angles are formed by a single vertex of a triangle. For the quadrilateral to be a rectangle, one of the angles in the congruent triangles has to be a right angle.

37. WRITE Why are all rectangles parallelograms, but all parallelograms are not rectangles? Explain. Sample answer: All rectangles are parallelograms because, by definition, both pairs of opposite sides are parallel. Parallelograms with right angles are rectangles, so some parallelograms are rectangles, but others with nonright angles are not.

38. CREATE Write the equations of four lines having intersections that form the vertices of a rectangle. Verify your answer using coordinate geometry. See Mod. 7 Answer Appendix.

39. ANALYZE Danny argues that to prove a parallelogram is a rectangle, it is sufficient to prove that it has one right angle. Do you agree? If so, explain why. If not, explain and draw a counterexample. Yes; sample answer: By Theorem 7.6, if a parallelogram has one right angle, then it has four right angles. Therefore, a parallelogram with one right angle must be a rectangle.

Right answers page

Answers

16. Proof
Statements (Reasons)
1. $QTVW$ is a rectangle, $\overline{QR} \cong \overline{ST}$ (Given)
2. $QTVW$ is a parallelogram. (Def. of rectangle)
3. $\overline{WQ} \cong \overline{VT}$ (Opp. sides of a parallelogram are ≅)
4. $\angle Q$ and $\angle T$ are right angles. (Def. of rectangle)
5. $\angle Q \cong \angle T$ (All right angles are ≅.)
6. $QR = ST$ (Def. of ≅ segments)
7. $\overline{RS} \cong \overline{RS}$ (Reflexive Property of ≅)
8. $RS = RS$ (Def. of ≅ segments)
9. $QR + RS = RS + ST$ (Addition Property of Equality)
10. $QS = QR + RS$, $RT = RS + ST$ (Segment Addition Postulate)
11. $QS = RT$ (Substitution)
12. $\overline{QS} \cong \overline{RT}$ (Def. of ≅ segments)
13. $\triangle SWQ \cong \triangle RVT$ (SAS)

17.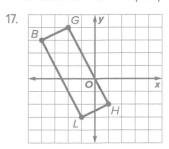

18.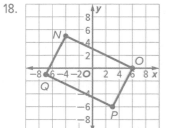

19.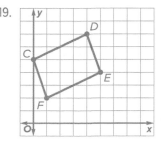

20.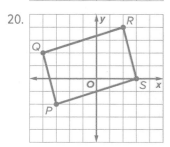

21.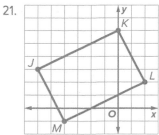

22.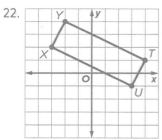

24. Proof
Statements (Reasons)
1. $\overline{PR} \cong \overline{QT}$; $PQRT$ is a parallelogram. (Given)
2. $\overline{PQ} \cong \overline{RT}$ and $\overline{PT} \cong \overline{QR}$. (If a quad. is a ▱, then opp. sides are ≅.)
3. $\overline{TR} \cong \overline{TR}$ (Reflexive Property of ≅)
4. $\triangle PTR \cong \triangle QRT$ (SSS)
5. $\angle PTR \cong \angle QRT$ (CPCTC)
6. $m\angle PTR = m\angle QRT$ (Def. of ≅ ∠s.)
7. $\angle PTR$ and $\angle QRT$ are supplementary. (If a quad. is a ▱, then its consec. ∠s are suppl.)
8. $m\angle PTR + m\angle QRT = 180°$ (Def. of suppl.)
9. $\angle PTR$ and $\angle QRT$ are right angles. (If 2 ∠s are ≅ and suppl., then each ∠ is a rt. ∠.)
10. $\angle TPQ$ and $\angle RQP$ are right angles. (If a ▱ has 1 rt. ∠, then it has 4 rt. ∠s.)
11. $PQRT$ is a rectangle. (Def. of a rectangle.)

Rhombi and Squares

LESSON GOAL

Students recognize and apply the properties of rhombi and squares.

1 LAUNCH

 Launch the lesson with a **Warm Up** and an introduction.

2 EXPLORE AND DEVELOP

Explore: Properties of Rhombi and Squares

Develop:

Properties of Rhombi and Squares
- Use the Definition of a Rhombus
- Use the Diagonals of a Rhombus
- Use the Definition of a Square

Tests for Rhombi and Squares
- Use Conditions for Rhombi and Squares
- Use Properties of a Rhombus
- Classify Parallelograms by Using Coordinate Geometry

You may want your students to complete the **Checks** online.

3 REFLECT AND PRACTICE

Exit Ticket

Practice

DIFFERENTIATE

 View reports of student progress on the **Checks** after each example.

Resources	AL	OL	BL	ELL
Remediation: Rate of Change and Slope	●	●		●
Extension: Searching for Squares		●	●	●

Language Development Handbook

Assign page 50 of the *Language Development Handbook* to help your students build mathematical language related to the properties of rhombi and squares.

ELL You can use the tips and suggestions on page T50 of the handbook to support students who are building English proficiency.

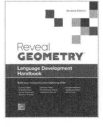

Suggested Pacing

90 min	**0.5 day**	
45 min	**1 day**	

Focus

Domain: Geometry

Standards for Mathematical Content:

G.CO.11 Prove theorems about parallelograms.

G.GPE.4 Use coordinates to prove simple geometric theorems algebraically.

Standards for Mathematical Practice:

2 Reason abstractly and quantitatively.

3 Construct viable arguments and critique the reasoning of others.

6 Attend to precision.

Coherence

Vertical Alignment

Previous
Students recognized and applied the properties of rectangles and used them to determine whether a parallelogram is a rectangle.
5.G.4, G.CO.11, G.GPE.4

Now
Students recognize and apply the properties of rhombi and squares.
G.CO.11, G.GPE.4

Next
Students will recognize and apply the properties of trapezoids and kites.
G.GPE.4

Rigor

The Three Pillars of Rigor

1 CONCEPTUAL UNDERSTANDING	2 FLUENCY	3 APPLICATION

Conceptual Bridge In this lesson, students extend their understanding of rectangles to prove theorems related to rhombi and squares. They build fluency and apply their understanding by solving real-world problems related to rhombi and squares.

Mathematical Background

A rhombus is a quadrilateral with all four sides congruent. The diagonals of a rhombus are perpendicular. If a quadrilateral is both a rhombus and a rectangle, then it is a square. A square is extremely specialized, having all the properties of a parallelogram, a rectangle, and a rhombus.

Interactive Presentation

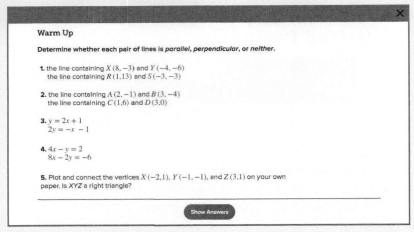

Warm Up

Determine whether each pair of lines is *parallel*, *perpendicular*, or *neither*.

1. the line containing $X(8, -3)$ and $Y(-4, -6)$
   the line containing $R(1, 13)$ and $S(-3, -3)$

2. the line containing $A(2, -1)$ and $B(3, -4)$
   the line containing $C(1, 6)$ and $D(3, 0)$

3. $y = 2x + 1$
   $2y = -x - 1$

4. $4x - y = 2$
   $8x - 2y = -6$

5. Plot and connect the vertices $X(-2, 1)$, $Y(-1, -1)$, and $Z(3, 1)$ on your own paper. Is XYZ a right triangle?

Show Answers

Warm Up

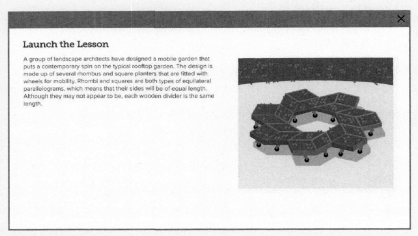

Launch the Lesson

A group of landscape architects have designed a mobile garden that puts a contemporary spin on the typical rooftop garden. The design is made up of several rhombus and square planters that are fitted with wheels for mobility. Rhombi and squares are both types of equilateral parallelograms, which means that their sides will be of equal length. Although they may not appear to be, each wooden divider is the same length.

Launch the Lesson

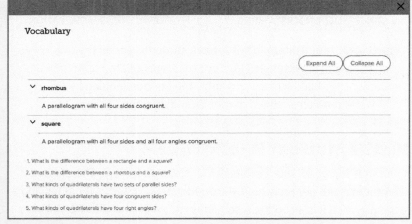

Vocabulary

Expand All | Collapse All

⌄ rhombus
  A parallelogram with all four sides congruent.

⌄ square
  A parallelogram with all four sides and all four angles congruent.

1. What is the difference between a rectangle and a *square*?
2. What is the difference between a *rhombus* and a *square*?
3. What kinds of quadrilaterals have two sets of parallel sides?
4. What kinds of quadrilaterals have four congruent sides?
5. What kinds of quadrilaterals have four right angles?

Today's Vocabulary

Warm Up

Prerequisite Skills

The Warm Up exercises address the following prerequisite skills for this lesson:

- identifying parallel and perpendicular lines
- identifying right triangles in the coordinate plane

Answers:

1. neither
2. parallel
3. perpendicular
4. parallel
5. yes

Launch the Lesson

 Teaching the Mathematical Practices

4 Apply Mathematics In this Launch the Lesson, students can see a real-world application of rhombi and squares.

🔍 **Go Online** to find additional teaching notes and questions to promote classroom discourse.

Today's Standards

Tell students that they will be addressing these content and practice standards in this lesson. You may wish to have a student volunteer read aloud *How can I meet these standards?* and *How can I use these practices?*, and connect these to the standards.

See the Interactive Presentation for I Can statements that align with the standards covered in this lesson.

Today's Vocabulary

Tell students that they will be using these vocabulary terms in this lesson. You can expand each row if you wish to share the definitions. Then, discuss the questions below with the class.

Explore Properties of Rhombi and Squares

Objective
Students use dynamic geometry software to determine the properties of rhombi and squares.

 Teaching the Mathematical Practices

6 Communicate Precisely Encourage students to routinely write or explain their solution methods. Point out that they should use clear definitions when they discuss their solutions with others.

Ideas for Use

Recommended Use Present the Inquiry Question, or have a student volunteer read it aloud. Have students work in pairs to complete the Explore activity on their devices. Pairs should discuss each of the questions. Monitor student progress during the activity. Upon completion of the Explore activity, have student volunteers share their responses to the Inquiry Question.

What if my students don't have devices? You may choose to project the activity on a whiteboard. A printable worksheet for each Explore is available online. You may choose to print the worksheet so that individuals or pairs of students can use it to record their observations.

Summary of the Activity

Students will complete guiding exercises throughout the Explore activity. Students use dynamic geometry software to manipulate and observe a rhombus. They complete guiding exercises leading them to observe that all four sides are congruent, the rhombus is a parallelogram, and that the diagonals are perpendicular bisectors. Then, students form a square and observe properties of the square, noting that it is also a rhombus, parallelogram, and rectangle. Then, students will answer the Inquiry Question.

(continued on the next page)

Interactive Presentation

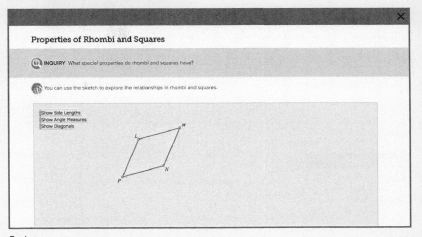

Explore

WEB SKETCHPAD

Students use a sketch to complete an activity in which they explore the properties of rhombi and squares.

1 CONCEPTUAL UNDERSTANDING | 2 FLUENCY | 3 APPLICATION

Interactive Presentation

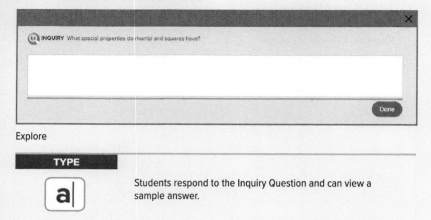

Explore

TYPE

Students respond to the Inquiry Question and can view a sample answer.

Explore Properties of Rhombi and Squares (*continued*)

MP Teaching the Mathematical Practices

3 Construct Arguments In the Explore, students will use stated assumptions, definitions, and previously established results to make a conjecture.

Questions

Have students complete the Explore activity.

Ask:

• What is the relationship between the diagonals of a rhombus?
  Sample answer: The diagonals of a rhombus are perpendicular.

ⓠ Inquiry

What special properties do rhombi and squares have? Sample answer: A rhombus is a parallelogram with four congruent sides. A square is a special rhombus with four right angles.

Go Online to find additional teaching notes and sample answers for the guiding exercises.

1 CONCEPTUAL UNDERSTANDING | **2 FLUENCY** | 3 APPLICATION

Learn Properties of Rhombi and Squares

Objective
Students recognize and apply the properties of rhombi and squares.

 Teaching the Mathematical Practices

7 Use Structure Help students to explore the structure of rhombi in this Learn.

Example 1 Use the Definition of a Rhombus

 Teaching the Mathematical Practices

6 Communicate Precisely Encourage students to routinely write or explain their solution methods. Point out that they should use clear definitions when they discuss their solutions with others.

Questions for Mathematical Discourse

AL Why can a rhombus and a square also be classified as equilateral parallelograms? Sample answer: All four sides are the same length and opposite sides are parallel.

OL In what ways can you classify rhombi and squares? Sample answer: A rhombus is an equilateral parallelogram. A square is a rhombus with all angles measuring 90°.

BL Is it possible for a rhombus to have exactly one 90° angle? Explain. Sample answer: A rhombus cannot have exactly one 90° angle, because if a parallelogram has one right angle, then it has four right angles.

Essential Question Follow-Up
Students learn properties of rhombi and squares.

Ask:

Why might properties of squares and rhombi be useful in the real world? Sample answer: Squares and rhombi appear in many places in the real world, so their properties could be useful any time those figures are used.

Go Online

- Find additional teaching notes.
- View performance reports of the Checks.
- Assign or present an Extra Example.

DIFFERENTIATE

Reteaching Activity **AL** **ELL**

Have students make a Venn diagram of the terms parallelogram, rhombus, rectangle, and square. Have students leave enough room to include the properties of each figure in the diagram. Ask about relevant properties.

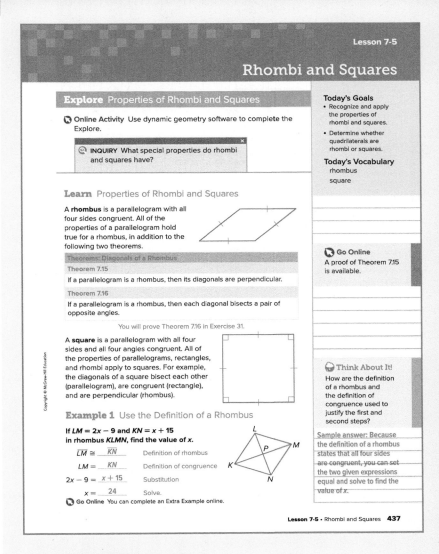

Lesson 7-5

Rhombi and Squares

Explore Properties of Rhombi and Squares

Online Activity Use dynamic geometry software to complete the Explore.

INQUIRY What special properties do rhombi and squares have?

Learn Properties of Rhombi and Squares

A **rhombus** is a parallelogram with all four sides congruent. All of the properties of a parallelogram hold true for a rhombus, in addition to the following two theorems.

Theorems: Diagonals of a Rhombus

Theorem 7.15
If a parallelogram is a rhombus, then its diagonals are perpendicular.

Theorem 7.16
If a parallelogram is a rhombus, then each diagonal bisects a pair of opposite angles.

You will prove Theorem 7.16 in Exercise 31.

A **square** is a parallelogram with all four sides and all four angles congruent. All of the properties of parallelograms, rectangles, and rhombi apply to squares. For example, the diagonals of a square bisect each other (parallelogram), are congruent (rectangle), and are perpendicular (rhombus).

Example 1 Use the Definition of a Rhombus

If $LM = 2x - 9$ and $KN = x + 15$ in rhombus $KLMN$, find the value of x.

$\overline{LM} \cong \overline{KN}$	Definition of rhombus
$LM = \underline{}$	Definition of congruence
$2x - 9 = \underline{x + 15}$	Substitution
$x = \underline{24}$	Solve.

Go Online You can complete an Extra Example online.

Today's Goals
- Recognize and apply the properties of rhombi and squares.
- Determine whether quadrilaterals are rhombi or squares.

Today's Vocabulary
rhombus
square

Go Online
A proof of Theorem 7.15 is available.

Think About It!
How are the definition of a rhombus and the definition of congruence used to justify the first and second steps?

Sample answer: Because the definition of a rhombus states that all four sides are congruent, you can set the two given expressions equal and solve to find the value of x.

Lesson 7-5 • Rhombi and Squares **437**

Interactive Presentation

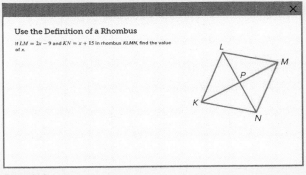

Use the Definition of a Rhombus

If $LM = 2x - 9$ and $KN = x + 15$ in rhombus $KLMN$, find the value of x.

Example 1

TYPE

Students answer a question to show they understand the definition of a rhombus.

1 CONCEPTUAL UNDERSTANDING   **2 FLUENCY**   3 APPLICATION

Your Notes

Check

Quadrilateral *WXYZ* is a rhombus. If *AZ* = 14, *ZY* = 22, and *m∠WYZ* = 35°, find each measure.

XZ = __28__   *m∠XYZ* = __70°__   *m∠WXZ* = __55°__

Talk About It!

Compare all of the properties of the following quadrilaterals: parallelograms, rectangles, rhombi, and squares.

Sample answer: Opposite sides of a parallelogram are parallel and congruent. Opposite angles of a parallelogram are congruent. The diagonals of a parallelogram bisect each other and each diagonal separates a parallelogram into two congruent triangles.

Rectangles, rhombi, and squares have all of the properties of parallelograms.

A rectangle has four right angles and its diagonals are congruent.

All sides of a rhombus are congruent. The diagonals of a rhombus are perpendicular and bisect the angles of the rhombus.

A square has all of the properties of a rectangle and a rhombus.

Example 2 Use the Diagonals of a Rhombus

The diagonals of rhombus *KLMN* intersect at *P*. If *m∠LMN* = 75°, find *m∠KNP*.

Because we know that *KLMN* is a rhombus, we can use the definition of a rhombus to say that ∠LKN and ∠LMN are congruent opposite angles that are bisected by diagonal $\overline{KM}$. Because $\overline{KM}$ is a bisector, $m\angle PKN = \frac{1}{2}m\angle LKN$. So $m\angle PKN = \frac{1}{2}(75°)$ or 37.5°. Because the diagonals of a rhombus are perpendicular, *m∠KPN* = 90° by the definition of perpendicular lines.

m∠PKN + *m∠PKN* + *m∠KNP* = 180   Triangle Angle-Sum Theorem

37.5 + 90 + *m∠KNP* = 180   Substitution

m∠KNP = __52.5°__   Solve.

Example 3 Use the Definition of a Square

EFGH is a square. If *FJ* = 19, find *FH*.

Because *EFGH* is square, it is both a parallelogram and a rectangle. Therefore, we know that its diagonals bisect each other and are congruent.

$\overline{FJ} \cong \overline{JH}$ Definition of a square

FJ = __JH__   Definition of congruence

__19__ = *JH*   Substitution

FJ + *JH* = __FH__   Definition of bisector

19 + __19__ = *FH*   Substitution

__38__ = *FH*   Simplify.

Check

In rhombus *PQRS*, *PQ* = 4*x* + 3, *QR* = 41, and *m∠PQT* = (2*x* + 4*y*)°. What must the value of *y* be for rhombus *PQRS* to be a square?

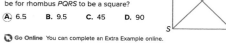

Ⓐ 6.5   **B.** 9.5   **C.** 45   **D.** 90

Go Online You can complete an Extra Example online.

438   Module 7 • Quadrilaterals

Interactive Presentation

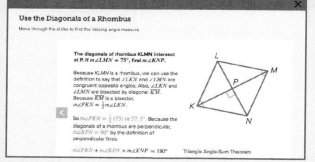

Use the Diagonals of a Rhombus

Move through the slides to find the missing angle measure.

Example 2

TAP

Students tap to find the missing angle measure.

CHECK

Students complete the Check online to determine whether they are ready to move on.

Example 2 Use the Diagonals of a Rhombus

MP Teaching the Mathematical Practices

2 Create Representations Guide students to write an equation that models the situation in this example. Then use the equation to solve the problem.

Questions for Mathematical Discourse

AL What do you know about the diagonals of rhombi? Sample answer: They are perpendicular bisectors and bisect opposite angles.

OL Which angles are congruent to ∠KLP? ∠MLP, ∠KNP, and ∠MNP

BL What is another way to find *m∠KLP*? Sample answer: ∠LMN is supplementary to ∠KLM, and ∠KLP measures half of ∠KLM.

Example 3 Use the Definition of a Square

MP Teaching the Mathematical Practices

6 Communicate Precisely Encourage students to routinely write or explain their solution methods. Point out that they should use clear definitions when they discuss their solutions with others.

Questions for Mathematical Discourse

AL What is the definition of a square? Sample answer: It is a quadrilateral with four congruent sides and four right angles.

OL Which segment is congruent to $\overline{FH}$? $\overline{EG}$

BL What is *EJ*? 19

DIFFERENTIATE

Language Development Activity ELL

Beginning Say key terms such as *parallelogram, rectangle, rhombus,* and *square,* from the lesson aloud, one at a time. Have students raise their hands if they have heard the term before. Have them use a word or phrase to tell something about the term. Use yes/no questions and prompts to help students complete a KWL Chart like the one below.

Intermediate Have students work with a partner to complete the K section of the chart to develop vocabulary. Have partners tell each other what they know about each term, concentrating on rhombi and squares.

Advanced After students complete the L section of the chart, have them work in small groups to compare answers and add each other's information to their own charts.

Advanced High Have students use the information on the KWL chart to give a short presentation about the lesson.

Rhombi and Squares	
K - What I Already Know	
W - What I Want to Learn	
L - What I Learned	

1 CONCEPTUAL UNDERSTANDING | **2 FLUENCY** | **3 APPLICATION**

Learn Tests for Rhombi and Squares

Objective
Students determine whether quadrilaterals are rhombi or squares.

MP Teaching the Mathematical Practices

3 Analyze Cases The Concept Check guides students to examine the cases of special parallelograms. Encourage students to familiarize themselves with all of the cases.

Example 4 Use Conditions for Rhombi and Squares

MP Teaching the Mathematical Practices

3 Construct Arguments In this example, students will use stated assumptions, definitions, and previously established results to complete the given proof.

Questions for Mathematical Discourse

AL What is the definition of a rectangle? a parallelogram with four right angles

OL Could you prove that *TUVW* is a rhombus using Theorem 7.17? Explain. Yes; sample answer: CPCTC says that $\angle UST \cong \angle WST$ and the two angles form a linear pair and are supplementary, so they are right angles. Theorem 7.17 says that a parallelogram whose diagonals are perpendicular is a rhombus, so *TUVW* is a rhombus.

BL If all four sides of a quadrilateral are congruent, can you prove that the quadrilateral is a rhombus? Explain. Yes; sample answer: If all four sides are congruent, then both pairs of opposite sides are congruent, so the quadrilateral is a parallelogram. Also, a pair of adjacent sides is congruent, so by Theorem 7.19 the quadrilateral is a rhombus.

🌐 Example 5 Use Properties of a Rhombus

MP Teaching the Mathematical Practices

4 Make Assumptions In the Study Tip, have students point out where an assumption or approximation was made in the solution.

Questions for Mathematical Discourse

AL What definitions and theorems can help you determine if the figure is a square? Sample answer: the definition of a square and Theorem 7.20

OL The given information is enough to determine that the figure is a rhombus. What else is needed to determine whether it is a square? Sample answer: to show that the figure is a rectangle

BL Why might it be easier to determine a length rather than an angle measurement? Sample answer: In the real world, people are more likely to have access to a ruler to measure length than a protractor to measure an angle.

Learn Tests for Rhombi and Squares

If a parallelogram meets certain conditions, you can conclude that it is a rhombus or a square.

Theorems: Conditions for Rhombi and Squares

Theorem 7.17
If the diagonals of a parallelogram are perpendicular, then the parallelogram is a rhombus.

Theorem 7.18
If one diagonal of a parallelogram bisects a pair of opposite angles, then the parallelogram is a rhombus.

Theorem 7.19
If two consecutive sides of a parallelogram are congruent, then the parallelogram is a rhombus.

Theorem 7.20
If a quadrilateral is both a rectangle and a rhombus, then it is a square.

You will prove Theorems 7.17, 7.19, and 7.20 in Exercises 32–34.

🔵 **Go Online** A proof of Theorem 7.18 is available.

You can use the properties of rhombi and squares to write proofs.

Example 4 Use Conditions for Rhombi and Squares

Write a paragraph proof.
Given: *TUVW* is a parallelogram.
  $\triangle TSW \cong \triangle TSU$
Prove: *TUVW* is a rhombus.
Proof:
Because it is given that $\triangle TSW \cong \triangle TSU$, it must be true that $\overline{WT} \cong \overline{UT}$. Because $\overline{WT}$ and $\overline{UT}$ are congruent, consecutive sides of the given parallelogram, we can prove that *TUVW* is a rhombus by using Theorem 7.19.

🌐 **Example 5** Use Properties of a Rhombus

GARMENT DESIGN Ananya is designing a sweater using an argyle pattern. All four sides of quadrilateral *ABCD* are 2 inches long. How can Ananya be sure that the argyle pattern is a square?

A square has all of the properties of a parallelogram, a rhombus, and a rectangle. To prove that quadrilateral *ABCD* is a square, prove that it is a parallelogram, a rhombus, and a rectangle.

(continued on the next page)

🔵 **Go Online** You can complete an Extra Example online.

Lesson 7-5 • Rhombi and Squares **439**

🔵 **Go Online** You may want to complete the Concept Check to check your understanding.

Math History Minute
Robert Ammann (1946–1994) was a programmer who considered himself an amateur mathematician. Although he did not study mathematics in college, Ammann discovered new ways to tile a plane by using quadrilaterals including rhombi. One of the tilings, the Ammann-Beenker tiling, is named for him.

Study Tip
Common Misconceptions The conditions for rhombi and squares only apply if you already know that a quadrilateral is a parallelogram.

Interactive Presentation

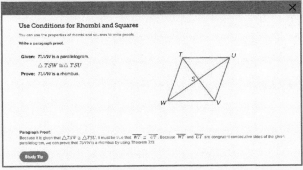

Use Conditions for Rhombi and Squares
You can use the properties of rhombi and squares to write proofs.
Write a paragraph proof.
Given: *TUVW* is a parallelogram.
  $\triangle TSW \cong \triangle TSU$
Prove: *TUVW* is a rhombus.

Paragraph Proof:
Because it is given that $\triangle TSW \cong \triangle TSU$, it must be true that $\overline{WT} \cong \overline{UT}$. Because $\overline{WT}$ and $\overline{UT}$ are congruent consecutive sides of the given parallelogram, we can prove that *TUVW* is a rhombus by using Theorem 7.19.

Study Tip

Example 4

TAP

Students tap to see a Study Tip.

1 CONCEPTUAL UNDERSTANDING | **2 FLUENCY** | 3 APPLICATION

🤔 **Think About It!**

How could Ananya show that the pattern is a square in a different way?

Sample answer: She could show that the sides of the pattern are equal and that the four angles are right angles.

Study Tip

Assumptions Although it would be difficult to measure a perfect square on a piece of fabric due to its stretching and shrinking qualities, we assume that the properties of a square will hold true, for example, the congruence of its diagonals.

🤔 **Think About It!**

What other way could you use to determine whether a quadrilateral is a rhombus?

Sample answer: Use the Distance Formula to compare the measures of all four sides. A rhombus has four congruent sides.

Study Tip

Make a Graph When analyzing a figure using coordinate geometry, graph the figure to help formulate a conjecture and also to help check the reasonableness of your answer. Use the same scale on the x- and y-axes so the representation is as accurate as possible. Be sure to choose a window that will allow you to see all of the vertices.

Because both pairs of opposite sides are congruent, ABCD is a ___parallelogram___.

Because ___consecutive___ sides of ▱ABCD are congruent, it is a rhombus.

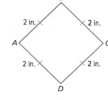

If the diagonals of a parallelogram are congruent, then the parallelogram is a ___rectangle___. So, if Ananya measures the length of each diagonal and finds that they are equal, then ABCD is a ___square___.

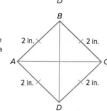

Example 6 Classify Parallelograms by Using Coordinate Geometry

Determine whether ▱ABCD with vertices A(−3, 2), B(−2, 6), C(2, 7), and D(1, 3) is a *rhombus*, a *rectangle*, a *square*, a *parallelogram*, or *none*. List all that apply. Explain.

Plot and connect the vertices on a coordinate plane. It appears that the figure is a ___parallelogram___.

ABCD appears to be a parallelogram, but is it also a rhombus? To check if the figure can be further classified, compare the slopes of the diagonals to determine whether they are perpendicular.

slope of $\overline{AC} = \frac{7-2}{2-(-3)} = \frac{5}{5}$ or 1

slope of $\overline{BD} = \frac{3-6}{1-(-2)} = \frac{-3}{3}$ or −1

Because the product of the slopes of the diagonals is ___−1___, the diagonals are ___perpendicular___, so ▱ABCD is a rhombus.

🔵 **Go Online** You can complete an Extra Example online.

Interactive Presentation

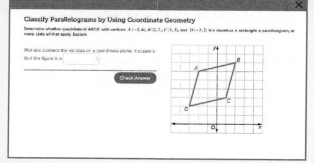

Example 6

SELECT

Students select the correct answers to complete the proof.

📊 **CHECK**

Students complete the Check online to determine whether they are ready to move on.

Example 6 Classify Parallelograms by Using Coordinate Geometry

🅼🅿 Teaching the Mathematical Practices

6 Use Quantities Use the Study Tip to guide students to clarifying their use of quantities in this example. Ensure that they specify the units of measure used in the problem and label axes appropriately.

Questions for Mathematical Discourse

AL How is a rhombus different from a square? Sample answer: A square has 4 right angles.

OL How can you show that the figure is a parallelogram? Sample answer: Show that the opposite sides are parallel.

BL Can the figure be a rhombus, a rectangle, and a square? Explain. Yes; sample answer: A square is also a rectangle because it is a parallelogram with 4 right angles. A square is also a rhombus because it is a parallelogram with 4 congruent sides.

Common Error

Students may think that the figure is a parallelogram because it looks like one. Remind them that there is enough information to prove that the figure is a parallelogram, and ask them what it is.

Exit Ticket

Recommended Use

At the end of class, go online to display the Exit Ticket prompt and ask students to respond using a separate piece of paper. Have students hand you their responses as they leave the room.

Alternate Use

At the end of class, go online to display the Exit Ticket prompt and ask students to respond verbally or by using a mini-whiteboard. Have students hold up their whiteboards so that you can see all student responses. Tap to reveal the answer when most or all students have completed the Exit Ticket.

Practice and Homework

Suggested Assignments

Use the table below to select appropriate exercises.

DOK	Topic	Exercises
1, 2	exercises that mirror the examples	1–22
2	exercises that use a variety of skills from this lesson	23–34
2	exercises that extend concepts learned in this lesson to new contexts	35–41
3	exercises that emphasize higher-order and critical-thinking skills	42–46

ASSESS AND DIFFERENTIATE

📊 Use the data from the **Checks** to determine whether to provide resources for extension, remediation, or intervention.

IF students score 90% or more on the Checks, `BL`
THEN assign:

- Practice, Exercises 1–41 odd, 42–46
- Extension: Searching for Squares
- ⬤ ALEKS· Parallelograms and Trapezoids

IF students score 66%–89% on the Checks, `OL`
THEN assign:

- Practice, Exercises 1–45 odd
- Remediation, Review Resources: Rate of Change and Slope
- Personal Tutors
- Extra Examples 1–6
- ⬤ ALEKS· Equations of Lines

IF students score 65% or less on the Checks, `AL`
THEN assign:

- Practice, Exercises 1–21 odd
- Remediation, Review Resources: Rate of Change and Slope
- *Quick Review Math Handbook:* Rhombi and Squares
- ⬤ ALEKS· Equations of Lines

Answers

11. Proof: Statements (Reasons)
 1. $ACDH$ and $BCDF$ are parallelograms, $\overline{BF} \cong \overline{AB}$. (Given)
 2. $\overline{BF} \cong \overline{CD}$; $\overline{CD} \cong \overline{AH}$ (If a quad. is a ▱, then its opp. sides are ≅.)
 3. $\overline{BF} \cong \overline{AH}$ (Transitive Property of ≅)
 4. $\overline{BC} \cong \overline{FD}$; $\overline{AC} \cong \overline{HD}$ (If a quad. is a ▱, then its opp. sides are ≅.)
 5. $BC = FD, AC = HD$ (Def. of ≅ segments)
 6. $AC = AB + BC, HD = HF + FD$ (Seg. Add. Post.)
 7. $AB + BC = HF + FD$ (Substitution)
 8. $AB + FD = HF + FD$ (Substitution)
 9. $AB = HF$ (Subtraction Property of =)
 10. $\overline{AB} \cong \overline{HF}$ (Def. of ≅ segments)
 11. $ABFH$ is a parallelogram. (If both pairs of opp. sides of a quad. are ≅, then the quad. is a ▱.)
 12. $ABFH$ is a rhombus. (If two consecutive sides of a ▱ are ≅, then the ▱ is a rhombus.)

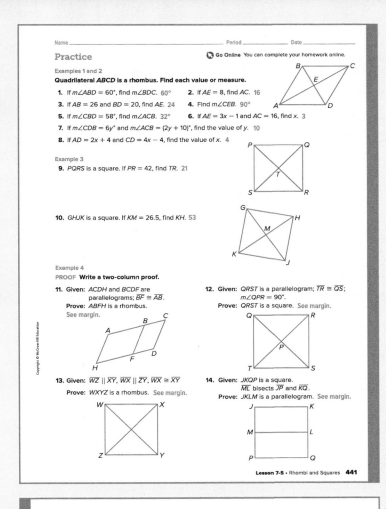

Name _____ Period _____ Date _____

Practice

🔄 **Go Online** You can complete your homework online.

Examples 1 and 2
Quadrilateral ABCD is a rhombus. Find each value or measure.

1. If $m\angle ABD = 60°$, find $m\angle BDC$. 60°
2. If $AE = 8$, find AC. 16
3. If $AB = 26$ and $BD = 20$, find AE. 24
4. Find $m\angle CEB$. 90°
5. If $m\angle CBD = 58°$, find $m\angle ACB$. 32°
6. If $AE = 3x - 1$ and $AC = 16$, find x. 3
7. If $m\angle CDB = 6y°$ and $m\angle ACB = (2y + 10)°$, find the value of y. 10
8. If $AD = 2x + 4$ and $CD = 4x - 4$, find the value of x. 4

Example 3

9. $PQRS$ is a square. If $PR = 42$, find TR. 21

10. $GHJK$ is a square. If $KM = 26.5$, find KH. 53

Example 4
PROOF Write a two-column proof.

11. Given: $ACDH$ and $BCDF$ are parallelograms; $\overline{BF} \cong \overline{AB}$.
 Prove: $ABFH$ is a rhombus.
 See margin.

12. Given: $QRST$ is a parallelogram; $\overline{TR} \cong \overline{QS}$; $m\angle QPR = 90°$.
 Prove: $QRST$ is a square. See margin.

13. Given: $\overline{WZ} \parallel \overline{XY}, \overline{WX} \parallel \overline{ZY}, \overline{WX} \cong \overline{XY}$
 Prove: $WXYZ$ is a rhombus. See margin.

14. Given: $JKQP$ is a square.
 $\overline{ML}$ bisects $\overline{JP}$ and $\overline{KQ}$.
 Prove: $JKLM$ is a parallelogram. See margin.

Lesson 7-5 • Rhombi and Squares 441

Example 5

15. PRECISION Jorge is using this box garden to plant his vegetables this year. What does Jorge need to know to ensure that the box garden is a square? Explain.
Sample answer: Because consecutive sides are congruent, the garden is a rhombus. Jorge needs to know if the diagonals of the garden are congruent to determine whether it is a square.

4 ft
4 ft

16. PRECISION Ingrid is designing a quilt with patches like the one shown. The patch is a parallelogram with all four angles having the same measure and the top and right sides having the same measure. Ingrid says that the patch is a square. Is she correct? Explain.
Yes; sample answer: The patch is a rectangle because all four angles have a measure of 90°, and it is a rhombus because two consecutive sides are congruent. Therefore, the patch is a square.

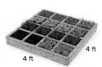

Example 6
REGULARITY **Determine whether quadrilateral ABCD is a rhombus, a rectangle, a square, a parallelogram, or none. List all that apply. Explain.**

17. $A(0, 2), B(2, 4), C(4, 2), D(2, 0)$
Parallelogram, rectangle, rhombus, square; the four sides are congruent and consecutive sides are perpendicular.

18. $A(-2, -1), B(0, 2), C(2, -1), D(0, -4)$
Parallelogram, rhombus; the four sides are congruent and consecutive sides are not perpendicular.

19. $A(-6, -1), B(4, -6), C(2, 5), D(-8, 10)$
Parallelogram, rhombus; all sides are congruent and the diagonals are perpendicular, but not congruent.

20. $A(2, -4), B(-6, -8), C(-10, 2), D(-2, 6)$
Parallelogram; opposite sides are congruent, but the diagonals are neither congruent nor perpendicular.

21. $A(1, 3), B(7, -3), C(1, -9), D(-5, -3)$
Parallelogram, rhombus, rectangle, square; all sides are congruent and the diagonals are perpendicular and congruent.

22. $A(-9, 1), B(2, 3), C(12, -2), D(1, -4)$
Parallelogram, rhombus; all sides are congruent and the diagonals are perpendicular, but not congruent.

Mixed Exercises
BCDF is a square with FD = 55. Find each measure.

23. BC 55
24. CD 55
25. GD 38.9
26. BD 77.8

442 Module 7 • Quadrilaterals

Name _____ Period _____ Date _____

WXYZ is a square. If WT = 3, find each measure.

27. ZX 6

28. XY $3\sqrt{2}$

29. m∠WTZ 90°

30. m∠WYX 45°

PROOF Write a two-column proof to prove each theorem.

31. Theorem 7.16
Given: *ABCD* is a rhombus.
Prove: $\overline{AC}$ bisects ∠DAB and ∠DCB.
$\overline{BD}$ bisects ∠ABC and ∠ADC.

Proof:
Statements (Reasons)
1. *ABCD* is a rhombus. (Given)
2. *ABCD* is a parallelogram. (Def. of rhombus)
3. ∠DAB ≅ ∠DCB, ∠ABC ≅ ∠ADC (If a quad. is a ▱, its opp. ∠s are ≅.)
4. $\overline{AB} ≅ \overline{BC} ≅ \overline{CD} ≅ \overline{AD}$ (Def. of rhombus)
5. △DAB ≅ △DCB, △ABC ≅ △ADC (SAS)
6. ∠8 ≅ ∠7, ∠3 ≅ ∠4, ∠1 ≅ ∠2, ∠5 ≅ ∠6 (CPCTC)
7. $\overline{AC}$ bisects ∠DAB and ∠DCB. $\overline{BD}$ bisects ∠ABC and ∠ADC. (Def. of angle bisector)

32. Theorem 7.17
Given: *PQRS* is a parallelogram; $\overline{PR} ⊥ \overline{QS}$.
Prove: *PQRS* is a rhombus.

Proof:
Statements (Reasons)
1. *PQRS* is a parallelogram; $\overline{PR} ⊥ \overline{QS}$. (Given)
2. ∠PTQ, ∠RTQ, ∠RTS, and ∠PTS are rt. ∠s. (⊥ lines form 4 rt. ∠s)
3. ∠PTQ ≅ ∠RTQ ≅ ∠RTS ≅ ∠PTS (All rt. ∠s are ≅.)
4. $\overline{PR}$ bisects $\overline{SQ}$, and $\overline{SQ}$ bisects $\overline{PR}$. (If a quad. is a ▱, its diagonals bisect each other.)
5. $\overline{ST} ≅ \overline{QT}, \overline{PT} ≅ \overline{RT}$ (Def. of segment bisector)
6. △PTQ ≅ △RTQ ≅ △RTS ≅ △PTS (SAS)
7. $\overline{PQ} ≅ \overline{RQ} ≅ \overline{RS} ≅ \overline{PS}$ (CPCTC)
8. *PQRS* is a rhombus. (Def. of rhombus)

33. Theorem 7.19
Given: *RSTU* is a parallelogram; $\overline{RS} ≅ \overline{ST}$.
Prove: *RSTU* is a rhombus.

Proof:
Statements (Reasons)
1. *RSTU* is a parallelogram; $\overline{RS} ≅ \overline{ST}$. (Given)
2. $\overline{RS} ≅ \overline{UT}, \overline{RU} ≅ \overline{ST}$ (If a quad. is a ▱, its opp. sides are ≅.)
3. $\overline{RS} ≅ \overline{RU}$ (Transitive Property of Congruence)
4. *RSTU* is a rhombus. (Def. of rhombus)

34. Theorem 7.20
Given: *WXYZ* is a rectangle and a rhombus.
Prove: *WXYZ* is a square. See margin.

Lesson 7-5 • Rhombi and Squares **443**

35. USE ESTIMATION The figure is an example of a quilt pattern. Estimate the type and number of shapes in the figure. Use a ruler or protractor to measure the shapes and then name the quadrilaterals used to form the figure. Compare this to your estimation.
The figure consists of 15 congruent rhombi.

Classify each quadrilateral.

36. rhombus **37.** square **38.** rectangle

USE TOOLS Use diagonals to construct each figure. Justify each construction.
39–40. See Mod. 7 Answer Appendix.

39. rhombus **40.** square

41. CAKE Douglas cuts a rhombus-shaped piece of cake along both diagonals. He ends up with four congruent triangles. Classify these triangles as *acute, obtuse,* or *right.* right triangles

Higher-Order Thinking Skills

42. PERSEVERE The area of square *ABCD* is 36 square units and the area of △EBF is 20 square units. If $\overline{EB} ⊥ \overline{BF}$ and *AE* = 2, find *CF*. 2

43. WRITE Compare all of the properties of the following quadrilaterals: parallelograms, rectangles, rhombi, and squares. See Mod. 7 Answer Appendix.

44. FIND THE ERROR In parallelogram *PQRS*, $\overline{PR} ≅ \overline{QS}$. Graciela thinks that the parallelogram is a square, and Xavier thinks that it is a rhombus. Is either of them correct? Explain your reasoning. No; sample answer: Because they do not know that the sides of the quadrilateral are congruent, they can only conclude that the quadrilateral is a rectangle.

45. ANALYZE Determine whether the statement is *true* or *false.* Then write the converse, inverse, and contrapositive of the statement and determine the truth value of each. Justify your argument. If a quadrilateral is a square, then it is a rectangle. See Mod. 7 Answer Appendix.

46. CREATE Find the vertices of a square with diagonals that are contained in the graphs of *y* = *x* and *y* = −*x* + 6. Justify your reasoning. Sample answer: (0, 0), (0, 6), (6, 6); The diagonals are perpendicular, and any four points on the lines equidistant from the intersection of the lines will be the vertices of the square.

Answers

12. Proof:
Statements (Reasons)
1. *QRST* is a parallelogram, $\overline{TR} ≅ \overline{QS}$, m∠QPR = 90° (Given)
2. *QRST* is a rectangle. (If the diag. of a parallelogram are ≅, the parallelogram is a rectangle.)
3. ∠QPR is a right angle. (Def. of right angle)
4. $\overline{QS} ⊥ \overline{TR}$ (Def. of perpendicular lines)
5. *QRST* is a rhombus. (If the diag. of a parallelogram are ⊥, the parallelogram is a rhombus.)
6. *QRST* is a square. (If a quad. is both a rectangle and a rhombus, then it is a square.)

13. Proof:
Statements (Reasons)
1. $\overline{WZ} ∥ \overline{XY}, \overline{WX} ∥ \overline{ZY}, \overline{WX} ≅ \overline{XY}$ (Given)
2. *WXYZ* is a parallelogram. (Both pairs of opposite sides are ∥.)
3. *WXYZ* is a rhombus. (If one pair of consec. sides of a parallelogram are ≅, then the parallelogram is a rhombus.)

14. Proof:
Statements (Reasons)
1. *JKQP* is a square, $\overline{ML}$ bisects $\overline{JP}$ and $\overline{KQ}$ (Given)
2. *JKQP* is a parallelogram. (All squares are parallelograms.)
3. $\overline{JM} ∥ \overline{KL}$ (Def. of a parallelogram)
4. $\overline{JP} ≅ \overline{KQ}$ (Opposite sides of a parallelogram are ≅.)
5. *JP* = *KQ* (Def. of ≅ segments)
6. *JM* = *MP*, *KL* = *LQ* (Def. of bisect)
7. *JP* = *JM* + *MP*, *KQ* = *KL* + *LQ* (Segment Addition Postulate)
8. *JP* = 2*JM*, *KQ* = 2*KL* (Substitution)
9. 2*JM* = 2*KL* (Substitution)
10. *JM* = *KL* (Division Property of Equality)
11. $\overline{KL} ≅ \overline{JM}$ (Def. of ≅ segments)
12. *JKLM* is a parallelogram. (If one pair of opp. sides is ≅ and ∥, then the quadrilateral is a parallelogram.)

34. Proof:
Statements (Reasons)
1. *WXYZ* is a rectangle and a rhombus. (Given)
2. *WXYZ* is a parallelogram. (Def. of a rectangle and a rhombus)
3. ∠W, ∠X, ∠Y, and ∠Z are right angles. (Def. of a rectangle)
4. $\overline{WX} ≅ \overline{XY} ≅ \overline{YZ} ≅ \overline{ZW}$ (Def. of a rhombus)
5. *WXYZ* is a square. (Def. of a square)

Trapezoids and Kites

LESSON GOAL

Students solve problems using the properties of trapezoids and kites.

1 LAUNCH

 Launch the lesson with a **Warm Up** and an introduction.

2 EXPLORE AND DEVELOP

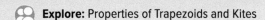 **Explore:** Properties of Trapezoids and Kites

 Develop:

Trapezoids
- Use Properties of Isosceles Trapezoids
- Isosceles Trapezoids and Coordinate Geometry

Midsegments of Trapezoids
- Midsegments of Trapezoids
- Find Missing Values in Trapezoids
- Midsegments and Coordinate Geometry

Kites
- Find Angle Measures in Kites
- Find Lengths in Kites

 You may want your students to complete the **Checks** online.

3 REFLECT AND PRACTICE

Exit Ticket

Practice

DIFFERENTIATE

View reports of student progress on the **Checks** after each example.

Resources	AL	OL	BL	ELL
Remediation: Similar Triangles: SSS and SAS Similarity	●	●		●
Extension: Mathematics and Music		●	●	●

Language Development Handbook

Assign page 51 of the *Language Development Handbook* to help your students build mathematical language related to the properties of trapezoids and kites.

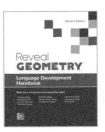

ELL You can use the tips and suggestions on page T51 of the handbook to support students who are building English proficiency.

Suggested Pacing

90 min	0.5 day
45 min	1 day

Focus

Domain: Geometry

Standards for Mathematical Content:

G.GPE.4 Use coordinates to prove simple geometric theorems algebraically.

Standards for Mathematical Practice:

3 Construct viable arguments and critique the reasoning of others.

6 Attend to precision.

8 Look for and express regularity in repeated reasoning.

Coherence

Vertical Alignment

Previous
Students recognized and applied the properties of rhombi and squares.
5.G.4, G.CO.11, G.GPE.4

Now
Students recognize and apply the properties of trapezoids and kites.
G.GPE.4

Next
Students will recognize and apply the properties of dilations.
G.SRT.1

Rigor

The Three Pillars of Rigor

1 CONCEPTUAL UNDERSTANDING	2 FLUENCY	3 APPLICATION

Conceptual Bridge In this lesson, students extend their understanding of quadrilaterals to prove theorems related to trapezoids and kites. They build fluency and apply their understanding by solving real-world problems related to trapezoids and kites.

Mathematical Background

A trapezoid is a quadrilateral with exactly one pair of parallel sides, called bases. The nonparallel sides are called legs. The median joins the midpoints of the legs of a trapezoid and is parallel to the bases. Its measure is one-half the sum of the measures of the bases.

Interactive Presentation

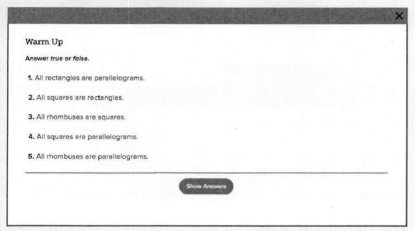

Warm Up

Warm Up

Prerequisite Skills

The Warm Up exercises address the following prerequisite skill for this lesson:

- identifying relationships between types of quadrilaterals

Answers:

1. true
2. true
3. false
4. true
5. true

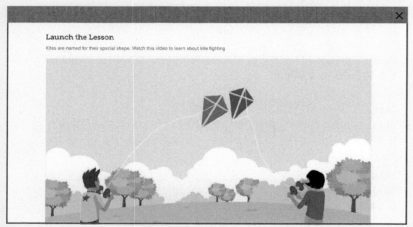

Launch the Lesson

Launch the Lesson

 Teaching the Mathematical Practices

> **4 Apply Mathematics** In this Launch the Lesson, students can see a real-world application of kites.

👆 **Go Online** to find additional teaching notes and questions to promote classroom discourse.

Today's Standards

Tell students that they will be addressing these content and practice standards in this lesson. You may wish to have a student volunteer read aloud *How can I meet these standards?* and *How can I use these practices?*, and connect these to the standards.

See the Interactive Presentation for I Can statements that align with the standards covered in this lesson.

Today's Vocabulary

Tell students that they will be using these vocabulary terms in this lesson. You can expand each row if you wish to share the definitions. Then, discuss the questions below with the class.

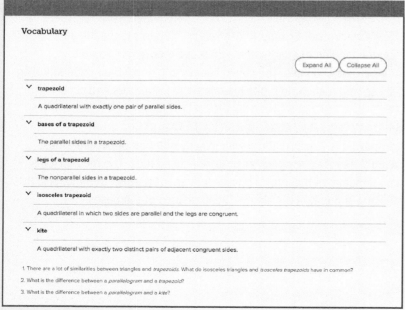

Today's Vocabulary

Explore Properties of Trapezoids and Kites

Objective

Students use dynamic geometry software to analyze data and make conjectures about the midsegments of trapezoids and angle relationships in kites.

 Teaching the Mathematical Practices

> **7 Look for a Pattern** Help students to see the pattern in this Explore.

Ideas for Use

Recommended Use Present the Inquiry Question, or have a student volunteer read it aloud. Have students work in pairs to complete the Explore activity on their devices. Pairs should discuss each of the questions. Monitor student progress during the activity. Upon completion of the Explore activity, have student volunteers share their responses to the Inquiry Question.

What if my students don't have devices? You may choose to project the activity on a whiteboard. A printable worksheet for each Explore is available online. You may choose to print the worksheet so that individuals or pairs of students can use it to record their observations.

Summary of the Activity

Students will complete guiding exercises throughout the Explore activity. Students explore the midsegment of a trapezoid and complete guiding exercises designed to lead them to making a conjecture about its length. Students then examine the diagonals of a kite and complete guiding exercises designed to lead them to conjecture that the diagonals are perpendicular. Finally, students measure the angles of the kite and complete guiding exercises designed to lead them to conjecture that two opposite angles are congruent. Then, students will answer the Inquiry Question.

(continued on the next page)

Interactive Presentation

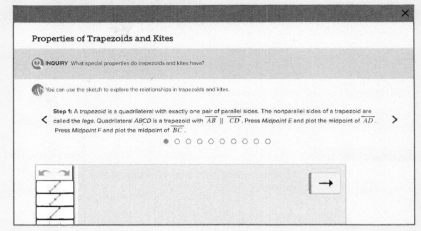

Explore

WEB SKETCHPAD

 Students use a sketch to complete an activity in which they explore properties of trapezoids and kites.

Interactive Presentation

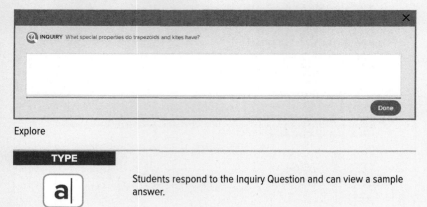

INQUIRY What special properties do trapezoids and kites have?

Done

Explore

| TYPE |

 Students respond to the Inquiry Question and can view a sample answer.

1 CONCEPTUAL UNDERSTANDING   2 FLUENCY | 3 APPLICATION

Explore Properties of Trapezoids and Kites (*continued*)

(MP) Teaching the Mathematical Practices

5 Use Mathematical Tools Point out that to solve the problem in this Explore, students will need to use dynamic geometry software. Work with students to explore and deepen their understanding of midsegments of trapezoids and angle relationships in kites.

Questions

Have students complete the Explore activity.

Ask:

- What is a conjecture that you can make about the interior angles of a kite? Sample answer: There exists one pair of congruent opposite angles in a kite.

Inquiry

What special properties do trapezoids and kites have? Sample answer: In a trapezoid, the length of the midsegment is half the sum of the lengths of the bases. In a kite, the diagonals are perpendicular, and there is one pair of congruent opposite angles.

Go Online to find additional teaching notes and sample answers for the guiding exercises.

1 CONCEPTUAL UNDERSTANDING   2 FLUENCY   3 APPLICATION

Learn Trapezoids

Objective
Students apply the properties of trapezoids to solve real-world and mathematical problems.

Teaching the Mathematical Practices
7 Use Structure Help students to explore the structure of trapezoids in this Learn.

Common Misconception
Students may think that parallelograms are trapezoids. Remind them to revisit the definitions of both types of quadrilaterals precisely. Parallelograms have two pairs of opposite parallel sides, and trapezoids have exactly one.

Essential Question Follow-Up
Students learn about trapezoids and kites.
Ask:
Why are properties of trapezoids and kites useful? Sample answer: When trapezoids and kites appear in real-world situations, you can use their properties to solve real-world problems.

Go Online
- Find additional teaching notes.
- View performance reports of the Checks.
- Assign or present an Extra Example.

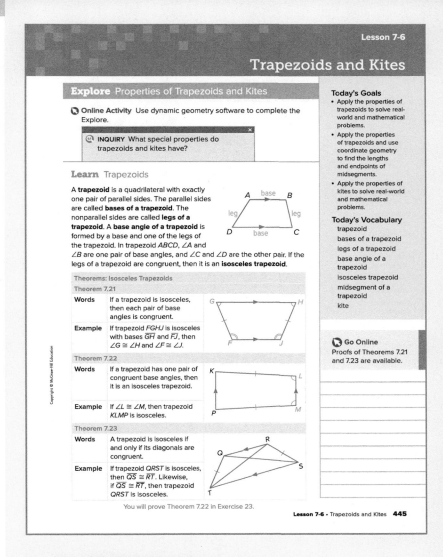

Lesson 7-6

Trapezoids and Kites

Explore Properties of Trapezoids and Kites

Online Activity Use dynamic geometry software to complete the Explore.

INQUIRY What special properties do trapezoids and kites have?

Learn Trapezoids

A **trapezoid** is a quadrilateral with exactly one pair of parallel sides. The parallel sides are called **bases of a trapezoid**. The nonparallel sides are called **legs of a trapezoid**. A **base angle of a trapezoid** is formed by a base and one of the legs of the trapezoid. In trapezoid $ABCD$, $\angle A$ and $\angle B$ are one pair of base angles, and $\angle C$ and $\angle D$ are the other pair. If the legs of a trapezoid are congruent, then it is an **isosceles trapezoid**.

Theorems: Isosceles Trapezoids

Theorem 7.21

Words	If a trapezoid is isosceles, then each pair of base angles is congruent.
Example	If trapezoid $FGHJ$ is isosceles with bases $\overline{GH}$ and $\overline{FJ}$, then $\angle G \cong \angle H$ and $\angle F \cong \angle J$.

Theorem 7.22

Words	If a trapezoid has one pair of congruent base angles, then it is an isosceles trapezoid.
Example	If $\angle L \cong \angle M$, then trapezoid $KLMP$ is isosceles.

Theorem 7.23

Words	A trapezoid is isosceles if and only if its diagonals are congruent.
Example	If trapezoid $QRST$ is isosceles, then $\overline{QS} \cong \overline{RT}$. Likewise, if $\overline{QS} \cong \overline{RT}$, then trapezoid $QRST$ is isosceles.

You will prove Theorem 7.22 in Exercise 23.

Today's Goals
- Apply the properties of trapezoids to solve real-world and mathematical problems.
- Apply the properties of trapezoids and use coordinate geometry to find the lengths and endpoints of midsegments.
- Apply the properties of kites to solve real-world and mathematical problems.

Today's Vocabulary
trapezoid
bases of a trapezoid
legs of a trapezoid
base angle of a trapezoid
isosceles trapezoid
midsegment of a trapezoid
kite

Go Online
Proofs of Theorems 7.21 and 7.23 are available.

Copyright © McGraw-Hill Education

Lesson 7-6 · Trapezoids and Kites 445

Interactive Presentation

Properties of Trapezoids

A **trapezoid** is a quadrilateral with exactly one pair of parallel sides. The parallel sides are called **bases of a trapezoid**. The nonparallel sides are called **legs of a trapezoid**. A base angle of a trapezoid is formed by a base and one of the legs of the trapezoid. In trapezoid $ABCD$, $\angle A$ and $\angle B$ are one pair of base angles, and $\angle C$ and $\angle D$ are the other pair. If the legs of a trapezoid are congruent, then it is an **isosceles trapezoid**.

Learn

DRAG & DROP

 Students drag reasons to complete a proof.

1 CONCEPTUAL UNDERSTANDING   2 FLUENCY   3 APPLICATION

Your Notes

🌐 Example 1 Use Properties of Isosceles Trapezoids

MUSIC The body of the guitar shown is a trapezoidal prism. The front face of the guitar is an isosceles trapezoid. $AB = 3x - 2$, $CD = 3x + 9$, $AD = 4x + 5$, and $BC = 5x - 6$.

Part A Prove $x = 11$.

Statements	Reasons
1. $ABCD$ is an isosceles trapezoid.	1. Given
2. $\overline{AD} \cong \overline{BC}$	2. Def. of isosceles trapezoid
3. $AD = BC$	3. Def. of congruent segments
4. $4x + 5 = 5x - 6$	4. Substitution
5. $5 = x - 6$	5. Subtraction Prop. of Equality
6. $11 = x$	6. Addition Prop. of Equality
7. $x = 11$	7. Symmetric Prop. of Equality

Reasons:

Addition Property of Equality

Definition of congruent angles

Definition of isosceles trapezoid

Definition of congruent segments

Given

Substitution

Subtraction Property of Equality

Symmetric Property of Equality

Part B Find $m\angle A$ if $m\angle C = 72°$.

Because $ABCD$ is an isosceles trapezoid, $\angle C$ and $\angle D$ are congruent base angles. So, $m\angle C = m\angle \underline{D} = 72°$.

Because $ABCD$ is a trapezoid, $\overline{AB} \parallel \overline{CD}$.

$m\angle A + m\angle \underline{D} = 180°$ Consecutive Interior Angles Theorem

$m\angle A + \underline{72} = 180$ Substitution

$m\angle A = \underline{108°}$ Solve.

Part C Find the perimeter of the front face of the guitar in centimeters.

$P = AB + BC + CD + AD$ Perimeter of trapezoid $ABCD$

$= 3x - 2 + 5x - 6 + 3x + 9 + 4x + 5$ Substitution

$= \underline{15x + 6}$ Combine like terms.

$= 15(\underline{11}) + 6$ $x = 11$

$= \underline{171}$ Simplify.

So, the perimeter of the front face of the guitar is 171 centimeters.

🌐 Example 1 Use Properties of Isosceles Trapezoids

ⓂⓅ Teaching the Mathematical Practices

4 Apply Mathematics In this example, students apply what they have learned about properties of trapezoids to solving a real-world problem.

Questions for Mathematical Discourse

AL Which pair of sides is parallel? $\overline{AB} \parallel \overline{CD}$

OL Which pair of sides is congruent? $\overline{AD}$ and $\overline{BC}$

BL What do you know about AC and BD? Sample answer: They are equal.

Common Error

Students may have difficulty determining which sides of the guitar are parallel and which are congruent, especially because the figure in the picture is not like the typical representation of a trapezoid where the parallel sides are horizontal and the upper side is shorter. Guide students to look carefully at the figure, sketch a copy, and mark sides with the appropriate information.

Interactive Presentation

Use Properties of Isosceles Trapezoids

🌐 MUSIC The body of the guitar is a trapezoidal prism. The front face of the guitar is an isosceles trapezoid. $AB = 3x - 2$, $CD = 3x + 9$, $AD = 4x + 5$, and $BC = 5x - 6$.

Example 1

TAP

Students tap to see steps in the solution.

Example 2 Isosceles Trapezoids and Coordinate Geometry

MP Teaching the Mathematical Practices

2 Different Properties Mathematically proficient students look for different ways to solve problems. Encourage them to work through both ways to solve the problem and to choose the method that works best for them.

Questions for Mathematical Discourse

AL How can you describe an isosceles trapezoid? Sample answer: An isosceles trapezoid is a trapezoid in which the legs are congruent.

OL How can you determine whether the figure is a trapezoid? Sample answer: I can analyze the slopes of the opposite sides to determine whether they are parallel.

BL How can you determine whether the trapezoid is isosceles? Sample answer: I can use the Distance Formula to find the length of each leg. If they are the same length, then the figure is an isosceles trapezoid.

DIFFERENTIATE

Language Development Activity **AL** **ELL**

There are several words that have multiple meanings within mathematics. The word isosceles can be applied to geometry in multiple ways. Have the students compare and contrast the meanings of isosceles when applied to a triangle and a trapezoid. Some comparisons are that both have a pair of congruent sides called legs, and that both have a pair of adjacent congruent angles. A contrast is that an isosceles triangle has only one other side while an isosceles trapezoid has two other parallel sides.

Learn Midsegments of Trapezoids

Objective

Students apply the properties of trapezoids and use coordinate geometry to find the lengths and endpoints of midsegments.

MP Teaching the Mathematical Practices

7 Use Structure Help students to explore the structure of midsegments of trapezoids in this Learn.

DIFFERENTIATE

Enrichment Activity **BL**

Students may notice that the midsegment divides a trapezoid into two smaller trapezoids. Ask students what they know about the corresponding angles in the three trapezoids. Students should be able to determine that corresponding angles in the three trapezoids are congruent.

Example 2 Isosceles Trapezoids and Coordinate Geometry

Quadrilateral QRST has vertices $Q(-8, -4)$, $R(0, 8)$, $S(6, 8)$, and $T(-6, -10)$. Show that QRST is a trapezoid, and determine whether QRST is an isosceles trapezoid.

Step 1 Graph quadrilateral QRST.

Graph and connect the vertices of QRST.

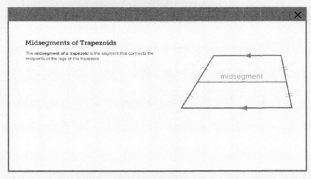

Step 2 Compare the slopes of the opposite sides.

Use the Slope Formula to compare the slopes of opposite sides $\overline{QR}$ and $\overline{ST}$ and opposite sides $\overline{QT}$ and $\overline{RS}$. A quadrilateral is a trapezoid if exactly one pair of opposite sides is parallel.

Opposite sides $\overline{QR}$ and $\overline{ST}$:

slope of $\overline{QR} = \frac{8-(-4)}{0-(-8)} = \frac{12}{8}$ or $\frac{3}{2}$

slope of $\overline{ST} = \frac{-10-8}{-6-6} = \frac{-18}{-12}$ or $\frac{3}{2}$

Because the slopes of $\overline{QR}$ and $\overline{ST}$ are equal, $\overline{QR} \parallel \overline{ST}$.

Opposite sides $\overline{QT}$ and $\overline{RS}$:

slope of $\overline{QT} = \frac{-10-(-4)}{-6-(-8)} = \frac{-6}{2}$ or -3

slope of $\overline{RS} = \frac{8-8}{6-0} = \frac{0}{6}$ or 0

Because the slopes of $\overline{QT}$ and $\overline{RS}$ are not equal, $\overline{QT} \nparallel \overline{RS}$. Because quadrilateral QRST has only one pair of opposite sides that are parallel, quadrilateral QRST is a trapezoid.

Step 3 Compare the lengths of the legs.

Use the Distance Formula to compare the lengths of the legs $\overline{QT}$ and $\overline{RS}$. A trapezoid is isosceles if its legs are congruent.

$QT = \sqrt{[-6-(-8)]^2 + [-10-(-4)]^2}$ or $\sqrt{40}$

$RS = \sqrt{(6-0)^2 + (8-8)^2} = \sqrt{36}$ or 6

Because $QT \neq RS$, legs $\overline{QT}$ and $\overline{RS}$ are *not* congruent. Therefore, trapezoid QRST is not isosceles.

Learn Midsegments of Trapezoids

The **midsegment of a trapezoid** is the segment that connects the midpoints of the legs of the trapezoid.

Theorem 7.24: Trapezoid Midsegment Theorem
The midsegment of a trapezoid is parallel to each base and its length is one half the sum of the lengths of the bases.

 Go Online A proof of Theorem 7.24 is available.

Go Online You can complete an Extra Example online.

Lesson 7-6 • Trapezoids and Kites **447**

💭 Think About It!
What other method could you have used to show that trapezoid QRST is not isosceles?

Sample answer: I could have used the Distance Formula to show that the diagonals of trapezoid QRST are not congruent.

Study Tip
Midsegment The midsegment of a trapezoid can also be called a *median*.

Interactive Presentation

Midsegments of Trapezoids
The midsegment of a trapezoid is the segment that connects the midpoints of the legs of the trapezoid.

midsegment

Learn

CHECK

Students complete the Check online to determine whether they are ready to move on.

Example 3 Midsegments of Trapezoids

In the figure, $\overline{UR}$ is the midsegment of trapezoid PQST. Find UR.

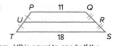

By the Trapezoid Midsegment Theorem, UR is equal to one half the sum of PQ and TS.

$UR = \frac{1}{2}(PQ + TS)$ Trapezoid Midsegment Theorem

$\underline{\quad} = \frac{1}{2}(11 + \underline{18}\quad)$ Substitution

$= \underline{14.5}$ Solve.

Example 4 Find Missing Values in Trapezoids

In the figure, $\overline{RN}$ is the midsegment of trapezoid LMPQ. What is the value of x?

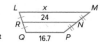

You can use the Trapezoid Midsegment Theorem to write an equation and find the value of x.

$RN = \frac{1}{2}(LM + QP)$ Trapezoid Midsegment Theorem

$\underline{24} = \frac{1}{2}(\underline{x} + \underline{16.7})$ Substitution

$\underline{48} = x + 16.7$ Multiply each side by 2.

$\underline{31.3} = x$ Solve.

Example 5 Midsegments and Coordinate Geometry

In trapezoid ABCD, $\overline{AD} \parallel \overline{BC}$. Find the endpoints of the midsegment.

You can use the Midpoint Formula to find the midpoints of $\overline{AB}$ and $\overline{DC}$. These midpoints are the endpoints of the midsegment of trapezoid ABCD.

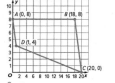

midpoint of $\overline{AB} = \left(\frac{0+18}{2}, \frac{8+8}{2}\right) = (9, \underline{8}\quad)$

midpoint of $\overline{DC} = \left(\frac{1+20}{2}, \frac{4+0}{2}\right) = (\underline{10.5}, 2)$

So, the endpoints of the midsegments are (9, 8) and (10.5, 2).

Go Online You can complete an Extra Example online.

💭 Think About It!

If the parallel sides of a trapezoid are contained by the lines $y = x + 4$ and $y = x - 8$, what equation represents the line containing the midsegment?

Sample answer: $y = x - 2$

Interactive Presentation

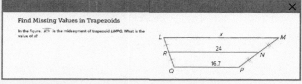

×

Find Missing Values in Trapezoids

In the figure, $\overline{RN}$ is the midsegment of trapezoid LMPQ. What is the value of x?

Example 4

TYPE

Students type to fill in steps in the solution.

CHECK

Students complete the Check online to determine whether they are ready to move on.

Example 3 Midsegments of Trapezoids

🔷 Teaching the Mathematical Practices

8 Attend to Details Mathematically proficient students continually ask themselves, "Does this make sense?" Point out that in this example, students will evaluate the reasonableness of their answer.

Questions for Mathematical Discourse

AL What do U and R represent in the figure? Sample answer: They are the midpoints of their respective sides.

OL If $UR = 26$ and $TS = 32$, then find PQ.   20

BL The midsegment of a trapezoid is also called a median. Compare and contrast the median of a triangle with the median of a trapezoid. Sample answer: The medians of a triangle and trapezoid connect the midpoint of a line segment to another location on the figure. The median of a triangle connects to a vertex while the median of a trapezoid connects the midpoints of the legs.

Example 4 Find Missing Values in Trapezoids

🔷 Teaching the Mathematical Practices

2 Create Representations Guide students to write an equation that models the situation in this example. Then use the equation to solve the problem.

Questions for Mathematical Discourse

AL What do R and N represent in terms of $\overline{LQ}$ and $\overline{MP}$? Sample answer: The points are the midpoints of the segments.

OL If we know that $LM = 22$ and $RN = 15$, what is QP?   8

BL For an isosceles trapezoid, as the difference between the measures of the two bases increases, how will the slope of the legs change, assuming the length of the midsegment remains constant? Sample answer: The slopes will approach zero.

Example 5 Midsegments and Coordinate Geometry

🔷 Teaching the Mathematical Practices

6 Communicate Precisely Encourage students to routinely write or explain their solution methods. Point out that they should use clear definitions when they discuss their solutions with others.

Questions for Mathematical Discourse

AL Why should you find the midpoints of $\overline{AB}$ and $\overline{DC}$ instead of $\overline{AD}$ and $\overline{BC}$? Sample answer: The midsegment has endpoints on the legs of the trapezoid. $\overline{AB}$ and $\overline{DC}$ are the legs of the trapezoid, whereas $\overline{AD}$ and $\overline{BC}$ are the bases.

OL Why do you have to use the Midpoint Formula to find the endpoints of the midsegment? Sample answer: The endpoints of the midsegments are the midpoints of the legs of the trapezoid. The diagram could be used to estimate the locations, but using the Midpoint Formula will give us the exact coordinates.

BL What is the slope of the midsegment? How is this slope related to the slopes of $\overline{AD}$ and $\overline{BC}$? $-\frac{1}{4}$; The slopes are equal because the midsegment is parallel to the bases.

Learn Kites

Objective
Students apply the properties of kites to solve real-world and mathematical problems.

 Teaching the Mathematical Practices

6 Communicate Precisely Encourage students to routinely write or explain their solution methods. Point out that they should use clear definitions when they discuss their solutions with others.

Important to Know
Notice that like trapezoids, kites are distinct from parallelograms. First, the two pairs of congruent sides in a kite are adjacent, rather than opposite. Second, the two pairs are distinct, so the pairs cannot include the same side, which would make a pair of opposite sides congruent. Third, there are exactly two pairs of congruent sides, so there is not another pair including one from each of the first two pairs. Thus a kite cannot have a pair of opposite congruent sides, and so cannot be a parallelogram.

Common Misconception
Students may think that rhombi are kites. Help students to look at the definition of a kite carefully to see why they are not.

Example 6 Find Angle Measures in Kites

 Teaching the Mathematical Practices

3 Compare Arguments Mathematically proficient students can compare arguments, determine which one is flawed, and explain the flaw. In this example, students have to identify the flawed argument and choose the correct one.

Questions for Mathematical Discourse

AL What does the Polygon Interior Angles Sum Theorem tell us about kites? Sample answer: The sum of the interior angles of a kite is 360°.

OL If the angles between the noncongruent adjacent sides each measure 120° and one of the other angles measures twice the other, what is the measure of the angle with least measure? 40°

BL Do you think that we could prove that the noncongruent angles of a kite are bisected by the diagonal between them? Explain. Yes; sample answer: We can prove that the pair of triangles formed by this diagonal are congruent using SSS, and then show that the two angles formed by the diagonal for each noncongruent angle are congruent using CPCTC.

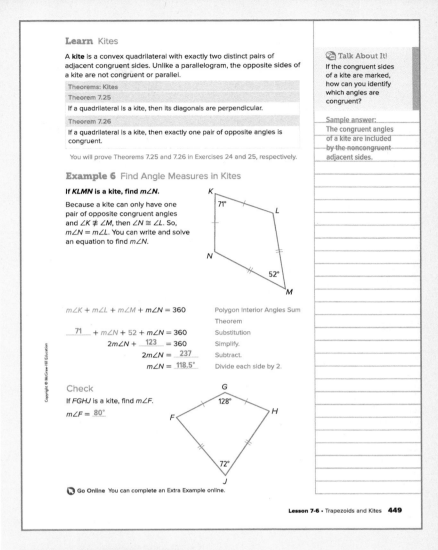

Learn Kites

A **kite** is a convex quadrilateral with exactly two distinct pairs of adjacent congruent sides. Unlike a parallelogram, the opposite sides of a kite are not congruent or parallel.

Theorems: Kites

Theorem 7.25
If a quadrilateral is a kite, then its diagonals are perpendicular.

Theorem 7.26
If a quadrilateral is a kite, then exactly one pair of opposite angles is congruent.

You will prove Theorems 7.25 and 7.26 in Exercises 24 and 25, respectively.

Talk About It!
If the congruent sides of a kite are marked, how can you identify which angles are congruent?

Sample answer: The congruent angles of a kite are included by the noncongruent adjacent sides.

Example 6 Find Angle Measures in Kites

If **KLMN** is a kite, find m∠N.

Because a kite can only have one pair of opposite congruent angles and ∠K ≇ ∠M, then ∠N ≅ ∠L. So, m∠N = m∠L. You can write and solve an equation to find m∠N.

$m\angle K + m\angle L + m\angle M + m\angle N = 360$	Polygon Interior Angles Sum Theorem
$\underline{71} + m\angle N + 52 + m\angle N = 360$	Substitution
$2m\angle N + \underline{123} = 360$	Simplify.
$2m\angle N = \underline{237}$	Subtract.
$m\angle N = \underline{118.5°}$	Divide each side by 2.

Check
If FGHJ is a kite, find m∠F.
m∠F = __80°__

Go Online You can complete an Extra Example online.

Lesson 7-6 · Trapezoids and Kites **449**

Interactive Presentation

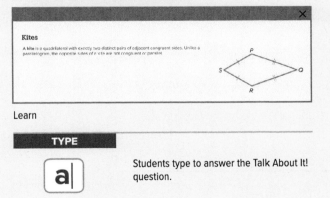

Kites

A kite is a quadrilateral with exactly two distinct pairs of adjacent congruent sides. Unlike a parallelogram, the opposite sides of a kite are not congruent or parallel.

Learn

TYPE

a|

Students type to answer the Talk About It! question.

| 1 CONCEPTUAL UNDERSTANDING | **2 FLUENCY** | 3 APPLICATION |

Example 7 Find Lengths in Kites

Quadrilateral *ABCD* is a kite.

Part A Find *AD*.

Because the diagonals of a kite are perpendicular, they divide *ABCD* into four right triangles. You can use the Pythagorean Theorem to find *AD*, the length of the hypotenuse of right △*AED*.

$$AE^2 + ED^2 = AD^2 \quad \text{Pythagorean Theorem}$$
$$12^2 + 24^2 = AD^2 \quad \text{Substitution}$$
$$144 + 576 = AD^2 \quad \text{Simplify.}$$
$$720 = AD^2 \quad \text{Simplify.}$$
$$\sqrt{720} = AD \quad \text{Take the square root of each side.}$$
$$12\sqrt{5} = AD \quad \text{Simplify.}$$

Part B Find the perimeter of kite *ABCD*.

From the figure, we know $\overline{AB} \cong \overline{BC}$ and $\overline{AD} \cong \overline{CD}$. So, $AB = BC$ and $AD = CD$. We know $AD = 12\sqrt{5}$. So, we can use the Pythagorean Theorem to find *AB*.

$$AE^2 + EB^2 = AB^2 \quad \text{Pythagorean Theorem}$$
$$12^2 + 6^2 = AB^2 \quad \text{Substitution}$$
$$144 + 36 = AB^2 \quad \text{Simplify.}$$
$$180 = AB^2 \quad \text{Simplify.}$$
$$\sqrt{180} = AB \quad \text{Take the square root of each side.}$$
$$6\sqrt{5} = AB \quad \text{Simplify.}$$

Use the values of *AB* and *AD* to find the perimeter of kite *ABCD*.

$$P = AB + BC + CD + AD \quad \text{Perimeter of kite}$$
$$= AB + AB + AD + AD \quad AB = BC \text{ and } AD = CD$$
$$= 2AB + 2AD \quad \text{Simplify.}$$
$$= 2(6\sqrt{5}) + 2(12\sqrt{5}) \quad AB = 6\sqrt{5} \text{ and } AD = 12\sqrt{5}$$
$$= 36\sqrt{5} \quad \text{Simplify.}$$

Check
Quadrilateral *ABCD* is a kite.
Part A Find *CD*. $\sqrt{89}$
Part B Find the perimeter of kite *ABCD*.
$26 + 2\sqrt{89}$

 Go Online You can complete an Extra Example online.

450 Module 7 • Quadrilaterals

Think About It!
How can you find the area of kite *ABCD*? Justify your argument.

Sample answer: In kite *ABCD*, △*ABD* ≅ △*CBD* by SSS. So, I can find the area of kite *ABCD* by finding the area of △*ABD* and multiplying it by 2.

 Go Online
to practice what you've learned about types of quadrilaterals in the Put It All Together over Lessons 7-2 through 7-6.

Example 7 Find Lengths in Kites

 Teaching the Mathematical Practices

3 Justify Conclusions Mathematically proficient students can explain the conclusions drawn when solving a problem. This example asks students to justify their conclusions.

Questions for Mathematical Discourse

AL What is *CD*? Explain. $12\sqrt{5}$; Sample answer: Because *ABCD* is a kite, $AD = CD$.

OL How do you know that you can use the Pythagorean Theorem? Sample answer: By Theorem 7.25, $\overline{AC} \perp \overline{BD}$.

BL If you were given the lengths *AD* and *AC*, could you find *DE*? Explain. Yes; sample answer: The diagonal $\overline{BD}$ bisects $\overline{AC}$, so you could find the length *AE* by dividing *AC* by 2. Then use the Pythagorean Theorem to write the equation $AE^2 + DE^2 = AD^2$ and solve to find *DE*.

Exit Ticket

Recommended Use

At the end of class, go online to display the Exit Ticket prompt and ask students to respond using a separate piece of paper. Have students hand you their responses as they leave the room.

Alternate Use

At the end of class, go online to display the Exit Ticket prompt and ask students to respond verbally or by using a mini-whiteboard. Have students hold up their whiteboards so that you can see all student responses. Tap to reveal the answer when most or all students have completed the Exit Ticket.

Interactive Presentation

Find Lengths in Kites
Quadrilateral *ABCD* is a kite.

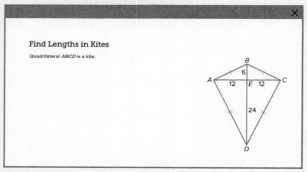

Example 7

TYPE

a|

Students type to fill in parts of the solution.

CHECK

Students complete the Check online to determine whether they are ready to move on.

Practice and Homework

Suggested Assignments

Use the table below to select appropriate exercises.

DOK	Topic	Exercises
1, 2	exercises that mirror the examples	1–16
2	exercises that use a variety of skills from this lesson	17–26
3	exercises that emphasize higher-order and critical-thinking skills	27–34

ASSESS AND DIFFERENTIATE

📊 Use the data from the **Checks** to determine whether to provide resources for extension, remediation, or intervention.

IF students score 90% or more on the Checks,   `BL`
THEN assign:

- Practice, Exercises 1–25 odd, 27–34
- Extension: Ratios in Trapezoids
- ⬛ **ALEKS**· Parallelograms and Trapezoids

IF students score 66%–89% on the Checks,   `OL`
THEN assign:

- Practice, Exercises 1–33 odd
- Remediation, Review Resources: Rhombi and Squares
- Personal Tutors
- Extra Examples 1–7
- ⬛ **ALEKS**· Parallelograms and Trapezoids

IF students score 65% or less on the Checks,   `AL`
THEN assign:

- Practice, Exercises 1–15 odd
- Remediation, Review Resources: Rhombi and Squares
- *Quick Review Math Handbook*: Trapezoids and Kites
- ⬛ **ALEKS**· Parallelograms and Trapezoids

Answers

1a. Proof:

Statements (Reasons)

1. *WXYZ* is an isosceles trapezoid. (Given)
2. $\overline{WZ} \cong \overline{XY}$ (Def. of isosceles trapezoid)
3. $WZ = XY$ (Def. of congruent segments)
4. $4x + 5 = 5x - 3$ (Substitution)
5. $5 = x - 3$ (Subtraction Prop. of Equality)
6. $8 = x$ (Addition Prop. of Equality)
7. $x = 8$ (Symmetric Prop. of Equality)

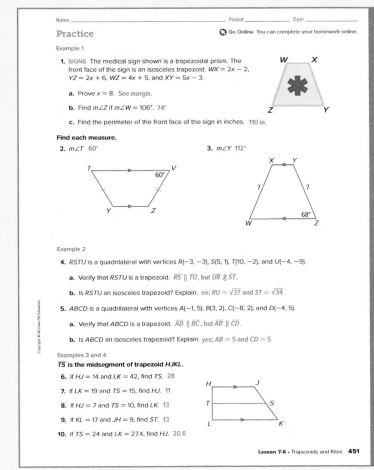

Name _____ Period _____ Date _____

Practice

🖥 Go Online You can complete your homework online.

Example 1

1. SIGNS The medical sign shown is a trapezoidal prism. The front face of the sign is an isosceles trapezoid. $WX = 2x - 2$, $YZ = 2x + 6$, $WZ = 4x + 5$, and $XY = 5x - 3$.

   a. Prove $x = 8$. See margin.

   b. Find $m\angle Z$ if $m\angle W = 106°$. 74°

   c. Find the perimeter of the front face of the sign in inches. 110 in.

Find each measure.

2. $m\angle T$ 60°

3. $m\angle Y$ 112°

Example 2

4. *RSTU* is a quadrilateral with vertices $R(-3, -3)$, $S(5, 1)$, $T(10, -2)$, and $U(-4, -9)$.

   a. Verify that *RSTU* is a trapezoid. $\overline{RS} \parallel \overline{TU}$, but $\overline{UR} \nparallel \overline{ST}$.

   b. Is *RSTU* an isosceles trapezoid? Explain. no; $RU = \sqrt{37}$ and $ST = \sqrt{34}$

5. *ABCD* is a quadrilateral with vertices $A(-1, 5)$, $B(3, 2)$, $C(-8, 2)$, and $D(-4, 5)$.

   a. Verify that *ABCD* is a trapezoid. $\overline{AD} \parallel \overline{BC}$, but $\overline{AB} \nparallel \overline{CD}$.

   b. Is *ABCD* an isosceles trapezoid? Explain. yes; $AB = 5$ and $CD = 5$

Examples 3 and 4

$\overline{TS}$ is the midsegment of trapezoid *HJKL*.

6. If $HJ = 14$ and $LK = 42$, find TS. 28

7. If $LK = 19$ and $TS = 15$, find HJ. 11

8. If $HJ = 7$ and $TS = 10$, find LK. 13

9. If $KL = 17$ and $JH = 9$, find ST. 13

10. If $TS = 24$ and $LK = 27.4$, find HJ. 20.6

Lesson 7-6 · Trapezoids and Kites   **451**

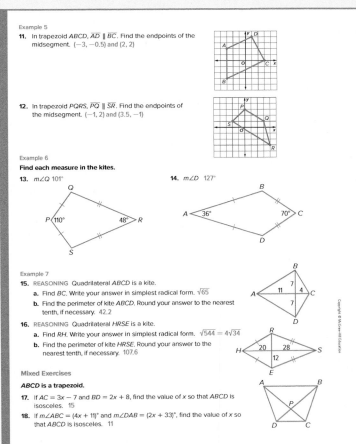

Example 5

11. In trapezoid *ABCD*, $\overline{AD} \parallel \overline{BC}$. Find the endpoints of the midsegment. $(-3, -0.5)$ and $(2, 2)$

12. In trapezoid *PQRS*, $\overline{PQ} \parallel \overline{SR}$. Find the endpoints of the midsegment. $(-1, 2)$ and $(3.5, -1)$

Example 6

Find each measure in the kites.

13. $m\angle Q$ 101°

14. $m\angle D$ 127°

Example 7

15. REASONING Quadrilateral *ABCD* is a kite.

    a. Find *BC*. Write your answer in simplest radical form. $\sqrt{65}$

    b. Find the perimeter of kite *ABCD*. Round your answer to the nearest tenth, if necessary. 42.2

16. REASONING Quadrilateral *HRSE* is a kite.

    a. Find *RH*. Write your answer in simplest radical form. $\sqrt{544} = 4\sqrt{34}$

    b. Find the perimeter of kite *HRSE*. Round your answer to the nearest tenth, if necessary. 107.6

Mixed Exercises

***ABCD* is a trapezoid.**

17. If $AC = 3x - 7$ and $BD = 2x + 8$, find the value of *x* so that *ABCD* is isosceles. 15

18. If $m\angle ABC = (4x + 11)°$ and $m\angle DAB = (2x + 33)°$, find the value of *x* so that *ABCD* is isosceles. 11

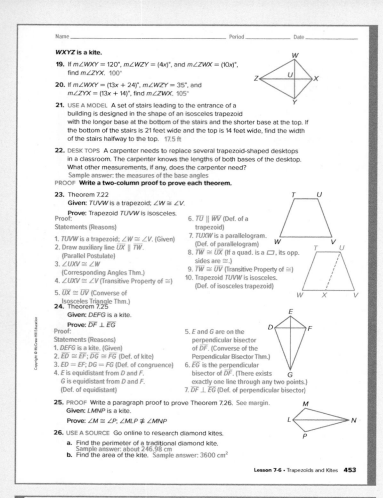

Name _____ Period _____ Date _____

WXYZ is a kite.

19. If $m\angle WXY = 120°$, $m\angle WZY = (4x)°$, and $m\angle ZWX = (10x)°$, find $m\angle ZYX$. **100°**

20. If $m\angle WXY = (13x + 24)°$, $m\angle WZY = 35°$, and $m\angle ZYX = (13x + 14)°$, find $m\angle ZWX$. **105°**

21. USE A MODEL A set of stairs leading to the entrance of a building is designed in the shape of an isosceles trapezoid with the longer base at the bottom of the stairs and the shorter base at the top. If the bottom of the stairs is 21 feet wide and the top is 14 feet wide, find the width of the stairs halfway to the top. **17.5 ft**

22. DESK TOPS A carpenter needs to replace several trapezoid-shaped desktops in a classroom. The carpenter knows the lengths of both bases of the desktop. What other measurements, if any, does the carpenter need? **Sample answer: the measures of the base angles**

PROOF Write a two-column proof to prove each theorem.

23. Theorem 7.22
Given: *TUVW* is a trapezoid; $\angle W \cong \angle V$.
Prove: Trapezoid *TUVW* is isosceles.
Proof:
Statements (Reasons)

1. *TUVW* is a trapezoid; $\angle W \cong \angle V$. (Given)
2. Draw auxiliary line $\overline{UX} \parallel \overline{TW}$. (Parallel Postulate)
3. $\angle UXV \cong \angle W$ (Corresponding Angles Thm.)
4. $\angle UXV \cong \angle V$ (Transitive Property of $\cong$)
5. $\overline{UX} \cong \overline{UV}$ (Converse of Isosceles Triangle Thm.)

6. $\overline{TU} \parallel \overline{WV}$ (Def. of a trapezoid)
7. *TUXW* is a parallelogram. (Def. of parallelogram)
8. $\overline{TW} \cong \overline{UX}$ (If a quad. is a ▱, its opp. sides are $\cong$.)
9. $\overline{TW} \cong \overline{UV}$ (Transitive Property of $\cong$)
10. Trapezoid *TUVW* is isosceles. (Def. of isosceles trapezoid)

24. Theorem 7.25
Given: *DEFG* is a kite.
Prove: $\overline{DF} \perp \overline{EG}$
Proof:
Statements (Reasons)
1. *DEFG* is a kite. (Given)
2. $\overline{ED} \cong \overline{EF}$; $\overline{DG} \cong \overline{FG}$ (Def. of kite)
3. $ED = EF$; $DG = FG$ (Def. of congruence)
4. *E* is equidistant from *D* and *F*. *G* is equidistant from *D* and *F*. (Def. of equidistant)

5. *E* and *G* are on the perpendicular bisector of $\overline{DF}$. (Converse of the Perpendicular Bisector Thm.)
6. $\overline{EG}$ is the perpendicular bisector of $\overline{DF}$. (There exists exactly one line through any two points.)
7. $\overline{DF} \perp \overline{EG}$ (Def. of perpendicular bisector)

25. PROOF Write a paragraph proof to prove Theorem 7.26. See margin.
Given: *LMNP* is a kite.
Prove: $\angle M \cong \angle P$, $\angle MLP \not\cong \angle MNP$

26. USE A SOURCE Go online to research diamond kites.
a. Find the perimeter of a traditional diamond kite. Sample answer: about 246.98 cm
b. Find the area of the kite. Sample answer: 3600 cm²

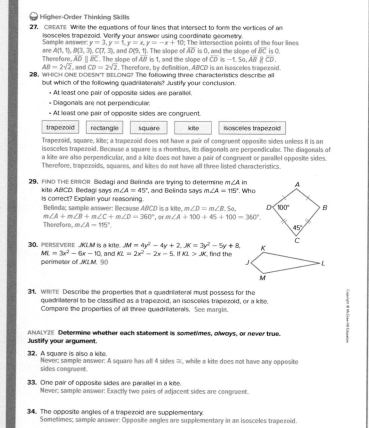

🌐 **Higher-Order Thinking Skills**

27. CREATE Write the equations of four lines that intersect to form the vertices of an isosceles trapezoid. Verify your answer using coordinate geometry.
Sample answer: $y = 3$, $y = 1$, $y = x$, $y = -x + 10$; The intersection points of the four lines are $A(1, 1)$, $B(3, 3)$, $C(7, 3)$, and $D(9, 1)$. The slope of $\overline{AD}$ is 0, and the slope of $\overline{BC}$ is 0. Therefore, $\overline{AD} \parallel \overline{BC}$. The slope of $\overline{AB}$ is 1, and the slope of $\overline{CD}$ is −1. So, $\overline{AB} \not\parallel \overline{CD}$. $AB = 2\sqrt{2}$, and $CD = 2\sqrt{2}$. Therefore, by definition, *ABCD* is an isosceles trapezoid.

28. WHICH ONE DOESN'T BELONG? The following three characteristics describe all but which of the following quadrilaterals? Justify your conclusion.
- At least one pair of opposite sides are parallel.
- Diagonals are not perpendicular.
- At least one pair of opposite sides are congruent.

trapezoid	rectangle	square	kite	isosceles trapezoid

Trapezoid, square, kite; a trapezoid does not have a pair of congruent opposite sides unless it is an isosceles trapezoid. Because a square is a rhombus, its diagonals are perpendicular. The diagonals of a kite are also perpendicular, and a kite does not have a pair of congruent or parallel opposite sides. Therefore, trapezoids, squares, and kites do not have all three listed characteristics.

29. FIND THE ERROR Bedagi and Belinda are trying to determine $m\angle A$ in kite *ABCD*. Bedagi says $m\angle A = 45°$, and Belinda says $m\angle A = 115°$. Who is correct? Explain your reasoning.
Belinda; sample answer: Because *ABCD* is a kite, $m\angle D = m\angle B$. So, $m\angle A + m\angle B + m\angle C + m\angle D = 360°$, or $m\angle A + 100 + 45 + 100 = 360°$. Therefore, $m\angle A = 115°$.

30. PERSEVERE *JKLM* is a kite. $JM = 4y^2 - 4y + 2$, $JK = 3y^2 - 5y + 8$, $ML = 3x^2 - 6x - 10$, and $KL = 2x^2 - 2x - 5$. If $KL > JK$, find the perimeter of *JKLM*. **90**

31. WRITE Describe the properties that a quadrilateral must possess for the quadrilateral to be classified as a trapezoid, an isosceles trapezoid, or a kite. Compare the properties of all three quadrilaterals. See margin.

ANALYZE Determine whether each statement is *sometimes*, *always*, or *never* true. Justify your argument.

32. A square is also a kite.
Never; sample answer: A square has all 4 sides $\cong$, while a kite does not have any opposite sides congruent.

33. One pair of opposite sides are parallel in a kite.
Never; sample answer: Exactly two pairs of adjacent sides are congruent.

34. The opposite angles of a trapezoid are supplementary.
Sometimes; sample answer: Opposite angles are supplementary in an isosceles trapezoid.

Answers

25. Proof: It is given that *LMNP* is a kite. By the definition of kite, $\overline{LM} \cong \overline{LP}$ and $\overline{MN} \cong \overline{PN}$. By the Reflexive Property of Congruence, $\overline{LN} \cong \overline{LN}$. Therefore, $\triangle LMN \cong \triangle LPN$ by SSS. $\angle M \cong \angle P$ by CPCTC. If both pairs of opposite angles of a quadrilateral are congruent, then the quadrilateral is a parallelogram. So, if $\angle MLP \cong \angle MNP$, then *LMNP* is a parallelogram. It is given the *LMNP* is a kite. Therefore, $\angle MLP \not\cong \angle MNP$.

31. Sample answer: A quadrilateral must have exactly one pair of sides parallel to be a trapezoid. If the legs are congruent, then the trapezoid is an isosceles trapezoid. If a quadrilateral has exactly two pairs of consecutive congruent sides with the opposite sides not congruent, the quadrilateral is a kite. A trapezoid and a kite both have four sides. In a trapezoid and isosceles trapezoid, both have exactly one pair of parallel sides.

Review

Rate Yourself

Have students return to the Module Opener to rate their understanding of the concepts presented in this module. They should see that their knowledge and skills have increased. After completing the chart, have them respond to the prompts in their *Interactive Student Edition* and share their responses with a partner.

ⓔ Answering the Essential Question

Before answering the Essential Question, have students review their answers to the Essential Question Follow-Up questions found throughout the module.

- Why is it important to know when a quadrilateral is a parallelogram in the real world?
- Why might properties of squares and rhombi be useful in the real world?
- Why are properties of trapezoids and kites useful?

Then have them write their answer to the Essential Question in the space provided.

DINAH ZIKE FOLDABLES

ELL A completed Foldable for this module should include the key concepts related to quadrilaterals.

LS LearnSmart Use LearnSmart as part of your test preparation plan to measure student topic retention. You can create a student assignment in LearnSmart for additional practice on these topics for **Congruence, Proof, and Constructions.**

- Prove Geometric Theorems
- Make Geometric Constructions

Module 7 • Quadrilaterals

Review

ⓔ Essential Question

What are the different types of quadrilaterals, and how can their characteristics be used to model real-world situations?

Sample answer: Parallelograms, rectangles, rhombi, squares, trapezoids, and kites; You can use these quadrilaterals to model real-world objects, and then you can use what you know about the properties of these shapes to approximate the measures of the real-world objects.

Module Summary

Lesson 7-1
Angles of Polygons
- The sum of the interior angle measures of an n-sided convex polygon is $(n - 2) \cdot 180°$.
- The sum of the exterior angle measures of a convex polygon, one angle at each vertex, is $360°$.

Lessons 7-2 and 7-3
Parallelograms
- A parallelogram is a quadrilateral with both pairs of opposite sides parallel.
- In a parallelogram, opposite sides and opposite angles are congruent.
- If the diagonals of a quadrilateral bisect each other, then the quadrilateral is a parallelogram.
- If one pair of opposite sides of a quadrilateral is both parallel and congruent, then the quadrilateral is a parallelogram.

Lesson 7-4
Rectangles
A rectangle has the following properties:
- All four angles are right angles.
- Opposite sides are parallel and congruent.
- Opposite angles are congruent.
- Consecutive angles are supplementary.
- Diagonals bisect each other.

Lesson 7-5
Rhombi and Squares
- A rhombus is a special type of parallelogram with all four sides congruent.
- A square is a special type of parallelogram with all four sides and all four angles congruent.
- If a quadrilateral is both a rectangle and a rhombus, then it is a square.

Lesson 7-6
Trapezoids and Kites
- A trapezoid is a quadrilateral with exactly one pair of parallel sides.
- If a trapezoid is isosceles, then each pair of base angles is congruent.
- The midsegment of a trapezoid is the segment that connects the midpoints of the legs of the trapezoid.
- The midsegment of a trapezoid is parallel to each base and its length is one half the sum of the lengths of the bases.
- A kite is a quadrilateral with exactly two distinct pairs of adjacent congruent sides.

Study Organizer

📖 **Foldables**
Use your Foldable to review this module. Working with a partner can be helpful. Ask for clarification of concepts as needed.

Module 7 Review • Quadrilaterals **455**

Test Practice

1. MULTIPLE CHOICE A home plate from a baseball field is modeled by the diagram. What is the value of x in degrees? (Lesson 7-1)

- (A) 45
- (B) 90
- (C) 120
- (D) 180

2. OPEN RESPONSE Find the measure of $\angle RKL$. (Lesson 7-1)

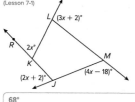

$68°$

3. MULTIPLE CHOICE A paper fan is made by folding the pattern shown in the diagram.

Angles A and C measure 80° and angle B measures 135°. If the remaining angles are congruent to each other, what is the measure of each angle? (Lesson 7-1)

- (A) 135°
- (B) 143°
- (C) 157°
- (D) 173°

4. OPEN RESPONSE Describe three different methods that you could use to prove that quadrilateral $ABCD$ is a parallelogram.

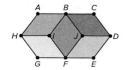

Sample answer: I could use the Slope Formula to show that opposite sides of the quadrilateral are parallel. I could use the Distance Formula to show that both pairs of opposite sides of the quadrilateral are congruent. I could use the Midpoint Formula to show that the diagonals of the quadrilateral bisect each other.

5. OPEN RESPONSE Quadrilateral $PQRS$ is a parallelogram. If $m\angle P = 72°$, then find $m\angle Q$ and $m\angle R$. (Lesson 7-2)

$m\angle Q = 108°$ and $m\angle R = 72°$

6. OPEN RESPONSE A repeating tile design is made from a rhombus and four congruent parallelograms. (Lesson 7-2)

If $m\angle IBJ = 54°$, find each angle measure.

$m\angle BIF = \_\_°$

$m\angle JBC = \_\_°$

$m\angle BJD = \_\_°$

$m\angle BIF = 126°, m\angle JBC = 63°,$
and $m\angle BJD = 117°$

Review and Assessment Options

The following online review and assessment resources are available for you to assign to your students. These resources include technology-enhanced questions that are auto-scored, as well as essay questions.

Review Resources

Put It All Together: Lessons 7-2 through 7-6
Vocabulary Activity
Module Review

Assessment Resources

Vocabulary Test
AL Module Test Form B
OL Module Test Form A
BL Module Test Form C
Performance Task*

*The module-level performance task is available online as a printable document. A scoring rubric is included.

Test Practice

You can use these pages to help your students review module content and prepare for online assessments. Exercises 1–17 mirror the types of questions your students will see on online assessments.

Question Type	Description	Exercise(s)
Multiple Choice	Students select one correct answer.	1, 3, 9, 11, 12, 14, 17
Multi-Select	Multiple answers may be correct. Students must select all correct answers.	15
Table Item	Students complete a table by entering in the correct values.	7, 13
Open Response	Students construct their own response in the area provided.	2, 4–6, 8, 10, 16

To ensure that students understand the standards, check students' success on individual exercises.

Standard(s)	Lesson(s)	Exercise(s)
G.MG.1	7-1	1, 3
G.CO.4	7-3	8
G.CO.9	7-1	2
G.CO.11	7-2, 7-3, 7-4, 7-5	5–7, 9–15
G.GPE.4	7-2, 7-6	4, 16, 17

Copyright © McGraw-Hill Education

Name _____ Period _____ Date _____

7. TABLE ITEM Identify whether each quadrilateral can be proven to be a parallelogram. (Lesson 7-3)

A. B.

C. D.

Quadrilateral	Parallelogram?	
	Yes	No
A		X
B	X	
C	X	
D	X	

8. OPEN RESPONSE If $\overline{AB}$ and $\overline{AC}$ are two sides of a figure, at which coordinates in Quadrant I should point D be placed so that ABDC is a parallelogram? (Lesson 7-3)

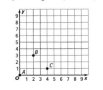

(6, 4)

9. MULTIPLE CHOICE Which measurements will ensure that PQRS is a parallelogram? (Lesson 7-3)

Ⓐ $PS = 5$ or $m\angle Q = 105°$

Ⓑ $PS = 4$ or $m\angle Q = 105°$

Ⓒ $PS = 5$ or $m\angle Q = 75°$

Ⓓ $PS = 4$ or $m\angle Q = 75°$

10. OPEN RESPONSE Given rectangle WXYZ, if $m\angle XZY = 27°$, then find $m\angle WYX$ and $m\angle WVZ$. (Lesson 7-4)

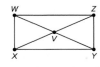

$m\angle WYX = 63°$ and $m\angle WVZ = 54°$

11. MULTIPLE CHOICE A carpenter builds a frame from two 6-foot long boards and two 8 foot long boards. Given these side lengths, how can the carpenter ensure that the frame is a rectangle? (Lesson 7-4)

Ⓐ If the diagonals are congruent, the frame must be a rectangle.

Ⓑ If the opposite sides are congruent, the frame must be a rectangle.

Ⓒ If the opposite angles are congruent, the frame must be a rectangle.

Ⓓ If the diagonals are perpendicular, the frame must be a rectangle.

Module 7 Review · Quadrilaterals 457

Name _____ Period _____ Date _____

12. MULTIPLE CHOICE In parallelogram *ABCD*, $AB = 2x$, $AC = 3x - 2$, and $AD = x + 2$. If the length of segment *BD* is 10, what value of *x* will ensure that *ABCD* is a rectangle? (Lesson 7-4)

Ⓐ 2

Ⓑ 4

Ⓒ 5

Ⓓ 8

13. TABLE ITEM If four bars of equal length are joined at their endpoints, which shape(s) can be created? (Lesson 7-5)

Shape	Can be created?	
	Yes	No
Kite		X
Parallelogram	X	
Rectangle	X	
Rhombus	X	
Square	X	
Trapezoid		X

14. MULTIPLE CHOICE Find the measure of ∠*B*. (Lesson 7-5)

Ⓐ 40°   Ⓒ 80°

Ⓑ 50°   Ⓓ 100°

15. MULTI-SELECT If *ABCD* is a rhombus that is not a square, select all of the true statements. (Lesson 7-5)

Ⓐ $\overline{AB} \cong \overline{CD}$

Ⓑ $\overline{AC} \perp \overline{BD}$

Ⓒ $\angle A \cong \angle C$

Ⓓ $\overline{AC} \cong \overline{BD}$

Ⓔ $\overline{BC} \cong \overline{DA}$

16. OPEN RESPONSE Given quadrilateral *JKLM* with $J(-12, 0)$, $K(0, 5)$, $L(6, 0)$, and $M(0, -5)$, how can it be determined whether the quadrilateral is a kite?

> Sample answer: By definition, a kite has exactly two pairs of adjacent congruent sides. For the quadrilateral to be a kite, use the Distance Formula to determine whether $KL = ML$ and $KJ = MJ$ or if $KJ = KL$ and $ML = MJ$.

17. MULTIPLE CHOICE Trapezoid *ABCD* has vertices $A(0, 0)$, $B(2, 5)$, $C(3, 5)$, and $D(8, 0)$. What is the length of its midsegment? (Lesson 7-6)

Ⓐ 4

Ⓑ 4.5

Ⓒ 5

Ⓓ 5.5

17. Given: *ABCD* is a parallelogram. ∠*A* is a right angle.

Prove: ∠*B*, ∠*C*, and ∠*D* are right angles.

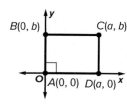

Proof:

slope of $\overline{AD} = \dfrac{0-0}{a-0} = 0$ slope of $\overline{BC} = \dfrac{b-b}{a-0} = 0$

slope of $\overline{AB}$ is undefined   slope of $\overline{CD}$ is undefined

Therefore, $\overline{AB} \perp \overline{BC}$, $\overline{BC} \perp \overline{CD}$, and $\overline{AB} \parallel \overline{CD}$. So, ∠*B*, ∠*C*, and ∠*D* are right angles.

18. Proof: $\overline{LN}$ divides quadrilateral *KLMN* into two triangles. The sum of the angle measures in each triangle is 180°, so the sum of the angle measures for both triangles is 360°. So, *m*∠*K* + *m*∠*L* + *m*∠*M* + *m*∠*N* = 360°. Because ∠*K* ≅ ∠*M* and ∠*N* ≅ ∠*L*, *m*∠*K* = *m*∠*M* and *m*∠*N* = *m*∠*L* by the definition of congruence. By the Substitution Property of Equality, *m*∠*K* + *m*∠*L* + *m*∠*K* + *m*∠*L* = 360°, so 2(*m*∠*K*) + 2(*m*∠*L*) = 360°. Dividing each side by 2 gives *m*∠*K* + *m*∠*L* = 180°. The consecutive angles are supplementary, so $\overline{KN} \parallel \overline{LM}$ by the Converse of the Consecutive Interior Angles Theorem. Likewise, 2(*m*∠*K*) + 2(*m*∠*N*) = 360°, or *m*∠*K* + *m*∠*N* = 180°. So these consecutive angles are supplementary and $\overline{KL} \parallel \overline{NM}$ by the Converse of the Consecutive Interior Angles Theorem. Opposite sides are parallel, so quadrilateral *KLMN* is a parallelogram.

19. Proof:

Statements (Reasons)

1. $\overline{PR}$ bisects $\overline{TQ}$; $\overline{TQ}$ bisects $\overline{PR}$. (Given)

2. $\overline{PV} \cong \overline{VR}$, $\overline{TV} \cong \overline{VQ}$ (Def. of bisector)

3. ∠*PVT* ≅ ∠*RVQ*, ∠*TVR* ≅ ∠*QVP* (Vertical Angles Thm.)

4. △*PVT* ≅ △*RVQ*, △*TVR* ≅ △*QVP* (SAS)

5. $\overline{PQ} \cong \overline{RT}$, $\overline{PT} \cong \overline{RQ}$ (CPCTC)

6. *PQRT* is a parallelogram. (If both pairs of opp. sides are ≅, then quad. is a ▱.)

28. By Theorem 7.11, if the diagonals of a quadrilateral bisect each other, then the quadrilateral is a parallelogram. Begin by drawing and bisecting a segment $\overline{AB}$. Then draw a line that intersects the first segment through its midpoint *D*. Mark a point *C* on one side of this line and then construct a segment $\overline{DE}$ congruent to $\overline{CD}$ on the other side of *D*. You now have intersecting segments which bisect each other. Connect point *A* to point *C*, point *C* to point *B*, point *B* to point *E*, and point *E* to point *A* to form ▱*ACBE*.

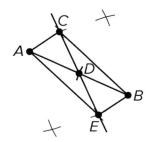

31. Given: *RSTV* is a quadrilateral. *A*, *B*, *C*, and *D* are midpoints of sides $\overline{RS}$, $\overline{ST}$, $\overline{TV}$, and $\overline{VR}$, respectively.

Prove: *ABCD* is a parallelogram.

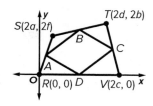

Proof:

Place quadrilateral *RSTV* on the coordinate plane and label the coordinates as shown. By the Midpoint Formula, the coordinates of *A*, *B*, *C*, and *D* are:

$A\left(\dfrac{2a}{2}, \dfrac{2f}{2}\right) = (a, f)$;

$B\left(\dfrac{2d+2a}{2}, \dfrac{2f+2b}{2}\right) = (d+a, f+b)$;

$C\left(\dfrac{2d+2c}{2}, \dfrac{2b}{2}\right) = (d+c, b)$; and $D\left(\dfrac{2c}{2}, \dfrac{0}{2}\right) = (c, 0)$.

Find the slopes of $\overline{AB}$ and $\overline{DC}$.

slope of $\overline{AB} = \dfrac{(f+b)-f}{(d+a)-a} = \dfrac{b}{d}$

slope of $\overline{DC} = \dfrac{0-b}{c-(d+c)} = \dfrac{-b}{-d} = \dfrac{b}{d}$

The slopes of $\overline{AB}$ and $\overline{DC}$ are the same, so the segments are parallel. Use the Distance Formula to find *AB* and *DC*.

$AB = \sqrt{(d+a-a)^2 + (f+b-f)^2} = \sqrt{d^2+b^2}$

$DC = \sqrt{(d+c-c)^2 + (b-0)^2} = \sqrt{d^2+b^2}$

Thus, *AB* = *DC* and $\overline{AB} \cong \overline{DC}$. Therefore, *ABCD* is a parallelogram because if one pair of opposite sides of a quadrilateral are both parallel and congruent, then the quadrilateral is a parallelogram.

34. Given: *ABCD* is a parallelogram and $\overline{AJ} \cong \overline{KC}$

Prove: Quadrilateral *JBKD* is a parallelogram.

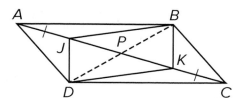

Proof:

Draw segment $\overline{DB}$. Because *ABCD* is a parallelogram, by Theorem 7.3, diagonals $\overline{DB}$ and $\overline{AC}$ bisect each other. Label their point of intersection *P*. By the definition of bisect, $\overline{AP} \cong \overline{PC}$, so *AP* = *PC*. By Segment Addition, *AP* = *AJ* + *JP* and *PC* = *PK* + *KC*. So *AJ* + *JP* = *PK* + *KC* by Substitution. Because $\overline{AJ} \cong \overline{KC}$, *AJ* = *KC* by the definition of congruence. Substituting yields *KC* + *JP* = *PK* + *KC*. By the Subtraction Property, *JP* = *PK*. So, by the definition of congruence, $\overline{JP} \cong \overline{PK}$. Thus, *P* is the midpoint of $\overline{JK}$. Because $\overline{JK}$ and $\overline{DB}$ bisect each other and are diagonals of quadrilateral *JBKD*, by Theorem 7.11, quadrilateral *JBKD* is a parallelogram.

Lesson 7-4

27. Sample answer: Because $\overline{RP} \perp \overline{PQ}$ and $\overline{SQ} \perp \overline{PQ}$, $m\angle P = m\angle Q = 90°$. Lines that are perpendicular to the same line are parallel, so $\overline{RP} \parallel \overline{SQ}$. The same compass setting was used to locate points R and S, so $\overline{RP} \cong \overline{SQ}$. If one pair of opposite sides of a quadrilateral is both parallel and congruent, then the quadrilateral is a parallelogram. A parallelogram with right angles is a rectangle. Thus, $PRSQ$ is a rectangle.

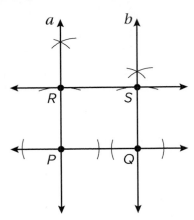

38. Sample answer: $x = 0$, $x = 6$, $y = 0$, $y = 4$;

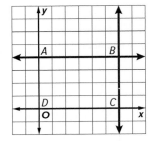

The length of $\overline{AB}$ is $6 - 0$ or 6 units and the length of $\overline{CD}$ is $6 - 0$ or 6 units. The slope of $\overline{AB}$ is 0 and the slope of $\overline{CD}$ is 0. Because a pair of sides of the quadrilateral is both parallel and congruent, the quadrilateral is a parallelogram. Because $\overline{AB}$ is horizontal and $\overline{BC}$ is vertical, the lines are perpendicular and the measure of the angle they form is $90°$. If a parallelogram has one right angle, then it has four right angles. Therefore, by definition, the parallelogram is a rectangle.

Lesson 7-5

39.

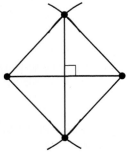

Sample answer: The diagonals bisect each other, so the quadrilateral is a parallelogram. Because the diagonals of the parallelogram are perpendicular to each other, the parallelogram is a rhombus.

40.

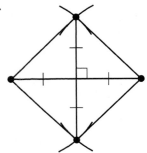

Sample answer: The diagonals bisect each other, so the quadrilateral is a parallelogram. Because the diagonals of the parallelogram are congruent and perpendicular, the parallelogram is a square.

43. Parallelogram: Opposite sides of a parallelogram are parallel and congruent. Opposite angles of a parallelogram are congruent. The diagonals of a parallelogram bisect each other and each diagonal separates a parallelogram into two congruent triangles.

Rectangle: A rectangle has all the properties of a parallelogram. A rectangle has four right angles. The diagonals of a rectangle are congruent.

Rhombus: A rhombus has all the properties of a parallelogram. All sides of a rhombus are congruent. The diagonals of a rhombus are perpendicular and bisect the angles of the rhombus.

Square: A square has all of the properties of a parallelogram. A square has all the properties of a rectangle. A square has all of the properties of a rhombus.

45. True; sample answer: A rectangle is a quadrilateral with four right angles and a square is both a rectangle and a rhombus, so a square is always a rectangle.

Converse: If a quadrilateral is a rectangle, then it is a square. False; sample answer: A rectangle is a quadrilateral with four right angles. It is not necessarily a rhombus, so it is not necessarily a square.

Inverse: If a quadrilateral is not a square, then it is not a rectangle. False; sample answer: A quadrilateral that has four right angles and two pairs of congruent sides is not a square, but it is a rectangle.

Contrapositive: If a quadrilateral is not a rectangle, then it is not a square. True; sample answer: If a quadrilateral is not a rectangle, it is also not a square by definition.

Module 8
Similarity

Module Goals

- Students identify similar polygons and use ratios and proportions to solve problem.
- Students use the AA Similarity Postulate and the SSS and SAS Similarity Theorems to solve problems.

Focus

Domain: Geometry

Standards for Mathematical Content:

G.SRT.4 Prove theorems about triangles.

G.SRT.5 Use congruence and similarity criteria for triangles to solve problems and to prove relationships in geometric figures.

Also addresses G.SRT.1, G.SRT.2, G.SRT.3, G.GPE.5, G.CO.2, G.CO.10, and G.CO.12.

Standards for Mathematical Practice:

All Standards for Mathematical Practice will be addressed in this module.

✪ Be Sure to Cover

To completely cover G.SRT.2, G.SRT.3, G.GPE.5 and G.CO.12, go online to assign the following activities:

- Similarity Transformations of Triangles (Explore, Lesson 8-3)
- Conditions that Prove Triangles Similar (Explore, Lesson 8-3)
- Proving the Slope Criteria (Expand, Lesson 8-4)
- Separate a Segment into Congruent Segments (Construction, Lesson 8-5)

Coherence

Vertical Alignment

Previous
Students understood similarity of two-dimensional figures using similarity transformations.
8.G.4

Now
Students use similarity criteria for triangles to solve problems and to prove relationships in geometric figures.
G.SRT.5

Next
Students will use trigonometric ratios and the Pythagorean Theorem to solve right triangles in applied problems.
G.SRT.6, G.SRT.8

Rigor

The Three Pillars of Rigor

To help students meet standards, they need to illustrate their ability to use the three pillars of rigor. Students gain conceptual understanding as they move from the Explore to Learn sections within a lesson. Once they understand the concept, they practice procedural skills and fluency and apply their mathematical knowledge as they go through the Examples and Practice.

| 1 CONCEPTUAL UNDERSTANDING | 2 FLUENCY | 3 APPLICATION |

EXPLORE ⟩ LEARN ⟩ EXAMPLE & PRACTICE

Suggested Pacing

Lessons		Standards	45-min classes	90-min classes
Module Pretest and Launch the Module Video			1	0.5
8-1	Dilations	G.CO.2, G.SRT.1	1	0.5
8-2	Similar Polygons	G.SRT.2	1	0.5
8-3	Similar Triangles: AA Similarity	G.SRT.2, G.SRT.3	1	0.5
8-4	Similar Triangles: SSS and SAS Similarity	G.SRT.2, G.SRT.5	1	0.5
Expand 8-4	Proving the Slope Criteria	G.GPE.5	1	0.5
Put It All Together: Lesson 8-3 and Lesson 8-4			1	0.5
8-5	Triangle Proportionality	G.SRT.4, G.CO.10, G.CO.12	2	1
8-6	Parts of Similar Triangles	G.SRT.4	1	0.5
Module Review			1	0.5
Module Assessment			1	0.5
		Total Days	**12**	**6**

CHERYL TOBEY MATH PROBES

Formative Assessment Math Probe
Similar Triangles

Analyze the Probe

Review the probe prior to assigning it to your students.

In this probe, students will determine which pairs of triangles fall into four categories and explain their choices.

Targeted Concepts Understand the information needed to prove triangle similarity.

Targeted Misconceptions

- Students assume that triangles are similar if they are shaped the same without analyzing side lengths for proportionality and/or angle measures for congruence.
- Students believe that similar triangles need to have the same orientation.
- Students assume nonsimilarity if insufficient information is given.
- Students do not consider HL in right triangles as the counterpart (SSA) does not work with nonright triangles.
- Students do not recognize congruent angles if information is given by showing parallel lines, stacked triangles, and/or vertical angles.

Use the Probe after Lesson 8-5.

Answers: similar triangles: C, D, F, H, I, K congruent triangles: G, L not similar: B, J not enough information: A, E

Collect and Assess Student Answers

If the student selects these responses...	**Then** the student likely...
similar triangles: A, B, C, E, J	is only using visual cues to determine similarity.
Not choosing *similar triangles* for D, F, or I or *congruent triangles* for G or L	is only considering figures with the same orientation for similarity or congruency. Check students' explanations as there might be additional misunderstandings.
not similar triangles: A or E	is assuming nonsimilarity if there is insufficient information to prove similarity.
errors with B or L	is having difficulty using the HL postulate with right triangles, does not recognize the tic marks in L, and/or does not check for side proportionality in B.
similar triangles: A or E	is not noticing that the tick marks and/or given side lengths only compare lengths from one triangle and do not show side congruence between the two triangles.
not choosing *similar triangles* for D, H, I, or K or *congruent triangles* for G	does not recognize congruent angles from parallel lines (G or K), stacked triangles (D or K), vertical angles (I), and/or the sum of the interior angles of a triangle (H).

Take Action

After the Probe Design a plan to address any possible misconceptions. You may wish to assign the following resources.

- **ALEKS·** Proving Triangle Similarity
- Lesson 8-5, all Learns, all Examples

Revisit the probe at the end of the module to be sure that your students no longer carry these misconceptions.

IGNITE!

The Ignite! activities, created by Dr. Raj Shah, cultivate curiosity and engage and challenge students. Use these open-ended, collaborative activities, located online in the module Launch section, to encourage your students to develop a growth mindset towards mathematics and problem solving. Use the teacher notes for implementation suggestions and support for encouraging productive struggle.

℮ Essential Question

At the end of this module, students should be able to answer the Essential Question.

What does it mean for objects to be similar, and how is similarity useful for modeling in the real world? Sample answer: Similar objects have corresponding sides that are proportional and corresponding angles that are congruent. Similarity can be used to scale objects in the real world.

What Will You Learn?

Prior to beginning this module, have your students rate their knowledge of each item listed. Then, at the end of the module, you will be reminded to have your students return to these pages to rate their knowledge again. They should see that their knowledge and skills have increased.

DINAH ZIKE FOLDABLES

Focus Students write notes about each lesson in this module.

Teach Have students make and label the Foldable. Students use their Foldables for notes, problem solving, and descriptions. As students read and work through each lesson of this module, have them record their questions. As students learn more about proportions and similarity, encourage students to answer their own questions. Self-questioning is a strategy that helps students stay focused during reading.

When to Use It Use the appropriate tabs as students cover each lesson in this module. Students can add to the vocabulary tab during each lesson.

Launch the Module

For this module, the Launch the Module video uses visuals from nature to introduce students to similarity. Students understand how similarity is found all around them.

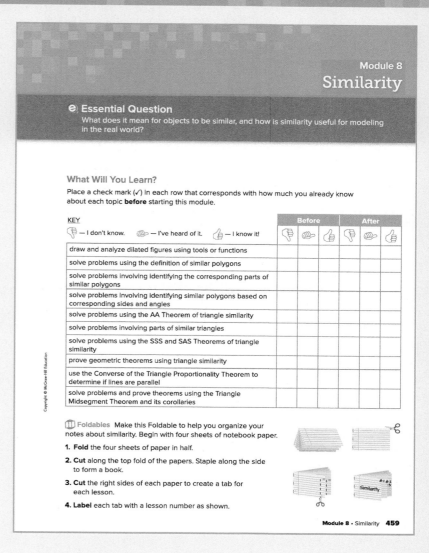

Interactive Presentation

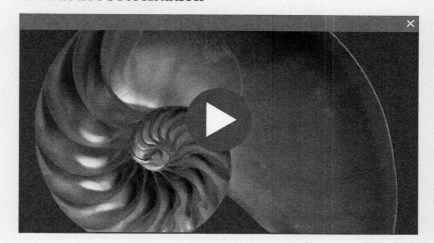

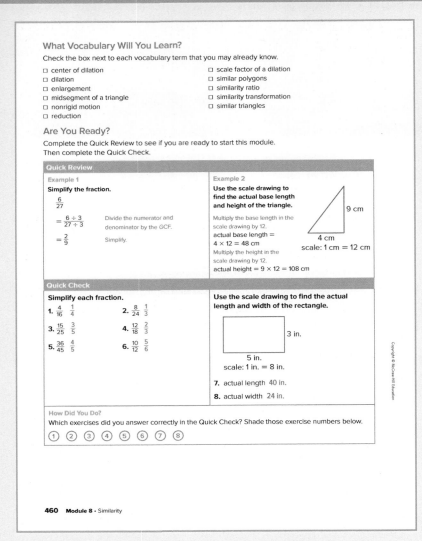

What Vocabulary Will You Learn?

Check the box next to each vocabulary term that you may already know.

☐ center of dilation   ☐ scale factor of a dilation
☐ dilation   ☐ similar polygons
☐ enlargement   ☐ similarity ratio
☐ midsegment of a triangle   ☐ similarity transformation
☐ nonrigid motion   ☐ similar triangles
☐ reduction

Are You Ready?

Complete the Quick Review to see if you are ready to start this module.
Then complete the Quick Check.

Quick Review

Example 1
Simplify the fraction.

$$\frac{6}{27}$$

$$= \frac{6 \div 3}{27 \div 3}$$ Divide the numerator and denominator by the GCF.

$$= \frac{2}{9}$$ Simplify.

Example 2
Use the scale drawing to find the actual base length and height of the triangle.

Multiply the base length in the scale drawing by 12.
actual base length =
4 × 12 = 48 cm
Multiply the height in the scale drawing by 12.
actual height = 9 × 12 = 108 cm

9 cm

4 cm
scale: 1 cm = 12 cm

Quick Check

Simplify each fraction.

1. $\frac{4}{16}$ $\frac{1}{4}$ 2. $\frac{8}{24}$ $\frac{1}{3}$

3. $\frac{15}{25}$ $\frac{3}{5}$ 4. $\frac{12}{18}$ $\frac{2}{3}$

5. $\frac{36}{45}$ $\frac{4}{5}$ 6. $\frac{10}{12}$ $\frac{5}{6}$

Use the scale drawing to find the actual length and width of the rectangle.

3 in.

5 in.
scale: 1 in. = 8 in.

7. actual length 40 in.

8. actual width 24 in.

How Did You Do?

Which exercises did you answer correctly in the Quick Check? Shade those exercise numbers below.

① ② ③ ④ ⑤ ⑥ ⑦ ⑧

What Vocabulary Will You Learn?

ELL As you proceed through the module, introduce the key vocabulary by using the following routine.

Define The scale factor of a dilation is the ratio of the lengths of the corresponding sides of two similar polygons.

Example In the diagram, $\triangle JKL \sim \triangle XYZ$.

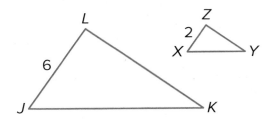

Ask What is the scale factor of $\triangle JKL$ to $\triangle XYZ$? $\frac{1}{3}$ What is the scale factor of $\triangle XYZ$ to $\triangle JKL$? 3

Are You Ready?

Students may need to review the following prerequisite skills to succeed in this module.

- simplifying fractions
- determining triangle congruence
- using scale drawings

🔵 ALEKS·

ALEKS is an adaptive, personalized learning environment that identifies precisely what each student knows and is ready to learn, ensuring student success at all levels.

You may want to use the **Similarity and Transformations** section to ensure student success in this module.

🧠 Mindset Matters

Regular Reflection

When students are asked to explain their thinking about their strategy they are engaging in thought organization, concise consolidation of knowledge, and deductive and inductive thinking.

How Can I Apply It?

Have students complete the **Exit Tickets** at the end of each lesson to reflect on their learning and communicate their thinking. Have students share by writing down their reflections or discussing with a partner or in small groups.

Dilations

LESSON GOAL

Students draw and analyze dilated figures using tools or functions.

1 LAUNCH

 Launch the lesson with a **Warm Up** and an introduction.

2 EXPLORE AND DEVELOP

Explore: Verifying the Properties of Dilations

Develop:

Dilations
- Identify a Dilation to Find Scale Factor
- Find and Use a Scale Factor

Dilations on the Coordinate Plane
- Dilate a Figure
- Find the Scale Factor of a Dilation

 You may want your students to complete the **Checks** online.

3 REFLECT AND PRACTICE

Exit Ticket

Practice

DIFFERENTIATE

View reports of student progress on the **Checks** after each example.

Resources	AL	OL	BL	ELL
Remediation: Graph Rational Numbers on a Number Line	●	●		●
Extension: Negative Scale Factors		●	●	●

Language Development Handbook

Assign page 52 of the *Language Development Handbook* to help your students build mathematical language related to drawing and analyzing dilated figures using tools or functions.

ELL You can use the tips and suggestions on page T52 of the handbook to support students who are building English proficiency.

Suggested Pacing

90 min	0.5 day
45 min	1 day

Focus

Domain: Geometry

Standards for Mathematical Content:

G.SRT.1 Verify experimentally the properties of dilations given by a center and a scale factor.

G.CO.2 Represent transformations in the plane using, e.g., transparencies and geometry software; describe transformations as functions that take points in the plane as inputs and give other points as outputs. Compare transformations that preserve distance and angle to those that do not.

Standards for Mathematical Practice:

1 Make sense of problems and persevere in solving them.
2 Reason abstractly and quantitatively.
5 Use appropriate tools strategically.
6 Attend to precision.

Coherence

Vertical Alignment

Previous
Students identified the effect of dilations on two-dimensional figures on the coordinate plane.
8.G.3

Now
Students identify and use dilations and dilations on the coordinate plane.
G.CO.2, G.SRT.1

Next
Students will solve problems using similar polygons.
G.SRT.2

Rigor

The Three Pillars of Rigor

1 CONCEPTUAL UNDERSTANDING	2 FLUENCY	3 APPLICATION

Conceptual Bridge In this lesson, students extend their understanding of congruence transformations to similarity transformations. They build fluency and apply their understanding by solving real-world dilation problems.

Mathematical Background

A similarity transformation is an operation that maps an original figure, the preimage, onto a new similar figure, the image. Dilations are one type of similarity transformation. A dilation is an enlargement if the scale factor is greater than 1, or a reduction if the scale factor is between 0 and 1.

Interactive Presentation

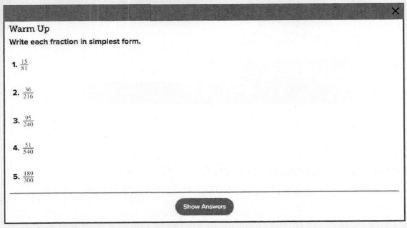

Warm Up

Write each fraction in simplest form.

1. $\frac{15}{81}$

2. $\frac{36}{216}$

3. $\frac{95}{240}$

4. $\frac{51}{540}$

5. $\frac{189}{300}$

Show Answers

Warm Up

Launch the Lesson

Watch this video to see how Tina uses dilations to create a new superhero in her comic book series.

Launch the Lesson

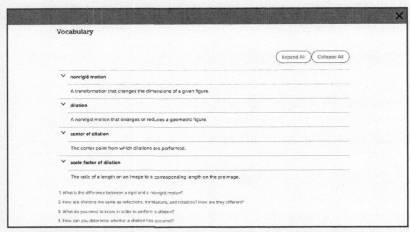

Vocabulary

Expand All   Collapse All

∨ **nonrigid motion**

A transformation that changes the dimensions of a given figure.

∨ **dilation**

A nonrigid motion that enlarges or reduces a geometric figure.

∨ **center of dilation**

The center point from which dilations are performed.

∨ **scale factor of dilation**

The ratio of a length on an image to a corresponding length on the preimage.

1. What is the difference between a rigid and a nonrigid motion?
2. How are dilations the same as reflections, translations, and rotations? How are they different?
3. What do you need to know in order to perform a dilation?
4. How can you determine whether a dilation has occurred?

Today's Vocabulary

Warm Up

Prerequisite Skills

The Warm Up exercises address the following prerequisite skill for this lesson:

- simplifying fractions

Answers:

1. $\frac{5}{27}$

2. $\frac{1}{6}$

3. $\frac{19}{48}$

4. $\frac{17}{180}$

5. $\frac{63}{100}$

Launch the Lesson

MP Teaching the Mathematical Practices

4 Apply Mathematics In this Launch the Lesson, students can see a real-world application of dilations.

Go Online to find additional teaching notes and questions to promote classroom discourse.

Today's Standards

Tell students that they will be addressing these content and practice standards in this lesson. You may wish to have a student volunteer read aloud *How can I meet these standards?* and *How can I use these practices?* and connect these to the standards.

See the Interactive Presentation for I Can statements that align with the standards covered in this lesson.

Today's Vocabulary

Tell students that they will be using these vocabulary terms in this lesson. You can expand each row if you wish to share the definitions. Then, discuss the questions below with the class.

Explore Verifying the Properties of Dilations

Objective

Students use dynamic geometry software to verify experimentally the properties of dilations given a center and a scale factor.

 Teaching the Mathematical Practices

2 Make Sense of Quantities Mathematically proficient students need to be able to make sense of quantities and their relationships. In this Explore, notice the relationship between the different segment lengths.

Ideas for Use

Recommended Use Present the Inquiry Question, or have a student volunteer read it aloud. Have students work in pairs to complete the Explore activity on their devices. Pairs should discuss each of the questions. Monitor student progress during the activity. Upon completion of the Explore activity, have student volunteers share their responses to the Inquiry Question.

What if my students don't have devices? You may choose to project the activity on a whiteboard. A printable worksheet for each Explore is available online. You may choose to print the worksheet so that individuals or pairs of students can use it to record their observations.

Summary of the Activity

Students will complete guiding exercises throughout the Explore activity. Students summarize the effects of dilations on line segments and on figures. Then, students will answer the Inquiry Question.

(continued on the next page)

Interactive Presentation

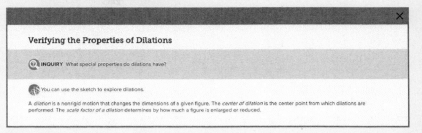

Explore

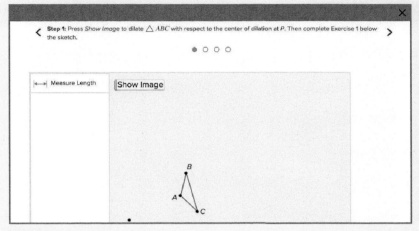

Explore

WEB SKETCHPAD

Students use a sketch to complete an activity in which they explore dilations.

TYPE

Students answer questions relating to dilations.

Interactive Presentation

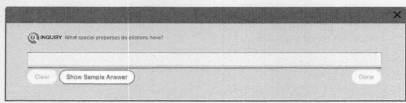

Explore

TYPE

 Students respond to the Inquiry Question and can view a sample answer.

1 **CONCEPTUAL UNDERSTANDING**   2 FLUENCY   3 APPLICATION

Explore Verifying the Properties of Dilations (continued)

Teaching the Mathematical Practices

5 Use Mathematical Tools Point out that to solve the problem in this Explore, students will need to use dynamic geometry software. Work with students to explore and deepen their understanding of properties of dilations.

Questions

Have students complete the Explore activity.

Ask:

- What happens when the scale factor is less than 1? Sample answer: When the scale factor is less than 1, it looks like the sides lengths are getting smaller which means the triangle is being reduced instead of enlarged.

- Why is it helpful to know that dilations of lines that do not pass through the center of dilation are parallel? Sample answer: You could use this relationship to verify if polygons are dilations by checking to see if their sides are parallel.

Inquiry

What special properties do dilations have? Sample answer: In a dilation, the ratio of a side length in the image to the corresponding side length in the preimage is equal to the scale factor. When a line is dilated and does not pass through the center of dilation, the image of the line is parallel to the original line. When a line is dilated and passes through the center of dilation, the line remains unchanged.

Go Online to find additional teaching notes and sample answers for the guiding exercises.

1 CONCEPTUAL UNDERSTANDING | 2 FLUENCY | 3 APPLICATION

Learn Dilations

Objective
Students verify that parts of dilated figures are longer or shorter in the ratio given by the scale factor, and use scale factors to calculate the dimensions of dilated images.

 Teaching the Mathematical Practices

> **7 Use Structure** Help students to explore the structure of dilations in this Learn.
>
> **1 Special Cases** Work with students to evaluate the various cases of dilations. Encourage students to familiarize themselves with each case.

Things to Remember
The scale factor of a dilation can be represented as a fraction, a decimal, or as a percent. For example, a scale factor of $\frac{2}{5}$ can also be written as 0.4 or as 40%. In addition, dilations can also have negative scale factors.

Example 1 Identify a Dilation to Find Scale Factor

 Teaching the Mathematical Practices

> **8 Attend to Details** Mathematically proficient students continually ask themselves, "Does this make sense?" Point out that in this example, students will evaluate the reasonableness of their answer.

Questions for Mathematical Discourse

AL What similarity statement compares the triangles?
Sample answer: $\triangle ABC \sim \triangle DEF$

OL What is the scale factor of $\triangle DEF$ to $\triangle ABC$? 3

BL Let the area of $\triangle ABC$ be 9 square centimeters. What is the area of $\triangle DEF$? 1 cm^2

Go Online

- Find additional teaching notes.
- View performance reports of the Checks.
- Assign or present an Extra Example.

DIFFERENTIATE

Language Development Activity AL BL ELL
Auditory/Musical Learners Students can relate dilations to music by how loud or soft a sound is. A harmonica's sound is magnified or dilated with a scale factor of *r* greater than 1 when a great force is used to create a musical note. The sound is much softer when the same note is produced with half the force. They can also correlate drawing a breath through the harmonica with a negative scale factor and exhaling into the harmonica with a positive scale factor.

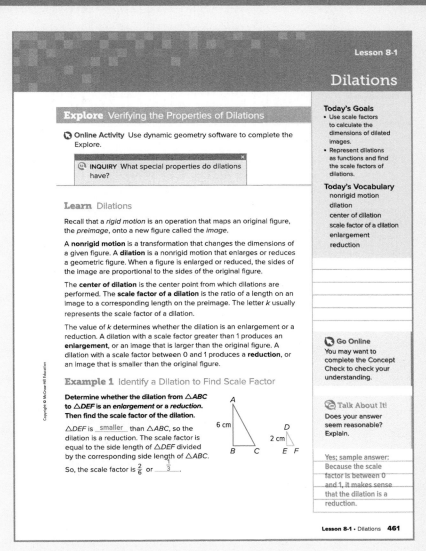

Interactive Presentation

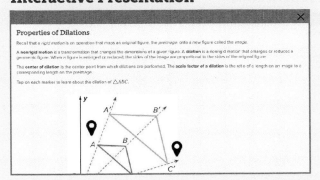

Learn

TAP

 Students will tap on markers to learn about the dilation of a triangle.

Your Notes

Study Tip

Multiple Representations
The scale factor of a dilation can be represented as a fraction, a decimal, or as a percent. For example, a scale factor of $\frac{2}{5}$ can also be written as 0.4 or as 40%.

Study Tip

Units of Measure
Sometimes when a figure is reduced or enlarged, the unit of measure should change to better fit the context of the problem. In Example 2, the dimensions of the banner are about 2.5 feet by 5.8 feet.

Check

Determine whether the dilation from *WXYZ* to *JKLM* is an *enlargement* or a *reduction*. Then find the scale factor of the dilation.

The dilation of *WXYZ* to *JKLM* is a(n) __reduction__

The scale factor of the dilation is $\frac{4}{7}$.

🌐 **Example 2** Find and Use a Scale Factor

SCHOOL SPIRIT
Jalal is printing a banner for his school's wheelchair tennis team based on the design shown. By what percent should Jalal enlarge his design so that the dimensions of the banner are 5 times that of the original design? What will be the dimensions of the banner?

Jalal wants to create an enlarged image of his banner design using a commercial printer. The scale factor of his enlargement is 5. Written as a percent, the scale factor is (5 × 100)% or __500__ %.

Now we can find the dimensions of the enlarged image using the scale factor.

width: 6 in. × 500% = __30__ in.   length: 14 in. × 500% = __70__ in.

The banner will be 30 inches by 70 inches.

Check

PORTRAITS Natalia wants to print an enlarged family portrait for her mother. By what percent should Natalia enlarge the portrait so that the dimensions of its image are 2.5 times that of the original? What will be the dimensions of the enlarged portrait?

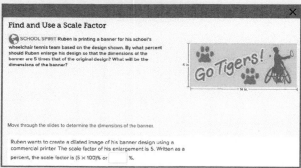

A. 125%; 22.5 cm by 30 cm   **B.** 125%; 45 cm by 60 cm
C. 250%; 22.5 cm by 30 cm   **D.** 250%; 45 cm by 60 cm

🌐 **Go Online** You can complete an Extra Example online.

🌐 **Example 2** Find and Use a Scale Factor

MP **Teaching the Mathematical Practices**

4 Apply Mathematics In this example, students apply what they have learned about dilations to solving a real-world problem.

Questions for Mathematical Discourse

AL By what percent should Jalal enlarge his design so that the dimensions of the banner are 3.5 times that of the original design? **350%**

OL If the scale factor of the enlargement is 10, what are the dimensions, in inches, of the enlarged design?
width = 60 in.; length = 140 in.

BL Is the area of the banner also enlarged by a scale factor of 5? Explain. No; sample answer: Because the dimensions are enlarged by a scale factor of 5, the area is enlarged by a factor of $5^2 = 25$.

Common Error

Have students estimate an answer before solving the problem to prevent careless errors.

🄴 Essential Question Follow-Up

Students have explored transformations and symmetry.
Ask:

How are dilations related to the concepts of symmetry and transformations? Sample answer: A dilation is a similarity transformation as it enlarges or reduces a figure proportionally. A dilation by a scale factor of 1 or −1 is also a congruence transformation.

Interactive Presentation

Find and Use a Scale Factor

🌐 SCHOOL SPIRIT Ruben is printing a banner for his school's wheelchair tennis team based on the design shown. By what percent should Ruben enlarge his design so that the dimensions of the banner are 5 times that of the original design? What will be the dimensions of the banner?

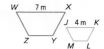

Move through the slides to determine the dimensions of the banner.

Ruben wants to create a dilated image of his banner design using a commercial printer. The scale factor of his enlargement is 5. Written as a percent, the scale factor is (5 × 100)% or ____ %.

Example 2

TYPE

Students complete calculations to find the dimensions of a new banner.

CHECK

Students complete the Check online to determine whether they are ready to move on.

1 CONCEPTUAL UNDERSTANDING | **2 FLUENCY** | 3 APPLICATION

Learn Dilations on the Coordinate Plane

Objective
Students represent dilations as functions and use preimages and images to find the scale factors of dilations.

 Teaching the Mathematical Practices

6 Communicate Precisely Encourage students to routinely write or explain their solution methods. Point out that they should use clear definitions when they discuss their solutions with others.

Example 3 Dilate a Figure

 Teaching the Mathematical Practices

1 Check Answers Mathematically proficient students continually ask themselves, "Does this make sense?" Point out that in this example, students need to check their answer. Point out that they should ask themselves whether their answer makes sense and whether they have answered the problem question.

Questions for Mathematical Discourse

AL If the scale factor is greater than 1, how do you find the coordinates of the dilated image? Multiply the scale factor by the coordinates of each vertex.

OL If the scale factor, k, is 2.5, what are the coordinates of the dilated image? $T'(-10, -12.5)$, $R'(0, 15)$, $S'(10, 7.5)$

BL If the coordinates of the dilated image are $T'(-6, -7.5)$, $R'(0, 9)$, and $S'(6, 4.5)$, what is the scale factor? $\frac{3}{2}$

Common Error
To check an answer, dilate $\triangle T'R'S'$ by the reciprocal of the original scale factor. If the coordinates of the vertices of the new image are the same as the coordinates of the vertices of $\triangle TRS$ then the answer is correct.

DIFFERENTIATE

Enrichment Activity BL
Ask students to describe how they would use the definition of similarity in terms of a dilation to determine if two figures are similar. Students should include examples that illustrate the properties of a dilation. Students should prove that their examples are dilations by identifying all proportional sides and congruent corresponding angles.

Learn Dilations on the Coordinate Plane

On the coordinate plane, a dilation is a function in which the coordinates of the vertices of a figure are multiplied by the same ratio k.

Key Concept • Dilations on the Coordinate Plane

Words	To dilate a figure by a scale factor of k with respect to the center of dilation (0, 0), multiply the x- and y-coordinate of each vertex by k.
Symbols	$(x, y) \longrightarrow (kx, ky)$
Example	The image of $\triangle PQR$ dilated by $k = 3$ is $\triangle P'Q'R'$.

 Think About It!
What is the relationship between PQ and $P'Q'$? How does this relate to the scale factor?

Sample answer: $P'Q'$ is 3 times PQ. The ratio between the lengths of the corresponding sides is the same as the scale factor.

Study Tip
Center of Dilation
Unless otherwise stated, all dilations on the coordinate plane use the origin as their center of dilation.

Example 3 Dilate a Figure

$\triangle TRS$ has vertices $T(-4, -5)$, $R(0, 6)$, and $S(4, 3)$. Find the coordinates of the vertices of $\triangle T'R'S'$ after a dilation of $\triangle TRS$ by a scale factor of $\frac{1}{2}$.

Because the scale factor is $\frac{1}{2}$, the coordinates of the vertices of $\triangle T'R'S'$ should be half of the value of the coordinates of the vertices of $\triangle TRS$.

Complete the calculations for the dilation when $k = \frac{1}{2}$.

$(x, y) \longrightarrow (kx, ky)$

$T(-4, -5) \longrightarrow T'\left(\frac{1}{2}(-4), \frac{1}{2}(-5)\right)$ or $T'(-2, -2.5)$

$R(0, 6) \longrightarrow R'\left(\frac{1}{2}(\underline{0}), \frac{1}{2}(\underline{6})\right)$ or $R'(0, 3)$

$S(4, 3) \longrightarrow S'\left(\frac{1}{2}(\underline{4}), \frac{1}{2}(\underline{3})\right)$ or $S'(2, 1.5)$

Check
$\triangle XYZ$ has vertices $X(3, -4)$, $Y(6, 5)$, and $Z(8, -2)$. Find the coordinates of the vertices of $\triangle X'Y'Z'$ after a dilation of $\triangle XYZ$ by a scale factor of 4.

$X'(\underline{12}, \underline{-16})$ $Y'(\underline{24}, \underline{20})$ $Z'(\underline{32}, \underline{-8})$

Go Online You can complete an Extra Example online.

Lesson 8-1 • Dilations **463**

Interactive Presentation

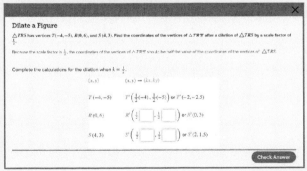

Example 3

TYPE

$a|$

Students complete the calculations to determine the coordinates of the vertices of a dilation.

1 CONCEPTUAL UNDERSTANDING | **2 FLUENCY** | 3 APPLICATION

Example 4 Find the Scale Factor of a Dilation

$\triangle A'B'C'$ is the image of $\triangle ABC$ after a dilation. Find the scale factor of the dilation.

To find the scale factor of the dilation, you must compare the lengths of corresponding sides in $\triangle ABC$ and $\triangle A'B'C'$.

Step 1 Identify two corresponding sides and their endpoints.

$\overline{AB}$ and $\overline{A'B'}$ are corresponding sides. The endpoints of $\overline{AB}$ are $A(\underline{-3}, \underline{0})$ and $B(\underline{0}, \underline{2})$. The endpoints of $\overline{A'B'}$ are $A'(\underline{-9}, \underline{0})$ and $B'(\underline{0}, \underline{6})$.

Step 2 Find the lengths of the corresponding sides.

Use the Distance Formula to find AB and $A'B'$.

$A(-3, 0)$ and $B(0, 2)$ $A'(-9, 0)$ and $B'(0, 6)$

$AB = \sqrt{[0 - (-3)]^2 + (2 - \underline{0})^2}$ $A'B' = \sqrt{[0-(-9)]^2 + (6 - \underline{0})^2}$

$\quad = \sqrt{\underline{3}^2 + 2^2}$ $= \sqrt{9^2 + \underline{6}^2}$

$\quad = \sqrt{13}$ $= \sqrt{117}$

Step 3 Calculate the scale factor.

To find the scale factor, find the ratio of $A'B'$ to AB.

$AB = \sqrt{13}$ and $A'B' = \sqrt{117}$

$\frac{A'B'}{AB} = \frac{\sqrt{117}}{\sqrt{13}} = \sqrt{\frac{117}{13}} = \sqrt{9} = 3$

So, the scale factor of the dilation is 3.

Check

$\triangle D'E'F'$ is the image of $\triangle DEF$ after a dilation. Find the scale factor of the dilation.

$k = \frac{1}{3}$

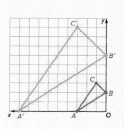

 Go Online You can complete an Extra Example online.

Interactive Presentation

Find the Scale Factor of a Dilation

$\triangle A'B'C'$ is the image of $\triangle ABC$ after a dilation. Find the scale factor of the dilation.

To find the scale factor of the dilation, you must compare the lengths of corresponding sides in $\triangle ABC$ and $\triangle A'B'C'$.

Example 4

CHECK

Students complete the Check online to determine whether they are ready to move on.

Example 4 Find the Scale Factor of a Dilation

 Teaching the Mathematical Practices

4 Analyze Relationships Mathematically Point out that to solve the problem in this example, students will need to analyze the mathematical relationships in the problem to draw a conclusion.

Questions for Mathematical Discourse

AL What are the other two pairs of two corresponding sides and their endpoints? AC and $A'C'$ are corresponding sides. The endpoints of AC are $A(-3, 0)$ and $C(-1, 3)$. The endpoints of $A'C'$ are $A'(-9, 0)$ and $C'(-3, 9)$. CB and $C'B'$ are corresponding sides. The endpoints of CB are $C(-1, 3)$ and $B(0, 2)$. The endpoints of $C'B'$ are $C'(-3, 9)$ and $B'(0, 6)$.

OL Is $\triangle ABC$ isosceles? Explain. Yes; sample answer: Use the Distance Formula to find AC. Because $AC = \sqrt{13}$, then $\overline{AC} \cong \overline{AB}$ and the triangle is isosceles.

BL What would have to be true of the two images in order for the scale factor to be $\frac{1}{3}$? $\triangle A'B'C'$ would need to be the preimage and $\triangle ABC$ would need to be the image.

Common Error

Remind students that dilations between 0 and 1 reduce the image size, and dilations greater than 1 enlarge the image.

Exit Ticket

Recommended Use

At the end of class, go online to display the Exit Ticket prompt and ask students to respond using a separate piece of paper. Have students hand you their responses as they leave the room.

Alternate Use

At the end of class, go online to display the Exit Ticket prompt and ask students to respond verbally or by using a mini-whiteboard. Have students hold up their whiteboards so that you can see all student responses. Tap to reveal the answer when most or all students have completed the Exit Ticket.

Important to Know

Digital Exercise Alert Exercise 21 requires representing a transformation in the plane and is not available online. To fully address G.CO.2, have students complete this exercise using their books.

Practice and Homework

Suggested Assignments

Use the table below to select appropriate exercises.

DOK	Topic	Exercises
1, 2	exercises that mirror the examples	1–12
2	exercises that use a variety of skills from this lesson	13–24
3	exercises that emphasize higher-order and critical-thinking skills	25–30

ASSESS AND DIFFERENTIATE

Use the data from the **Checks** to determine whether to provide resources for extension, remediation, or intervention.

IF students score 90% or more on the Checks, **BL**
THEN assign:

- Practice, Exercises 1–23 odd, 25–30
- Extension: Negative Scale Factors
- **ALEKS'** Dilations

IF students score 66%–89% on the Checks, **OL**
THEN assign:

- Practice, Exercises 1–29 odd
- Remediation, Review Resources: Rational Numbers
- Personal Tutors
- Extra Examples 1–4
- **ALEKS'** Simplifying Fractions

IF students score 65% or less on the Checks, **AL**
THEN assign:

- Practice, Exercises 1–11 odd
- Remediation, Review Resources: Rational Numbers
- *Quick Review Math Handbook:* Dilations
- **ALEKS'** Simplifying Fractions

Answers

6. $J'(-4, 0), K'(-2, 2), L'(-1, 0)$

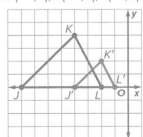

7. $S'(0, 0), T'(-5, 0), V'(-10, -10)$

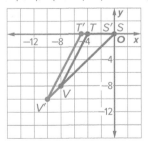

8. $A'(3, 3), B'(1, 1), C'(2, 0)$

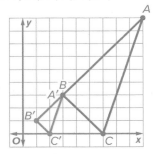

9. $D'(3, 3), F'(0, 0), G'(6, 0)$

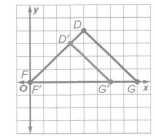

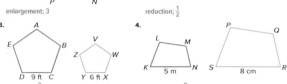

Name _____ Period _____ Date _____

Practice — Go Online You can complete your homework online.

Example 1

Determine whether the dilation from the figure on the left to the figure on the right is an *enlargement* or a *reduction*. Then find the scale factor of the dilation.

1.

enlargement; 3

2.

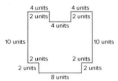

reduction; $\frac{1}{2}$

3.

reduction; $\frac{2}{3}$

4.

enlargement; $\frac{8}{5}$

Example 2

5. BLUEPRINTS Ezra is redrawing the blueprint shown of a stage he is planning to build for his band. By what percentage should he multiply the dimensions of the stage so that the dimensions of the image are $\frac{1}{2}$ the size of the original blueprint? What will be the perimeter of the updated blueprint? 50%; The perimeter of the updated blueprint will be 26 units.

Example 3

For each set of triangle vertices, find and graph the coordinates of the vertices of the image after a dilation of the triangle by the given scale factor. 6–9. See margin.

6. $J(-8, 0), K(-4, 4), L(-2, 0), k = 0.5$

7. $S(0, 0), T(-4, 0), V(-8, -8), k = 1.25$

8. $A(9, 9), B(3, 3), C(6, 0), k = \frac{1}{3}$

9. $D(4, 4), F(0, 0), G(8, 0), k = 0.75$

Lesson 8-1 • Dilations **465**

Example 4

Find the scale factor of the dilation.

10. $\triangle J'K'P'$ is the image of $\triangle JKP$. 2

11. $\triangle D'F'G'$ is the image of $\triangle DFG$. 1.5

12. Tyrone drew a logo and a dilation of the same logo on the coordinate plane. What is the scale factor of the dilation? 2.5

Mixed Exercises

Graph the image of each polygon with the given vertices after a dilation centered at the origin with the given scale factor. 13–16. See margin.

13. $F(-10, 4), G(-4, 4), H(-4, -8), k = 0.25$

14. $X(2, -1), Y(-6, 4), Z(-2, -5), k = \frac{5}{4}$

15. $M(4, 6), N(-6, 2), P(0, -8), k = \frac{3}{4}$

16. $R(-2, 6), S(0, -1), T(-5, 3), k = 1.5$

Find the scale factor of the dilation.

17. $A'B'C'D'$ is the image of $ABCD$. $\frac{2}{3}$

18. $\triangle P'Q'R'$ is the image of $\triangle PQR$. 1.5

466 Module 8 • Similarity

Name _____ Period _____ Date _____

19. Determine whether the dilation from Figure N to N' is an *enlargement* or a *reduction*. Find the scale factor of the dilation. enlargement; 2

20. $\triangle ABC$ has vertices $A(2, 2)$, $B(3, 4)$, and $C(5, 2)$. What are the coordinates of point C of the image of the triangle after a dilation centered at the origin with a scale factor of 2.5? (12.5, 5)

21. USE TOOLS Use a ruler to draw the image of the figure under a dilation with center M and a scale factor of $\frac{1}{5}$. See margin.

22. Davion is using a coordinate plane to experiment with quadrilaterals, as shown in the figure. Davion creates $M'N'P'Q'$ by enlarging $MNPQ$ with a dilation with a scale factor of 2. Then he creates $M''N''P''Q''$ by dilating $M'N'P'Q'$ with a scale factor of $\frac{1}{3}$. The center of dilation for each dilation is the origin.

  a. Draw and label the final image, $M''N''P''Q''$. See margin.

  b. Can Davion map $MNPQ$ directly to $M''N''P''Q''$ with a single transformation? If so, what transformation should he use? yes; a dilation with a scale factor of $\frac{2}{3}$

  c. In general, what can you say about a dilation with scale factor k_1 that is followed by a dilation with scale factor k_2? The new dilation factor is $k_1 \cdot k_2$.

23. The point P' is the image of point $P(a, b)$ under a dilation centered at the origin with scale factor $k \neq 1$.

  a. Assuming that point P does not lie on the y-axis, what is the slope of $\overline{PP'}$? Explain how you know. $\frac{b}{a}$; Sample answer: The coordinates of P' are (ka, kb). The slope of $\overline{PP'}$ is $\frac{kb-b}{ka-a} = \frac{b(k-1)}{a(k-1)} = \frac{b}{a}$.

  b. In part **a**, why is it important that P does not lie on the y-axis? Sample answer: If P lies on the y-axis, then its image P' will also lie on the y-axis. In this case, $\overline{PP'}$ will be vertical, and the slope will be undefined.

24. $WXYZ$ has vertices $W(6, 2)$, $X(3, 7)$, $Y(-1, 4)$, and $Z(4, -2)$.

  a. Find the perimeter of $WXYZ$. ≈ 23.1

  b. Find the perimeter of the image of $WXYZ$ after a dilation of $\frac{1}{2}$ centered at the origin and compare it to the perimeter of $WXYZ$. ≈ 11.6; The perimeter of the dilated figure is half of the perimeter of $WXYZ$.

Higher-Order Thinking Skills

25. PERSEVERE Find the equation for the dilated image of the line $y = 4x - 2$ if the dilation is centered at the origin with a scale factor of 1.5. $y = 4x - 3$

26. WRITE Are parallel lines (parallelism) and collinear points (collinearity) preserved under all transformations? Explain. See margin.

27. ANALYZE An *invariant point* is a point that remains fixed under a transformation. Determine whether invariant points are *sometimes*, *always*, or *never* maintained for the transformations described below. If so, describe the invariant point(s). If not, explain why invariant points are not possible. a–e. See margin.

  a. dilation of $ABCD$ with scale factor of 1

  b. rotation of $\overline{AB}$ 74° about B

  c. reflection of $\triangle MNP$ in the x-axis

  d. translation of $PQRS$ along $(7, 3)$

  e. dilation of $\triangle XYZ$ centered at the origin with scale factor 2

28. CREATE Graph a triangle. Dilate the triangle so that its area is four times the area of the original triangle. State the scale factor and center of your dilation. See Mod. 8 Answer Appendix.

29. WRITE Can you use transformations to create congruent figures? Explain. Sample answer: Translations, reflections, and rotations produce congruent figures because the sides and angles of the preimage are congruent to the corresponding sides and angles of the image.

30. ANALYZE Determine whether each statement is *sometimes*, *always*, or *never* true. Justify your argument.

  a. If c is a real number, then a dilation centered at the origin maps the line $y = cx$ to itself. Always; the line $y = cx$ passes through the origin and a dilation leaves lines through the center of dilation unchanged.

  b. If $k > 1$, then a dilation with scale factor k maps $\overline{AB}$ to a segment that is congruent to $\overline{AB}$. Never; $A'B' = k(AB)$, and $k > 1$, so $A'B' \neq AB$. This means $\overline{AB}$ cannot be congruent to its image.

13.

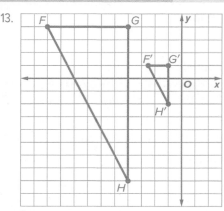

14.

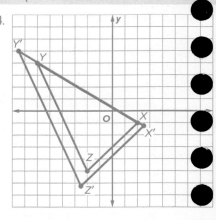

15.

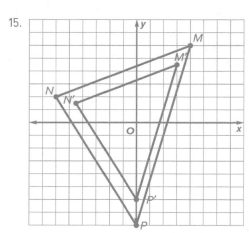

16.

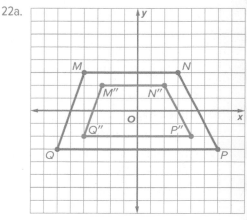

21.

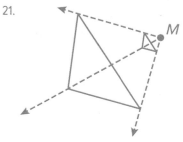

22a.

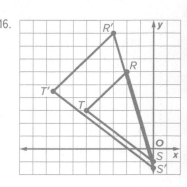

26. Yes; sample answer: In translations, reflections, and rotations, congruent figures are formed, which means that sides that were parallel before transformation will be parallel after transformation and points that were collinear before transformation will still be collinear after transformation. Both parallel sides and collinear points are also preserved under dilations because a similar figure is formed, which has the same shape, but in a different proportion.

27a. Always; sample answer: Points remain invariant under the dilation.

27b. Always; sample answer: Because the rotation is centered at B, point B will always remain invariant under the rotation.

27c. Sometimes; sample answer: If one of the vertices is on the x-axis, then that point will remain invariant under reflection. If two vertices are on the x-axis, then the two vertices located on the x-axis will remain invariant under reflection.

27d. Never; sample answer: When a figure is translated, all points move an equal distance. Therefore, no points can remain invariant under translation.

27e. Sometimes; sample answer: If one of the vertices of the triangle is located at the origin, then that vertex would remain invariant under the dilation. If none of the points of $\triangle XYZ$ are located at the origin, then no points will remain invariant under the dilation.

Similar Polygons

LESSON GOAL

Students solve problems using the definition of similar polygons.

1 LAUNCH

Launch the lesson with a **Warm Up** and an introduction.

2 EXPLORE AND DEVELOP

Explore: Similarity in Polygons

Develop:

Similar Polygons
- Use a Similarity Statement
- Identify Similar Polygons
- Use Similar Figures to Find Missing Measures

Perimeters of Similar Polygons
- Use Similar Polygons to Find Perimeter

You may want your students to complete the **Checks** online.

3 REFLECT AND PRACTICE

Exit Ticket

Practice

DIFFERENTIATE

View reports of student progress on the **Checks** after each example.

Resources	AL	OL	BL	ELL
Remediation: Congruent Triangles	●	●		●
Extension: Constructing Similar Polygons		●	●	●

Language Development Handbook

Assign page 53 of the *Language Development Handbook* to help your students build mathematical language related to the definition of similar polygons.

ELL You can use the tips and suggestions on page T53 of the handbook to support students who are building English proficiency.

Suggested Pacing

90 min	**0.5 day**
45 min	**1 day**

Focus

Domain: Geometry

Standards for Mathematical Content:

G.SRT.2 Given two figures, use the definition of similarity in terms of similarity transformations to decide if they are similar; explain using similarity transformations the meaning of similarity for triangles as the equality of all corresponding pairs of angles and the proportionality of all corresponding pairs of sides.

Standards for Mathematical Practice:

3 Construct viable arguments and critique the reasoning of others.

5 Use appropriate tools strategically.

6 Attend to precision.

Coherence

Vertical Alignment

Previous
Students identified and used dilations on the coordinate plane.
G.CO.2, G.SRT.1

Now
Students solve problems using the definition of similar polygons.
G.SRT.2

Next
Students will use the AA similarity criterion to solve problems and prove triangles similar.
G.SRT.2, G.SRT.3

Rigor

The Three Pillars of Rigor

1 CONCEPTUAL UNDERSTANDING	2 FLUENCY	3 APPLICATION

Conceptual Bridge In this lesson, students develop an understanding of similarity in terms of similarity transformations. They build fluency and apply their understanding by solving real-world problems with similar polygons.

Mathematical Background

Two polygons are similar if and only if their corresponding angles are congruent and the measures of their corresponding sides are proportional. The ratio of the lengths of two corresponding sides of two similar polygons is the scale factor.

Interactive Presentation

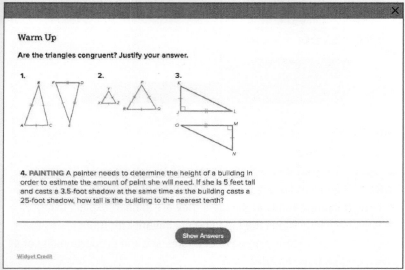

Warm Up

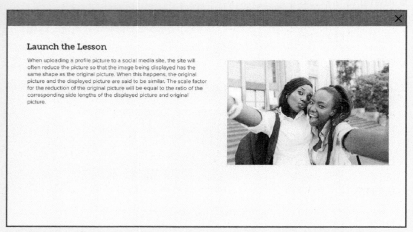

Launch the Lesson

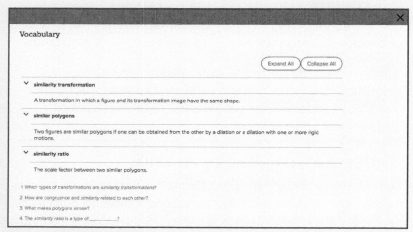

Today's Vocabulary

Warm Up

Prerequisite Skills

The Warm Up exercises address the following prerequisite skill for this lesson:

- identifying congruent triangles

Answers:

1. yes; SSS
2. no
3. yes; SAS
4. 35.7 ft

Launch the Lesson

 Teaching the Mathematical Practices

4 Apply Mathematics In this Launch the Lesson, students can see a real-world application of similar polygons.

Go Online to find additional teaching notes and questions to promote classroom discourse.

Today's Standards

Tell students that they will be addressing these content and practice standards in this lesson. You may wish to have a student volunteer read aloud *How can I meet these standards?* and *How can I use these practices?* and connect these to the standards.

See the Interactive Presentation for I Can statements that align with the standards covered in this lesson.

Today's Vocabulary

Tell students that they will be using these vocabulary terms in this lesson. You can expand each row if you wish to share the definitions. Then, discuss the questions below with the class.

Explore Similarity in Polygons

Objective
Students use dynamic geometry software and the definition of similarity in terms of similarity transformations to decide if figures are similar.

Inquiry
How can you identify whether two polygons are similar? Sample answer: You must determine whether one of the polygons can be obtained by dilating the other polygon or dilating and performing one or more rigid motions, such as a translation, on the other polygon.

(MP) Teaching the Mathematical Practices
3 Construct Arguments In this Explore, students will use stated assumptions, definitions, and previously established results to construct an argument.

Ideas for Use

Recommended Use Present the Inquiry Question, or have a student volunteer read it aloud. Have students work in pairs to complete the Explore activity on their devices. Pairs should discuss each of the questions. Monitor student progress during the activity. Upon completion of the Explore activity, have student volunteers share their responses to the Inquiry Question.

What if my students don't have devices? You may choose to project the activity on a whiteboard. A printable worksheet for each Explore is available online. You may choose to print the worksheet so that individuals or pairs of students can use it to record their observations.

Summary of the Activity
Students will complete guiding exercises throughout the Explore activity. Students will use a sketch to explore dilations and to decide if figures are similar. Then, students will answer the Inquiry Question.

(continued on the next page)

Interactive Presentation

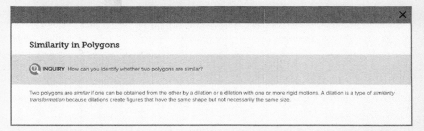

Explore

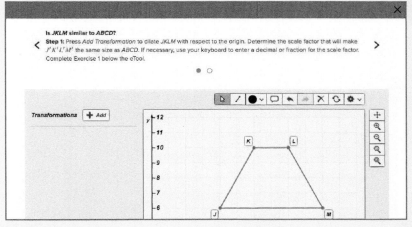

Explore

WEB SKETCHPAD

Students use a sketch to complete an activity in which they explore similar polygons.

Interactive Presentation

INQUIRY How can you identify whether two polygons are similar?

Done

×

Explore

TYPE

Students respond to the Inquiry Question and can view a sample answer.

---

1 CONCEPTUAL UNDERSTANDING | 2 FLUENCY | 3 APPLICATION

Explore Similarity in Polygons (*continued*)

Teaching the Mathematical Practices

5 Use Mathematical Tools Point out that to solve the problem in this Explore, students will need to use dynamic geometry software. Work with students to explore and deepen their understanding of similarity and similarity transformations.

Questions

Have students complete the Explore activity.

Ask:

- Does a dilation alone map *JKLM* to *ABCD*? Why or why not? No; sample answer: The dilation can get the shapes to be the same size, but the location of *ABCD* is such that *A* is not along the line from the origin to *J*.

- Would dilating kite *PQRS* and then translating it make the kites similar? Describe the transformations used in your answer. No; sample answer: If you use a dilation with scale factor of 0.5 centered at the origin followed by a translation along $\langle 6, 1 \rangle$, the shapes are still not similar because points *Z* and *S"* do not match up.

Inquiry

How can you identify whether two polygons are similar? Sample answer: You must determine whether one of the polygons can be obtained by dilating the other polygon or dilating and performing one or more rigid motions, such as a translation, on the other polygon.

 Go Online to find additional teaching notes and sample answers for the guiding exercises.

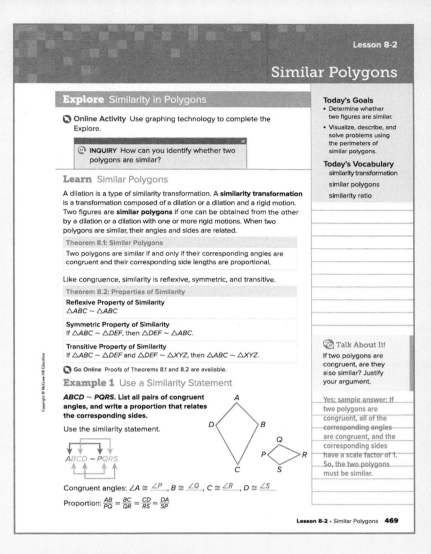

Learn Similar Polygons

Objective

Students determine whether two figures are similar based on the equality of all corresponding pairs of angles and the proportionality of all corresponding sides.

(MP) Teaching the Mathematical Practices

7 Use Structure Help students to explore the structure of similar polygons in this Learn.

6 Communicate Precisely Encourage students to routinely write or explain their solution methods. Point out that they should use clear definitions when they discuss their solutions with others.

Important to Know

If two polygons are congruent, they are also similar. All of the corresponding angles are congruent, and the lengths of the corresponding sides have a ratio of 1 : 1.

Example 1 Use a Similarity Statement

(MP) Teaching the Mathematical Practices

1 Explain Correspondences Encourage students to explain the relationships between the two similar figures in this example.

Questions for Mathematical Discourse

AL What does it mean if two triangles are similar? Sample answer: The two triangles have congruent corresponding angles and proportional corresponding sides.

OL What are the advantages of using the similarity statement to write the proportion instead of the drawing? Explain. Sample answer: If you use the drawing, you may confuse the order of the vertices, but if you use the similarity statement it is easy to see which vertices correspond.

BL Why do you think the proportion of the sides of two similar polygons is important? Sample answer: You can use the proportion to find the lengths of the sides.

(e) Essential Question Follow-Up

Students have explored proportions, similar triangles, and similarity theorems.

Ask:

How can you determine whether two objects are similar? Sample answer: You can compare corresponding angle measures to see if they are congruent and corresponding side lengths to see if they are proportional.

(R) Go Online

- Find additional teaching notes.
- View performance reports of the Checks.
- Assign or present an Extra Example.

Interactive Presentation

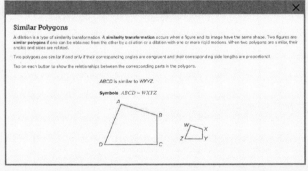

Learn

TAP

Students tap on each button to see the relationships between corresponding parts in similar polygons.

1 CONCEPTUAL UNDERSTANDING | **2 FLUENCY** | 3 APPLICATION

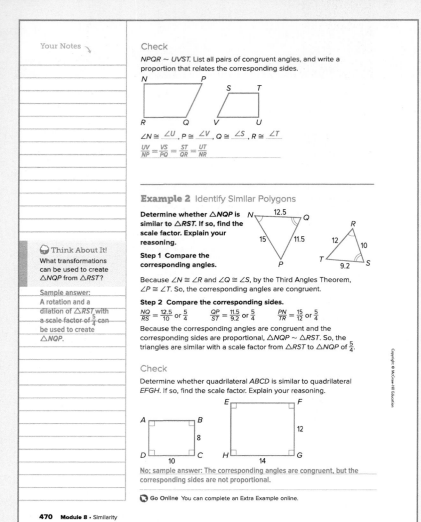

Your Notes

Check

NPQR ~ UVST. List all pairs of congruent angles, and write a proportion that relates the corresponding sides.

$\angle N \cong \angle U$, $P \cong \angle V$, $Q \cong \angle S$, $R \cong \angle T$

$\frac{UV}{NP} = \frac{VS}{PQ} = \frac{ST}{QR} = \frac{UT}{NR}$

Example 2 Identify Similar Polygons

Determine whether △*NQP* is similar to △*RST*. If so, find the scale factor. Explain your reasoning.

Step 1 Compare the corresponding angles.

Because $\angle N \cong \angle R$ and $\angle Q \cong \angle S$, by the Third Angles Theorem, $\angle P \cong \angle T$. So, the corresponding angles are congruent.

Step 2 Compare the corresponding sides.

$\frac{NQ}{RS} = \frac{12.5}{10}$ or $\frac{5}{4}$ $\frac{QP}{ST} = \frac{11.5}{9.2}$ or $\frac{5}{4}$ $\frac{PN}{TR} = \frac{15}{12}$ or $\frac{5}{4}$

Because the corresponding angles are congruent and the corresponding sides are proportional, △*NQP* ~ △*RST*. So, the triangles are similar with a scale factor from △*RST* to △*NQP* of $\frac{5}{4}$.

Check

Determine whether quadrilateral *ABCD* is similar to quadrilateral *EFGH*. If so, find the scale factor. Explain your reasoning.

No; sample answer: The corresponding angles are congruent, but the corresponding sides are not proportional.

💬 **Go Online** You can complete an Extra Example online.

💭 **Think About It!**
What transformations can be used to create △*NQP* from △*RST*?

Sample answer: A rotation and a dilation of △*RST* with a scale factor of $\frac{5}{4}$ can be used to create △*NQP*.

Interactive Presentation

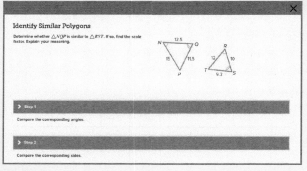

Identify Similar Polygons

Determine whether △*NQP* is similar to △*RST*. If so, find the scale factor. Explain your reasoning.

> Step 1
Compare the corresponding angles.

> Step 2
Compare the corresponding sides.

Example 2

TYPE

Students will complete statements to identify similar polygons.

Example 2 Identify Similar Polygons

MP Teaching the Mathematical Practices

6 Communicate Precisely Encourage students to routinely write or explain their solution methods. Point out that they should use clear definitions when they discuss their solutions with others.

Questions for Mathematical Discourse

AL What does the scale factor between two similar polygons tell you?
the ratio of the lengths of all corresponding sides

OL If △*JKL* has side lengths *JK* = 25, *KL* = 23, and *JL* = 30, is △*JKL* similar to △*NQP*? If so, what is the scale factor? yes; 2

BL What is the scale factor when △*NQP* is transformed to △*RST*? $\frac{4}{5}$

DIFFERENTIATE

Reteaching Activity AL

Show students how to be consistent when analyzing figures for similarity. For example, they may choose to always compare the figure on the left to the figure on the right. Show students ways to organize their work so that they reference corresponding vertices in the correct order.

DIFFERENTIATE

Language Development Activity ELL

Beginning Help students access text by working through the examples using an interactive whiteboard. Point out each part of the similar polygons and which are being used in each step of the solution, explaining using short phrases.

1 CONCEPTUAL UNDERSTANDING | **2 FLUENCY** | 3 APPLICATION

Example 3 Use Similar Figures to Find Missing Measures

Teaching the Mathematical Practices

3 Construct Arguments In this example, students will use stated assumptions, definitions, and previously established results to construct an argument.

Questions for Mathematical Discourse

AL Which side in *PQRS* corresponds to side *WZ*? *PS*

OL What is the scale factor of *WXYZ* to *PQRS*? $\frac{3}{4}$

BL What is *ZY*? 8

Common Error

Some students may have difficulty identifying corresponding parts in similar figures. Have students redraw the given diagram so the similar figures have the same orientation. This will allow them to easily compare corresponding parts and set up a similarity proportion. Students can also use different colors to circle letters of congruent angles to identify corresponding parts.

Learn Perimeters of Similar Polygons

Objective

Students apply geometric properties and create geometric models to visualize, describe, and solve problems using the perimeters of similar polygons.

Teaching the Mathematical Practices

7 Use Structure Help students to explore the structure of perimeters of similar polygons in this Learn.

Example 3 Use Similar Figures to Find Missing Measures

In the diagram, *WXYZ* ~ *PQRS*. Find the value of *y*.

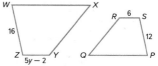

Use the corresponding side lengths to write a proportion.

$\frac{WZ}{PS} = \frac{YZ}{RS}$	Similarity proportion
$\frac{16}{12} = \frac{5y-2}{6}$	Substitute.
$16(6) = 12(5y-2)$	Multiplication Property of Equality
$96 = \underline{60}\ y - \underline{24}$	Multiply.
$\underline{120} = 60y$	Add 24 to each side.
$\underline{2} = y$	Divide each side by 60.

Check

In the diagram, △*JLM* ~ △*QST*. Find the value of *x*. Round to the nearest tenth, if necessary.

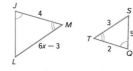

$x = \underline{1.5}$

 Go Online You can complete an Extra Example online.

Learn Perimeters of Similar Polygons

In similar polygons, the ratio of any two corresponding lengths is equal to the scale factor or **similarity ratio** between them. So, you can write a proportion to relate them. This leads to the following theorem about the perimeters of two similar polygons.

Theorem 8.3: Perimeters of Similar Polygons Theorem
If two polygons are similar, then their perimeters are proportional in the same ratio as the scale factor between them.

You will prove Theorem 8.3 in Exercise 21.

Problem-Solving Tip

Redraw Diagrams
When solving problems that use similar figures, sometimes it is difficult to identify corresponding parts. Redraw the given diagram so the similar figures have the same orientation. This will allow you to easily compare corresponding parts and set up a similarity proportion.

🗨 Think About It!

Will any two regular polygons with the same number of sides be similar? Justify your argument.

Sample answer: All of the angles and sides in a regular polygon are congruent. The angles will be congruent regardless of the size of the figure, and because all of the sides within a figure are congruent, the ratios of the sides of one regular polygon to a second regular polygon with the same number of sides will all be the same. Therefore, all regular polygons with the same number of sides are similar.

Interactive Presentation

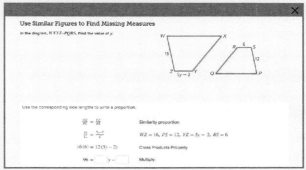

Example 3

CHECK

Students complete the Check online to determine whether they are ready to move on.

✪ Example 4 Use Similar Polygons to Find Perimeter

STATE FAIR Geoffrey plans on going to the state fair this summer. He has downloaded a map of the fairgrounds that shows all of the attractions. Geoffrey plans to visit the concert hall, the Ferris wheel, and the sports center. On the map, the distance between the concert hall and the Ferris wheel is 9 centimeters, the distance between the Ferris wheel and the sports center is 8 centimeters, and the distance between the sports center and the concert hall is 4 centimeters.

Part A Describe Geoffrey's path.

Geoffrey wants to visit the concert hall, the Ferris wheel, and the sports center. If Geoffrey returns to the concert hall after visiting the sports center, what polygon can be used to model Geoffrey's path between the three attractions?

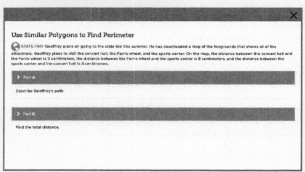

Geoffrey's path can be modeled by a _triangle_ .

On the map, draw line segments between the three attractions. Then label the points that represent the three attractions. Label the concert hall as C, the sports center as S, and the Ferris wheel as F.

Part B Find the total distance.

If the actual distance between the concert hall and the sports center is 20 meters, how far will Geoffrey have to travel to visit all three attractions and then return to his starting point?

$\triangle CSF$ will be similar to the triangle formed by Geoffrey as he walks to the three attractions. Let's call the figure formed by Geoffrey's path $\triangle C'S'F'$. So, $\triangle CSF \sim \triangle C'S'F'$. To find how far Geoffrey will have to travel to visit all three attractions, find the perimeter of $\triangle C'S'F'$.

Because 1 meter = 100 centimeters, 20 meters is equal to _2000_ centimeters. So, $C'S' = 2000$ centimeters.

The scale factor of $\triangle CSF$ to $\triangle C'S'F'$ is $\frac{C'S'}{CS} = \frac{2000}{4}$ or _500_ .

The perimeter of $\triangle CSF$ is $4 + \underline{\ 8\ } + 9$ or _21_ .

Use the perimeter of $\triangle CSF$ and the scale factor to write a proportion. Let w represent the perimeter of $\triangle C'S'F'$.

$$\frac{1}{500} = \frac{\text{perimeter of } \triangle CSF}{\text{perimeter of } \triangle C'S'F'}$$

$$\frac{1}{500} = \frac{21}{w}$$

$$w = \underline{\ 500\ } (21)$$

$$w = \underline{\ 10{,}500\ }$$

So, the perimeter of $\triangle C'S'F'$ is 10,500 centimeters or 105 meters.

🌐 **Go Online** You can complete an Extra Example online.

Think About It!
What assumption did you make while solving this problem?

Sample answer: I assumed that Geoffrey had a clear path from one attraction to the next and that he was able to walk in a straight line between all of the attractions.

Study Tip
Units of Measure
When finding a scale factor, the measurements being compared must have the same unit of measure. If they do not have the same unit of measure, you will need to convert one of the measurements.

Copyright © McGraw-Hill Education

Example 4 Use Similar Polygons to Find Perimeter

ⓜⓟ Teaching the Mathematical Practices

4 Make Assumptions Have students explain an assumption or approximation that was made to solve the problem.

Questions for Mathematical Discourse

AL What is the difference between congruency and similarity in polygons? Congruent polygons have the same angle measures and side lengths. Similar polygons have the same angle measures and proportional side lengths.

OL What is the actual distance between each of the three attractions? $CS = 20$ m, $SF = 40$ m, and $CF = 45$ m

BL If on the map, the distance between the sports center and the concert hall is 5 centimeters, what is the actual distance Geoffrey must travel? 88 meters

Common Error

Students may try to apply the Perimeters of Similar Polygons Theorem to areas. Work through this example to show that this is not the case.

Exit Ticket

Recommended Use

At the end of class, go online to display the Exit Ticket prompt and ask students to respond using a separate piece of paper. Have students hand you their responses as they leave the room.

Alternate Use

At the end of class, go online to display the Exit Ticket prompt and ask students to respond verbally or by using a mini-whiteboard. Have students hold up their whiteboards so that you can see all student responses. Tap to reveal the answer when most or all students have completed the Exit Ticket.

Interactive Presentation

> **Use Similar Polygons to Find Perimeter**
>
> ✪ STATE FAIR Geoffrey plans on going to the state fair this summer. He has downloaded a map of the fairgrounds that shows all of the attractions. Geoffrey plans to visit the concert hall, the Ferris wheel, and the sports center. On the map, the distance between the concert hall and the Ferris wheel is 9 centimeters, the distance between the Ferris wheel and the sports center is 8 centimeters, and the distance between the sports center and the concert hall is 4 centimeters.
>
> **❯ Part A**
>
> Describe Geoffrey's path.
>
> **❯ Part B**
>
> Find the total distance.

Example 4

TYPE

| a| |

Students type words and values to complete calculations.

WEB SKETCHPAD

Students use a sketch to model a path on the map.

CHECK

Students complete the Check online to determine whether they are ready to move on.

Practice and Homework

Suggested Assignments

Use the table below to select appropriate exercises.

DOK	Topic	Exercises
1, 2	exercises that mirror the examples	1–16
2	exercises that use a variety of skills from this lesson	17–26
3	exercises that emphasize higher-order and critical-thinking skills	27–31

ASSESS AND DIFFERENTIATE

📊 Use the data from the **Checks** to determine whether to provide resources for extension, remediation, or intervention.

IF students score 90% or more on the Checks,   `OL` `BL`
THEN assign:

- Practice, Exercises 1–25 odd, 27–31
- Extension: Constructing Similar Polygons
- 🔵 **ALEKS** Similar Figures

IF students score 66%–89% on the Checks,   `AL` `OL`
THEN assign:

- Practice, Exercises 1–31 odd
- Remediation, Review Resources: Congruent Triangles
- Personal Tutors
- BrainPOP Video: Using Proportions
- Extra Examples 1–4
- 🔵 **ALEKS** Congruent Triangles

IF students score 65% or less on the Checks,   `AL`
THEN assign:

- Practice, Exercises 1–15 odd
- Remediation, Review Resources: Congruent Triangles
- *Quick Review Math Handbook*: Similar Polygons
- 🔵 **ALEKS** Congruent Triangles

Answers

10. Yes; $\triangle BDC \sim \triangle FGC$ because $\angle B \cong \angle F$, $\angle D \cong \angle G$, $\angle BCD \cong \angle FCG$, and $\frac{BD}{FG} = \frac{DC}{GC} = \frac{CB}{CF}$, $\frac{3}{5}$.

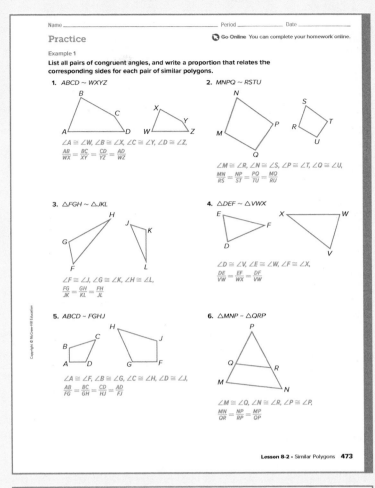

Name _____ Period _____ Date _____

Practice

🔵 **Go Online** You can complete your homework online.

Example 1

List all pairs of congruent angles, and write a proportion that relates the corresponding sides for each pair of similar polygons.

1. $ABCD \sim WXYZ$

$\angle A \cong \angle W$, $\angle B \cong \angle X$, $\angle C \cong \angle Y$, $\angle D \cong \angle Z$,
$\frac{AB}{WX} = \frac{BC}{XY} = \frac{CD}{YZ} = \frac{AD}{WZ}$

2. $MNPQ \sim RSTU$

$\angle M \cong \angle R$, $\angle N \cong \angle S$, $\angle P \cong \angle T$, $\angle Q \cong \angle U$,
$\frac{MN}{RS} = \frac{NP}{ST} = \frac{PQ}{TU} = \frac{MQ}{RU}$

3. $\triangle FGH \sim \triangle JKL$

$\angle F \cong \angle J$, $\angle G \cong \angle K$, $\angle H \cong \angle L$,
$\frac{FG}{JK} = \frac{GH}{KL} = \frac{FH}{JL}$

4. $\triangle DEF \sim \triangle VWX$

$\angle D \cong \angle V$, $\angle E \cong \angle W$, $\angle F \cong \angle X$,
$\frac{DE}{VW} = \frac{EF}{WX} = \frac{DF}{VW}$

5. $ABCD \sim FGHJ$

$\angle A \cong \angle F$, $\angle B \cong \angle G$, $\angle C \cong \angle H$, $\angle D \cong \angle J$,
$\frac{AB}{FG} = \frac{BC}{GH} = \frac{CD}{HJ} = \frac{AD}{FJ}$

6. $\triangle MNP \sim \triangle QRP$

$\angle M \cong \angle Q$, $\angle N \cong \angle R$, $\angle P \cong \angle P$,
$\frac{MN}{QR} = \frac{NP}{RP} = \frac{MP}{QP}$

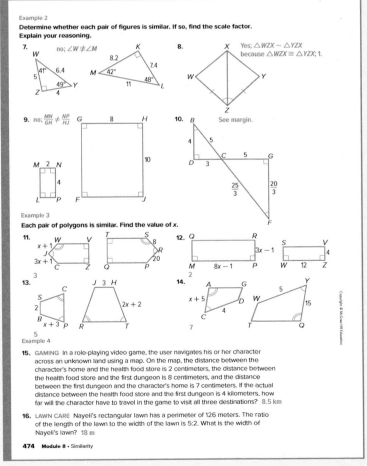

Example 2

Determine whether each pair of figures is similar. If so, find the scale factor. Explain your reasoning.

7. no; $\angle W \not\cong \angle M$

8. Yes; $\triangle WZX \sim \triangle YZX$ because $\triangle WZX \cong \triangle YZX$; 1.

9. no; $\frac{MN}{GH} \neq \frac{NP}{HJ}$

10. See margin.

Example 3

Each pair of polygons is similar. Find the value of x.

11.

12.

13.

14.

Example 4

15. GAMING In a role-playing video game, the user navigates his or her character across an unknown land using a map. On the map, the distance between the character's home and the health food store is 2 centimeters, the distance between the health food store and the first dungeon is 8 centimeters, and the distance between the first dungeon and the character's home is 7 centimeters. If the actual distance between the health food store and the first dungeon is 4 kilometers, how far will the character have to travel in the game to visit all three destinations? 8.5 km

16. LAWN CARE Nayeli's rectangular lawn has a perimeter of 126 meters. The ratio of the length of the lawn to the width of the lawn is 5:2. What is the width of Nayeli's lawn? 18 m

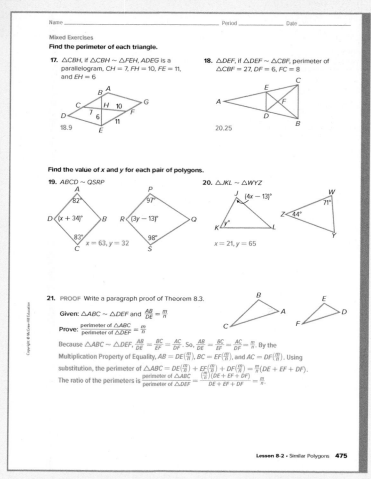

Name _____ Period _____ Date _____

Mixed Exercises

Find the perimeter of each triangle.

17. △CBH, if △CBH ~ △FEH, ADEG is a parallelogram, CH = 7, FH = 10, FE = 11, and EH = 6

18.9

18. △DEF, if △DEF ~ △CBF, perimeter of △CBF = 27, DF = 6, FC = 8

20.25

Find the value of x and y for each pair of polygons.

19. ABCD ~ QSRP

x = 63, y = 32

20. △JKL ~ △WYZ

x = 21, y = 65

21. PROOF Write a paragraph proof of Theorem 8.3.

Given: △ABC ~ △DEF and $\frac{AB}{DE} = \frac{m}{n}$

Prove: $\frac{\text{perimeter of } \triangle ABC}{\text{perimeter of } \triangle DEF} = \frac{m}{n}$

Because △ABC ~ △DEF, $\frac{AB}{DE} = \frac{BC}{EF} = \frac{AC}{DF}$. So, $\frac{AB}{DE} = \frac{BC}{EF} = \frac{AC}{DF} = \frac{m}{n}$. By the Multiplication Property of Equality, $AB = DE(\frac{m}{n})$, $BC = EF(\frac{m}{n})$, and $AC = DF(\frac{m}{n})$. Using substitution, the perimeter of $\triangle ABC = DE(\frac{m}{n}) + EF(\frac{m}{n}) + DF(\frac{m}{n}) = \frac{m}{n}(DE + EF + DF)$. The ratio of the perimeters is $\frac{\text{perimeter of } \triangle ABC}{\text{perimeter of } \triangle DEF} = \frac{(\frac{m}{n})(DE + EF + DF)}{DE + EF + DF} = \frac{m}{n}$.

Lesson 8-2 · Similar Polygons   **475**

22. If △ABC ~ △DEC, find the value of x and the scale factor from △DEC to △ABC.
x = 4; scale factor 5:4

23. Rectangle ABCD ~ rectangle EFGH, the perimeter of ABCD is 54 centimeters, and the perimeter of EFGH is 36 centimeters. What is the scale factor from EFGH to ABCD? $\frac{3}{2}$

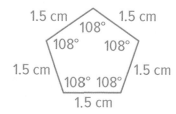

24. △ABC is an isosceles triangle.

a. Write a possible ratio for the lengths of the sides of △ABC if its perimeter is 42 inches. Sample answer: 3:2:2 (Note: Check to be sure that the sum of any two sides of the triangle is greater than the third side. For example, a ratio of 1:1:2 would not be acceptable.)

b. Name possible measures for the sides of △ABC using your answer to part a. Sample answer: 18, 12, 12

c. If △WXY is also isosceles and has a perimeter of 28 and △ABC has sides with the measures you gave in part b, what must be the measure of the sides of △WXY so that △WXY ~ △ABC? Sample answer: 12, 8, 8

25. ICE HOCKEY An official Olympic-sized ice hockey rink measures 30 meters by 60 meters. The ice hockey rink at the local community college measures 25.5 meters by 51 meters. Are the ice hockey rinks similar? Explain your reasoning. Yes; the ratio of the longer dimensions of the rinks is $\frac{20}{17}$, and the ratio of the smaller dimensions of the rinks is $\frac{20}{17}$.

26. BIOLOGY A paramecium is a small, single-cell organism. The magnified paramecium shown is actually one-tenth of a millimeter long.

a. If you want to make a photograph of the original paramecium so that its image is 1 centimeter long, by what scale factor should you magnify it? 100

b. If you want to make a photograph of the original paramecium so that its image is 15 centimeters long, by what scale factor should you magnify it? 1500

c. By approximately what scale factor has the paramecium been enlarged to make the image shown? 120

🌐 **Higher-Order Thinking Skills**

27. PERSEVERE For what value(s) of x is BEFA ~ EDCB? 4

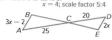

28. ANALYZE Recall that an *equivalence relation* is any relationship that satisfies the Reflexive, Symmetric, and Transitive Properties. Is similarity an equivalence relation? Explain. See margin.

29. CREATE Find a counterexample of the following statement. See margin.
All rectangles are similar.

30. ANALYZE Draw two regular pentagons of different sizes. Are the pentagons similar? Will any two regular polygons with the same number of sides be similar? Explain. See margin.

31. WRITE How can you describe the relationship between two figures? See margin.

Answers

28. Yes; sample answer: Similarity is reflexive, symmetric and transitive.
△ABC ~ △ABC (Reflexive)
If △ABC ~ △DEF, then △DEF ~ △ABC. (Symmetric)
If △ABC ~ △DEF and △DEF ~ △MNP, then △ABC ~ △MNP. (Transitive)

29. Sample answer: $\frac{4}{3} \neq \frac{4}{10}$

4 cm

4 cm

3 cm

10 cm

30. Yes; yes; sample answer: The pentagons are similar because their corresponding angles are congruent and their corresponding sides are proportional. All of the angles and sides in a regular polygons are congruent. The angles will be congruent regardless of the size of the figure, and because all of the sides are congruent, the ratios of the sides of one regular figure to a second regular figure with the same number of sides will be the same. Therefore, all regular polygons with the same number of sides are similar.

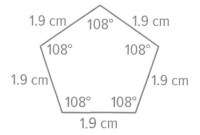

1.5 cm   108°   1.5 cm
108°   108°
1.5 cm   1.5 cm
108° 108°
1.5 cm

1.9 cm   108°   1.9 cm
108°   108°
1.9 cm   1.9 cm
108° 108°
1.9 cm

31. Sample answer: The figures could be described as congruent if they are the same size and shape, similar if their corresponding angles are congruent and their corresponding sides are proportional, and equal if they are the same figure, or none of those.

Similar Triangles: AA Similarity

LESSON GOAL

Students use the AA similarity criterion to solve problems and prove triangles similar.

1 LAUNCH

 Launch the lesson with a **Warm Up** and an introduction.

2 EXPLORE AND DEVELOP

 Explore:

- Similarity Transformations and Triangles
- Conditions that Prove Triangles Similar

 Develop:

Similar Triangles: AA Similarity
- Use the AA Similarity Postulate
- Use Parts of Similar Triangles

 You may want your students to complete the **Checks** online.

3 REFLECT AND PRACTICE

 Exit Ticket

 Practice

DIFFERENTIATE

 View reports of student progress on the **Checks** after each example.

Resources	AL	OL	BL	ELL
Remediation: Similarity and Transformations	●	●		●
Extension: Moving Shadows		●	●	●

Language Development Handbook

Assign page 54 of the *Language Development Handbook* to help your students build mathematical language related to using the AA similarity criterion to solve problems and prove triangles similar.

ELL You can use the tips and suggestions on page T54 of the handbook to support students who are building English proficiency.

Suggested Pacing

90 min	**0.5 day**
45 min	**1 day**

Focus

Domain: Geometry

Standards for Mathematical Content:

G.SRT.2 Given two figures, use the definition of similarity in terms of similarity transformations to decide if they are similar; explain using similarity transformations the meaning of similarity for triangles as the equality of all corresponding pairs of angles and the proportionality of all corresponding pairs of sides.

G.SRT.3 Use the properties of similarity transformations to establish the AA criterion for two triangles to be similar.

Standards for Mathematical Practice:

3 Construct viable arguments and critique the reasoning of others.
4 Model with mathematics.
5 Use appropriate tools strategically.

Coherence

Vertical Alignment

Previous
Students solved problems using the definition of similar polygons.
G.SRT.2

Now
Students use the AA similarity criterion to solve problems and prove triangles similar.
G.SRT.2, G.SRT.3

Next
Students will use the SSS and SAS Similarity criteria to solve problems and prove triangles similar.
G.SRT.2, G.SRT.5

Rigor

The Three Pillars of Rigor

1 CONCEPTUAL UNDERSTANDING	2 FLUENCY	3 APPLICATION

Conceptual Bridge In this lesson, students expand on their understanding of similarity to include similar triangles. They build fluency by deciding whether pairs of triangles are similar, and they apply their understanding by using similarity criteria to solve real-world problems.

Mathematical Background

In similar triangles, all of the corresponding angles are congruent and all of the corresponding sides are proportional. However, you don't need to show that all of the criteria are met to show that two triangles are similar. Angle-Angle Similarity is one of several shortcuts.

Interactive Presentation

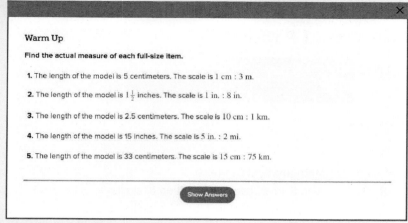

Warm Up

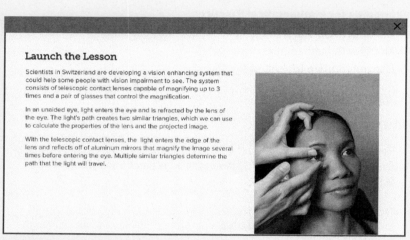

Launch the Lesson

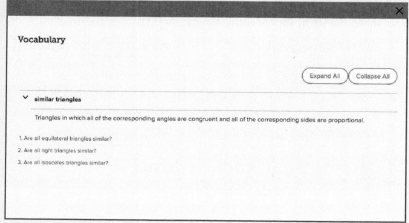

Today's Vocabulary

Warm Up

Prerequisite Skills

The Warm Up exercises address the following prerequisite skill for this lesson:

• using scale drawings

Answers:

1. 15 m

2. 12 in.

3. 0.25 km

4. 6 mi

5. 165 km

Launch the Lesson

MP **Teaching the Mathematical Practices**

4 Apply Mathematics In this Launch the Lesson, students can see a real-world application of similar triangles.

 **Go Online** to find additional teaching notes and questions to promote classroom discourse.

Today's Standards

Tell students that they will be addressing these content and practice standards in this lesson. You may wish to have a student volunteer read aloud *How can I meet these standards?* and *How can I use these practices?* and connect these to the standards.

See the Interactive Presentation for I Can statements that align with the standards covered in this lesson.

Today's Vocabulary

Tell students that they will be using this vocabulary term in this lesson. You can expand the row if you wish to share the definition. Then, discuss the questions below with the class.

Explore Similarity Transformations and Triangles

Objective
Students use dynamic geometry software to explore the meaning of similarity for triangles using similarity transformations.

MP Teaching the Mathematical Practices

3 Make Conjectures In this Explore, students will make conjectures and then build a logical progression of statements to validate the conjectures. Once students have made their conjectures, guide the students to validate them.

Ideas for Use

Recommended Use Present the Inquiry Question, or have a student volunteer read it aloud. Have students work in pairs to complete the Explore activity on their devices. Pairs should discuss each of the questions. Monitor student progress during the activity. Upon completion of the Explore activity, have student volunteers share their responses to the Inquiry Question.

What if my students don't have devices? You may choose to project the activity on a whiteboard. A printable worksheet for each Explore is available online. You may choose to print the worksheet so that individuals or pairs of students can use it to record their observations.

Summary of the Activity
Students will complete guiding exercises throughout the Explore activity. Students will use a sketch to explore similar triangles and how corresponding sides are proportional. Then, students will answer the Inquiry Question.

(continued on the next page)

Interactive Presentation

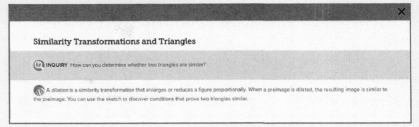

Explore

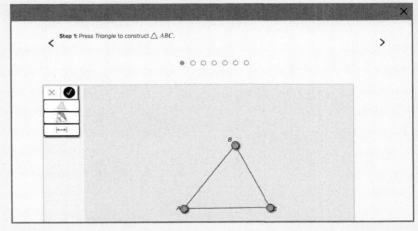

Explore

WEB SKETCHPAD

 Students use a sketch to complete an activity in which they explore similar triangles.

Interactive Presentation

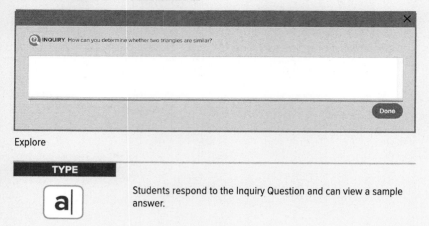

Explore

TYPE

a|

Students respond to the Inquiry Question and can view a sample answer.

Explore Similarity Transformations and Triangles (*continued*)

Questions

Have students complete the Explore activity.

Ask:

- What would happen if the corresponding angles were also multiplied by the scale factor? Why does this not make sense? Sample answer: If the angles were also multiplied by the scale factor, then you would end up with a sum either less than or greater than 180°. This doesn't make sense, because the sum of the interior angles of any triangle is always 180°.

- Can you argue that two congruent triangles are also two similar triangles? Why or why not? Yes; sample answer: The corresponding pairs of angles are all congruent. The corresponding sides are equal, so the ratio of the corresponding sides would all have a ratio of 1, so the ratios are all equal.

ⓠ Inquiry

How can you determine whether two triangles are similar? Sample answer: Two triangles are similar if all corresponding pairs of angles are congruent, and all corresponding pairs of sides are proportional.

🔎 Go Online to find additional teaching notes and sample answers for the guiding exercises.

Explore Conditions that Prove Triangles Similar

Objective

Students use dynamic geometry software and similarity transformations to explore the AA Similarity criterion.

Teaching the Mathematical Practices

3 Justify Conclusions Mathematically proficient students can explain the conclusions drawn when solving a problem. This Explore asks students to justify their conclusions.

Ideas for Use

Recommended Use Present the Inquiry Question, or have a student volunteer read it aloud. Have students work in pairs to complete the Explore activity on their devices. Pairs should discuss each of the questions. Monitor student progress during the activity. Upon completion of the Explore activity, have student volunteers share their responses to the Inquiry Question.

What if my students don't have devices? You may choose to project the activity on a whiteboard. A printable worksheet for each Explore is available online. You may choose to print the worksheet so that individuals or pairs of students can use it to record their observations.

Summary of the Activity

Students will complete guiding exercises throughout the Explore activity. Students use a sketch to explore how two triangles can be proven similar by showing that all corresponding angles are congruent and all corresponding sides are proportional, which leads them to the AA Similarity criterion. Then, students will answer the Inquiry Question.

(continued on the next page)

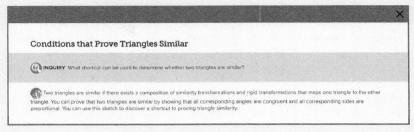

Conditions that Prove Triangles Similar

INQUIRY What shortcut can be used to determine whether two triangles are similar?

Two triangles are similar if there exists a composition of similarity transformations and rigid transformations that maps one triangle to the other triangle. You can prove that two triangles are similar by showing that all corresponding angles are congruent and all corresponding sides are proportional. You can use this sketch to discover a shortcut to proving triangle similarity.

Explore

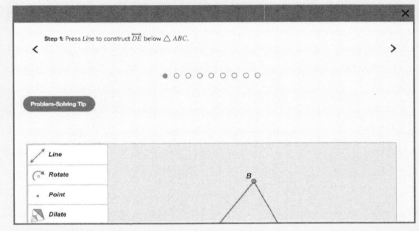

Step 1: Press *Line* to construct $\overrightarrow{DE}$ below $\triangle ABC$.

Problem-Solving Tip

	Line
	Rotate
	Point
	Dilate

Explore

WEB SKETCHPAD

Students use a sketch to complete an activity in which they explore AA Similarity criterion.

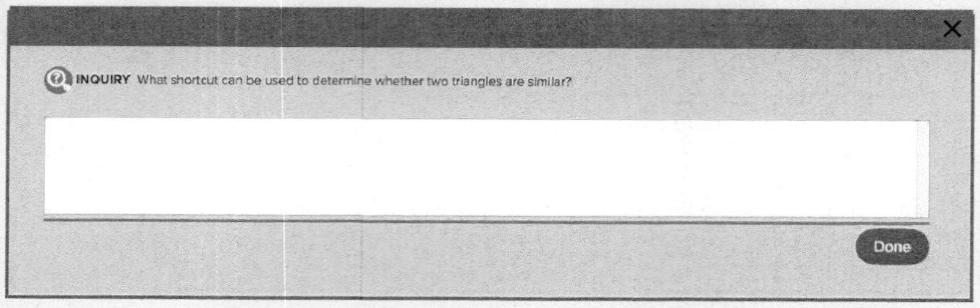

INQUIRY What shortcut can be used to determine whether two triangles are similar?

Done

Explore

TYPE

a|

Students respond to the Inquiry Question and can view a sample answer.

Explore Conditions that Prove Triangles Similar (*continued*)

Questions
Have students complete the Explore activity.

Ask:
- Why are the lines rotated at angles equal to $m\angle BAC$ and $m\angle BCA$? Sample answer: By rotating the lines equal to those angles, you are constructing two corresponding pairs of angles with congruent measures.

- If you know the measures of two angles in a triangle, can you find the measure of the non-corresponding angle in a similar triangle? Why or why not? Yes; sample answer: If I know the two triangles are similar, then the measures of the corresponding angles are equal. I can use the Triangle Angle-Sum Theorem to find the measure of the third angle.

Inquiry
What shortcut can be used to determine whether two triangles are similar? Sample answer: If two triangles have two pairs of congruent angles, then the two triangles are similar.

Go Online to find additional teaching notes and sample answers for the guiding exercises.

1 CONCEPTUAL UNDERSTANDING | **2 FLUENCY** | 3 APPLICATION

Learn Similar Triangles: AA Similarity

Objective
Students use the AA Similarity criterion to solve problems and prove triangles similar.

MP Teaching the Mathematical Practices

7 Use Structure Help students to explore the structure of Angle-Angle Similarity in this Learn to determine if two triangles are similar.

Important to Know
Students may find it helpful to draw the similar triangles in the same orientation.

Example 1 Use the AA Similarity Postulate

MP Teaching the Mathematical Practices

3 Justify Conclusions Mathematically proficient students can explain the conclusions drawn when solving a problem. This example asks students to explain their reasoning and justify their conclusions.

Questions for Mathematical Discourse

AL Why is ∠LPQ ≅ ∠LJK? Corresponding Angles Theorem

OL Which other pair of angles can you prove congruent to prove the AA Similarity postulate? Explain. ∠PQL ≅ ∠JKL by the Corresponding Angles Theorem.

BL If PQ is moved closer to point L, are the two triangles still similar? Explain. Yes; sample answer: The angles of the triangles would remain congruent.

🖱 Go Online
- Find additional teaching notes.
- View performance reports of the Checks.
- Assign or present an Extra Example.

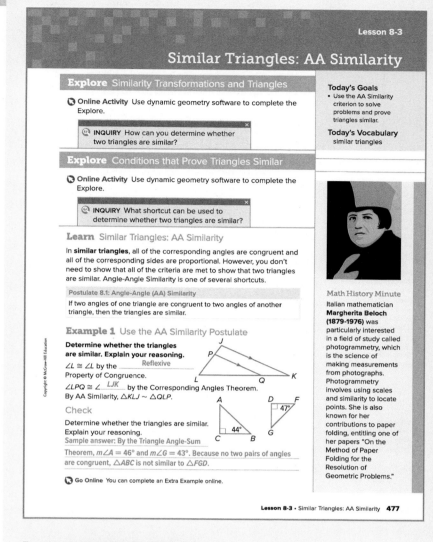

Lesson 8-3

Similar Triangles: AA Similarity

Explore Similarity Transformations and Triangles

🔵 **Online Activity** Use dynamic geometry software to complete the Explore.

INQUIRY How can you determine whether two triangles are similar?

Explore Conditions that Prove Triangles Similar

🔵 **Online Activity** Use dynamic geometry software to complete the Explore.

INQUIRY What shortcut can be used to determine whether two triangles are similar?

Learn Similar Triangles: AA Similarity

In **similar triangles**, all of the corresponding angles are congruent and all of the corresponding sides are proportional. However, you don't need to show that all of the criteria are met to show that two triangles are similar. Angle-Angle Similarity is one of several shortcuts.

Postulate 8.1: Angle-Angle (AA) Similarity
If two angles of one triangle are congruent to two angles of another triangle, then the triangles are similar.

Example 1 Use the AA Similarity Postulate

Determine whether the triangles are similar. Explain your reasoning.

∠L ≅ ∠L by the _____Reflexive_____ Property of Congruence.

∠LPQ ≅ ∠__LJK__ by the Corresponding Angles Theorem. By AA Similarity, △KLJ ~ △QLP.

Check
Determine whether the triangles are similar. Explain your reasoning.
Sample answer: By the Triangle Angle-Sum Theorem, m∠A = 46° and m∠G = 43°. Because no two pairs of angles are congruent, △ABC is not similar to △FGD.

🔵 **Go Online** You can complete an Extra Example online.

Today's Goals
- Use the AA Similarity criterion to solve problems and prove triangles similar.

Today's Vocabulary
similar triangles

Math History Minute
Italian mathematician **Margherita Beloch (1879-1976)** was particularly interested in a field of study called photogrammetry, which is the science of making measurements from photographs. Photogrammetry involves using scales and similarity to locate points. She is also known for her contributions to paper folding, entitling one of her papers "On the Method of Paper Folding for the Resolution of Geometric Problems."

Lesson 8-3 • Similar Triangles: AA Similarity **477**

Interactive Presentation

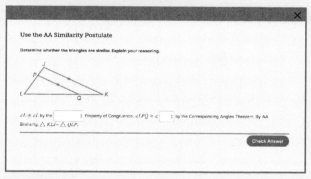

Use the AA Similarity Postulate

Determine whether the triangles are similar. Explain your reasoning.

∠L ≅ ∠L by the _____ : Property of Congruence. ∠LPQ ≅ ∠ _____ by the Corresponding Angles Theorem. By AA Similarity, △ KLJ ~ △ QLP.

Check Answer

Example 1

TYPE

a|

Students complete the statements to determine whether the triangles are similar.

1 CONCEPTUAL UNDERSTANDING | **2 FLUENCY** | **3 APPLICATION**

Your Notes

⊘ Example 2 Use Parts of Similar Triangles

HANDBALL Demarco is teaching Taye how to play handball. Taye prefers to return the ball on a serve when it bounces to a height of 42 inches. When Demarco serves the ball, where should he aim for the ball to hit the front wall to ensure that it bounces at the short line and up to Taye standing 11 feet behind the short line? Assume that the angles formed by the path of the bouncing handball are congruent.

Create and Describe the Model

- The ball should bounce at the short line, 25 feet from the front wall.
- The ball should bounce to Taye, who is standing 11 feet from the short line.
- Taye will hit the ball when it bounces to a height of <u>42 inches</u>.
- Find the point on the front wall x where the ball bounces.
- You can model the path of the handball using two triangles.

💭 Think About It!
What assumptions did you make when creating your model for the path of the handball?

Sample answer: I assumed that the handball traveled in a straight line from the front wall to the ground and up to Taye. I also assumed that the handball only moved along the length of the court and did not travel any distance horizontally along the width of the court.

- You are given that the angles formed by the bouncing handball are congruent. The front wall forms a <u>90</u>° angle with the ground, and the height to which the ball bounces forms a 90° angle with the ground. Therefore, the two triangles are similar by the <u>AA Similarity Postulate</u>.

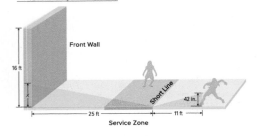

Watch Out!
Units Remember to convert inches to feet when you solve for x in the example.

Solve

Because the two triangles are similar, the corresponding sides are proportional.

$$\frac{11 \text{ ft}}{25 \text{ ft}} = \frac{42 \text{ in.}}{x} \qquad \text{AA Similarity Postulate}$$

$$\frac{11 \text{ ft}}{25 \text{ ft}} = \frac{3.5 \text{ ft}}{x} \qquad 12 \text{ inches} = 1 \text{ foot}$$

$$x = 7.95 \text{ ft} \qquad \text{Solve.}$$

🖥 Go Online You can complete an Extra Example online.

478 **Module 8** · Similarity

Interactive Presentation

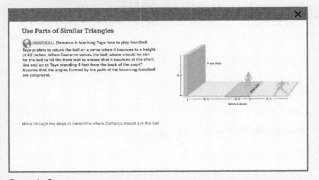

Use Parts of Similar Triangles

⊘ HANDBALL Demarco is teaching Taye how to play handball. Taye prefers to return the ball on a serve when it bounces to a height of 42 inches. When Demarco serves the ball, where should he aim for the ball to hit the front wall to ensure that it bounces at the short line and up to Taye standing 4 feet from the back of the court? Assume that the angles formed by the path of the bouncing handball are congruent.

Move through the steps to determine where Demarco should aim the ball.

Example 2

CHECK

Students complete the Check online to determine whether they are ready to move on.

⊕ **Example 2** Use Parts of Similar Triangles

MP Teaching the Mathematical Practices

> **2 Create Representations** Guide students to write an equation that models the situation in this example. Then use the equation to solve the problem.

Questions for Mathematical Discourse

AL What needs to be shown for two triangles to be similar using the Angle-Angle Similarity postulate? there are two sets of congruent corresponding angles in the triangle

OL Estimate how much longer the base of the larger triangle is than the base of the smaller triangle. Using your estimate, about how high should Demarco hit the front wall? Sample answer: The length of the base of the larger triangle is slightly more than twice the length of the base of the smaller triangle. So, Demarco should hit the ball higher than 2 × 42 in. = 84 in. = 7 ft on the front wall.

BL If two triangles with parallel bases share a common vertex, do you think the triangles will always be similar? Explain. No; sample answer: The angles formed at the common vertex may not always be congruent.

Common Error

Remind students to convert inches to feet when solving for x in the example.

Exit Ticket

Recommended Use

At the end of class, go online to display the Exit Ticket prompt and ask students to respond using a separate piece of paper. Have students hand you their responses as they leave the room.

Alternate Use

At the end of class, go online to display the Exit Ticket prompt and ask students to respond verbally or by using a mini-whiteboard. Have students hold up their whiteboards so that you can see all student responses. Tap to reveal the answer when most or all students have completed the Exit Ticket.

1 CONCEPTUAL UNDERSTANDING	2 FLUENCY	3 APPLICATION

Practice and Homework

Suggested Assignments

Use the table below to select appropriate exercises.

DOK	Topic	Exercises
1, 2	exercises that mirror the examples	1–8
2	exercises that use a variety of skills from this lesson	9–13
3	exercises that emphasize higher-order and critical-thinking skills	14–16

ASSESS AND DIFFERENTIATE

📊 Use the data from the **Checks** to determine whether to provide resources for extension, remediation, or intervention.

IF students score 90% or more on the Checks, **BL**
THEN assign:

- Practice, Exercises 1–13 odd, 14–16
- Extension: Moving Shadows
- ⊙ **ALEKS** Proving Triangle Similarity

IF students score 66%–89% on the Checks, **OL**
THEN assign:

- Practice, Exercises 1–15 odd
- Remediation, Review Resources: Similarity and Transformations
- Personal Tutors
- BrainPOP Video: Similar Triangles
- Extra Examples 1–2
- ⊙ **ALEKS** Using Scale Drawings

IF students score 65% or less on the Checks, **AL**
THEN assign:

- Practice, Exercises 1–7 odd
- Remediation, Review Resources: Similarity and Transformations
- *Quick Review Math Handbook*: Establishing Triangle Similarity
- ⊙ **ALEKS** Using Scale Drawings

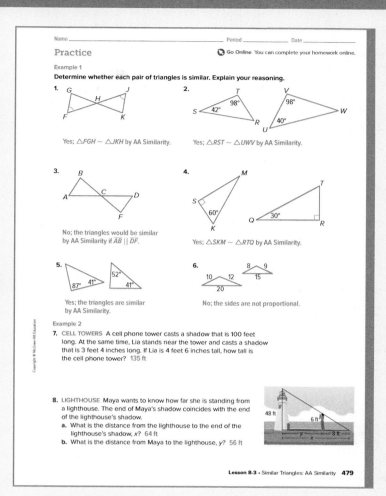

Name _____ Period _____ Date _____

Practice

🔵 Go Online You can complete your homework online.

Example 1

Determine whether each pair of triangles is similar. Explain your reasoning.

1.

Yes; △FGH ~ △JKH by AA Similarity.

2.

Yes; △RST ~ △UWV by AA Similarity.

3.

No; the triangles would be similar by AA Similarity if $\overline{AB} \parallel \overline{DF}$.

4.

Yes; △SKM ~ △RTQ by AA Similarity.

5.

Yes; the triangles are similar by AA Similarity.

6.

No; the sides are not proportional.

Example 2

7. CELL TOWERS A cell phone tower casts a shadow that is 100 feet long. At the same time, Lia stands near the tower and casts a shadow that is 3 feet 4 inches long. If Lia is 4 feet 6 inches tall, how tall is the cell phone tower? 135 ft

8. LIGHTHOUSE Maya wants to know how far she is standing from a lighthouse. The end of Maya's shadow coincides with the end of the lighthouse's shadow.
   a. What is the distance from the lighthouse to the end of the lighthouse's shadow, x? 64 ft
   b. What is the distance from Maya to the lighthouse, y? 56 ft

Lesson 8-3 · Similar Triangles: AA Similarity **479**

1 CONCEPTUAL UNDERSTANDING | **2 FLUENCY** | 3 APPLICATION

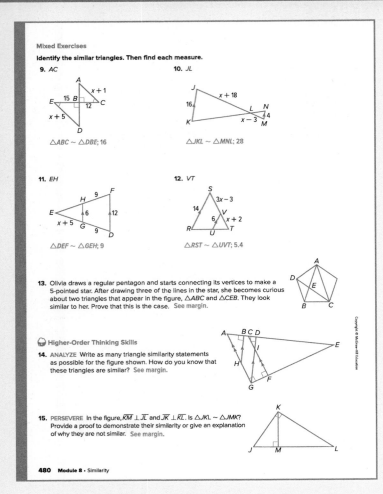

Mixed Exercises

Identify the similar triangles. Then find each measure.

9. *AC*

△*ABC* ~ △*DBE*; 16

10. *JL*

△*JKL* ~ △*MNL*; 28

11. *EH*

△*DEF* ~ △*GEH*; 9

12. *VT*

△*RST* ~ △*UVT*; 5.4

13. Olivia draws a regular pentagon and starts connecting its vertices to make a 5-pointed star. After drawing three of the lines in the star, she becomes curious about two triangles that appear in the figure, △*ABC* and △*CEB*. They look similar to her. Prove that this is the case. **See margin.**

🗨 **Higher-Order Thinking Skills**

14. ANALYZE Write as many triangle similarity statements as possible for the figure shown. How do you know that these triangles are similar? **See margin.**

15. PERSEVERE In the figure, $\overline{KM} \perp \overline{JL}$ and $\overline{JK} \perp \overline{KL}$. Is △*JKL* ~ △*JMK*? Provide a proof to demonstrate their similarity or give an explanation of why they are not similar. **See margin.**

Answers

13. Sample answer: $m\angle ADB = 108°$, so $m\angle DBA = 36°$ because base angles of an isosceles triangle are congruent. Thus, $m\angle ABC = 72°$. Similarly, $m\angle DCB = 36°$ and $m\angle ACB = 72°$. So, $m\angle BEC = 72°$ and $m\angle BAC = 36°$. Therefore, △*ABC* and △*BCE* are similar.

14. △*ABH* ~ △*CDI* ~ △*GFI* ~ △*ADG* ~ △*GDE* ~ △*CFE* ~ △*AGE* by AA Similarity.

15. Yes; sample answer: The triangles are similar. It is given that $\overline{KM} \perp \overline{JL}$ and $\overline{JK} \perp \overline{KL}$. $\angle JKL \cong \angle JMK$ because they are both right angles. By the Reflexive Property of Congruence, we know that $\angle J \cong \angle J$. Therefore, by the AA Similarity Postulate, we can conclude that △*JKL* ~ △*JMK*.

Similar Triangles: SSS and SAS Similarity

LESSON GOAL

Students use the SSS and SAS Similarity criteria to solve problems and prove triangles similar.

1 LAUNCH

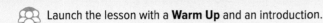 Launch the lesson with a **Warm Up** and an introduction.

2 EXPLORE AND DEVELOP

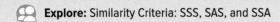 **Explore:** Similarity Criteria: SSS, SAS, and SSA

....

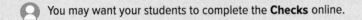 **Develop:**

Similar Triangles: SSS and SAS Similarity
- Use the SSS and SAS Similarity Theorems
- Parts of Similar Triangles
- Use Similar Triangles to Solve Problems

....

 You may want your students to complete the **Checks** online.

3 REFLECT AND PRACTICE

 Exit Ticket

....

Practice

DIFFERENTIATE

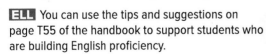 View reports of student progress on the **Checks** after each example.

Resources	AL	OL	BL	ELL
Remediation: Similarity and Corresponding Parts	●	●		●
Extension: Medial and Orthic Triangles		●	●	●

Language Development Handbook

Assign page 55 of the *Language Development Handbook* to help your students build mathematical language related to using the SSS and SAS Similarity criteria to solve problems and prove triangles similar.

ELL You can use the tips and suggestions on page T55 of the handbook to support students who are building English proficiency.

Reveal
GEOMETRY
Language Development
Handbook

Suggested Pacing

| 90 min | 0.5 day |
| 45 min | 1 day |

Focus

Domain: Geometry

Standards for Mathematical Content:

G.SRT.2 Given two figures, use the definition of similarity in terms of similarity transformations to decide if they are similar; explain using similarity transformations the meaning of similarity for triangles as the equality of all corresponding pairs of angles and the proportionality of all corresponding pairs of sides.

G.SRT.5 Use congruence and similarity criteria for triangles to solve problems and to prove relationships in geometric figures.

Standards for Mathematical Practice:

3 Construct viable arguments and critique the reasoning of others.

6 Attend to precision.

7 Look for and make use of structure.

Coherence

Vertical Alignment

Previous
Students used the AA similarity criterion to solve problems and proved triangles similar.
G.SRT.2, G.SRT.3

Now
Students use the SSS and SAS Similarity criteria to solve problems and prove triangles similar.
G.SRT.2, G.SRT.5

Next
Students will use triangle proportionality to solve problems and prove theorems.
G.SRT.4, G.CO.10, G.CO.12

Rigor

The Three Pillars of Rigor

1 CONCEPTUAL UNDERSTANDING	2 FLUENCY	3 APPLICATION

Conceptual Bridge In this lesson, students continue to develop their understanding of similar triangles. They build fluency by deciding whether pairs of triangles are similar, and they apply their understanding by using similarity criteria to solve real-world problems.

Interactive Presentation

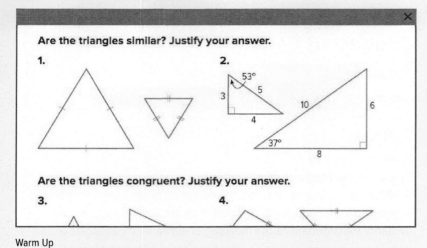

Warm Up

Launch the Lesson

Warm Up

Prerequisite Skills

The Warm Up exercises address the following prerequisite skill for this lesson:

- using triangle similarity and congruence

Answers:

1. yes; SSS

2. yes; AA

3. yes; SAS

4. yes; SSS

5. SAS, SSS, ASA, AAS, HL

Launch the Lesson

MP Teaching the Mathematical Practices

4 Apply Mathematics In this Launch the Lesson, students can see an application of similar triangles.

Go Online to find additional teaching notes and questions to promote classroom discourse.

Today's Standards

Tell students that they will be addressing these content and practice standards in this lesson. You may wish to have a student volunteer read aloud *How can I meet these standards?* and *How can I use these practices?* and connect these to the standards.

See the Interactive Presentation for I Can statements that align to the standards covered in this lesson.

Mathematical Background

You can use the AA Similarity Postulate to prove the Side-Side-Side (SSS) Similarity and the Side-Angle-Side (SAS) Similarity Theorems. The SSS Similarity Theorem states that if the corresponding side lengths of two triangles are proportional, then the triangles are similar. The SAS Similarity Theorem states that if the lengths of two sides of one triangle are proportional to the lengths of two corresponding sides of another triangle and the included angles are congruent, then the triangles are similar.

Explore Similarity Criteria: SSS, SAS, and SSA

Objective

Students use dynamic geometry software and similarity transformations to explore the SSS and SAS Similarity criteria and to determine whether SSA can be used to prove triangles similar.

Teaching the Mathematical Practices

> **5 Use Mathematical Tools** Point out that to solve the problem in this Explore, students will need to use dynamic geometry software. Work with students to explore and deepen their understanding of the SSS and SAS similarity criteria.

Ideas for Use

Recommended Use Present the Inquiry Question, or have a student volunteer read it aloud. Have students work in pairs to complete the Explore activity on their devices. Pairs should discuss each of the questions. Monitor student progress during the activity. Upon completion of the Explore activity, have student volunteers share their responses to the Inquiry Question.

What if my students don't have devices? You may choose to project the activity on a whiteboard. A printable worksheet for each Explore is available online. You may choose to print the worksheet so that individuals or pairs of students can use it to record their observations.

Summary of the Activity

Students will complete guiding exercises throughout the Explore activity. Students use a sketch and similarity transformations to explore how the SSS and SAS Similarity criteria can be used to prove that two triangles are similar and to explore how SSA cannot be used to prove that two triangles are similar. Then, students will answer the Inquiry Question.

(continued on the next page)

Interactive Presentation

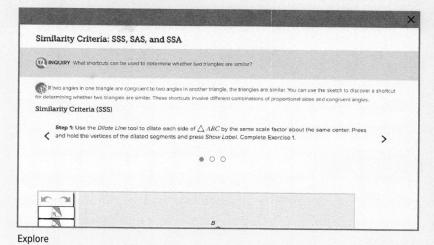

Explore

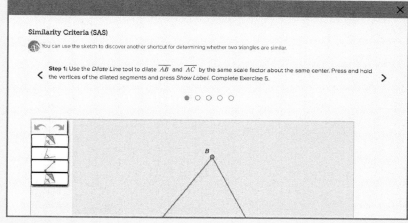

Explore

WEB SKETCHPAD

 Students use a sketch to complete an activity in which they explore the SSS, SAS, and SSA similarity criteria.

G.SRT.2

Interactive Presentation

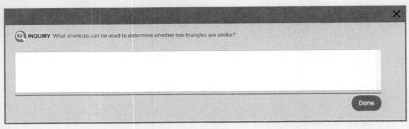

Explore

TYPE

Students respond to the Inquiry Question and can view a sample answer.

Explore Similarity Criteria: SSS, SAS, and SSA (*continued*)

MP Teaching the Mathematical Practices

3 Make Conjectures In this Explore, students will make conjectures and then build a logical progression of statements to validate the conjectures. Once students have made their conjectures, guide the students to validate them.

Questions

Have students complete the Explore activity.

Ask:

• How is SSS similarity different than SSS congruence? Sample answer: For SSS similarity, you are finding if the scale factors (or ratios of corresponding sides) are equal rather than the measures of the sides being equal.

• Why do you think ASA is not included as a shortcut for finding similarity? Sample answer: If you know two angles are congruent, you already know the triangles are similar. You don't need to also find the scale factor for the included sides.

Inquiry

What shortcuts can be used to determine whether two triangles are similar? Sample answer: Two triangles can be identified as similar if they have three pairs of proportional corresponding sides or if they have two pairs of proportional corresponding sides and a congruent included angle.

Go Online to find additional teaching notes and sample answers for the guiding exercises.

1 CONCEPTUAL UNDERSTANDING | **2 FLUENCY** | 3 APPLICATION

Learn Similar Triangles: SSS and SAS Similarity

Objective
Students use the SSS and SAS Similarity criteria to solve problems and prove triangles similar.

 Teaching the Mathematical Practices

7 Draw an Auxiliary Line Help students see the need to draw an auxiliary line to prove Theorem 8.4.

Common Misconception
Students may try to use SSA to prove similar triangles. Remind them that they prove similarity using the AA Similarity Postulate, the SSS Similarity Theorem, and the SAS Similarity Theorem.

Example 1 Use the SSS and SAS Similarity Theorems

 Teaching the Mathematical Practices

3 Justify Conclusions Mathematically proficient students can explain the conclusions drawn when solving a problem. This example asks students to explain their reasoning and justify their conclusions.

Questions for Mathematical Discourse

AL Why can you use the SSS Similarity Theorem in this example? Sample answer: Because the corresponding side lengths of the two triangles are proportional, then the triangles are similar.

OL In what other way can a similarity statement be written for the two triangles? Sample answer: $\triangle KLJ \sim \triangle MPQ$

BL Is $\triangle JKL$ similar to $\triangle MPQ$? Explain. No; sample answer: The corresponding side lengths are not proportional.

Go Online

- Find additional teaching notes.
- View performance reports of the Checks.
- Assign or present an Extra Example.

DIFFERENTIATE

Language Development Activity AL BL ELL
Interpersonal Learners Have students choose a partner. Ask each pair of students to measure the height of the school building by using their own shadows and similar triangles.

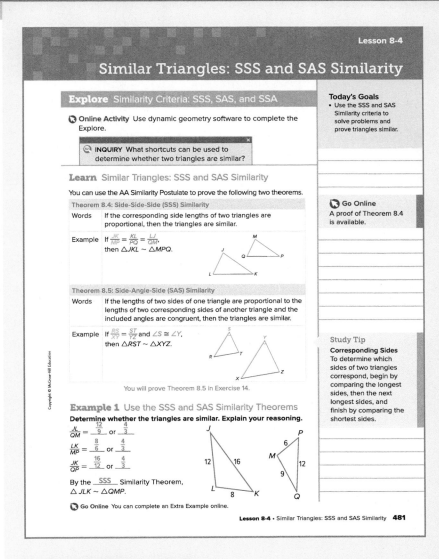

Lesson 8-4

Similar Triangles: SSS and SAS Similarity

Explore Similarity Criteria: SSS, SAS, and SSA

Online Activity Use dynamic geometry software to complete the Explore.

INQUIRY What shortcuts can be used to determine whether two triangles are similar?

Learn Similar Triangles: SSS and SAS Similarity

You can use the AA Similarity Postulate to prove the following two theorems.

Theorem 8.4: Side-Side-Side (SSS) Similarity

Words | If the corresponding side lengths of two triangles are proportional, then the triangles are similar.

Example | If $\frac{JK}{MP} = \frac{KL}{PQ} = \frac{LJ}{QM}$, then $\triangle JKL \sim \triangle MPQ$.

Theorem 8.5: Side-Angle-Side (SAS) Similarity

Words | If the lengths of two sides of one triangle are proportional to the lengths of two corresponding sides of another triangle and the included angles are congruent, then the triangles are similar.

Example | If $\frac{RS}{XY} = \frac{ST}{YZ}$ and $\angle S \cong \angle Y$, then $\triangle RST \sim \triangle XYZ$.

You will prove Theorem 8.5 in Exercise 14.

Example 1 Use the SSS and SAS Similarity Theorems
Determine whether the triangles are similar. Explain your reasoning.

$\frac{JL}{QM} = \frac{12}{9}$ or $\frac{4}{3}$

$\frac{LK}{MP} = \frac{8}{6}$ or $\frac{4}{3}$

$\frac{JK}{QP} = \frac{16}{12}$ or $\frac{4}{3}$

By the __SSS__ Similarity Theorem, $\triangle JLK \sim \triangle QMP$.

Go Online You can complete an Extra Example online.

Today's Goals
- Use the SSS and SAS Similarity criteria to solve problems and prove triangles similar.

Go Online
A proof of Theorem 8.4 is available.

Study Tip
Corresponding Sides
To determine which sides of two triangles correspond, begin by comparing the longest sides, then the next longest sides, and finish by comparing the shortest sides.

Interactive Presentation

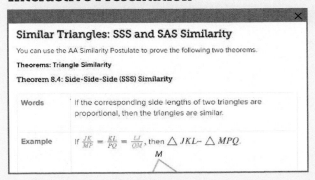

Similar Triangles: SSS and SAS Similarity

You can use the AA Similarity Postulate to prove the following two theorems.

Theorems: Triangle Similarity

Theorem 8.4: Side-Side-Side (SSS) Similarity

Words | If the corresponding side lengths of two triangles are proportional, then the triangles are similar.

Example | If $\frac{JK}{MP} = \frac{KL}{PQ} = \frac{LJ}{QM}$, then $\triangle JKL \sim \triangle MPQ$.

Learn

TAP

 Students move through the steps to see the proof of Side-Side-Side Similarity.

1 CONCEPTUAL UNDERSTANDING | **2 FLUENCY** | 3 APPLICATION

Your Notes

Check

Determine whether the triangles are similar. Explain your reasoning.

Sample answer: $\triangle TWZ \sim \triangle YWX$ by SAS Similarity, because $\angle W \cong \angle W$ and $\frac{TW}{YW} = \frac{WZ}{WX} = \frac{1}{2}$.

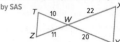

Go Online
An alternate method is available for this example.

Example 2 Parts of Similar Triangles

Find *QN* and *PO*. Justify your answer.

Step 1 Show that $\triangle NQM \sim \triangle OPM$.

Because $\frac{MP}{MQ} = \frac{8}{5}$ and $\frac{MO}{MN} = \frac{9\frac{3}{5}}{6}$ or $\frac{8}{5}$, these two sides of $\triangle NQM$ and $\triangle OPM$ are proportional. By the Reflexive Property of Congruence, $\angle M \cong \angle M$. So, by the SAS Similarity Theorem, $\triangle NQM \sim \triangle OPM$.

Step 2 Find *QN* and *PO*.

$\frac{MP}{MQ} = \frac{PO}{QN}$	Definition of similar polygons
$\frac{8}{5} = \frac{x + 2\frac{1}{4}}{x}$	Substitution
$8x = 5x + 11\frac{1}{4}$	Multiplication Property of Equality
$x = 3\frac{3}{4}$	Solve for *x*.
$QN = 3\frac{3}{4}$	Substitution
$PO = 3\frac{3}{4} + 2\frac{1}{4}$ or 6	Solve.

Check

Find *WR* and *RT*.

$WR =$ __8__

$RT =$ __10__

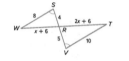

Go Online You can complete an Extra Example online.

Example 2 Parts of Similar Triangles

MP Teaching the Mathematical Practices

1 Understand the Approaches of Others Work with students to look at the Alternate Method. Ask students to compare and contrast the original method and the alternate method.

Questions for Mathematical Discourse

AL Why can you use the SAS Similarity Theorem in this example? Sample answer: Because the lengths of two sides of one triangle are proportional to the lengths of two sides of the second triangle and the included angles are congruent, the triangles are similar.

OL What are the perimeters of triangles *NQM* and *OPM*? The perimeter of $\triangle NQM = 14\frac{3}{4}$ and the perimeter of $\triangle OPM = 23\frac{3}{5}$.

BL Is showing that *MP* is proportional to *MQ*, *MO* is proportional to *MN*, and $\angle MQN \cong \angle MPO$ enough to prove the triangles similar? Explain. No; sample answer: Because the congruent angles are not the included angles, the SAS Similarity Theorem cannot be used.

Interactive Presentation

Parts of Similar Triangles

Find *QN* and *PO*. Justify your answer.

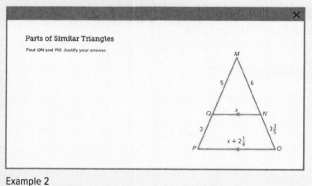

Example 2

EXPAND

Students tap to see the steps to find the side lengths of similar triangles.

1 CONCEPTUAL UNDERSTANDING   **2 FLUENCY** | 3 APPLICATION

🌐 **Example 3** Use Similar Triangles to Solve Problems

📐 Teaching the Mathematical Practices

2 Create Representations Guide students to write an equation that models the situation in this example. Then use the equation to solve the problem.

Questions for Mathematical Discourse

AL Are there any similar triangles in the image? Explain. Yes; sample answer: By the SAS Similarity Theorem or the AA Similarity Postulate, it can be proven that triangles *ABC* and *ADE* are similar.

OL Describe how you could use the AA Similarity Postulate to show that the triangles are similar. Sample answer: Because *ED* ∥ *CB*, ∠*AED* ≅ ∠*ACB* by the Corresponding Angles Postulate. ∠*A* ≅ ∠*A* by the Reflexive Property of Congruence, so the two triangles are similar by the AA Similarity Postulate.

BL How does the length of the base of the house and the length of the balcony relate to the ratios you found in Step 3? The ratio of the base to the balcony is also 1.6.

🌐 **Example 3** Use Similar Triangles to Solve Problems

ARCHITECTURAL DESIGN Julia is designing an A-frame house. The entire house will be 40 feet tall and the base of the house will be 60 feet long. She will build a second-floor balcony around the outside of the house, 15 feet above the ground. The left side of the house will be 50 feet long and the balcony will intersect the side 18.75 feet from the bottom. The height of the house bisects the base of the house and the balcony. Calculate the total length of the balcony.

Step 1 Draw a diagram.

Step 2 Create a model.

You can model the side of the house with two triangles. Use the information that you know to label the triangles.

Step 3 Describe the model.

$\frac{AC}{AE} = \frac{50}{31.25}$ or 1.6

$\frac{AB}{AD} = \frac{40}{25}$ or 1.6

By the Reflexive Property of Congruence, ∠*A* ≅ ∠*A*. Therefore, the two triangles are similar by the SAS Similarity Theorem.

Step 4 Solve.

Because the two triangles are similar, the corresponding sides are proportional.

$\frac{50 \text{ ft}}{31.25 \text{ ft}} = \frac{30 \text{ ft}}{ED}$ SAS Similarity Theorem

ED = 18.75 ft.   Solve.

The height of the triangle bisects the length of the balcony, so the total length of the balcony is 2(18.75) or 37.5 feet.

💭 **Think About It!**
What assumptions did you make when creating your model for the side of the house?

Sample answer: I assumed that the sides of the house and the length of the balcony are perfectly straight lines.

Lesson 8-4 • Similar Triangles: SSS and SAS Similarity   **483**

Interactive Presentation

Use Similar Triangles to Solve Problems

🌐 ARCHITECTURAL DESIGN Jessica is designing an A-frame house. The entire house will be 40 feet tall and the base of the house will be 60 feet long. She will build a second-floor balcony around the outside of the house, 15 feet above the ground. The left side of the house will be 50 feet long and the balcony will intersect the side 18.75 feet from the bottom. The height of the house bisects the base of the house and the balcony. Jessica wants to calculate the total length of the balcony.

Example 3

TAP

Students move through slides to see how to calculate the total length of the balcony.

🌐 **Go Online**
to practice what you've learned about similar triangles in the Put It All Together over Lessons 8-3 through 8-4.

🌐 **Go Online**
to learn how to prove the slope criteria in Expand 8-4.

Check

TENNIS Justin is playing tennis. When serving, he stands 12 feet away from the net, which is 3 feet tall. The ball is served from a height of 7.5 feet. Justin thinks the ball travels about 21.4 feet before it hits the ground 8 feet from the net on the opposite side.

Part A

How far does the ball travel before it reaches the net? Round your answer to the nearest tenth, if necessary.

_12.8_ ft

Part B

What assumptions did you make to solve for the distance that the ball travels?

Sample answer: I assumed that the ball traveled in a straight line and barely passed over the net. I assumed that the measure of the angle between the net and the ground was 90°, and I assumed that the measure of the angle between Justin and the ground was 90°.

Pause and Reflect

Did you struggle with anything in this lesson? If so, how did you deal with it?

 See students' observations.

Interactive Presentation

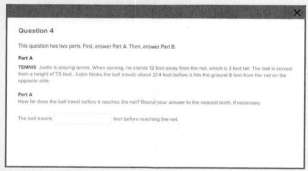

Check

CHECK

📊 Students complete the Check online to determine whether they are ready to move on.

Exit Ticket

Recommended Use

At the end of class, go online to display the Exit Ticket prompt and ask students to respond using a separate piece of paper. Have students hand you their responses as they leave the room.

Alternate Use

At the end of class, go online to display the Exit Ticket prompt and ask students to respond verbally or by using a mini-whiteboard. Have students hold up their whiteboards so that you can see all student responses. Tap to reveal the answer when most or all students have completed the Exit Ticket.

Practice and Homework

Suggested Assignments

Use the table below to select appropriate exercises.

DOK	Topic	Exercises
1, 2	exercises that mirror the examples	1–12
2	exercises that use a variety of skills from this lesson	13–14
2	exercises that emphasize higher-order and critical-thinking skills	15–18

ASSESS AND DIFFERENTIATE

📊 Use the data from the **Checks** to determine whether to provide resources for extension, remediation, or intervention.

IF students score 90% or more on the Checks,   **BL**
THEN assign:

- Practice, Exercises 1–13 odd, 15–18
- Extension: Medial and Orthic Triangles
- 🔲 **ALEKS**' Proving Triangle Similarity

IF students score 66%–89% on the Checks,   **OL**
THEN assign:

- Practice, Exercises 1–17 odd
- Remediation, Review Resources: Similarity and Corresponding Parts
- Personal Tutors
- BrainPOP Video: Similar Triangles
- Extra Examples 1–3
- 🔲 **ALEKS**' Triangle Similarity and Congruence

IF students score 65% or less on the Checks,   **AL**
THEN assign:

- Practice, Exercises 1–11 odd
- Remediation, Review Resources: Similarity and Corresponding Parts
- *Quick Review Math Handbook*: Similar Triangles
- 🔲 **ALEKS**' Triangle Similarity and Congruence

Answers

1. Yes; $\triangle RST \sim \triangle WSX$ (or $\triangle XSW$) by SAS Similarity

2. Yes; $\triangle ABC \sim \triangle PQR$ (or $\triangle QPR$) by SSS Similarity

3. Yes; $\triangle STU \sim \triangle JPM$ by SAS Similarity

4. No; sample answer: The triangles would be similar by SSS Similarity if $\overline{AC} \cong \overline{DF}$ or by SAS Similarity if $\angle B \cong \angle E$.

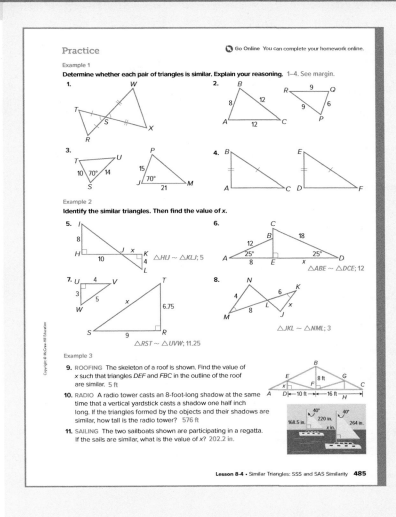

Practice

🔲 Go Online You can complete your homework online.

Example 1

Determine whether each pair of triangles is similar. Explain your reasoning. 1–4. See margin.

1.
2.
3.
4.

Example 2

Identify the similar triangles. Then find the value of x.

5. $\triangle HIJ \sim \triangle KLJ$; 5

6. $\triangle ABE \sim \triangle DCE$; 12

7. $\triangle RST \sim \triangle UVW$; 11.25

8. $\triangle JKL \sim \triangle NML$; 3

Example 3

9. ROOFING The skeleton of a roof is shown. Find the value of x such that triangles *DEF* and *FBC* in the outline of the roof are similar. 5 ft

10. RADIO A radio tower casts an 8-foot-long shadow at the same time that a vertical yardstick casts a shadow one half inch long. If the triangles formed by the objects and their shadows are similar, how tall is the radio tower? 576 ft

11. SAILING The two sailboats shown are participating in a regatta. If the sails are similar, what is the value of *x*? 202.2 in.

Lesson 8-4 · Similar Triangles: SSS and SAS Similarity   **485**

12. MOUNTAIN PEAKS Marcus and Skye want to estimate how far a mountain peak is from their houses. After taking some measurements, they construct a diagram.

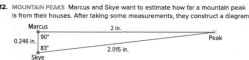

The actual distance between Marcus and Skye's houses is $1\frac{1}{2}$ miles.

a. What is the actual distance from Marcus's house to the peak of the mountain? Round your answer to the nearest tenth of a mile.   12.2 mi

b. What is the actual distance from Skye's house to the peak of the mountain? Round your answer to the nearest tenth of a mile.   12.3 mi

Mixed Exercises

13. Mia drew triangles *STU* and *SQR*. She claims that △*STU* and △*SQR* are similar. Is she correct? Justify your reasoning. See margin.

14. PROOF Write a two-column proof for the Side-Angle-Side (SAS) Similarity Proof. (Theorem 8.5)

Given: $\angle B \cong \angle E$, $\overline{QP} \parallel \overline{BC}$, $\overline{QP} \cong \overline{EF}$, $\frac{AB}{DE} = \frac{BC}{EF}$

Prove: △*ABC* ~ △*DEF*   See margin.

🧠 Higher-Order Thinking Skills

15. WRITE Compare and contrast the AA Similarity Postulate, the SSS Similarity Theorem, and the SAS Similarity Theorem. See margin.

16. PERSEVERE $\overline{YW}$ is an altitude of △*XYZ*. Find *YW*. $\frac{5\sqrt{2}}{2}$

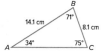

17. ANALYZE A pair of similar triangles has angles that measure 50°, 85°, and 45°. The sides of one triangle measure 3, 3.25, and 4.23 units, and the sides of the second triangle measure $x - 0.46$, x, and $x + 1.81$ units. Find the value of *x* to the nearest integer.   6

18. CREATE Draw a triangle that is similar to △*ABC* shown. Explain how you know that it is similar.   See margin.

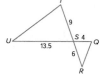

13. Sample answer: $m\angle TSU = m\angle QSR$ because they are vertical angles. $\frac{ST}{SQ}$ is proportional to $\frac{SU}{SR}$. Therefore, △*STU* and △*SQR* are similar by the SAS Similarity Theorem.

14. Proof:

Statements (Reasons)

1. $\angle B \cong \angle E$, $\overline{QP} \parallel \overline{BC}$, $\overline{QP} \cong \overline{EF}$, $\frac{AB}{DE} = \frac{BC}{EF}$ (Given)

2. $\angle APQ \cong \angle C$, $\angle AQP \cong \angle B$ (Corresponding Angles Theorem)

3. $\angle AQP \cong \angle E$ (Substitution)

4. △*ABC* ~ △*AQP* (AA Similarity)

5. $\frac{AB}{AQ} = \frac{BC}{QP}$ (Definition of similar triangles)

6. $AB \cdot QP = AQ \cdot BC$, $AB \cdot EF = DE \cdot BC$ (Multiplication Property of Equality)

7. $QP = EF$ (Definition of congruence)

8. $AB \cdot EF = AQ \cdot BC$ (Substitution)

9. $AQ \cdot BC = DE \cdot BC$ (Substitution)

10. $AQ = DE$ (Division Property)

11. $\overline{AQ} \cong \overline{DE}$ (Definition of congruence)

12. △*AQP* ≅ △*DEF* (SAS)

13. $\angle APQ \cong \angle F$ (CPCTC)

14. $\angle C \cong \angle F$ (Substitution)

15. △*ABC* ~ △*DEF* (AA Similarity)

15. Sample answer: The AA Similarity Postulate, SSS Similarity Theorem, and SAS Similarity Theorem are all tests that can be used to determine whether two triangles are similar. The AA Similarity Postulate is used when two pairs of congruent angles of two triangles are given. The SSS Similarity Theorem is used when the corresponding proportional side lengths of two triangles are given. The SAS Similarity Theorem is used when two corresponding proportional side lengths and the included angle of two triangles are given.

18. Sample answer:

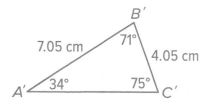

△*ABC* ~ △*A'B'C'* because the measures of each side is half the measure of the corresponding side and the measures of corresponding angles are equal.

Triangle Proportionality

LESSON GOAL

Students use triangle proportionality to solve problems and prove theorems.

1 LAUNCH

 Launch the lesson with a **Warm Up** and an introduction.

2 EXPLORE AND DEVELOP

 Explore: Proportions in Triangles

 Develop:

Triangle Proportionality:
- Use Triangle Proportions to Find the Length of a Side
- Use Triangle Proportions to Determine if Lines are Parallel

Midsegments and Parallel Lines
- Use the Triangle Midsegment Theorem
- Use Proportional Segments of Transversals
- Use Congruent Segments of Transversals

You may want your students to complete the **Checks** online.

3 REFLECT AND PRACTICE

Exit Ticket

Practice

Formative Assessment Math Probe

DIFFERENTIATE

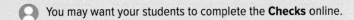 View reports of student progress on the **Checks** after each example.

Resources	AL	OL	BL	ELL
Remediation: Similar Polygons	●	●		●
Extension: Parallel Lines and Congruent Parts		●	●	●

Language Development Handbook

Assign page 56 of the *Language Development Handbook* to help your students build mathematical language related to using triangle proportionality to solve problems and prove triangles similar.

ELL You can use the tips and suggestions on page T56 of the handbook to support students who are building English proficiency.

Suggested Pacing

90 min	**1 day**
45 min	**2 days**

Focus

Domain: Geometry

Standards for Mathematical Content:

G.SRT.4 Prove theorems about triangles.

G.CO.10 Prove theorems about triangles.

G.CO.12 Make formal geometric constructions with a variety of tools and methods.

Standards for Mathematical Practice:

2 Reason abstractly and quantitatively.

5 Use appropriate tools strategically.

8 Look for and express regularity in repeated reasoning.

Coherence

Vertical Alignment

Previous
Students used proportional relationships to solve real-world problems.
7.RP, A.CED.1, A.REI.3 (Algebra 1)

Now
Students use triangle proportionality to solve problems and prove theorems.
G.SRT.4, G.CO.10, G.CO.12

Next
Students will solve problems and prove theorems about parts of similar triangles by using triangle similarity.
G.SRT.4

Rigor

The Three Pillars of Rigor

1 CONCEPTUAL UNDERSTANDING	2 FLUENCY	3 APPLICATION

Conceptual Bridge In this lesson, students focus on understanding the relationships that occur with similar triangles that have a common angle. They build fluency by proving theorems about triangles, and apply their understanding by using proportionality to solve real-world problems.

Mathematical Background

If a line is parallel to one side of a triangle and intersects the other two sides in two distinct points, then it separates these sides into segments of proportional lengths. A *midsegment* is a segment with endpoints that are the midpoints of two sides of the triangle and is parallel to one side of the triangle.

Interactive Presentation

Warm Up

Determine whether the figures are similar.

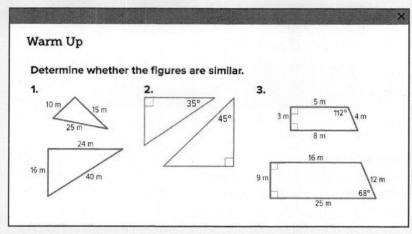

Warm Up

Launch the Lesson

The further away an object gets from your viewpoint, the smaller it looks. In order to accurately portray this, artists use what is known as vanishing point perspective, or single-point perspective. This technique has been used since 5 B.C., and the way it works is that images in the foreground of a picture appear larger and objects in the background appear smaller. Using this logic, it makes sense that the distance between two parallel lines will also appear to become smaller as the lines recede into the background, which is what makes them appear to converge at a point called the vanishing point.

Launch the Lesson

Vocabulary

Expand All   Collapse All

⌄ **midsegment of a triangle**

The segment that connects the midpoints of the legs of a triangle.

1. How many *midsegments* do you think there are in a triangle?
2. How are the *midsegments of a triangle* related to the sides of the triangle?
3. How is the *midsegment of a trapezoid* different from the midsegment of a triangle?

Today's Vocabulary

Warm Up

Prerequisite Skills

The Warm Up exercises address the following prerequisite skill for this lesson:

- identifying similar figures

Answers:

1. yes
2. no
3. no
4. 73°
5. 14 m
6. 25 in.

Launch the Lesson

Teaching the Mathematical Practices

4 Apply Mathematics In this Launch the Lesson, students can see a real-world application of triangle proportionality.

Go Online to find additional teaching notes and questions to promote classroom discourse.

Today's Standards

Tell students that they will be addressing these content and practice standards in this lesson. You may wish to have a student volunteer read aloud *How can I meet these standards?* and *How can I use these practices?* and connect these to the standards.

See the Interactive Presentation for I Can statements that align with the standards covered in this lesson.

Today's Vocabulary

Tell students that they will be using this vocabulary term in this lesson. You can expand the row if you wish to share the definition. Then, discuss the questions below with the class.

Explore Proportions in Triangles

Objective
Students use dynamic geometry software to make conjectures about the midsegments of triangles.

(MP) Teaching the Mathematical Practices

8 Look for a Pattern Help students to see the pattern in this Explore.

Ideas for Use

Recommended Use Present the Inquiry Question, or have a student volunteer read it aloud. Have students work in pairs to complete the Explore activity on their devices. Pairs should discuss each of the questions. Monitor student progress during the activity. Upon completion of the Explore activity, have student volunteers share their responses to the Inquiry Question.

What if my students don't have devices? You may choose to project the activity on a whiteboard. A printable worksheet for each Explore is available online. You may choose to print the worksheet so that individuals or pairs of students can use it to record their observations.

Summary of the Activity

Students will complete guiding exercises throughout the Explore activity. Students use a sketch to complete an activity that leads them to make a conjecture that the midsegment of a triangle is half the length of the side to which it is parallel. Then, students will answer the Inquiry Question.

(continued on the next page)

Interactive Presentation

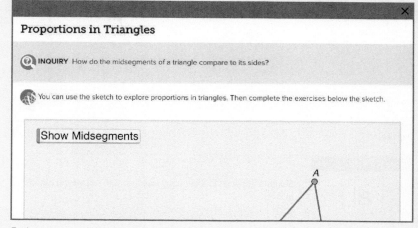

Explore

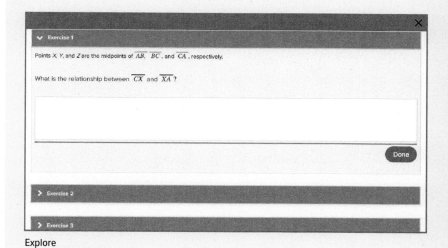

Explore

WEB SKETCHPAD

 Students use a sketch to complete an activity in which they explore the midsegments of triangles.

Interactive Presentation

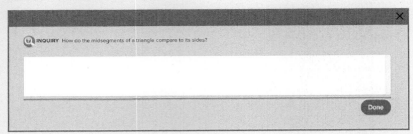

Explore

TYPE

Students respond to the Inquiry Question and can view a sample answer.

Explore Proportions in Triangles (*continued*)

MP Teaching the Mathematical Practices

> **8 Look for a Pattern** Help students to see the pattern in this Explore.

Questions

Have students complete the Explore activity.

Ask:

- What is the relationship between *CX* and *ZY*? Sample answer: The segments *CX* and *ZY* appear to be congruent. Because *X* is the midpoint of $\overline{CA}$, it is exactly half of *CA*, which is also the measure of $\overline{ZY}$.

- How could you verify a segment is a midsegment on the coordinate plane? Sample answer: Use the slope formula to confirm that the slopes are equal, which means the segments are parallel. Then, you could use the Distance Formula to make sure that the length of the midsegment is half of the side parallel to it.

Inquiry

How do the midsegments of a triangle compare to its sides? Sample answer: The midsegments of a triangle are formed by connecting two of its midpoints and dividing the sides of the triangle into equal parts. Each midsegment is parallel to a side of the triangle and has a length that is half of this side.

Go Online to find additional teaching notes and sample answers for the exercises.

1 CONCEPTUAL UNDERSTANDING | **2 FLUENCY** | 3 APPLICATION

Learn Triangle Proportionality

Objective
Students solve problems and prove theorems by using triangle proportionality.

 Teaching the Mathematical Practices

> **7 Use Structure** Help students to explore the structure of triangle proportionality in this Learn.

Example 1 Use Triangle Proportions to Find the Length of a Side

 Teaching the Mathematical Practices

> **6 Communicate Precisely** Encourage students to routinely write or explain their solution methods. Point out that they should use clear definitions when they discuss their solutions with others.

Questions for Mathematical Discourse

AL What is one similarity statement for these triangles? Sample answer: $\triangle PBQ \sim \triangle CBD$

OL What is the ratio between the lengths of the corresponding sides of $\triangle BCD$ and $\triangle BPQ$? 0.375

BL If P and Q are moving towards B, and C and D remain stationary, how will the ratio between the sides change? Sample answer: It will be less.

Go Online

- Find additional teaching notes.
- View performance reports of the Checks.
- Assign or present an Extra Example.

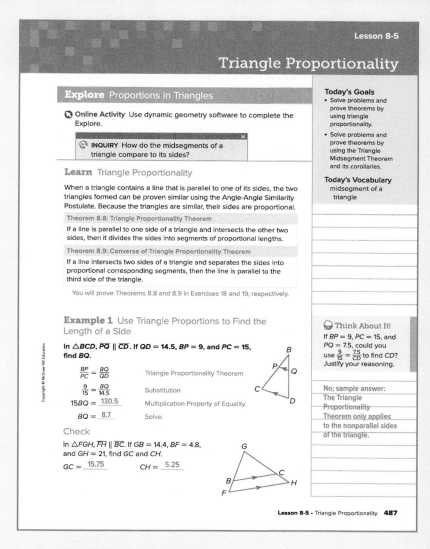

Lesson 8-5

Triangle Proportionality

Explore Proportions in Triangles

Online Activity Use dynamic geometry software to complete the Explore.

INQUIRY How do the midsegments of a triangle compare to its sides?

Learn Triangle Proportionality

When a triangle contains a line that is parallel to one of its sides, the two triangles formed can be proven similar using the Angle-Angle Similarity Postulate. Because the triangles are similar, their sides are proportional.

Theorem 8.8: Triangle Proportionality Theorem

If a line is parallel to one side of a triangle and intersects the other two sides, then it divides the sides into segments of proportional lengths.

Theorem 8.9: Converse of Triangle Proportionality Theorem

If a line intersects two sides of a triangle and separates the sides into proportional corresponding segments, then the line is parallel to the third side of the triangle.

You will prove Theorems 8.8 and 8.9 in Exercises 18 and 19, respectively.

Example 1 Use Triangle Proportions to Find the Length of a Side

In $\triangle BCD$, $\overline{PQ} \parallel \overline{CD}$. If $QD = 14.5$, $BP = 9$, and $PC = 15$, find BQ.

$\dfrac{BP}{PC} = \dfrac{BQ}{QD}$	Triangle Proportionality Theorem
$\dfrac{9}{15} = \dfrac{BQ}{14.5}$	Substitution
$15BQ = \underline{130.5}$	Multiplication Property of Equality
$BQ = \underline{8.7}$	Solve.

Check

In $\triangle FGH$, $\overline{FH} \parallel \overline{BC}$. If $GB = 14.4$, $BF = 4.8$, and $GH = 21$, find GC and CH.

$GC = \underline{15.75}$ $\qquad$ $CH = \underline{5.25}$

Today's Goals
- Solve problems and prove theorems by using triangle proportionality.
- Solve problems and prove theorems by using the Triangle Midsegment Theorem and its corollaries.

Today's Vocabulary
midsegment of a triangle

Think About It!
If $BP = 9$, $PC = 15$, and $PQ = 7.5$, could you use $\dfrac{9}{15} = \dfrac{7.5}{CD}$ to find CD? Justify your reasoning.

No; sample answer: The Triangle Proportionality Theorem only applies to the nonparallel sides of the triangle.

Lesson 8-5 · Triangle Proportionality **487**

Interactive Presentation

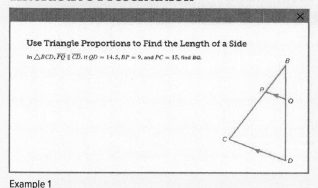

Use Triangle Proportions to Find the Length of a Side

In $\triangle BCD$, $\overline{FQ} \parallel \overline{CD}$. If $QD = 14.5$, $BP = 9$, and $PC = 15$, find BQ.

Example 1

TYPE

Students answer a question to determine whether they understand the Triangle Proportionality Theorem.

1 CONCEPTUAL UNDERSTANDING | **2 FLUENCY** | 3 APPLICATION

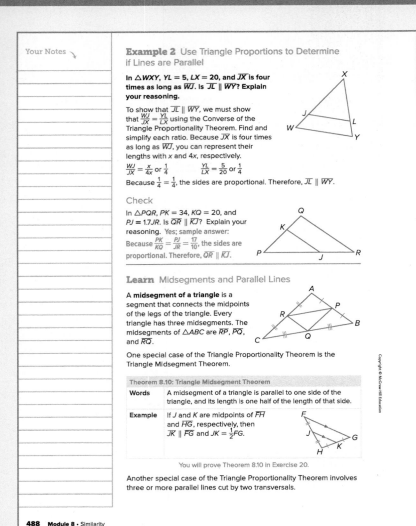

Your Notes

Example 2 Use Triangle Proportions to Determine if Lines are Parallel

In △WXY, YL = 5, LX = 20, and $\overline{JX}$ is four times as long as $\overline{WJ}$. Is $\overline{JL} \parallel \overline{WY}$? Explain your reasoning.

To show that $\overline{JL} \parallel \overline{WY}$, we must show that $\frac{WJ}{JX} = \frac{YL}{LX}$ using the Converse of the Triangle Proportionality Theorem. Find and simplify each ratio. Because $\overline{JX}$ is four times as long as $\overline{WJ}$, you can represent their lengths with x and 4x, respectively.

$\frac{WJ}{JX} = \frac{x}{4x}$ or $\frac{1}{4}$ $\frac{YL}{LX} = \frac{5}{20}$ or $\frac{1}{4}$

Because $\frac{1}{4} = \frac{1}{4}$, the sides are proportional. Therefore, $\overline{JL} \parallel \overline{WY}$.

Check

In △PQR, PK = 34, KQ = 20, and PJ = 1.7JR. Is $\overline{QR} \parallel \overline{KJ}$? Explain your reasoning. Yes; sample answer: Because $\frac{PK}{KQ} = \frac{PJ}{JR} = \frac{17}{10}$, the sides are proportional. Therefore, $\overline{QR} \parallel \overline{KJ}$.

Learn Midsegments and Parallel Lines

A **midsegment of a triangle** is a segment that connects the midpoints of the legs of the triangle. Every triangle has three midsegments. The midsegments of △ABC are $\overline{RP}$, $\overline{PQ}$, and $\overline{RQ}$.

One special case of the Triangle Proportionality Theorem is the Triangle Midsegment Theorem.

Theorem 8.10: Triangle Midsegment Theorem	
Words	A midsegment of a triangle is parallel to one side of the triangle, and its length is one half of the length of that side.
Example	If J and K are midpoints of $\overline{FH}$ and $\overline{HG}$, respectively, then $\overline{JK} \parallel \overline{FG}$ and $JK = \frac{1}{2}FG$.

You will prove Theorem 8.10 in Exercise 20.

Another special case of the Triangle Proportionality Theorem involves three or more parallel lines cut by two transversals.

Example 2 Use Triangle Proportions to Determine if Lines are Parallel

ⓂⓅ Teaching the Mathematical Practices

3 Construct Arguments In this example, students will see how to use stated assumptions, definitions, and previously established results to determine if lines are parallel.

Questions for Mathematical Discourse

AL Could you write the proportion in a different way? If so, how? Yes; sample answer: $\frac{XL}{LY} = \frac{XJ}{JW}$

OL If you used x to represent YL and 4x to represent LX, would the result be the same? Yes; LX is 4 times YL.

BL If WJ = 2, JX = 7, and LX = 10 more than YL, can you show that WY is parallel to JL? Explain. No; sample answer: If you represent YL with x and LX with x + 10, the x-terms cannot be eliminated to show that the corresponding sides of the triangles are proportional.

Learn Midsegments and Parallel Lines

Objective
Students solve problems and prove theorems by using the Triangle Midsegment Theorem and its corollaries.

ⓂⓅ Teaching the Mathematical Practices

7 Use Structure Help students to explore the structure of triangle midsegments and parallel lines in this Learn.

Important to Know
The three midsegments of a triangle form the *midsegment triangle*.

Interactive Presentation

Use Triangle Proportions to Determine if Lines are Parallel

In △WXY, YL = 5, LX = 20, and $\overline{JX}$ is four times as long as $\overline{WJ}$. Is $\overline{JL} \parallel \overline{WY}$?

Move through the slides to determine if the two lines are parallel.

To show that $\overline{JL} \parallel \overline{WY}$ by the Converse of the Triangle Proportionality Theorem, we must show that $\frac{WJ}{JX} = \frac{YL}{LX}$.

Find and simplify each ratio. Because $\overline{JX}$ is four times as long as $\overline{WJ}$, you can represent their lengths with x and 4x, respectively.

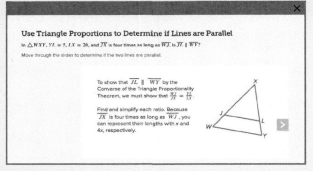

Example 2

TAP

Students move through the slides to determine if two lines are parallel.

CHECK

Students complete the Check online to determine whether they are ready to move on.

1 CONCEPTUAL UNDERSTANDING   **2 FLUENCY**   3 APPLICATION

Example 3 Use the Triangle Midsegment Theorem

MP Teaching the Mathematical Practices

2 Create Representations Guide students to write equations that model the situation in this example. Then use the equations to solve the problem.

Questions for Mathematical Discourse

AL What points do *E*, *F*, and *D* represent? the midpoints of the sides

OL If *CB* = 10, what is *DF*? 5

BL Do you have enough information to find the measure of ∠*CEF*? Explain. No; sample answer: You would need to also know the measure of ∠*DEB*.

Common Error

When students use the Triangle Proportionality Theorem, direct them to write a proportion. Remind them that if they are finding the length of an entire side of a triangle, they must use the entire side of the similar triangle.

DIFFERENTIATE

Reteaching Activity AL
Have students use string, masking tape, and a tiled floor to mark off congruent segments on parallel lines made with masking tape on the floor. Use the string to show that if three or more parallel lines form congruent segments on one transversal, they form congruent segments on another transversal.

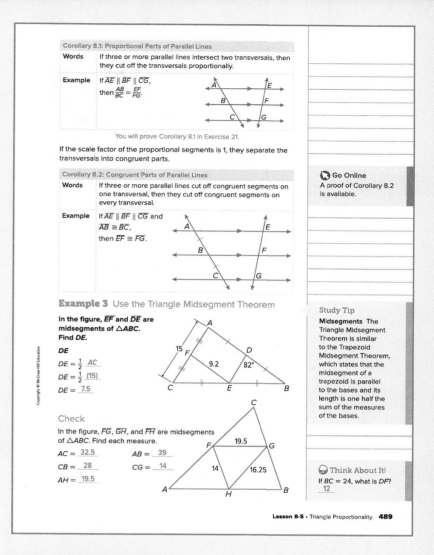

Corollary 8.1: Proportional Parts of Parallel Lines

Words	If three or more parallel lines intersect two transversals, then they cut off the transversals proportionally.
Example	If $\overline{AE} \parallel \overline{BF} \parallel \overline{CG}$, then $\frac{AB}{BC} = \frac{EF}{FG}$.

You will prove Corollary 8.1 in Exercise 21.

If the scale factor of the proportional segments is 1, they separate the transversals into congruent parts.

Corollary 8.2: Congruent Parts of Parallel Lines

Words	If three or more parallel lines cut off congruent segments on one transversal, then they cut off congruent segments on every transversal.
Example	If $\overline{AE} \parallel \overline{BF} \parallel \overline{CG}$ and $\overline{AB} \cong \overline{BC}$, then $\overline{EF} \cong \overline{FG}$.

Go Online
A proof of Corollary 8.2 is available.

Example 3 Use the Triangle Midsegment Theorem

In the figure, $\overline{EF}$ and $\overline{DE}$ are midsegments of △*ABC*. Find *DE*.

DE
$DE = \frac{1}{2} \; AC$
$DE = \frac{1}{2} \; (15)$
$DE = \; 7.5$

Study Tip
Midsegments The Triangle Midsegment Theorem is similar to the Trapezoid Midsegment Theorem, which states that the midsegment of a trapezoid is parallel to the bases and its length is one half the sum of the measures of the bases.

Check
In the figure, $\overline{FG}$, $\overline{GH}$, and $\overline{FH}$ are midsegments of △*ABC*. Find each measure.

$AC = \; 32.5$ $AB = \; 39$
$CB = \; 28$ $CG = \; 14$
$AH = \; 19.5$

Think About It!
If *BC* = 24, what is *DF*?
12

Lesson 8-5 · Triangle Proportionality **489**

Interactive Presentation

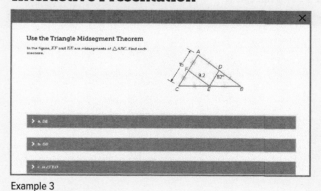

Use the Triangle Midsegment Theorem
In the figure, *EF* and *DE* are midsegments of △*ABC*. Find each measure.

> a. DE
> b. GE
> c. m∠FED

Example 3

EXPAND

Students tap to see how to find measures using the Triangle Midsegment Theorem.

1 CONCEPTUAL UNDERSTANDING | 2 FLUENCY | 3 APPLICATION

🌐 **Example 4** Use Proportional Segments of Transversals

REAL ESTATE A developer is looking to purchase lots 18 and 19 on the lake and wants to determine the length of the property's boundary that runs along the lake, a measurement known as frontage. Find the lake frontage for Lot 18 to the nearest tenth of a foot.

By Corollary 8.1, because the three boundaries are parallel, the segments formed by the front and back property lines are divided into proportional parts. Let x represent the missing length.

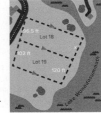

$$\frac{102}{120} = \frac{96.5}{x}$$ Corollary 8.1

$102x = 11580$ Multiplication Property of Equality

$x = 113.5$ Divide each side by 102.

Example 5 Use Congruent Segments of Transversals

Find the values of x and y.

Because $\overleftrightarrow{AJ} \parallel \overleftrightarrow{BK} \parallel \overleftrightarrow{CL}$ and $\overline{JK} \cong \overline{KL}$, then $\overline{AB} \cong \overline{BC}$.

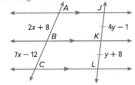

Find the value of x.

$AB = BC$ Definition of congruence

$2x + 8 = \underline{7x - 12}$ Substitution

$8 = \underline{5}\ x - 12$ Subtract $2x$ from each side.

$\underline{20} = 5x$ Add 12 to each side.

$\underline{4} = x$ Divide each side by 5.

Find the value of y.

$JK = KL$ Definition of congruence

$4y - 1 = \underline{y + 8}$ Substitution

$\underline{3}\ y - 1 = 8$ Subtract y from each side.

$3y = \underline{9}$ Add 1 to each side.

$y = \underline{3}$ Divide each side by 3.

🌐 **Go Online** You can complete an Extra Example online.

Go Online
You may want to complete the construction activities for this lesson.

490 Module 8 · Similarity

Interactive Presentation

×

Use Proportional Segments of Transversals

🌐 REAL ESTATE A developer is looking to purchase lots 18 and 19 on the lake and wants to determine the length of the property's boundary that runs along the lake, a measurement known as frontage. Find the lake frontage for lot 18 to the nearest tenth of a yard.

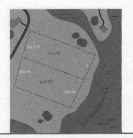

Example 4

CHECK

📊

Students complete the Check online to determine whether they are ready to move on.

🌐 **Example 4** Use Proportional Segments of Transversals

Ⓜ️ Teaching the Mathematical Practices

8 Attend to Details Mathematically proficient students continually ask themselves, "Does this make sense?" Point out that in this example, students should evaluate the reasonableness of their answer.

Questions for Mathematical Discourse

AL In this situation, what are the transversals? the frontage and the boundary that runs along the road

OL Write another proportion that could be used to solve for x. Sample answer: $\frac{96.5}{102} = \frac{x}{120}$

BL What is the total length of the frontage? 233.5 ft

Example 5 Use Congruent Segments of Transversals

Ⓜ️ Teaching the Mathematical Practices

1 Check Answers Mathematically proficient students continually ask themselves, "Does this make sense?" Point out that in this example, students should check their answer by substituting for x and y in the original expressions.

Questions for Mathematical Discourse

AL Does the Congruent Parts of Parallel Lines Corollary address the relationships between the parallel segments? Explain. No; sample answer: It only pertains to the transversals.

OL How can you check your solution? Substitute the values of x and y into the original expressions and confirm that $AB = BC$ and $JK = KL$.

BL If you extended lines AC and JL until they intersect, how many pairs of congruent segments would be formed? 3

Exit Ticket

Recommended Use

At the end of class, go online to display the Exit Ticket prompt and ask students to respond using a separate piece of paper. Have students hand you their responses as they leave the room.

Alternate Use

At the end of class, go online to display the Exit Ticket prompt and ask students to respond verbally or by using a mini-whiteboard. Have students hold up their whiteboards so that you can see all student responses. Tap to reveal the answer when most or all students have completed the Exit Ticket.

Practice and Homework

Suggested Assignments

Use the table below to select appropriate exercises.

DOK	Topic	Exercises
1, 2	exercises that mirror the examples	1–12
2	exercises that use a variety of skills from this lesson	12–25
3	exercises that emphasize higher-order and critical-thinking skills	26–30

ASSESS AND DIFFERENTIATE

📊 Use the data from the **Checks** to determine whether to provide resources for extension, remediation, or intervention.

IF students score 90% or more on the Checks,　`OL` `BL`
THEN assign:

- Practice Exercises 1–25 odd, 26–30
- Extension: Parallel Lines and Congruent Parts
- ⊙ **ALEKS** Proving Triangle Similarity

IF students score 66%–89% on the Checks,　`AL` `OL`
THEN assign:

- Practice Exercises 1–29 odd
- Remediation, Review Resources: Similar Polygons
- Personal Tutors
- Extra Examples 1–5
- ⊙ **ALEKS** Similar Figures

IF students score 65% or less on the Checks,　`AL`
THEN assign:

- Practice Exercises 1–11 odd
- Remediation, Review Resources: Similar Polygons
- *Quick Review Math Handbook*: Parallel Lines and Proportional Parts
- ⊙ **ALEKS** Similar Figures

Important to Know

Digital Exercise Alert Exercise 29 requires a construction and is not available online. To fully address G.CO.12, have students complete this exercise using their books.

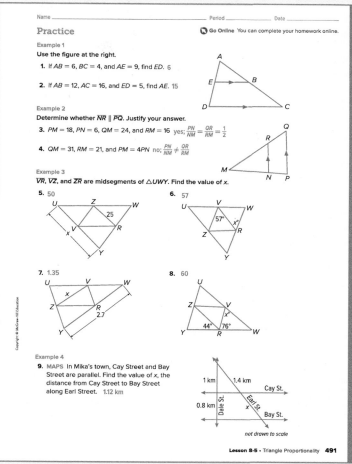

Name _____ Period _____ Date _____

Practice　🔵 Go Online You can complete your homework online.

Example 1
Use the figure at the right.

1. If $AB = 6$, $BC = 4$, and $AE = 9$, find ED.　6

2. If $AB = 12$, $AC = 16$, and $ED = 5$, find AE.　15

Example 2
Determine whether $\overline{NR} \parallel \overline{PQ}$. Justify your answer.

3. $PM = 18$, $PN = 6$, $QM = 24$, and $RM = 16$　yes; $\frac{PN}{NM} = \frac{QR}{RM} = \frac{1}{2}$

4. $QM = 31$, $RM = 21$, and $PM = 4PN$　no; $\frac{PN}{NM} \ne \frac{QR}{RM}$

Example 3
$\overline{VR}$, $\overline{VZ}$, and $\overline{ZR}$ are midsegments of $\triangle UWY$. Find the value of x.

5.　50

6.　57

7.　1.35

8.　60

Example 4

9. **MAPS** In Mika's town, Cay Street and Bay Street are parallel. Find the value of x, the distance from Cay Street to Bay Street along Earl Street.　1.12 km

not drawn to scale

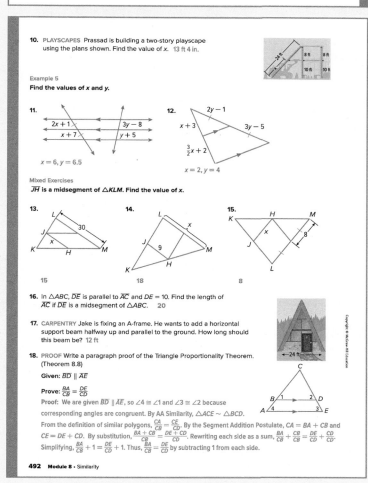

10. **PLAYSCAPES** Prassad is building a two-story playscape using the plans shown. Find the value of x.　13 ft 4 in.

Example 5
Find the values of x and y.

11.

$x = 6$, $y = 6.5$

12.

$x = 2$, $y = 4$

Mixed Exercises
$\overline{JH}$ is a midsegment of $\triangle KLM$. Find the value of x.

13.

15

14.

18

15.

8

16. In $\triangle ABC$, $\overline{DE}$ is parallel to $\overline{AC}$ and $DE = 10$. Find the length of $\overline{AC}$ if $\overline{DE}$ is a midsegment of $\triangle ABC$.　20

17. **CARPENTRY** Jake is fixing an A-frame. He wants to add a horizontal support beam halfway up and parallel to the ground. How long should this beam be?　12 ft

18. **PROOF** Write a paragraph proof of the Triangle Proportionality Theorem. (Theorem 8.8)

Given: $\overline{BD} \parallel \overline{AE}$

Prove: $\frac{BA}{CB} = \frac{DE}{CD}$

Proof: We are given $\overline{BD} \parallel \overline{AE}$, so $\angle 4 \cong \angle 1$ and $\angle 3 \cong \angle 2$ because corresponding angles are congruent. By AA Similarity, $\triangle ACE \sim \triangle BCD$. From the definition of similar polygons, $\frac{CA}{CB} = \frac{CE}{CD}$. By the Segment Addition Postulate, $CA = BA + CB$ and $CE = DE + CD$. By substitution, $\frac{BA + CB}{CB} = \frac{DE + CD}{CD}$. Rewriting each side as a sum, $\frac{BA}{CB} + \frac{CB}{CB} = \frac{DE}{CD} + \frac{CD}{CD}$. Simplifying, $\frac{BA}{CB} + 1 = \frac{DE}{CD} + 1$. Thus, $\frac{BA}{CB} = \frac{DE}{CD}$ by subtracting 1 from each side.

1 CONCEPTUAL UNDERSTANDING | 2 FLUENCY | 3 APPLICATION

Name _____ Period _____ Date _____

19. PROOF Write a paragraph proof of the Converse of the Triangle Proportionality Theorem. (Theorem 8.9). See margin.

Given: $\frac{AD}{DB} = \frac{AE}{EC}$

Prove: $\overline{DE} \parallel \overline{BC}$

(*Hint: Explain how you can use the given proportion to show that $\frac{AB}{AD} = \frac{AC}{EC}$. Then, use this proportion to complete the proof.*)

20. PROOF Write a two-column proof of the Triangle Midsegment Theorem. (Theorem 8.10)

Given: △ABC; D is the midpoint of $\overline{AB}$; E is the midpoint of $\overline{AC}$.

Prove: $\overline{DE} \parallel \overline{BC}, DE = \frac{1}{2}BC$ See margin.

21. PROOF Write a paragraph proof of Corollary 8.1.

Given: $\overrightarrow{AE} \parallel \overrightarrow{BF} \parallel \overrightarrow{CG}$

Prove: $\frac{AB}{BC} = \frac{EF}{FG}$

Proof: We are given that $\overrightarrow{AE} \parallel \overrightarrow{BF} \parallel \overrightarrow{CG}$. Draw $\overrightarrow{AG}$ so that $\overrightarrow{AG}$ intersects $\overrightarrow{BF}$ at D.

In △ACG, $\overleftrightarrow{CG} \parallel \overline{BD}$. By the Triangle Proportionality Theorem, $\frac{AB}{BC} = \frac{AD}{DG}$. In △AGE, $\overline{AE} \parallel \overline{DF}$. By the Triangle Proportionality Theorem, $\frac{AD}{DG} = \frac{EF}{FG}$. Therefore, by the Transitive Property, $\frac{AB}{BC} = \frac{EF}{FG}$.

22. REGULARITY In the figure, $\overline{DE} \parallel \overline{BC}$, BD = 12, EC = 10, and AE = 15. Explain how to find the length of $\overline{AD}$. See margin.

23. ART The divider bars between the pieces of colored glass in a stained glass window are called *cames*. In the stained window at the right, the total length of the cames for △PQR is 78 centimeters. What is the total length of the cames for △JKL? Give an argument to support your answer. See margin.

Lesson 8-5 · Triangle Proportionality **493**

---

24. SHUFFLEBOARD A crew is laying out a shuffleboard court using the plan shown at the right. Explain how they can find the lengths of $\overline{AB}, \overline{BD},$ and $\overline{DF}$ to the nearest tenth of a foot. See margin.

25. In △PQR, the length of $\overline{PQ}$ is 16 units. A series of midsegments are drawn such that $\overline{ST}$ is the midsegment of △PQR, $\overline{UV}$ is the midsegment of △STR, and $\overline{WX}$ is the midsegment of △UVR.

a. What is the length of each midsegment?

ST = 8   UV = 4   WX = 2

b. What would be the measure of midsegment $\overline{YZ}$ of △WXR?
Based on the pattern, the length of the midsegment of △WXR = 1.

🔲 **Higher-Order Thinking Skills**

26. FIND THE ERROR Jacinda and Elaine are finding the value of x in △JHL. Jacinda says that MP is one half of JL, so x is 4.5. Elaine says that JL is one half of MP, so x is 18. Is either of them correct? Explain your reasoning. Jacinda; sample answer: $\overline{MP}$ is the midsegment, so $MP = \frac{1}{2}JL$.

27. ANALYZE In △ABC, AF = FB and AH = HC. If D is $\frac{3}{4}$ of the way from A to B and E is $\frac{3}{4}$ of the way from A to C, is DE *sometimes, always,* or *never* $\frac{3}{4}$ of BC? Justify your argument. See Mod. 8 Answer Appendix.

28. PROOF Write a two-column proof.
Given: AB = 4, BC = 4, and CD = DE
Prove: $\overline{BD} \parallel \overline{AE}$ See Mod. 8 Answer Appendix.

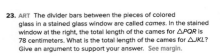

29. CREATE Construct segments a, b, c, and d of all different lengths such that $\frac{a}{b} = \frac{c}{d}$. See Mod. 8 Answer Appendix.

30. WRITE Compare the Triangle Proportionality Theorem and the Triangle Midsegment Theorem. See Mod. 8 Answer Appendix.

Answers

19. Because $\frac{AD}{DB} = \frac{AE}{EC}$, an equivalent proportion is $\frac{DB}{AD} = \frac{EC}{AE}$. Add 1 to each side of the proportion as follows: $\frac{DB}{AD} + \frac{AD}{AD} = \frac{EC}{AE} + \frac{AE}{AE}$. Therefore, $\frac{DB + AD}{AD} = \frac{EC + AE}{AE}$. By the Segment Addition Postulate, this is equivalent to $\frac{AB}{AD} = \frac{AC}{AE}$. Because $\frac{AB}{AD} = \frac{AC}{AE}$ and $\angle A \cong \angle A$ by the Reflexive Property of Congruence, △ADE ∼ △ABC by the SAS Similarity Theorem. Therefore, $\angle ADE \cong \angle ABC$ because they are corresponding angles of similar triangles; so $\overline{DE} \parallel \overline{BC}$, because if corresponding angles are congruent, then the lines are parallel.

20. Proof:
Statements (Reasons)

1. D is the midpoint of $\overline{AB}$, E is the midpoint of $\overline{AC}$. (Given)

2. $\overline{AD} \cong \overline{DB}, \overline{AE} \cong \overline{EC}$, (Midpoint Theorem)

3. AD = DB, AE = EC (Definition of congruent segments)

4. AB = AD + DB, AC = AE + EC (Segment Addition Postulate)

5. AB = AD + AD, AC = AE + AE (Substitution)

6. AB = 2AD, AC = 2AE (Substitution)

7. $\frac{AB}{AD} = 2, \frac{AC}{AE} = 2$ (Division Property)

8. $\frac{AB}{AD} = \frac{AC}{AE}$ (Transitive Property)

9. $\angle A \cong \angle A$ (Reflexive Property)

10. △ADE ∼ △ABC (SAS Similarity)

11. $\angle ADE \cong \angle ABC$ (Definition of similar polygons)

12. $\overline{DE} \parallel \overline{BC}$ (Converse of Corresponding Angles Theorem)

13. $\frac{BC}{DE} = \frac{AB}{AD}$ (Definition of similar polygons)

14. $\frac{BC}{DE} = 2$ (Substitution Property)

15. 2DE = BC (Multiplication Property)

16. $DE = \frac{1}{2}BC$ (Division Property)

22. Sample answer: Write a proportion: $\frac{AD}{BD} = \frac{AE}{EC}$. Solving for the length of $\overline{AD}$, $\frac{AD}{12} = \frac{15}{10}$ results in 10 · AD = 12 · 15, and so AD = 12 · $\frac{15}{10}$ = 18.

23. 39 cm; Sample answer: Because J, K, and L are midpoints of their respective sides, $JK = \frac{1}{2}QR, KL = \frac{1}{2}PQ,$ and $JL = \frac{1}{2}PR$ by the Triangle Midsegment Theorem. So $JK + KL + JL = \frac{1}{2}(QR + PQ + PR) = \frac{1}{2}(78) = 39$.

24. Sample answer: Using the Pythagorean Theorem, $AF = \sqrt{3^2 + 9^2} = \sqrt{90} \approx 9.49$ ft. The horizontal lines cut off congruent segments on the vertical transversal at the left of the figure, so they cut off congruent segments on $\overline{AF}$, so $AB = BD = DF = \frac{1}{3}AF \approx 3.2$ ft.

Parts of Similar Triangles

LESSON GOAL

Students solve problems and prove theorems about parts of similar triangles by using triangle similarity.

1 LAUNCH

Launch the lesson with a **Warm Up** and an introduction.

2 EXPLORE AND DEVELOP

Explore: Special Segments in Triangles

....

Develop:

Parts of Similar Triangles
- Use Special Segments in Similar Triangles
- Use Similar Triangles to Solve Problems
- Use the Triangle Angle Bisector Theorem

....

You may want your students to complete the **Checks** online.

3 REFLECT AND PRACTICE

Exit Ticket

....

Practice

DIFFERENTIATE

 View reports of student progress on the **Checks** after each example.

Resources	AL	OL	BL	ELL
Remediation: Similar Triangles: AA Similarity	●	●		●
Extension: A Proof of the Pythagorean Theorem		●	●	●

Language Development Handbook

Assign page 57 of the *Language Development Handbook* to help your students build mathematical language related to solving problems and proving theorems about parts of similar triangles by using triangle similarity.

ELL You can use the tips and suggestions on page T57 of the handbook to support students who are building English proficiency.

Reveal
GEOMETRY
Language Development
Handbook

Suggested Pacing

| 90 min | 0.5 day |
| 45 min | 1 day |

Focus

Domain: Geometry
Standards for Mathematical Content:
G.SRT.4 Prove theorems about triangles.
Standards for Mathematical Practice:
1 Make sense of problems.
3 Construct viable arguments.
6 Attend to precision.

Coherence

Vertical Alignment

Previous
Students used proportional relationships to solve real-world problems.
7.RP, A.CED.1, A.REI.3 (Algebra 1)

Now
Students solve problems and prove theorems about parts of similar triangles by using triangle similarity.
G.SRT.4

Next
Students will solve problems involving relationships between parts of a right triangle and the altitude to its hypotenuse using the geometric mean.
G.SRT.4, G.SRT.5

Rigor

The Three Pillars of Rigor

1 CONCEPTUAL UNDERSTANDING	2 FLUENCY	3 APPLICATION
Conceptual Bridge In this lesson, students focus on understanding the relationships that occur with parts of similar triangles. They build fluency by proving theorems about triangles, and apply their understanding by using proportionality to solve real-world problems.		

Mathematical Background

If two triangles are similar, then the perimeters and altitudes are proportional to the measures of corresponding sides. This relationship holds true for angle bisectors and medians as well.

Interactive Presentation

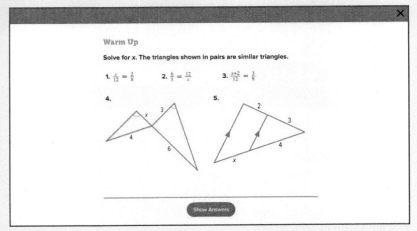

Warm Up

Launch the Lesson

Warm Up

Prerequisite Skills

The Warm Up exercises address the following prerequisite skill for this lesson:

- using triangle proportionality

Answers:

  1. 3   2. 10   3. $2\frac{1}{2}$ 4. 2   5. $\frac{8}{3}$

Launch the Lesson

MP Teaching the Mathematical Practices

> **4 Apply Mathematics** In this Launch the Lesson, students can see a real-world application of similar triangles.

Go Online to find additional teaching notes and questions to promote classroom discourse.

Today's Standards

Tell students that they will be addressing these content and practice standards in this lesson. You may wish to have a student volunteer read aloud *How can I meet these standards?* and *How can I use these practices?* and connect these to the standards.

See the Interactive Presentation for I Can statements that align with the standards covered in this lesson.

Explore Special Segments in Triangles

Objective
Students use dynamic geometry software to make conjectures about the special segments in similar triangles.

Teaching the Mathematical Practices

> **3 Make Conjectures** In this Explore, students will make conjectures and then build a logical progression of statements to validate the conjectures. Once students have made their conjectures, guide the students to validate them.

Ideas for Use

Recommended Use Present the Inquiry Question, or have a student volunteer read it aloud. Have students work in pairs to complete the Explore activity on their devices. Pairs should discuss each of the questions. Monitor student progress during the activity. Upon completion of the Explore activity, have student volunteers share their responses to the Inquiry Question.

What if my students don't have devices? You may choose to project the activity on a whiteboard. A printable worksheet for each Explore is available online. You may choose to print the worksheet so that individuals or pairs of students can use it to record their observations.

Summary of the Activity

Students will complete guiding exercises throughout the Explore activity. Students use a sketch to complete an activity that leads them to make conjectures that similar triangles have corresponding angle bisectors proportional to corresponding sides, similar triangles have corresponding medians proportional to corresponding sides, and similar triangles have corresponding altitudes proportional to corresponding sides. Then, students will answer the Inquiry Question.

(continued on the next page)

Interactive Presentation

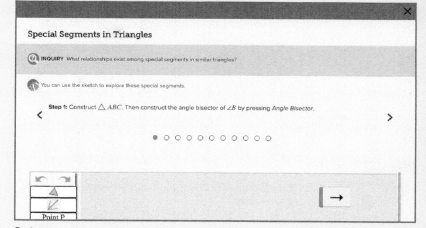

Explore

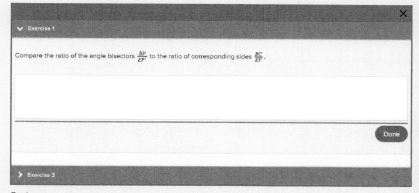

Explore

WEB SKETCHPAD

Students use a sketch to complete an activity in which they explore special segments in similar triangles.

Interactive Presentation

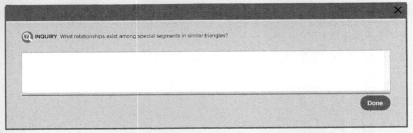

Explore

TYPE

a|

Students respond to the Inquiry Question and can view a sample answer.

Explore Special Segments in Triangles (*continued*)

 Teaching the Mathematical Practices

5 Use Mathematical Tools Point out that to solve the problem in this Explore, students will need to use dynamic geometry software. Work with students to explore and deepen their understanding of special segments in similar triangles.

Questions

Have students complete the Explore activity.

Ask:

- Does it make sense that the angle bisectors of similar triangles have a special relationship? Yes; sample answer: The corresponding angles in similar triangles are congruent. If you bisect the angles, the new corresponding angles will also be congruent.

- What happens when the altitude is outside the triangle? Do you think the ratios are still the same? Sample answer: The sketch continues to show the two triangles looking similar, but the ratio for $\frac{BP}{EP}$ is not visible. The ratios should still be similar, because you can draw altitudes outside of triangles.

Inquiry

What relationships exist among special segments in triangles? Sample answer: Corresponding sides and segments are proportional in similar triangles.

Go Online to find additional teaching notes and sample answers for the guiding exercises.

1 CONCEPTUAL UNDERSTANDING | 2 FLUENCY | 3 APPLICATION

Learn Parts of Similar Triangles

Objective
Students solve problems and prove theorems about parts of similar triangles by using triangle similarity.

Teaching the Mathematical Practices

7 Use Structure Help students to explore the structure of parts of similar triangles and the Triangle Angle Bisector Theorem in this Learn.

7 Draw an Auxiliary Line Help students see the need to draw an auxiliary line to prove Theorem 8.11.

Common Misconception
Students may believe that the corresponding angles of two similar triangles have the same ratio as the corresponding sides. Emphasize that the corresponding angles of two similar triangles must be congruent.

Go Online

- Find additional teaching notes.
- View performance reports of the Checks.
- Assign or present an Extra Example.

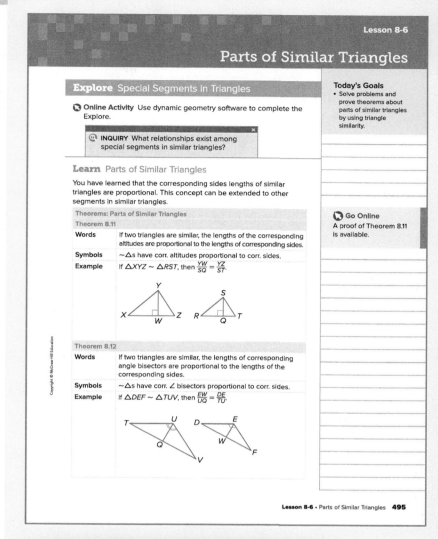

Lesson 8-6

Parts of Similar Triangles

Explore Special Segments in Triangles

Online Activity Use dynamic geometry software to complete the Explore.

INQUIRY What relationships exist among special segments in similar triangles?

Learn Parts of Similar Triangles

You have learned that the corresponding sides lengths of similar triangles are proportional. This concept can be extended to other segments in similar triangles.

Theorems: Parts of Similar Triangles

Theorem 8.11

Words	If two triangles are similar, the lengths of the corresponding altitudes are proportional to the lengths of corresponding sides.
Symbols	~△s have corr. altitudes proportional to corr. sides.
Example	If $\triangle XYZ \sim \triangle RST$, then $\frac{YW}{SQ} = \frac{YZ}{ST}$.

Theorem 8.12

Words	If two triangles are similar, the lengths of corresponding angle bisectors are proportional to the lengths of the corresponding sides.
Symbols	~△s have corr. ∠ bisectors proportional to corr. sides.
Example	If $\triangle DEF \sim \triangle TUV$, then $\frac{EW}{UQ} = \frac{DE}{TU}$.

Today's Goals
- Solve problems and prove theorems about parts of similar triangles by using triangle similarity.

Go Online
A proof of Theorem 8.11 is available.

Lesson 8-6 • Parts of Similar Triangles **495**

Parts of Similar Triangles

Theorems: Parts of Similar Triangles

Theorem 8.11

Words	If two triangles are similar, the lengths of the corresponding altitudes are proportional to the lengths of corresponding sides.
Symbols	~ △ s have corr. altitudes proportional to corr. sides.
Example	If $\triangle XYZ \sim \triangle RST$, then $\frac{YW}{SQ} = \frac{YZ}{ST}$.

Learn

EXPAND

Students tap to see a proof of Theorem 8.11.

DRAG & DROP

Students drag relationships to show whether they can be proven or need to be proven.

Your Notes

Theorem 8.13

Words	If two triangles are similar, the lengths of corresponding medians are proportional to the lengths of corresponding sides.
Symbols	~△s have corr. medians proportional to corr. sides.
Example	If $\triangle PQR \sim \triangle FGH$, then $\frac{RS}{HJ} = \frac{PQ}{FG}$.

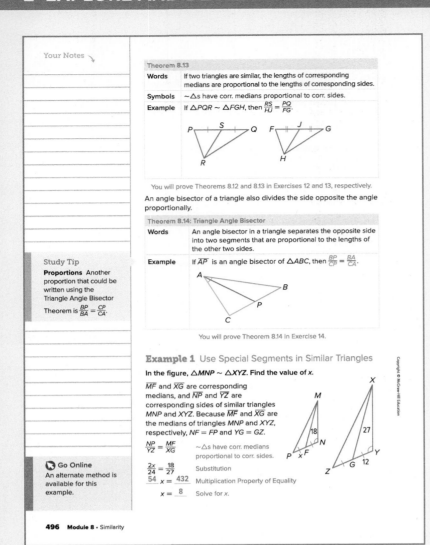

You will prove Theorems 8.12 and 8.13 in Exercises 12 and 13, respectively.

An angle bisector of a triangle also divides the side opposite the angle proportionally.

Theorem 8.14: Triangle Angle Bisector

Words	An angle bisector in a triangle separates the opposite side into two segments that are proportional to the lengths of the other two sides.
Example	If $\overline{AP}$ is an angle bisector of $\triangle ABC$, then $\frac{BP}{CP} = \frac{BA}{CA}$.

You will prove Theorem 8.14 in Exercise 14.

Study Tip

Proportions Another proportion that could be written using the Triangle Angle Bisector Theorem is $\frac{BP}{BA} = \frac{CP}{CA}$.

Example 1 Use Special Segments in Similar Triangles

In the figure, $\triangle MNP \sim \triangle XYZ$. Find the value of x.

$\overline{MF}$ and $\overline{XG}$ are corresponding medians, and $\overline{NP}$ and $\overline{YZ}$ are corresponding sides of similar triangles MNP and XYZ. Because $\overline{MF}$ and $\overline{XG}$ are the medians of triangles MNP and XYZ, respectively, NF = FP and YG = GZ.

$\frac{NP}{YZ} = \frac{MF}{XG}$ ~△s have corr. medians proportional to corr. sides.

$\frac{2x}{24} = \frac{18}{27}$ Substitution

$54\,x = 432$ Multiplication Property of Equality

$x = 8$ Solve for x.

Go Online
An alternate method is available for this example.

496   Module 8 · Similarity

Example 1 Use Special Segments in Similar Triangles

Teaching the Mathematical Practices

6 Communicate Precisely Encourage students to routinely write or explain their solution methods. Point out that they should use clear definitions when they discuss their solutions with others.

Questions for Mathematical Discourse

AL Would the relationship be the same if *MF* and *XG* were angle bisectors instead of medians? Explain. Yes; sample answer: An angle bisector also separates the opposite side into two segments that are proportional to the lengths of the other two sides.

OL Is it true that the corresponding angles of two similar triangles have the same ratio as the corresponding sides? Explain. No; sample answer: The corresponding angles of two similar triangles must be congruent.

BL Do you think perpendicular bisectors would divide similar triangles proportionally? Sample answer: Perpendicular bisectors only intersect the opposite vertex in special cases, but the segments produced would still be proportional for similar triangles.

Common Error

Similar triangles may be oriented differently. Remind students to look at markings on the figures to determine congruent angles and corresponding sides.

Interactive Presentation

×

Use Special Segments in Similar Triangles

In the figure, $\triangle MNP \sim \triangle XYZ$. Find the value of x.

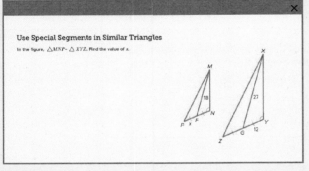

Example 1

TYPE

Students complete a calculation to find the unknown value.

1 CONCEPTUAL UNDERSTANDING | **2 FLUENCY** | **3 APPLICATION**

🌐 Apply Example 2 Use Similar Triangles to Solve Problems

MP Teaching the Mathematical Practices

> **1 Make Sense of Problems and Persevere in Solving Them,**
> **4 Model with Mathematics** Students will be presented with a task. They will first seek to understand the task, and then determine possible entry points to solving it. As students come up with their own strategies, they may propose mathematical models to aid them. As they work to solve the problem, encourage them to evaluate their model and/or progress, and change direction, if necessary.

Common Error

Remind students that not all altitudes separate a triangle proportionally. The altitudes of an obtuse triangle are outside of the triangle and don't separate the triangle at all.

Recommended Use

Have students work in pairs or small groups. You may wish to present the task, or have a volunteer read it aloud. Then allow students the time to make sure they understand the task, think of possible strategies, and work to solve the problem.

Encourage Productive Struggle

As students work, monitor their progress. Instead of instructing them on a particular strategy, encourage them to use their own strategies to solve the problem and to evaluate their progress along the way. They may or may not find that they need to change direction or try out several strategies.

Signs of Non-Productive Struggle

If students show signs of non-productive struggle, such as feeling overwhelmed, frustrated, or disengaged, intervene to encourage them to think of alternate approaches to the problem. Some sample questions are shown.

- Which angles are congruent in the diagram?
- What does the focal distance mean in photography?

✏️ Write About It!

Have students share their responses with another pair/group of students or the entire class. Have them clearly state or describe the mathematical reasoning they can use to defend their solution.

🌐 Apply Example 2 Use Similar Triangles to Solve Problems

PHOTOGRAPHY **A digital camera projects an image through its lens and onto its sensor, where it is converted into a digital image. The distance between the camera's lens and its sensor is known as the focal length and is adjusted depending on the size of the object being photographed and its distance from the camera lens. Ms. Elgin sets her camera up 3 meters away from her subject, who is 1.6 meters tall. If the sensor on her camera is 4.8 millimeters tall, what is the optimal focal length?**

1 What is the task?

Describe the task in your own words. Then list any questions that you may have. How can you find answers to your questions?

Sample answer: I need to find the optimal focal length for the digital camera. Are the triangles that model the situation similar? What theorem relating the measures within similar triangles can I use to find the focal length? To answer these questions, I will draw a diagram and use what I know about triangle similarity.

2 How will you approach the task? What have you learned that you can use to help you complete the task?

Sample answer: I will draw a diagram. Then I will identify congruent angles and corresponding sides. I will determine whether the triangles are similar. Then I will write a proportion and solve for the optimal focal length.

3 What is your solution?

Use your strategy to solve the problem.

Complete the diagram. Assume that $\overline{CK}$ and $\overline{CL}$ are altitudes of $\triangle ACB$ and $\triangle DCF$, respectively, and that $\overline{AB} \parallel \overline{DF}$.

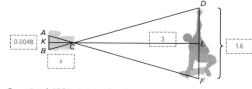

Prove that $\triangle ABC$ is similar to $\triangle FDC$.

Sample answer: Because $\overline{AB} \parallel \overline{DF}$, $\angle BAC \cong \angle DFC$ and $\angle CBA \cong \angle CDF$ by the Alternate Interior Angles Theorem. $\triangle ABC \sim \triangle FDC$ by AA Similarity.

What is the measure of the optimal focal length of the digital camera?

___9___ mm

(continued on the next page)

Study Tip
Assumptions In this example, we assume that the sensor on the camera is pointing straight, creating altitudes in triangles *ABC* and *DCF*.

Watch Out!
Altitudes Not all altitudes separate a triangle proportionally. The altitudes of an obtuse triangle are outside of the triangle and don't separate the triangle at all.

Interactive Presentation

Use Similar Triangles to Solve Problems

🌐 PHOTOGRAPHY A digital camera projects an image through its lens and onto its sensor, where it is converted into a digital image. The distance between the camera's lens and its sensor is known as the focal length and is adjusted depending on the size of the object being photographed and its distance from the camera lens. Ms. Elgin sets her camera up 3 meters away from her subject, who is 1.6 meters tall. If the sensor on her camera is 4.8 mm tall, what is the optimal focal length?

Tap on each step of the four-step plan to solve the problem.

Apply Example 2

DRAG & DROP

 Students complete the diagram by dragging the correct labels.

1 CONCEPTUAL UNDERSTANDING | **2 FLUENCY** | **3 APPLICATION**

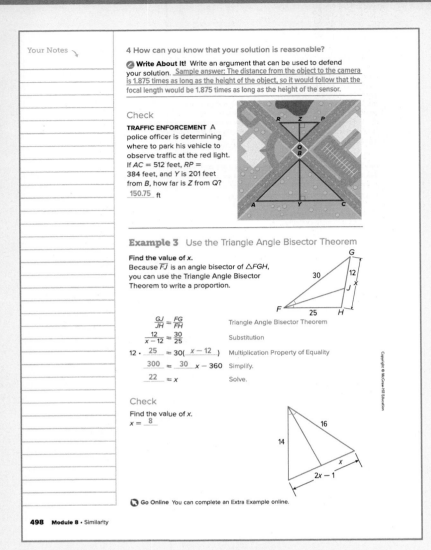

Your Notes ↘

4 How can you know that your solution is reasonable?

✏️ **Write About It!** Write an argument that can be used to defend your solution. _Sample answer: The distance from the object to the camera is 1.875 times as long as the height of the object, so it would follow that the focal length would be 1.875 times as long as the height of the sensor._

Check

TRAFFIC ENFORCEMENT A police officer is determining where to park his vehicle to observe traffic at the red light. If $AC = 512$ feet, $RP = 384$ feet, and Y is 201 feet from B, how far is Z from Q?

_150.75_ ft

Example 3 Use the Triangle Angle Bisector Theorem

Find the value of x.
Because $\overline{FJ}$ is an angle bisector of $\triangle FGH$, you can use the Triangle Angle Bisector Theorem to write a proportion.

$\dfrac{GJ}{JH} = \dfrac{FG}{FH}$ Triangle Angle Bisector Theorem

$\dfrac{12}{x-12} = \dfrac{30}{25}$ Substitution

$12 \cdot \underline{25} = 30(\underline{x-12})$ Multiplication Property of Equality

$\underline{300} = \underline{30}\,x - 360$ Simplify.

$\underline{22} = x$ Solve.

Check
Find the value of x.
$x = \underline{8}$

🔵 **Go Online** You can complete an Extra Example online.

498 Module 8 · Similarity

Example 3 Use the Triangle Angle Bisector Theorem

MP Teaching the Mathematical Practices

2 Create Representations Guide students to write an equation that models the situation in this example. Then use the equation to solve the problem.

Questions for Mathematical Discourse

AL Does this prove that $\triangle FGJ \sim \triangle FHJ$? Explain. No; sample answer: The Triangle Angle Bisector Theorem only tells you that the segments formed by the angle bisector are proportional to the lengths of the other sides.

OL What is another proportion you can write to solve this problem? Sample answer: $\dfrac{FG}{GJ} = \dfrac{FH}{HJ}$

BL Give a counterexample to show that not all altitudes separate a triangle proportionally. Sample answer: In a right triangle, two of the altitudes are legs, so they do not separate the triangle at all.

Exit Ticket

Recommended Use
At the end of class, go online to display the Exit Ticket prompt and ask students to respond using a separate piece of paper. Have students hand you their responses as they leave the room.

Alternate Use
At the end of class, go online to display the Exit Ticket prompt and ask students to respond verbally or by using a mini-whiteboard. Have students hold up their whiteboards so that you can see all student responses. Tap to reveal the answer when most or all students have completed the Exit Ticket.

Interactive Presentation

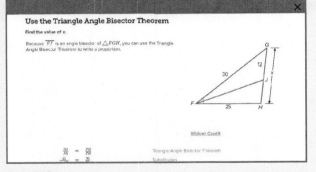

Example 3

CHECK

Students complete the Check online to determine whether they are ready to move on.

Practice and Homework

Suggested Assignments

Use the table below to select appropriate exercises.

DOK	Topic	Exercises
1, 2	exercises that mirror the examples	1–9
2	exercises that use a variety of skills from this lesson	10–14
3	exercises that emphasize higher-order and critical-thinking skills	15–18

ASSESS AND DIFFERENTIATE

📊 Use the data from the **Checks** to determine whether to provide resources for extension, remediation, or intervention.

IF students score 90% or more on the Checks, `OL` `BL`
THEN assign:

- Practice, Exercises 1–13 odd, 15–18
- Extension: A Proof of the Pythagorean Theorem
- ⊚ **ALEKS**· Similar Figures

IF students score 66%–89% on the Checks, `AL` `OL`
THEN assign:

- Practice, Exercises 1–17 odd
- Remediation, Review Resources: Similar Triangles: AA Similarity
- Personal Tutors
- Extra Examples 1–3
- ⊚ **ALEKS**· Triangle Proportionality

IF students score 65% or less on the Checks, `AL`
THEN assign:

- Practice, Exercises 1–9 odd
- Remediation, Review Resources: Similar Triangles: AA Similarity
- *Quick Review Math Handbook*: Parts of Similar Triangles
- ⊚ **ALEKS**· Triangle Proportionality

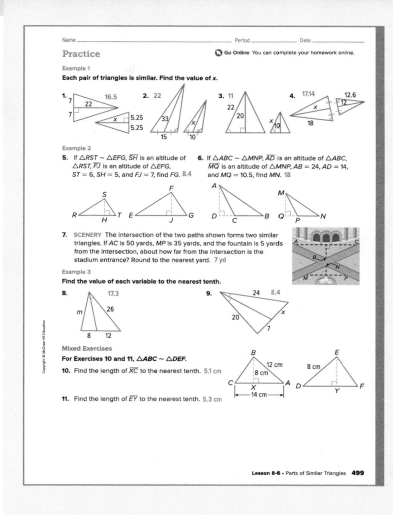

1 CONCEPTUAL UNDERSTANDING | 2 FLUENCY | 3 APPLICATION

12. PROOF Write a paragraph proof of Theorem 8.12.

Given: $\triangle RTS \sim \triangle EGF$; $\overline{TA}$ and $\overline{GB}$ are angle bisectors.

Prove: $\frac{TA}{GB} = \frac{RT}{EG}$ Proof: It is given that $\triangle RTS \sim \triangle EGF$ and that $\overline{TA}$ and $\overline{GB}$ are angle bisectors. By the definition of similar triangles, $\angle R \cong \angle E$ and $\angle RTS \cong \angle EGF$. Because $\angle RTS$ and $\angle EGF$ or $\angle FGE$ are bisected, we know that $\frac{1}{2}m\angle RTS = \frac{1}{2}m\angle EGF$ or $m\angle RTA = m\angle EGB$. By the definition of congruence, $\angle RTA \cong \angle EGB$. $\triangle RTA \sim \triangle EGB$ by AA Similarity. Thus, $\frac{TA}{GB} = \frac{RT}{EG}$.

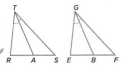

13. PROOF Write a two-column proof of Theorem 8.13.

Given: $\triangle ABC \sim \triangle RST$; $\overline{AD}$ is a median of $\triangle ABC$ and $\overline{RU}$ is a median of $\triangle RST$.

Prove: $\frac{AD}{RU} = \frac{AB}{RS}$ See margin.

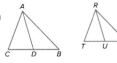

14. PROOF Write a two-column proof of the Triangle Angle Bisector Theorem. (Theorem 8.14)

Given: $\overline{CD}$ bisects $\angle ACB$. By construction, $\overline{AE} \parallel \overline{CD}$.

Prove: $\frac{AD}{DB} = \frac{AC}{BC}$ See margin.

Higher-Order Thinking Skills

15. FIND THE ERROR Chun and Traci are determining the value of x in the figure. Chun says to solve the proportion $\frac{5}{8} = \frac{15}{x}$, but Traci says to find the value of x, the proportion $\frac{5}{x} = \frac{8}{15}$ should be solved. Is either of them correct? Explain your reasoning.

Chun; sample answer: By the Angle Bisector Theorem, the correct proportion is $\frac{5}{8} = \frac{15}{x}$.

16. CREATE Draw two triangles so that the measures of an altitude and side of one triangle are proportional to the measures of an altitude and side of another triangle, but the triangles are not similar. See margin.

17. PERSEVERE The perimeter of $\triangle PQR$ is 94 units. $\overline{QS}$ bisects $\angle PQR$. Find PS and RS. Round to the nearest tenth, if necessary. $PS = 18.4$, $RS = 24$

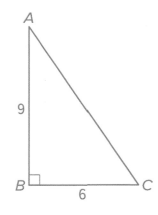

Answers

13. Proof:

Statements (Reasons)

1. $\triangle ABC \sim \triangle RST$, $\overline{AD}$ is a median of $\triangle ABC$ and $\overline{RU}$ is a median of $\triangle RST$. (Given)

2. $CD = DB$, $TU = US$ (Definition of median)

3. $\frac{AB}{RS} = \frac{CB}{TS}$ (Definition of similar triangles)

4. $CB = CD + DB$, $TS = TU + US$ (Segment Addition Postulate)

5. $\frac{AB}{RS} = \frac{CD + DB}{TU + US}$ (Substitution)

6. $\frac{AB}{RS} = \frac{DB + DB}{US + US} = \frac{2(DB)}{2(US)}$ (Substitution)

7. $\frac{AB}{RS} = \frac{DB}{US}$ (Substitution)

8. $\angle B \cong \angle S$ (Definition of similar triangles)

9. $\triangle ABD \sim \triangle RSU$ (SAS Similarity)

10. $\frac{AD}{RU} = \frac{AB}{RS}$ (Definition of similar triangles)

14. Proof:

Statements (Reasons)

1. $\overline{CD}$ bisects $\angle ACB$. By construction, $\overline{AE} \parallel \overline{CD}$. (Given)

2. $\frac{AD}{DB} = \frac{EC}{BC}$ (Triangle Proportionality Theorem)

3. $\angle 1 \cong \angle 2$ (Definition of angle bisector)

4. $\angle 3 \cong \angle 1$ (Alternate Interior Angles Theorem)

5. $\angle 2 \cong \angle E$ (Corresponding Angles Theorem)

6. $\angle 3 \cong \angle E$ (Transitive Property)

7. $\overline{EC} \cong \overline{AC}$ (Converse of Isosceles Triangle Theorem)

8. $EC = AC$ (Definition of congruence)

9. $\frac{AD}{DB} = \frac{AC}{BC}$ (Substitution)

16. $\frac{AB}{BC} = \frac{XW}{YZ}$, but $\triangle ABC$ is not similar to $\triangle XYZ$.

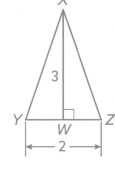

Review

Rate Yourself! 👎 ✋ 👍

Have students return to the Module Opener to rate their understanding of the concepts presented in this module. They should see that their knowledge and skills have increased. After completing the chart, have them respond to the prompts in their *Interactive Student Edition* and share their responses with a partner.

ⓔ Answering the Essential Question

Before answering the Essential Question, have students review their answers to the Essential Question Follow-Up questions found throughout the module.

- What does it mean for objects to be similar, and how is similarity useful for modeling in the real world?
- How are dilations related to the concepts of symmetry and transformations?

Then have them write their answer to the Essential Question in the space provided.

DINAH ZIKE FOLDABLES

ELL A completed Foldable for this module should include the key concepts related to similarity.

LS **LearnSmart** Use LearnSmart as part of your test preparation plan to measure student topic retention. You can create a student assignment in LearnSmart for additional practice on these topics for **Similarity, Proof, and Trigonometry**.

- Understand similarity in terms of similarity transformations
- Prove theorems involving similarity

ⓔ Essential Question

What does it mean for objects to be similar, and how is similarity useful for modeling in the real world?

Sample answer: Objects are similar when they are the same shape but not necessarily the same size. Their measures are in proportion to one another. Similar shapes are used when making scale drawings, such as blueprints, and scale models, such as replicas.

Module Summary

Lessons 8-1 and 8-2

Dilations and Similar Polygons

- A dilation is a nonrigid transformation that enlarges or reduces a geometric figure.
- When a figure is enlarged or reduced, the sides of the image are proportional to the sides of the original figure.
- To dilate a figure by a scale factor of k with respect to (0, 0), multiply the x- and y-coordinate of each vertex by k.
- Two figures are similar if one can be obtained from the other by a dilation or a dilation with one or more rigid motions.

Lessons 8-3 and 8-4

Criteria for Similar Triangles

- Angle-Angle (AA) Similarity: If two angles of one triangle are congruent to two angles of another triangle, then the triangles are similar.
- Side-Side-Side (SSS) Similarity: If the corresponding side lengths of two triangles are proportional, then the triangles are similar.
- Side-Angle-Side (SAS) Similarity: If the lengths of two sides of one triangle are proportional to the lengths of two corresponding sides of another triangle and the included angles are congruent, then the triangles are similar.

Lesson 8-5

Triangle Proportionality

- If a line is parallel to one side of a triangle and intersects the other two sides, then it divides the sides into segments of proportional lengths.
- If three or more parallel lines intersect two transversals, then they cut off the transversals proportionally.

Lesson 8-6

Parts of Similar Triangles

- If two triangles are similar, the lengths of the corresponding altitudes are proportional to the lengths of corresponding sides.
- If two triangles are similar, the lengths of corresponding angle bisectors are proportional to the lengths of the corresponding sides.

Study Organizer

📖 Foldables

Use your Foldable to review this module. Working with a partner can be helpful. Ask for clarification of concepts as needed.

Test Practice

1. MULTIPLE CHOICE Which kind of dilation is the transformation from trapezoid *EFGH* to trapezoid *JKLM*? (Lesson 8-1)

Ⓐ Enlargement with a scale factor of $\frac{5}{3}$

Ⓑ Enlargement with a scale factor of $\frac{3}{5}$

Ⓒ Reduction with a scale factor of $\frac{5}{3}$

Ⓓ Reduction with a scale factor of $\frac{3}{5}$

2. TABLE ITEM Match each effect on a figure with its corresponding dilation scale factor value. (Lesson 8-1)

	Scale Factor		
	−1 to 0	0 to 1	>1
reduction		X	
rotation and reduction	X		
enlargement			X

3. OPEN RESPONSE The vertices of △*ABC* are *A*(5, 4), *B*(10, 8), and *C*(20, 0). A dilation centered at the origin with a scale factor of $\frac{4}{5}$ maps △*ABC* onto △*A'B'C'*. What are the coordinates of the vertices of △*A'B'C'*? (Lesson 8-1)

> *A'*(4, 3.2), *B'*(8, 6.4), and *C'*(16, 0)

4. OPEN RESPONSE Given parallelogram *WXYZ*, what are the coordinates of *W'X'Y'Z'* after a dilation centered at the origin with a scale factor of $\frac{3}{2}$? (Lesson 8-1)

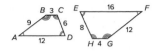

> $W'\left(\frac{3}{2}, \frac{15}{2}\right)$, *X'*(9, 9), *Y'*(9, 3), $Z'\left(\frac{3}{2}, \frac{3}{2}\right)$

5. OPEN RESPONSE Using the definition of similarity, show that the two quadrilaterals are similar. (Lesson 8-2)

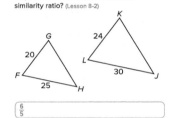

$\angle A \cong \angle F, \angle B \cong \angle G, \angle C \cong \angle H, \angle D \cong \angle E$

$\frac{AB}{FG} = \frac{BC}{GH} = \frac{CD}{HE} = \frac{DA}{EF}$

$\frac{9}{12} = \frac{3}{4} = \frac{6}{8} = \frac{12}{16}$

$\frac{3}{4} = \frac{3}{4} = \frac{3}{4} = \frac{3}{4}$

Therefore, quadrilateral *ABCD* ~ quadrilateral *FGHE*.

6. OPEN RESPONSE If a similarity transformation maps △*FGH* onto △*LKJ*, what is the similarity ratio? (Lesson 8-2)

> $\frac{6}{5}$

Review and Assessment Options

The following online review and assessment resources are available for you to assign to your students. These resources include technology-enhanced questions that are auto-scored, as well as essay questions.

Review Resources

Put It All Together: Lessons 8–1 through 8–4

Vocabulary Activity

Module Review

Assessment Resources

Vocabulary Test

AL Module Test Form B

OL Module Test Form A

BL Module Test Form C

Performance Task*

*The module-level performance task is available online as a printable document. A scoring rubric is included.

Test Practice

You can use these pages to help your students review module content and prepare for online assessments. Exercises 1–17 mirror the types of questions your students will see on online assessments.

Question Type	Description	Exercise(s)
Multiple Choice	Students select one correct answer.	1, 7, 9, 11, 17
Multi-Select	Multiple answers may be correct. Students must select all correct answers.	14
Table Item	Students complete a table by entering in the correct values.	2, 13
Open Response	Students construct their own response in the area provided.	3–6, 8, 10, 12, 15, 16

To ensure that students understand the standards, check students' success on individual exercises.

Standard(s)	Lesson(s)	Exercise(s)
G.CO.2	8-1	3, 4
G.SRT.1	8-1	1, 2, 4
G.SRT.2	8-2, 8-4	5–7, 12
G.SRT.3	8-3	8–10
G.SRT.4	8-6	17
G.SRT.5	8-3, 8-4	8–12
G.CO.10	8-5	13–15
G.CO.12	8-6	16

Name _____   Period _____   Date _____

7. MULTIPLE CHOICE On a blueprint, a rectangular kitchen has a length of 4 inches and a width of 3 inches. If the length of the kitchen is 6 feet, what is the perimeter of the kitchen in feet? (Lesson 8-2)

- (A) 18 feet
- (B) 20 feet
- (C) 21 feet
- (D) 24 feet

8. OPEN RESPONSE Given any two equilateral triangles. Are the triangles similar? Justify your answer. (Lesson 8-3)

Sample answer: Because equilateral triangles have angles that are each 60°, all the angles in one equilateral triangle are congruent to the angles in the second triangle. Therefore, by AA similarity, all equilateral triangles are similar.

9. MULTIPLE CHOICE Given: $\angle B \cong \angle E$
Prove: $\triangle ADE \sim \triangle CDB$

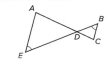

Complete the paragraph proof.

It is given that $\angle B \cong \angle E$. $\angle ADE \cong \angle CDB$ by the ___. Therefore, $\triangle ADE$ is similar to $\triangle CDB$ by the ___. (Lesson 8-3)

- (A) Corresponding Angles Postulate, Angle-Angle Similarity Postulate
- (B) Corresponding Angles Postulate, Third Angles Theorem
- (C) Vertical Angles Theorem, Angle-Angle Similarity Postulate
- (D) Vertical Angles Theorem, Third Angles Theorem

10. OPEN RESPONSE In $\triangle ABC$, $m\angle A = 44°$ and $m\angle B = 56°$. In $\triangle DEF$, $m\angle D = 44°$ and $m\angle F = 80°$. Is $\triangle ABC$ similar to $\triangle DEF$? Justify your answer. (Lesson 8-3)

Yes; sample answer: The measure of $\angle C$ is $180 - 44 - 56 = 80°$, so $\angle C$ is congruent to $\angle F$. Thus, the triangles are similar by the Angle-Angle Similarity Postulate.

11. MULTIPLE CHOICE What can be used to prove that $\triangle ABC$ is similar to $\triangle DBE$? (Lesson 8-4)

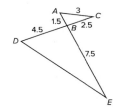

- (A) AA Similarity Postulate
- (B) SAS Similarity Theorem
- (C) SSS Similarity Theorem
- (D) AAS Similarity Theorem

12. OPEN RESPONSE What proves that $\triangle CDE$ is not similar to $\triangle FGH$? (Lesson 8-4)

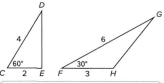

Sample answer: Corresponding angles are not congruent.

13. TABLE ITEM If $\overline{BD} \parallel \overline{AE}$ and $AC = 4$, identify the lengths of the other sides. (Lesson 8-5)

Sides	Lengths			
	1.6	2.0	2.4	3.6
$\overline{AB}$	X			
$\overline{BD}$				X
$\overline{BC}$			X	

14. MULTI-SELECT Select all of the true statements about the figure. (Lesson 8-5)

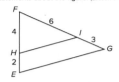

- Ⓐ $\overline{HI} \parallel \overline{EG}$
- Ⓑ $\frac{FH}{HE} = \frac{FI}{IG}$
- Ⓒ $\frac{FH}{HE} = \frac{HI}{EG}$
- Ⓓ $\frac{FH}{GI} = \frac{FI}{EH}$
- Ⓔ $\frac{HE}{FH} = \frac{FI}{IG}$

15. OPEN RESPONSE If lines k, m, and n are parallel, what is the value of x? (Lesson 8-5)

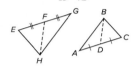

8

16. OPEN RESPONSE Suppose $AD = 7$. What is the length of $\overline{AB}$? Round your answer to the nearest thousandth. (Lesson 8-6)

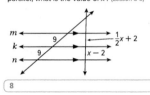

2.625 units

17. MULTIPLE CHOICE If $\triangle ABC \sim \triangle GHE$, which theorem proves $\frac{FH}{BD} = \frac{GH}{AB}$? (Lesson 8-6)

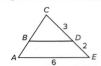

- Ⓐ If two triangles are similar, then the lengths of corresponding medians are proportional to the lengths of the corresponding sides.

- Ⓑ If two triangles are similar, then the lengths of corresponding altitudes are proportional to the lengths of the corresponding sides.

- Ⓒ If two triangles are similar, then the lengths of corresponding angle bisectors are proportional to the lengths of the corresponding sides.

- Ⓓ An angle bisector in a triangle separates the opposite side into two segments that are proportional to the lengths of the other two sides.

Lesson 8-1

28. Sample answer: $k = 2$; The center of dilation is B.

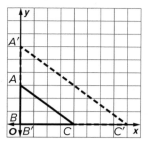

Lesson 8-5

27. Always; sample answer: FH is a midsegment. Let $BC = x$, then $FH = \frac{1}{2}x$. $FHCB$ is a trapezoid, so $DE = \frac{1}{2}(BC + FH) = \frac{1}{2}\left(x + \frac{1}{2}x\right) = \frac{1}{2}x + \frac{1}{4}x = \frac{3}{4}x$. Therefore, $DE = \frac{3}{4}BC$.

28. Proof:

Statements (Reasons)

1. $AB = 4$, $BC = 4$ (Given)
2. $AB = BC$ (Substitution)
3. $AB + BC = AC$ (Segment Addition Postulate)
4. $BC + BC = AC$ (Substitution)
5. $2BC = AC$ (Substitution)
6. $AC = 2BC$ (Symmetric Property of Equality)
7. $\frac{AC}{BC} = 2$ (Division Property of Equality)
8. $ED = DC$ (Given)
9. $ED + DC = EC$ (Segment Addition Postulate)
10. $DC + DC = EC$ (Substitution)
11. $2DC = EC$ (Substitution)
12. $2 = \frac{EC}{DC}$ (Division Property of Equality)
13. $\frac{AC}{BC} = \frac{EC}{DC}$ (Transitive Property or Equality)
14. $\angle C \cong \angle C$ (Reflexive Property of Congruence)
15. $\triangle ACE \sim \triangle BCD$ (SAS Similarity)
16. $\angle CAE \cong \angle CBD$ (Definition of similar polygons)
17. $\overline{BD} \parallel \overline{AE}$ (If corresponding angles are congruent, lines are parallel.)

29. Sample answer: By Corollary 8.1, $\frac{a}{b} = \frac{c}{d}$.

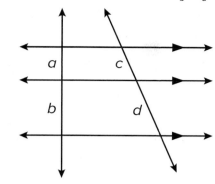

30. Sample answer: Both theorems deal with a parallel line inside the triangle. The Midsegment Theorem is a special case of the Converse of the Proportionality Theorem.

Module Goals

- Students use trigonometric ratios and the Pythagorean Theorem to solve right triangles in applied problems.
- Students explain and use the relationship between the sine and cosine of complementary angles.
- Students prove the Laws of Sines and Cosines and use them to solve problems.

Focus

Domain: Geometry

Standards for Mathematical Content:

G.SRT.6 Understand that by similarity, side ratios in right triangles are properties of the angles in the triangle, leading to definitions of trigonometric ratios for acute angles.

G.SRT.8 Use trigonometric ratios and the Pythagorean Theorem to solve right triangles in applied problems.

Also addresses G.SRT.4, G.SRT.5, G.SRT.7, G.SRT.9, G.SRT.10, and G.SRT.11.

Standards for Mathematical Practice:

All Standards for Mathematical Practice will be addressed in this module.

✪ Be Sure to Cover

To completely cover G.SRT.6, go online to assign the following activity:

- Trigonometry and Similarity (Explore Lesson 9-5)

Coherence

Vertical Alignment

Previous
Students solved problems involving right triangles using the Pythagorean Theorem.
8.G.7, 8.G.8

Now
Students use trigonometric ratios and the Pythagorean Theorem to solve right triangles in applied problems.
G.SRT.6, G.SRT.8

Next
Students will solve problems using the relationships in circles, tangents, secants, and associated angles.
G.C.1, G.C.2

Rigor

The Three Pillars of Rigor

To help students meet standards, they need to illustrate their ability to use the three pillars of rigor. Students gain conceptual understanding as they move from the Explore to Learn sections within a lesson. Once they understand the concept, they practice procedural skills and fluency and apply their mathematical knowledge as they go through the Examples and Practice.

1 CONCEPTUAL UNDERSTANDING	2 FLUENCY	3 APPLICATION

EXPLORE ⟩ LEARN ⟩ EXAMPLE & PRACTICE

Suggested Pacing

Lessons	Standards	45-min classes	90-min classes
Module Pretest and Launch the Module Video		1	0.5
9-1 Geometric Mean	G.SRT.4, G.SRT.5	1	0.5
9-2 Pythagorean Theorem and Its Converse	G.SRT.4, G.SRT.8	1	0.5
9-3 Coordinates in Space		1	0.5
9-4 Special Right Triangles	G.SRT.6	1	0.5
9-5 Trigonometry	G.SRT.6, G.SRT.7	2	1
9-6 Applying Trigonometry	G.SRT.8, G.SRT.9	1	0.5
9-7 The Law of Sines	G.SRT.10, G.SRT.11	1	0.5
9-8 The Law of Cosines	G.SRT.10, G.SRT.11	1	0.5
Put It All Together: Lessons 9-5 through 9-8		1	0.5
Module Review		1	0.5
Module Assessment		1	0.5
Total Days		**13**	**6.5**

Formative Assessment Math Probe
Solving Trigonometric Equations

NAME _____ DATE_____ PERIOD _____

Cheryl Tobey Math Probe
Solving Trigonometric Equations

Which solution shows a correct way to solve for x in each equation below?

A. $x = \tan 42 \cdot 12$ B. $x = \frac{42}{\tan}$ C. $x = \frac{12}{\tan 42}$

D. $x = 12 \tan 42$ E. $x = \frac{\tan 42}{12}$ F. $x = \tan^{-1} \frac{42}{12}$

Circle your choice.	Explain your choice.
1. $\tan 42 = \frac{x}{12}$ A. Solution A B. Solution B C. Solution C D. Solution D E. Solution E F. Solution F	
2. $\tan 42 = \frac{12}{x}$ A. Solution A B. Solution B C. Solution C D. Solution D E. Solution E F. Solution F	
3. $\tan x = \frac{42}{12}$ A. Solution A B. Solution B C. Solution C D. Solution D E. Solution E F. Solution F	

Cheryl Tobey Math Probe • Solving Trigonometric Equations   © McGraw-Hill Education

Answers: 1. D; 2. C; 3. F

Analyze the Probe

Review the probe prior to assigning it to your students.

In this probe, students will determine the correct ways to solve trigonometric equations and explain their choices.

Targeted Concepts Understand the relationships between numbers, variables, and symbols in trigonometric equations.

Targeted Misconceptions

- When solving for an unknown side length in a trigonometric equation, students may incorrectly multiply or divide the angle measure instead of finding the sine, cosine, or tangent of the angle.

- When students do not understand the relationships among the numbers, variables, and/or symbols used in trigonometric equations, they often incorrectly solve for unknown side lengths that are in the denominator by

  - "flipping" only one side of the equation,
  - leaving the variable in the denominator and trying to "work around it," or
  - moving the variable to the numerator without maintaining the equality.

- Students may incorrectly believe that to solve for an unknown angle, each side of the equation needs to be divided by sine, cosine, or tangent instead of taking the inverse trigonometric function of each side.

Use the Probe after Lesson 9-5.

Collect and Assess Student Answers

If the student selects these responses...	**Then** the student likely...
1. A	is multiplying each side by 12 to solve for x, but incorrectly multiplies the angle measure (42°) by 12 instead of the tangent of the angle (tan 42°).
2. E	does not understand the relationship between tangent, the numbers, and/or the variable, and tried to solve the equation without using the proper steps to maintain equality.
3. B	sees tan x as tangent times x, and solves for x by dividing each side by tan.

Take Action

After the Probe Design a plan to address any possible misconceptions. You may wish to assign the following resources.

- **ALEKS** Right Triangle Trigonometry
- Lesson 9-5, all Learns, all Examples

Revisit the probe at the end of the module to be sure that your students no longer carry these misconceptions.

IGNITE!

The Ignite! activities, created by Dr. Raj Shah, cultivate curiosity and engage and challenge students. Use these open-ended, collaborative activities, located online in the module Launch section, to encourage your students to develop a growth mindset towards mathematics and problem solving. Use the teacher notes for implementation suggestions and support for encouraging productive struggle.

ⓔ Essential Question

At the end of this module, students should be able to answer the Essential Question.

How are right triangle relationships useful in solving real-world problems? Sample answer: The Pythagorean Theorem can be used to find missing side lengths of right triangles that occur in the real world.

What Will You Learn?

Prior to beginning this module, have your students rate their knowledge of each item listed. Then, at the end of the module, you will be reminded to have your students return to these pages to rate their knowledge again. They should see that their knowledge and skills have increased.

DINAH ZIKE FOLDABLES

Focus Students read about right triangle trigonometry.

Teach Throughout the module, have students take notes under the tabs of their Foldables while working through each lesson. They should include definitions, terms, and key concepts. Encourage students to record examples of each right triangle relationship from a lesson on the back of their Foldable.

When to Use It Use the appropriate tabs as students cover each lesson in this module. Students should add to the vocabulary tab during each lesson.

Launch the Module

For this module, the Launch the Module video uses Mount Everest to demonstrate how it is possible to measure the height of a mountain without climbing it. Students learn that right triangles and trigonometry can be used to find locations, distances, and routes.

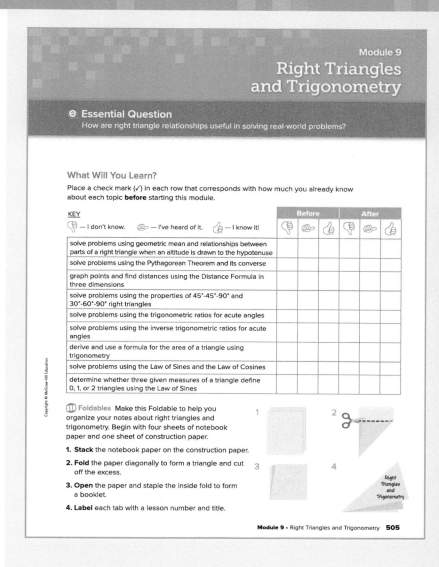

Interactive Presentation

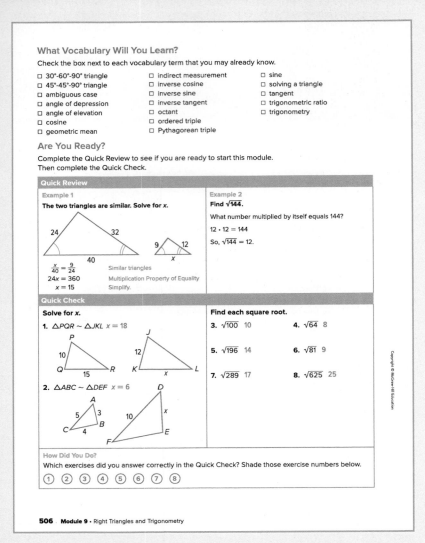

What Vocabulary Will You Learn?

Check the box next to each vocabulary term that you may already know.

- ☐ 30°-60°-90° triangle
- ☐ 45°-45°-90° triangle
- ☐ ambiguous case
- ☐ angle of depression
- ☐ angle of elevation
- ☐ cosine
- ☐ geometric mean
- ☐ indirect measurement
- ☐ inverse cosine
- ☐ inverse sine
- ☐ inverse tangent
- ☐ octant
- ☐ ordered triple
- ☐ Pythagorean triple
- ☐ sine
- ☐ solving a triangle
- ☐ tangent
- ☐ trigonometric ratio
- ☐ trigonometry

Are You Ready?

Complete the Quick Review to see if you are ready to start this module.
Then complete the Quick Check.

Quick Review

Example 1

The two triangles are similar. Solve for x.

$\frac{x}{40} = \frac{9}{24}$ Similar triangles

$24x = 360$ Multiplication Property of Equality

$x = 15$ Simplify.

Example 2

Find $\sqrt{144}$.

What number multiplied by itself equals 144?

$12 \cdot 12 = 144$

So, $\sqrt{144} = 12$.

Quick Check

Solve for x.

1. $\triangle PQR \sim \triangle JKL$ $x = 18$

2. $\triangle ABC \sim \triangle DEF$ $x = 6$

Find each square root.

3. $\sqrt{100}$ 10

4. $\sqrt{64}$ 8

5. $\sqrt{196}$ 14

6. $\sqrt{81}$ 9

7. $\sqrt{289}$ 17

8. $\sqrt{625}$ 25

How Did You Do?

Which exercises did you answer correctly in the Quick Check? Shade those exercise numbers below.

① ② ③ ④ ⑤ ⑥ ⑦ ⑧

What Vocabulary Will You Learn?

ELL As you proceed through the module, introduce the key vocabulary by using the following routine.

Define The geometric mean of two positive real numbers a and b is the number x such that $\frac{a}{x} = \frac{x}{b}$.

Example The geometric mean of 1 and 16 is 4.

Ask Is the geometric mean the average of the two numbers? What are equivalent ways to show the relationship given by the geometric mean? No; $\frac{a}{x} = \frac{x}{b}$, $x^2 = ab$, $x = \sqrt{ab}$.

Are You Ready?

Students may need to review the following prerequisite skills to succeed in this module.

- using similar triangles
- finding square roots
- graphing ordered pairs
- using the Pythagorean Theorem
- identifying the adjacent side, opposite side, and hypotenuse
- using similar triangles to measure indirectly
- solving proportions
- finding trigonometric ratios

⊙ ALEKS®

ALEKS is an adaptive, personalized learning environment that identifies precisely what each student knows and is ready to learn, ensuring student success at all levels.

You may want to use the **Right Triangles and Trigonometry** section to ensure student success in this module.

🧠 Mindset Matters

"Not Yet" Doesn't Mean Never

Students with a growth mindset come to understand that just because they haven't yet found a solution, that doesn't mean they can't find one with additional effort and reasoning. It takes time to reason through the different strategies that can be used to solve a problem.

How Can I Apply It?

Assign students the **Math Probes** that are available for each module. Have them complete the probe before starting the module and again at the specified point in the module or at the end of the module so that they can see their progress.

Geometric Mean

LESSON GOAL

Students solve problems involving relationships between parts of a right triangle and the altitude to its hypotenuse using the geometric mean.

1 LAUNCH

 Launch the lesson with a **Warm Up** and an introduction.

2 EXPLORE AND DEVELOP

 Explore: Relationships in Right Triangles

....

 Develop:

Geometric Mean
- Find a Geometric Mean
- Identify Similar Right Triangles
- Use the Geometric Mean with Right Triangles
- Use Indirect Measurement

....

 You may want your students to complete the **Checks** online.

3 REFLECT AND PRACTICE

 Exit Ticket

....

 Practice

DIFFERENTIATE

 View reports of student progress on the **Checks** after each example.

Resources	AL	OL	BL	ELL
Remediation: Similar Triangles: SSS and SAS Similarity	•	•		•
Extension: Mathematics and Music		•	•	•

Language Development Handbook

Assign page 58 of the *Language Development Handbook* to help your students build mathematical language related to using the geometric mean to solve problems.

ELL You can use the tips and suggestions on page T58 of the handbook to support students who are building English proficiency.

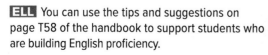

Suggested Pacing

90 min	**0.5 day**
45 min	**1 day**

Focus

Domain: Geometry

Standards for Mathematical Content:

G.SRT.4 Prove theorems about triangles.

G.SRT.5 Use congruence and similarity criteria for triangles to solve problems and to prove relationships in geometric figures.

Standards for Mathematical Practice:

2 Reason abstractly and quantitatively.

3 Construct viable arguments and critique the reasoning of others.

4 Model with mathematics.

5 Use appropriate tools strategically.

6 Attend to precision.

Coherence

Vertical Alignment

Previous
Students solved problems involving right triangles using the Pythagorean Theorem.
8.G.7, 8.G.8

Now
Students solve problems using geometric means in right triangles.
G.SRT.4, G.SRT.5

Next
Students will solve problems using the Pythagorean Theorem and its converse.
G.SRT.4, G.SRT.8

Rigor

The Three Pillars of Rigor

1 CONCEPTUAL UNDERSTANDING	2 FLUENCY	3 APPLICATION

Conceptual Bridge In this lesson, students extend their understanding of right triangles to prove theorems related to geometric means of right triangles. They build fluency and apply their understanding by solving real-world problems related to geometric means.

Mathematical Background

The *geometric mean* between two numbers is the square root of their product. The geometric mean has a particular application for a right triangle.

Interactive Presentation

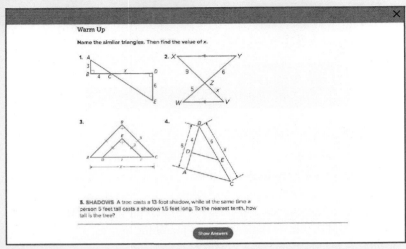

Warm Up

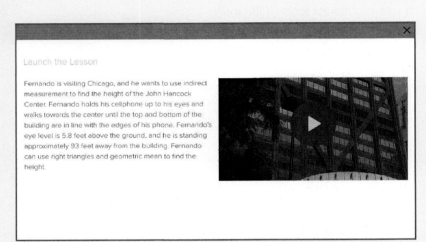

Launch the Lesson

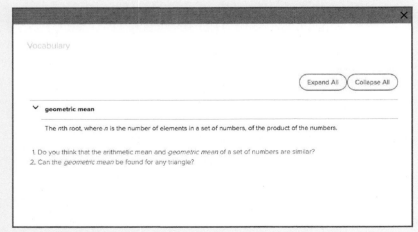

Today's Vocabulary

Warm Up

Prerequisite Skills

The Warm Up exercises address the following prerequisite skill for this lesson:

- using similar triangles

Answers:

1. $\triangle ABC \sim \triangle EDC$; 8
2. $\triangle XYZ \sim \triangle VWZ$; 7.5
3. $\triangle ABC \sim \triangle DEF$; 21
4. $\triangle ABC \sim \triangle DBE$; 9
5. 43.3 ft

Launch the Lesson

Teaching the Mathematical Practices

4 Apply Mathematics In this Launch the Lesson, students can see a real-world application of right triangles and geometric mean.

Go Online to find additional teaching notes and questions to promote classroom discourse.

Today's Standards

Tell students that they will be addressing these content and practice standards in this lesson. You may wish to have a student volunteer read aloud *How can I meet these standards?* and *How can I use these practices?* and connect these to the standards.

See the Interactive Presentation for I Can statements that align with the standards covered in this lesson.

Today's Vocabulary

Tell students that they will be using this vocabulary term in this lesson. You can expand the row if you wish to share the definition. Then, discuss the questions below with the class.

Explore Relationships in Right Triangles

Objective
Students use dynamic geometry software and similarity criteria for triangles to solve problems and explore the relationships that exist when the altitude is drawn to the hypotenuse of a right triangle.

Teaching the Mathematical Practices

3 Justify Conclusions Mathematically proficient students can explain the conclusions drawn when solving a problem. This Explore asks students to justify their conclusions.

Ideas for Use

Recommended Use Present the Inquiry Question, or have a student volunteer read it aloud. Have students work in pairs to complete the Explore activity on their devices. Pairs should discuss each of the questions. Monitor student progress during the activity. Upon completion of the Explore activity, have student volunteers share their responses to the Inquiry Question.

What if my students don't have devices? You may choose to project the activity on a whiteboard. A printable worksheet for each Explore is available online. You may choose to print the worksheet so that individuals or pairs of students can use it to record their observations.

Summary of the Activity

Students will complete guiding exercises throughout the Explore activity. Students first construct the altitude to the hypotenuse of a right triangle. Then students measure the angles of the original triangle and the two triangles into which the altitude divides the original triangle. Students observe that the three triangles are similar. Students then are given measurements for the two parts of the hypotenuse and are tasked with finding the length of the altitude. Throughout the activity students complete guiding exercises. Then, students will answer the Inquiry Question.

(continued on the next page)

Interactive Presentation

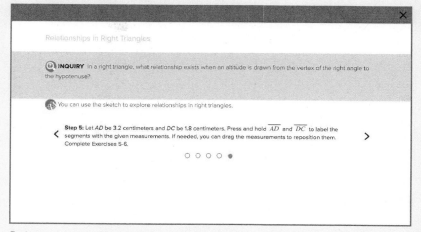

Explore

WEB SKETCHPAD

Students use a sketch to explore relationships in right triangles.

Interactive Presentation

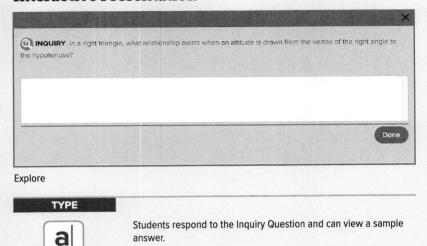

Explore

TYPE

a|

Students respond to the Inquiry Question and can view a sample answer.

Explore Relationships in Right Triangles *(continued)*

Teaching the Mathematical Practices

3 Justify Conclusions Mathematically proficient students can explain the conclusions drawn when solving a problem. Exercise 4 asks students to justify their conclusions.

Questions

Have students complete the Explore activity.

Ask:

- Why don't we draw an altitude from points *A* or *C*? Sample answer: Drawing altitudes from these points would be the same as drawing the legs of the right triangle.
- Can you say that ∠B is congruent in every triangle? Explain. No; sample answer: ∠B is the right angle in the original triangle, but then it is cut into unknown measures to make the other two triangles.

Inquiry

In a right triangle, what relationship exists when an altitude is drawn from the vertex of the right angle to the hypotenuse? Sample answer: The altitude forms two new right triangles. These two right triangles are similar to each other and to the original triangle.

Go Online to find additional teaching notes and sample answers for the guiding exercises.

1 CONCEPTUAL UNDERSTANDING | 2 FLUENCY | 3 APPLICATION

Learn Geometric Mean

Objective
Students use similarity criteria for triangles and geometric means to solve problems and to prove relationships in geometric figures.

MP Teaching the Mathematical Practices

7 Use Structure Help students to explore the structure of the geometric mean in this Learn.

What Students Are Learning
The altitude to the hypotenuse divides a right triangle into two smaller triangles, both similar to the original. This creates a number of proportional relationships between parts of the triangle that form geometric means. The altitude is the geometric mean of the two parts of the hypotenuse. Each leg is the geometric mean of the part of the hypotenuse adjacent to the leg and the whole hypotenuse.

Common Misconception
Emphasize the difference between the geometric mean and the arithmetic mean and for what situations either one should be used.

Go Online
- Find additional teaching notes.
- View performance reports of the Checks.
- Assign or present an Extra Example.

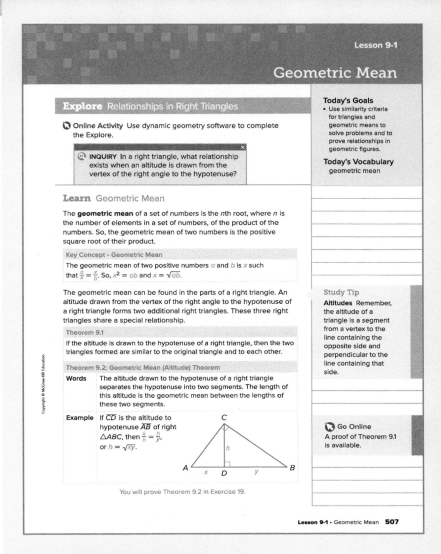

Lesson 9-1

Geometric Mean

Explore Relationships in Right Triangles

Online Activity Use dynamic geometry software to complete the Explore.

INQUIRY In a right triangle, what relationship exists when an altitude is drawn from the vertex of the right angle to the hypotenuse?

Learn Geometric Mean

The **geometric mean** of a set of numbers is the nth root, where n is the number of elements in a set of numbers, of the product of the numbers. So, the geometric mean of two numbers is the positive square root of their product.

Key Concept · Geometric Mean

The geometric mean of two positive numbers a and b is x such that $\frac{a}{x} = \frac{x}{b}$. So, $x^2 = ab$ and $x = \sqrt{ab}$.

The geometric mean can be found in the parts of a right triangle. An altitude drawn from the vertex of the right angle to the hypotenuse of a right triangle forms two additional right triangles. These three right triangles share a special relationship.

Theorem 9.1

If the altitude is drawn to the hypotenuse of a right triangle, then the two triangles formed are similar to the original triangle and to each other.

Theorem 9.2: Geometric Mean (Altitude) Theorem

Words The altitude drawn to the hypotenuse of a right triangle separates the hypotenuse into two segments. The length of this altitude is the geometric mean between the lengths of these two segments.

Example If $\overline{CD}$ is the altitude to hypotenuse $\overline{AB}$ of right $\triangle ABC$, then $\frac{x}{h} = \frac{h}{y}$, or $h = \sqrt{xy}$.

You will prove Theorem 9.2 in Exercise 19.

Today's Goals
- Use similarity criteria for triangles and geometric means to solve problems and to prove relationships in geometric figures.

Today's Vocabulary
geometric mean

Study Tip

Altitudes Remember, the altitude of a triangle is a segment from a vertex to the line containing the opposite side and perpendicular to the line containing that side.

Go Online
A proof of Theorem 9.1 is available.

Lesson 9-1 · Geometric Mean **507**

Interactive Presentation

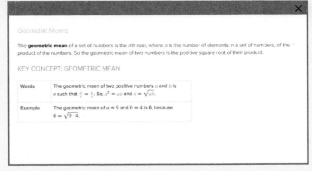

Geometric Means

The **geometric mean** of a set of numbers is the nth root, where n is the number of elements in a set of numbers, of the product of the numbers. So, the geometric mean of two numbers is the positive square root of their product.

KEY CONCEPT: GEOMETRIC MEAN

Words	The geometric mean of two positive numbers a and b is x such that $\frac{a}{x} = \frac{x}{b}$. So, $x^2 = ab$ and $x = \sqrt{ab}$.
Example	The geometric mean of $a = 9$ and $b = 4$ is 6, because $6 = \sqrt{9 \cdot 4}$.

Learn

TAP

 Students tap to reveal a Study Tip and steps in a proof.

1 CONCEPTUAL UNDERSTANDING | **2 FLUENCY** | 3 APPLICATION

Your Notes

Theorem 9.3: Geometric Mean (Leg) Theorem

Words The altitude drawn to the hypotenuse of a right triangle separates the hypotenuse into two segments. The length of a leg of this triangle is the geometric mean between the length of the hypotenuse and the segment of the hypotenuse adjacent to that leg.

Example If $\overline{CD}$ is the altitude to hypotenuse $\overline{AB}$ of right $\triangle ABC$, then $\frac{c}{b} = \frac{b}{x}$, or $b = \sqrt{xc}$ and $\frac{c}{a} = \frac{a}{y}$ or $a = \sqrt{yc}$.

You will prove Theorem 9.3 in Exercise 20.

Example 1 Find a Geometric Mean

Find the geometric mean between 5 and 45.

$x = \sqrt{ab}$ Definition of geometric mean

$= \sqrt{5 \cdot 45}$ $a = 5$ and $b = \underline{45}$

$= \underline{15}$ Simplify.

The geometric mean between 5 and 45 is ___15___.

Check

Find the geometric mean between 12 and 15. Write your answer in simplest radical form, if necessary. $6\sqrt{5}$

Example 2 Identify Similar Right Triangles

Write a similarity statement identifying the three similar right triangles in the figure.

The diagram below shows the three triangles with their corresponding angles and sides in the same position as the largest triangle. Complete the labels in the diagram.

So by Theorem 9.1, $\triangle STR \sim \triangle \underline{QTS} \sim \triangle \underline{QSR}$.

Check

Write a similarity statement identifying the three similar right triangles in the figure.
$\triangle KML \sim \triangle KPM \sim \triangle MPL$

🔗 **Go Online** You can complete an Extra Example online.

Interactive Presentation

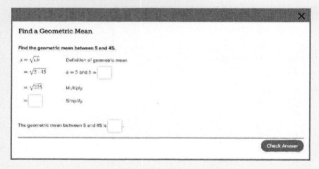

Example 1

TYPE

| a| |

Students can complete the calculations to find the geometric mean.

Example 1 Find a Geometric Mean

 Teaching the Mathematical Practices

> **2 Create Representations** Guide students to write an equation that models the situation in this example. Then use the equation to solve the problem.

Questions for Mathematical Discourse

AL What is the prime factorization of 225? $3 \cdot 3 \cdot 5 \cdot 5$

OL How can you rewrite 225 as the product of squares? 15^2; $3^2 \cdot 5^2$

BL What would you do if the number in the square root symbol was not a perfect square? You would reduce the square root by factoring out any perfect squares, or you would estimate the value of the square root with a calculator.

Common Error

Students may not remember how to reduce or compute square roots properly. If so, spend some time reminding them of the properties of square roots and how to reduce them.

Example 2 Identify Similar Right Triangles

 Teaching the Mathematical Practices

> **4 Analyze Relationships Mathematically** Point out that to solve the problem in this example, students will need to analyze the mathematical relationships in the problem to draw a conclusion.

Questions for Mathematical Discourse

AL How do we know that $\angle R \cong \angle QST$? We know that $m\angle R + m\angle Q + 90° = 180°$ and $m\angle QST + m\angle Q + 90° = 180°$, so $m\angle R = m\angle QST$.

OL Can you also write $\triangle STR \sim \triangle STQ$? Explain. No; $\angle R$ does not correspond to $\angle Q$.

BL Can you split any triangle into two triangles similar to the first triangle using an altitude? Explain. No; the altitude forms a right angle with a side of the triangle, so this only works with right triangles.

1 CONCEPTUAL UNDERSTANDING   **2 FLUENCY**   3 APPLICATION

Example 3 Use the Geometric Mean with Right Triangles

Ⓜ Teaching the Mathematical Practices

6 Communicate Precisely Encourage students to routinely write or explain their solution methods. Point out that they should use clear definitions when they discuss their solutions with others.

Questions for Mathematical Discourse

AL Why are there three different geometric means we can write for the triangles formed by the altitude of a right triangle? because three similar triangles are formed

OL If $AD = 2$ and $DC = 50$, what is BD? 10

BL What proportion can you write to solve for z? $\frac{25}{z} = \frac{z}{33}$

Common Error

Students may use the two legs of the triangle to find the altitude using the geometric mean, rather than the two segments that make up the hypotenuse. Have them use the Avoid a Common Error feature online.

DIFFERENTIATE

Language Development Activity **AL** **ELL**

In Module 7, a comparison was made between words that have multiple meanings within mathematics. The word *mean* can be applied to geometry or statistics. In their own words, have students describe the meaning of *mean* when applied to a triangle.

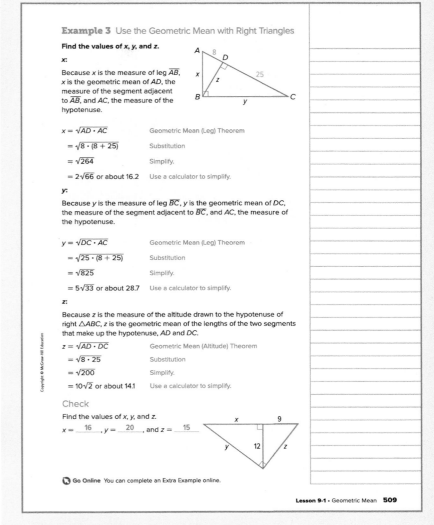

Example 3 Use the Geometric Mean with Right Triangles

Find the values of x, y, and z.

x:

Because x is the measure of leg $\overline{AB}$, x is the geometric mean of AD, the measure of the segment adjacent to $\overline{AB}$, and AC, the measure of the hypotenuse.

$x = \sqrt{AD \cdot AC}$ Geometric Mean (Leg) Theorem

$= \sqrt{8 \cdot (8 + 25)}$ Substitution

$= \sqrt{264}$ Simplify.

$= 2\sqrt{66}$ or about 16.2   Use a calculator to simplify.

y:

Because y is the measure of leg $\overline{BC}$, y is the geometric mean of DC, the measure of the segment adjacent to $\overline{BC}$, and AC, the measure of the hypotenuse.

$y = \sqrt{DC \cdot AC}$ Geometric Mean (Leg) Theorem

$= \sqrt{25 \cdot (8 + 25)}$ Substitution

$= \sqrt{825}$ Simplify.

$= 5\sqrt{33}$ or about 28.7   Use a calculator to simplify.

z:

Because z is the measure of the altitude drawn to the hypotenuse of right $\triangle ABC$, z is the geometric mean of the lengths of the two segments that make up the hypotenuse, AD and DC.

$z = \sqrt{AD \cdot DC}$ Geometric Mean (Altitude) Theorem

$= \sqrt{8 \cdot 25}$ Substitution

$= \sqrt{200}$ Simplify.

$= 10\sqrt{2}$ or about 14.1   Use a calculator to simplify.

Check

Find the values of x, y, and z.

$x = \underline{\ 16\ }$, $y = \underline{\ 20\ }$, and $z = \underline{\ 15\ }$

Ⓖ **Go Online** You can complete an Extra Example online.

Interactive Presentation

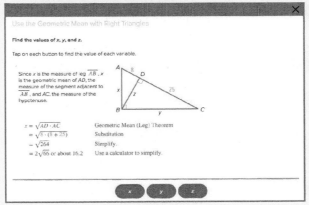

Example 3

TAP

Students tap to see parts of the solution.

Example 4 Use Indirect Measurement

SKATEBOARDING Diego wants to find the height of a half pipe ramp at a skate park near his house. To find this height, Diego holds a book up to his eyes so that the top and bottom of the ramp are in line with the bottom edge and binding of the book. If Diego's eye level is 5.5 feet above the ground and he stands 6 feet from the ramp, how tall is the ramp to the nearest foot?

Step 1 Visualize and describe the situation.

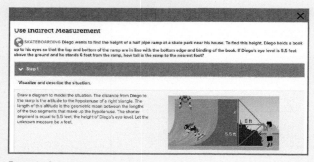

Draw a diagram to model the situation. The distance from Diego to the ramp is the altitude to the hypotenuse of a right triangle. The length of this altitude is the geometric mean between the lengths of the two segments that make up the hypotenuse. The shorter segment is equal to 5.5 feet, the height of Diego's eye level. Let the unknown measure be x feet.

Step 2 Find the height.

You can use the Geometric Mean (Altitude) Theorem to find x.

$6 = \sqrt{5.5 \cdot x}$	Geometric Mean (Altitude) Theorem
$36 = 5.5x$	Square each side.
$6.55 \approx x$	Divide each side by 5.5.

The height of the ramp is the total length of the hypotenuse, $6.55 + \underline{5.5}$, or about 12 feet.

Check

EVENTS Katelyn wants to make a banner for homecoming that will cover a wall in the cafeteria of her high school. To find the height of the wall, Katelyn holds a folder up to her eyes so that the top and bottom of the wall are in line with the edges of the folder. If Katelyn's eye level is 5.4 feet above the ground and she stands 11 feet from the wall, how tall is the wall to the nearest foot? __28__ ft

Go Online You can complete an Extra Example online.

Example 4 Use Indirect Measurement

MP Teaching the Mathematical Practices

2 Create Representations Guide students to write an equation that models the situation in this example. Then use the equation to solve the problem.

Questions for Mathematical Discourse

AL What is one possible problem when measuring the height of a very tall object? Sample answer: The ground next to the object may not be level.

OL What must Diego do to make sure he can use the geometric mean to measure the height? Diego must stand so that the angle from his line of sight to the bottom of the ramp and his line of sight to the top of the ramp is a right angle.

BL What measure or measures do you need when using the geometric mean to photograph a very tall object? You need the distance of the viewer to the object and the height of the viewer's eye.

DIFFERENTIATE

Enrichment Activity BL

Have students measure the height of a tall object or a high ceiling in your school using indirect measurement and the geometric mean as in Example 4.

Exit Ticket

Recommended Use

At the end of class, go online to display the Exit Ticket prompt and ask students to respond using a separate piece of paper. Have students hand you their responses as they leave the room.

Alternate Use

At the end of class, go online to display the Exit Ticket prompt and ask students to respond verbally or by using a mini-whiteboard. Have students hold up their whiteboards so that you can see all student responses. Tap to reveal the answer when most or all students have completed the Exit Ticket.

Interactive Presentation

Use Indirect Measurement

SKATEBOARDING Diego wants to find the height of a half pipe ramp at a skate park near his house. To find this height, Diego holds a book up to his eyes so that the top and bottom of the ramp are in line with the bottom edge and binding of the book. If Diego's eye level is 5.5 feet above the ground and he stands 6 feet from the ramp, how tall is the ramp to the nearest foot?

Step 1

Visualize and describe the situation.

Draw a diagram to model the situation. The distance from Diego to the ramp is the altitude to the hypotenuse of a right triangle. The length of this altitude is the geometric mean between the lengths of the two segments that make up the hypotenuse. The shorter segment is equal to 5.5 feet, the height of Diego's eye level. Let the unknown measure be x feet.

Example 4

TAP

Students tap to reveal parts of the solution.

CHECK

Students complete the Check online to determine whether they are ready to move on.

Practice and Homework

Suggested Assignments

Use the table below to select appropriate exercises.

DOK	Topic	Exercises
1, 2	exercises that mirror the examples	1–17
2	exercises that use a variety of skills from this lesson	18–20
3	exercises that emphasize higher-order and critical-thinking skills	21–25

ASSESS AND DIFFERENTIATE

📊 Use the data from the **Checks** to determine whether to provide resources for extension, remediation, or intervention.

IF students score 90% or more on the Checks,   `BL`
THEN assign:

- Practice, Exercises 1–19 odd, 21–25
- Extension: Mathematics and Music
- 🅰 **ALEKS** The Pythagorean Theorem

IF students score 66%–89% on the Checks,   `OL`
THEN assign:

- Practice, Exercises 1–25 odd
- Remediation, Review Resources: Similar Triangles: SSS and SAS Similarity
- Personal Tutors
- Extra Examples 1–4
- 🅰 **ALEKS** Proving Triangle Similarity

IF students score 65% or less on the Checks,   `AL`
THEN assign:

- Practice, Exercises 1–17 odd
- Remediation, Review Resources: Similar Triangles: SSS and SAS Similarity
- *Quick Review Math Handbook:* Special Segments in Right Triangles
- 🅰 **ALEKS** Proving Triangle Similarity

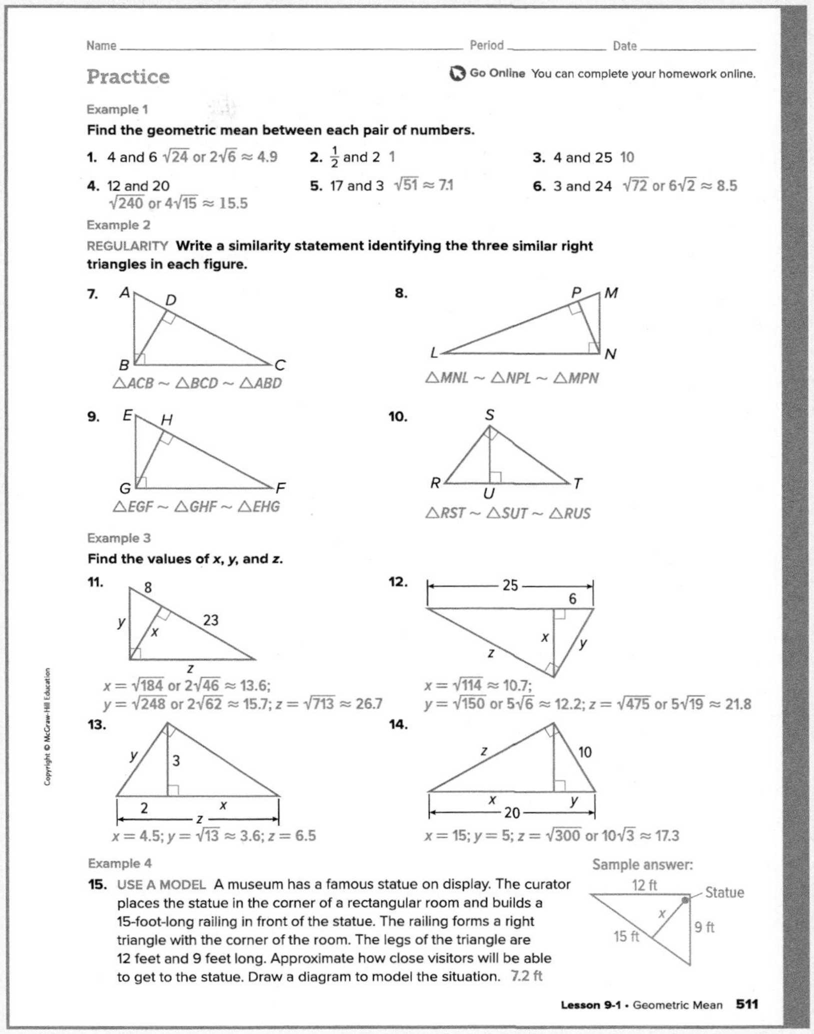

Name _____ Period _____ Date _____

Practice

🌐 **Go Online** You can complete your homework online.

Example 1
Find the geometric mean between each pair of numbers.

1. 4 and 6 $\sqrt{24}$ or $2\sqrt{6} \approx 4.9$ 2. $\frac{1}{2}$ and 2   1   3. 4 and 25   10

4. 12 and 20   5. 17 and 3 $\sqrt{51} \approx 7.1$ 6. 3 and 24 $\sqrt{72}$ or $6\sqrt{2} \approx 8.5$
  $\sqrt{240}$ or $4\sqrt{15} \approx 15.5$

Example 2
REGULARITY **Write a similarity statement identifying the three similar right triangles in each figure.**

7.
$\triangle ACB \sim \triangle BCD \sim \triangle ABD$

8.
$\triangle MNL \sim \triangle NPL \sim \triangle MPN$

9.
$\triangle EGF \sim \triangle GHF \sim \triangle EHG$

10.
$\triangle RST \sim \triangle SUT \sim \triangle RUS$

Example 3
Find the values of x, y, and z.

11.
$x = \sqrt{184}$ or $2\sqrt{46} \approx 13.6$;
$y = \sqrt{248}$ or $2\sqrt{62} \approx 15.7$; $z = \sqrt{713} \approx 26.7$

12.
$x = \sqrt{114} \approx 10.7$;
$y = \sqrt{150}$ or $5\sqrt{6} \approx 12.2$; $z = \sqrt{475}$ or $5\sqrt{19} \approx 21.8$

13.
$x = 4.5$; $y = \sqrt{13} \approx 3.6$; $z = 6.5$

14.
$x = 15$; $y = 5$; $z = \sqrt{300}$ or $10\sqrt{3} \approx 17.3$

Example 4

15. USE A MODEL A museum has a famous statue on display. The curator places the statue in the corner of a rectangular room and builds a 15-foot-long railing in front of the statue. The railing forms a right triangle with the corner of the room. The legs of the triangle are 12 feet and 9 feet long. Approximate how close visitors will be able to get to the statue. Draw a diagram to model the situation.   7.2 ft

Sample answer:

Copyright © McGraw Hill Education

1 CONCEPTUAL UNDERSTANDING   2 FLUENCY   3 APPLICATION

16. USE A MODEL Noah wants to take a picture of a beach front. He wants to make sure two palm trees located at points *A* and *B* are just inside the edges of the photograph. He walks out on a walkway that goes over the ocean to get the shot. Point *A* is 90 feet from the entrance of the walkway, and point *B* is 40 feet from the entrance. If the walkway is perpendicular to *AB*, and Noah's camera has a viewing angle of 90°, at what distance down the walkway should Noah stop to take his photograph? Draw a diagram to model the situation. **60 ft**

Sample answer:
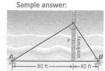

17. CIVIL ENGINEERING An airport, a factory, and a shopping center are at the vertices of a right triangle formed by three highways. The airport and factory are 6.0 miles apart. Their distances from the shopping center are 3.6 miles and 4.8 miles, respectively. A service road will be constructed from the shopping center to the highway that connects the airport and factory. What is the shortest possible length for the service road? Round to the nearest hundredth. **2.88 mi**

Mixed Exercises

18. REASONING The geometric mean of a number and four times the number is 22. What is the number? **11**

PROOF Write the specified type of proof to prove each theorem. 19–20. See margin.

19. paragraph proof Theorem 9.2
Given: △*ADC* is a right triangle.
DB is an altitude of △*ADC*.
Prove: $\frac{AB}{DB} = \frac{DB}{CB}$ See margin.

20. two-column proof Theorem 9.3
Given: ∠*ADC* is a right angle.
DB is an altitude of △*ADC*.
Prove: $\frac{AB}{AD} = \frac{AD}{AC}, \frac{BC}{DC} = \frac{DC}{AC}$
See margin.

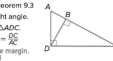

🧠 **Higher-Order Thinking Skills** 21. *x* = 5.2; *y* = 6.8; *z* = 11.1

21. PERSEVERE Refer to the figure at the right. Find the values of *x*, *y*, and *z*. Round to the nearest tenth.

22. WRITE Compare and contrast the arithmetic and geometric means of two numbers. When will the two means be equal? Justify your reasoning. See margin.

23. CREATE Find two pairs of whole numbers with a geometric mean that is also a whole number. What condition must be met in order for a pair of numbers to produce a whole-number geometric mean? See margin.

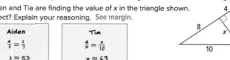

24. FIND THE ERROR Aiden and Tia are finding the value of *x* in the triangle shown. Is either of them correct? Explain your reasoning. See margin.

Aiden	Tia
$\frac{4}{3} = \frac{x}{7}$	$\frac{4}{x} = \frac{x}{10}$
$x \approx 5.3$	$x \approx 6.3$

25. ANALYZE Determine whether each statement is *sometimes*, *always*, or *never* true. Justify your argument. a–c. See margin.
a. The geometric mean for consecutive positive integers is the mean of the two numbers.
b. The geometric mean for two perfect squares is a positive integer.
c. The geometric mean for two positive integers is another integer.

Answers

19. Proof:
It is given that △*ADC* is a right triangle and *DB* is an altitude of △*ADC*. ∠*ADC* is a right angle by the definition of a right triangle. Therefore, △*ADB* ~ △*DCB*, because if the altitude is drawn from the vertex of the right angle to the hypotenuse of a right triangle, then the two triangles formed are similar to the given triangle and to each other. So, $\frac{AB}{DB} = \frac{DB}{CB}$ by the definition of similar triangles.

20. Proof:
Statements (Reasons)
1. ∠*ADC* is a right angle. *DB* is an altitude of △*ADC*. (Given)
2. △*ADC* is a right triangle. (Definition of right triangle)
3. △*ABD* ~ △*ADC*; △*DBC* ~ △*ADC* (If the altitude is drawn from the vertex of the rt. ∠ to the hypotenuse of a rt. △, then the 2 △s formed are similar to the given △ and to each other.)
4. $\frac{AB}{AD} = \frac{AD}{AC}, \frac{BC}{DC} = \frac{DC}{AC}$ (Definition of similar triangles)

22. Sample answer: Both the arithmetic and the geometric mean calculate a value between two given numbers. The arithmetic mean of two numbers *a* and *b* is $\frac{a+b}{2}$, and the geometric mean of two numbers *a* and *b* is $\sqrt{ab}$. The two means will be equal when *a* = *b*.

Justification:

$$\frac{a+b}{2} = \sqrt{ab}$$
$$\left(\frac{a+b}{2}\right)^2 = ab$$
$$(a+b)^2 = 4ab$$
$$a^2 + 2ab + b^2 = 4ab$$
$$a^2 - 2ab + b^2 = 0$$
$$(a-b)^2 = 0$$
$$a - b = 0$$
$$a = b$$

23. Sample answer: 9 and 4, 8 and 8; For two whole numbers to result in a whole-number geometric mean, their product must be a perfect square.

24. Neither; sample answer: On the similar triangles created by the altitude, the leg that is *x* units long on the smaller triangle corresponds with the leg that is 8 units long on the larger triangle, so the correct proportion is $\frac{4}{x} = \frac{x}{8}$ and *x* is about 5.7.

25a. Never; sample answer: The geometric mean of two consecutive integers is $\sqrt{x(x+1)}$, and the average of two consecutive integers is $\frac{x+(x+1)}{2}$. If you set the two expressions equal to each other, the equation has no solution.

25b. Always; sample answer: Because $\sqrt{ab}$ is equal to $\sqrt{a} \cdot \sqrt{b}$, the geometric mean for two perfect squares will always be the product of two positive integers, which is a positive integer.

25c. Sometimes; sample answer: When the product of two integers is a perfect square, the geometric mean will be a positive integer.

Pythagorean Theorem and Its Converse

LESSON GOAL

Students solve problems using the Pythagorean Theorem and its converse.

1 LAUNCH

 Launch the lesson with a **Warm Up** and an introduction.

2 EXPLORE AND DEVELOP

 Explore: Proving the Pythagorean Theorem

 Develop:

The Pythagorean Theorem
- Find Missing Measures by Using the Pythagorean Theorem
- Use a Pythagorean Triple
- Use the Pythagorean Theorem

Converse of the Pythagorean Theorem
- Classify Triangles

 You may want your students to complete the **Checks** online.

3 REFLECT AND PRACTICE

 Exit Ticket

 Practice

DIFFERENTIATE

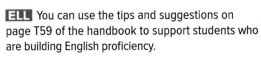 View reports of student progress on the **Checks** after each example.

Resources	AL	OL	BL	ELL
Remediation: Roots	●	●		●
Extension: Generating Pythagorean Triples		●	●	●

Language Development Handbook

Assign page 59 of the *Language Development Handbook* to help your students build mathematical language related to the Pythagorean Theorem and its converse.

ELL You can use the tips and suggestions on page T59 of the handbook to support students who are building English proficiency.

Suggested Pacing

90 min	**0.5 day**	
45 min	**1 day**	

Focus

Domain: Geometry

Standards for Mathematical Content:

G.SRT.4 Prove theorems about triangles.

G.SRT.8 Use trigonometric ratios and the Pythagorean Theorem to solve righ triangles in applied problems.

Standards for Mathematical Practice:

3 Construct viable arguments and critique the reasoning of others.

4 Model with mathematics.

5 Use appropriate tools strategically.

6 Attend to precision.

Coherence

Vertical Alignment

Previous
Students solved problems using geometric means in right triangles.
G.SRT.4, G.SRT.5

Now
Students solve problems using the Pythagorean Theorem and its converse.
G.SRT.4, G.SRT.8

Next
Students will graph points and find distances in three dimensions.

Rigor

The Three Pillars of Rigor

1 CONCEPTUAL UNDERSTANDING	2 FLUENCY	3 APPLICATION

Conceptual Bridge In this lesson, students expand on their understanding of and fluency with using the Pythagorean Theorem (first studied in Grade 8) to prepare for finding volumes. They apply their understanding by using the Pythagorean Theorem to solve problems related to real-world right triangles.

Mathematical Background

In a right triangle, the sum of the measures of the legs squared equals the square of the measure of the hypotenuse. A Pythagorean triple is a group of three whole numbers that satisfy the equation $a^2 + b^2 = c^2$.

Interactive Presentation

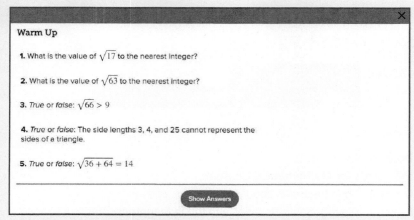

Warm Up

1. What is the value of $\sqrt{17}$ to the nearest integer?

2. What is the value of $\sqrt{63}$ to the nearest integer?

3. *True or false:* $\sqrt{66} > 9$

4. *True or false:* The side lengths 3, 4, and 25 cannot represent the sides of a triangle.

5. *True or false:* $\sqrt{36 + 64} = 14$

Show Answers

Warm Up

Launch the Lesson

Many cities are redesigning major intersections to prevent accidents for drivers and pedestrians. These intersections are being updated to have scramble crosswalks. A scramble crosswalk stops all vehicular traffic and allows pedestrians to cross in any direction, including diagonally. In a scramble crosswalk, the diagonal crosswalk is the hypotenuse of a right triangle. The legs of the right triangle are the vertical and horizontal crosswalks. If you know the distance between the street corners of an intersection, you can use the Pythagorean Theorem to find the approximate length of the diagonal crosswalk.

Launch the Lesson

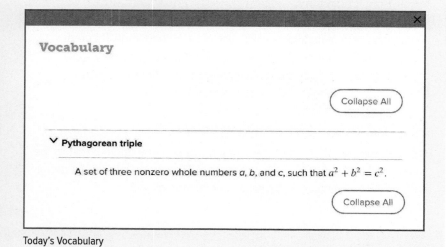

Vocabulary

Collapse All

⌄ **Pythagorean triple**

A set of three nonzero whole numbers a, b, and c, such that $a^2 + b^2 = c^2$.

Collapse All

Today's Vocabulary

Warm Up

Prerequisite Skills

The Warm Up exercises address the following prerequisite skill for this lesson:

- finding square roots

Answers:

1. 4
2. 8
3. false
4. true
5. false

Launch the Lesson

Ⓜ️ Teaching the Mathematical Practices

4 Apply Mathematics In this Launch the Lesson, students can see a real-world application of the Pythagorean Theorem.

🔎 **Go Online** to find additional teaching notes and questions to promote classroom discourse.

Today's Standards

Tell students that they will be addressing these content and practice standards in this lesson. You may wish to have a student volunteer read aloud *How can I meet these standards?* and *How can I use these practices?* and connect these to the standards.

See the Interactive Presentation for I Can statements that align with the standards covered in this lesson.

Today's Vocabulary

Tell students that they will be using this vocabulary term in this lesson. You can expand the row if you wish to share the definition. Then, discuss the questions below with the class.

Explore Proving the Pythagorean Theorem

Objective
Students use dynamic geometry software and triangle similarity to prove the Pythagorean Theorem.

 Teaching the Mathematical Practices

> **3 Construct Arguments** In this Explore, students will use stated assumptions, definitions, and previously established results to complete the given proof.

Ideas for Use

Recommended Use Present the Inquiry Question, or have a student volunteer read it aloud. Have students work in pairs to complete the Explore activity on their devices. Pairs should discuss each of the questions. Monitor student progress during the activity. Upon completion of the Explore activity, have student volunteers share their responses to the Inquiry Question.

What if my students don't have devices? You may choose to project the activity on a whiteboard. A printable worksheet for each Explore is available online. You may choose to print the worksheet so that individuals or pairs of students can use it to record their observations.

Summary of the Activity

Students will complete guiding exercises throughout the Explore activity. Students use their knowledge of the Pythagorean Theorem to write an equation for a given right triangle. Then students use a sketch of the given right triangle to draw two similar triangles using the altitude to the hypotenuse. Students complete guiding exercises designed to help them write a proof of the Pythagorean Theorem using similar right triangles. Then, students will answer the Inquiry Question.

(continued on the next page)

Interactive Presentation

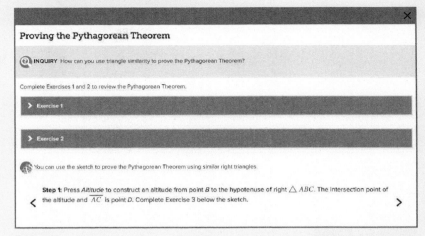

Proving the Pythagorean Theorem

 INQUIRY How can you use triangle similarity to prove the Pythagorean Theorem?

Complete Exercises 1 and 2 to review the Pythagorean Theorem.

> Exercise 1

> Exercise 2

You can use the sketch to prove the Pythagorean Theorem using similar right triangles.

Step 1: Press *Altitude* to construct an altitude from point *B* to the hypotenuse of right $\triangle ABC$. The intersection point of the altitude and $\overline{AC}$ is point *D*. Complete Exercise 3 below the sketch.

Explore

WEB SKETCHPAD

Students use a sketch to explore a proof of the Pythagorean Theorem using triangle similarity.

G.SRT.4

Interactive Presentation

INQUIRY Use triangle similarity to complete the paragraph proof of the Pythagorean Theorem.

Let △ ABC be a right triangle with the right angle located at point ▢ . Draw an altitude from point B to the hypotenuse of the right

triangle $\overline{AC}$. Let the intersection of the altitude and $\overline{AC}$ be point ▢ . By Theorem 9.1, altitude $\overline{BD}$ forms three similar triangles:

△ ABC~ △ ▢ ~ △ BDC. Because △ ABC~ △ ADB, by the definition of similar polygons, $\frac{AB}{AC} = \frac{AD}{AB}$. So, ▢

▢ $^2 = AC \cdot AD$. Because △ ABC~ △ ▢ . $\frac{BC}{AC} = \frac{DC}{BC}$. So, ▢ $^2 = AC \cdot DC$. $AB^2 + BC^2 = AC \cdot AD + AC \cdot AD$ by

substitution. By ▢ , $AB^2 + BC^2 = AC(AD + DC)$. By the Segment Addition Postulate,

$AD +$ ▢ $= AC$. So, $AB^2 + BC^2 = AC \cdot AC$ by substitution. Therefore, $AB^2 + BC^2 = $ ▢ ^{2}.

[Check Answer]

Explore

TYPE

Students respond to the Inquiry Question and can view a sample answer.

---

1 **CONCEPTUAL UNDERSTANDING**   2 FLUENCY | 3 APPLICATION

Explore Proving the Pythagorean Theorem (*continued*)

MP **Teaching the Mathematical Practices**

3 Construct Arguments In the Explore, students will use stated assumptions, definitions, and previously established results to complete the given proof.

Questions

Have students complete the Explore activity.

Ask:

- What is the Pythagorean Theorem? $a^2 + b^2 = c^2$

- Why should we prove the Pythagorean Theorem? Sample answer: Proving the Pythagorean Theorem allows us to use newly learned concepts to prove a relationship that has been stated before. This can also help us understand why something is true.

Inquiry

How can you use triangle similarity to prove the Pythagorean Theorem? Sample answer: Let △ABC be a right triangle with the right angle located at point B. Draw an altitude from point B to the hypotenuse of the right triangle $\overline{AC}$. Let the intersection of the altitude and $\overline{AC}$ be point D. By Theorem 9.1, altitude $\overline{BD}$ forms three similar triangles: △$ABC \sim$ △$ADB \sim$ △BDC. Because △$ABC \sim$ △ADB, by the definition of similar polygons, $\frac{AB}{AC} = \frac{AD}{AB}$. So, $AB^2 = AC \cdot AD$. Because △$ABC \sim$ △BDC, $\frac{BC}{AC} = \frac{DC}{BC}$. So, $BC^2 = AC \cdot DC$. $AB^2 + BC^2 = AC \cdot AD + AC \cdot DC$ by substitution. By factoring, $AB^2 + BC^2 = AC(AD + DC)$. By the Segment Addition Postulate, $AD + DC = AC$. So, $AB^2 + BC^2 = AC \cdot AC$ by substitution. Therefore, $AB^2 + BC^2 = AC^2$.

Go Online to find additional teaching notes and sample answers for the guiding exercises.

1 CONCEPTUAL UNDERSTANDING | **2 FLUENCY** | 3 APPLICATION

Learn The Pythagorean Theorem

Objective
Students use the Pythagorean Theorem to solve problems involving right triangles.

 Teaching the Mathematical Practices

> **7 Use Structure** Help students to explore the structure of the Pythagorean Theorem in this Learn.

About the Key Concept
There are many ways to prove the Pythagorean Theorem. The proofs in this Lesson are not the only ones. Have students research the Pythagorean Theorem on the internet to discover more proofs.

Example 1 Find Missing Measures by Using the Pythagorean Theorem

 Teaching the Mathematical Practices

> **2 Create Representations** Guide students to write an equation that models the situation in this example. Then use the equation to solve the problem.

Questions for Mathematical Discourse

AL Which side of a right triangle is represented by the letter c in the Pythagorean Theorem? the hypotenuse

OL If the legs of a right triangle measure 8 and 15, what is the length of the hypotenuse? 17

BL If the hypotenuse of an isosceles right triangle measures 8 units, what are the lengths of the legs? $4\sqrt{2}$

Common Error
Students may substitute for the wrong variables in the Pythagorean Theorem, especially if they are solving for a leg rather than the hypotenuse. Remind them to draw a sketch of the right triangle and label the sides with their variable names and known lengths. Then they should use their sketch to remember which lengths to substitute for which variables.

 Go Online

- Find additional teaching notes.
- View performance reports of the Checks.
- Assign or present an Extra Example.

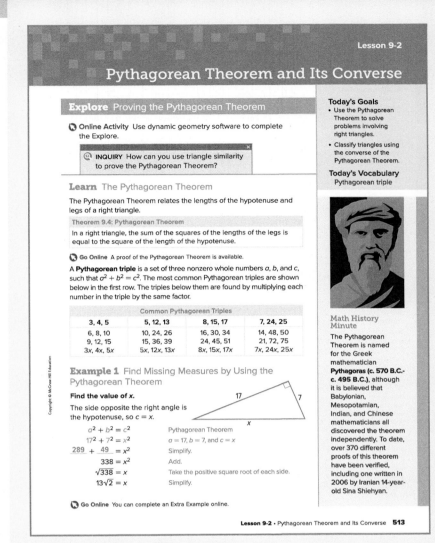

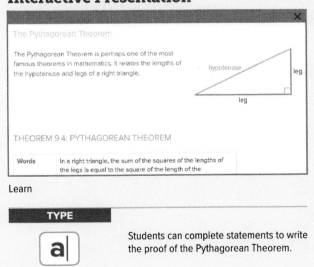

Interactive Presentation

Learn

TYPE

a| Students can complete statements to write the proof of the Pythagorean Theorem.

DRAG & DROP

Students drag ratios to complete equations.

1 CONCEPTUAL UNDERSTANDING | 2 FLUENCY | 3 APPLICATION

Your Notes

Go Online
An alternate method is available for this example.

Talk About It!
Draw a right triangle with side lengths that form a Pythagorean triple. If you double the length of each side, is the resulting triangle *acute*, *right*, or *obtuse*? If you halve the length of each side? Justify your argument.

Right; sample answer: If you double or halve the side lengths, all three sides of the new triangles are proportional to the sides of the original triangle. Using the Side-Side-Side Similarity Theorem, you know that both of the new triangles are similar to the original triangle, so they are both right triangles.

Think About It!
Is your answer reasonable? Use estimation to justify your reasoning.

Yes; sample answer: 803,125 is approximately 810,000. Because the square root of 810,000 is 900, it is reasonable that the square root of 803,125 is 896.17.

Example 2 Use a Pythagorean Triple

Use a Pythagorean triple to find the value of x.

Notice that 14 and 50 are both multiples of 2, because 14 = 2 · 7 and 50 = 2 · 25. Because 7, 24, 25 is a Pythagorean triple, the missing leg length x is 2 · 24 or 48 .

Check
Use a Pythagorean triple to find the value of x.

x = 52

Example 3 Use the Pythagorean Theorem

ZIP LINING A summer camp is building a new zip lining course. The designer of the course wants the last zip line to start at a platform 450 meters above the ground and end 775 meters away from the base of the platform. How long must the zip line be to meet the designer's specifications?

Step 1 Visualize and describe the situation.

The base of the platform and the ground should be approximately perpendicular. We need to find the length of the zip line, which is the hypotenuse of the right triangle. Draw a diagram that models the situation.

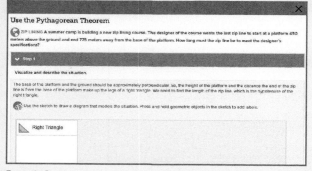
450 m
775 m

Step 2 Find the length of the zip line.

Use the Pythagorean Theorem to find the length x of the zip line.

$$450^2 + 775^2 = x^2 \quad \text{Pythagorean Theorem}$$
$$202,500 + 600,625 = x^2 \quad \text{Simplify.}$$
$$803,125 = x^2 \quad \text{Add.}$$
$$\sqrt{803,125} = x \quad \text{Take the positive square root of each side.}$$
$$25\sqrt{1285} = x \quad \text{Simplify.}$$

So, the length of the zip line is $25\sqrt{1285}$ or about 896.17 meters.

Go Online You can complete an Extra Example online.

514   Module 9 · Right Triangles and Trigonometry

Example 2 Use a Pythagorean Triple

MP Teaching the Mathematical Practices

1 Understand the Approaches of Others Work with students to look at the Alternate Method. Ask students to compare and contrast the original method and the alternate method.

Questions for Mathematical Discourse

AL What is a common factor of 14 and 50? 2

OL When you divide 14 and 50 by a common factor, what do you get? 7 and 25

BL What is another related Pythagorean Triple? Sample answer: 21, 72, 75

Example 3 Use the Pythagorean Theorem

MP Teaching the Mathematical Practices

8 Attend to Details Mathematically proficient students continually ask themselves, "Does this make sense?" Point out that in this example, students will evaluate the reasonableness of their answer.

Questions for Mathematical Discourse

AL How do we know that the platform support, the zip line, and the ground form a right triangle? Sample answer: because the side of the platform support is perpendicular to the ground

OL If the campground instead wants to install a 750-meter zip line, how far from the platform would it extend? 600 m

BL Another zip line platform will have a 425-meter zip line ending 375 meters away. How tall is the platform? 200 m

Common Error

Students may not realize that the zip line should end at ground level. Make sure that students understand what a zip line is and help them sketch a diagram of the situation.

Interactive Presentation

Use the Pythagorean Theorem

ZIP LINING A summer camp is building a new zip lining course. The designer of the course wants the last zip line to start at a platform 450 meters above the ground and end 775 meters away from the base of the platform. How long must the zip line be to meet the designer's specifications?

Step 1

Visualize and describe the situation.

The base of the platform and the ground should be approximately perpendicular. So, the height of the platform and the distance the end of the zip line is from the base of the platform make up the legs of a right triangle. We need to find the length of the zip line, which is the hypotenuse of the right triangle.

Use the sketch to draw a diagram that models the situation. Press and hold geometric objects in the sketch to add labels.

Right Triangle

Example 3

TAP

Students tap to reveal parts of the solution.

WEB SKETCHPAD

Students use a sketch to create a diagram of the situation in the problem.

CHECK

Students complete the Check online to determine whether they are ready to move on.

1 CONCEPTUAL UNDERSTANDING | **2 FLUENCY** | **3 APPLICATION**

Learn Converse of the Pythagorean Theorem

Objective
Students classify triangles using the converse of the Pythagorean Theorem.

 Teaching the Mathematical Practices

> **1 Explain Correspondences** Encourage students to explain the relationships between the Pythagorean Theorem and its converse in this Learn.

Essential Question Follow-Up
Students learn the converse of the Pythagorean Theorem.
Ask:

Why might the converse of the Pythagorean Theorem be useful in the real world? Sample answer: The converse of the Pythagorean Theorem can be used to test whether an angle is a right angle. Many situations in the real world need a right angle, so a way to test this is useful.

DIFFERENTIATE

Language Development Activity ELL

Beginning Read the lesson opener or an Example aloud one sentence at a time. At the end of each sentence, ask students to say a word or short phrase that describes an important piece of information from the sentence. Model recording the information in preparation for solving the problem. Have students use your model to record information in their notes.

Intermediate Slowly read the lesson opener or an Example aloud. After each sentence or two, pause and ask volunteers to identify an important piece of information.Have students write the important idea in their notes.

Advanced Tell students to listen without taking notes while you read aloud. After you have finished, have students write down what they remember from your reading. Have students work in small groups to compare their notes. Then have each group discuss the problem and its solution.

Advanced High Have students practice active listening as you read aloud by taking notes. Then have students work in pairs to summarize the information and solve the problem. Have pairs share with the class.

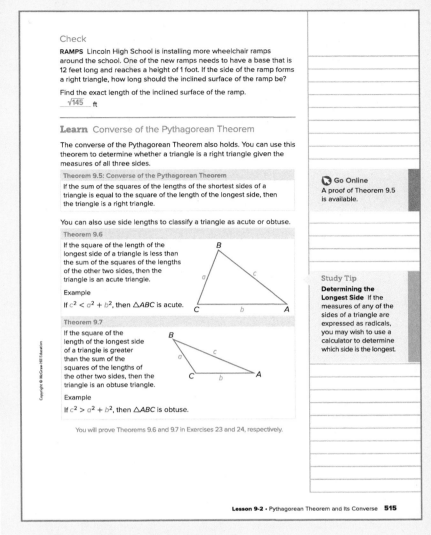

Check

RAMPS Lincoln High School is installing more wheelchair ramps around the school. One of the new ramps needs to have a base that is 12 feet long and reaches a height of 1 foot. If the side of the ramp forms a right triangle, how long should the inclined surface of the ramp be?

Find the exact length of the inclined surface of the ramp.

$\sqrt{145}$ ft

Learn Converse of the Pythagorean Theorem

The converse of the Pythagorean Theorem also holds. You can use this theorem to determine whether a triangle is a right triangle given the measures of all three sides.

Theorem 9.5: Converse of the Pythagorean Theorem
If the sum of the squares of the lengths of the shortest sides of a triangle is equal to the square of the length of the longest side, then the triangle is a right triangle.

You can also use side lengths to classify a triangle as acute or obtuse.

Theorem 9.6
If the square of the length of the longest side of a triangle is less than the sum of the squares of the lengths of the other two sides, then the triangle is an acute triangle.

Example
If $c^2 < a^2 + b^2$, then $\triangle ABC$ is acute.

Theorem 9.7
If the square of the length of the longest side of a triangle is greater than the sum of the squares of the lengths of the other two sides, then the triangle is an obtuse triangle.

Example
If $c^2 > a^2 + b^2$, then $\triangle ABC$ is obtuse.

You will prove Theorems 9.6 and 9.7 in Exercises 23 and 24, respectively.

Go Online
A proof of Theorem 9.5 is available.

Study Tip
Determining the Longest Side If the measures of any of the sides of a triangle are expressed as radicals, you may wish to use a calculator to determine which side is the longest.

Interactive Presentation

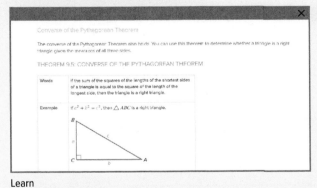

Converse of the Pythagorean Theorem

Learn

TAP

 Students tap to reveal a Study Tip.

Example 4 Classify Triangles

Determine whether the points $A(2, 2)$, $B(5, 7)$, and $C(10, 6)$ can be the vertices of a triangle. If so, classify the triangle as *acute*, *right*, or *obtuse*. Justify your answer.

Step 1 Calculate the measures of the sides.

Use the Distance Formula to calculate the measures of $\overline{AB}$, $\overline{BC}$, and $\overline{AC}$.

$$AB = \sqrt{(5-2)^2 + (7-2)^2} \qquad\qquad BC = \sqrt{(10-5)^2 + (6-7)^2}$$

$$= \sqrt{3^2 + 5^2} \qquad\qquad\qquad\qquad = \sqrt{5^2 + (-1)^2}$$

$$= \sqrt{34} \qquad\qquad\qquad\qquad\qquad = \sqrt{26}$$

$$AC = \sqrt{(10-2)^2 + (6-2)^2}$$

$$= \sqrt{8^2 + 4^2}$$

$$= \sqrt{80}$$

$$= 4\sqrt{5}$$

Use a calculator to approximate the measure of each side. So, $AB \approx 5.83$, $BC \approx 5.10$, and $AC \approx 8.94$.

Step 2 Determine whether the measures can form a triangle.

Use the Triangle Inequality Theorem to determine whether the measures 5.83, 5.10, and 8.94 can form a triangle.

$5.83 + 5.10 > 8.94$ ✓ $5.83 + 8.94 > 5.10$ ✓ $5.10 + 8.94 > 5.83$ ✓

The side lengths 5.83, 5.10, and 8.94 __can__ form a triangle.

Step 3 Classify the triangle.

Classify the triangle by comparing the square of the longest side to the sum of the squares of the other two sides.

$$c^2 \overset{?}{=} a^2 + b^2 \qquad\qquad \text{Compare } c^2 \text{ and } a^2 + b^2.$$

$$8.94^2 \overset{?}{=} 5.83^2 + 5.10^2 \qquad c = 8.94, a = 5.83, \text{ and } b = 5.10$$

$$79.9 > 60.0 \qquad\qquad\qquad \text{Simplify and compare.}$$

Because $c^2 > a^2 + b^2$, the triangle is __obtuse__.

Check

Determine whether the points $J(1, 6)$, $K(3, 2)$, and $L(5, 3)$ can be the vertices of a triangle. If so, classify the triangle as *acute*, *right*, or *obtuse*. __yes; right__

 Go Online You can complete an Extra Example online.

516   Module 9 · Right Triangles and Trigonometry

Copyright © McGraw-Hill Education

Study Tip

Approximations
When finding the side lengths of a triangle using the Distance Formula, it may be easier to work with the side lengths after using a calculator to approximate their measures. However, when classifying a triangle, your final calculations will be more accurate if you keep the side lengths in radical form.

 Think About It!
Does your conclusion seem reasonable? Explain.

Yes; sample answer: If you graph the triangle on the coordinate plane, it appears to be obtuse.

Example 4 Classify Triangles

MP Teaching the Mathematical Practices

4 Make Assumptions In the Study Tip, have students point out where an assumption or approximation was made in the solution.

Questions for Mathematical Discourse

AL Which is the possible hypotenuse of this triangle? Explain.
$\overline{AC}$ because it is the longest side.

OL What is another way to do step 3? Use the square roots rather than the approximations.

BL What is another way to check if the points can make a triangle? Graph them and check that they are not collinear.

DIFFERENTIATE

Reteaching Activity **AL** **ELL**

Give students the coordinates of two points on the coordinate plane. Have them come up with a third point that fits each possible classification of acute, right, obtuse, or not a triangle. Have students share graphs of their triangles and non-triangles.

Exit Ticket

Recommended Use

At the end of class, go online to display the Exit Ticket prompt and ask students to respond using a separate piece of paper. Have students hand you their responses as they leave the room.

Alternate Use

At the end of class, go online to display the Exit Ticket prompt and ask students to respond verbally or by using a mini-whiteboard. Have students hold up their whiteboards so that you can see all student responses. Tap to reveal the answer when most or all students have completed the Exit Ticket.

Interactive Presentation

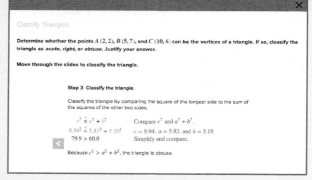

Classify Triangles

Determine whether the points $A(2, 2)$, $B(5, 7)$, and $C(10, 6)$ can be the vertices of a triangle. If so, classify the triangle as *acute*, *right*, or *obtuse*. Justify your answer.

Move through the slides to classify the triangle.

Step 3 Classify the triangle.

Classify the triangle by comparing the square of the longest side to the sum of the squares of the other two sides.

$$c^2 \overset{?}{=} a^2 + b^2 \qquad \text{Compare } c^2 \text{ and } a^2 + b^2.$$
$$8.94^2 \overset{?}{=} 5.83^2 + 5.10^2 \qquad c = 8.94, a = 5.83, \text{ and } b = 5.10$$
$$79.9 > 60.0 \qquad \text{Simplify and compare.}$$

Because $c^2 > a^2 + b^2$, the triangle is obtuse.

Example 4

TAP

Students tap to see steps in the solution.

CHECK

Students complete the Check online to determine whether they are ready to move on.

Practice and Homework

Suggested Assignments

Use the table below to select appropriate exercises.

DOK	Topic	Exercises
1, 2	exercises that mirror the examples	1–18
2	exercises that use a variety of skills from this lesson	19–39
3	exercises that emphasize higher-order and critical-thinking skills	40–43

ASSESS AND DIFFERENTIATE

📊 Use the data from the **Checks** to determine whether to provide resources for extension, remediation, or intervention.

IF students score 90% or more on the Checks,   `BL`
THEN assign:

- Practice, Exercises 1–39 odd, 40–43
- Extension: Generating Pythagorean Triples
- ⊘ **ALEKS** The Pythagorean Theorem

IF students score 66%–89% on the Checks,   `OL`
THEN assign:

- Practice, Exercises 1–43 odd
- Remediation, Review Resources: Roots
- Personal Tutors
- BrainPOP Video: The Pythagorean Theorem
- Extra Examples 1–4
- ⊘ **ALEKS** Square Roots and Irrational Numbers

IF students score 65% or less on the Checks,   `AL`
THEN assign:

- Practice, Exercises 1–17 odd
- Remediation, Review Resources: Roots
- *Quick Review Math Handbook*: The Pythagorean Theorem and Its Converse
- ⊘ **ALEKS** Square Roots and Irrational Numbers

Answers

15. Yes; right; sample answer: The measures of the sides would be $XY = \sqrt{8} \approx 2.83$, $YZ = \sqrt{2} \approx 1.41$, and $XZ = \sqrt{10} \approx 3.16$. Because $2.83 + 1.41 > 3.16$, $2.83 + 3.16 > 1.41$, and $1.41 + 3.16 > 2.83$, the side lengths can form a triangle. Because $(\sqrt{8})^2 + (\sqrt{2})^2 = (\sqrt{10})^2$, we know that the triangle is a right triangle.

16. Yes; acute; sample answer: The measures of the sides would be $XY = \sqrt{29} \approx 5.39$, $YZ = \sqrt{20} \approx 4.47$, and $XZ = \sqrt{13} \approx 3.61$. Because $5.39 + 4.47 > 3.61$, $5.39 + 3.61 > 4.47$, and $3.61 + 4.47 > 5.39$, the side lengths can form a triangle. Because $(\sqrt{13})^2 + (\sqrt{20})^2 > (\sqrt{29})^2$, we know that the triangle is an acute triangle.

17. Yes; obtuse; sample answer: The measures of the sides would be $XY = 5$, $YZ = 2$, and $XZ = \sqrt{41} \approx 6.40$. Because $5 + 2 > 6.40$, $5 + 6.40 > 2$, and $2 + 6.40 > 5$, the side lengths can form a triangle. Because $5^2 + 2^2 < (\sqrt{41})^2$, we know that the triangle is an obtuse triangle.

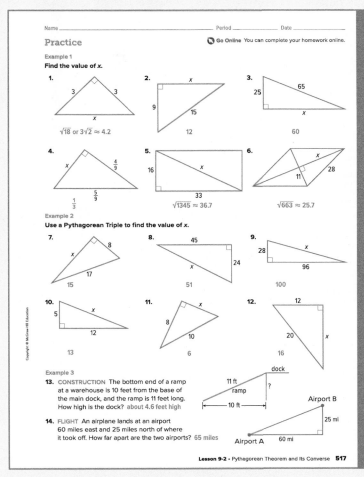

Name _____ Period _____ Date _____

Practice   ⊘ **Go Online** You can complete your homework online.

Example 1
Find the value of x.

1. $\sqrt{18}$ or $3\sqrt{2} \approx 4.2$
2.
3.
4.
5. $\sqrt{1345} \approx 36.7$
6. $\sqrt{663} \approx 25.7$

Example 2
Use a Pythagorean Triple to find the value of x.

7.
8.
9.
10.
11.
12.

Example 3

13. CONSTRUCTION The bottom end of a ramp at a warehouse is 10 feet from the base of the main dock, and the ramp is 11 feet long. How high is the dock? about 4.6 feet high

14. FLIGHT An airplane lands at an airport 60 miles east and 25 miles north of where it took off. How far apart are the two airports? 65 miles

Lesson 9-2 • Pythagorean Theorem and Its Converse **517**

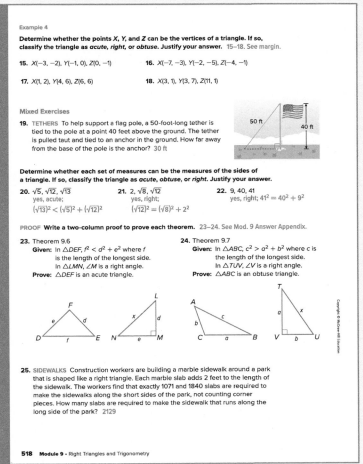

Example 4

Determine whether the points X, Y, and Z can be the vertices of a triangle. If so, classify the triangle as *acute*, *right*, or *obtuse*. Justify your answer. 15–18. See margin.

15. $X(-3, -2)$, $Y(-1, 0)$, $Z(0, -1)$
16. $X(-7, -3)$, $Y(-2, -5)$, $Z(-4, -1)$
17. $X(1, 2)$, $Y(4, 6)$, $Z(6, 6)$
18. $X(3, 1)$, $Y(3, 7)$, $Z(11, 1)$

Mixed Exercises

19. TETHERS To help support a flag pole, a 50-foot-long tether is tied to the pole at a point 40 feet above the ground. The tether is pulled taut and tied to an anchor in the ground. How far away from the base of the pole is the anchor? 30 ft

Determine whether each set of measures can be the measures of the sides of a triangle. If so, classify the triangle as *acute*, *obtuse*, or *right*. Justify your answer.

20. $\sqrt{5}$, $\sqrt{12}$, $\sqrt{13}$
yes, acute;
$(\sqrt{13})^2 < (\sqrt{5})^2 + (\sqrt{12})^2$

21. 2, $\sqrt{8}$, $\sqrt{12}$
yes, right;
$(\sqrt{12})^2 = (\sqrt{8})^2 + 2^2$

22. 9, 40, 41
yes, right; $41^2 = 40^2 + 9^2$

PROOF Write a two-column proof to prove each theorem. 23–24. See Mod. 9 Answer Appendix.

23. Theorem 9.6
Given: In $\triangle DEF$, $f^2 < d^2 + e^2$ where f is the length of the longest side. In $\triangle LMN$, $\angle M$ is a right angle.
Prove: $\triangle DEF$ is an acute triangle.

24. Theorem 9.7
Given: In $\triangle ABC$, $c^2 > a^2 + b^2$ where c is the length of the longest side. In $\triangle TUV$, $\angle V$ is a right angle.
Prove: $\triangle ABC$ is an obtuse triangle.

25. SIDEWALKS Construction workers are building a marble sidewalk around a park that is shaped like a right triangle. Each marble slab adds 2 feet to the length of the sidewalk. The workers find that exactly 1071 and 1840 slabs are required to make the sidewalks along the short sides of the park, not counting corner pieces. How many slabs are required to make the sidewalk that runs along the long side of the park? 2129

518 **Module 9** • Right Triangles and Trigonometry

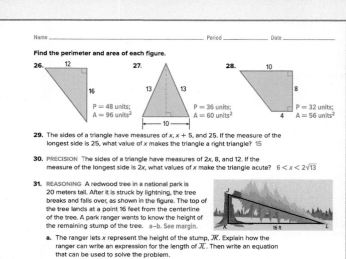

Name _____ Period _____ Date _____

Find the perimeter and area of each figure.

26.

12

16

P = 48 units;
A = 96 units²

27.

13   13

10

P = 36 units;
A = 60 units²

28.

10

8

4

P = 32 units;
A = 56 units²

29. The sides of a triangle have measures of x, $x + 5$, and 25. If the measure of the longest side is 25, what value of x makes the triangle a right triangle? 15

30. PRECISION The sides of a triangle have measures of $2x$, 8, and 12. If the measure of the longest side is $2x$, what values of x make the triangle acute? $6 < x < 2\sqrt{13}$

31. REASONING A redwood tree in a national park is 20 meters tall. After it is struck by lightning, the tree breaks and falls over, as shown in the figure. The top of the tree lands at a point 16 feet from the centerline of the tree. A park ranger wants to know the height of the remaining stump of the tree. a–b. See margin.

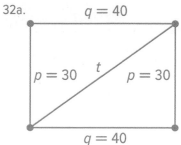

a. The ranger lets x represent the height of the stump, $\overline{JK}$. Explain how the ranger can write an expression for the length of $\overline{JL}$. Then write an equation that can be used to solve the problem.

b. Show how to solve the equation from part **a** to find the height of the stump.

32. CONSTRUCT ARGUMENTS Valeria and Sanjia are staking out a garden that has one pair of opposite sides measuring 30 feet and the other pair of sides measuring 40 feet. Using only a 60-foot-long tape measure, how can they be sure that their garden is a rectangle? a–c. See margin.

a. Draw a model of the garden with diagonal t. Let $p = 30$ and $q = 40$.

b. If the garden is a rectangle, what must be true about p, q, and t? Why?

c. Sanjia measures the diagonal and finds that it is 50 feet long. Is there enough information to determine whether their garden is a rectangle? Explain.

Find the value of x.

33.

x

$x - 4$

8

34.

$x - 3$

x

9

15

35.

x

$x + 1$

$\sqrt{2}$

$\frac{1}{2}$

36. HDTV The screen aspect ratio, or the ratio of the width to the height, of a high-definition television is 16:9. The size of the television is given by the diagonal distance across the screen. If the height of Raj's HDTV screen is 32 inches, what is the screen size to the nearest inch? 65 in.

32 in.

37. DISTANCE Eduardo and Lisa both leave school on their bikes at the same time. Eduardo rides due east at 18 miles per hour for 30 minutes and Lisa rides due south at 16 miles per hour for 30 minutes. Complete the diagram to represent the problem. To the nearest hundredth of a mile, how far apart are they when they stop riding their bikes? See margin.

School

Eduardo

Lisa

38. OFFICE PARK An office park has a rectangular lawn with the dimensions shown. Employees often take a shortcut by walking from P to R, rather than from P to S to R. What is the total distance an employee saves in a week by taking the shortcut twice a day for five days? Explain. See margin.

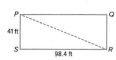

P   Q

41 ft

S   R

98.4 ft

39. STRUCTURE Ms. Jones assigned her fifth-period geometry class the following problem. Let m and n be two positive integers with $m > n$.

Let $a = m^2 - n^2$, $b = 2mn$, and $c = m^2 + n^2$. a–c. See margin.

a. Show that there is a right triangle with side lengths a, b, and c.

b. Complete the table shown at the right.

c. Find a Pythagorean triple that corresponds to a right triangle with a hypotenuse $25^2 = 625$ units long. (*Hint:* Use the table you completed for part **b** to find two positive integers m and n with $m > n$ and $m^2 + n^2 = 625$.)

m	n	a	b	c
2	1	3	4	5
3	1			
3	2			
4	1			
4	2			
4	3			
5	1			

🧠 **Higher-Order Thinking Skills**

40. ANALYZE *True* or *false*? Any two right triangles with the same hypotenuse have the same area. Explain your reasoning. See Mod. 9 Answer Appendix.

41. CREATE Draw a right triangle with side lengths that form a Pythagorean triple. If you double the length of each side, is the resulting triangle *acute*, *right*, or *obtuse*? If you halve the length of each side? Explain. See Mod. 9 Answer Appendix.

42. PERSEVERE Find the value of x in the figure at the right. 5.4197

43. WRITE Research *incommensurable magnitudes*, and describe how this phrase relates to the use of irrational numbers in geometry. Include one example of an irrational number used in geometry. See Mod. 9 Answer Appendix.

11.6

x 2.7

13

7.5   15

Answers

18. Yes; right; sample answer: The measures of the sides would be $XY = 6$, $YZ = 10$, and $XZ = 8$. Because $6 + 10 > 8$, $6 + 8 > 10$, and $8 + 10 > 6$, the side lengths can form a triangle. Because $6^2 + 8^2 = 10^2$, we know that the triangle is a right triangle.

31a. Because the height of the tree is 20 m, $JL = 20 - x$. By the Pythagorean Theorem, $16^2 + x^2 = (20 - x)^2$.

31b. $16^2 + x^2 = (20 - x)^2$, so $256 + x^2 = 400 - 40x + x^2$. Subtracting x^2 from both sides gives $256 = 400 - 40x$. Therefore, $-144 = -40x$. Dividing both sides by -40 gives $3.6 = x$. The stump of the tree is 3.6 meters tall.

32a.

$q = 40$

$p = 30$ t $p = 30$

$q = 40$

32b. If the garden is a rectangle, then sides p and q form a right angle because all rectangles have 4 right angles. The diagonal t is the hypotenuse of the right triangle with legs p and q.

32c. Yes, the garden is a rectangle; sample answer: The quadrilateral is a parallelogram because both pairs of opposite sides are congruent. Because the diagonal and sides form a Pythagorean triple ($50^2 = 30^2 + 40^2$), the diagonal forms 2 right triangles. Because consecutive angles are supplementary, the other pair of opposite angles is right angles. The garden is a rectangle by definition.

37.

School   9 mi   Eduardo

8 mi

12.04 miles

Lisa

38. By the Pythagorean Theorem, $PR = 106.6$ ft. The distance saved on each trip is $(41 + 98.4) - 106.6 = 32.8$ ft. There are 10 trips per week, so the total distance saved is 328 ft.

39a. Sample answer: $a^2 + b^2 = (m^2 - n^2)^2 + (2mn)^2 = m^4 - 2m^2n^2 + n^4 + 4m^2n^2 = m^4 + 2m^2n^2 + n^4$ and $c^2 = (m^2 + n^2)^2 = m^4 + 2m^2n^2 + n^4$. This means that $a^2 + b^2 = c^2$, so a, b, and c do form the sides of a right triangle by the Converse of the Pythagorean Theorem.

39b.

m	n	a	b	c
2	1	3	4	5
3	1	8	6	10
3	2	5	12	13
4	1	15	8	17
4	2	12	16	20
4	3	7	24	25
5	1	24	10	26

39c. Sample answer: Take $m = 24$ and $n = 7$ to get $a = 527$, $b = 336$, and $c = 625$.

Coordinates in Space

LESSON GOAL

Students graph points and find distances using the distance formula for three dimensions.

1 LAUNCH

 Launch the lesson with a **Warm Up** and an introduction.

2 EXPLORE AND DEVELOP

 Explore: Proving the Distance Formula in Space

 Develop:

Coordinates in Space
- Graph a Rectangular Solid
- Distance Formula in Space
- Midpoint Formula in Space

You may want your students to complete the **Checks** online.

3 REFLECT AND PRACTICE

Exit Ticket

Practice

DIFFERENTIATE

View reports of student progress on the **Checks** after each example.

Resources	AL	OL	BL	ELL
Remediation: The Coordinate Plane	●	●		●
Extension: Transformation of Points in Space		●	●	●

Language Development Handbook

Assign page 60 of the *Language Development Handbook* to help your students build mathematical language related to graphing points and finding distances using the distance formula for three dimensions.

ELL You can use the tips and suggestions on page T60 of the handbook to support students who are building English proficiency.

Suggested Pacing

| 90 min | 0.5 day |
| 45 min | 1 day |

Focus

Domain: Geometry

Standards for Mathematical Practice:

3 Construct viable arguments and critique the reasoning of others.

4 Model with mathematics.

6 Attend to precision.

Coherence

Vertical Alignment

Previous
Students solved problems using the Pythagorean Theorem and its converse.
G.SRT.4, G.SRT.8

Now
Students graph points and find distances in three dimensions.

Next
Students will solve problems by using the properties of special right triangles.
G.SRT.6

Rigor

The Three Pillars of Rigor

1 CONCEPTUAL UNDERSTANDING	2 FLUENCY	3 APPLICATION

Conceptual Bridge In this lesson, students extend on their understanding of the Pythagorean Theorem and Distance Formula in two dimensions to three dimensions. They apply their understanding by solving real-world problems related to space.

Mathematical Background

You have used ordered pairs of two coordinates to describe the location of a point on the coordinate plane. Because space has three dimensions, a point requires three numbers, or coordinates, to describe its location in space. A point in space is represented by an *ordered triple* of real numbers (x, y, z).

Interactive Presentation

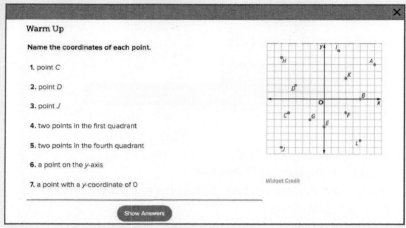

Warm Up

Launch the Lesson

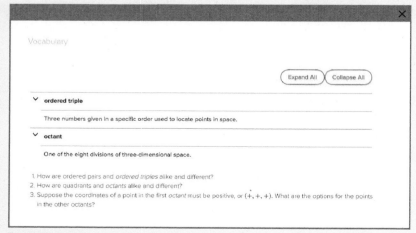

Today's Vocabulary

Warm Up

Prerequisite Skills
The Warm Up exercises address the following prerequisite skill for this lesson:

• graphing ordered pairs

Answers:

1. $(-5, -2)$
2. $(-4, 2)$
3. $(-6, -7)$
4. $A(7, 5)$, $I(2, 7)$, and $K(3, 3)$
5. $F(3, -2)$ and $L(5, -6)$
6. $E(0, -4)$
7. $B(5, 0)$

Launch the Lesson

 Teaching the Mathematical Practices

4 Apply Mathematics In this Launch the Lesson, students can see a real-world application of three-dimensional coordinate space.

Go Online to find additional teaching notes and questions to promote classroom discourse.

Today's Standards

Tell students that they will be addressing these content and practice standards in this lesson. You may wish to have a student volunteer read aloud *How can I meet these standards?* and *How can I use these practices?* and connect these to the standards.

See the Interactive Presentation for I Can statements that align with the standards covered in this lesson.

Today's Vocabulary

Tell students that they will be using these vocabulary terms in this lesson. You can expand each row if you wish to share the definitions. Then, discuss the questions below with the class.

Explore Proving the Distance Formula in Space

Objective
Students use the Pythagorean Theorem to prove the Distance Formula in three-dimensional coordinate space.

 Teaching the Mathematical Practices

> **3 Construct Arguments** In this Explore, students will use stated assumptions, definitions, and previously established results to construct an argument.

Ideas for Use

Recommended Use Present the Inquiry Question, or have a student volunteer read it aloud. Have students work in pairs to complete the Explore activity on their devices. Pairs should discuss each of the questions. Monitor student progress during the activity. Upon completion of the Explore activity, have student volunteers share their responses to the Inquiry Question.

What if my students don't have devices? You may choose to project the activity on a whiteboard. A printable worksheet for each Explore is available online. You may choose to print the worksheet so that individuals or pairs of students can use it to record their observations.

Summary of the Activity

Students will complete guiding exercises throughout the Explore activity. Students begin by completing guiding exercises to lead them to the use of the Pythagorean Theorem to develop the Distance Formula in three-dimensional space. The students then complete guiding exercises to use two right triangles in a rectangular prism and the Pythagorean Theorem to develop the Distance Formula in three-dimensional space. Then, students will answer the Inquiry Question.

(continued on the next page)

Interactive Presentation

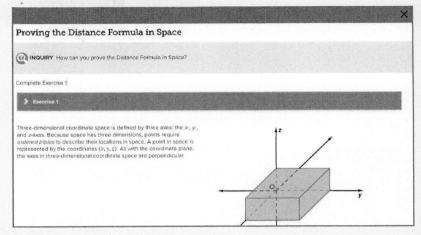

Explore

TAP

Students tap to move through steps of the proof and to complete the solution.

Interactive Presentation

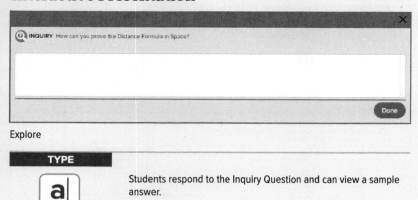

Explore

TYPE

Students respond to the Inquiry Question and can view a sample answer.

Explore Proving the Distance Formula in Space (*continued*)

MP Teaching the Mathematical Practices

6 Use Quantities Use the exercises to guide students to clarify their use of quantities in this Explore. Ensure that they label axes appropriately.

Questions

Have students complete the Explore activity.

Ask:

- How are coordinates in space similar to coordinates on the Cartesian plane? How are they different? Sample answer: Both involve the *x*- and *y*-axes, but coordinates in space also use the *z*-axis.

- What real world examples can help you think about the distance formula in space? Sample answer: A diagonal line from one corner of the classroom floor to the opposite corner of the classroom ceiling.

Inquiry

How can you prove the Distance Formula in Space? Sample answer: I can create a right triangle in space and define the coordinates of each vertex of the triangle as an ordered triple. Then I can use the Distance Formula and the Pythagorean Theorem in two-dimensions to find the lengths of the legs of the right triangle in space. Then I can use the Pythagorean Theorem to find the length of the hypotenuse of the triangle in space. The length of the hypotenuse is equal to the distance between the endpoints of the hypotenuse.

Go Online to find additional teaching notes and sample answers for the guiding exercises.

Learn Coordinates in Space

Objective
Students graph points and find distances between points on a three-dimensional coordinate plane.

 Teaching the Mathematical Practices

7 Use Structure Help students to explore the structure of coordinates in space in this Learn.

Things to Remember
The right-hand rule can be used to depict the coordinate system in any direction. Demonstrate: First, point the fingers of your right hand in the direction of the positive *x*-axis. Then, curl your fingers towards the positive *y*-axis. Your thumb will point in the direction of the positive *z*-axis.

Example 1 Graph a Rectangular Solid

 Teaching the Mathematical Practices

6 Communicate Precisely Encourage students to routinely write or explain their solution methods. Point out that they should use clear definitions when they discuss their solutions with others.

Questions for Mathematical Discourse

AL Describe the positions of the three axes in your own words. The *z*-axis is vertical, the *y*-axis is horizontal, and the *x*-axis is drawn at a non-right angle to the other two axes.

OL Where is the point (3, 4, 2) in relation to the prism? It is outside the prism, appearing on the paper slightly below the prism.

BL If a rectangular prism included the origin and the point (3, 4, −2), where would it appear in the drawing? Sample answer: It would appear below the *y*-axis and to the right of the *x*-axis.

DIFFERENTIATE

Reteaching Activity **AL** **ELL**
Have students use a rectangular solid such as a shoe box to find coordinates in space. Use items such as toothpicks and mini marshmallows to represent line segments and points. Have students draw grid lines inside the box and select random values for points in the space. For example, use *J*(3, 6, 9) and *K*(−3, −5, 7). Have them work in teams to find *JK* using the Distance Formula in Space and coordinates of the midpoint *M* of the line segment $\overline{JK}$.

 Go Online

- Find additional teaching notes.
- View performance reports of the Checks.
- Assign or present an Extra Example.

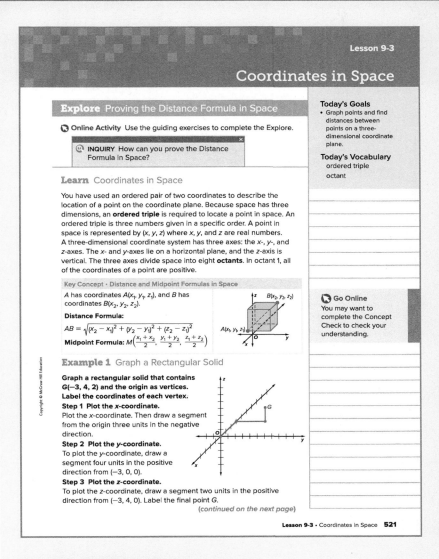

Lesson 9-3

Coordinates in Space

Explore Proving the Distance Formula in Space

Online Activity Use the guiding exercises to complete the Explore.

INQUIRY How can you prove the Distance Formula in Space?

Learn Coordinates in Space

You have used an ordered pair of two coordinates to describe the location of a point on the coordinate plane. Because space has three dimensions, an **ordered triple** is required to locate a point in space. An ordered triple is three numbers given in a specific order. A point in space is represented by (*x, y, z*) where *x, y,* and *z* are real numbers. A three-dimensional coordinate system has three axes: the *x*-, *y*-, and *z*-axes. The *x*- and *y*-axes lie on a horizontal plane, and the *z*-axis is vertical. The three axes divide space into eight **octants**. In octant 1, all of the coordinates of a point are positive.

Key Concept · Distance and Midpoint Formulas in Space

A has coordinates $A(x_1, y_1, z_1)$, and *B* has coordinates $B(x_2, y_2, z_2)$.

Distance Formula:
$$AB = \sqrt{(x_2 - x_1)^2 + (y_2 - y_1)^2 + (z_2 - z_1)^2}$$

Midpoint Formula: $M\left(\dfrac{x_1 + x_2}{2}, \dfrac{y_1 + y_2}{2}, \dfrac{z_1 + z_2}{2}\right)$

Example 1 Graph a Rectangular Solid

Graph a rectangular solid that contains *G*(−3, 4, 2) and the origin as vertices. Label the coordinates of each vertex.

Step 1 Plot the *x*-coordinate.
Plot the *x*-coordinate. Then draw a segment from the origin three units in the negative direction.

Step 2 Plot the *y*-coordinate.
To plot the *y*-coordinate, draw a segment four units in the positive direction from (−3, 0, 0).

Step 3 Plot the *z*-coordinate.
To plot the *z*-coordinate, draw a segment two units in the positive direction from (−3, 4, 0). Label the final point *G*.

(continued on the next page)

Today's Goals
- Graph points and find distances between points on a three-dimensional coordinate plane.

Today's Vocabulary
ordered triple
octant

 Go Online
You may want to complete the Concept Check to check your understanding.

Interactive Presentation

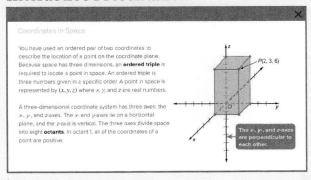

Coordinates in Space

You have used an ordered pair of two coordinates to describe the location of a point on the coordinate plane. Because space has three dimensions, an **ordered triple** is required to locate a point in space. An ordered triple is three numbers given in a specific order. A point in space is represented by (*x, y, z*) where *x, y,* and *z* are real numbers.

A three-dimensional coordinate system has three axes: the *x*-, *y*-, and *z*-axes. The *x*- and *y*-axes lie on a horizontal plane, and the *z*-axis is vertical. The three axes divide space into eight **octants**. In octant 1, all of the coordinates of a point are positive.

The *x*-, *y*-, and *z*-axes are perpendicular to each other.

Learn

TAP

Students tap to reveal the Distance and Midpoint Formulas in Space.

Your Notes

💬 Talk About It!

What is the relationship between the origin and the coordinates of a point?

Sample answer: The coordinates of a point represent the distance the point is from the origin on each of the three axes.

💭 Think About It!

What assumption did you make while solving this problem? Explain why this assumption caused your answer to be an approximation.

Sample answer: I assumed that the man's spine is straight. Because spines are curved, the length I calculated is shorter than the actual length of the spine. So, my answer is an approximation.

🌐 Go Online

You can complete an Extra Example online.

Step 4 Draw the rectangular prism.

Draw the rectangular prism and label each vertex: $G(-3, 4, 2)$, $F(-3, 0, 2)$, $E(0, 0, 2)$, $D(0, 4, 2)$, $H(0, 4, 0)$, $I(0, 0, 0)$, $J(-3, 0, 0)$, and $K(-3, 4, 0)$.

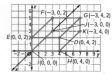

🌐 Example 2 Distance Formula in Space

MEDICINE Doctors use three-dimensional coordinate systems for medical imaging. Medical imaging and positioning systems allow doctors to analyze a person's anatomy from a three-dimensional perspective. On an anatomical coordinate system, the top of a man's spine is located at $(5, 0, 65)$, and the bottom of his spine is located at $(3, 0, -6)$. If each unit on the coordinate system represents a centimeter, what is the length of the man's spine?

Write the coordinates to find the length of the man's spine.

$$D = \sqrt{(x_2 - x_1)^2 + (y_2 - y_1)^2 + (z_2 - z_1)^2}$$ Distance Formula in Space

$$= \sqrt{(5 - 3)^2 + (0 - 0)^2 + [65 - (-6)]^2}$$ Substitution

$$= \sqrt{2^2 + 0^2 + 71^2}$$ Subtract.

$$= \sqrt{5045} \text{ or about } 71.0$$ Use a calculator.

So, the length of the man's spine is about ___71.0___ centimeters.

Check

AVIATION Air traffic controllers use three-dimensional coordinate space to track the locations of aircraft. By assigning coordinates to every aircraft in the sky, air traffic controllers can describe the positions of other aircraft to pilots to prevent accidents. An airplane is at $(17, -14, 23)$, and the air traffic control tower is at $(0, 0, 0)$. If each unit on the coordinate system represents a kilometer, what is the distance between the airplane and the tower? Round your answer to the nearest tenth, if necessary. ___31.8___ km

🌐 Example 3 Midpoint Formula in Space

Determine the coordinates of the midpoint M of $\overline{DE}$ with endpoints $D(-4, -3, 5)$ and $E(6, 1, -9)$.

$$M = \left(\frac{x_1 + x_2}{2}, \frac{y_1 + y_2}{2}, \frac{z_1 + z_2}{2}\right)$$ Midpoint Formula in Space

$$= \left(\frac{-4 + 6}{2}, \frac{-3 + 1}{2}, \frac{5 + (-9)}{2}\right)$$ Substitution

$$= (\underline{1}, \underline{-1}, \underline{-2})$$ Simplify.

Check

Determine the coordinates of the midpoint M of $\overline{AB}$ with endpoints $A(-7, 9, 4)$ and $B(5, -3, -4)$.

$M(\underline{-1}, \underline{3}, \underline{0})$

Interactive Presentation

Distance Formula in Space

🌐 MEDICINE Doctors use three-dimensional coordinate systems for medical imaging. Medical imaging and positioning systems allow doctors to analyze a person's anatomy from a three-dimensional perspective. On an anatomical coordinate system the top of a man's spine is located at $(5, 0, 65)$, and the bottom of his spine is located at $(3, 0, -6)$. If each unit on the coordinate system represents a centimeter, what is the length of the man's spine?

Example 2

DRAG

Students drag coordinates to the correct locations in the Distance Formula in Space.

CHECK

Students complete the Check online to determine whether they are ready to move on.

🌐 Example 2 Distance Formula in Space

MP Teaching the Mathematical Practices

4 Apply Mathematics In this example, students apply what they have learned about the Distance Formula in Space to solving a real-world problem.

Questions for Mathematical Discourse

AL Which point is represented by (x_1, y_1, z_1)? $(5, 0, 65)$

OL What is the difference between the z-coordinates? 71

BL Would it be possible to represent this spine with a two-dimensional coordinate system? Explain. Yes, if you use just the x- and z-coordinates, because the y-coordinates are both 0.

Example 3 Midpoint Formula in Space

MP Teaching the Mathematical Practices

4 Use Tools Point out that to solve the problem in this example, students will need to use the Midpoint Formula in Space.

Questions for Mathematical Discourse

AL What is the average of the x-coordinates of the two points? 1

OL How do you find each coordinate of the midpoint? Find the average of the corresponding coordinates of the two points.

BL If the midpoint of $\overline{DF}$ is $N(-2, 1, 1)$, what are the coordinates of F? $(0, 5, -3)$

Common Error

Students may divide the first coordinate in each average by 2 before adding, without dividing the second.

Exit Ticket

Recommended Use

At the end of class, go online to display the Exit Ticket prompt and ask students to respond using a separate piece of paper. Have students hand you their responses as they leave the room.

Alternate Use

At the end of class, go online to display the Exit Ticket prompt and ask students to respond verbally or by using a mini-whiteboard. Have students hold up their whiteboards so that you can see all student responses. Tap to reveal the answer when most or all students have completed the Exit Ticket.

| 1 CONCEPTUAL UNDERSTANDING | 2 FLUENCY | 3 APPLICATION |

Practice and Homework

Suggested Assignments

Use the table below to select appropriate exercises.

DOK	Topic	Exercises
1, 2	exercises that mirror the examples	1–18
2	exercises that use a variety of skills from this lesson	19–25
3	exercises that emphasize higher-order and critical-thinking skills	26–29

ASSESS AND DIFFERENTIATE

📊 Use the data from the **Checks** to determine whether to provide resources for extension, remediation, or intervention.

IF students score 90% or more on the Checks, **BL**
THEN assign:

- Practice, Exercises 1–25 odd, 26–29
- Extension: Transformation of Points in Space

IF students score 66%–89% on the Checks, **OL**
THEN assign:

- Practice, Exercises 1–29 odd
- Remediation, Review Resources: Compare and Order Rational Numbers
- Personal Tutors
- Extra Examples 1–3
- ⊙ **ALEKS** Converting Between Fractions and Decimals; Ordered Pairs

IF students score 65% or less on the Checks, **AL**
THEN assign:

- Practice, Exercises 1–17 odd
- Remediation, Review Resources: Compare and Order Rational Numbers
- ⊙ **ALEKS** Converting Between Fractions and Decimals; Ordered Pairs

Answers

1.

2.

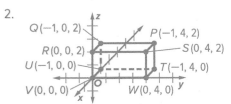

Name _____ Period _____ Date _____

Practice

🔵 **Go Online** You can complete your homework online.

Example 1

Graph a rectangular solid that contains the given point and the origin as vertices. Label the coordinates of each vertex. 1–6. See margin.

1. $A(2, 1, 5)$
2. $P(-1, 4, 2)$
3. $C(-2, 2, 2)$

4. $R(3, -4, 1)$
5. $H(4, 5, -3)$
6. $G(4, 1, -3)$

Example 2

Determine the distance between each pair of points.

7. $F(0, 0, 0)$ and $G(2, 4, 3)$ $\sqrt{29}$
8. $X(-2, 5, -1)$ and $Y(9, 0, 4)$ $\sqrt{171}$ or $3\sqrt{19}$

9. $A(4, -6, 0)$ and $B(1, 0, 1)$ $\sqrt{46}$
10. $C(8, 7, -2)$ and $D(0, 0, 0)$ $\sqrt{117}$ or $3\sqrt{13}$

11. **AIR TRAFFIC CONTROLLERS** An air traffic controller knows that the most recent position of an aircraft was at the coordinates shown on the three-dimensional coordinate system to the right. If the control tower is at $(0, 0, 0)$, then what is the distance between the aircraft and the tower if each unit on the coordinate system represents one mile? Round your answer to the nearest tenth, if necessary.
20.2 mi

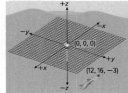

12. **ANIMATORS** An animator is using three-dimensional software to create the character shown. She labels the coordinates of point R and point T. Point R represents the nose of the dog, and point T represents the tip of the dog's tail. What is the distance between these two points in the animation? Round your answer to the nearest tenth, if necessary.
18.7 units

$R(-9, 2, -1)$ $T(9, -2, 2)$

Example 3

Determine the coordinates of the midpoint M of the segment joining each pair of points.

13. $K(-2, -4, -4)$ and $L(4, 2, 0)$ $(1, -1, -2)$
14. $W(-1, -3, -6)$ and $Z(-1, 5, 10)$ $(-1, 1, 2)$

15. $R(3, 3, 4)$ and $V(5, 4, 13)$ $\left(4, \frac{7}{2}, \frac{17}{2}\right)$
16. $A(4, 6, -8)$ and $B(0, 0, 0)$ $(2, 3, -4)$

17. $C(8, 7, 11)$ and $D(2, 1, 8)$ $\left(5, 4, \frac{19}{2}\right)$
18. $T(-1, -7, 9)$ and $U(5, -1, -6)$ $\left(2, -4, \frac{3}{2}\right)$

Lesson 9-3 • Coordinates in Space 523

Mixed Exercises

REGULARITY **Determine the distance between each pair of points. Then determine the coordinates of the midpoint M of the segment joining the pair of points.** 19–24. See margin.

19. $P(-5, -2, -1)$ and $Q(-1, 0, 3)$

20. $J(1, 1, 1)$ and $K(-1, -1, -1)$

21. $F\left(\frac{3}{5}, 0, \frac{4}{5}\right)$ and $G(0, 3, 0)$

22. $G(1, -1, 6)$ and $H\left(\frac{1}{5}, -\frac{2}{5}, 2\right)$

23. $B(\sqrt{3}, 2, 2\sqrt{2})$ and $C(-2\sqrt{3}, 4, 4\sqrt{2})$

24. $S(6\sqrt{3}, 4, 4\sqrt{2})$ and $T(4\sqrt{3}, 5, \sqrt{2})$

25. PROOF Write a coordinate proof of the Midpoint Formula in Space.
See margin.

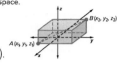

Given: Points $A(x_1, y_1, z_1)$ and $B(x_2, y_2, z_2)$;
M is the midpoint of $\overline{AB}$.

Prove: The coordinates of point M are $\left(\frac{x_1 + x_2}{2}, \frac{y_1 + y_2}{2}, \frac{z_1 + z_2}{2}\right)$.

🧠 **Higher-Order Thinking Skills**

26. WRITE Compare and contrast the Distance and Midpoint Formulas on the coordinate plane and in three-dimensional coordinate space. See Mod. 9 Answer Appendix.

27. FIND THE ERROR Camilla and Teion were asked to find the distance between the points $A(2, 5, -8)$ and $B(3, -1, 0)$. Who is correct? Explain your reasoning.
See Mod. 9 Answer Appendix.

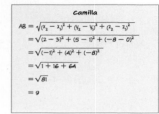

28. CREATE Graph a cube that has the following characteristics:
- the origin is one of the vertices,
- one of the edges lies on the negative y-axis, and
- one of the faces lies in the negative xz-plane. See Mod. 9 Answer Appendix.

29. PERSEVERE Suppose the sphere has a radius of 9 units and passes through point P. Find the missing z-coordinate of point P. $2\sqrt{19}$

Answers

3.

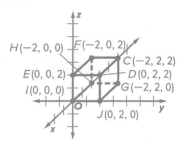

4.

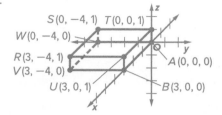

5.

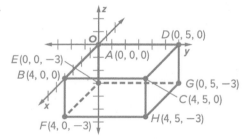

6.

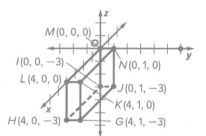

19. $PQ = \sqrt{36}$ or 6; $(-3, -1, 1)$

20. $JK = \sqrt{12}$ or $2\sqrt{3}$; $(0, 0, 0)$

21. $FG = \sqrt{10}$; $\left(\frac{3}{10}, \frac{3}{2}, \frac{2}{5}\right)$

22. $GH = \sqrt{17}$; $\left(\frac{3}{5}, -\frac{7}{10}, 4\right)$

23. $BC = \sqrt{39}$; $\left(-\frac{\sqrt{3}}{2}, 3, 3\sqrt{2}\right)$

24. $ST = \sqrt{31}$; $\left(5\sqrt{3}, \frac{9}{2}, \frac{5\sqrt{2}}{2}\right)$

25. Proof: Points $A(x_1, y_1, z_1)$ and $B(x_2, y_2, z_2)$ are given. It is also given that M is the midpoint of $\overline{AB}$. To find the coordinates of point M, you must find the coordinates of a point that is $\frac{1}{2}$ of the distance from point A to point B in three-dimensional space. The difference between the x-, y-, and z-coordinates of points A and B are $x_2 - x_1$, $y_2 - y_1$, and $z_2 - z_1$, respectively. Because M is halfway between points A and B, the distances between the x-, y-, and z-coordinates of points A and M are $\frac{1}{2}(x_2 - x_1)$, $\frac{1}{2}(y_2 - y_1)$, and $\frac{1}{2}(z_2 - z_1)$, respectively. To find the coordinates of point M, add the fractional distances to the coordinates of point A.

coordinates of point $M =$

$$\left(x_1 + \frac{1}{2}(x_2 - x_1), y_1 + \frac{1}{2}(y_2 - y_1), z_1 + \frac{1}{2}(z_2 - z_1)\right) =$$

$$\left(\frac{2x_1 + x_2 - x_1}{2}, \frac{2y_1 + y_2 - y_1}{2}, \frac{2z_1 + z_2 - z_1}{2}\right) =$$

$$\left(\frac{x_1 + x_2}{2}, \frac{y_1 + y_2}{2}, \frac{z_1 + z_2}{2}\right)$$

Special Right Triangles

LESSON GOAL

Students solve problems by using the properties of 45°-45°-90° and 30°-60°-90° triangles.

1 LAUNCH

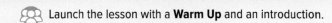 Launch the lesson with a **Warm Up** and an introduction.

2 EXPLORE AND DEVELOP

Explore: Properties of Special Right Triangles

Develop:

45°-45°-90° Triangles
- Find the Hypotenuse Length Given an Angle Measure
- Find the Hypotenuse Length Given a Side Measure
- Find Leg Lengths in a 45°-45°-90° Triangle

30°-60°-90° Triangles
- Find Leg Lengths in a 30°-60°-90° Triangle
- Use Properties of 30°-60°-90° Triangles

You may want your students to complete the **Checks** online.

3 REFLECT AND PRACTICE

Exit Ticket

Practice

DIFFERENTIATE

 View reports of student progress on the **Checks** after each example.

Resources	AL	OL	BL	ELL
Remediation: The Pythagorean Theorem	●	●		●
Extension: Wheel of Theodorus		●	●	●

Language Development Handbook

Assign page 61 of the *Language Development Handbook* to help your students build mathematical language related to special right triangles.

ELL You can use the tips and suggestions on page T61 of the handbook to support students who are building English proficiency.

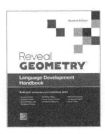

Suggested Pacing

| 90 min | 0.5 day |
| 45 min | 1 day |

Focus

Domain: Geometry

Standards for Mathematical Content:

G.SRT.6 Understand that by similarity, side ratios in right triangles are properties of the angles in the triangle, leading to definitions of trigonometric ratios for acute angles.

Standards for Mathematical Practice:

1 Make sense of problems and persevere in solving them.

3 Construct viable arguments and critique the reasoning of others.

8 Look for and express regularity in repeated reasoning.

Coherence

Vertical Alignment

Previous
Students graphed points and found distances in three dimensions.

Now
Students solve problems by using the properties of special right triangles.
G.SRT.6

Next
Students will solve problems using trigonometric ratios and their inverses for acute angles.
G.SRT.6, G.SRT.7

Rigor

The Three Pillars of Rigor

1 CONCEPTUAL UNDERSTANDING	2 FLUENCY	3 APPLICATION

Conceptual Bridge In this lesson, students expand on their understanding of right triangles to find similarities between right triangles with common measures. They build fluency and apply their understanding by solving real-world problems related to special right triangles.

Mathematical Background

A *45°-45°-90° triangle* is the only type of isosceles right triangle. The hypotenuse is $\sqrt{2}$ times the length of a leg. A *30°-60°-90° triangle* also has special properties. The measures of the sides are x, $x\sqrt{3}$, and $2x$. Knowing these properties can save valuable time when you are solving problems involving special right triangles.

Interactive Presentation

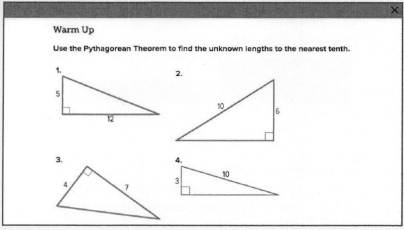

Warm Up

Launch the Lesson

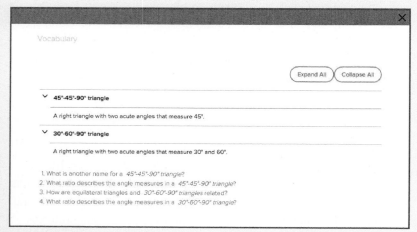

Today's Vocabulary

Warm Up

Prerequisite Skills

The Warm Up exercises address the following prerequisite skill for this lesson:

• using the Pythagorean Theorem

Answers:

1. 13
2. 8
3. 8.1
4. 9.5
5. no

Launch the Lesson

MP **Teaching the Mathematical Practices**

4 Apply Mathematics In this Launch the Lesson, students can see a real-world application of special right triangles.

Go Online to find additional teaching notes and questions to promote classroom discourse.

Today's Standards

Tell students that they will be addressing these content and practice standards in this lesson. You may wish to have a student volunteer read aloud *How can I meet these standards?* and *How can I use these practices?* and connect these to the standards.

See the Interactive Presentation for I Can statements that align with the standards covered in this lesson.

Today's Vocabulary

Tell students that they will be using these vocabulary terms in this lesson. You can expand each row if you wish to share the definitions. Then, discuss the questions below with the class.

Explore Properties of Special Right Triangles

Objective
Students use dynamic geometry software to explain that by similarity, side ratios in special right triangles are properties of the angles in the triangles.

(MP) Teaching the Mathematical Practices

5 Use Mathematical Tools Point out that to solve the problem in this Explore, students will need to use dynamic geometry software. Work with students to explore and deepen their understanding of special right triangles.

Ideas for Use

Recommended Use Present the Inquiry Question, or have a student volunteer read it aloud. Have students work in pairs to complete the Explore activity on their devices. Pairs should discuss each of the questions. Monitor student progress during the activity. Upon completion of the Explore activity, have student volunteers share their responses to the Inquiry Question.

What if my students don't have devices? You may choose to project the activity on a whiteboard. A printable worksheet for each Explore is available online. You may choose to print the worksheet so that individuals or pairs of students can use it to record their observations.

Summary of the Activity

Students will complete guiding exercises throughout the Explore activity. Students begin by constructing an isosceles right triangle using dynamic geometry software. They complete guiding exercises to find that the ratios of side lengths in isosceles right triangles are 1: 1: $\sqrt{2}$. Then students construct an equilateral triangle and the midpoint of one side. Students determine that this divides the equilateral triangle into two congruent right triangles. Next, students complete guiding exercises to determine that the ratios of side lengths in all such right triangles is 1: $\sqrt{3}$: 2. Then, students will answer the Inquiry Question.

(continued on the next page)

Interactive Presentation

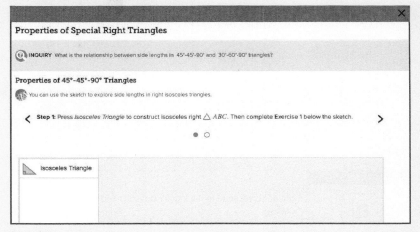

Explore

WEB SKETCHPAD

Students use a sketch to explore special right triangles.

Interactive Presentation

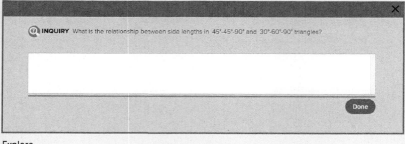

Explore

TYPE

Students respond to the Inquiry Question and can view a sample answer.

Explore Properties of Special Right Triangles (*continued*)

MP **Teaching the Mathematical Practices**

6 Communicate Precisely Encourage students to routinely write or explain their solution methods. Point out that they should use clear definitions when they discuss their solutions with others.

Questions

Have students complete the Explore activity.

Ask:

- Why is a 45°-45°-90° triangle an isosceles right triangle? Sample answer: An isosceles triangle has two congruent sides and two congruent angles. You are given two angle measures that are equal, so you know that two side lengths will also be equal and the triangle is isosceles. The last angle measure is 90°, so the triangle is a right triangle.

- If the shortest leg of a 30°-60°-90° triangle has a measure of 3, what are the measures of the other two sides? Sample answer: The ratio of the sides of a 30°-60°-90° triangle is $1: \sqrt{3}: 2$, so the side lengths are 3, $3\sqrt{3}$, and 6.

Inquiry

What is the relationship between side lengths in 45°-45°-90° and 30°-60°-90° triangles? Sample answer: In a 45°-45°-90° triangle, the side lengths are in the ratio $1: 1: \sqrt{2}$. In a 30°-60°-90° triangle, the side lengths are in the ratio $1: \sqrt{3}: 2$.

Go Online to find additional teaching notes and sample answers for the guiding exercises.

Learn 45°-45°-90° Triangles

Objective
Students understand that by similarity, side ratios in 45°-45°-90° triangles are related to the angles in the triangles.

 Teaching the Mathematical Practices

6 Communicate Precisely Encourage students to routinely write or explain their solution methods. Point out that they should use clear definitions when they discuss their solutions with others.

Things to Remember
Special right triangles are triangles with special properties in the angle measurements and side lengths. These triangles are also useful in some real-world situations. Because of this, knowing these properties provides students a useful shortcut for solving both mathematical and real-world problems.

Example 1 Find the Hypotenuse Length Given an Angle Measure

 Teaching the Mathematical Practices

6 Communicate Precisely Encourage students to routinely write or explain their solution methods. Point out that they should use clear definitions when they discuss their solutions with others.

Questions for Mathematical Discourse

AL What is the length of the unlabeled leg? 4

OL What do you know about this triangle? Because it is a 45°-45°-90° triangle, the hypotenuse is $\sqrt{2}$ times the length of a leg.

BL If the area of a 45°-45°-90° triangle is 4.5 square centimeters, what is the length of the hypotenuse? $3\sqrt{2}$ cm

Go Online
- Find additional teaching notes.
- View performance reports of the Checks.
- Assign or present an Extra Example.

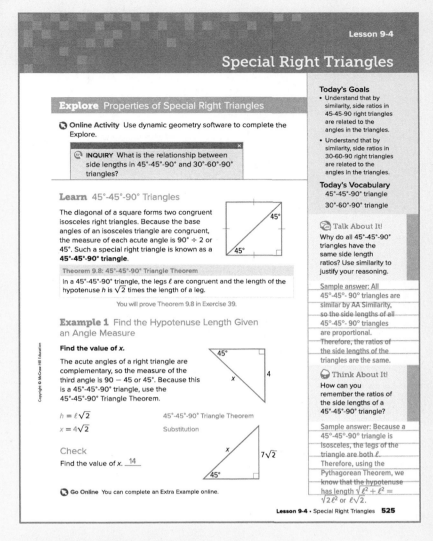

Lesson 9-4

Special Right Triangles

Today's Goals
- Understand that by similarity, side ratios in 45-45-90 right triangles are related to the angles in the triangles.
- Understand that by similarity, side ratios in 30-60-90 right triangles are related to the angles in the triangles.

Today's Vocabulary
45°-45°-90° triangle
30°-60°-90° triangle

Explore Properties of Special Right Triangles

Online Activity Use dynamic geometry software to complete the Explore.

INQUIRY What is the relationship between side lengths in 45°-45°-90° and 30°-60°-90° triangles?

Learn 45°-45°-90° Triangles

The diagonal of a square forms two congruent isosceles right triangles. Because the base angles of an isosceles triangle are congruent, the measure of each acute angle is 90° ÷ 2 or 45°. Such a special right triangle is known as a **45°-45°-90° triangle**.

Theorem 9.8: 45°-45°-90° Triangle Theorem
In a 45°-45°-90° triangle, the legs ℓ are congruent and the length of the hypotenuse h is $\sqrt{2}$ times the length of a leg.

You will prove Theorem 9.8 in Exercise 39.

Example 1 Find the Hypotenuse Length Given an Angle Measure

Find the value of x.

The acute angles of a right triangle are complementary, so the measure of the third angle is 90 − 45 or 45°. Because this is a 45°-45°-90° triangle, use the 45°-45°-90° Triangle Theorem.

$h = \ell\sqrt{2}$ 45°-45°-90° Triangle Theorem

$x = 4\sqrt{2}$ Substitution

Check
Find the value of x. ___14___

Go Online You can complete an Extra Example online.

Talk About It!
Why do all 45°-45°-90° triangles have the same side length ratios? Use similarity to justify your reasoning.

Sample answer: All 45°-45°-90° triangles are similar by AA Similarity, so the side lengths of all 45°-45°-90° triangles are proportional. Therefore, the ratios of the side lengths of the triangles are the same.

Think About It!
How can you remember the ratios of the side lengths of a 45°-45°-90° triangle?

Sample answer: Because a 45°-45°-90° triangle is isosceles, the legs of the triangle are both ℓ. Therefore, using the Pythagorean Theorem, we know that the hypotenuse has length $\sqrt{\ell^2 + \ell^2} = \sqrt{2\ell^2}$ or $\ell\sqrt{2}$.

Interactive Presentation

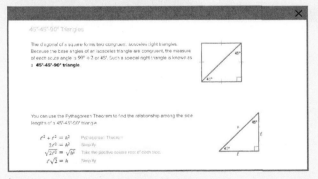

Learn

TYPE

a|

Students can type to answer the Talk About It! question.

Your Notes

Example 2 Find the Hypotenuse Length Given a Side Measure

Find the value of x.

The legs of this right triangle have the same measure, so it is isosceles. Because this is a 45°-45°-90° triangle, use the 45°-45°-90° Triangle Theorem.

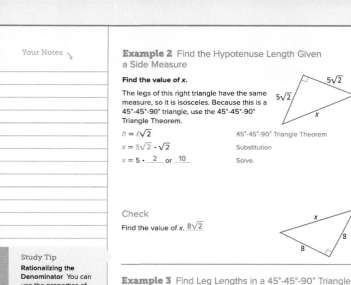

$h = \ell\sqrt{2}$ 45°-45°-90° Triangle Theorem

$x = 5\sqrt{2} \cdot \sqrt{2}$ Substitution

$x = 5 \cdot \underline{2}$ or $\underline{10}$ Solve.

Check

Find the value of x. $8\sqrt{2}$

Study Tip

Rationalizing the Denominator You can use the properties of square roots to rationalize the denominator of a fraction with a radical. This involves multiplying the numerator and denominator by a factor that eliminates radicals in the denominator. In this example, $\frac{18}{\sqrt{2}}$ can be simplified by multiplying the numerator and denominator by $\sqrt{2}$.

Example 3 Find Leg Lengths in a 45°-45°-90° Triangle

Find the value of x.

The acute angles of a right triangle are complementary, so the measure of the third angle is 90 − 45 or 45°. So, the triangle is a 45°-45°-90° triangle. Use the 45°-45°-90° Triangle Theorem to find the value of x.

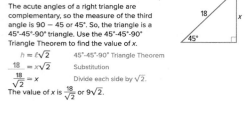

$h = \ell\sqrt{2}$ 45°-45°-90° Triangle Theorem

$18 = x\sqrt{2}$ Substitution

$\frac{18}{\sqrt{2}} = x$ Divide each side by $\sqrt{2}$.

The value of x is $\frac{18}{\sqrt{2}}$ or $9\sqrt{2}$.

Check

Find the value of x. $\underline{5}$

Go Online You can complete an Extra Example online.

526   **Module 9 ·** Right Triangles and Trigonometry

Interactive Presentation

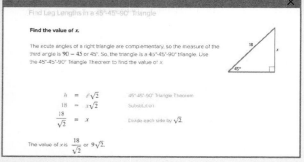

Example 3

TAP

Students tap to learn about rationalizing the denominator.

CHECK

Students complete the Check online to determine whether they are ready to move on.

Example 2 Find the Hypotenuse Length Given a Side Measure

MP Teaching the Mathematical Practices

2 Create Representations Guide students to write an equation that models the situation in this example. Then use the equation to solve the problem.

Questions for Mathematical Discourse

AL What is the relationship between the legs in a 45°-45°-90° triangle? They are congruent.

OL If a leg of a 45°-45°-90° triangle measures $6\sqrt{3}$, what is the length of the hypotenuse? $6\sqrt{6}$

BL If the hypotenuse of a 45°-45°-90° triangle measures $10\sqrt{3}$, what is the length of a leg? $5\sqrt{6}$

Common Error

Students may confuse the leg length with the hypotenuse when the given leg length has a $\sqrt{2}$ in its representation. Help them to be careful to connect the information for the correct part of the triangle.

Example 3 Find Leg Lengths in a 45°-45°-90° Triangle

MP Teaching the Mathematical Practices

2 Create Representations Guide students to write an equation that models the situation in this example. Then use the equation to solve the problem.

Questions for Mathematical Discourse

AL For which part of the triangle do you know the length? the hypotenuse

OL Should you multiply or divide 18 by $\sqrt{2}$? divide

BL What is the leg length if the hypotenuse has a length of $10\sqrt{6}$? $10\sqrt{3}$

Common Error

Students may incorrectly divide 18 by $\sqrt{2}$. Use the Study Tip to help students remember how to rationalize denominators.

1 CONCEPTUAL UNDERSTANDING | **2 FLUENCY** | 3 APPLICATION

Learn 30°-60°-90° Triangles

Objective
Students understand that by similarity, side ratios in 30°-60°-90° triangles are related to the angles in the triangles.

 Teaching the Mathematical Practices

3 Find the Error This Learn requires students to read the arguments of others, decide whether they make sense, and ask useful questions to clarify or improve the arguments.

Common Misconception
Advise students that a common mistake that can be made is to assume that the longer leg of a 30°-60°-90° triangle is twice the length of the shorter leg. Demonstrate that this cannot be true by providing one or more counterexamples.

Example 4 Find Leg Lengths in a 30°-60°-90° Triangle

 Teaching the Mathematical Practices

3 Compare Arguments Mathematically proficient students can compare arguments, determine which one is flawed, and explain the flaw. In this example, students have to identify the flawed argument and choose the correct one.

Questions for Mathematical Discourse

AL In a 30°-60°-90° triangle, how do we know which is the shorter leg? The shorter leg is opposite the 30° angle.

OL In a 30°-60°-90° triangle, if we are given any side length, can we find the other two? Explain. Yes; sample answer: Regardless of the side length you are given, you can find the other two because they are all related to the given side length.

BL Write the equation for the shorter side s and hypotenuse h in terms of the longer side ℓ. $s = \dfrac{\ell\sqrt{3}}{3}, h = \dfrac{2\ell\sqrt{3}}{3}$

DIFFERENTIATE

Enrichment Activity **BL**

Have students draw a 45°-45°-90° triangle and a 30°-60°-90° triangle and label each side length. Have the students use their drawings to choose one of the acute angles and find the ratio of the measure of the opposite leg to the measure of the adjacent leg. Explain that this ratio is called the tangent ratio. Discuss their findings. Tangent is the measure of the opposite leg divided by the measure of the adjacent leg.

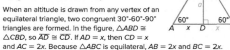

Learn 30°-60°-90° Triangles

A **30°-60°-90° triangle** is a special right triangle or right triangle with side lengths that share a special relationship. You can use an equilateral triangle to find this relationship.

When an altitude is drawn from any vertex of an equilateral triangle, two congruent 30°-60°-90° triangles are formed. In the figure, $\triangle ABD \cong \triangle CBD$, so $\overline{AD} \cong \overline{CD}$. If $AD = x$, then $CD = x$ and $AC = 2x$. Because $\triangle ABC$ is equilateral, $AB = 2x$ and $BC = 2x$.

Use the Pythagorean Theorem to find a, the length of the altitude $\overline{BD}$, which is also the longer leg of $\triangle BDC$.

$a^2 + x^2 = (2x)^2$ Pythagorean Theorem
$a^2 + x^2 = 4x^2$ Simplify.
$a^2 = 3x^2$ Subtract x^2 from each side.
$a = x\sqrt{3}$ Simplify.

Theorem 9.9: 30°-60°-90° Triangle Theorem
In a 30°-60°-90° triangle, the length of the hypotenuse h is 2 times the length of the shorter leg s, and the longer leg ℓ is $\sqrt{3}$ times the length of the shorter leg.

You will prove Theorem 9.9 in Exercise 40.

Example 4 Find Leg Lengths in a 30°-60°-90° Triangle

Find the values of x and y.

Use the 30°-60°-90° Triangle Theorem to find the value of x, the length of the shorter side.

$s\sqrt{3} = \ell$ 30°-60°-90° Triangle Theorem
$x\sqrt{3} = 12$ Substitution
$x = \dfrac{12}{\sqrt{3}}$ or $4\sqrt{3}$ Divide each side by $\sqrt{3}$.

Now use the 30°-60°-90° Triangle Theorem to find y, the length of the hypotenuse.

$h = 2s$ 30°-60°-90° Triangle Theorem
$y = 2\left(\dfrac{12}{\sqrt{3}}\right)$ Substitution
$y = \dfrac{24}{\sqrt{3}}$ or $8\sqrt{3}$ Simplify.

Check

Find the values of x and y.
$x = \dfrac{15}{\sqrt{3}}$ or $5\sqrt{3}$ $y = \dfrac{30}{\sqrt{3}}$ or $10\sqrt{3}$

 Go Online You can complete an Extra Example online.

Lesson 9-4 • Special Right Triangles   **527**

Think About It!
Ian states that in a 30°-60°-90° triangle, sometimes the 30° angle is opposite the longer leg and the 60° angle is opposite the shorter leg. Do you *agree* or *disagree* with Ian? Justify your answer.

Disagree; sample answer: In a triangle, the smallest angle is always opposite the shortest side. So, the 30° angle will always be opposite the shorter leg, and the 60° angle will be opposite the longer leg.

Study Tip
Use Ratios The lengths of the sides of a 30°-60°-90° triangle are in a ratio of 1 to $\sqrt{3}$ to 2 or 1: $\sqrt{3}$: 2.

Interactive Presentation

Find Leg Lengths in a 30°-60°-90° Triangle

Find the values of x and y.

Use the 30°-60°-90° Triangle Theorem to find the value of x, the length of the shorter side.

$s\sqrt{3} = \ell$ 30°-60°-90° Triangle Theorem

Example 4

TYPE

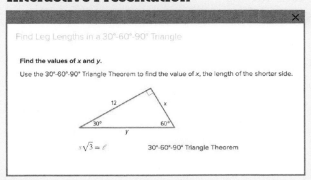

Students describe the error made in a solution and find the correct value.

1 CONCEPTUAL UNDERSTANDING | 2 FLUENCY | **3 APPLICATION**

🌐 Apply Example Use Properties of 30°-60°-90° Triangles

JEWELRY Destiny makes and sells upcycled earrings. The earrings shown are made from congruent equilateral triangles. Each triangle has a height of 2 centimeters. The hooks attached to the top of the earrings are 1 centimeter tall. Destiny needs to mail this pair of earrings to a customer. If she mails the earrings in a rectangular box, what width and length must the base of the box have so the earrings will fit if they are placed side by side in the bottom of the box?

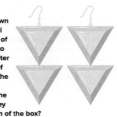

1 What is the task?
Describe the task in your own words. Then list any questions that you may have. How can you find answers to your questions?
Sample answer: To find the width and length of the box, I should calculate the height and width of the earrings. How does the information provided in the problem relate to the earrings? I can draw and label a diagram to represent the earrings.

2 How will you approach the task? What have you learned that you can use to help you complete the task?
Sample answer: I will draw and label the altitude of the triangle, calculate the length of the base of the triangle, and then calculate the width and length of the box. I will use what I know about equilateral and special right triangles to solve for missing measures.

3 What is your solution?
The altitude of the triangle measures __2__ centimeters.
The length of the base of one earring is $\frac{4}{\sqrt{3}}$ or $\frac{4\sqrt{3}}{3}$.
The width of the box must be at least $\frac{8}{\sqrt{3}}$ or about __4.62__ centimeters.
The length of the box must be at least __5__ centimeters.

4 How can you know that your solution is reasonable?
🖊 **Write About It!** Write an argument that can be used to defend your solution.
Sample answer: Because the equilateral triangles are congruent, it makes sense that the width and length of the box are twice the length of the base and the height of one equilateral triangle, respectively.

🌐 **Go Online** You can complete an Extra Example online.

Think About It!
What assumption did you make while solving this problem?

Sample answer: I assumed that Destiny would not leave any space around or between the earrings when placing them in the box.

Copyright © McGraw-Hill Education

Interactive Presentation

Use Properties of 30°-60°-90° Triangles

🌐 **JEWELRY** Destiny makes and sells upcycled earrings. The earrings shown are made from congruent equilateral triangles. Each triangle has a height of 2 centimeters. The hooks attached to the top of the earrings are 1 centimeter tall. Destiny needs to mail this pair of earrings to a customer. If she mails the earrings in a rectangular box, what width and length must the base of the box have so the earrings will fit?

Apply Example 5

TAP

Students tap to see the steps in the solution.

CHECK

Students complete the Check online to determine whether they are ready to move on.

🌐 Apply Example 5 Use Properties of 30°-60°-90° Triangles

Recommended Use
Have students work in pairs or small groups. You may wish to present the task, or have a volunteer read it aloud. Then allow students the time to make sure they understand the task, think of possible strategies, and work to solve the problem.

Encourage Productive Struggle
As students work, monitor their progress. Instead of instructing them on a particular strategy, encourage them to use their own strategies to solve the problem and to evaluate their progress along the way. They may or may not find that they need to change direction or try out several strategies.

Signs of Non-Productive Struggle
If students show signs of non-productive struggle, such as feeling overwhelmed, frustrated, or disengaged, intervene to encourage them to think of alternate approaches to the problem. Some sample questions are shown.

- What do we know about the angle measures from the given information?
- How does the length of the box relate to the height of each triangle?

🖊 Write About It!
Have students share their responses with another pair/group of students or the entire class. Have them clearly state or describe the mathematical reasoning they can use to defend their solution.

DIFFERENTIATE

Reteaching Activity 🟦AL🟦
Visual/Spatial Learners Explain that many artists use right triangles in their works because they are so appealing to the eye. Right triangles can serve as guidelines to draw mountains in the background or to create vanishing points and perspective. Ask students to construct one or more right triangles on a blank sheet of paper, find the lengths of the sides and then try to compose a picture using the triangles in an image or as a guide for an image. Examples could be a picture of a road vanishing in the distance or a house with right triangles as part of its roof.

Exit Ticket

Recommended Use

At the end of class, go online to display the Exit Ticket prompt and ask students to respond using a separate piece of paper. Have students hand you their responses as they leave the room.

Alternate Use

At the end of class, go online to display the Exit Ticket prompt and ask students to respond verbally or by using a mini-whiteboard. Have students hold up their whiteboards so that you can see all student responses. Tap to reveal the answer when most or all students have completed the Exit Ticket.

Practice and Homework

Suggested Assignments

Use the table below to select appropriate exercises.

DOK	Topic	Exercises
1, 2	exercises that mirror the examples	1–28
2	exercises that use a variety of skills from this lesson	29–44
3	exercises that emphasize higher-order and critical-thinking skills	45–49

ASSESS AND DIFFERENTIATE

.ılı Use the data from the **Checks** to determine whether to provide resources for extension, remediation, or intervention.

IF students score 90% or more on the Checks, **BL**
THEN assign:
- Practice, Exercises 1–43 odd, 45–49
- Extension: Wheel of Theodorus
- **ALEKS** Similar Right Triangles and Special Right Triangles

IF students score 66%–89% on the Checks, **OL**
THEN assign:
- Practice, Exercises 1–49 odd
- Remediation, Review Resources: The Pythagorean Theorem
- Personal Tutors
- Extra Examples 1–5
- **ALEKS** Applying the Pythagorean Theorem

IF students score 65% or less on the Checks, **AL**
THEN assign:
- Practice, Exercises 1–27 odd
- Remediation, Review Resources: The Pythagorean Theorem
- *Quick Review Math Handbook*: Special Right Triangles
- **ALEKS** Applying the Pythagorean Theorem

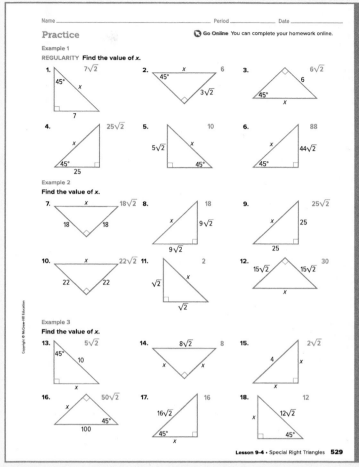

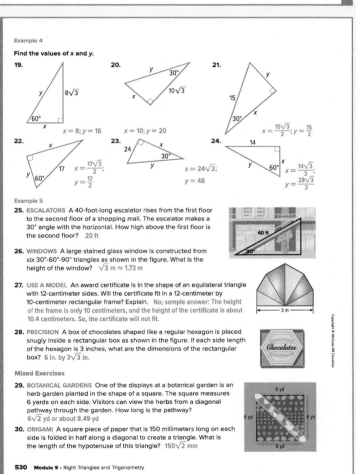

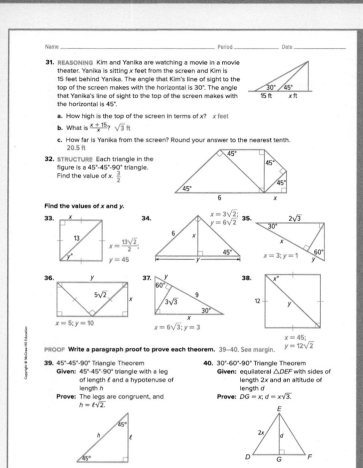

Name _____ Period _____ Date _____

31. REASONING Kim and Yanika are watching a movie in a movie theater. Yanika is sitting x feet from the screen and Kim is 15 feet behind Yanika. The angle that Kim's line of sight to the top of the screen makes with the horizontal is 30°. The angle that Yanika's line of sight to the top of the screen makes with the horizontal is 45°.

  a. How high is the top of the screen in terms of x? *x feet*

  b. What is $\frac{x+15}{x}$? $\sqrt{3}$ ft

  c. How far is Yanika from the screen? Round your answer to the nearest tenth. 20.5 ft

32. STRUCTURE Each triangle in the figure is a 45°-45°-90° triangle. Find the value of x. $\frac{3}{2}$

Find the values of x and y.

33. x, 13

34. 6, x; $x=\frac{13\sqrt{2}}{2}$; $y=45$

35. $x=3\sqrt{2}$; $y=6\sqrt{2}$; 30°, $2\sqrt{3}$, 60°; $x=3$; $y=1$

36. y, $5\sqrt{2}$, x; $x=5$; $y=10$

37. y, 60°, $3\sqrt{3}$, 9, 30°, x; $x=6\sqrt{3}$; $y=3$

38. x°, y; $x=45$; $y=12\sqrt{2}$

PROOF Write a paragraph proof to prove each theorem. 39–40. See margin.

39. 45°-45°-90° Triangle Theorem
Given: 45°-45°-90° triangle with a leg of length ℓ and a hypotenuse of length h
Prove: The legs are congruent, and $h=\ell\sqrt{2}$.

40. 30°-60°-90° Triangle Theorem
Given: equilateral △DEF with sides of length 2x and an altitude of length d
Prove: $DG=x$; $d=x\sqrt{3}$.

Lesson 9-4 • Special Right Triangles **531**

41. △XYZ is a 45°-45°-90° triangle with right angle Z. Find the coordinates of X in Quadrant I for Y(−1, 2) and Z(6, 2). (6, 9)

42. △EFG is a 30°-60°-90° triangle with m∠F = 90°. Find the coordinates of E in Quadrant III for F(−3, −4) and G(−3, 2). FG is the longer leg. $(-3-2\sqrt{3}, -4)$

43. USE TOOLS Melody is in charge of building a ramp for a loading dock. According to the plan, the ramp makes a 30° angle with the ground. The plan also states that $\overline{ST}$ is 4 feet longer than $\overline{RS}$. Use a calculator to find the lengths of the three sides of the ramp to the nearest thousandth. $RS\approx5.464$ ft; $ST\approx9.464$ ft; $RT\approx10.928$ ft

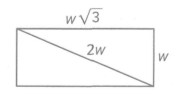

44. STATE YOUR ASSUMPTION Liling is making a quilt. She starts with two small squares of material and cuts them along the diagonal. Then she arranges the four resulting triangles to make a large square quilt block. She wants the large quilt block to have an area of 36 square inches. a–b. See margin.

  a. What side lengths should Liling use for the two small squares of material? Explain.

  b. Explain any assumption that you make to answer part **a.**

Higher-Order Thinking Skills

45. PERSEVERE Find the perimeter of quadrilateral ABCD. Round your answer to the nearest tenth. 59.8

27, A, D, 7, 135°, B, C

46. WRITE Why are some right triangles considered *special*? See margin.

47. FIND THE ERROR Carmen and Audrey want to find the value of x in the triangle shown. Who is correct? Explain your reasoning. See margin.

6, x

Carmen	Audrey
$x=\frac{6\sqrt{3}}{2}$	$x=\frac{6\sqrt{2}}{2}$
$x=3\sqrt{3}$	$x=3\sqrt{2}$

48. ANALYZE The ratio of the measure of the angles of a triangle is 1:2:3. The length of the shortest side is 8. What is the perimeter of the triangle? Round your answer to the nearest tenth. 37.9

49. CREATE Draw a rectangle that has a diagonal twice as long as its width. Then write an equation to find the length of the rectangle. See margin.

532 Module 9 • Right Triangles and Trigonometry

Answers

39. Proof: A 45°-45° -90° triangle with a leg of length ℓ and a hypotenuse of length h is given. Because the measure of each acute angle in the triangle is 45°, by the definition of congruent angles, the angles are congruent. Therefore, by the Converse of the Isosceles Triangle Theorem, the legs of the triangle are congruent. Because the legs are congruent, the measure of each leg is ℓ. By the Pythagorean Theorem, $\ell^2+\ell^2=h^2$. This equation simplifies to $2\ell^2=h^2$. Take the postive square root of each side to get $\sqrt{2\ell^2}=\sqrt{h^2}$. So, $\ell\sqrt{2}=h$. By the Symmetric Property of Equality, $h=\ell\sqrt{2}$.

40. Given: equilateral △DEF with sides of length 2x and altitude of length d
Prove: $DG=x$; $d=x\sqrt{3}$.

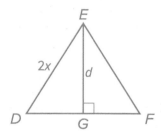

Proof: Because △DEF is equilateral, $DE=2x$ and $DF=2x$. When an altitude is drawn from any vertex of an equilateral triangle, two congruent 30°-60°-90° triangles are formed. In the figure shown, △DEG ≅ △FEG, so $\overline{DG}\cong\overline{FG}$. If $DE=2x$, then $DG=\frac{1}{2}(DF)$. By substitution, $DG=x$. Use the Pythagorean Theorem to find d, the length of the altitude $\overline{EG}$, which is the longer leg of △DGE.
$d^2+x^2=(2x)^2$ (Pythagorean Theorem)
$d^2+x^2=4x^2$ (Substitution)
$d^2=3x^2$ (Subtraction Property)
$d=\sqrt{3x^2}$ (A property of square roots)
$d=x\sqrt{3}$ (Substitution)

44a. $3\sqrt{2}$ in. or about 4.2 in.; Sample answer: For the block to have an area of 36 square inches, each side must be 6 inches. This means the hypotenuse of each small right triangle is 6 inches. By the 45°-45°-90° Triangle Theorem, the sides of these triangles measure $\frac{6}{\sqrt{2}}$ or $3\sqrt{2}$ inches.

44b. Sample answer: The assumption is that the cuts are made with accuracy. Also, that sewing seams of small rectangles together does not use up any material.

46. Sample answer: Once you identify that a right triangle is special or has a 30°, 60°, or 45° angle measure, you can solve the triangle without the use of a calculator.

47. Carmen; sample answer: Because the three angles of the larger triangle are congruent, it is an equilateral triangle and the right triangles formed by the altitude are 30°-60°-90° triangles. The hypotenuse is 6, so the shorter leg is 3 and the longer leg x is $3\sqrt{3}$.

49. Sample answer:

$w\sqrt{3}$, 2w, w

Let ℓ represent the length.
$\ell^2+w^2=(2w)^2$; $\ell^2=3w^2$; $\ell=w\sqrt{3}$.

Trigonometry

LESSON GOAL

Students solve problems using the trigonometric ratios and the inverse trigonometric ratios for acute angles.

1 LAUNCH

 Launch the lesson with a **Warm Up** and an introduction.

2 EXPLORE AND DEVELOP

 Explore:

- Sines and Cosines of Complementary Angles
- Trigonometry and Similarity

 Develop:

Trigonometry
- Find Trigonometric Ratios
- Use a Special Right Triangle to Find Trigonometric Ratios
- Estimate Measures by Using Trigonometry

Inverse Trigonometric Ratios
- Find Angle Measures by Using Inverse Trigonometric Ratios
- Solve a Right Triangle

 You may want your students to complete the **Checks** online.

3 REFLECT AND PRACTICE

 Exit Ticket

 Practice

 Formative Assessment Math Probe

DIFFERENTIATE

 View reports of student progress on the **Checks** after each example.

Resources	AL	OL	BL	ELL
Remediation: Triangles	●	●		●
Extension: Sine and Cosine of Angles		●	●	●

Language Development Handbook

Assign page 62 of the *Language Development Handbook* to help your students build mathematical language related to trigonometry.

ELL You can use the tips and suggestions on page T62 of the handbook to support students who are building English proficiency.

Suggested Pacing

90 min	**1 day**	
45 min	**2 days**	

Focus

Domain: Geometry

Standards for Mathematical Content:

G.SRT.6 Understand that by similarity, side ratios in right triangles are properties of the angles in the triangle, leading to definitions of trigonometric ratios for acute angles.

G.SRT.7 Explain and use the relationship between the sine and cosine of complementary angles.

Standards for Mathematical Practice:

5 Use appropriate tools strategically.

7 Look for and make use of structure.

Coherence

Vertical Alignment

Previous
Students understood ratios, similiarity, and right triangles in Grades 6-8.
6.RP, 7.RP, 8.G.4, 8.G.6, 8.G.7, 8.G.8

Now
Students solve problems using trigonometric ratios and their inverses for acute angles.
G.SRT.6, G.SRT.7

Next
Students will apply trigonometry to real-world situations and to triangle area.
G.SRT.8, G.SRT.9

Rigor

The Three Pillars of Rigor

1 CONCEPTUAL UNDERSTANDING	2 FLUENCY	3 APPLICATION

Conceptual Bridge In this lesson, students extend their understanding of special right triangles to develop definitions of the trigonometric ratios. They build fluency by exploring the relationship between the sines and cosines of complementary angles, and they apply trigonometry to solve real-world problems.

Mathematical Background

A ratio of the lengths of the sides of a right triangle is called a trigonometric ratio. The three most common *trigonometric ratios* are *sine, cosine,* and *tangent*. Trigonometric ratios are used to find missing measures of a right triangle. The inverse of each trigonometric ratio yields the angle measure.

Interactive Presentation

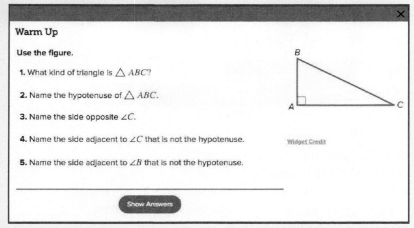

Warm Up

Use the figure.

1. What kind of triangle is △ABC?

2. Name the hypotenuse of △ABC.

3. Name the side opposite ∠C.

4. Name the side adjacent to ∠C that is not the hypotenuse.

5. Name the side adjacent to ∠B that is not the hypotenuse.

Widget Credit

Show Answers

Warm Up

Launch the Lesson

Scientists can approximate the depth of a crater on the Moon's surface by analyzing the length of the shadow formed by the rim of the crater. To make this calculation, a scientist must first measure the length of the crater's shadow and the Sun's elevation angle. Then the scientist can use a trigonometric ratio, such as the tangent ratio, to calculate the depth of the crater.

Launch the Lesson

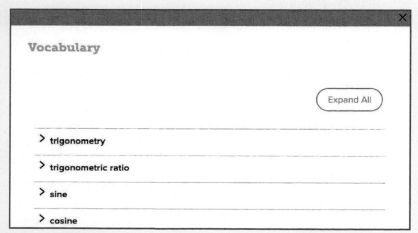

Vocabulary

Expand All

> trigonometry

> trigonometric ratio

> sine

> cosine

Today's Vocabulary

Warm Up

Prerequisite Skills

The Warm Up exercises address the following prerequisite skill for this lesson:

- identifying the adjacent side, opposite side, and hypotenuse

Answers:

1. right
2. $\overline{BC}$
3. $\overline{AB}$
4. $\overline{AC}$
5. $\overline{AB}$

Launch the Lesson

MP Teaching the Mathematical Practices

> **4 Apply Mathematics** In this Launch the Lesson, students can see a real-world application of trigonometric ratios.

Go Online to find additional teaching notes and questions to promote classroom discourse.

Today's Standards

Tell students that they will be addressing these content and practice standards in this lesson. You may wish to have a student volunteer read aloud *How can I meet these standards?* and *How can I use these practices?* and connect these to the standards.

See the Interactive Presentation for I Can statements that align with the standards covered in this lesson.

Today's Vocabulary

Tell students that they will be using these vocabulary terms in this lesson. You can expand each row if you wish to share the definitions. Then, discuss the questions below with the class.

Explore Sines and Cosines of Complementary Angles

Objective
Students use dynamic geometry software to explain the relationship between the sine and cosine of complementary angles.

 Teaching the Mathematical Practices

3 Make Conjectures In this Explore, students will make conjectures and then build a logical progression of statements to validate the conjectures. Once students have made their conjectures, guide the students to validate them.

Ideas for Use

Recommended Use Present the Inquiry Question, or have a student volunteer read it aloud. Have students work in pairs to complete the Explore activity on their devices. Pairs should discuss each of the questions. Monitor student progress during the activity. Upon completion of the Explore activity, have student volunteers share their responses to the Inquiry Question.

What if my students don't have devices? You may choose to project the activity on a whiteboard. A printable worksheet for each Explore is available online. You may choose to print the worksheet so that individuals or pairs of students can use it to record their observations.

Summary of the Activity

Students will complete guiding exercises throughout the Explore activity. Students construct a right triangle using dynamic geometry software. Then students use the software to calculate ratios between sides of the right triangle. Students then learn that these are the trigonometric ratios *sine*, *cosine*, and *tangent*. Students move parts of a right triangle to notice that the sine ratio of one acute angle in the triangle is always the same as the cosine of the other acute angle, and vice versa. Then, students will answer the Inquiry Question.

(continued on the next page)

Interactive Presentation

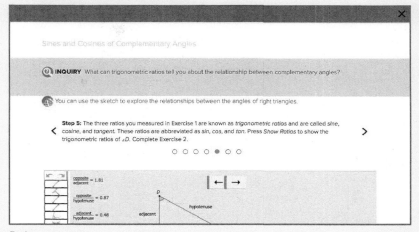

Explore

WEB SKETCHPAD

Students will use a sketch to explore the sine and cosine of complementary angles.

Interactive Presentation

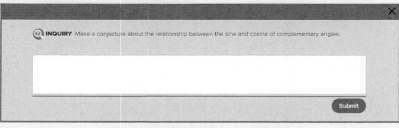

Explore

TYPE

Students respond to the Inquiry Question and view a sample answer.

Explore Sines and Cosines of Complementary Angles (*continued*)

Teaching the Mathematical Practices

7 Interpret Complicated Expressions Mathematically proficient students can see a complicated expressions as single objects or as being composed of several objects. In this Explore, guide students to see what information they can gather about the expression just from looking at it.

Questions

Have students complete the Explore activity.

Ask:

- What is always true about the sides opposite to D and F in relation to each other? Sample answer: The side opposite D is adjacent to F, and the side opposite F is adjacent to D.

- If you know the sine of $\angle F$ what do you know about $\angle D$? Sample answer: You know the cosine of $\angle D$.

Inquiry

Make a conjecture about the relationship between the sine and cosine of complementary angles. Sample answer: The sine of any angle is equal to the cosine of the complement of the angle.

Go Online to find additional teaching notes and sample answers for the guiding exercises.

Explore Trigonometry and Similarity

Objective
Students use dynamic geometry software to understand that side ratios in right triangles are properties of the angles in the triangle.

 Teaching the Mathematical Practices

5 Use Mathematical Tools Point out that to solve the problem in the Explore, students will need to use dynamic geometry software. Work with students to explore and deepen their understanding of similarity in right triangles and trigonometric ratios.

Ideas for Use

Recommended Use Present the Inquiry Question, or have a student volunteer read it aloud. Have students work in pairs to complete the Explore activity on their devices. Pairs should discuss each of the questions. Monitor student progress during the activity. Upon completion of the Explore activity, have student volunteers share their responses to the Inquiry Question.

What if my students don't have devices? You may choose to project the activity on a whiteboard. A printable worksheet for each Explore is available online. You may choose to print the worksheet so that individuals or pairs of students can use it to record their observations.

Summary of the Activity
Students will complete guiding exercises throughout the Explore activity. Students construct a right triangle using dynamic geometry software. Then students use the software to calculate ratios between sides of the right triangle. Students move parts of the triangle to create similar and non-similar triangles, and observe that the ratios stay the same in similar triangles. Then, students will answer the Inquiry Question.

(continued on the next page)

Interactive Presentation

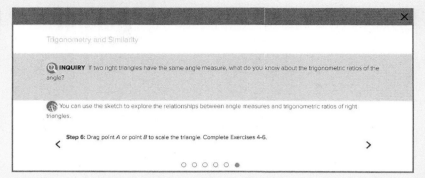

Trigonometry and Similarity

INQUIRY If two right triangles have the same angle measure, what do you know about the trigonometric ratios of the angle?

You can use the sketch to explore the relationships between angle measures and trigonometric ratios of right triangles.

Step 6: Drag point A or point B to scale the triangle. Complete Exercises 4-6.

Explore

WEB SKETCHPAD

Students use a sketch to explore similarity in right triangles to discover trigonometric ratios.

Interactive Presentation

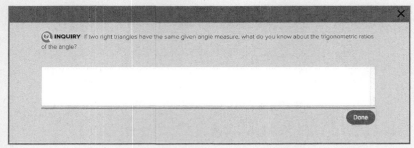

Explore

TYPE

Students respond to the Inquiry Question and can view a sample answer.

Explore Trigonometry and Similarity (*continued*)

MP Teaching the Mathematical Practices

7 Use Structure Help students to explore the structure of right triangles in the Explore to discover the trigonometric ratios.

Questions

Have students complete the Explore activity.

Ask:

- What do you know about the sides of similar triangles? Sample answer: The sides of similar triangles are proportional, or the corresponding sides have ratios that are congruent.

- How are trigonometric ratios related to the sides of similar triangles? Sample answer: Trigonometric ratios are ratios of the sides in a triangle. For a given angle measure, this means that the ratio of the sides is equal to a fixed value. We know that similar triangles have proportional sides and so the ratios would reduce to (or be equal to) that fixed value.

② Inquiry

If two right triangles have the same angle measure, what do you know about the trigonometric ratios of the angle? Sample answer: If an angle measure is the same in any two right triangles, then the trigonometric ratios of the angle are equal.

Go Online to find additional teaching notes and sample answers for the guiding exercises.

1 CONCEPTUAL UNDERSTANDING | 2 FLUENCY | 3 APPLICATION

Learn Trigonometry

Objective
Students solve problems by using the trigonometric ratios for acute angles.

Teaching the Mathematical Practices

7 Use Structure Help students to explore the structure of trigonometry and trigonometric ratios in this Learn.

About the Key Concept
The definition of trigonometric functions as the ratio of side lengths of any right triangle with a particular angle only works for acute angles. In order to extend the domain of trigonometric functions to any angle, mathematicians use a definition based on the unit circle.

Common Misconception
Many students get confused about functions such as sine or cosine. Emphasize the connection to the ratios between the sides of similar right triangles.

DIFFERENTIATE

Reteaching Activity AL

Auditory/Musical Learners The easiest way for auditory learners to remember the ratios for sine, cosine, and tangent is for them to chant SOH-CAH-TOA. When introducing this mnemonic device to students, have them repeat it as a class a few times in rhythm. Point out that SOH and CAH each have one syllable because the "H" is silent, so students can remember that one "silent" hypotenuse is involved for the sine and cosine ratios. TOA has two syllables and involves the two legs for the tangent ratio.

Go Online

- Find additional teaching notes.
- View performance reports of the Checks.
- Assign or present an Extra Example.

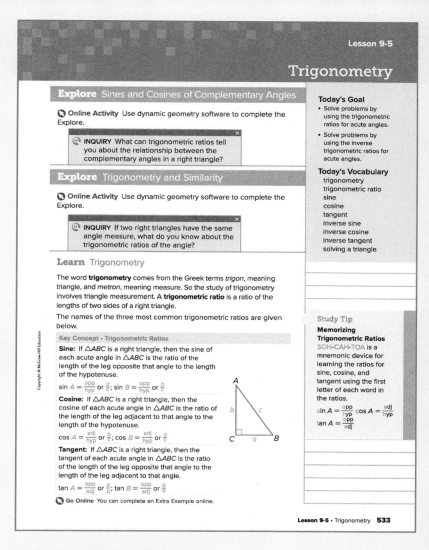

Lesson 9-5

Trigonometry

Explore Sines and Cosines of Complementary Angles

Online Activity Use dynamic geometry software to complete the Explore.

INQUIRY What can trigonometric ratios tell you about the relationship between the complementary angles in a right triangle?

Explore Trigonometry and Similarity

Online Activity Use dynamic geometry software to complete the Explore.

INQUIRY If two right triangles have the same angle measure, what do you know about the trigonometric ratios of the angle?

Learn Trigonometry

The word **trigonometry** comes from the Greek terms *trigon*, meaning triangle, and *metron*, meaning measure. So the study of trigonometry involves triangle measurement. A **trigonometric ratio** is a ratio of the lengths of two sides of a right triangle.

The names of the three most common trigonometric ratios are given below.

Key Concept • Trigonometric Ratios

Sine: If $\triangle ABC$ is a right triangle, then the sine of each acute angle in $\triangle ABC$ is the ratio of the length of the leg opposite that angle to the length of the hypotenuse.

$\sin A = \frac{opp}{hyp}$ or $\frac{a}{c}$; $\sin B = \frac{opp}{hyp}$ or $\frac{b}{c}$

Cosine: If $\triangle ABC$ is a right triangle, then the cosine of each acute angle in $\triangle ABC$ is the ratio of the length of the leg adjacent to that angle to the length of the hypotenuse.

$\cos A = \frac{adj}{hyp}$ or $\frac{b}{c}$; $\cos B = \frac{adj}{hyp}$ or $\frac{a}{c}$

Tangent: If $\triangle ABC$ is a right triangle, then the tangent of each acute angle in $\triangle ABC$ is the ratio of the length of the leg opposite that angle to the length of the leg adjacent to that angle.

$\tan A = \frac{opp}{adj}$ or $\frac{a}{b}$; $\tan B = \frac{opp}{adj}$ or $\frac{b}{a}$

Go Online You can complete an Extra Example online.

Today's Goal
- Solve problems by using the trigonometric ratios for acute angles.
- Solve problems by using the inverse trigonometric ratios for acute angles.

Today's Vocabulary
trigonometry
trigonometric ratio
sine
cosine
tangent
inverse sine
inverse cosine
inverse tangent
solving a triangle

Study Tip
Memorizing Trigonometric Ratios SOH-CAH-TOA is a mnemonic device for learning the ratios for sine, cosine, and tangent using the first letter of each word in the ratios.
$\sin A = \frac{opp}{hyp}$ $\cos A = \frac{adj}{hyp}$
$\tan A = \frac{opp}{adj}$

Lesson 9-5 • Trigonometry **533**

Interactive Presentation

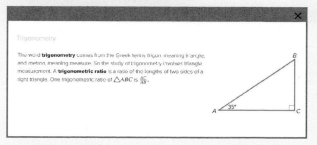

Trigonometry

The word **trigonometry** comes from the Greek terms *trigon*, meaning triangle, and *metron*, meaning measure. So the study of trigonometry involves triangle measurement. A **trigonometric ratio** is a ratio of the lengths of two sides of a right triangle. One trigonometric ratio of $\triangle ABC$ is $\frac{AC}{AB}$.

Learn

TAP

Students tap to reveal information on each of the trigonometric ratios.

1 CONCEPTUAL UNDERSTANDING | **2 FLUENCY** | 3 APPLICATION

Left page panel

Your Notes

Think About It!
How are sin *J* and cos *K* related?

Sample answer: They are the same.

Example 1 Find Trigonometric Ratios

Find sin *J*, cos *J*, tan *J*, sin *K*, cos *K*, and tan *K*. Express each ratio as a fraction and as a decimal to the nearest hundredth.

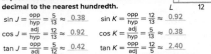

$\sin J = \frac{opp}{hyp} = \frac{5}{13} \approx 0.38$ $\sin K = \frac{opp}{hyp} = \frac{12}{13} \approx 0.92$

$\cos J = \frac{adj}{hyp} = \frac{12}{13} \approx 0.92$ $\cos K = \frac{adj}{hyp} = \frac{5}{13} \approx 0.38$

$\tan J = \frac{opp}{adj} = \frac{5}{12} \approx 0.42$ $\tan K = \frac{opp}{adj} = \frac{12}{5} \approx 2.40$

Special right triangles can be used to find the sine, cosine, and tangent of 30°, 45°, and 60° angles.

Example 2 Use a Special Right Triangle to Find Trigonometric Ratios

Use a special right triangle to express the sine of 60° as a fraction and as a decimal to the nearest hundredth.

Using the 30°-60°-90° Triangle Theorem, write the correct side lengths for each leg of the right triangle with *x* as the length of the shorter leg.

$\sin 60° = \frac{opp}{hyp}$ Definition of sine ratio

$= \frac{x\sqrt{3}}{2x}$ Substitution

≈ 0.87 Use a calculator.

Example 3 Estimate Measures by Using Trigonometry

ACCESSIBILITY Mathias builds a ramp so his sister can access the back door of their house. The 12-foot ramp to the house slopes upward from the ground at a 4° angle. What is the horizontal distance between the foot of the ramp and the house? What is the height of the ramp?

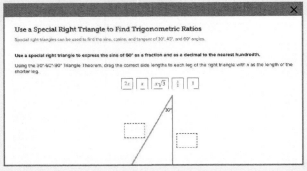

Find the horizontal distance.

Let *m*∠*A* = 4°. The horizontal distance between the foot of the ramp and the house is *x*, the measure of the leg adjacent to ∠*A*. The length of the ramp is the measure of the hypotenuse, 12 feet. Because the lengths of the leg adjacent to a given angle and the hypotenuse are involved, write an equation using the cosine ratio.

$\cos A = \frac{adj}{hyp}$ Definition of cosine ratio

$\cos 4° = \frac{x}{12}$ Substitution

$12 \cos 4° = x$ Multiply each side by 12.

$x \approx 11.97$ Use a calculator.

The horizontal distance between the foot of the ramp and the house is about 11.97 feet.

Study Tip

Graphing Calculator
Be sure that your graphing calculator is in degree mode rather than radian mode. Then, use the trigonometric functions [cos] and [sin] to find *x* and *y*, respectively.

12 [cos] 4 [enter] 11.9707686

12 [sin] 4 [enter] 0.8370777

Go Online
You can complete an Extra Example online.

534   Module 9 · Right Triangles and Trigonometry

Interactive Presentation

Use a Special Right Triangle to Find Trigonometric Ratios

Special right triangles can be used to find the sine, cosine, and tangent of 30°, 45°, and 60° angles.

Use a special right triangle to express the sine of 60° as a fraction and as a decimal to the nearest hundredth.

Using the 30°-60°-90° Triangle Theorem, drag the correct side lengths to each leg of the right triangle with *x* as the length of the shorter leg.

Example 2

DRAG & DROP

Students drag labels to parts of a special triangle.

Right page column

Example 1 Find Trigonometric Ratios

MP Teaching the Mathematical Practices

6 Communicate Precisely Encourage students to routinely write or explain their solution methods. Point out that they should use clear definitions when they discuss their solutions with others.

Questions for Mathematical Discourse

AL Why isn't it appropriate to find the trigonometric ratios for ∠*L*? Trigonometric ratios only apply to the acute angles in a right triangle.

OL How are cos *J* and sin *K* related? Do you think this will always be true for the acute angles of a right triangle? Explain. They are the same. Yes; sample answer: For acute angles of a right triangle, the side adjacent to one angle will always be the side opposite the other angle, so the cosine of one angle will always be the same as the sine of the other angle.

BL How are the tangents of ∠*J* and ∠*K* related? Do you think this will always be true for the acute angles of a right triangle? Explain. They are multiplicative inverses. Yes; sample answer: The sides adjacent to and opposite one angle will always be the reverse of the other acute angle in the triangle, so the tangents of the two acute angles will always be multiplicative inverses.

Example 2 Use Special Right Triangle to Find Trigonometric Ratios

MP Teaching the Mathematical Practices

7 Use Structure Help students to use the structure of special right triangles in this example to find trigonometric ratios of certain angles.

Questions for Mathematical Discourse

AL Is $\frac{\sqrt{3}}{2}$ the sine of the 60° angle for all 30°-60°-90° triangles? Explain. Yes; sample answer: Because we used the relationships between the sides and not specific lengths, the sine for the 60° angle for all 30°-60°-90° triangles will be the same.

OL What is the sine of the of the 30° angle for all 30°-60°-90° triangles? $\frac{1}{2}$

BL What is the tangent of the of the 30° angle for all 30°-60°-90° triangles? $\frac{\sqrt{3}}{3}$ or about 0.58.

Example 3 Estimate Measures by Using Trigonometry

MP Teaching the Mathematical Practices

4 Apply Mathematics In this example, students apply what they have learned about trigonometry to solving a real-world problem.

(continued on the next page)

1 CONCEPTUAL UNDERSTANDING | **2 FLUENCY** | 3 APPLICATION

Questions for Mathematical Discourse

AL When would you need to use trigonometry to estimate a measurement? Sample answer: when you can't easily measure a distance, length, or angle, but you have enough information to use trigonometry

OL If Mathias built a ramp with the same slope that is 18 ft long, what would the height of the ramp be? Explain. About 15 inches; sample answer: 18 ft is one and a half times the original length of the ramp, so the new height would be one and a half times the original height.

BL How is the horizontal distance covered by the ramp affected if the angle of the ramp increases and the length of the ramp stays the same? The horizontal distance decreases.

Learn Inverse Trigonometric Ratios

Objective
Students solve problems by using the inverse trigonometric ratios for acute angles.

MP Teaching the Mathematical Practices

6 Communicate Precisely Encourage students to routinely write or explain their solution methods. Point out that they should use clear definitions when they discuss their solutions with others.

Example 4 Find Angle Measures Using Inverse Trigonometric Ratios

MP Teaching the Mathematical Practices

5 Use Mathematical Tools Point out that to solve the problem in this example, students will need to use a calculator. Work with students to explore and deepen their understanding of inverse trigonometric ratios for acute angles.

Questions for Mathematical Discourse

AL What does it mean to be the *inverse* of something? Explain. Sample answer: The inverse of something is the opposite. For example, the inverse of multiplication is division.

OL How would you find the measure of angle *B*? Explain. Find the inverse sine of $\frac{3}{15}$ or $\sin^{-1}\frac{3}{15}$ which is $m\angle B$.

BL Can you find the angle measure of any angle of a right triangle given any two sides of the triangle? Explain. Yes; sample answer: If you are given any two sides of the triangle, you can use them to find one of the three trigonometric ratios for any angle.

Find the height.
The height of the ramp is y, the measure of the leg opposite from $\angle A$. Because the lengths of the leg opposite to a given angle and the hypotenuse are involved, write an equation using a sine ratio.

$$\sin A = \frac{opp}{hyp} \qquad \text{Definition of sine ratio}$$
$$\sin 4° = \frac{y}{12} \qquad \text{Substitution}$$
$$12 \cdot \sin 4° = y \qquad \text{Multiply each side by 12.}$$
$$y \approx 0.84 \qquad \text{Use a calculator.}$$

The height y of the ramp is about 0.84 feet or about 10 inches.

Learn Inverse Trigonometric Ratios

If you know the value of a trigonometric ratio for an acute angle, you can use a calculator to find the measure of the angle, which is the inverse of the trigonometric ratio.

Key Concept • Inverse Trigonometric Ratios

Inverse Sine	Inverse Cosine	Inverse Tangent
Words		
If $\angle A$ is an acute angle and the sine of A is x, then the **inverse sine** of x is the measure of $\angle A$.	If $\angle A$ is an acute angle and the cosine of A is x, then the **inverse cosine** of x is the measure of $\angle A$.	If $\angle A$ is an acute angle and the tangent of A is x, then the **inverse tangent** of x is the measure of $\angle A$.
Symbols		
If $\sin A = x$, then $\sin^{-1}x = m\angle A$.	If $\cos A = x$, then $\cos^{-1}x = m\angle A$.	If $\tan A = x$, then $\tan^{-1}x = m\angle A$.

Example 4 Find Angle Measures by Using Inverse Trigonometric Ratios

Use a calculator to find $m\angle A$ to the nearest tenth.
The measures given are those of the leg adjacent to $\angle A$ and the hypotenuse, so write an equation using the ___cosine___ ratio.
$$\cos A = \frac{3}{15} \text{ or } \frac{1}{5} \qquad \cos A = \frac{adj}{hyp}$$
$$\cos^{-1}\left(\frac{1}{5}\right) = m\angle A.$$
So, $m\angle A \approx$ ___78.5°___ . Use a calculator.

Go Online You can complete an Extra Example online.

Study Tip
Inverse Trigonometric Ratios The expression $\sin^{-1}x$ is read *the inverse sine of x* and is interpreted as the angle with sine x. Be careful not to confuse this notation with the notation for negative exponents. That is, $\sin^{-1}x \neq \frac{1}{\sin x}$. Instead, this notation is similar to the notation for an inverse function, $f^{-1}(x)$.

Go Online
You can watch a video to see how to solve a right triangle using trigonometry.

Study Tip
Graphing Calculators The second functions of the [sin] [cos] and [tan] keys are usually their inverses.

Talk About It!
What other method could you use to find $m\angle A$? Explain.

Sample answer: Find the inverse sine of $\frac{3}{15}$ or $\sin^{-1}\frac{3}{15}$, which is $m\angle B$. Then subtract from 90°.

Interactive Presentation

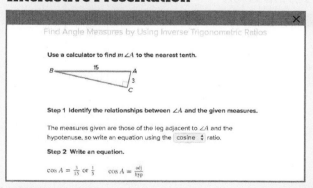

Find Angle Measures by Using Inverse Trigonometric Ratios

Use a calculator to find $m\angle A$ to the nearest tenth.

Step 1 Identify the relationships between $\angle A$ and the given measures.

The measures given are those of the leg adjacent to $\angle A$ and the hypotenuse, so write an equation using the cosine ratio.

Step 2 Write an equation.

$$\cos A = \frac{3}{15} \text{ or } \frac{1}{5} \qquad \cos A = \frac{adj}{hyp}$$

Example 4

TAP
Students tap to reveal steps in the solution and complete the solution.

CHECK
Students complete the Check online to determine whether they are ready to move on.

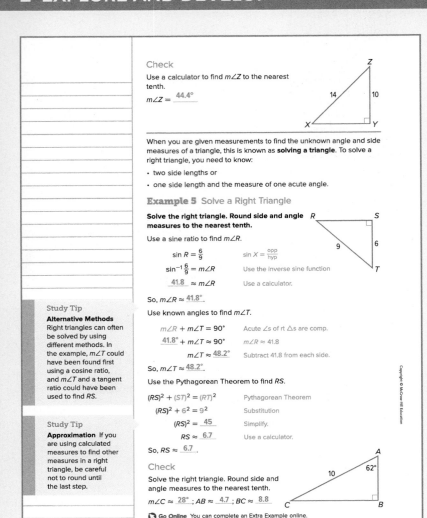

Check

Use a calculator to find $m\angle Z$ to the nearest tenth.

$m\angle Z = \underline{44.4°}$

When you are given measurements to find the unknown angle and side measures of a triangle, this is known as **solving a triangle**. To solve a right triangle, you need to know:

- two side lengths or
- one side length and the measure of one acute angle.

Example 5 Solve a Right Triangle

Solve the right triangle. Round side and angle measures to the nearest tenth.

Use a sine ratio to find $m\angle R$.

$\sin R = \frac{6}{9}$ $\sin X = \frac{opp}{hyp}$

$\sin^{-1}\frac{6}{9} = m\angle R$ Use the inverse sine function

$\underline{41.8} \approx m\angle R$ Use a calculator.

So, $m\angle R \approx \underline{41.8°}$.

Use known angles to find $m\angle T$.

$m\angle R + m\angle T = 90°$ Acute $\angle$s of rt $\triangle$s are comp.

$\underline{41.8°} + m\angle T \approx 90°$ $m\angle R \approx 41.8$

$m\angle T \approx \underline{48.2°}$ Subtract 41.8 from each side.

So, $m\angle T \approx \underline{48.2°}$.

Use the Pythagorean Theorem to find RS.

$(RS)^2 + (ST)^2 = (RT)^2$ Pythagorean Theorem

$(RS)^2 + 6^2 = 9^2$ Substitution

$(RS)^2 = \underline{45}$ Simplify.

$RS \approx \underline{6.7}$ Use a calculator.

So, $RS \approx \underline{6.7}$.

Check

Solve the right triangle. Round side and angle measures to the nearest tenth.

$m\angle C \approx \underline{28°}$; $AB \approx \underline{4.7}$; $BC \approx \underline{8.8}$

🖥 **Go Online** You can complete an Extra Example online.

Study Tip

Alternative Methods
Right triangles can often be solved by using different methods. In the example, $m\angle T$ could have been found first using a cosine ratio, and $m\angle T$ and a tangent ratio could have been used to find RS.

Study Tip

Approximation If you are using calculated measures to find other measures in a right triangle, be careful not to round until the last step.

Interactive Presentation

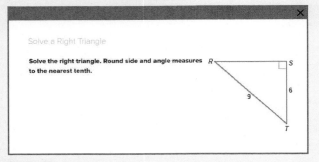

Solve a Right Triangle

Solve the right triangle. Round side and angle measures to the nearest tenth.

Example 5

TAP

Students tap to reveal steps in the solution.

CHECK

Students complete the Check online to determine whether they are ready to move on.

Example 5 Solve a Right Triangle

MP Teaching the Mathematical Practices

2 Create Representations Guide students to write equations that model the situation in this example. Then use the equations to solve the problem.

Questions for Mathematical Discourse

AL What does it mean to solve a right triangle? to determine all of the angle measures and side lengths that are not given

OL Could you use only trigonometry to solve this triangle? Explain. Yes; you could use a cosine ratio to find $m\angle T$ and another cosine ratio to find RS.

BL If a right triangle has one angle that measures 35° and the length of the hypotenuse is 11, what are the missing measures? The other angle measures 55°. The length of the shorter leg is about 6.3. The length of the longer leg is about 9.

Common Error

Students often want to round decimals in intermediate steps, as warned against in the Study Tip. Remind them that rounding creates an approximation, and using this approximation for later values may introduce further error.

Exit Ticket

Recommended Use

At the end of class, go online to display the Exit Ticket prompt and ask students to respond using a separate piece of paper. Have students hand you their responses as they leave the room.

Alternate Use

At the end of class, go online to display the Exit Ticket prompt and ask students to respond verbally or by using a mini-whiteboard. Have students hold up their whiteboards so that you can see all student responses. Tap to reveal the answer when most or all students have completed the Exit Ticket.

Practice and Homework

Suggested Assignments

Use the table below to select appropriate exercises.

DOK	Topic	Exercises
1, 2	exercises that mirror the examples	1–27
2	exercises that use a variety of skills from this lesson	28–38
3	exercises that emphasize higher-order and critical-thinking skills	39–44

ASSESS AND DIFFERENTIATE

📊 Use the data from the **Checks** to determine whether to provide resources for extension, remediation, or intervention.

IF students score 90% or more on the Checks,   `BL`
THEN assign:

- Practice, Exercises 1–37 odd, 39–44
- Extension: Sine and Cosine of Angles
- 🖥 **ALEKS** Right Triangle Trigonometry

IF students score 66%–89% on the Checks,   `OL`
THEN assign:

- Practice, Exercises 1–44 odd
- Remediation, Review Resources: Triangles
- Personal Tutors
- Extra Examples 1–5
- 🖥 **ALEKS** Triangle Constructions and Triangle Inequalities

---

IF students score 65% or less on the Checks,   `AL`
THEN assign:

- Practice, Exercises 1–27 odd
- Remediation, Review Resources: Triangles
- *Quick Review Math Handbook*: Trigonometry
- 🖥 **ALEKS** Triangle Constructions and Triangle Inequalities

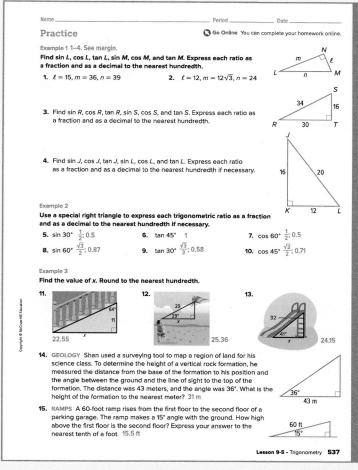

Name _____ Period _____ Date _____

Practice

🔵 **Go Online** You can complete your homework online.

Example 1 1–4. See margin.
Find sin *L*, cos *L*, tan *L*, sin *M*, cos *M*, and tan *M*. Express each ratio as a fraction and as a decimal to the nearest hundredth.

1. $\ell = 15$, $m = 36$, $n = 39$ 2. $\ell = 12$, $m = 12\sqrt{3}$, $n = 24$

3. Find sin *R*, cos *R*, tan *R*, sin *S*, cos *S*, and tan *S*. Express each ratio as a fraction and as a decimal to the nearest hundredth.

4. Find sin *J*, cos *J*, tan *J*, sin *L*, cos *L*, and tan *L*. Express each ratio as a fraction and as a decimal to the nearest hundredth if necessary.

Example 2
Use a special right triangle to express each trigonometric ratio as a fraction and as a decimal to the nearest hundredth if necessary.

5. sin 30° $\frac{1}{2}$; 0.5   6. tan 45° 1   7. cos 60° $\frac{1}{2}$; 0.5

8. sin 60° $\frac{\sqrt{3}}{2}$; 0.87   9. tan 30° $\frac{\sqrt{3}}{3}$; 0.58   10. cos 45° $\frac{\sqrt{2}}{2}$; 0.71

Example 3
Find the value of *x*. Round to the nearest hundredth.

11. 22.55   12. 25.36   13. 24.15

14. **GEOLOGY** Shan used a surveying tool to map a region of land for his science class. To determine the height of a vertical rock formation, he measured the distance from the base of the formation to his position and the angle between the ground and the line of sight to the top of the formation. The distance was 43 meters, and the angle was 36°. What is the height of the formation to the nearest meter? 31 m

15. **RAMPS** A 60-foot ramp rises from the first floor to the second floor of a parking garage. The ramp makes a 15° angle with the ground. How high above the first floor is the second floor? Express your answer to the nearest tenth of a foot. 15.5 ft

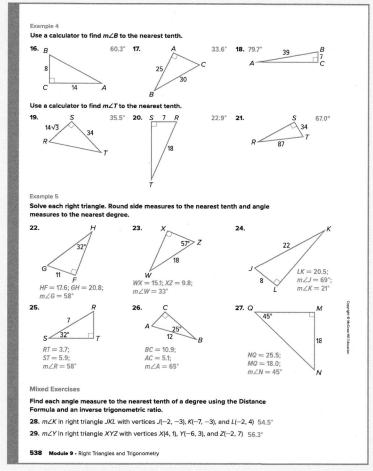

Example 4
Use a calculator to find *m∠B* to the nearest tenth.

16. 60.3°   17. 33.6°   18. 79.7°

Use a calculator to find *m∠T* to the nearest tenth.

19. 35.5°   20. 22.9°   21. 67.0°

Example 5
Solve each right triangle. Round side measures to the nearest tenth and angle measures to the nearest degree.

22. $HF = 17.6$; $GH = 20.8$; $m\angle G = 58°$

23. $WX = 15.1$; $XZ = 9.8$; $m\angle W = 33°$

24. $LK = 20.5$; $m\angle J = 69°$; $m\angle K = 21°$

25. $RT = 3.7$; $ST = 5.9$; $m\angle R = 58°$

26. $BC = 10.9$; $AC = 5.1$; $m\angle A = 65°$

27. $NQ = 25.5$; $MQ = 18.0$; $m\angle N = 45°$

Mixed Exercises

Find each angle measure to the nearest tenth of a degree using the Distance Formula and an inverse trigonometric ratio.

28. *m∠K* in right triangle *JKL* with vertices *J*(−2, −3), *K*(−7, −3), and *L*(−2, 4)   54.5°

29. *m∠Y* in right triangle *XYZ* with vertices *X*(4, 1), *Y*(−6, 3), and *Z*(−2, 7)   56.3°

Name _____ Period ___ Date ___

REASONING Find the perimeter and area of each triangle. Round to the nearest hundredth.

30. 5 in.   59°   13.84 in.; 7.51 in²

31. 18°   12 cm   28.52 cm; 23.39 cm²

32. 48°   8.44 ft; 3.05 ft²   3.5 ft

33. NEIGHBORS Amy, Barry, and Chris live in the same neighborhood. Chris lives up the street and around the corner from Amy, and Barry lives at the corner between Amy and Chris. The three homes are the vertices of a right triangle.

Chris 64° Barry 26° Amy

  a. Give two trigonometric expressions for the ratio of Barry's distance from Amy to Chris's distance from Amy. cos 26° or sin 64°

  b. Give two trigonometric expressions for the ratio of Barry's distance from Chris to Amy's distance from Chris. cos 64° or sin 26°

  c. Give a trigonometric expression for the ratio of Amy's distance from Barry to Chris's distance from Barry. tan 64°

34. CONSTRUCT ARGUMENTS A cell phone tower is supported by a guy wire as shown. Chilam wants to determine the height of the tower. She finds that the guy wire makes an angle of 53° with the ground and it is attached to the ground 65 feet from the base of the tower.

S R 53° 65 ft T

  a. Let the height of the tower be x. Which trigonometric ratio should you use to write an equation that you can solve for x? Justify your choice. Tangent; sample answer: The tangent ratio relates the two pieces of given information to the missing information.

  b. Write and solve an equation for the height of the tower. Round to the nearest tenth of a foot. tan 53° = $\frac{x}{65}$; x ≈ 86.3 ft

  c. Suppose Chilam had wanted to find the length of the guy wire. What would you have done differently to solve the problem? Justify your argument. Let y represent the length of the guy wire and use the cosine ratio to write the equation cos 53° = $\frac{65}{y}$. Solving for y shows that y = $\frac{65}{\cos 53°}$, or ≈ 108.0 feet. The length of the guy wire is about 108.0 feet.

35. COMPLEMENTARY ANGLES In the right triangle shown, sin α = 0.6428 and cos α = 0.7660. Find sin β and cos β and explain your reasoning. Sample answer: The sine of an angle equals the cosine of its complement. So, sin β = cos α = 0.7660. Similarly, cos β = sin α = 0.6428.

β α

Lesson 9-5 · Trigonometry **539**

Find the values of x and y. Round to the nearest tenth.

36. 40   x°   22   y°
x = 37.2; y = 33.4

37. 8   x   43°   y
x = 9.2; y = 11.7

38. STRUCTURE Explain how you can use only the table at the right to find the value of cos 20°. Sample answer: The cosine of an angle equals the sine of its complement, so cos 20° = sin 70° or 0.9397.

m∠A	sin A
65°	0.9063
70°	0.9397
75°	0.9659
80°	0.9848
85°	0.9962

🧠 **Higher-Order Thinking Skills**

39. FIND THE ERROR Lakasha and Treyvon were both solving the same trigonometry problem. However, after they finished their computations, Lakasha said the answer was 52 sin 27° and Treyvon said the answer was 52 cos 63°. Could they both be correct? Explain your reasoning. Yes, they are both correct; sample answer: Because 27 + 63 = 90, the sine of 27° is the same ratio as the cosine of 63°.

40. PERSEVERE Solve △ABC. Round each measure to the nearest whole number.
m∠A = 53°, m∠B = 90°, m∠C = 37°, AB = 12, BC = 16, AC = 20

B (7x − 1)° 2y + 2 y + 5 (4x + 1)° (3x − 2)° C A 3y − 1

41. ANALYZE Are the values of sine and cosine for an acute angle of a right triangle always less than 1? Explain. See margin.

42. WHICH ONE DOESN'T BELONG? If the directions say to Solve the right triangle, then which of the triangles shown does not belong? Justify your conclusion. △ABC; sample answer: In order to solve a right triangle, you need 2 side length or 1 side length and 1 acute angle measure.

C 36° 54° A B   Y 12 63° X W   M 12 P 3 N

43. WRITE Explain how you can use ratios of the side lengths to find the angle measures of the acute angles in a right triangle. See margin.

44. CREATE Draw a right triangle with a tangent ratio of $\frac{3}{2}$ for one of the acute angles. Then find the measure of the other acute angle to the nearest tenth of a degree. See margin.

540 Module 9 · Right Triangles and Trigonometry

Answers

1. sin L = $\frac{5}{13}$ ≈ 0.38; cos L = $\frac{12}{13}$ ≈ 0.92; tan L = $\frac{5}{12}$ ≈ 0.42; sin M = $\frac{12}{13}$ ≈ 0.92; cos M = $\frac{5}{13}$ ≈ 0.38; tan M = $\frac{12}{5}$ = 2.4

2. sin L = $\frac{1}{2}$ = 0.50; cos L = $\frac{\sqrt{3}}{2}$ ≈ 0.87; tan L = $\frac{1}{\sqrt{3}}$ or $\frac{\sqrt{3}}{3}$ ≈ 0.58; sin M = $\frac{\sqrt{3}}{2}$ ≈ 0.87; cos M = $\frac{1}{2}$ = 0.50; tan M = $\sqrt{3}$ ≈ 1.73

3. sin R = $\frac{8}{17}$ ≈ 0.47; cos R = $\frac{15}{17}$ ≈ 0.88; tan R = $\frac{8}{15}$ ≈ 0.53; sin S = $\frac{15}{17}$ ≈ 0.88; cos S = $\frac{8}{17}$ ≈ 0.47; tan S = $\frac{15}{8}$ ≈ 1.88

4. sin J = $\frac{3}{5}$ = 0.6; cos J = $\frac{4}{5}$ = 0.8; tan J = $\frac{3}{4}$ = 0.75; sin L = $\frac{4}{5}$ = 0.8; cos L = $\frac{3}{5}$ = 0.6; tan L = $\frac{4}{3}$ ≈ 1.33

41. Yes; sample answer: Because the values of sine and cosine are both calculated by dividing one of the legs of a right triangle by the hypotenuse, and the hypotenuse is always the longest side of a right triangle, the values will always be less than 1. You will always be dividing the smaller number by the larger number.

43. Sample answer: To find the measure of an acute angle of a right triangle, you can find the ratio of the leg opposite the angle to the hypotenuse and use a calculator to find the inverse sine of the ratio; you can find the ratio of the leg adjacent to the angle to the hypotenuse and use a calculator to find the inverse cosine of the ratio; or you can find the ratio of the leg opposite the angle to the leg adjacent to the angle and use a calculator to find the inverse tangent of the ratio.

44. Sample answer: Suppose right △ABC has acute angles at A and C. If tan C = $\frac{3}{2}$, then C = tan⁻¹ $\frac{3}{2}$ ≈ 56.3°. So, m∠A = 90° − m∠C ≈ 90° − 56.3° ≈ 33.7°.

A 6 B 4 C

Applying Trigonometry

LESSON GOAL

Students solve real-world problems using the trigonometric ratios and their inverses.

1 LAUNCH

 Launch the lesson with a **Warm Up** and an introduction.

2 EXPLORE AND DEVELOP

 Explore:
- Angles of Elevation and Depression
- Measuring Angles of Elevation

 Develop:

Angles of Elevation and Depression
- Angle of Elevation
- Angle of Depression
- Use Two Angles of Elevation or Depression

Trigonometry and Areas of Triangles
- Find the Area of a Triangle When Given the Included Angle
- Find the Area of Any Triangle

 You may want your students to complete the **Checks** online.

3 REFLECT AND PRACTICE

 Exit Ticket

 Practice

DIFFERENTIATE

 View reports of student progress on the **Checks** after each example.

Resources	AL	OL	BL	ELL
Remediation: Indirect Measurement	●	●		●
Extension: Best Seat in the House		●	●	●

Language Development Handbook

Assign page 63 of the *Language Development Handbook* to help your students build mathematical language related to applying trigonometry.

ELL You can use the tips and suggestions on page T63 of the handbook to support students who are building English proficiency.

Suggested Pacing

90 min	0.5 day	
45 min	1 day	

Focus

Domain: Geometry

Standards for Mathematical Content:

G.SRT.8 Use trigonometric ratios and the Pythagorean Theorem to solve right triangles in applied problems.

G.SRT.9 Derive the formula $A = \frac{1}{2} ab \sin(C)$ for the area of a triangle by drawing an auxiliary line from a vertex perpendicular to the opposite side.

Standards for Mathematical Practice:

4 Model with mathematics.

5 Use appropriate tools strategically.

Coherence

Vertical Alignment

Previous
Students solved problems using trigonometric ratios and their inverses for acute angles.
G.SRT.6, G.SRT.7

Now
Students apply trigonometry to real-world situations and to triangle area.
G.SRT.8, G.SRT.9

Next
Students will solve problems using the Law of Sines.
G.SRT.10, G.SRT.11

Rigor

The Three Pillars of Rigor

1 CONCEPTUAL UNDERSTANDING	2 FLUENCY	3 APPLICATION

Conceptual Bridge In this lesson, students apply their understanding of trigonometry to solving real-world problems related to angles of elevation and depression. They also build fluency by applying trigonometry to general triangles.

Mathematical Background

An *angle of elevation* is the angle between the line of sight and the horizontal when an observer looks upward. An *angle of depression* is the angle between the line of sight and the horizontal when an observer looks downward. Trigonometric ratios can be used to solve problems involving these angles.

Interactive Presentation

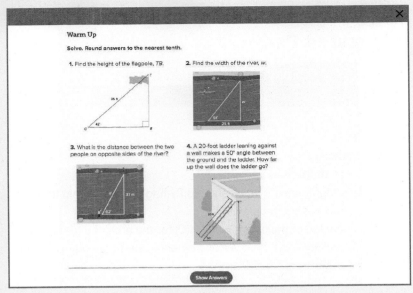

Warm Up

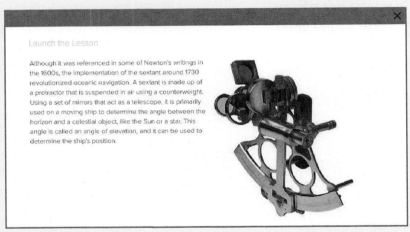

Launch the Lesson

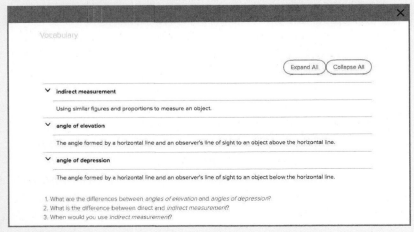

Today's Vocabulary

Warm Up

Prerequisite Skills

The Warm Up exercises address the following prerequisite skill for this lesson:

- using similar triangles to measure indirectly

Answers:

1. 23.4 ft
2. 30.9 ft
3. 41.9 m
4. 15.3 ft

Launch the Lesson

MP Teaching the Mathematical Practices

4 Apply Mathematics In this Launch the Lesson, students can see a real-world application of angles of elevation.

Go Online to find additional teaching notes and questions to promote classroom discourse.

Today's Standards

Tell students that they will be addressing these content and practice standards in this lesson. You may wish to have a student volunteer read aloud *How can I meet these standards?* and *How can I use these practices?* and connect these to the standards.

See the Interactive Presentation for I Can statements that align with the standards covered in this lesson.

Today's Vocabulary

Tell students that they will be using these vocabulary terms in this lesson. You can expand each row if you wish to share the definitions. Then, discuss the questions below with the class.

Explore Angles of Elevation and Depression

Objective
Students understand how to use right triangles to estimate distance and lengths by exploring their properties in a real-world setting.

Teaching the Mathematical Practices

> **5 Use Mathematical Tools** Point out that to solve the problem in this Explore, students will need to use a protractor. Work with students to explore and deepen their understanding of applications of trigonometry.

Ideas for Use

Recommended Use Present the Inquiry Question, or have a student volunteer read it aloud. Have students work in pairs to complete the Explore activity on their devices. Pairs should discuss each of the questions. Monitor student progress during the activity. Upon completion of the Explore activity, have student volunteers share their responses to the Inquiry Question.

What if my students don't have devices? You may choose to project the activity on a whiteboard. A printable worksheet for each Explore is available online. You may choose to print the worksheet so that individuals or pairs of students can use it to record their observations.

Summary of the Activity

Students will complete guiding exercises throughout the Explore activity. Students use a protractor with a string and a weight to measure the height of a tall object. First, they determine the distance between them and the object. Then they determine the angle of elevation or depression to the top of the object in question using the protractor. Next they include their own height, and complete guiding exercises to compute the height of the object. Then, students will answer the Inquiry Question.

(continued on the next page)

Interactive Presentation

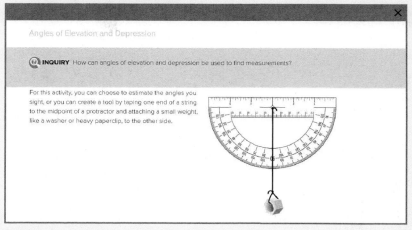

Explore

TAP

Students tap to reveal steps in solving the problem and to enter answers to guiding exercises.

Interactive Presentation

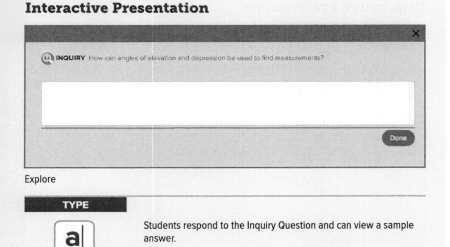

Explore

TYPE

a|

Students respond to the Inquiry Question and can view a sample answer.

Explore Angles of Elevation and Depression (*continued*)

𝖬𝖯 Teaching the Mathematical Practices

4 Use Tools Point out that to solve the problem in this Explore, students will need to use diagrams.

Questions

Have students complete the Explore activity.

Ask:

- How does lying on the ground change the scenario? Sample answer: If you are lying on the ground, you don't have to take your height into consideration with the measurements.

- Do you think you could use a given height and distance to find the angle of elevation? Sample answer: You can set up the ratio with the height and distance with respect to the angle, then find the angle that makes this ratio true. For example, if you were given the height and the distance to a building, you would use the tangent ratio and then solve for the angle.

ℚ Inquiry

How can angles of elevation and depression be used to find measurements? Sample answer: An angle of elevation or depression is the angle your line of sight to an object you are sighting makes with a horizontal line. The right triangle created by these two legs and the vertical line that passes through the object you are sighting can be solved to determine specific lengths.

🔘 **Go Online** to find additional teaching notes and sample answers for the guiding exercises.

Explore Measuring Angles of Elevation

Objective

Students understand how to use right triangles to estimate distances and lengths by exploring their properties in a real-world setting.

Teaching the Mathematical Practices

> **6 Use Precision** In this Explore, students learn how to calculate accurately and efficiently and to express numerical answers with a degree of precision appropriate to the problem context.

Ideas for Use

Recommended Use Present the Inquiry Question, or have a student volunteer read it aloud. Have students work in pairs to complete the Explore activity on their devices. Pairs should discuss each of the questions. Monitor student progress during the activity. Upon completion of the Explore activity, have student volunteers share their responses to the Inquiry Question.

What if my students don't have devices? You may choose to project the activity on a whiteboard. A printable worksheet for each Explore is available online. You may choose to print the worksheet so that individuals or pairs of students can use it to record their observations.

Summary of the Activity

Students will complete guiding exercises throughout the Explore activity. Students create a spreadsheet with one column having the fixed distance from an object in each cell, any 10 angle measures in order in the next column, and the tangent of the angle in the third column. Then students calculate the height of the object as the product of the distance from the object and the tangent of the angle. Students then complete guiding exercises to help them understand angles of elevation and their use in finding the height of tall objects. Then, students will answer the Inquiry Question.

(continued on the next page)

Interactive Presentation

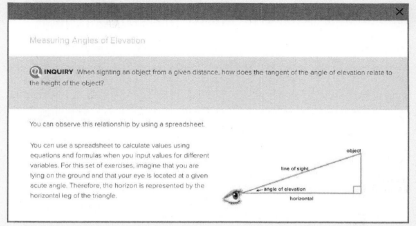

Measuring Angles of Elevation

INQUIRY When sighting an object from a given distance, how does the tangent of the angle of elevation relate to the height of the object?

You can observe this relationship by using a spreadsheet.

You can use a spreadsheet to calculate values using equations and formulas when you input values for different variables. For this set of exercises, imagine that you are lying on the ground and that your eye is located at a given acute angle. Therefore, the horizon is represented by the horizontal leg of the triangle.

Explore

TAP

Students tap to reveal steps to create a spreadsheet and enter answers to guiding exercises.

Interactive Presentation

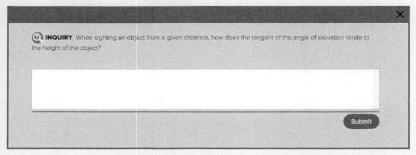

Explore

TYPE

Students respond to the Inquiry Question and can view a sample answer.

---

1 CONCEPTUAL UNDERSTANDING | 2 FLUENCY | 3 APPLICATION

Explore Measuring Angles of Elevation (*continued*)

Teaching the Mathematical Practices

4 Apply Mathematics In this Explore, students apply what they have learned about right triangles to solving a real-world problem.

Questions

Have students complete the Explore activity.

Ask:
- Why do you need to know the horizontal distance between yourself and the object you're sighting? Sample answer: You should have at least one measure in the triangle that you are using to model the situation.

- Why can't you use the sine ratio to find the height? Sample answer: The sine ratio does involve the side opposite where you are standing, but it also uses the hypotenuse of the triangle, which is a distance that you can't measure. If you were given the distance from yourself to the top of the building, you could use the sine ratio to find the height.

Inquiry

When sighting an object from a given distance, how does the tangent of the angle of elevation relate to the height of the object? Sample answer: The tangent of the angle of elevation times the distance between the object and you is equal to the height of the object.

Go Online to find additional teaching notes and sample answers for the guiding exercises.

1 CONCEPTUAL UNDERSTANDING | **2 FLUENCY** | **3 APPLICATION**

Learn Angles of Elevation and Depression

Objective
Students solve real-world problems by using the trigonometric ratios and their inverses.

MP Teaching the Mathematical Practices

6 Communicate Precisely Encourage students to routinely write or explain their solution methods. Point out that they should use clear definitions when they discuss their solutions with others.

Essential Question Follow-Up
Students apply trigonometry to real-world situations.

Ask:

Why is trigonometry important in the real world? Sample answer: Trigonometry helps us find the length of distances we can't measure directly.

Example 1 Angle of Elevation

MP Teaching the Mathematical Practices

6 Communicate Precisely Encourage students to routinely write or explain their solution methods. Point out that they should use clear definitions when they discuss their solutions with others.

Questions for Mathematical Discourse

AL What two rays form the angle of elevation? $\overrightarrow{AB}$ and $\overrightarrow{AC}$

OL What is the measure of $\angle ABC$? 60°

BL If the drone is at the same height, would the angle of elevation be greater if the drone is closer or further away? closer

Go Online

- Find additional teaching notes.
- View performance reports of the Checks.
- Assign or present an Extra Example.

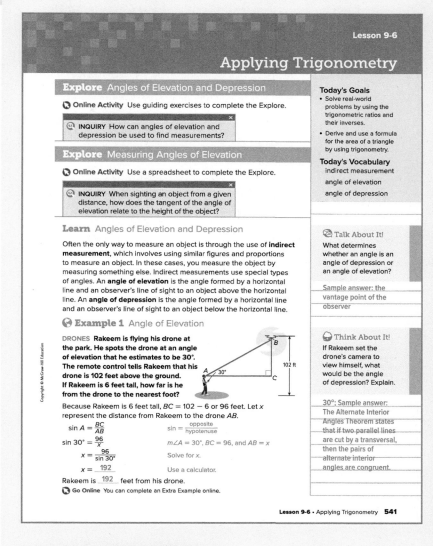

Lesson 9-6

Applying Trigonometry

Explore Angles of Elevation and Depression

Online Activity Use guiding exercises to complete the Explore.

INQUIRY How can angles of elevation and depression be used to find measurements?

Explore Measuring Angles of Elevation

Online Activity Use a spreadsheet to complete the Explore.

INQUIRY When sighting an object from a given distance, how does the tangent of the angle of elevation relate to the height of the object?

Learn Angles of Elevation and Depression

Often the only way to measure an object is through the use of **indirect measurement**, which involves using similar figures and proportions to measure an object. In these cases, you measure the object by measuring something else. Indirect measurements use special types of angles. An **angle of elevation** is the angle formed by a horizontal line and an observer's line of sight to an object above the horizontal line. An **angle of depression** is the angle formed by a horizontal line and an observer's line of sight to an object below the horizontal line.

Example 1 Angle of Elevation

DRONES **Rakeem is flying his drone at the park. He spots the drone at an angle of elevation that he estimates to be 30°. The remote control tells Rakeem that his drone is 102 feet above the ground. If Rakeem is 6 feet tall, how far is he from the drone to the nearest foot?**

Because Rakeem is 6 feet tall, $BC = 102 - 6$ or 96 feet. Let x represent the distance from Rakeem to the drone AB.

$$\sin A = \frac{BC}{AB} \qquad \sin = \frac{\text{opposite}}{\text{hypotenuse}}$$

$$\sin 30° = \frac{96}{x} \qquad m\angle A = 30°, BC = 96, \text{ and } AB = x$$

$$x = \frac{96}{\sin 30°} \qquad \text{Solve for } x.$$

$$x = \underline{192} \qquad \text{Use a calculator.}$$

Rakeem is $\underline{192}$ feet from his drone.

Go Online You can complete an Extra Example online.

Today's Goals
- Solve real-world problems by using the trigonometric ratios and their inverses.
- Derive and use a formula for the area of a triangle by using trigonometry.

Today's Vocabulary
indirect measurement
angle of elevation
angle of depression

Talk About It!
What determines whether an angle is an angle of depression or an angle of elevation?

Sample answer: the vantage point of the observer

Think About It!
If Rakeem set the drone's camera to view himself, what would be the angle of depression? Explain.

30°; Sample answer: The Alternate Interior Angles Theorem states that if two parallel lines are cut by a transversal, then the pairs of alternate interior angles are congruent.

Interactive Presentation

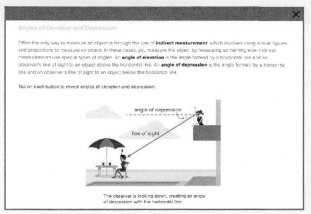

Angles of Elevation and Depression

Often the only way to measure an object is through the use of **indirect measurement**, which involves using similar figures and proportions to measure an object. In these cases, you measure the object by measuring something else. Indirect measurements use special types of angles. An **angle of elevation** is the angle formed by a horizontal line and an observer's line of sight to an object above the horizontal line. An **angle of depression** is the angle formed by a horizontal line and an observer's line of sight to an object below the horizontal line.

Tap on each button to reveal angles of elevation and depression.

The observer is looking down, creating an angle of depression with the horizontal line.

Learn

TAP

Students tap to reveal information about angles of elevation and depression.

Your Notes

Check

SEARCH AND RESCUE A flare is shot vertically into the air approximately 200 meters from base camp. The angle of elevation to the maximum height of the flare is 35°. The group at base camp needs to know the altitude of the flare.

Part A Write the equation that represents the situation if *a* represents the height of the flare.

$\tan 35° = \frac{a}{200}$

Part B What is the maximum height of the flare to the nearest meter?

140 m

⊕ Example 2 Angle of Depression

SIGHTSEEING Cottonwood, Idaho's Dog Bark Park Inn is a popular tourist attraction featuring a hotel in the shape of a 30-foot wood-carved beagle. Pedro looks out the window 30 feet from the ground and spots a fire hydrant on the ground at an estimated angle of depression of 40°. What is the horizontal distance from Pedro to the hydrant to the nearest foot?

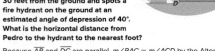

Because $\overline{AB}$ and $\overline{DC}$ are parallel, $m\angle BAC = m\angle ACD$ by the Alternate Interior Angles Theorem.

Let *x* represent the ___horizontal___ distance from the base of the hotel to the hydrant.

$\tan C = \frac{AD}{DC}$	$\tan = \frac{\text{opposite}}{\text{adjacent}}$
$\tan 40° = \frac{30}{x}$	$C = 40°, AD = 30,$ and $DC = x$
$x \tan 40° = 30$	Multiply each side by *x*.
$x = \frac{30}{\tan 40°}$	Divide each side by tan 40°.
$x \approx 35.8$	Use a calculator.

The horizontal distance from Pedro to the hydrant is about ___36___ feet.

Check

LIFEGUARDING Braylen stands on an 8-foot platform and sights a swimmer at an angle of depression of 5°. If Braylen is 6 feet tall, how far away is the swimmer from the base of the platform to the nearest foot? ___160___ ft

⊕ **Go Online** You can complete an Extra Example online.

Study Tip

Angles of Elevation and Depression To avoid mislabeling, remember that angles of elevation and depression are always formed with a horizontal line, never with a vertical line.

Use a Source

Chaz hikes to the top of Mount Elbert in Colorado. He uses binoculars to sight his car in the parking lot at the trailhead, which is at an altitude of 10,040 feet. The angle of depression at which he sites his car is about 23.6°. Use available resources to find the total height of Mount Elbert. Then, calculate the distance Chaz is from his car to the nearest foot.

Chaz is about ___11,722___ feet from his car.

⊕ **Example 2** Angle of Depression

MP Teaching the Mathematical Practices

5 Use a Source Guide students to find external information to answer the questions posed in the Use a Source feature.

Questions for Mathematical Discourse

AL How do we know this is an angle of depression? Pedro is looking down at the fire hydrant.

OL What is the actual distance from Pedro to the hydrant? 46.7 ft

BL If Pedro looks out a window 8 ft lower than his current location, what is the new angle of depression? 31.6°

DIFFERENTIATE

Reteaching Activity **AL**

Kinesthetic Learners Using a meterstick and a calculator, groups of students can find angles of elevation and depression for different objects in the classroom. Groups can measure one person's eye level from the floor, and the topmost height of a wall clock from the floor. The person stands 5 feet away from the clock, and the group calculates the angle of elevation from the person's line of sight to the top of the object. Repeat for items placed on the floor, and include variations like having the person stand on a platform, or placing two objects on the floor a certain distance from each other.

Interactive Presentation

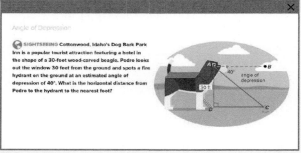

Example 2

TYPE

Students can complete the calculations to find an angle of depression.

1 CONCEPTUAL UNDERSTANDING | 2 FLUENCY | **3 APPLICATION**

🌐 **Example 3** Use Two Angles of Elevation or Depression

🔠 Teaching the Mathematical Practices

6 Use Quantities Use the Study Tip to guide students to clarifying their use of quantities in this example. Ensure that they specify the units of measure used in the problem and label axes appropriately.

Questions for Mathematical Discourse

AL Why do we need to use two angles of elevation in this case?
Sample answer: We might not have known how far she was from the second floor at the first sighting, and might not have been able to measure the angle of elevation in her second sighting.

OL For what types of situations does this type of estimation make sense? In a situation where you don't know how far you are from an object or how tall it is, but you can estimate the angle you use to sight it from two different points that you can measure the distance between.

BL If Wei sights the bottom of the roof at an angle of elevation of 40°, moves forward 30 feet, and sights the same place at an angle of elevation of 60°, how high is the roof? 28.2 ft

---

DIFFERENTIATE

Language Development Activity AL BL ELL

Have students draw a triangle and construct the altitude to two of the sides. Then have them measure the lengths of the two sides, the included angle, and the altitudes. Have students compute the area of the triangle three ways, twice using a different altitude as the height, and one using trigonometry. Have students compare the values they get from each method.

🌐 **Example 3** Use Two Angles of Elevation or Depression

MALL Wei is estimating the height of the second floor in the mall. She sights the second floor at a 10° angle of elevation. She then steps forward 50 feet, until she is 5.5 feet from the wall and sights the second floor again. If Wei's line of sight is 66 inches above the ground, at what angle of elevation does she sight the second floor?

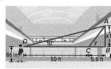

$\triangle ABC$ and $\triangle ABD$ are right triangles. To find the angle of elevation, first find the height of the second floor of the mall. This height is the sum of Wei's height and AB.

Use $\triangle ABD$ to write an equation for AB.

$\tan 10° = \frac{AB}{BD}$ $\tan \theta = \frac{\text{opposite}}{\text{adjacent}}$ and $m\angle ADB = 10$

$\tan 10° = \frac{AB}{55.5}$ $BD = 50 + 5.5$

$55.5 \tan 10° = AB$ Multiply each side by 55.5.

Use $\triangle ABC$ to write an equation for AB.

$\tan y° = \frac{AB}{BC}$ $\tan \theta = \frac{\text{opposite}}{\text{adjacent}}$

$\tan y° = \frac{AB}{5.5}$ $BC = 5.5$

$5.5 \tan y° = AB$ Multiply each side by 5.5.

Use the equation for AB from $\triangle ABD$ in the equation for $\triangle ABC$ and solve for y.

$5.5 \tan y° = AB$

$5.5 \tan y° = 55.5 \tan 10°$

$\tan y° = \frac{55.5 \tan 10°}{5.5}$

$y \approx 60.66$

Using the equation from $\triangle ABC$, $AB = 5.5 \tan 60.7°$ or about ___9.8___. The height of the second floor of the mall is about $9.8 + 5.5$ or 15.3, which is about 15 feet.

Check

SIGHTSEEING Looking north, two skyscrapers are sighted from the viewing deck of the Empire State Building at 1250 feet up. One skyscraper is sighted at a 20° angle of depression and a second skyscraper is sighted at a 30° angle of depression. How far apart are the two skyscrapers to the nearest foot?

___525___ ft

🌐 **Go Online** You can complete an Extra Example online.

Lesson 9-6 • Applying Trigonometry **543**

Interactive Presentation

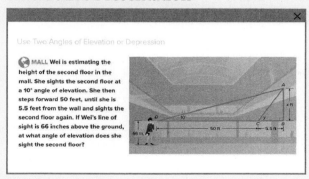

Use Two Angles of Elevation or Depression

🌐 **MALL** Wei is estimating the height of the second floor in the mall. She sights the second floor at a 10° angle of elevation. She then steps forward 50 feet, until she is 5.5 feet from the wall and sights the second floor again. If Wei's line of sight is 66 inches above the ground, at what angle of elevation does she sight the second floor?

Example 3

TAP

 Students tap to reveal steps of the solution.

CHECK

 Students complete the Check online to determine whether they are ready to move on.

1 CONCEPTUAL UNDERSTANDING | **2 FLUENCY** | 3 APPLICATION

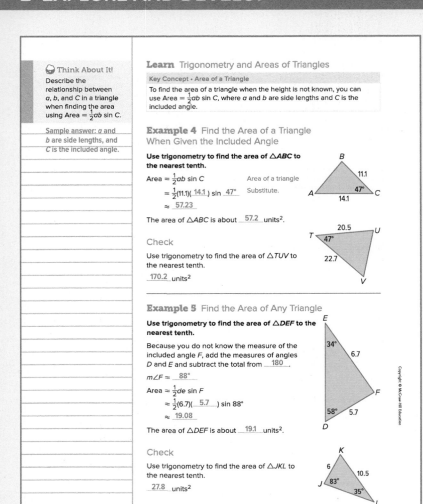

🧠 Think About It!

Describe the relationship between a, b, and C in a triangle when finding the area using Area = $\frac{1}{2}ab$ sin C.

Sample answer: a and b are side lengths, and C is the included angle.

Learn Trigonometry and Areas of Triangles

Key Concept • Area of a Triangle

To find the area of a triangle when the height is not known, you can use Area = $\frac{1}{2}ab$ sin C, where a and b are side lengths and C is the included angle.

Example 4 Find the Area of a Triangle When Given the Included Angle

Use trigonometry to find the area of △ABC to the nearest tenth.

Area = $\frac{1}{2}ab$ sin C   Area of a triangle

= $\frac{1}{2}$(11.1)(14.1) sin 47°   Substitute.

≈ 57.23

The area of △ABC is about 57.2 units².

Check

Use trigonometry to find the area of △TUV to the nearest tenth.

 170.2 units²

Example 5 Find the Area of Any Triangle

Use trigonometry to find the area of △DEF to the nearest tenth.

Because you do not know the measure of the included angle F, add the measures of angles D and E and subtract the total from 180 .

m∠F ≈ 88°

Area ≈ $\frac{1}{2}de$ sin F

≈ $\frac{1}{2}$(6.7)(5.7) sin 88°

≈ 19.08

The area of △DEF is about 19.1 units².

Check

Use trigonometry to find the area of △JKL to the nearest tenth.

 27.8 units²

🔲 Go Online You can complete an Extra Example online.

Interactive Presentation

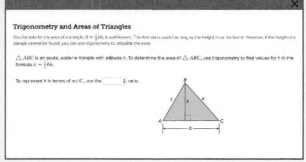

Trigonometry and Areas of Triangles

Learn

TAP

Students select answer choices to complete an argument.

CHECK

Students complete the Check online to determine whether they are ready to move on.

Learn Trigonometry and Areas of Triangles

Objective

Students derive and use a formula for the area of a triangle by using trigonometry.

Example 4 Find the Area of a Triangle When Given the Included Angle

🔲 Teaching the Mathematical Practices

3 Construct Arguments In this example, students will use stated assumptions, definitions, and previously established results to construct an argument.

Questions for Mathematical Discourse

AL What extra line segment do we need to draw in the diagram to solve this problem? the altitude or height of the triangle

OL If you are given △RST and the values of RS, RT, and m∠R, what is the area of the triangle? $A = \frac{1}{2}RS \cdot RT$ sin ∠R

BL Can you find the area of a triangle given two sides and a nonincluded angle? Explain. No; sample answer: This information follows the SSA pattern which is not a pattern in any of the triangle congruence theorems, so this information may belong to multiple different triangles.

Example 5 Find the Area of any Triangle

🔲 Teaching the Mathematical Practices

6 Use Precision In this example, students must calculate accurately and efficiently and express numerical answers with a degree of precision appropriate to the problem context.

Questions for Mathematical Discourse

AL Why do we need to find m∠F? ∠F is the included angle between the two given side lengths.

OL Why do we need two angle measures in this problem? In order to use the area formula we need the measure of the angle included between the given sides, and we need both the other angles to find the included angle measure.

BL Why do we need the included angle to be acute? The definition of sine requires that the angle be a nonright angle in a right triangle, so the angle must be acute.

Exit Ticket

Recommended Use

At the end of class, go online to display the Exit Ticket prompt and ask students to respond using a separate piece of paper. Have students hand you their responses as they leave the room.

Alternate Use

At the end of class, go online to display the Exit Ticket prompt and ask students to respond verbally or by using a mini-whiteboard. Have students hold up their whiteboards so that you can see all student responses. Tap to reveal the answer when most or all students have completed the Exit Ticket.

Practice and Homework

Suggested Assignments

Use the table below to select appropriate exercises.

DOK	Topic	Exercises
1, 2	exercises that mirror the examples	1–21
2	exercises that use a variety of skills from this lesson	22–31
3	exercises that emphasize higher-order and critical-thinking skills	32–36

ASSESS AND DIFFERENTIATE

Use the data from the **Checks** to determine whether to provide resources for extension, remediation, or intervention.

IF students score 90% or more on the Checks, **BL**
THEN assign:

- Practice, Exercises 1–31 odd, 32–36
- Extension: Best Seat in the House
- **ALEKS** Right Triangle Trigonometry

IF students score 66%–89% on the Checks, **OL**
THEN assign:

- Practice, Exercises 1–35 odd
- Remediation, Review Resources: Indirect Measurement
- Personal Tutors
- Extra Examples 1–5
- **ALEKS** Similar Figures

IF students score 65% or less on the Checks, **AL**
THEN assign:

- Practice, Exercises 1–21 odd
- Remediation, Review Resources: Indirect Measurement
- *Quick Review Math Handbook*: Angles of Elevation and Depression
- **ALEKS** Similar Figures

Name _____ Period _____ Date _____

Practice

Go Online You can complete your homework online.

Example 1

1. **LIGHTHOUSES** Sailors on a ship at sea spot the light from a lighthouse at an angle of elevation of 25°. The light of the lighthouse is 30 meters above sea level. How far from the shore is the ship? Round your answer to the nearest meter. 64 m

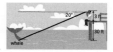

2. **WATER TOWERS** A student can see a water tower from the edge of a soccer field at San Lobos High School. The edge of the field is about 110 feet from the water tower, and the water tower stands at a height of 32.5 feet. What is the angle of elevation if the eye level of the student viewing the tower is 6 feet above the ground? Round your answer to the nearest tenth. about 13.5°

3. **CONSTRUCTION** A roofer props a ladder against a wall so the top of the ladder just reaches a 30-foot roof that needs repair. If the angle of elevation from the bottom of the ladder to the roof is 55°, how far is the ladder from the base of the wall? Round your answer to the nearest foot. about 21 ft

4. **MOUNTAIN BIKING** On a mountain bike trip along the Gemini Bridges Trail in Moab, Utah, Nabuko stopped on the canyon floor to get a good view of the twin sandstone bridges. Nabuko is standing about 60 meters from the base of the canyon cliff, and the natural arch bridges are about 100 meters up the canyon wall. If her line of sight is 5 meters above the ground, what is the angle of elevation to the top of the bridges? Round to the nearest tenth of a degree. about 57.7°

Example 2

5. **ROOFTOP** Lucia is 5.5 feet tall. She is standing on the roof of a building that is 80 feet tall. She spots a fountain at ground level that she knows to be 122 feet away from the base of the building. What is the measure of the angle of depression formed by Lucia's horizontal line of sight and her line of sight to the fountain? Round your answer to the nearest degree. about 35°

6. **AIR TRAFFIC** From the top of the 120-foot-high tower, an air traffic controller observes an airplane on the runway at an angle of depression of 19°. How far from the base of the tower is the airplane? Round to the nearest tenth of a foot. 348.5 ft

7. **AVIATION** Due to a storm, a pilot flying at an altitude of 528 feet has to land. If he has a horizontal landing distance of 2000 feet until he reaches the landing strip, what angle of depression should he use to land? Round to the nearest tenth of a degree. 14.8°

---

8. **INDIRECT MEASUREMENT** Kenneth is sitting at the end of a pier and using binoculars to watch a whale surface. The pier is 30 feet above the water, and Kenneth's eye level is 3 feet above the pier. If the angle of depression to the whale is 20°, how far is the whale from Kenneth's binoculars? Round your answer to the nearest tenth of a foot. 96.5 ft

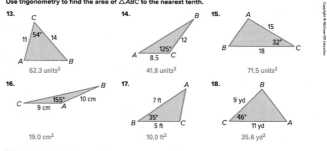

Example 3

9. **GARAGE** To estimate the height of a garage, Carlos sights the top of the garage at a 42° angle of elevation. He then steps back 20 feet and sights the top of the garage at a 10° angle. If Carlos is 6 feet tall, how tall is the garage to the nearest foot? 10 feet tall

10. **CLIFF** Sarah stands on the ground and sights the top of a steep cliff at a 60° angle of elevation. She then steps back 50 meters and sights the top of the cliff at a 30° angle. If Sarah is 1.8 meters tall, how tall is the cliff to the nearest meter? 45 m

11. **BALLOON** The angle of depression from a hot air balloon to a person on the ground is 36°. When the person steps back 10 feet, the new angle of depression is 25°. If the person is 6 feet tall, how far above the ground is the hot air balloon to the nearest foot? 19 ft

12. **INDIRECT MEASUREMENT** Mr. Dominguez is standing on a 40-foot ocean bluff near his home. He can see his two friends on the beach below. If his line of sight is 6 feet above the ground and the angles of depression to his friends are 34° and 48°, how far apart are his friends to the nearest foot? 27 ft

Example 4

Use trigonometry to find the area of △ABC to the nearest tenth.

13.

11, 54°, 14

A, B

62.3 units²

14.

B, 12

125°

A, 8.5, C

41.8 units²

15.

A, 15

32°

B, 18, C

71.5 units²

16.

B

155°, 10 cm

C, 9 cm, A

19.0 cm²

17.

A, 7 ft

35°

B, 5 ft, C

10.0 ft²

18.

B, 9 yd

46°

C, 11 yd, A

35.6 yd²

1 CONCEPTUAL UNDERSTANDING | **2 FLUENCY** | **3 APPLICATION**

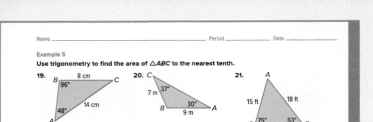

Name _____ Period _____ Date _____

Example 5

Use trigonometry to find the area of △ABC to the nearest tenth.

19.
B 96° 8 cm C
14 cm
48° A
32.9 cm²

20. C
7 m 37°
B 30° A
9 m
29.0 m²

21. A
15 ft 18 ft
C 75° 53° B
106.4 ft²

Mixed Exercises

22. USE ESTIMATION The angle of elevation to an airplane viewed from the air traffic control tower at an airport is 7°. The tower is 200 feet tall, and the pilot reports that the altitude of the airplane is 5127 feet.

   a. Explain how you can use angles of elevation and depression to estimate the distance from the air traffic control tower to the airplane. Sample answer: Because the altitude of the plane and the height of the air traffic control tower are known, I can find the difference between these heights. Then, I can use this difference and the 7° angle of elevation to estimate the distance.

   b. About how far away is the airplane from the air traffic control tower to the nearest foot? 40,429 ft

23. USE ESTIMATION A hiker dropped his backpack over one side of a canyon onto a ledge below. Because of the shape of the cliff, he could not see exactly where it landed. A park ranger is located on the other side of the canyon, at the same height, 113 feet away from the hiker. The ranger sights the backpack at an angle of depression of 32°.

   a. Explain how you can use angles of elevation and depression to estimate the distance that the backpack fell. Sample answer: Because the horizontal distance between the hiker and the park ranger is known, I can use the 32° angle of depression to estimate the distance that the backpack fell.

   b. About how far down did the backpack fall to the nearest foot? 71 ft

24. USE A MODEL Jermaine and John are standing 10 meters apart watching a helicopter hover above the ground.

   a. Find two different expressions that can be used to find *h*, the height of the helicopter. $h = x \tan 55°$; $h = (x + 10) \tan 48°$

   b. Equate the two expressions you found for part **a** to solve for *x*. Round your answer to the nearest hundredth. 34.98 m

   c. How high above the ground is the helicopter? Round your answer to the nearest hundredth. 49.95 m

Jermaine 10 m John x

Lesson 9-6 • Applying Trigonometry **547**

25. USE A SOURCE Go online to research the Sandia Peak Tramway in New Mexico. If you were to stand at the top terminal of Sandia Peak Tramway and look at the base of the second tower along the tramway route, what would be the angle of depression for your line of sight? Round your answer to the nearest tenth of a degree. 12.2°

26. REGULARITY A geologist wants to determine the height of a rock formation. She stands *d* meters from the formation and sights the top of the formation at an angle of *x*°, as shown. The geologist's height is 1.8 m. Write a general formula that the geologist can use to find the height *h* of the rock formation if she knows the values of *d* and *x*. $h = 1.8 + d \tan x°$

1.8 m d

Find the area of △ABC to the nearest tenth.

27. $m\angle A = 20°$, $c = 4$ cm, $b = 7$ cm
4.8 cm²

28. $m\angle C = 55°$, $a = 10$ m, $b = 15$ m
61.4 m²

29. $a = 5.6$ ft, $c = 3.7$ ft, $m\angle A = 37°$, $m\angle C = 24°$
9.1 ft²

30. $a = 6.3$ in., $c = 7$ in., $m\angle A = 42°$, $m\angle C = 49°$
22.0 in²

31. THEATER Albert is helping to build the set for a play. One piece of scenery is a large triangle that will be constructed out of wood and be painted to represent a mountain. Albert would like to know the area of the piece of scenery so that he can buy the right amount of paint. What is the area of this triangle? Round your answer to the nearest tenth of a foot. 22.4 ft²

8 ft
34°
10 ft

Higher-Order Thinking Skills

32. FIND THE ERROR Terrence and Rodrigo are trying to determine the relationship between angles of elevation and depression. Terrence says that if you are looking up at someone with an angle of elevation of 35°, then they are looking down at you with an angle of depression of 55°, which is the complement of 35°. Rodrigo disagrees and says that the other person would be looking down at you with an angle of depression equal to your angle of elevation or 35°. Who is correct? Explain your reasoning. See margin.

33. CREATE A classmate finds the angle of elevation of an object, but she is trying to find the angle of depression. Write a question to help her solve the problem. Sample answer: What is the relationship between the angle of elevation and the angle of depression?

34. ANALYZE Classify the statement below as *true* or *false*. Explain your reasoning. See margin.

> As a person moves closer to an object he or she is sighting, the angle of elevation increases.

35. PERSEVERE Find the value of *x*. Round to the nearest tenth. 7.8

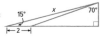

15° x 70°
2

36. WRITE Describe a way that you can estimate the height of an object without using trigonometry. Explain your reasoning. See margin.

Answers

32. Rodrigo; sample answer: Because your horizontal line of site is parallel to the other person's horizontal line of sight, the angles of elevation and depression are congruent according to the Alternate Interior Angles Theorem.

34. True; sample answer: As a person moves closer to an object, the horizontal distance decreases, but the height of the object is constant. The tangent ratio will increase, and therefore the measure of the angle also increases.

36. Sample answer: If you sight something with a 45° angle of elevation, you do not have to use trigonometry to determine the height of the object. Because the legs of a 45°-45°-90° are congruent, the height of the object will be the same as your horizontal distance from the object.

The Law of Sines

LESSON GOAL

Students solve problems using the Law of Sines.

1 LAUNCH

Launch the lesson with a **Warm Up** and an introduction.

2 EXPLORE AND DEVELOP

Explore: Trigonometric Ratios in Nonright Triangles

Develop:

The Law of Sines
- The Law of Sines (AAS)
- The Law of Sines (ASA)
- Indirect Measurement with the Law of Sines

The Ambiguous Case
- The Ambiguous Case with One Solution
- The Ambiguous Case with No Solution
- The Ambiguous Case with More than One Solution

You may want your students to complete the **Checks** online.

3 REFLECT AND PRACTICE

Exit Ticket

Practice

DIFFERENTIATE

View reports of student progress on the **Checks** after each example.

Resources	AL	OL	BL	ELL
Remediation: Solving Proportions	●	●		●
Extension: Trigonometric Identities		●	●	●

Language Development Handbook

Assign page 64 of the *Language Development Handbook* to help your students build mathematical language related to solving problems using the Law of Sines.

ELL You can use the tips and suggestions on page T64 of the handbook to support students who are building English proficiency.

Suggested Pacing

90 min	**0.5 day**
45 min	**1 day**

Focus

Domain: Geometry

Standards for Mathematical Content:

G.SRT.10 Prove the Laws of Sines and Cosines and use them to solve problems.

G.SRT.11 Understand and apply the Law of Sines and the Law of Cosines to find unknown measurements in right and non-right triangles.

Standards for Mathematical Practice:

3 Construct viable arguments and critique the reasoning of others.

4 Model with mathematics.

5 Use appropriate tools strategically.

Coherence

Vertical Alignment

Previous
Students applied trigonometry to real-world situations and to triangle area.
G.SRT.8, G.SRT.9

Now
Students solve problems using the Law of Sines.
G.SRT.10, G.SRT.11

Next
Students will solve problems using the Law of Cosines.
G.SRT.10, G.SRT.11

Rigor

The Three Pillars of Rigor

1 CONCEPTUAL UNDERSTANDING	2 FLUENCY	3 APPLICATION

Conceptual Bridge In this lesson, students develop an understanding of the Law of Sines. They build fluency and apply their understanding by using the Law of Sines to solve real-world problems.

Mathematical Background

The Law of Sines is used to solve triangles that are not right triangles given the measures of two angles and any side of a triangle or the measures of two sides and an angle opposite one of these sides.

Interactive Presentation

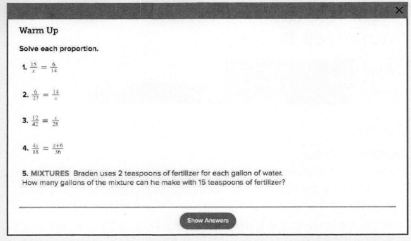

Warm Up

Solve each proportion.

1. $\frac{15}{x} = \frac{6}{14}$

2. $\frac{6}{27} = \frac{14}{x}$

3. $\frac{12}{42} = \frac{x}{28}$

4. $\frac{4x}{18} = \frac{x+6}{36}$

5. **MIXTURES** Braden uses 2 teaspoons of fertilizer for each gallon of water. How many gallons of the mixture can he make with 15 teaspoons of fertilizer?

Show Answers

Warm Up

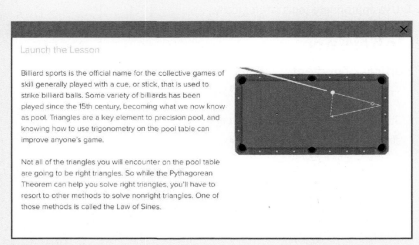

Launch the Lesson

Billiard sports is the official name for the collective games of skill generally played with a cue, or stick, that is used to strike billiard balls. Some variety of billiards has been played since the 15th century, becoming what we now know as pool. Triangles are a key element to precision pool, and knowing how to use trigonometry on the pool table can improve anyone's game.

Not all of the triangles you will encounter on the pool table are going to be right triangles. So while the Pythagorean Theorem can help you solve right triangles, you'll have to resort to other methods to solve nonright triangles. One of those methods is called the Law of Sines.

Launch the Lesson

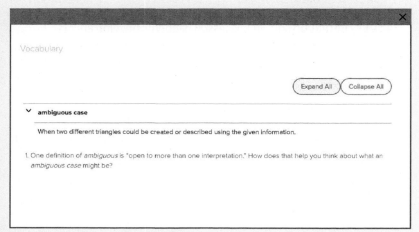

Vocabulary

Expand All   Collapse All

⌄ **ambiguous case**

When two different triangles could be created or described using the given information.

1. One definition of *ambiguous* is "open to more than one interpretation." How does that help you think about what an *ambiguous case* might be?

Today's Vocabulary

Warm Up

Prerequisite Skills

The Warm Up exercises address the following prerequisite skill for this lesson:

- solving proportions

Answers:

1. 35
2. 63
3. 8
4. $\frac{6}{7}$
5. 7.5 gal

Launch the Lesson

MP **Teaching the Mathematical Practices**

4 Apply Mathematics In this Launch the Lesson, students can see a real-world application of the Law of Sines.

Go Online to find additional teaching notes and questions to promote classroom discourse.

Today's Standards

Tell students that they will be addressing these content and practice standards in this lesson. You may wish to have a student volunteer read aloud *How can I meet these standards?* and *How can I use these practices?* and connect these to the standards.

See the Interactive Presentation for I Can statements that align with the standards covered in this lesson.

Today's Vocabulary

Tell students that they will be using this vocabulary term in this lesson. You can expand the row if you wish to share the definition. Then, discuss the question below with the class.

Explore Trigonometric Ratios in Nonright Triangles

Objective
Students use dynamic geometry software to make conjectures about trigonometric ratios in nonright triangles.

 Teaching the Mathematical Practices

3 Reason Inductively In this Explore, students will use inductive reasoning to make plausible arguments.

Ideas for Use

Recommended Use Present the Inquiry Question, or have a student volunteer read it aloud. Have students work in pairs to complete the Explore activity on their devices. Pairs should discuss each of the questions. Monitor student progress during the activity. Upon completion of the Explore activity, have student volunteers share their responses to the Inquiry Question.

What if my students don't have devices? You may choose to project the activity on a whiteboard. A printable worksheet for each Explore is available online. You may choose to print the worksheet so that individuals or pairs of students can use it to record their observations.

Summary of the Activity

Students will complete guiding exercises throughout the Explore activity. Students first use dynamic geometry software to change parts of a nonright triangle and observe the changes in side lengths, angle measures, and the sine ratios of the angle measures. Then students complete a table of these measures and the ratios of the sine of each angle and the length of its opposite side. Students complete guiding exercises which include completing a similar table for a different nonright triangle and writing a conjecture based on these ratios. Then, students will answer the Inquiry Question.

(continued on the next page)

Interactive Presentation

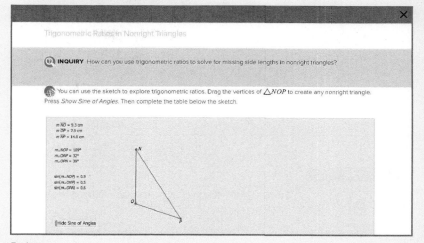

Explore

WEB SKETCHPAD

Students use a sketch to explore trigonometry in nonright triangles.

1 CONCEPTUAL UNDERSTANDING | 2 FLUENCY | 3 APPLICATION

Interactive Presentation

Explore

TYPE

Students respond to the Inquiry Question and can view a sample answer.

Explore Trigonometric Ratios in Nonright Triangles (*continued*)

Teaching the Mathematical Practices

3 Construct Arguments In the Explore, students will use stated assumptions, definitions, and previously established results to make a conjecture.

Questions

Have students complete the Explore activity.

Ask:

• Does dragging the vertices to make an obtuse triangle prevent you from getting sine measurements? Sample answer: No, you can drag the vertices to any locations and the sine of each angle is still shown.

• Why do you think we don't use the Law of Sines when one angle is 90°? Use the sketch to check your reasoning. Sample answer: By definition the sine ratio is used for right triangles. Using the sketch, you can see that the sine of a 90° angle is 1.

Inquiry

How can you use a trigonometric ratio to solve for missing side lengths in nonright triangles? Sample answer: The ratios between the angles of a nonright triangle and their opposite sides are equivalent for all three pairs of angles and sides.

Go Online to find additional teaching notes and sample answers for the guiding exercises.

| 1 CONCEPTUAL UNDERSTANDING | 2 FLUENCY | 3 APPLICATION |

Learn The Law of Sines

Objective

Students understand and apply the Law of Sines to find unknown measurements in right and nonright triangles.

 Teaching the Mathematical Practices

> **3 Analyze Cases** The Concept Check guides students to examine the cases of uses of the Law of Sines. Encourage students to familiarize themselves with all of the cases.

About the Key Concept

The Law of Sines is one of two formulas that extend trigonometry to nonright triangles. The Law of Sines also works for right triangles, so it is useful for any type of triangle. This includes obtuse triangles. The definitions of the trigonometric ratios earlier in the module were only for acute angles. The sine value of obtuse angles will be defined in Postulate 9.1 in the next Learn. To extend the sine ratio to right angles, note that as acute angles get closer to 90°, their sine values get closer to 1, so sin 90° = 1.

Example 1 The Law of Sines (AAS)

 Teaching the Mathematical Practices

> **3 Construct Arguments** In this example, students will use stated assumptions, definitions, and previously established results to construct an argument.

Questions for Mathematical Discourse

AL In your own words, what is the Law of Sines? Sample answer: A method of using trigonometry in nonright triangles.

OL What is AC? approximately 10.6

BL If $BC = 25$, what is x? approximately 16.9

Go Online

- Find additional teaching notes.
- View performance reports of the Checks.
- Assign or present an Extra Example.

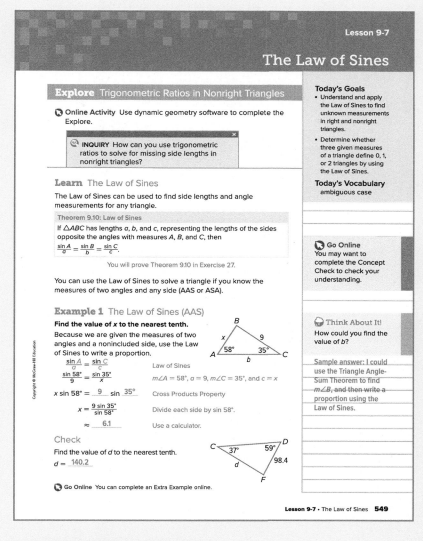

Lesson 9-7

The Law of Sines

Explore Trigonometric Ratios in Nonright Triangles

Online Activity Use dynamic geometry software to complete the Explore.

> **INQUIRY** How can you use trigonometric ratios to solve for missing side lengths in nonright triangles?

Learn The Law of Sines

The Law of Sines can be used to find side lengths and angle measurements for any triangle.

Theorem 9.10: Law of Sines

If △ABC has lengths a, b, and c, representing the lengths of the sides opposite the angles with measures A, B, and C, then
$$\frac{\sin A}{a} = \frac{\sin B}{b} = \frac{\sin C}{c}$$

You will prove Theorem 9.10 in Exercise 27.

You can use the Law of Sines to solve a triangle if you know the measures of two angles and any side (AAS or ASA).

Example 1 The Law of Sines (AAS)

Find the value of x to the nearest tenth.

Because we are given the measures of two angles and a nonincluded side, use the Law of Sines to write a proportion.

$$\frac{\sin A}{a} = \frac{\sin C}{c} \qquad \text{Law of Sines}$$

$$\frac{\sin 58°}{9} = \frac{\sin 35°}{x} \qquad m\angle A = 58°, a = 9, m\angle C = 35°, \text{ and } c = x$$

$$x \sin 58° = 9 \sin 35° \qquad \text{Cross Products Property}$$

$$x = \frac{9 \sin 35°}{\sin 58°} \qquad \text{Divide each side by sin 58°.}$$

$$\approx 6.1 \qquad \text{Use a calculator.}$$

Check

Find the value of d to the nearest tenth.

$$d = 140.2$$

Go Online You can complete an Extra Example online.

Today's Goals
- Understand and apply the Law of Sines to find unknown measurements in right and nonright triangles.
- Determine whether three given measures of a triangle define 0, 1, or 2 triangles by using the Law of Sines.

Today's Vocabulary
ambiguous case

Go Online
You may want to complete the Concept Check to check your understanding.

Think About It!
How could you find the value of b?

Sample answer: I could use the Triangle Angle-Sum Theorem to find $m\angle B$, and then write a proportion using the Law of Sines.

Lesson 9-7 · The Law of Sines **549**

Interactive Presentation

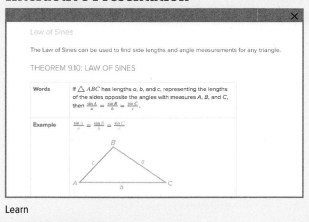

Law of Sines

The Law of Sines can be used to find side lengths and angle measurements for any triangle.

THEOREM 9.10: LAW OF SINES

| Words | If △ABC has lengths a, b, and c, representing the lengths of the sides opposite the angles with measures A, B, and C, then $\frac{\sin A}{a} = \frac{\sin B}{b} = \frac{\sin C}{c}$. |
| Example | $\frac{\sin A}{a} = \frac{\sin B}{b} = \frac{\sin C}{c}$ |

Learn

TYPE

Students enter values to find the side length using the Law of Sines.

1 CONCEPTUAL UNDERSTANDING | 2 FLUENCY | 3 APPLICATION

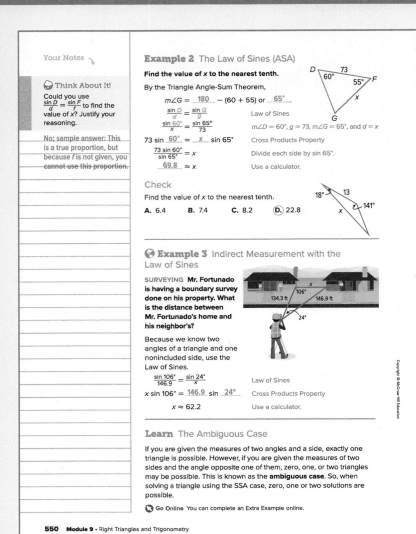

Example 2 The Law of Sines (ASA)

MP Teaching the Mathematical Practices

1 Understand the Approaches of Others Mathematically proficient students can explain the methods used to solve a problem. The Think About It! feature asks students to justify their reasoning.

Questions for Mathematical Discourse

AL Does the ratio change if we are given $m\angle G$ instead of $m\angle F$? No, you could just use the ratio without having to find $m\angle G$ first.

OL What is DG? about 66

BL If $m\angle D = 55$, what is x? about 63.6

DIFFERENTIATE

Reteaching Activity **AL** **ELL**

Interpersonal Learners Organize students into groups of three students to work through exercises. One group member can select the exercise. The second member sets up the equation for the Law of Sines and fills in the values. The third member uses a calculator to solve the problem. Group members rotate tasks so each member participates in each responsibility.

🌐 **Example 3** Indirect Measurement with the Law of Sines

MP Teaching the Mathematical Practices

4 Apply Mathematics In this example, students apply what they have learned about the Law of Sines to solving a real-world problem.

Questions for Mathematical Discourse

AL Why is it a good idea to use the Law of Sines to solve this problem? The triangle is nonright.

OL Can you solve this problem using the Law of Sines without knowing the measure of the 106° angle? Explain. No; sample answer: If you did not have that angle measure, you would not know the measure of an angle and its opposite side, which you need in order to use the Law of Sines.

BL If you couldn't remember the Law of Sines, could you still solve this problem? Explain. Yes; sample answer: You can draw the altitude to the side of length x. This creates two right triangles that you can solve to find the length of x.

Interactive Presentation

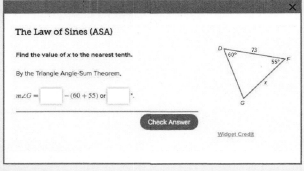

Example 2

TAP

Students tap to reveal steps in the solution.

CHECK

Students complete the Check online to determine whether they are ready to move on.

1 CONCEPTUAL UNDERSTANDING | **2 FLUENCY** | 3 APPLICATION

DIFFERENTIATE

Reteaching Activity **AL**
Kinesthetic Learners Have students draw triangles and measure two angles and the included side. Have them trade triangles with another student. Have the other student use the Law of Sines to find the measures of the remaining parts of the triangle.

Learn The Ambiguous Case

Objective
Students determine whether three given measures of a triangle define 0, 1, or 2 triangles by using the Law of Sines.

MP Teaching the Mathematical Practices
7 Use Structure Help students to explore the structure of the ambiguous case in this Learn.

What Students Are Learning
The ambiguous case occurs in the Law of Sines when a problem gives two sides of a triangle and a nonincluded angle. This fits the pattern SSA, which is not one of the triangle congruence theorems, so the given information fits 0, 1, or 2 triangles. In the case with 2 possible triangles, the side adjacent to the given angle is opposite an angle that could have an acute measure or an obtuse measure. The two possible measures are supplementary, so they have the same sine value. The inverse sine function cannot determine the measure of that angle in this case.

Common Misconception
Students may have difficulty remembering which case they are in, especially for acute angles. Encourage them to draw diagrams of the possible cases to help them remember how to determine which case they are in.

Example 4 The Ambiguous Case with One Solution

MP Teaching the Mathematical Practices
3 Construct Arguments In this example, students will use stated assumptions, definitions, and previously established results to construct an argument.

Questions for Mathematical Discourse

AL Which angle corresponds to ∠A in this problem? ∠N

OL Why don't you need to find h in this problem? Sample answer: Because n > p, you already know that there will be one solution without finding h.

BL If n is changed to length 2.1, is there still only one solution? Explain. Yes; h = 4 sin 32° = 2.1, so n = h.

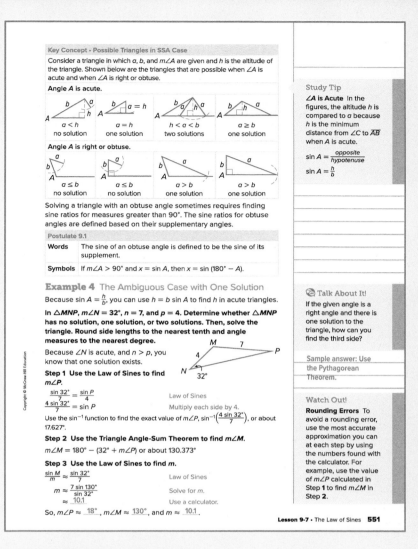

Interactive Presentation

Learn

TAP

Students tap to see the various cases.

1 CONCEPTUAL UNDERSTANDING   **2 FLUENCY**   3 APPLICATION

Left Page

Think About It!

If ∠R were acute and r < s, how could you find the number of possible solutions?

Sample answer: I would have to find the length of altitude h and compare it to r.

Example 5 The Ambiguous Case with No Solution

In △RST, m∠R = 95°, r = 10, and s = 12. Determine whether △RST has no solution, one solution, or two solutions. Then, solve the triangle. Round side lengths to the nearest tenth and angle measures to the nearest degree.

Because ∠R is obtuse, and 10 < 12, there is __no solution__.

Example 6 The Ambiguous Case with More than One Solution

In △ABC, m∠A = 32°, a = 15, and b = 18. Determine whether △ABC has no solution, one solution, or two solutions. Then, solve the triangle. Round side lengths to the nearest tenth and angle measures to the nearest degree.

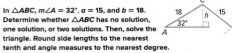

Because ∠A is acute, and 15 < 18, find h and compare it to a.

$b \sin A = 18 \sin 32°$	$b = 18$ and $m\angle A = 32°$
$\approx \underline{9.5}$	Use a calculator.

Because 9.5 < 15 < 18, or h < a < b, there are __two__ solutions.

∠B is acute.		∠B is obtuse.	
Find m∠B.		**Find m∠B.**	
$\frac{\sin B}{18} = \frac{\sin 32°}{15}$	Law of Sines	Find an obtuse angle B for which sin B ≈ 0.6359.	
$\sin B = \frac{18 \sin 32°}{15}$	Solve for sin B.	$m\angle B \approx 180° - 39°$	Postulate 9.1
$\sin B \approx 0.6359$	Use a calculator.	or 141°	
$B \approx 39.487$	Use the $\sin^{-1}$ function.		
Find m∠C.		**Find m∠C.**	
$m\angle C \approx 180 - (32 + B)$ or 109°.		$m\angle C \approx 180 - (32 + 141)$ or 7°.	
Find c.		**Find c.**	
$\frac{\sin C}{c} = \frac{\sin 32°}{15}$	Law of Sines	$\frac{\sin C}{c} = \frac{\sin 32°}{15}$	Law of Sines
$c = \frac{15 \sin 109°}{\sin 32°}$	Solve for c.	$c = \frac{15 \sin 7°}{\sin 32°}$	Solve for c.
$c \approx 26.8$	Use a calculator.	$c \approx 3.4$	Use a calculator.

So, one solution is m∠B ≈ 39°, m∠C ≈ 109°, and c ≈ 26.8, and another solution is m∠B ≈ 141°, m∠C ≈ 7°, and c ≈ 3.4.

Go Online You can complete an Extra Example online.

Interactive Presentation

The Ambiguous Case with More than One Solution

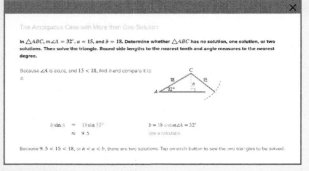

Example 6

TAP

Students tap to reveal parts of the solution.

CHECK

Students complete the Check online to determine whether they are ready to move on.

Right Page

Example 5 The Ambiguous Case with No Solution

Teaching the Mathematical Practices

6 Communicate Precisely Encourage students to routinely write or explain their solution methods. Point out that they should use clear definitions when they discuss their solutions with others.

Questions for Mathematical Discourse

AL What are the possible cases for the given angle? Because ∠R is obtuse, the two cases are one triangle if r > s and no triangle if r ≤ s.

OL How many triangles would there be if r = 12? Explain. None, because r = s.

BL What measures of r would yield one triangle? r > 12

Example 6 The Ambiguous Case with More than One Solution

Teaching the Mathematical Practices

1 Special Cases Work with students to evaluate the two cases shown. Encourage students to familiarize themselves with both cases, and to understand the solution of each one.

Questions for Mathematical Discourse

AL What do we know about the ambiguous case with more than one solution? It happens when the given angle is acute and the measure of the nonadjacent side is between h and the measure of the adjacent side.

OL Does saying that the resulting triangle is obtuse give only one solution? Explain. No; in the first solution ∠C is obtuse, and in the second solution, ∠B is obtuse.

BL What possible range of values contains m∠B? 0 < m∠B < 147°

Exit Ticket

Recommended Use

At the end of class, go online to display the Exit Ticket prompt and ask students to respond using a separate piece of paper. Have students hand you their responses as they leave the room.

Alternate Use

At the end of class, go online to display the Exit Ticket prompt and ask students to respond verbally or by using a mini-whiteboard. Have students hold up their whiteboards so that you can see all student responses. Tap to reveal the answer when most or all students have completed the Exit Ticket.

Practice and Homework

Suggested Assignments

Use the table below to select appropriate exercises.

DOK	Topic	Exercises
1, 2	exercises that mirror the examples	1–26
2	exercises that use a variety of skills from this lesson	27–44
3	exercises that emphasize higher-order and critical-thinking skills	45–49

ASSESS AND DIFFERENTIATE

📊 Use the data from the **Checks** to determine whether to provide resources for extension, remediation, or intervention.

IF students score 90% or more on the Checks, **BL**
THEN assign:

- Practice, Exercises 1–43 odd, 45–49
- Extension: Trigonometric Identities
- **ALEKS** Laws of Sines and Cosines

IF students score 66%–89% on the Checks, **OL**
THEN assign:

- Practice, Exercises 1–49 odd
- Remediation, Review Resources: Solving Proportions
- Personal Tutors
- Extra Examples 1–6
- **ALEKS** Proportions

IF students score 65% or less on the Checks, **AL**
THEN assign:

- Practice, Exercises 1–25 odd
- Remediation, Review Resources: Solving Proportions
- *Quick Review Math Handbook:* The Law of Sines
- **ALEKS** Proportions

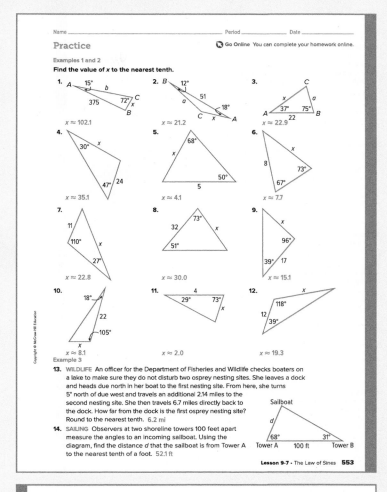

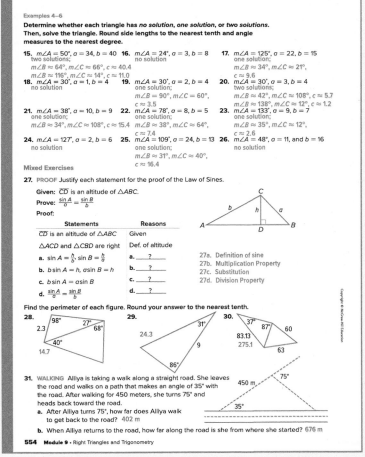

1 CONCEPTUAL UNDERSTANDING   2 FLUENCY   3 APPLICATION

Name _____ Period _____ Date _____

32. CAMERAS A security camera is located on top of a building at a certain distance from the sidewalk. The camera revolves counterclockwise at a steady rate of one revolution per minute. At one point in the revolution it directly faces a point on the sidewalk that is 20 meters from the camera. Four seconds later, it directly faces a point 10 meters down the sidewalk.

  a. How many degrees does the camera rotate in 4 seconds? 24°

  b. To the nearest tenth of a meter, how far is the security camera from the sidewalk? 19.6 m

33. FISHING A fishing pole is resting against the railing of a boat making an angle of 22° with the deck. The fishing pole is 5 feet long, and the hook hangs 3 feet from the tip of the pole. The movement of the boat causes the hook to sway back and forth. Determine which angles the fishing line must make with the pole in order for the hook to be level with the boat's deck. 119.4° or 16.6°

34. REASONING Angle A is obtuse. How many triangles can be formed if $a = b$? if $a < b$? if $a > b$? 0; 0; 1

REGULARITY Determine whether the given measures define 0, 1, or 2 triangles. Justify your answers. 35–43. See margin for justifications.

35. $a = 14, b = 16, m\angle A = 55°$ 2   **36.** $a = 7, b = 11, m\angle A = 68°$ 0   **37.** $a = 22, b = 25, m\angle A = 39°$ 2

38. $a = 13, b = 12, m\angle A = 81°$ 1   **39.** $a = 10, b = 10, m\angle A = 45°$ 1   **40.** $a = 17, b = 15, m\angle A = 128°$ 1

41. $a = 13, b = 17, m\angle A = 52°$ 0   **42.** $a = 5, b = 9, c = 6$ 1   **43.** $a = 10, b = 15, m\angle A = 33°$ 2

44. TOWERS Cell towers A, B, and C form a triangular region in one of the suburban districts of Fairfield County. Towers A and B are 8 miles apart. The angle formed at tower A is 112°, and the angle formed at tower B is 40°. How far apart are towers B and C? about 15.8 mi

---

Answers

35. $b \sin A = 16 \sin 55°$, or about 13.1; Because $\angle A$ is acute, $14 < 16$, and $14 > 13.1$, the measures define 2 triangles.

36. $b \sin A = 11 \sin 68°$ or about 10.2; Because $\angle A$ is acute and $7 < 10.2$, the measures define 0 triangles.

37. $b \sin A = 25 \sin 39°$ or about 15.7; Because $\angle A$ is acute, $22 < 25$, and $22 > 15.7$, the measures define 2 triangles.

38. Because $\angle A$ is acute and $13 > 12$, the measures define 1 triangle.

39. Because $\angle A$ is acute and $a = b = 10$, the measures define 1 triangle.

40. Because $\angle A$ is obtuse and $17 > 15$, the measures define 1 triangle.

41. $b \sin A = 17 \sin 52°$ or about 13.4; Because $\angle A$ is acute and $13 < 13.4$, the measures define 0 triangles.

42. Three side measures (SSS) determine exactly 1 triangle.

43. $b \sin A = 15 \sin 33°$ or about 8.2; Because $\angle A$ is acute, $10 < 15$, and $10 > 8.2$, the measures define 2 triangles.

🧠 Higher-Order Thinking Skills

45. FIND THE ERROR In $\triangle RST$, $m\angle R = 56°$, $r = 24$, and $t = 12$. Cameron and Gabriela are using the Law of Sines to find $m\angle T$. Who is correct? Explain your reasoning. Cameron; sample answer: $\angle R$ is acute and $r > t$, so there is one solution.

Cameron	Gabriela
$\frac{\sin T}{12} = \frac{\sin 56°}{24}$ $\sin T = 0.4145$ $m\angle T = 24.5$	Because $r > t$, there is no solution.

46. WRITE What two methods can be used to find the value of x in $\triangle ABC$? Write two equations using the different methods and explain your reasoning. $\sin 35° = \frac{x}{10}$ and $\frac{\sin 35°}{x} = \frac{\sin 90°}{10}$; Sample answer: Because $\triangle ABC$ is a right triangle, the sine ratio can be used to find the value of x. The Law of Sines can also be used because a side length and two angle measures are given.

47. PERSEVERE Find both solutions for $\triangle ABC$ if $a = 15$, $b = 21$, and $m\angle A = 42°$. Round angle measures to the nearest degree and side measures to the nearest tenth.

  a. For solution 1, assume that $\angle B$ is acute, and use the Law of Sines to find $m\angle B$. Then find $m\angle C$. Finally, use the Law of Sines again to find the value of c. $m\angle B \approx 70°$, $m\angle C \approx 68°$, $c \approx 20.9$

  b. For solution 2, assume that $\angle B$ is obtuse. Let this obtuse angle be $\angle B'$. Use $m\angle B$ you found in solution 1 and the diagram shown to find $m\angle B'$. Then find $m\angle C$. Finally, use the Law of Sines to find the value of c. $m\angle B \approx 110°$, $m\angle C \approx 28°$, $c \approx 10.4$

48. ANALYZE Determine whether the statement below is *true* or *false*. Explain your reasoning.

  The Law of Sines can always be used to solve a triangle if the measures of two sides and their included angle are known.

False; sample answer: The Law of Sines can only be used when given AAS, ASA, and SSA. If the measures of two sides and their included angle are known, then the SAS case is being considered.

49. CREATE Give measures for a, b, and an acute $\angle A$ that define the given number of triangles. Sample answers given.

  a. 0 triangles   **b.** exactly one triangle   **c.** two triangles
    $a = 22, b = 25, m\angle A = 70°$ $a = 25, b = 22, m\angle A = 95°$ $a = 22, b = 30, m\angle A = 43°$

The Law of Cosines

LESSON GOAL

Students solve problems using the Law of Cosines.

1 LAUNCH

 Launch the lesson with a **Warm Up** and an introduction.

2 EXPLORE AND DEVELOP

 Explore: Trigonometric Relationships in Nonright Triangles

 Develop:

The Law of Cosines
- The Law of Cosines (SAS)
- The Law of Cosines (SSS)
- Indirect Measurement with the Law of Cosines
- Solve a Nonright Triangle with the Law of Cosines
- Solve a Right Triangle with the Law of Cosines

You may want your students to complete the **Checks** online.

3 REFLECT AND PRACTICE

Exit Ticket

Practice

DIFFERENTIATE

View reports of student progress on the **Checks** after each example.

Resources	AL	OL	BL	ELL
Remediation: Trigonometry	●	●		●
Extension: Law of Tangents		●	●	●

Language Development Handbook

Assign page 65 of the *Language Development Handbook* to help your students build mathematical language related to solving problems using the Law of Cosines.

ELL You can use the tips and suggestions on page T65 of the handbook to support students who are building English proficiency.

Suggested Pacing

90 min	**0.5 day**
45 min	**1 day**

Focus

Domain: Geometry

Standards for Mathematical Content:

G.SRT.10 Prove the Laws of Sines and Cosines and use them to solve problems.

G.SRT.11 Understand and apply the Law of Sines and the Law of Cosines to find unknown measurements in right and non-right triangles.

Standards for Mathematical Practice:

3 Construct viable arguments and critique the reasoning of others.

6 Attend to precision.

Coherence

Vertical Alignment

Previous
Students solved problems using the Law of Sines.
G.SRT.10, G.SRT.11

Now
Students solve problems using the Law of Cosines.
G.SRT.10, G.SRT.11

Next
Students will extend their understanding of trigonometric ratios to trigonometric functions.
F.TF (Algebra 2)

Rigor

The Three Pillars of Rigor

1 CONCEPTUAL UNDERSTANDING	2 FLUENCY	3 APPLICATION

📖 **Conceptual Bridge** In this lesson, students develop an understanding of the Law of Cosines. They build fluency and apply their understanding by using the Law of Cosines to solve real-world problems.

Mathematical Background

The Law of Cosines is used to solve triangles that are not right triangles. The Law of Cosines is used when the measures of two sides and the included angle or three sides are known.

Interactive Presentation

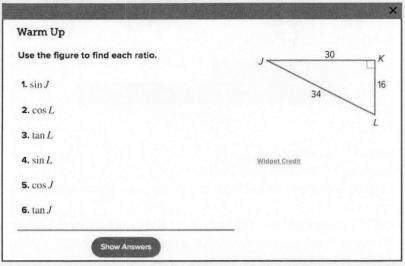

Warm Up

Use the figure to find each ratio.

1. sin J
2. cos L
3. tan L
4. sin L
5. cos J
6. tan J

Widget Credit

Show Answers

Warm Up

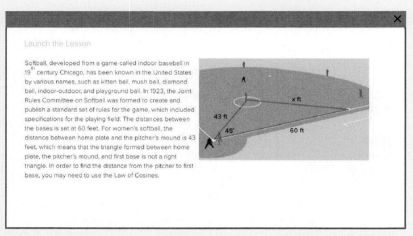

Launch the Lesson

Softball, developed from a game called indoor baseball in 19th century Chicago, has been known in the United States by various names, such as kitten ball, mush ball, diamond ball, indoor-outdoor, and playground ball. In 1923, the Joint Rules Committee on Softball was formed to create and publish a standard set of rules for the game, which included specifications for the playing field. The distances between the bases is set at 60 feet. For women's softball, the distance between home plate and the pitcher's mound is 43 feet, which means that the triangle formed between home plate, the pitcher's mound, and first base is not a right triangle. In order to find the distance from the pitcher to first base, you may need to use the Law of Cosines.

Launch the Lesson

Warm Up

Prerequisite Skills

The Warm Up exercises address the following prerequisite skill for this lesson:

- finding trigonometric ratios

Answers:

1. $\frac{8}{17}$
2. $\frac{8}{17}$
3. $\frac{15}{8}$
4. $\frac{15}{17}$
5. $\frac{15}{17}$
6. $\frac{8}{15}$

Launch the Lesson

MP **Teaching the Mathematical Practices**

4 Apply Mathematics In this Launch the Lesson, students can see a real-world application of the Law of Cosines.

Go Online to find additional teaching notes and questions to promote classroom discourse.

Today's Standards

Tell students that they will be addressing these content and practice standards in this lesson. You may wish to have a student volunteer read aloud *How can I meet these standard?* and *How can I use these practices?* and connect these to the standards.

See the Interactive Presentation for I Can statements that align with the standards covered in this lesson.

Explore Trigonometric Relationships in Nonright Triangles

Objective
Students use the Law of Sines to generate the Law of Cosines.

 Teaching the Mathematical Practices

> **6 Communicate Precisely** Encourage students to routinely write or explain their solution methods. Point out that they should use clear definitions when they discuss their solutions with others.

Ideas for Use

Recommended Use Present the Inquiry Question, or have a student volunteer read it aloud. Have students work in pairs to complete the Explore activity on their devices. Pairs should discuss each of the questions. Monitor student progress during the activity. Upon completion of the Explore activity, have student volunteers share their responses to the Inquiry Question.

What if my students don't have devices? You may choose to project the activity on a whiteboard. A printable worksheet for each Explore is available online. You may choose to print the worksheet so that individuals or pairs of students can use it to record their observations.

Summary of the Activity

Students will complete guiding exercises throughout the Explore activity. Students begin by noting that if they have the lengths of the three sides of a triangle, they cannot determine the measures of the angles using the Law of Sines. Students then complete a series of guiding exercises to derive the Law of Cosines. The first step is drawing a diagram of a triangle and an altitude that falls within the triangle. The students are guided to give variable names to the various measures. They then use the Pythagorean Theorem to write two equations from the two right triangles formed by the altitude. They solve both equations for the square of the altitude and substitute one equation into the other. The students then eliminate all variables except the measures of the triangle using algebra and the definition of cosine for right triangles. The result is the Law of Cosines. Then, students will answer the Inquiry Question.

(continued on the next page)

Interactive Presentation

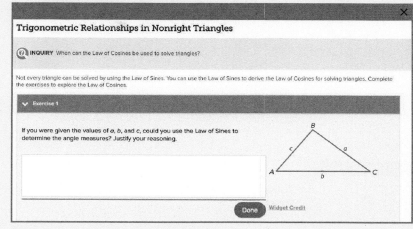

Explore

TYPE

Students type to complete the guiding exercises.

G.SRT.10

Interactive Presentation

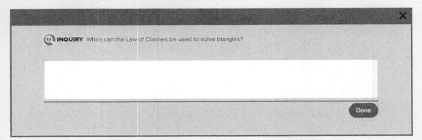

INQUIRY When can the Law of Cosines be used to solve triangles?

Done

Explore

TYPE

Students respond to the Inquiry Question and can view a sample answer.

Explore Trigonometric Relationships in Nonright Triangles (*continued*)

MP Teaching the Mathematical Practices

3 Construct Arguments In Example 1, students will use stated assumptions, definitions, and previously established results to construct an argument.

Questions

Have students complete the Explore activity.

Ask:

- Why does it help to create two right triangles in the non-right triangle with given side lengths? Sample answer: We know a relationship between the sides of right triangles because of the Pythagorean Theorem. If we are given side lengths in any triangle, we can create right triangles to discover the relationship between these side lengths as well.

- What happens to $c^2 = a^2 + b^2 - 2ab \cos C$ when C is a right angle? Sample answer: Using a calculator, find that $\cos 90° = 0$. So, the final term in the Law of Cosines becomes 0, and you are left with the Pythagorean Theorem.

Inquiry

When can the Law of Cosines be used to solve triangles? Sample answer: The Law of Cosines can be used to find missing measures in nonright triangles when you know three side measures or when you cannot use the Law of Sines.

Go Online to find additional teaching notes and sample answers for the guiding exercises.

1 CONCEPTUAL UNDERSTANDING | 2 FLUENCY | 3 APPLICATION

Learn Law of Cosines

Objective

Students understand and apply the Law of Cosines to find unknown measurements in right and nonright triangles.

Ⓜ Teaching the Mathematical Practices

3 Construct Arguments In this Learn, students will use stated assumptions, definitions, and previously established results to construct an argument.

Things to Remember

The Law of Cosines is an extension of the Pythagorean Theorem to nonright triangles. In a right triangle, if the angle used in the Law of Cosines is the right angle of the triangle, $\cos 90° = 0$, the cosine term in the equation is 0. The remaining parts of the equation in the Law of Cosines match the Pythagorean Theorem.

Common Misconception

Students may have difficulty determining when they should use the Law of Cosines rather than the Law of Sines. Remind them that they used the Law of Sines given ASA or AAS information about a triangle. They should use the Law of Cosines when they are given SAS or SSS information about a triangle.

Example 1 The Law of Cosines (SAS)

Ⓜ Teaching the Mathematical Practices

6 Communicate Precisely Encourage students to routinely write or explain their solution methods. Point out that they should use clear definitions when they discuss their solutions with others.

Questions for Mathematical Discourse

AL How would you describe the relationship between the three given triangle measures? The given measures are for two sides and the included angle.

OL If $m\angle C = 35°$, what is x? about 2.7

BL After finding x, can we find the other angle measures? Explain.
Yes; sample answer: We can use the Law of Sines to find one of the other angles, then the Triangle Angle-Sum Theorem to find the other.

Ⓖ Go Online

- Find additional teaching notes.
- View performance reports of the Checks.
- Assign or present an Extra Example.

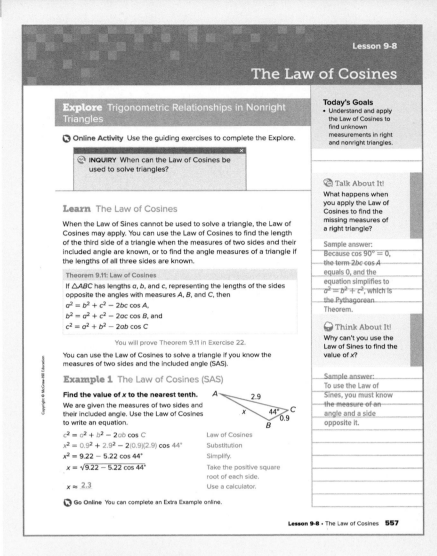

Lesson 9-8

The Law of Cosines

Today's Goals
- Understand and apply the Law of Cosines to find unknown measurements in right and nonright triangles.

Explore Trigonometric Relationships in Nonright Triangles

Ⓞ **Online Activity** Use the guiding exercises to complete the Explore.

Ⓠ INQUIRY When can the Law of Cosines be used to solve triangles?

Learn The Law of Cosines

When the Law of Sines cannot be used to solve a triangle, the Law of Cosines may apply. You can use the Law of Cosines to find the length of the third side of a triangle when the measures of two sides and their included angle are known, or to find the angle measures of a triangle if the lengths of all three sides are known.

Theorem 9.11: Law of Cosines
If $\triangle ABC$ has lengths a, b, and c, representing the lengths of the sides opposite the angles with measures A, B, and C, then
$a^2 = b^2 + c^2 - 2bc \cos A$,
$b^2 = a^2 + c^2 - 2ac \cos B$, and
$c^2 = a^2 + b^2 - 2ab \cos C$

You will prove Theorem 9.11 in Exercise 22.

You can use the Law of Cosines to solve a triangle if you know the measures of two sides and the included angle (SAS).

Example 1 The Law of Cosines (SAS)

Find the value of x to the nearest tenth.
We are given the measures of two sides and their included angle. Use the Law of Cosines to write an equation.

$c^2 = a^2 + b^2 - 2ab \cos C$ — Law of Cosines
$x^2 = 0.9^2 + 2.9^2 - 2(0.9)(2.9) \cos 44°$ — Substitution
$x^2 = 9.22 - 5.22 \cos 44°$ — Simplify.
$x = \sqrt{9.22 - 5.22 \cos 44°}$ — Take the positive square root of each side.
$x \approx 2.3$ — Use a calculator.

Ⓖ **Go Online** You can complete an Extra Example online.

Ⓐ Talk About It!
What happens when you apply the Law of Cosines to find the missing measures of a right triangle?

Sample answer: Because $\cos 90° = 0$, the term $2bc \cos A$ equals 0, and the equation simplifies to $a^2 = b^2 + c^2$, which is the Pythagorean Theorem.

Ⓣ Think About It!
Why can't you use the Law of Sines to find the value of x?

Sample answer: To use the Law of Sines, you must know the measure of an angle and a side opposite it.

Lesson 9-8 • The Law of Cosines 557

Interactive Presentation

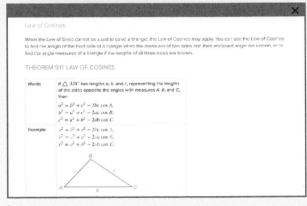

Learn

TYPE

Students answer a question to show they understand the Law of Cosines.

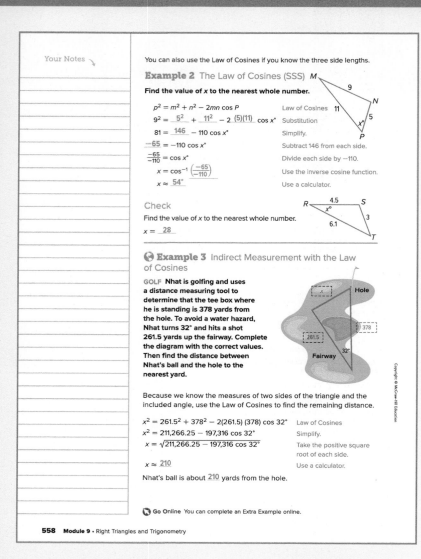

Your Notes

You can also use the Law of Cosines if you know the three side lengths.

Example 2 The Law of Cosines (SSS) M

Find the value of x to the nearest whole number.

$$p^2 = m^2 + n^2 - 2mn \cos P \qquad \text{Law of Cosines}$$
$$9^2 = \underline{5}^2 + \underline{11}^2 - 2\,\underline{(5)(11)}\cos x° \qquad \text{Substitution}$$
$$81 = \underline{146} - 110 \cos x° \qquad \text{Simplify.}$$
$$\underline{-65} = -110 \cos x° \qquad \text{Subtract 146 from each side.}$$
$$\frac{-65}{-110} = \cos x° \qquad \text{Divide each side by } -110.$$
$$x = \cos^{-1}\left(\frac{-65}{-110}\right) \qquad \text{Use the inverse cosine function.}$$
$$x \approx \underline{54}° \qquad \text{Use a calculator.}$$

Check

Find the value of x to the nearest whole number.

$$x = \underline{28}$$

Example 3 Indirect Measurement with the Law of Cosines

GOLF Nhat is golfing and uses a distance measuring tool to determine that the tee box where he is standing is 378 yards from the hole. To avoid a water hazard, Nhat turns 32° and hits a shot 261.5 yards up the fairway. Complete the diagram with the correct values. Then find the distance between Nhat's ball and the hole to the nearest yard.

Because we know the measures of two sides of the triangle and the included angle, use the Law of Cosines to find the remaining distance.

$$x^2 = 261.5^2 + 378^2 - 2(261.5)(378)\cos 32° \qquad \text{Law of Cosines}$$
$$x^2 = 211{,}266.25 - 197{,}316 \cos 32° \qquad \text{Simplify.}$$
$$x = \sqrt{211{,}266.25 - 197{,}316 \cos 32°} \qquad \text{Take the positive square root of each side.}$$
$$x \approx \underline{210} \qquad \text{Use a calculator.}$$

Nhat's ball is about 210 yards from the hole.

Go Online You can complete an Extra Example online.

Interactive Presentation

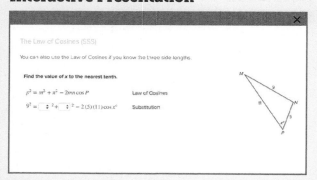

Example 2

TAP

Students select values to complete the calculations and find a missing side length using the Law of Cosines.

---

e **Essential Question Follow-Up**

Students learn the Law of Sines and the Law of Cosines.

Ask:

Why are the Law of Sines and the Law of Cosines important in the real world? *Sample answer: The Law of Sines and the Law of Cosines allow you to solve nonright triangles, which is useful for indirect measurement and other real world problems.*

DIFFERENTIATE

Reteaching Activity AL ELL

Interpersonal Learners Organize students into groups of three students to work through exercises. One group member can select the exercise. The second member sets up the equation for the Law of Cosines and fills in the values. The third member uses a calculator to solve the problem. Group members rotate tasks so each member participates in each responsibility.

Example 2 The Law of Cosines (SSS)

MP **Teaching the Mathematical Practices**

2 Create Representations Guide students to write an equation that models the situation in this example. Then use the equation to solve the problem.

Questions for Mathematical Discourse

AL If you are given the lengths of all three sides, can you find the measure of any angle using the Law of Cosines? Explain. *Yes; the angle should be in the cosine part of the equation while the side opposite is on the left side of the equation.*

OL If $MN = 7$, what is $m\angle P$? *about 28°*

BL If the sides measure 7, 8, and 11, what is the measure of the angle opposite the longest side? *about 94°*

Example 3 Indirect Measurement with the Law of Cosines

MP **Teaching the Mathematical Practices**

4 Apply Mathematics In this example, students apply what they have learned about the Law of Cosines to solving a real-world problem.

Questions for Mathematical Discourse

AL Why is it necessary to use the Law of Cosines to solve this problem? *With the information given, only the Law of Cosines will allow you to find x in one step.*

OL If you couldn't remember the Law of Cosines, could you still solve this problem? *Yes, if you drew an altitude to the triangle and used trigonometry to find parts of the two right triangles formed.*

BL Why do you take the positive square root in the third step of solving the equation? *x represents a distance so the value must be positive.*

1 CONCEPTUAL UNDERSTANDING   2 FLUENCY | 3 APPLICATION

Example 4 Solve a Nonright Triangle with the Law of Cosines

Teaching the Mathematical Practices

1 Monitor and Evaluate Point out that in this example, students must stop and evaluate their progress and change course to find the ultimate solution.

Questions for Mathematical Discourse

AL Why do we need to use the Law of Cosines in the first step? We don't have enough information to use the Law of Sines, and we do have enough information to use the Law of Cosines.

OL Does it matter which angle you choose to find the measure of first when solving a triangle given all three side lengths? Explain. No; you can solve for the angles in any order.

BL For what given information is your only option for the first step to solve a nonright triangle to use the Law of Sines? the Law of Cosines if you are given two angles and one side; If you are given all three sides or if you are given two sides and the included angle

Common Error

Students may have difficulty determining whether to use the Law of Cosines or the Law of Sines at each step in solving a nonright triangle. Help them to analyze the given information to help them determine which formula to use.

Check

CELL PHONE TOWERS A cell phone company builds two towers that are 2 miles apart. They choose a random location 1.1 miles from tower A and 1.5 miles from tower B to test the towers' signal strengths. Find the value of x to the nearest degree.

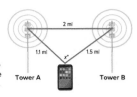

$x = \underline{99°}$

When solving right triangles, you can use sine, cosine, or tangent. When solving any triangle, you can use the Law of Sines or the Law of Cosines, depending on what information is given.

Example 4 Solve a Nonright Triangle with the Law of Cosines

Solve △ABC. Round to the nearest degree.

Because $7^2 + 8^2 \neq 11^2$, this is not a right triangle. The measures of all three sides are given (SSS), so decide which angle measure you want to find. Then use the Law of Cosines.

$a^2 = b^2 + c^2 - 2bc \cos A$	Law of Cosines
$7^2 = \underline{11}^2 + \underline{8}^2 - 2(11)(8) \cos A$	Substitute.
$\underline{49} = 185 - \underline{176} \cos A$	Simplify.
$\underline{-136} = -176 \cos A$	Subtract 185 from each side.
$\frac{-136}{-176} = \cos A$	Divide each side by −176.
$m\angle A = \cos^{-1}\left(\frac{-136}{-176}\right)$	Use the inverse cosine function.
$m\angle A = 39.400°$	Use a calculator.

Use the Law of Sines to find $m\angle B$.

$\frac{\sin A}{a} = \frac{\sin B}{b}$	Law of Sines
$\frac{\sin A}{7} = \frac{\sin B}{11}$	$a = 7$ and $b = 11$
$11 \sin A = \underline{7} \sin B$	Multiplication Property of Equality
$\left(\frac{11 \sin A}{7}\right) = \sin B$	Divide each side by 7.
$m\angle B = \sin^{-1}\left(\frac{11 \sin A}{7}\right)$	Use the inverse sine function.
$m\angle B \approx 85.904°$	Use a calculator.

By the Triangle Angle-Sum Theorem, $m\angle C \approx 180 - (39 + 86)$ or 55°.

Go Online You can complete an Extra Example online.

> **Study Tip**
>
> **Rounding** When you round a numerical solution and then use it in later calculations, your answers may be inaccurate. Wait until after you have completed all of your calculations to round.

Lesson 9-8 • The Law of Cosines   **559**

Interactive Presentation

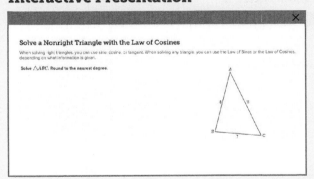

Example 4

TYPE

Students enter values to calculate the missing angle measures using the Law of Cosines.

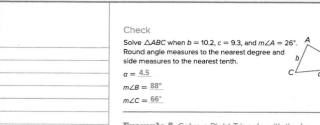

Check

Solve $\triangle ABC$ when $b = 10.2$, $c = 9.3$, and $m\angle A = 26°$. Round angle measures to the nearest degree and side measures to the nearest tenth.

$a = \underline{4.5}$

$m\angle B = \underline{88°}$

$m\angle C = \underline{66°}$

Example 5 Solve a Right Triangle with the Law of Cosines

Solve $\triangle FGH$. Round angle measures to the nearest degree and side measures to the nearest tenth.

Find FG.

$h^2 = f^2 + g^2$	Pythagorean Theorem
$h^2 = \underline{2}^2 + \underline{3}^2$	Substitution
$h^2 = \underline{13}$	Simplify.
$h = \underline{\sqrt{13}}$	Take the positive square root of each side.
$h \approx \underline{3.6}$	Use a calculator.

So, $FG \approx 3.6$.

Find $m\angle F$.

$f^2 = g^2 + h^2 - 2gh \cos F$	Law of Cosines
$2^2 = 3^2 + (\sqrt{13})^2 - 2(3)(\sqrt{13}) \cos \underline{F}$	Substitution
$\underline{4} = 22 - 6\sqrt{13} \cos \underline{F}$	Simplify.
$\underline{-18} = -6\sqrt{13} \cos \underline{F}$	Subtract 22 from each side.
$\dfrac{-18}{-6\sqrt{3}} = \cos F$	Divide each side by $-6\sqrt{13}$.
$\underline{34} \approx m\angle F$	Use a calculator.

So, $m\angle F \approx 34°$.

Find $m\angle G$.

Because we know that $m\angle H = 90°$ and $m\angle F \approx 34°$, find $m\angle G$.

$m\angle G = 90° - \underline{34°}$ or $\underline{56°}$

Check

Solve $\triangle EFG$. Round angle measures to the nearest degree and side measures to the nearest tenth.

$e = \underline{17}$

$m\angle F = \underline{28°}$

$m\angle G = \underline{62°}$

🔵 **Go Online** You can complete an Extra Example online.

Study Tip

Obtuse Angles There are also values for sin A, cos A, and tan A when $m\angle A \geq 90°$. Values of the ratios for these angles can be found by using the trigonometric functions on your calculator. It is good practice to solve for smaller angles first, and then use the Triangle Angle-Sum Theorem to find the measure of the largest, third angle.

🔵 **Go Online** to practice what you've learned about solving triangles in the Put It All Together over Lessons 9-7 through 9-8.

Interactive Presentation

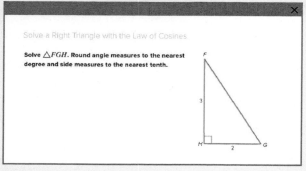

Example 5

TAP

Students move through the steps to solve a right triangle with the Law of Cosines.

CHECK

Students complete the Check online to determine whether they are ready to move on.

---

1 CONCEPTUAL UNDERSTANDING　　**2 FLUENCY**　　3 APPLICATION

Example 5 Solve a Right Triangle with the Law of Cosines

MP Teaching the Mathematical Practices

1 Monitor and Evaluate Point out that in this example, students must stop and evaluate their progress and change course to find the ultimate solution.

Questions for Mathematical Discourse

AL Could you use the Law of Cosines in the first step? Yes, but because cos 90° = 0, you will end up with the same equation as the Pythagorean Theorem.

OL Does it matter which angle you choose to find the measure of first? No; you can solve for the angles in any order.

BL Do you need to use the Law of Cosines or the Law of Sines to solve a right triangle? No, if you are not given that it is a right triangle, you will have all three side lengths. In that case, you can use the Converse of the Pythagorean Theorem to determine that it is a right triangle. Then you can find the other angle measures using trigonometry.

DIFFERENTIATE

Enrichment Activity BL

Have the students draw nonright triangles. Then have them use rulers to find the length of the three sides. The students should use the Law of Sines and the Law of Cosines to find the measures of the angles of the triangles. Have them check their answers by measuring the angles with a protractor.

Exit Ticket

Recommended Use

At the end of class, go online to display the Exit Ticket prompt and ask students to respond using a separate piece of paper. Have students hand you their responses as they leave the room.

Alternate Use

At the end of class, go online to display the Exit Ticket prompt and ask students to respond verbally or by using a mini-whiteboard. Have students hold up their whiteboards so that you can see all student responses. Tap to reveal the answer when most or all students have completed the Exit Ticket.

Practice and Homework

Suggested Assignments

Use the table below to select appropriate exercises.

DOK	Topic	Exercises
1, 2	exercises that mirror the examples	1–14
2	exercises that use a variety of skills from this lesson	15–22
3	exercises that emphasize higher-order and critical-thinking skills	23–26

ASSESS AND DIFFERENTIATE

📊 Use the data from the **Checks** to determine whether to provide resources for extension, remediation, or intervention.

IF students score 90% or more on the Checks,   `BL`
THEN assign:

- Practice, Exercises 1–21 odd, 23–26
- Extension: Law of Tangents
- 🅐 **ALEKS'** Laws of Sines and Cosines

IF students score 66%–89% on the Checks,   `OL`
THEN assign:

- Practice, Exercises 1–26 odd
- Remediation, Review Resources: Trigonometry
- Personal Tutors
- Extra Examples 1–5
- 🅐 **ALEKS'** Right Triangle Trigonometry

IF students score 65% or less on the Checks,   `AL`
THEN assign:

- Practice, Exercises 1–13 odd
- Remediation, Review Resources: Trigonometry
- *Quick Review Math Handbook:* The Law of Cosines
- 🅐 **ALEKS'** Right Triangle Trigonometry

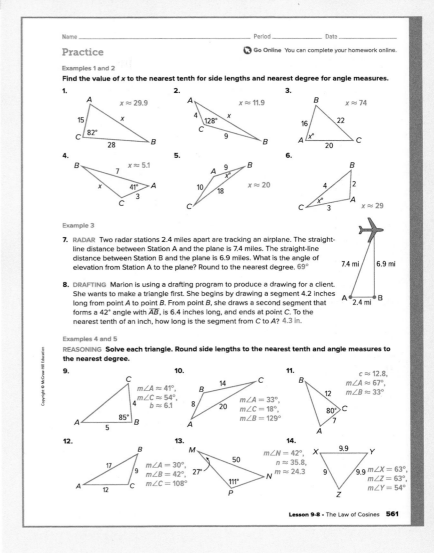

Name _____ Period _____ Date _____

Practice

🔵 **Go Online** You can complete your homework online.

Examples 1 and 2

Find the value of x to the nearest tenth for side lengths and nearest degree for angle measures.

1. $x \approx 29.9$

2. $x \approx 11.9$

3. $x \approx 74$

4. $x \approx 5.1$

5. $x \approx 20$

6. $x \approx 29$

Example 3

7. **RADAR** Two radar stations 2.4 miles apart are tracking an airplane. The straight-line distance between Station A and the plane is 7.4 miles. The straight-line distance between Station B and the plane is 6.9 miles. What is the angle of elevation from Station A to the plane? Round to the nearest degree. 69°

8. **DRAFTING** Marion is using a drafting program to produce a drawing for a client. She wants to make a triangle first. She begins by drawing a segment 4.2 inches long from point A to point B. From point B, she draws a second segment that forms a 42° angle with $\overline{AB}$, is 6.4 inches long, and ends at point C. To the nearest tenth of an inch, how long is the segment from C to A? 4.3 in.

Examples 4 and 5

REASONING Solve each triangle. Round side lengths to the nearest tenth and angle measures to the nearest degree.

9. $m\angle A \approx 41°$, $m\angle C \approx 54°$, $b \approx 6.1$

10. $m\angle A = 33°$, $m\angle C = 18°$, $m\angle B = 129°$

11. $c \approx 12.8$, $m\angle A \approx 67°$, $m\angle B \approx 33°$

12. $m\angle A = 30°$, $m\angle B = 42°$, $m\angle C = 108°$

13.

14. $m\angle N = 42°$, $n \approx 35.8$, $m \approx 24.3$ $m\angle X = 63°$, $m\angle Z = 63°$, $m\angle Y = 54°$

Mixed Exercises

REGULARITY **Determine whether each triangle should be solved by beginning with the *Law of Sines* or the *Law of Cosines*. Then solve the triangle.**

15. $m\angle A = 11°$, $m\angle C = 27°$, $c = 50$
Law of Sines; $m\angle B = 142°$, $a \approx 21.0$, $b \approx 67.8$

16. $m\angle B = 47°$, $a = 20$, $c = 24$
Law of Cosines; $m\angle A \approx 55°$, $m\angle C \approx 78°$, $b \approx 17.9$

17. $m\angle A = 37°$, $a = 20$, $b = 18$
Law of Sines; $m\angle B \approx 33°$, $m\angle C \approx 110°$, $c \approx 31.2$

18. $m\angle C = 35°$, $a = 18$, $b = 24$
Law of Cosines; $m\angle A \approx 48°$, $m\angle B \approx 97°$, $c \approx 13.9$

19. POOLS The Perth County pool has a lifeguard station in both the deep-water and shallow-water sections of the pool. The distance between each station and the bottom of the slide is known, but the manager would like to calculate more information about the pool setup.

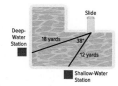

   a. When the lifeguards switch positions, the lifeguard at the deep-water station swims to the shallow-water station. How far does the lifeguard swim? about 11.3 yd

   b. If the lifeguard at the deep-water station is directly facing the bottom of the slide, what angle does she need to turn in order to face the lifeguard at the shallow-water station? about 40.9°

20. PROOF Write a two-column proof to prove the Law of Cosines. See margin.

   Given: The altitude of $\triangle ABC$ is h.

   Prove: $a^2 = b^2 + c^2 - 2bc \cos A$

🧠 **Higher-Order Thinking Skills**

21. PERSEVERE Find the value of x in the figure at the right. 5.6

22. ANALYZE Explain why the Pythagorean Theorem is a specific case of the Law of Cosines. See margin.

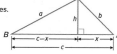

23. WRITE What methods can you use to solve a triangle? See margin.

24. CREATE Draw and label a triangle that can be solved: a–b. See margin.

   a. using only the Law of Sines.

   b. using only the Law of Cosines.

Answers

20. Given: h is an altitude of $\triangle ABC$. Prove: $a^2 = b^2 + c^2 - 2bc \cos A$ Proof:
   1. h is an altitude of $\triangle ABC$ (Given)
   2. Altitude h separates $\triangle ABC$ into two right triangles (Definition of altitude)
   3. $a^2 = (c - x)^2 + h^2$ (Pythagorean Theorem)
   4. $a^2 = c^2 - 2cx + x^2 + h^2$ (Substitution)
   5. $x^2 + h^2 = b^2$ (Pythagorean Theorem)
   6. $a^2 = c^2 - 2cx + b^2$ (Substitution)
   7. $\cos A = \dfrac{x}{b}$ (Definition of cosine)
   8. $b \cos A = x$ (Multiplication Property)
   9. $a^2 = c^2 - 2c(b \cos A) + b^2$ (Substitution)
   10. $a^2 = b^2 + c^2 - 2bc \cos A$ (Commutative Property)

22. The Law of Cosines relates the measures of two sides a and b of any triangle to the measure of the third side c given the measure of the angle C between those two sides using the equation $a^2 + b^2 - 2ab \cos C = c^2$. When $m\angle C = 90$, we have $a^2 + b^2 - 2ab \cos 90° = c^2$.

Because $\cos 90°$ is 0, this equation simplifies $a^2 + b^2 - 2ab (0) = c^2$ or $a^2 + b^2 = c^2$.

23. Sample answer: When solving a right triangle, you can use the Pythagorean Theorem to find missing side lengths and trigonometric ratios to find missing side lengths or angle measures. To solve any triangle, you can use the Law of Sines or the Law of Cosines, depending on what measures you are given.

24a.

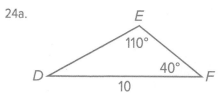

24b.

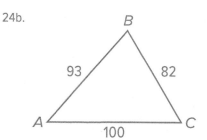

Review

Rate Yourself!

Have students return to the Module Opener to rate their understanding of the concepts presented in this module. They should see that their knowledge and skills have increased. After completing the chart, have them respond to the prompts in their *Interactive Student Edition* and share their responses with a partner.

Ⓔ Answering the Essential Question

Before answering the Essential Question, have students review their answers to the Essential Question Follow-Up questions found throughout the module.

- Why might the converse of the Pythagorean Theorem be useful in the real world?
- Why is trigonometry important in the real world?
- Why are the Law of Sines and the Law of Cosines important in the real world?

Then, have them write their answer to the Essential Question in the space provided.

DINAH ZIKE FOLDABLES

ELL A completed Foldable for this module should include the key concepts related to right triangles and trigonometry.

LS **LearnSmart** Use LearnSmart as part of your test preparation plan to measure student topic retention. You can create a student assignment in LearnSmart for additional practice on these topics for **Similarity, Proof, and Trigonometry**.

- Define trigonometric ratios and solve problems involving right triangles
- Apply trigonometry to general triangles

Ⓔ **Essential Question**

How are right triangle relationships useful in solving real-world problems?

Sample answer: The Pythagorean Theorem can be used to find missing side lengths of right triangles that occur in the real world.

Module Summary

Lesson 9-1

Geometric Mean
- The geometric mean of two positive numbers a and b is x such that $\frac{a}{x} = \frac{x}{b}$.
  So, $x^2 = ab$ and $x = \sqrt{ab}$.

Lesson 9-2

Pythagorean Theorem
- If $\triangle ABC$ is a right triangle with right angle C, then $a^2 + b^2 = c^2$.

Lesson 9-3

Coordinates in Space
- A point in space is represented by (x, y, z) where $x, y,$ and z are real numbers.
- A three-dimensional coordinate system has three axes: the x-, y-, and z-axes. The x- and y-axes lie on a horizontal plane, and the z-axis is vertical.

Lesson 9-4

Special Right Triangles
- In a 45°-45°-90° triangle, the legs ℓ are congruent and the length of the hypotenuse h is $\sqrt{2}$ times the length of a leg.
- In a 30°-60°-90° triangle, the length of the hypotenuse h is 2 times the length of the shorter leg s, and the longer leg ℓ is $\sqrt{3}$ times the length of the shorter leg.

Lesson 9-5

Trigonometry
- $\sin A = \frac{\text{opp}}{\text{hyp}}$, $\cos A = \frac{\text{adj}}{\text{hyp}}$, and $\tan A = \frac{\text{opp}}{\text{adj}}$.
- If $\sin A = x$, then $\sin^{-1} x = m\angle A$. If $\cos A = x$, then $\cos^{-1} x = m\angle A$. If $\tan A = x$, then $\tan^{-1} x = m\angle A$.

Lessons 9-6 through 9-8

Applications of Trigonometry
- Area $= \frac{1}{2}ab \sin C$, where a and b are side lengths and C is the included angle.
- Law of Sines: If $\triangle ABC$ has lengths a, b, and c, representing the lengths of the sides opposite the angles with measures A, B, and C, then $\frac{\sin A}{a} = \frac{\sin B}{b} = \frac{\sin C}{c}$.
- Law of Cosines: If $\triangle ABC$ has lengths a, b, and c, representing the lengths of the sides opposite the angles with measures A, B, and C, then $a^2 = b^2 + c^2 - 2bc\cos A$, $b^2 = a^2 + c^2 - 2ac\cos B$, and $c^2 = a^2 + b^2 - 2ab\cos C$.

Study Organizer

📖 **Foldables**
Use your Foldable to review this module. Working with a partner can be helpful. Ask for clarification of concepts as needed.

Right Triangles and Trigonometry

Test Practice

Name _____ Period _____ Date _____

1. MULTIPLE CHOICE What is the geometric mean between 6 and 12? (Lesson 9-1)

Ⓐ $6\sqrt{2}$ Ⓑ $3\sqrt{2}$

Ⓒ 9   Ⓓ 36

2. MULTIPLE CHOICE What is the geometric mean between 9 and 15? (Lesson 9-1)

Ⓐ $9\sqrt{15}$ Ⓑ 12

Ⓒ $3\sqrt{15}$ Ⓓ 135

3. MULTI-SELECT Which of the following triangles is similar to △JKL? Select all that apply. (Lesson 9-1)

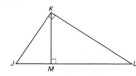

Ⓐ △JMK   Ⓑ △MKL

Ⓒ △JKM   Ⓓ △KML

Ⓔ △LJK

4. OPEN RESPONSE A path forms a diagonal of a rectangular city park. A bench is placed along the path at a point that is closest to the fountain. This point is 30 yards from one end of the path and 50 yards from the other end of the path. What is the distance from the bench to the fountain, to the nearest yard? (Lesson 9-1)

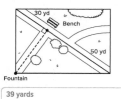

39 yards

5. OPEN RESPONSE Given right △ABC with point D such that $\overleftrightarrow{CD}$ is perpendicular to $\overleftrightarrow{AB}$ and △ACB is similar to △ADC and to △CDB, complete the proof to show $AC^2 + BC^2 = AB^2$. (Lesson 9-1)

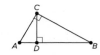

	Statements		Reasons
1.	△ABC is a right triangle with point D such that $\overleftrightarrow{CD}$ is perpendicular to $\overleftrightarrow{AB}$ and △ACB is similar to △ADC and to △CDB.	1.	Given
2.	$\frac{BC}{BA} = \frac{BD}{BC}$	2.	Definition of similar triangles
3.	$\frac{AC}{AB} = \frac{AD}{AC}$	3.	Definition of similar triangles
4.	$BC^2 = (BA)(BD)$ and $AC^2 = (AB)(AD)$	4.	
5.	$AC^2 + BC^2 = (BA)(BD) + (AB)(AD)$	5.	Addition Property
6.	$AC^2 + BC^2 = (AB)(BD + AD)$	6.	
7.	$BD + AD = AB$	7.	Segment Addition Postulate
8.	$AC^2 + BC^2 = AB^2$	8.	Substitution

Multiplication Property of Equality; Distributive Property

Review and Assessment Options

The following online review and assessment resources are available for you to assign to your students. These resources include technology-enhanced questions that are auto-scored, as well as essay questions.

Review Resources

Put It All Together: Lessons 9–5 through 9–8

Vocabulary Activity

Module Review

Assessment Resources

Vocabulary Test

AL Module Test Form B

OL Module Test Form A

BL Module Test Form C

Performance Task*

*The module-level performance task is available online as a printable document. A scoring rubric is included.

Test Practice

You can use these pages to help your students review module content and prepare for online assessments. Exercises 1–18 mirror the types of questions your students will see on online assessments.

Question Type	Description	Exercise(s)
Multiple Choice	Students select one correct answer.	1, 2, 8, 13
Multi-Select	Multiple answers may be correct. Students must select all correct answers.	3
Table Item	Students complete a table by entering in the correct values.	6, 12
Open Response	Students construct their own response in the area provided.	4, 5, 7, 9–11, 14

To ensure that students understand the standards, check students' success on individual exercises.

Standard(s)	Lesson(s)	Exercise(s)
G.SRT.4	9-1	5
G.SRT.5	9-1	1–4
G.SRT.6	9-4, 9-5	7–9, 11
G.SRT.7	9-5	10, 12
G.SRT.8	9-2, 9-5	6, 13, 14

---

6. TABLE ITEM In $\triangle DEF$, $DE = 8$ and $EF = 15$. Match the length of the third side to the type of triangle it would create. (Lesson 9-2)

Third Side	Type of Triangle		
	Acute	Right	Obtuse
15	X		
16	X		
17		X	
18			X

7. OPEN RESPONSE Use the figure. If $AB = 3\sqrt{15}$, what is BD? Write the answer in simplest radical form. (Lesson 9-4)

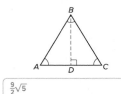

$\frac{9}{2}\sqrt{5}$

8. MULTIPLE CHOICE What is the value of y? (Lesson 9-4)

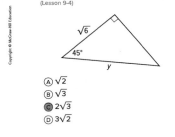

ⓐ $\sqrt{2}$
ⓑ $\sqrt{3}$
ⓒ $2\sqrt{3}$
ⓓ $3\sqrt{2}$

9. OPEN RESPONSE A 10-foot-long ladder leans against a wall so that the ladder and the wall form a 30° angle. What is the distance to the nearest tenth of a foot from the ground to the point where the ladder touches the wall? (Lesson 9-4)

8.7 feet

10. TABLE ITEM Match the trigonometric ratio with its decimal value. (Lesson 9-5)

Ratio	Decimal Value		
	0.6	0.75	0.8
sin B	X		
cos B			X
tan B		X	

11. OPEN RESPONSE Use special right triangles to evaluate sin 45°. Give an exact answer. (Lesson 9-5)

$\frac{\sqrt{2}}{2}$

12. MULTIPLE CHOICE A support wire for an electric pole makes a 50° angle with the ground. If the bottom of the support wire is 8 feet from the base of the pole, which of the following equations can be used to find the height at which the support wire is attached to the pole? (Lesson 9-6)

Ⓐ $\frac{x}{8} = \tan 50°$

Ⓑ $\frac{8}{x} = \tan 50°$

Ⓒ $\frac{x}{8} = \sin 50°$

Ⓓ $\frac{8}{x} = \sin 50°$

13. OPEN RESPONSE Paula stands on the side of a river and sights the opposite bank at an angle of depression of 7°. If Paula is 5.5 feet tall, approximately how wide is the river, to the nearest foot? (Lesson 9-6)

> 45 ft

14. MULTI-SELECT In $\triangle DEF$, $e = 7$, $f = 5$, and $m\angle F = 44°$. What are the possible measures of $\angle E$, to the nearest degree? Select all that apply. (Lesson 9-7)

Ⓐ 32°   Ⓑ 44°

Ⓒ 60°   Ⓓ 77°

Ⓔ 103°   Ⓕ 120°

15. OPEN RESPONSE What is the value of a, to the nearest tenth? (Lesson 9-7)

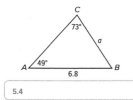

> 5.4

16. MULTIPLE CHOICE Two ships leave from the same location. The first ship travels due south for 13 miles. The second ship travels 50° east of due south for 11 miles. What is the distance between the ships? (Lesson 9-8)

Ⓐ 6.9 miles

Ⓑ 9.2 miles

Ⓒ 10.3 miles

Ⓓ 10.9 miles

17. MULTIPLE CHOICE What is $m\angle E$, to the nearest degree? (Lesson 9-8)

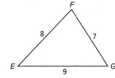

Ⓐ 40°

Ⓑ 42°

Ⓒ 45°

Ⓓ 48°

18. MULTIPLE CHOICE What is JK to the nearest tenth? (Lesson 9-8)

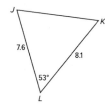

Ⓐ 7.0 units   Ⓑ 15.4 units

Ⓒ 49.3 units   Ⓓ 74.1 units

Lesson 9-2

23. Proof:

Statements (Reasons)

1. In $\triangle DEF$, $f^2 < d^2 + e^2$ where f is the length of the longest side. In $\triangle LMN$, $\angle M$ is a right angle. (Given)

2. $d^2 + e^2 = x^2$ (Pythagorean Theorem)

3. $f^2 < x^2$ (Substitution)

4. $f < x$ (Take the positive square root.)

5. $m\angle M = 90°$ (Definition of right angle)

6. $m\angle F < m\angle M$ (Converse of the Hinge Theorem)

7. $m\angle F < 90°$ (Substitution)

8. $\angle F$ is an acute angle. (Definition of acute angle)

9. $m\angle D < m\angle F$, $m\angle E < m\angle F$ (If one side of a $\triangle$ is longer than another side, then the $\angle$ opp. the longer side has a greater measure than the $\angle$ opp. the shorter side.)

10. $m\angle D < 90°$, $m\angle E < 90°$ (Transitive Prop. of Inequality)

11. $\triangle DEF$ is an acute triangle. (Definition of acute triangle)

24. Proof:

Statements (Reasons)

1. In $\triangle ABC$, $c^2 > a^2 + b^2$ where c is the length of the longest side. In $\triangle TUV$, $\angle V$ is a right angle. (Given)

2. $a^2 + b^2 = x^2$ (Pythagorean Theorem)

3. $c^2 > x^2$ (Substitution Property)

4. $c > x$ (A property of square roots.)

5. $m\angle V = 90°$ (Definition of right angle)

6. $m\angle C > m\angle V$ (Converse of the Hinge Theorem)

7. $m\angle C > 90°$ (Substitution Property)

8. $\angle C$ is an obtuse angle. (Definition of obtuse angle)

9. $\triangle ABC$ is an obtuse triangle. (Definition of obtuse triangle)

40. False; sample answer: A right triangle with legs measuring 3 inches and 4 inches has a hypotenuse of 5 inches and an area of $\frac{1}{2} \times 3 \times 4$ or 6 square inches. A right triangle with legs measuring 2 inches and $\sqrt{21}$ inches also has a hypotenuse of 5 inches, but its area is $\frac{1}{2} \times 2 \times \sqrt{21}$ or $\sqrt{21}$ square inches, which is not equivalent to 6 square inches.

41.

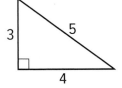

Right; sample answer: If you double or halve the side lengths, all three sides of the new triangles are proportional to the sides of the original triangle. Using the Side-Side-Side Similarity Theorem, you know that both of the new triangles are similar to the original triangle, so they are both right.

43. Sample answer: Incommensurable magnitudes are magnitudes of the same kind that do not have a common unit of measure. Irrational numbers were invented to describe geometric relationships, such as ratios of incommensurable magnitudes that cannot be described using rational numbers. For example, to express the measures of the sides of a square with an area of 2 square units, the irrational number $\sqrt{2}$ is needed.

Lesson 9-3

26. The formulas for the coordinate plane involve two coordinates and the formulas for three-dimensional space involve three coordinates. Both distance formulas involve square root of the squares of the differences of the coordinates. Both midpoint formulas involve the averages of the coordinates.

27. Teion; sample answer: Camilla made a mistake when substituting the value for y_1.

28.

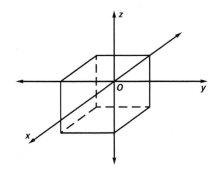

Module Goals

- Students measure and find relationships between arcs, chords, and inscribed angles of circles.
- Students solve problems using relationships between tangents, secants, and circumscribed angles of circles.
- Students determine and use equations of conic sections.

Focus

Domain: Geometry

Standards for Mathematical Content:

G.C.2 Identify and describe relationships among inscribed angles, radii, and chords.

G.GPE.1 Derive the equation of a circle of given center and radius using the Pythagorean Theorem; complete the square to find the center and radius of a circle given by an equation.

Also addresses G.CO.13, G.C.1, G.C.3, G.C.4, G.C.5, G.GMD.1, G.GPE.2, and G.GPE.4.

Standards for Mathematical Practice:

All Standards for Mathematical Practice will be addressed in this module.

✪ Be Sure to Cover

To completely cover G.GMD.1, G.C.5, G.CO.12, and G.GPE.4, go online to assign the following activities:

- Discovering the Formula for Circumference (Explore, Lesson 10-1)
- Relationships Between Arc Lengths and Radii (Explore, Lesson 10-2)
- Deriving Equations of Circles (Explore, Lesson 10-7)
- All Construction Activities (Lessons 10-3 through 10-5)

Coherence

Vertical Alignment

Previous
Students understood the formulas for circumference and area of circles and used them to solve problems.
7.G.4

Now
Students solve problems using the relationships in circles, tangents, secants, and associated angles.
G.C.1, G.C.2

Next
Students will derive and use surface area and volume formulas for cylinders, pyramids, cones, and spheres.
G.GMD.3

Rigor

The Three Pillars of Rigor

To help students meet standards, they need to illustrate their ability to use the three pillars of rigor. Students gain conceptual understanding as they move from the Explore to Learn sections within a lesson. Once they understand the concept, they practice procedural skills and fluency and apply their mathematical knowledge as they go through the Examples and Practice.

1 CONCEPTUAL UNDERSTANDING	2 FLUENCY	3 APPLICATION

EXPLORE 〉 LEARN 〉 **EXAMPLE & PRACTICE**

Suggested Pacing

Lessons	Standards	45-min classes	90-min classes
Module Pretest and Launch the Module Video		1	0.5
10-1 Circles and Circumference	G.C.1, G.GMD.1	1	0.5
10-2 Measuring Angles and Arcs	G.C.2, G.C.5	1	0.5
10-3 Arcs and Chords	G.C.2	1	0.5
10-4 Inscribed Angles	G.C.2, G.C.3	1	0.5
10-5 Tangents	G.C.4, G.CO.13	1	0.5
10-6 Tangents, Secants, and Angle Measures	G.C.2	1	0.5
Put It All Together: Lessons 10-1 through 10-6		1	0.5
10-7 Equations of Circles	G.GPE.1, G.GPE.4	1	0.5
10-8 Equations of Parabolas	G.GPE.2	2	1
Module Review		1	0.5
Module Assessment		1	0.5
Total Days		**13**	**6.5**

Formative Assessment Math Probe
Circles and Angles

Analyze the Probe

Review the probe prior to assigning it to your students.

In this probe, students will determine which of four students has made a correct assumption and explain their choices.

Targeted Concepts Understand how the measures of central angles, inscribed angles, and intercepted arcs can be used to find other missing angle measures.

Targeted Misconceptions

- Students may not consider the relationship between central and inscribed angles when they share an intercepted arc.
- Students may try to guess angle measures based on appearance or segment lengths forming the angle.

Use the Probe after Lesson 10-4.

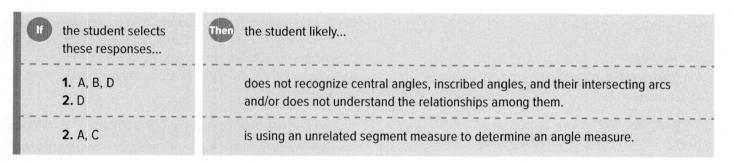

Answers:
1. Student C   2. Student B

Collect and Assess Student Answers

If the student selects these responses...	Then the student likely...
1. A, B, D **2.** D	does not recognize central angles, inscribed angles, and their intersecting arcs and/or does not understand the relationships among them.
2. A, C	is using an unrelated segment measure to determine an angle measure.

Take Action

After the Probe Design a plan to address any possible misconceptions. You may wish to assign the following resources.

- **ALEKS** Inscribed Angles and Polygons
- Lesson 10-4, all Learns, all Examples

Revisit the probe at the end of the module to be sure that your students no longer carry these misconceptions.

IGNITE!

The Ignite! activities, created by Dr. Raj Shah, cultivate curiosity and engage and challenge students. Use these open-ended, collaborative activities, located online in the module Launch section, to encourage your students to develop a growth mindset towards mathematics and problem solving. Use the teacher notes for implementation suggestions and support for encouraging productive struggle.

Ⓔ Essential Question

At the end of this module, students should be able to answer the Essential Question.

How can circles and parts of circles be used to model situations in the real world? Sample answer: Anything round can be modeled by a circle. Engineers and architects use circles to model moving parts of models they build. Banquet managers use circles to model tables so they know how much room they have to set up an event.

What Will You Learn?

Prior to beginning this module, have your students rate their knowledge of each item listed. Then, at the end of the module, you will be reminded to have your students return to these pages to rate their knowledge again. They should see that their knowledge and skills have increased.

DINAH ZIKE FOLDABLES

Focus Students read about circles.

Teach Throughout the module, have students take notes under the tabs of their Foldables while working through each lesson. They should include definitions, terms, and key concepts. Encourage students to record examples of each concept from a lesson on the back of their Foldable.

📖 **When to Use It** Use the appropriate tabs as students cover each lesson in this module. Students should add to the vocabulary tab during each lesson.

Launch the Module

In this module, the launch the module video uses the mechanics of a bicycle to describe the properties of circles and arcs. Students learn how the parts of a bicycle are a construction of circles and semicircles.

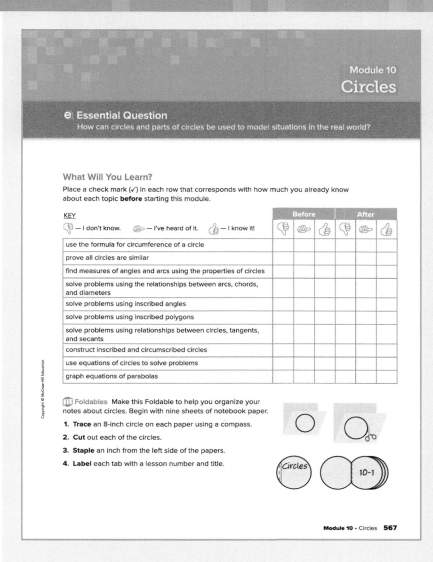

Interactive Presentation

What Vocabulary Will You Learn?

Check the box next to each vocabulary term that you may already know.

☐ adjacent arcs
☐ arc
☐ arc length
☐ center of a circle
☐ central angle of a circle
☐ chord of a circle
☐ circle

☐ circumscribed angle
☐ circumscribed polygon
☐ common tangent
☐ concentric circles
☐ congruent arcs
☐ degree
☐ diameter of a circle
☐ directrix

☐ focus
☐ inscribed angle
☐ inscribed polygon
☐ intercepted arc
☐ major arc
☐ minor arc
☐ parabola
☐ pi

☐ point of tangency
☐ radian
☐ radius of a circle
☐ secant
☐ semicircle
☐ tangent to a circle

Are You Ready?

Complete the Quick Review to see if you are ready to start this module.
Then complete the Quick Check.

Quick Review

Example 1

Find the value of h.

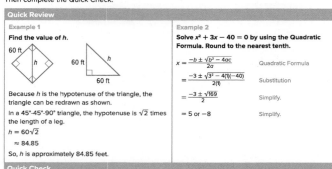

Because h is the hypotenuse of the triangle, the triangle can be redrawn as shown.

In a 45°-45°-90° triangle, the hypotenuse is $\sqrt{2}$ times the length of a leg.

$h = 60\sqrt{2}$

≈ 84.85

So, h is approximately 84.85 feet.

Example 2

Solve $x^2 + 3x - 40 = 0$ by using the Quadratic Formula. Round to the nearest tenth.

$x = \dfrac{-b \pm \sqrt{b^2 - 4ac}}{2a}$ Quadratic Formula

$= \dfrac{-3 \pm \sqrt{3^2 - 4(1)(-40)}}{2(1)}$ Substitution

$= \dfrac{-3 \pm \sqrt{169}}{2}$ Simplify.

$= 5 \text{ or } -8$ Simplify.

Quick Check

Find the value of h in each triangle.

1.
8 in.

2.
3 cm   45° $3\sqrt{2}$ cm

Solve each equation by using the Quadratic Formula. Round to the nearest tenth if necessary.

3. $5x^2 + 4x - 20 = 0$ $-2.4, 1.6$
4. $x^2 = x + 12$ $-3, 4$
5. $3x^2 - x - 12 = 0$ $-1.8, 2.2$
6. $4x^2 - 16x - 18 = 0$ $-0.9, 4.9$

How Did You Do?

Which exercises did you answer correctly in the Quick Check? Shade those exercise numbers below.

① ② ③ ④ ⑤ ⑥

What Vocabulary Will You Learn?

ELL As you proceed through the module, introduce the key vocabulary by using the following routine.

Define Concentric circles are coplanar circles that share the same center.

Example

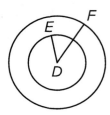

Ask Are concentric circles similar or congruent? Explain. The circles are similar because all circles are similar. The circles are not congruent because they have different radii.

Are You Ready?

Students may need to review the following prerequisite skills to succeed in this module.

- using radii and diameters
- comparing arc lengths
- comparing chord lengths
- comparing angle measures
- using the Pythagorean Theorem
- testing angle knowledge
- using the Distance Formula

⬡ ALEKS·

ALEKS is an adaptive, personalized learning environment that identifies precisely what each student knows and is ready to learn, ensuring student success at all levels.

You may want to use the **Circles** and **Area and Volume** sections to ensure student success in this module.

🧠 Mindset Matters

Reward Effort, Not Talent

When adults praise students for their hard work toward a solution, rather than praising them for being smart or talented, it supports students' development of a growth mindset. Reward *actions* like hard work, determination, and perseverance instead of *traits* like inherent skill or talent.

How Can I Apply It?

Have students complete the **Performance Task** for the module. Allow students a forum to discuss their process or strategy that they used and give them positive feedback on their diligence in completing the task.

Circles and Circumference

LESSON GOAL

Students find and apply the formulas for the circumference and area of a circle.

1 LAUNCH

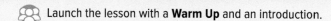

Launch the lesson with a **Warm Up** and an introduction.

2 EXPLORE AND DEVELOP

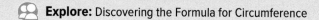

Explore: Discovering the Formula for Circumference

Develop:

Parts of Circles
- Identify Segments in a Circle
- Use Radius and Diameter Relationships
- Find Circumference
- Find Diameter and Radius

Pairs of Circles
- Find Measures in Intersecting Circles

You may want your students to complete the **Checks** online.

3 REFLECT AND PRACTICE

Exit Ticket

Practice

DIFFERENTIATE

View reports of student progress on the **Checks** after each example.

Resources	AL	OL	BL	ELL
Remediation: Circumference of Circles	●	●		●
Extension: Circumference and RPMs		●	●	●

Language Development Handbook

Assign page 66 of the *Language Development Handbook* to help your students build mathematical language related to the circumference and area of a circle.

ELL You can use the tips and suggestions on page T66 of the handbook to support students who are building English proficiency.

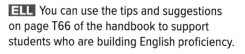

Suggested Pacing

90 min	0.5 day
45 min	1 day

Focus

Domain: Geometry

Standards for Mathematical Content:

G.C.1 Prove that all circles are similar.

G.GMD.1 Give an informal argument for the formulas for the circumference of a circle, area of a circle, volume of a cylinder, pyramid, and cone.

Standards for Mathematical Practice:

3 Construct viable arguments and critique the reasoning of others.

4 Model with mathematics.

5 Use appropriate tools strategically.

6 Attend to precision.

7 Look for and make use of structure.

Coherence

Vertical Alignment

Previous
Students solved problems using the Law of Cosines.
G.SRT.10

Now
Students find and apply the formulas for the circumference and area of a circle.
G.GMD.1

Next
Students will find measures of angles and arcs in circles.
G.C.2, G.C.5

Rigor

The Three Pillars of Rigor

1 CONCEPTUAL UNDERSTANDING	2 FLUENCY	3 APPLICATION

Conceptual Bridge In this lesson, students review and expand on their understanding of circles and circumference. They develop fluency and apply their understanding by solving real-world problems related to circles.

Mathematical Background

A *circle* is the locus of all points in a plane equidistant from a given point, which is the center of the circle. A circle is usually named by its center point. Any segment with endpoints on the circle is a *chord of the circle*. The circumference of a circle is the distance around the circle. The ratio of the circumference to the diameter of a circle is always equal to π. For a circumference of C units and a diameter of d units or a radius of r units, $C = \pi d$ or $C = 2\pi r$.

Interactive Presentation

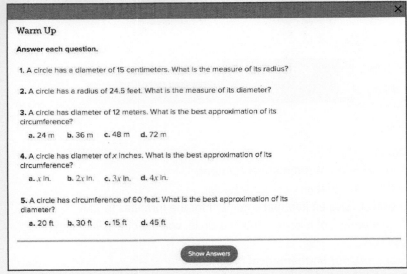

Warp Up

Answer each question.

1. A circle has a diameter of 15 centimeters. What is the measure of its radius?

2. A circle has a radius of 24.5 feet. What is the measure of its diameter?

3. A circle has diameter of 12 meters. What is the best approximation of its circumference?
   a. 24 m   b. 36 m   c. 48 m   d. 72 m

4. A circle has diameter of x inches. What is the best approximation of its circumference?
   a. x in.   b. $2x$ in.   c. $3x$ in.   d. $4x$ in.

5. A circle has circumference of 60 feet. What is the best approximation of its diameter?
   a. 20 ft   b. 30 ft   c. 15 ft   d. 45 ft

Warm Up

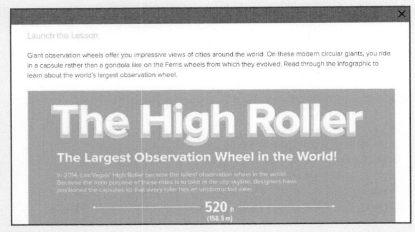

Launch the Lesson

Giant observation wheels offer you impressive views of cities around the world. On these modern circular giants, you ride in a capsule rather than a gondola like on the Ferris wheels from which they evolved. Read through the infographic to learn about the world's largest observation wheel.

The High Roller

The Largest Observation Wheel in the World!

In 2014, Las Vegas' High Roller became the tallest observation wheel in the world. Because the main purpose of these rides is to take in the city skyline, designers have positioned the capsules so that every rider has an unobstructed view.

520 ft
(158.5 m)

Launch the Lesson

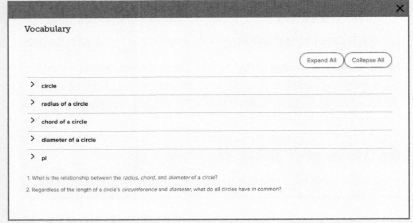

Vocabulary

Expand All   Collapse All

> circle
> radius of a circle
> chord of a circle
> diameter of a circle
> pi

1. What is the relationship between the *radius*, *chord*, and *diameter* of a circle?

2. Regardless of the length of a circle's *circumference* and *diameter*, what do all circles have in common?

Today's Vocabulary

Warm Up

Prerequisite Skills
The Warm Up exercises address the following prerequisite skill for this lesson:

- using radii and diameters

Answers:
1. 7.5 cm
2. 49 ft
3. b
4. c
5. a

Launch the Lesson

MP Teaching the Mathematical Practices

4 Apply Mathematics In this Launch the Lesson, students can see a real-world application of circles.

Go Online to find additional teaching notes and questions to promote classroom discourse.

Today's Standards

Tell students that they will be addressing these content and practice standards in this lesson. You may wish to have a student volunteer read aloud *How can I meet these standards?* and *How can I use these practices?* and connect these to the standards.

See the Interactive Presentation for I Can statements that align with the standards covered in this lesson.

Today's Vocabulary

Tell students that they will be using these vocabulary terms in this lesson. You can expand each row if you wish to share the definitions. Then, discuss the questions below with the class.

Explore Discovering the Formula for Circumference

Objective
Students use dynamic geometry software and informal limit arguments to discover the formula for the circumference of a circle.

 Teaching the Mathematical Practices

7 Interpret Complicated Expressions Mathematically proficient students can see complicated expressions as single objects or as being composed of several objects. In this Explore, guide students to see what information they can gather about the expression just from looking at it.

Ideas for Use

Recommended Use Present the Inquiry Question, or have a student volunteer read it aloud. Have students work in pairs to complete the Explore activity on their devices. Pairs should discuss each of the questions. Monitor student progress during the activity. Upon completion of the Explore activity, have student volunteers share their responses to the Inquiry Question.

What if my students don't have devices? You may choose to project the activity on a whiteboard. A printable worksheet for each Explore is available online. You may choose to print the worksheet so that individuals or pairs of students can use it to record their observations.

Summary of the Activity

Students will complete guiding exercises throughout the Explore activity. Students begin by answering some guiding questions comparing the perimeter of a regular octagon inscribed in a circle to the radius of the circle. Then students use dynamic geometry software to explore the perimeter of a regular polygon inscribed in a circle to see what happens when the number of sides of the polygon changes. Next, students answer more guiding questions to write the ratio between the radius of the circle and the circumference. Finally they use the ratio to write the formula for circumference. Then, students will answer the Inquiry Question.

(continued on the next page)

Interactive Presentation

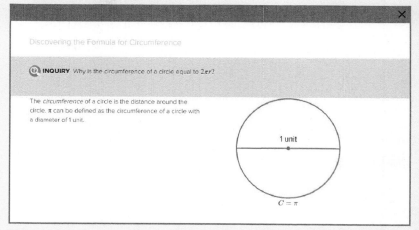

Explore

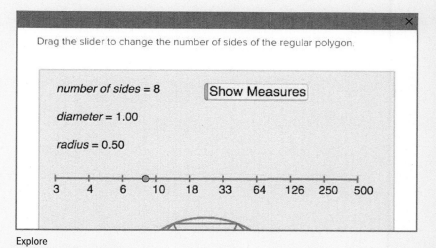

Explore

WEB SKETCHPAD

 Students use the sketch to explore circumference.

Interactive Presentation

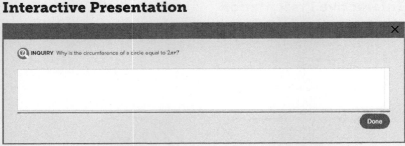

Explore

TYPE

Students respond to the Inquiry Question and can view a sample answer.

Explore Discovering the Formula for Circumference (*continued*)

Questions
Have students complete the Explore activity.

Ask:
- Do you think the sketch should have included the option for more than 500 sides? Why or why not? No; sample answer: It's clear that the shape of the polygon gets closer to a circle as the number of sides increases, and the perimeter was already a very close approximation of π.
- Would the formula for the circumference have changed if the diameter in the sketch was 2 units? Sample answer: If the diameter was 2 units, the radius would be 1 unit and all other measures would be twice the original values. The ratio of circumference to radius would be the same so you would still get $C = 2\pi r$.

Inquiry
Why is the circumference of a circle equal to $2\pi r$? Sample answer: When a circle has a diameter of 1 unit, the ratio of the circumference of the circle to the radius of the circle is $\pi : \frac{1}{2}$. When you solve the proportion $\frac{C}{r} = \frac{\pi}{\frac{1}{2}}$ for C, $C = 2\pi r$. So, the circumference of a circle with radius r is $2\pi r$.

Go Online to find additional teaching notes and sample answers for the guiding exercises.

1 CONCEPTUAL UNDERSTANDING | 2 FLUENCY | 3 APPLICATION

Learn Parts of Circles

Objective
Students know the precise definition of a circle and find the circumferences of circles.

MP Teaching the Mathematical Practices

7 Use Structure Help students to explore the structure of circles in this Learn.

1 Explain Correspondences Encourage students to explain the relationships between the radius, diameter, and circumference of a circle in this Learn.

Common Misconception

Students sometimes think that π is just a symbol that they have to use when solving circle problems. In this case they do not understand that π is an actual number that is on the number line but is unlike most numbers they are familiar with, like integers and fractions. Encourage students to find approximate values of numerical expressions involving π.

Go Online

- Find additional teaching notes.
- View performance reports of the Checks.
- Assign or present an Extra Example.

DIFFERENTIATE

Reteaching Activity AL

Hands-On Learners Find a number of differently sized circular bottles and cans of food or drink. Give a different one and a cloth tape measure to each pair of students and have them measure the diameter and circumference. Then have students compute the ratio between the circumference and the diameter. Next make a chart of all the values. Students should notice that the ratios are all close to π.

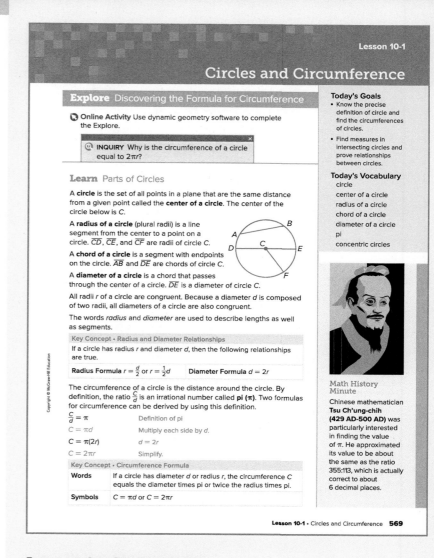

Lesson 10-1

Circles and Circumference

Explore Discovering the Formula for Circumference

⤴ **Online Activity** Use dynamic geometry software to complete the Explore.

🔍 **INQUIRY** Why is the circumference of a circle equal to $2\pi r$?

Learn Parts of Circles

A **circle** is the set of all points in a plane that are the same distance from a given point called the **center of a circle**. The center of the circle below is C.

A **radius of a circle** (plural radii) is a line segment from the center to a point on a circle. $\overline{CD}$, $\overline{CE}$, and $\overline{CF}$ are radii of circle C.

A **chord of a circle** is a segment with endpoints on the circle. $\overline{AB}$ and $\overline{DE}$ are chords of circle C.

A **diameter of a circle** is a chord that passes through the center of a circle. $\overline{DE}$ is a diameter of circle C.

All radii r of a circle are congruent. Because a diameter d is composed of two radii, all diameters of a circle are also congruent.

The words *radius* and *diameter* are used to describe lengths as well as segments.

Key Concept • Radius and Diameter Relationships

If a circle has radius r and diameter d, then the following relationships are true.

Radius Formula $r = \frac{d}{2}$ or $r = \frac{1}{2}d$ Diameter Formula $d = 2r$

The circumference of a circle is the distance around the circle. By definition, the ratio $\frac{C}{d}$ is an irrational number called **pi (π)**. Two formulas for circumference can be derived by using this definition.

$\frac{C}{d} = \pi$	Definition of pi
$C = \pi d$	Multiply each side by d.
$C = \pi(2r)$	$d = 2r$
$C = 2\pi r$	Simplify.

Key Concept • Circumference Formula

Words	If a circle has diameter d or radius r, the circumference C equals the diameter times pi or twice the radius times pi.
Symbols	$C = \pi d$ or $C = 2\pi r$

Lesson 10-1 • Circles and Circumference **569**

Today's Goals
- Know the precise definition of circle and find the circumferences of circles.
- Find measures in intersecting circles and prove relationships between circles.

Today's Vocabulary
circle
center of a circle
radius of a circle
chord of a circle
diameter of a circle
pi
concentric circles

Math History Minute

Chinese mathematician **Tsu Ch'ung-chih (429 AD–500 AD)** was particularly interested in finding the value of π. He approximated its value to be about the same as the ratio 355:113, which is actually correct to about 6 decimal places.

Copyright © McGraw-Hill Education

Interactive Presentation

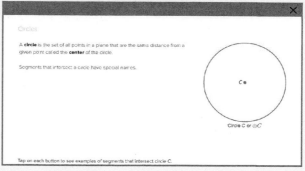

Circles

A **circle** is the set of all points in a plane that are the same distance from a given point called the **center** of the circle.

Segments that intersect a circle have special names.

Circle C or $\odot C$

Tap on each button to see examples of segments that intersect circle C.

Learn

TAP

Students tap to reveal information about circles.

Left page (student notes)

Your Notes

Example 1 Identify Segments in a Circle

Name the circle and identify a radius, a chord, and a diameter of the circle.

The circle has a center at *X*, so it is named circle *X* or ⊙*X*.

Four radii are shown: $\overline{XV}$, $\overline{XT}$, $\underline{\overline{XU}}$, and $\underline{\overline{XZ}}$.

Two chords are shown: $\overline{RS}$ and $\underline{\overline{TZ}}$.

$\overline{TZ}$ contains the center, so $\overline{TZ}$ is the __diameter__.

Example 2 Use Radius and Diameter Relationships

If *TU* = 14 feet, what is the radius of ⊙*Q*?

$r = \frac{d}{2}$ Radius Formula

$r = \frac{14}{2}$ or 7   Substitute and simplify.

The radius of ⊙*Q* is 7 feet.

Check

If *LM* = 11 inches, what is the diameter ⊙*L*?

__22__ in.

😀 **Think About It!**

What assumption did you make while solving this problem?

Sample answer: I assumed that the car remained 18 meters from the center of the island as it drove around the traffic circle.

Use a Source

Find the diameter of a famous traffic circle. Then calculate the circumference of the traffic circle.

Answers will vary.

🌐 **Example 3** Find Circumference

TRAFFIC CIRCLES Traffic circles, also known as roundabouts, are circular roadways that reflow traffic in one direction around an island. A car enters a traffic circle and is 18 meters from the center of the island. If the car drives around the traffic circle until it is back to its original position, what is the circumference of the car's path?

Because the car is 18 meters from the center of the island, the radius of the car's path is __18__ meters.

$C = 2\pi r$ Circumference Formula

$= 2\pi(\underline{18})$ Substitution

$= \underline{36}\ \pi$ Simplify.

$\approx \underline{113.1}$ Use a calculator.

The circumference of the car's path is __36__ π or about __113.1__ meters.

🌐 **Go Online** You can complete an Extra Example online.

570 Module 10 · Circles

Interactive Presentation

Identify Segments in a Circle ✕

Name the circle and identify a radius, a chord, and a diameter of the circle.

Tap on each button to identify and name the parts of the circle.

$\overline{TZ}$ contains the center, so $\overline{TZ}$ is a diameter.

Example 1

TAP

Students tap to reveal parts of a solution.

TYPE

Students answer a question to show they understand how to identify segments in a circle.

Right page

Example 1 Identify Segments in a Circle

MP Teaching the Mathematical Practices

6 Communicate Precisely Encourage students to routinely write or explain their solution methods. Point out that they should use clear definitions when they discuss their solutions with others.

Questions for Mathematical Discourse

AL Define a chord in your own words. Sample answer: A chord is any segment that has both endpoints on the same circle.

OL How many chords and radii are in a diameter? one chord; two radii

BL How can you tell if a chord is a diameter? A chord is a diameter if it contains the center of the circle.

Example 2 Use Radius and Diameter Relationships

MP Teaching the Mathematical Practices

4 Use Tools Point out that to solve the problem in this example, students will need to use the Radius Formula.

Questions for Mathematical Discourse

AL If the radius of a circle is 5 cm, what is the diameter? 10 cm

OL If the diameter of a circle is 15 in, what is the radius of the circle? 7.5 in.

BL If the radius of a circle is $x + 3$ and the diameter is $3x + 1$, what is x? 5

Common Error

Students may use mental math to solve this problem, and may confuse whether to multiply or divide by 2. Remind them to check their work, because the radius must be shorter than the diameter.

🌐 Example 3 Find Circumference

MP Teaching the Mathematical Practices

5 Use a Source Guide students to find external information to answer the questions posed in the Use a Source feature.

Questions for Mathematical Discourse

AL To what measure in polygons does circumference correspond? perimeter

OL If the radius of a circle is 9 ft, what is the circumference of the circle? about 56.5 ft

BL The circumference of a circle is 33 cm. What is the diameter of the circle to the nearest tenth? 10.5 cm

1 CONCEPTUAL UNDERSTANDING   **2 FLUENCY**   3 APPLICATION

Example 4 Find Diameter and Radius

MP Teaching the Mathematical Practices

6 Use Precision In this example, students must calculate accurately and efficiently and express numerical answers with a degree of precision appropriate to the problem context.

Questions for Mathematical Discourse

AL If the circumference is 345 mm, what is the radius? about 54.9 mm

OL What is the formula for the circumference in terms of radius r?
$C = 2\pi r$

BL If the circumference of a circle is $2\pi x + 6\pi$, what is the radius?
$x + 3$

DIFFERENTIATE

Enrichment Activity BL

Have students answer the following question. An asteroid hit Earth and created a huge round crater. Scientists measured the distance around the crater as 78.5 miles. What was the diameter of the crater?
about 25 miles

Check

AUTOMOBILES Many automobiles have customized rims that are attached to wheels and align with the inner edges of the tires. The rim of a tire has a radius of 7.5 inches, and the width of the tire is 6 inches.

Part A Find the circumference of the rim.

A. $\frac{15\pi}{2}$ in.   B. 13.5π in.   C.) 15π in.   D. 27π in.

Part B What assumptions did you make while solving this problem? Select all that apply.

A. I assumed the radius of the tire rim.
B.) I assumed that the tire rim was a perfect circle.
C. I assumed the width of the tire.
D.) I assumed there was no space between the tire and the rim.
E. I assumed the tire and rim were not the same shape.

Example 4 Find Diameter and Radius

Find the diameter and radius of a circle to the nearest hundredth if the circumference of the circle is 77.8 centimeters.

Find the diameter.

$C = \pi d$	Circumference Formula
$\underline{77.8} = \pi d$	Substitution
$\frac{77.8}{\pi} = d$	Divide each side by π.
$\underline{24.76} \approx d$	Use a calculator.

The diameter of the circle is about 24.76 centimeters. Use the diameter of the circle to find the radius.

$r = \frac{1}{2}d$	Radius Formula
$\approx \frac{1}{2}(\underline{24.76})$	$d \approx 24.76$
$\approx \underline{12.38}$	Use a calculator.

So, the radius of the circle is about $\underline{12.38}$ centimeters.

Check

Find the diameter and radius of a circle to the nearest hundredth if the circumference of the circle is 94.2 yards.

Part A Select the most appropriate estimates of the diameter and radius.

A. 15.7 yd; 7.85 yd.   B. 26.91 yd; 13.46 yd
C. 18.84 yd; 9.42 yd   D.) 31.4 yd; 15.7 yd

Part B Find the diameter and radius of the circle to the nearest hundredth.

diameter = $\underline{29.98}$ yd
radius = $\underline{14.99}$ yd

 Go Online You can complete an Extra Example online.

Copyright © McGraw-Hill Education

> **Study Tip**
>
> **Levels of Accuracy**
> Because π is irrational, its value cannot be given as a terminating decimal. Using a value of 3 for π provides a quick estimate in calculations. Using a value of 3.14 or $\frac{22}{7}$ provides a closer approximation. For the most accurate approximation, use the π key on a calculator. Unless stated otherwise, assume that in this course, a calculator with a π key was used to generate answers.

Lesson 10-1 · Circles and Circumference 571

Interactive Presentation

Example 4

TAP	
	Students tap to move through the steps to find the diameter and radius.

CHECK	
	Students complete the Check online to determine whether they are ready to move on.

1 CONCEPTUAL UNDERSTANDING | **2 FLUENCY** | 3 APPLICATION

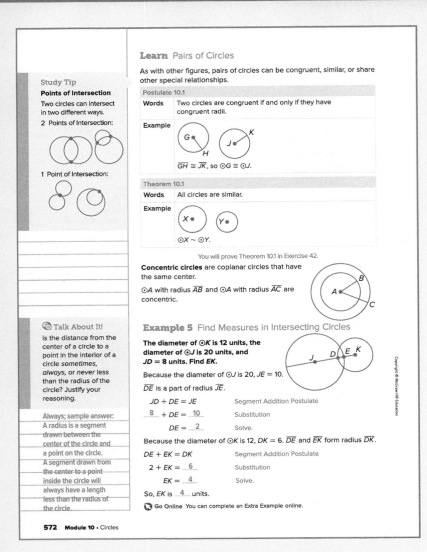

Learn Pairs of Circles

As with other figures, pairs of circles can be congruent, similar, or share other special relationships.

Study Tip

Points of Intersection

Two circles can intersect in two different ways.

2 Points of Intersection:

1 Point of Intersection:

Postulate 10.1

Words	Two circles are congruent if and only if they have congruent radii.
Example	$\overline{GH} \cong \overline{JK}$, so $\odot G \cong \odot J$.

Theorem 10.1

Words	All circles are similar.
Example	$\odot X \sim \odot Y.$

You will prove Theorem 10.1 in Exercise 42.

Concentric circles are coplanar circles that have the same center.

$\odot A$ with radius $\overline{AB}$ and $\odot A$ with radius $\overline{AC}$ are concentric.

Talk About It!

Is the distance from the center of a circle to a point in the interior of a circle *sometimes*, *always*, or *never* less than the radius of the circle? Justify your reasoning.

Always; sample answer: A radius is a segment drawn between the center of the circle and a point on the circle. A segment drawn from the center to a point inside the circle will always have a length less than the radius of the circle.

Example 5 Find Measures in Intersecting Circles

The diameter of $\odot K$ is 12 units, the diameter of $\odot J$ is 20 units, and $JD = 8$ units. Find EK.

Because the diameter of $\odot J$ is 20, $JE = 10$.

$\overline{DE}$ is a part of radius $\overline{JE}$.

$JD + DE = JE$	Segment Addition Postulate
$8 + DE = 10$	Substitution
$DE = 2$	Solve.

Because the diameter of $\odot K$ is 12, $DK = 6$. $\overline{DE}$ and $\overline{EK}$ form radius $\overline{DK}$.

$DE + EK = DK$	Segment Addition Postulate
$2 + EK = 6$	Substitution
$EK = 4$	Solve.

So, EK is 4 units.

Go Online You can complete an Extra Example online.

Interactive Presentation

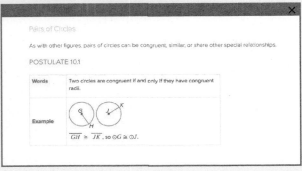

Pairs of Circles

As with other figures, pairs of circles can be congruent, similar, or share other special relationships.

POSTULATE 10.1

Words	Two circles are congruent if and only if they have congruent radii.
Example	$\overline{GH} \cong \overline{JK}$, so $\odot G \cong \odot J$.

Learn

TYPE

Students answer a question to show they understand the parts of a circle.

CHECK

Students complete the Check online to determine whether they are ready to move on.

Learn Pairs of Circles

Objective

Students find measures in intersecting circles and prove relationships between circles.

MP Teaching the Mathematical Practices

3 Construct Arguments In this Learn, students will use stated assumptions, definitions, and previously established results to construct an argument.

Example 5 Find Measures in Intersecting Circles

MP Teaching the Mathematical Practices

6 Communicate Precisely Encourage students to routinely write or explain their solution methods. Point out that they should use clear definitions when they discuss their solutions with others.

Questions for Mathematical Discourse

AL Why is $JE = 10$? It is a radius of $\odot J$ and the diameter is 20 units.

OL What is JK? 14 units

BL What is the length of the figure formed by both circles through the centers of both circles? 30 units

Exit Ticket

Recommended Use

At the end of class, go online to display the Exit Ticket prompt and ask students to respond using a separate piece of paper. Have students hand you their responses as they leave the room.

Alternate Use

At the end of class, go online to display the Exit Ticket prompt and ask students to respond verbally or by using a mini-whiteboard. Have students hold up their whiteboards so that you can see all student responses. Tap to reveal the answer when most or all students have completed the Exit Ticket.

Practice and Homework

Suggested Assignments

Use the table below to select appropriate exercises.

DOK	Topic	Exercises
1, 2	exercises that mirror the examples	1–26
2	exercises that use a variety of skills from this lesson	27–41
2	exercises that extend concepts learned in this lesson to new contexts	42–47
3	exercises that emphasize higher-order and critical-thinking skills	48–51

ASSESS AND DIFFERENTIATE

📊 Use the data from the **Checks** to determine whether to provide resources for extension, remediation, or intervention.

IF students score 90% or more on the Checks,   **BL**
THEN assign:

- Practice, Exercises 1–47 odd, 48–51
- Extension: Circumference and RPMs
- 🅰 **ALEKS** Circumferences and Areas of Circles, Segments in a Circle and Tangent Lines

IF students score 66%–89% on the Checks,   **OL**
THEN assign:

- Practice, Exercises 1–51 odd
- Remediation, Review Resources: Circumference of Circles
- Personal Tutors
- Extra Examples 1–5
- 🅰 **ALEKS** Using Radii and Diameters

IF students score 65% or less on the Checks,   **AL**
THEN assign:

- Practice, Exercises 1–25 odd
- Remediation, Review Resources: Circumference of Circles
- *Quick Review Math Handbook*: Circles and Circumference
- 🅰 **ALEKS** Using Radii and Diameters

Name _____ Period _____ Date _____

Practice

🖥 **Go Online** You can complete your homework online.

Example 1

For Exercises 1–3, refer to the circle at the right.

1. Name the circle. $\odot O$

2. Name the radii of the circle. $\overline{AO}, \overline{BO}, \overline{CO},$ and $\overline{DO}$

3. Name the chords of the circle. $\overline{AB}$ and $\overline{CD}$

For Exercises 4–8, refer to the circle at the right.

4. Name the circle. $\odot P$

5. Name the radii of the circle. $\overline{PA}, \overline{PB},$ and $\overline{PC}$

6. Name the chords of the circle. $\overline{AB}$ and $\overline{DE}$

7. Name a diameter of the circle. $\overline{AB}$

8. Name a radius not drawn as part of a diameter. $\overline{PC}$

Example 2

For Exercises 9–11, refer to $\odot R$.

9. If $AB = 18$ millimeters, find AR. 9 mm

10. If $RY = 10$ inches, find AR and AB. $AR = 10$ in.; $AB = 20$ in.

11. Is $\overline{AB} \cong \overline{XY}$? Explain.
Yes; all diameters of the same circle are congruent.

For Exercises 12–14, refer to $\odot L$.

12. Suppose the radius of the circle is 3.5 yards. Find the diameter. 7 yd

13. If $RT = 19$ meters, find LW. 9.5 m

14. If $LT = 4.2$ inches, what is the diameter of $\odot L$? 8.4 inches

Example 3

15. TIRES A bicycle has tires with a diameter of 26 inches. Find the radius and circumference of each tire. Round your answer to the nearest hundredth, if necessary. 13 in.; 81.68 in.

---

16. STATE YOUR ASSUMPTION Herman purchased a sundial to use as the centerpiece for a garden. The diameter of the sundial is 9.5 inches.

   a. Find the radius of the sundial. 4.75 in.

   b. Find the circumference of the sundial to the nearest hundredth. 29.85 in.

   c. Explain any assumptions that you make while solving this problem. Sample answer: I assumed that the sundial was a perfect circle.

Example 4

Find the diameter and radius of a circle to the nearest hundredth with the given circumference.

17. $C = 40$ in. 12.73 in.; 6.37 in.   18. $C = 256$ ft 81.49 ft; 40.74 ft

19. $C = 15.62$ m 4.97 m; 2.49 m   20. $C = 9$ cm 2.86 cm; 1.43 cm

21. $C = 79.5$ yd 25.31 yd; 12.65 yd   22. $C = 204.16$ m 64.99 m; 32.49 m

Example 5

The diameters of $\odot F$ and $\odot G$ are 5 and 6 units, respectively. Find each measure.

23. BF 0.5   24. AB 2

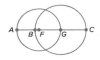

The diameters of $\odot L$ and $\odot M$ are 20 and 13 units, respectively, and $QR = 4$. Find each measure.

25. LQ 6   26. RM 2.5

Mixed Exercises

The radius, diameter, or circumference of a circle is given. Find each missing measure to the nearest hundredth.

27. $d = 8\frac{1}{2}$ in., $r = \underline{\ ?\ }$, $C = \underline{\ ?\ }$
4.25 in.; 26.70 in.

28. $r = 11\frac{2}{5}$ ft, $d = \underline{\ ?\ }$, $C = \underline{\ ?\ }$
22.80 ft; 71.63 ft

29. $C = 628$ m, $d = \underline{\ ?\ }$, $r = \underline{\ ?\ }$
199.90 m; 99.95 m

30. $d = \frac{3}{4}$ yd, $r = \underline{\ ?\ }$, $C = \underline{\ ?\ }$
0.38 yd; 2.36 yd

31. $C = 35x$ cm, $d = \underline{\ ?\ }$, $r = \underline{\ ?\ }$
11.14x cm; 5.57x cm

32. $r = \frac{x}{8}$, $d = \underline{\ ?\ }$, $C = \underline{\ ?\ }$
0.25x; 0.79x

1 CONCEPTUAL UNDERSTANDING   2 FLUENCY   3 APPLICATION

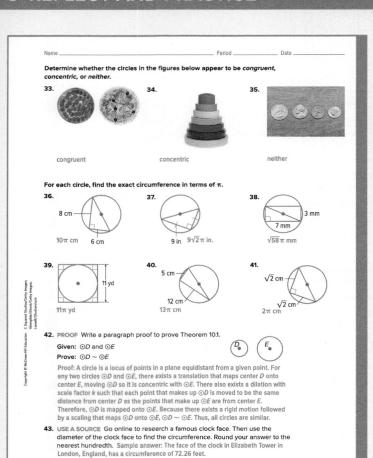

Name _____ Period _____ Date _____

Determine whether the circles in the figures below appear to be *congruent*, *concentric*, or *neither*.

33.   34.   35.

congruent   concentric   neither

For each circle, find the exact circumference in terms of π.

36.   37.   38.

8 cm   3 mm
                                             7 mm
10π cm   6 cm   9 in   9√2π in.   √58π mm

39.   40.   41.

        11 yd   5 cm   √2 cm
                       12 cm   √2 cm
11π yd   13π cm   2π cm

42. **PROOF** Write a paragraph proof to prove Theorem 10.1.

   Given: ⊙D and ⊙E
   Prove: ⊙D ~ ⊙E

   Proof: A circle is a locus of points in a plane equidistant from a given point. For any two circles ⊙D and ⊙E, there exists a translation that maps center D onto center E, moving ⊙D so it is concentric with ⊙E. There also exists a dilation with scale factor k such that each point that makes up ⊙D is moved to be the same distance from center D as the points that make up ⊙E are from center E. Therefore, ⊙D is mapped onto ⊙E. Because there exists a rigid motion followed by a scaling that maps ⊙D onto ⊙E, ⊙D ~ ⊙E. Thus, all circles are similar.

43. **USE A SOURCE** Go online to research a famous clock face. Then use the diameter of the clock face to find the circumference. Round your answer to the nearest hundredth. Sample answer: The face of the clock in Elizabeth Tower in London, England, has a circumference of 72.26 feet.

44. **WHEELS** Zack is designing wheels for a concept car. The diameter of the wheel is 18 inches. Zack wants to make spokes in the wheel that run from the center of the wheel to the rim. In other words, each spoke is a radius of the wheel. How long are these spokes? 9 in.

45. **PRECISION** Kathy slices through a circular cake. The cake has a diameter of 14 inches. The slice that Kathy made is straight and has a length of 11 inches. Did Kathy cut along a *radius*, a *diameter*, or a *chord* of the circle? chord

46. **REASONING** Three identical circular coins are lined up in a row as shown. The distance between the centers of the first and third coins is 3.2 centimeters. What is the radius of one of these coins? 0.8 cm
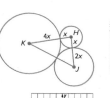

|← 3.2 cm →|

47. **EXERCISE HOOPS** Taiga wants to make a circular loop that he can twirl around his body for exercise. He will use a tube that is 2.5 meters long.

   a. What will be the diameter of Taiga's exercise hoop? Round your answer to the nearest thousandth of a meter. 0.796 m

   b. What will be the radius of Taiga's exercise hoop? Round your answer to the nearest thousandth of a meter. 0.398 m

Higher-Order Thinking Skills

48. **WRITE** How can we describe the relationships that exist between circles and line segments? See margin.

49. **PERSEVERE** The sum of the circumferences of circles H, J, and K shown at the right is 56π units. Find KJ. 24 units

50. **ANALYZE** Is the distance from the center of a circle to a point in the interior of a circle *sometimes*, *always*, or *never* less than the radius of the circle? Justify your argument. Always; a radius is a segment drawn between the center of the circle and a point on the circle. A segment drawn from the center to a point inside the circle will always have a length less than the radius of the circle.

51. **CREATE** Design a sequence of transformations that can be used to prove that ⊙D is similar to ⊙E. See margin.

Answers

48. Sample answer: A line segment with endpoints on a circle can be described as a chord. If the chord passes through the center of the circle, it can be described as a diameter. A line segment with endpoints at the center and on the circle can be described as a radius.

51. Sample answer: First apply the translation $(x, y) \rightarrow (x - 3, y - 4)$ to ⊙D. The dilation should have a scale factor of 3 and be centered at $(-1, -1)$. The translation and dilation are similarity transformations, so ⊙D is similar to ⊙E.

Measuring Angles and Arcs

LESSON GOAL

Students find measures of angles and arcs using the properties of circles.

1 LAUNCH

 Launch the lesson with a **Warm Up** and an introduction.

2 EXPLORE AND DEVELOP

 Develop:

Measuring Angles and Arcs
- Find Measures of Central Angles
- Classify Arcs and Find Arc Measures
- Find Arc Measures in Circle Graphs
- Use Arc Addition to Find Measures of Arcs

 Explore: Relationships Between Arc Lengths and Radii

 Develop:

Arc Length and Radian Measure
- Find Arc Length by Using Degrees
- Convert From Degrees to Radian Measure
- Convert From Radian Measure to Degrees
- Find Arc Length by Using Radian Measure

 You may want your students to complete the **Checks** online.

3 REFLECT AND PRACTICE

 Exit Ticket

 Practice

DIFFERENTIATE

 View reports of student progress on the **Checks** after each example.

Resources	AL	OL	BL	ELL
Remediation: Circles and Circumference	●	●		●
Extension: Curves of Constant Width		●	●	●

Language Development Handbook

Assign page 67 of the *Language Development Handbook* to help your students build mathematical language related to the properties of circles.

ELL You can use the tips and suggestions on page T67 of the handbook to support students who are building English proficiency.

Suggested Pacing

90 min	**0.5 day**	
45 min		**1 day**

Focus

Domain: Geometry

Standards for Mathematical Content:

G.C.2 Identify and describe relationships among inscribed angles, radii, and chords.

G.C.5 Derive using similarity the fact that the length of the arc intercepted by an angle is proportional to the radius, and define the radian measure of the angle as the constant of proportionality; derive the formula for the area of a sector.

Standards for Mathematical Practice:

1 Make sense of problems and persevere in solving them.

2 Reason abstractly and quantitatively.

3 Construct viable arguments and critique the reasoning of others.

Coherence

Vertical Alignment

Previous
Students found and applied the formulas for the circumference and area of a circle.
7.G.4, G.GMD.1

Now
Students find measures of angles and arcs in circles.
G.C.2, G.C.5

Next
Students will solve problems using the relationships between arcs, chords, and diameters.
G.C.2

Rigor

The Three Pillars of Rigor

1 CONCEPTUAL UNDERSTANDING	2 FLUENCY	3 APPLICATION

Conceptual Bridge In this lesson, students extend their understanding of circles to parts of circles. They build fluency by deriving the definition of the lengths of arcs, and they apply their understanding by solving real-world problems.

Mathematical Background

A *central angle of a circle* has the center of the circle as its vertex, and its sides are two radii of the circle. A central angle separates the circle into two parts, each of which is an *arc*. The measure of each arc is related to the measure of its central angle. A *minor arc* degree measure equals the measure of the central angle and is less than 180°. A *semicircle* is also considered an arc and has a measure of 180°.

Interactive Presentation

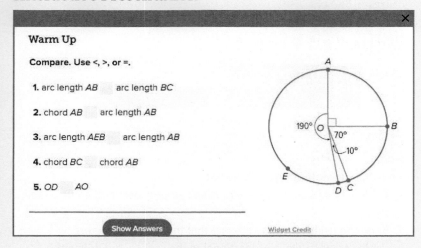

Warm Up

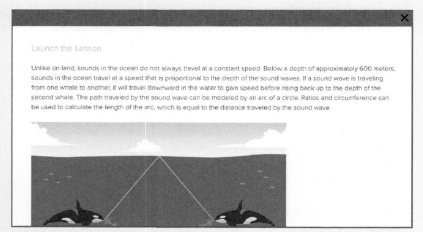

Launch the Lesson

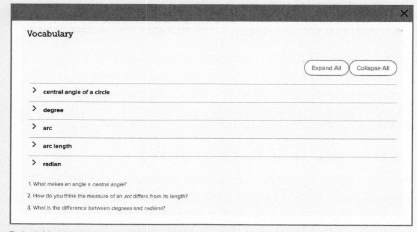

Today's Vocabulary

Warm Up

Prerequisite Skills

The Warm Up exercises address the following prerequisite skill for this lesson:

- comparing chord lengths and arc lengths

Answers:

1. $>$
2. $<$
3. $>$
4. $<$
5. $=$

Launch the Lesson

 Teaching the Mathematical Practices

4 Apply Mathematics In this Launch the Lesson, students can see a real-world application of arcs of circles.

Go Online to find additional teaching notes and questions to promote classroom discourse.

Today's Standards

Tell students that they will be addressing these content and practice standards in this lesson. You may wish to have a student volunteer read aloud *How can I meet these standards?* and *How can I use these practices?*, and connect these to the standards.

See the Interactive Presentation for I Can statements that align with the standards covered in this lesson.

Today's Vocabulary

Tell students that they will be using these vocabulary terms in this lesson. You can expand each row if you wish to share the definitions. Then, discuss the questions below with the class.

Explore Relationships Between Arc Lengths and Radii

Objective

Students use dynamic geometry software and similarity to derive the fact that the length of an arc intercepted by an angle is proportional to the radius and define the radian measure of the angle as the constant of proportionality.

 Teaching the Mathematical Practices

> **2 Represent a Situation Symbolically** Guide students to define variables to solve the problem in this Explore. Help students to identify the independent and dependent variables. Then work with them to find the other relationships in the problem.

Ideas for Use

Recommended Use Present the Inquiry Question, or have a student volunteer read it aloud. Have students work in pairs to complete the Explore activity on their devices. Pairs should discuss each of the questions. Monitor student progress during the activity. Upon completion of the Explore activity, have student volunteers share their responses to the Inquiry Question.

What if my students don't have devices? You may choose to project the activity on a whiteboard. A printable worksheet for each Explore is available online. You may choose to print the worksheet so that individuals or pairs of students can use it to record their observations.

Summary of the Activity

Students will complete guiding exercises throughout the Explore activity. Students begin by using dynamic geometry software to measure the radius and arc length for the same angle using three different circles. In each case students compute the ratio of the arc length to the radius. Students then complete guiding questions to conjecture that this ratio does not change when the circle changes, and that the ratio is equal to the radian measure of the angle. Students then write an equation for arc length. Then, students will answer the Inquiry Question.

(continued on the next page)

Interactive Presentation

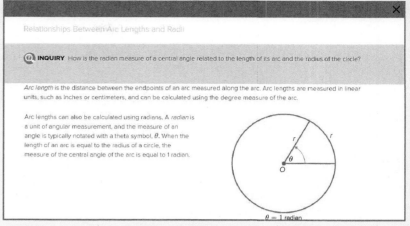

Explore

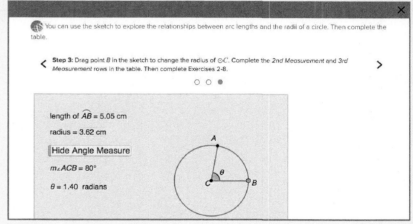

Explore

WEB SKETCHPAD

Students use a sketch to explore the relationship between arc lengths, radii, and central angles.

1 CONCEPTUAL UNDERSTANDING | 2 FLUENCY | 3 APPLICATION

Interactive Presentation

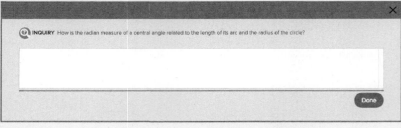

Explore

TYPE

a| Students respond to the Inquiry Question and can view a sample answer.

Explore Relationships Between Arc Lengths and Radii (*continued*)

MP Teaching the Mathematical Practices

> **2 Represent a Situation Symbolically** Guide students to define variables to solve the problem in this Explore. Help students to identify the independent and dependent variables. Then work with them to find the other relationships in the problem.

Questions

Have students complete the Explore activity.

Ask:
- Why do you think the arc length is used in relation to the angle? Sample answer: The arc length appears to be the part of the circle formed by the central angle. It makes sense to focus on just that length if we're looking for a way to measure that angle.
- How many radians do you think are in half a revolution of the circle? Sample answer: If one full revolution is 2π radians, then half a revolution should be π radians.

Inquiry

How is the radian measure of a central angle related to the length of its arc and the radius of the circle? Sample answer: The radian measure of a central angle is equal to the length of its arc divided by the radius of the circle.

 Go Online to find additional teaching notes and sample answers for the guiding exercises.

1 CONCEPTUAL UNDERSTANDING | 2 FLUENCY | 3 APPLICATION

Learn Measuring Angles and Arcs

Objective
Students find measures of angles and arcs using the properties of circles.

 Teaching the Mathematical Practices

7 Use Structure Help students to explore the structure of central angles of circles in this Learn.

What Students Are Learning

There are two ways to apply measurement to arcs, so helping students determine which type of measure they should use in a problem is important. The first way to measure arcs is with the *arc measure*, the degree or radian measure of the central angle corresponding to the arc. It is more useful in problems dealing with central angles and related concepts. The second method is *arc length*, the distance around the portion of the circumference the arc represents. This method comes up when considering distance along the circle or circumference in problems.

Go Online

- Find additional teaching notes.
- View performance reports of the Checks.
- Assign or present an Extra Example.

DIFFERENTIATE

Language Development Activity ELL

Intermediate Before reading the lesson, have students take a close look at the visual support. Have them use the diagrams in the Key Concepts as they work in pairs to form questions about measuring angles and arcs. After reading, have partners discuss how their ideas changed or stayed the same. Move around the room to monitor progress.

Advanced Have student pairs take turns reading the text to one another. Move around the room, correcting pronunciation as necessary. Ask students what they learn from the title and how the title makes them approach the text. What do they know about angles or arcs of circles, and what do they expect to learn? Have them share with the class. Record their contributions on the board.

Advanced High Have students write a paragraph explaining and evaluating the diagrams in the Key Concepts and Theorems in relation to the content of the lesson. What was its purpose? How effective was it? Have volunteers share their evaluations with the group.

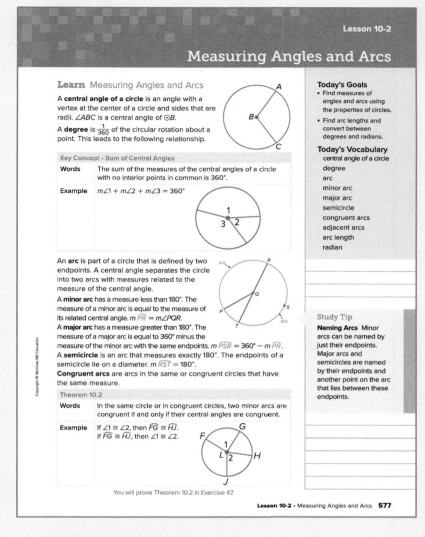

Lesson 10-2

Measuring Angles and Arcs

Learn Measuring Angles and Arcs

A **central angle of a circle** is an angle with a vertex at the center of a circle and sides that are radii. $\angle ABC$ is a central angle of $\odot B$.

A **degree** is $\frac{1}{360}$ of the circular rotation about a point. This leads to the following relationship.

Key Concept · Sum of Central Angles

Words	The sum of the measures of the central angles of a circle with no interior points in common is 360°.
Example	$m\angle 1 + m\angle 2 + m\angle 3 = 360°$

An **arc** is part of a circle that is defined by two endpoints. A central angle separates the circle into two arcs with measures related to the measure of the central angle.

A **minor arc** has a measure less than 180°. The measure of a minor arc is equal to the measure of its related central angle. $m\overset{\frown}{PR} = m\angle PQR$.

A **major arc** has a measure greater than 180°. The measure of a major arc is equal to 360° minus the measure of the minor arc with the same endpoints. $m\overset{\frown}{PSR} = 360° - m\overset{\frown}{PR}$.

A **semicircle** is an arc that measures exactly 180°. The endpoints of a semicircle lie on a diameter. $m\overset{\frown}{RST} = 180°$.

Congruent arcs are arcs in the same or congruent circles that have the same measure.

Theorem 10.2

Words	In the same circle or in congruent circles, two minor arcs are congruent if and only if their central angles are congruent.
Example	If $\angle 1 \cong \angle 2$, then $\overset{\frown}{FG} \cong \overset{\frown}{HJ}$. If $\overset{\frown}{FG} \cong \overset{\frown}{HJ}$, then $\angle 1 \cong \angle 2$.

You will prove Theorem 10.2 in Exercise 47.

Lesson 10-2 · Measuring Angles and Arcs 577

Today's Goals
- Find measures of angles and arcs using the properties of circles.
- Find arc lengths and convert between degrees and radians.

Today's Vocabulary
central angle of a circle
degree
arc
minor arc
major arc
semicircle
congruent arcs
adjacent arcs
arc length
radian

Study Tip
Naming Arcs Minor arcs can be named by just their endpoints. Major arcs and semicircles are named by their endpoints and another point on the arc that lies between these endpoints.

Interactive Presentation

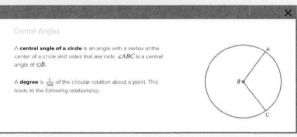

Central Angles

A **central angle of a circle** is an angle with a vertex at the center of a circle and sides that are radii. $\angle ABC$ is a central angle of $\odot B$.

A **degree** is $\frac{1}{360}$ of the circular rotation about a point. This leads to the following relationship.

Learn

TAP

Students tap to see more information about minor arcs, major arcs, and semicircles.

1 CONCEPTUAL UNDERSTANDING | 2 FLUENCY | 3 APPLICATION

Your Notes

 Go Online
You can watch a video to see the characteristics of arcs.

 Go Online
You may want to complete the Concept Check to check your understanding.

💭 **Think About It!**
What part of a circle is represented by the sides of a central angle?

radii

Arcs in a circle that have exactly one point in common are called **adjacent arcs**. In ⊙M, $\overparen{HJ}$ and $\overparen{JK}$ are adjacent arcs. As with adjacent angles, you can add the measures of adjacent arcs.

Postulate 10.2: Arc Addition Postulate

Words	The measure of an arc formed by two adjacent arcs is the sum of the measures of the two arcs.
Example	$m\overparen{XZ} = m\overparen{XY} + m\overparen{YZ}$.

Example 1 Find Measures of Central Angles

Find the value of x.

$m\angle EAB + m\angle BAC + m\angle CAD + m\angle DAE = 360°$ Sum of central angles

$90 + 40 + 85 + x = 360$ Substitution

$\underline{215} + x = 360$ Simplify.

$x = \underline{145}$ Solve.

Check

Find the value of x.

$x = \underline{50}$

Example 2 Classify Arcs and Find Arc Measures

$\overline{PM}$ is a diameter of ⊙R. Identify each arc as a *major arc*, *minor arc*, or *semicircle*. Then find its measure.

a. $\overparen{MQ}$

$\overparen{MQ}$ is a minor arc, so $m\overparen{MQ} = m\angle MRQ$. Because ∠MRQ and ∠PRQ are linear pairs, $m\angle MRQ = 180 - 115$ or $\underline{65°}$. So, $m\overparen{MQ} = \underline{65°}$.

🖥 **Go Online** You can complete an Extra Example online.

578 Module 10 • Circles

Interactive Presentation

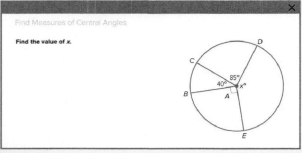

Find Measures of Central Angles

Find the value of x.

Example 1

TYPE

 a|

Students type to complete the solution.

Example 1 Find Measures of Central Angles

🅜🅟 **Teaching the Mathematical Practices** —

6 Communicate Precisely Encourage students to routinely write or explain their solution methods. Point out that they should use clear definitions when they discuss their solutions with others.

Questions for Mathematical Discourse

AL How do we know that $m\angle BAE$ is 90°? Sample answer: The diagram includes a right angle mark for ∠BAE.

OL How can we check the reasonableness of our solution? Sample answer: Compare ∠DAE to ∠CAE.

BL What would the measure of the central angle created by a diameter of the circle be? 180°

Example 2 Classify Arcs and Find Arc Measures

🅜🅟 **Teaching the Mathematical Practices** —

8 Attend to Details Mathematically proficient students continually ask themselves, "Does this make sense?" Point out that in this example, students will evaluate the reasonableness of their answer.

Questions for Mathematical Discourse

AL Describe the difference between a major arc, a minor arc, and a semicircle. Sample answer: A major arc has a measure greater than 180° and less than 360°. A minor arc measures less than 180°. A semicircle measures exactly 180°.

OL What is $m\overparen{NMQ}$? 155°

BL Can a circle contain both a major arc and a semicircle? Explain. Yes; sample answer: The major arc and the semicircle must overlap, but a circle can contain each.

2222

Example 3 Find Arc Measures in Circle Graphs

MP Teaching the Mathematical Practices

3 Construct Arguments In this example, students will use stated assumptions, definitions, and previously established results to construct an argument.

Questions for Mathematical Discourse

AL Why did we find 12% of 360°? because 360° represents the whole circle and we are looking for 12% of the whole

OL Find the arc measure for the area representing Social Media. 158.4°

BL Which activity is represented by a sector with arc measure 72°? videos

Talk About It! Answer:

No; sample answer: Because no section of the circle graph is 12% or can be combined with an adjacent section to form 12% of the graph, there is no arc that has the same measure as $\widehat{DE}$. Therefore, no arc is congruent to $\widehat{DE}$.

Example 4 Use Arc Addition to Find Measures of Arcs

MP Teaching the Mathematical Practices

2 Create Representations Guide students to write an equation that models the situation in this example. Then use the equation to solve the problem.

Questions for Mathematical Discourse

AL How would you find $m\widehat{XYZ}$? $m\widehat{XY} + m\widehat{YZ}$

OL What is $m\widehat{XWY}$? 298°

BL Can you find $m\widehat{XYZ}$? Explain. No; sample answer: You do not have enough information to find $m\widehat{YZ}$, so you cannot add that to 62° to get $m\widehat{XYZ}$.

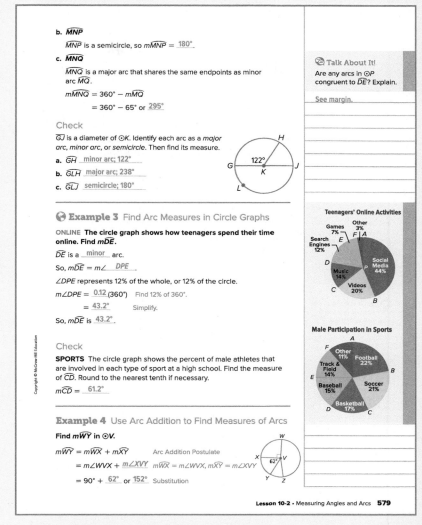

b. $\widehat{MNP}$

$\widehat{MNP}$ is a semicircle, so $m\widehat{MNP} = 180°$.

c. $\widehat{MNQ}$

$\widehat{MNQ}$ is a major arc that shares the same endpoints as minor arc $\widehat{MQ}$.

$m\widehat{MNQ} = 360° - m\widehat{MQ}$

$= 360° - 65°$ or $295°$

Check

$\overline{GJ}$ is a diameter of $\odot K$. Identify each arc as a *major arc, minor arc,* or *semicircle.* Then find its measure.

a. $\widehat{GH}$ minor arc; 122°

b. $\widehat{GLH}$ major arc; 238°

c. $\widehat{GLJ}$ semicircle; 180°

Talk About It!
Are any arcs in $\odot P$ congruent to $\widehat{DE}$? Explain.

See margin.

Example 3 Find Arc Measures in Circle Graphs

ONLINE **The circle graph shows how teenagers spend their time online. Find $m\widehat{DE}$.**

$\widehat{DE}$ is a minor arc.

So, $m\widehat{DE} = m\angle$ DPE .

$\angle DPE$ represents 12% of the whole, or 12% of the circle.

$m\angle DPE = 0.12 (360°)$ Find 12% of 360°.

$= 43.2°$ Simplify.

So, $m\widehat{DE}$ is $43.2°$.

Check

SPORTS The circle graph shows the percent of male athletes that are involved in each type of sport at a high school. Find the measure of $\widehat{CD}$. Round to the nearest tenth if necessary.

$m\widehat{CD} = 61.2°$

Example 4 Use Arc Addition to Find Measures of Arcs

Find $m\widehat{WY}$ in $\odot V$.

$m\widehat{WY} = m\widehat{WX} + m\widehat{XY}$ Arc Addition Postulate

$= m\angle WVX + m\angle XVY$ $m\widehat{WX} = m\angle WVX, m\widehat{XY} = m\angle XVY$

$= 90° + 62°$ or $152°$ Substitution

Lesson 10-2 • Measuring Angles and Arcs **579**

Interactive Presentation

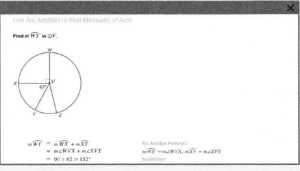

Example 4

TAP

Students tap to see steps in a solution.

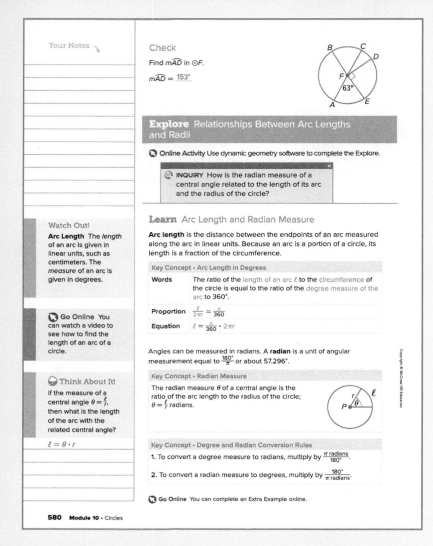

1 CONCEPTUAL UNDERSTANDING | **2 FLUENCY** | 3 APPLICATION

Learn Arc Length and Radian Measure

Objective
Students find arc lengths and convert between degrees and radians.

Teaching the Mathematical Practices

6 Use Quantities Use the Watch Out! to guide students to clarify their use of quantities in this example. Ensure that they specify the units of measure used in the problem and label axes appropriately.

6 Communicate Precisely Encourage students to routinely write or explain their solution methods. Point out that they should use clear definitions when they discuss their solutions with others.

Interactive Presentation

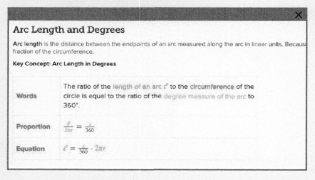

Arc Length and Degrees

Arc length is the distance between the endpoints of an arc measured along the arc in linear units. Because fraction of the circumference.

Key Concept: Arc Length in Degrees

Words	The ratio of the length of an arc ℓ to the circumference of the circle is equal to the ratio of the degree measure of the arc to 360°.
Proportion	$\frac{\ell}{2\pi r} = \frac{x}{360}$
Equation	$\ell = \frac{x}{360} \cdot 2\pi r$

TAP

Students tap to learn more about arc length, circumference, and degree measure of the arc.

CHECK

Students complete the Check online to determine whether they are ready to move on.

1 CONCEPTUAL UNDERSTANDING   **2 FLUENCY**   3 APPLICATION

Example 5 Find Arc Length by Using Degrees

Teaching the Mathematical Practices

1 Understand the Approaches of Others Work with students to look at the Alternate Method. Ask students to compare and contrast the original method and the alternate method.

Questions for Mathematical Discourse

AL Why did we use 7 instead of 14 for r? 14 is the diameter, so the radius r is 7.

OL If the radius is 6 m, what is $\widehat{AB}$? about 8.38 m

BL What is the length of the major arc formed by the endpoints A and B? about 34.21 m

Example 6 Convert From Degrees to Radian Measure

Teaching the Mathematical Practices

2 Consider Units Point out that it is important to note the units involved in this problem.

Questions for Mathematical Discourse

AL Why do you multiply by $\frac{\pi}{180°}$ in this problem instead of $\frac{180°}{\pi}$?
Sample answer: This way the degrees cancel to get just radians.

OL What is the approximate value of $\frac{3\pi}{4}$? 2.36

BL What is $\frac{5\pi}{6}$ in degrees? 150°

Example 7 Convert From Radian Measure to Degrees

Teaching the Mathematical Practices

3 Compare Arguments Mathematically proficient students can compare arguments, determine which one is flawed, and explain the flaw. In this example, students have to identify the flawed argument and choose the correct one.

Questions for Mathematical Discourse

AL Why do you multiply by $\frac{180°}{\pi}$ in this problem instead of $\frac{\pi}{180°}$? Sample answer: This way the radians cancel to get just degrees.

OL What is 1 radian in degrees? about 57.3

BL What is 1 degree in radians? about 0.017

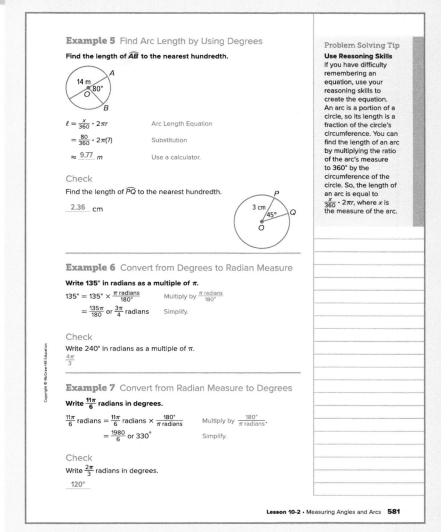

Example 5 Find Arc Length by Using Degrees

Find the length of $\widehat{AB}$ to the nearest hundredth.

$\ell = \frac{x}{360} \cdot 2\pi r$ Arc Length Equation

   $= \frac{80}{360} \cdot 2\pi(7)$ Substitution

   $\approx \underline{9.77}$ m   Use a calculator.

Check
Find the length of $\widehat{PQ}$ to the nearest hundredth.

   $\underline{2.36}$ cm

Example 6 Convert from Degrees to Radian Measure

Write 135° in radians as a multiple of π.

$135° = 135° \times \frac{\pi \text{ radians}}{180°}$ Multiply by $\frac{\pi \text{ radians}}{180°}$

     $= \frac{135\pi}{180}$ or $\frac{3\pi}{4}$ radians   Simplify.

Check
Write 240° in radians as a multiple of π.
$\frac{4\pi}{3}$

Example 7 Convert from Radian Measure to Degrees

Write $\frac{11\pi}{6}$ radians in degrees.

$\frac{11\pi}{6}$ radians $= \frac{11\pi}{6}$ radians $\times \frac{180°}{\pi \text{ radians}}$ Multiply by $\frac{180°}{\pi \text{ radians}}$.

     $= \frac{1980}{6}$ or 330°   Simplify.

Check
Write $\frac{2\pi}{3}$ radians in degrees.
   $\underline{120°}$

Problem Solving Tip
Use Reasoning Skills
If you have difficulty remembering an equation, use your reasoning skills to create the equation. An arc is a portion of a circle, so its length is a fraction of the circle's circumference. You can find the length of an arc by multiplying the ratio of the arc's measure to 360° by the circumference of the circle. So, the length of an arc is equal to $\frac{x}{360} \cdot 2\pi r$, where x is the measure of the arc.

Lesson 10-2 · Measuring Angles and Arcs   **581**

Interactive Presentation

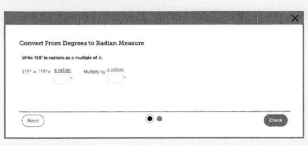

Example 6

TYPE

Students enter values to calculate the solution.

Your Notes

Example 8 Find Arc Length by Using Radian Measure

Find the length of $\widehat{ZY}$ to the nearest hundredth.

🤔 **Think About It!**

Check your answer to the problem.

What method did you use to check your answer?

Sample answer: I converted the radian measure $\frac{3\pi}{4}$ to degrees and calculated the length of $\widehat{ZY}$ using the arc length equation $\ell = \frac{x}{360} \cdot 2\pi r$.

$\theta = \frac{\ell}{r}$	Arc length Equation
$\frac{3\pi}{4} = \frac{\ell}{9}$	$\theta = \frac{3\pi}{4}, r = 9$
$9\left(\frac{3\pi}{4}\right) = \ell$	Multiply each side by 9.
$\frac{27\pi}{4} = \ell$	Use a calculator.
$21.21 \approx \ell$	

So, the length of $\widehat{ZY}$ is about __21.21__ centimeters.

Check

Find the length of $\widehat{MN}$ to the nearest hundredth.

__3.67__ in.

Pause and Reflect

Did you struggle with anything in this lesson? If so, how did you deal with it?

💬 Record your observations here.   See students' observations.

🔵 **Go Online** You can complete an Extra Example online.

582 Module 10 · Circles

Example 8 Find Arc Length by Using Radian Measure

Questions for Mathematical Discourse

AL How are radians similar to degrees? Different? Sample answer: Both are used to measure central angles of a circle. Degrees are not based on arc length and radius of the circle, but radians are.

OL What is the arc length of $\widehat{ZY}$ if the radius is 10 cm? 13.46 cm

BL Do you think you can compare a radian value and a degree value? Explain. Yes; sample answer: If you convert either value to the other unit, you can compare the values.

Exit Ticket

Recommended Use

At the end of class, go online to display the Exit Ticket prompt and ask students to respond using a separate piece of paper. Have students hand you their responses as they leave the room.

Alternate Use

At the end of class, go online to display the Exit Ticket prompt and ask students to respond verbally or by using a mini-whiteboard. Have students hold up their whiteboards so that you can see all student responses. Tap to reveal the answer when most or all students have completed the Exit Ticket.

Interactive Presentation

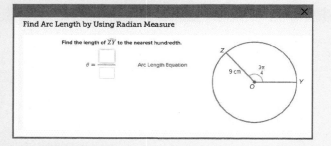

Find Arc Length by Using Radian Measure

TYPE

Students enter values to calculate the arc length.

CHECK

Students complete the Check online to determine whether they are ready to move on.

Practice and Homework

Suggested Assignments

Use the table below to select appropriate exercises.

DOK	Topic	Exercises
1, 2	exercises that mirror the examples	1–41
2	exercises that use a variety of skills from this lesson	42–46
2	exercises that extend concepts learned in this lesson to new contexts	47–55
3	exercises that emphasize higher-order and critical-thinking skills	56–63

ASSESS AND DIFFERENTIATE

📊 Use the data from the **Checks** to determine whether to provide resources for extension, remediation, or intervention.

IF students score 90% or more on the Checks,   `BL`
THEN assign:

- Practice, Exercises 1–55 odd, 56–63
- Extension: Curves of Constant Width
- **ALEKS'** Chords and Arcs

IF students score 66%–89% on the Checks,   `OL`
THEN assign:

- Practice, Exercises 1–63 odd
- Remediation, Review Resources: Circles and Circumference
- Personal Tutors
- Extra Examples 1–8
- **ALEKS'** Comparing Chord and Arc Lengths

IF students score 65% or less on the Checks,   `AL`
THEN assign:

- Practice, Exercises 1–41 odd
- Remediation, Review Resources: Circles and Circumference
- *Quick Review Math Handbook*: Measuring Angles and Arcs
- **ALEKS'** Comparing Chord and Arc Lengths

Important to Know

Digital Exercise Alert Exercise 61 requires a construction and is not available online.

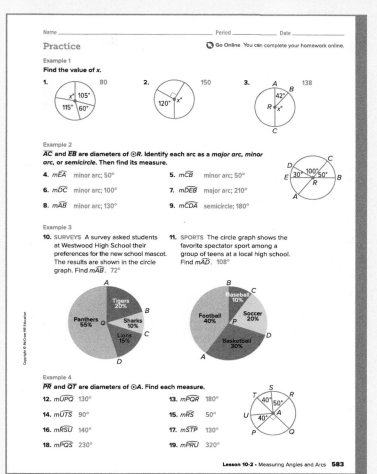

Practice

Go Online You can complete your homework online.

Example 1
Find the value of x.

1. 80   2. 150   3. 138

Example 2
$\overline{AC}$ and $\overline{EB}$ are diameters of $\odot R$. Identify each arc as a *major arc, minor arc,* or *semicircle.* Then find its measure.

4. $m\widehat{EA}$ minor arc; 50°
5. $m\widehat{CB}$ minor arc; 50°
6. $m\widehat{DC}$ minor arc; 100°
7. $m\widehat{DEB}$ major arc; 210°
8. $m\widehat{AB}$ minor arc; 130°
9. $m\widehat{CDA}$ semicircle; 180°

Example 3

10. SURVEYS A survey asked students at Westwood High School their preferences for the new school mascot. The results are shown in the circle graph. Find $m\widehat{AB}$.   72°

11. SPORTS The circle graph shows the favorite spectator sport among a group of teens at a local high school. Find $m\widehat{AD}$.   108°

Example 4
$\overline{PR}$ and $\overline{QT}$ are diameters of $\odot A$. Find each measure.

12. $m\widehat{UPQ}$ 130°
13. $m\widehat{PQR}$ 180°
14. $m\widehat{UTS}$ 90°
15. $m\widehat{RS}$ 50°
16. $m\widehat{RSU}$ 140°
17. $m\widehat{STP}$ 130°
18. $m\widehat{PQS}$ 230°
19. $m\widehat{PRU}$ 320°

Lesson 10-2 • Measuring Angles and Arcs   **583**

Example 5
Use $\odot D$ to find the length of each arc to the nearest hundredth. $\overline{NL}$ is a diameter.

20. $\widehat{LM}$ if the radius is 5 inches   8.73 in.
21. $\widehat{MN}$ if the diameter is 3 yards   2.09 yd
22. $\widehat{KL}$ if $JD = 7$ centimeters   7.33 cm
23. $\widehat{NJK}$ if $NL = 12$ feet   12.57 ft
24. $\widehat{KLM}$ if $DM = 9$ millimeters   25.13 mm
25. $\widehat{JK}$ if $KD = 15$ inches   13.09 in.

Example 6
Write each degree measure in radians as a multiple of π.

26. 120° $\frac{2\pi}{3}$ radians
27. 45° $\frac{\pi}{4}$ radians
28. 30° $\frac{\pi}{6}$ radians
29. 90° $\frac{\pi}{2}$ radians
30. 180° π radians
31. 225° $\frac{5\pi}{4}$ radians

Example 7
Write each radian measure in degrees.

32. $\frac{3\pi}{4}$ radians   135°
33. $\frac{3\pi}{2}$ radians   270°
34. $\frac{\pi}{3}$ radians   60°
35. $\frac{5\pi}{6}$ radians   150°
36. 2π radians   360°
37. $\frac{\pi}{12}$ radians   15°

Example 8
Use $\odot Z$ to find the length of each arc to the nearest hundredth.

38. $\widehat{QR}$, if $PZ = 12$ feet   12.57 ft
39. $\widehat{ST}$, if $SZ = 8$ inches   2.79 in.
40. $\widehat{PQ}$, if $TZ = 14$ centimeters   21.99 cm
41. $\widehat{PT}$, if $TR = 20$ inches   5.24 in.

Mixed Exercises

42. CLOCKS Shiatsu is a type of Japanese physical therapy. One of the beliefs is that various body functions are most active at various times during the day. To illustrate this, they use a Chinese clock that is based on a circle divided into 12 equal sections by radii. What are the degree and radian measures of any one of the 12 equal central angles?   30°; $\frac{\pi}{6}$ radians

43. RIBBONS Cora is wrapping a ribbon around a cylinder-shaped gift box. The box has a diameter of 15 inches, and the ribbon is 60 inches long. Cora is able to wrap the ribbon all the way around the box once and then continue so that the second end of the ribbon passes the first end. What is the measure of the central angle formed by the arc between the ends of the ribbon? Round your answer to the nearest tenth of a degree.   98.4°

584   Module 10 • Circles

Name _____ Period _____ Date _____

44. PIES Shekeia has divided a circular apple pie into 4 slices by cutting the pie along 4 radii. If the measures of the central angles of the 4 slices are represented by $3x°$, $(6x − 10)°$, $(4x + 10)°$, and $5x°$, what are the measures of the central angles? 60°, 110°, 90°, and 100°

45. BIKE WHEELS Louis has to buy a new wheel for his bike. The bike wheel has a diameter of 20 inches.

  a. If Louis rolls the wheel one complete rotation along the ground, how far will the wheel travel? Round your answer to the nearest hundredth of an inch. 62.83 in.

  b. If the bike wheel is rolled along the ground so that it rotates 45°, how far will the wheel travel? Round your answer to the nearest hundredth of an inch. 7.85 in.

  c. If the bike wheel is rolled along the ground for 10 inches, through what angle does the wheel rotate? Round your answer to the nearest tenth of a degree. 57.3°

46. USE TOOLS The table on the right shows the number of hours students at Leland High School say they spend on homework each night.

Homework	
<1	8
1–2	29
2–3	58
3–4	3
>4	2

  a. If you were to construct a circle graph of the data, how many degrees would be allotted to each category? < 1 hour: 28.8°; 1−2 hours: 104.4°; 2−3 hours: 208.8°; 3−4 hours: 10.8°; > 4 hours: 7.2°

  b. Describe the types of arcs associated with each category. The arc associated with 2–3 hours is a major arc; minor arcs are associated with the remaining categories.

47. PROOF Write a two-column proof of Theorem 10.2.

  Given: $\angle BAC \cong \angle DAE$

  Prove: $\overarc{BC} \cong \overarc{DE}$

  Proof: Statements (Reasons)

  1. $\angle BAC \cong \angle DAE$ (Given)

  2. $m\angle BAC = m\angle DAE$ (Def. of congruent angles)

  3. $m\angle BAC = m\overarc{BC}$ and $m\angle DAE = m\overarc{DE}$ (Def. of arc measure)

  4. $m\overarc{BC} = m\overarc{DE}$ (Substitution)

  5. $\overarc{BC} \cong \overarc{DE}$ (Def. of congruent arcs)

REASONING Find each measure. Round each linear measure to the nearest hundredth and each arc measure to the nearest degree.

48. circumference of ⊙S   40.83 in.   **49.** $m\overarc{CD}$ 150°   **50.** radius of ⊙K   9.50 ft

70°   7.94 in.

1.31 m   0.5 m

J L   340°   56.37 ft

In ⊙C, $m\angle HCG = 2x°$ and $m\angle HCD = (6x + 28)°$. $\overline{HE}$ and $\overline{GD}$ are diameters of the circle. Find each measure.

51. $m\overarc{EF}$ 52   **52.** $m\overarc{HD}$ 142   **53.** $m\overarc{HGF}$ 128

Lesson 10-2 • Measuring Angles and Arcs   **585**

---

54. STRUCTURE An arc has a related central angle of 45°. Complete the table by finding the length of the arc in terms of π for each given radius.

Radius of Circle, r	3	5	11	15	r
Length of Arc, ℓ	$\frac{3\pi}{4}$	$\frac{5\pi}{4}$	$\frac{11\pi}{4}$	$\frac{15\pi}{4}$	$\frac{\pi}{4}r$

55. REGULARITY An architect is designing the seating area for a theater. The seating area is formed by a region that lies between two circles. The architect is planning to place a brass rail in front of the first row of seats.

  a. The architect wants to know the length of the rail. Express the length in terms of π and to the nearest tenth of a foot. 10π or about 31.4 ft

  b. The architect is considering changing the radius of ⊙T or changing the measure of $\overarc{RS}$. Describe a general method she can use to find the length of $\overarc{RS}$. See margin.

🧠 **Higher-Order Thinking Skills**

ANALYZE For Exercises 56–58, determine whether each statement is *sometimes, always,* or *never* true. Justify your argument.

56. The measure of a minor arc is less than 180°. Always; sample answer: By definition, an arc that measures less than 180° is a minor arc.

57. If a central angle is obtuse, its corresponding arc is a major arc. Never; sample answer: Obtuse angles intersect arcs that measure between 90° and 180°.

58. The sum of the measures of adjacent arcs of a circle depends on the measure of the radius. Never; sample answer: The sum of the measures of adjacent arcs depends on the measures of the arcs.

59. FIND THE ERROR Brody says that $\overarc{WX}$ and $\overarc{YZ}$ are congruent because their central angles have the same measure. Selena says they are not congruent. Who is correct? Explain your reasoning. Selena; sample answer: The circles are not congruent because they do not have congruent radii. So, the arcs are not congruent.

60. PERSEVERE The time shown on an analog clock is 8:10. What is the measure of the angle formed by the hands of the clock? 175°

61. CREATE Draw a circle and locate three points on the circle. Estimate the measures of the three nonoverlapping arcs that are formed. Then use a protractor to find the measure of each arc. Label your circle with the arc measures. See margin.

62. WRITE Describe the three different types of arcs in a circle and a method for finding the measure of each one. See margin.

63. PERSEVERE The measures of $\overarc{LM}$, $\overarc{MN}$, and $\overarc{NL}$ are in the ratio 5:3:4. Find the measure of each arc. $m\overarc{LM} = 150°$; $m\overarc{MN} = 90°$; $m\overarc{NL} = 120°$

Answers

55b. Sample answer: She can find the circumference of the entire circle and then use the arc measure to find the appropriate fraction of the circle. If the radius of the circle is r and the measure of the arc is x, then the arc length is $\frac{x}{360°} \cdot 2\pi r$.

61. Sample answer:

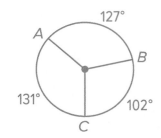

127°, A, B, 131°, 102°, C

62. Sample answer: Minor arc, major arc, semicircle; the measure of a minor arc equals the measure of the corresponding central angle. The measure of a major arc equals 360° minus the measure of the minor arc with the same endpoints. The measure of a semicircle is 180°.

Arcs and Chords

LESSON GOAL

Students solve problems using the relationships between arcs, chords, and diameters.

1 LAUNCH

 Launch the lesson with a **Warm Up** and an introduction.

2 EXPLORE AND DEVELOP

 Explore: Chords in Circles

 Develop:

Arcs and Chords

- Use Congruent Arcs to Find Arc Measures
- Use Congruent Arcs to Find Chord Length
- Use a Radius Perpendicular to a Chord
- Use a Diameter Perpendicular to a Chord
- Chords Equidistant from the Center

 You may want your students to complete the **Checks** online.

3 REFLECT AND PRACTICE

 Exit Ticket

 Practice

DIFFERENTIATE

 View reports of student progress on the **Checks** after each example.

Resources	AL	OL	BL	ELL
Remediation: Measuring Angles and Arcs	●	●		●
Extension: Patterns from Chords		●	●	●

Language Development Handbook

Assign page 68 of the *Language Development Handbook* to help your students build mathematical language related to arcs, chords, and diameters.

ELL You can use the tips and suggestions on page T68 of the handbook to support students who are building English proficiency.

Suggested Pacing

90 min	**0.5 day**	
45 min		**1 day**

Focus

Domain: Geometry

Standards for Mathematical Content:

G.C.2 Identify and describe relationships among inscribed angles, radii, and chords.

Standards for Mathematical Practice:

1 Make sense of problems and persevere in solving them.

3 Construct viable arguments and critique the reasoning of others.

4 Model with mathematics.

6 Attend to precision.

Coherence

Vertical Alignment

Previous
Students found measures of angles and arcs in circles.
G.C.2, G.C.5

Now
Students solve problems involving arcs, chords, and diameters.
G.C.2

Next
Students will solve problems using inscribed angles and polygons.
G.C.2, G.C.3

Rigor

The Three Pillars of Rigor

1 CONCEPTUAL UNDERSTANDING	2 FLUENCY	3 APPLICATION

Conceptual Bridge In this lesson, students develop understanding of the relationships between arcs and chords. They build fluency by making constructions using a variety of methods, and they apply their understanding by solving real-world problems related to arcs and chords.

Mathematical Background

The endpoints of a chord are also endpoints of an arc. Arcs and chords have a special relationship. In a circle or in congruent circles, two minor arcs are congruent if and only if their corresponding chords are congruent. In a circle or congruent circles, two chords are congruent if and only if they are equidistant from the center of the circle. The chords of adjacent arcs can form a polygon. Such a polygon is said to be inscribed in the circle because all its vertices lie on the circle. The circle circumscribes the polygon.

Interactive Presentation

Warm Up

Answer *true* or *false*.

1. The longest chord in a circle is the diameter.

2. If a chord has length equal to half of the diameter, it is a radius.

3. In any circle, the length of a chord *AB* is less than the length of arc *AB*.

4. A circle has infinitely many chords of different lengths.

5. For any given chord *AB* in a circle, there is only one chord that is perpendicular to it.

Show Answers

Warm Up

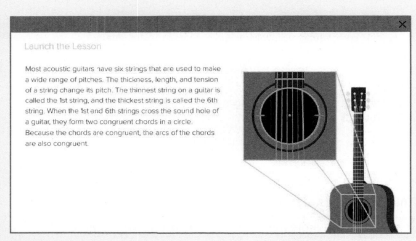

Launch the Lesson

Most acoustic guitars have six strings that are used to make a wide range of pitches. The thickness, length, and tension of a string change its pitch. The thinnest string on a guitar is called the 1st string, and the thickest string is called the 6th string. When the 1st and 6th strings cross the sound hole of a guitar, they form two congruent chords in a circle. Because the chords are congruent, the arcs of the chords are also congruent.

Launch the Lesson

Warm Up

Prerequisite Skills

The Warm Up exercises address the following prerequisite skill for this lesson:

- comparing chord lengths

Answers:

1. true
2. false
3. true
4. true
5. false

Launch the Lesson

MP Teaching the Mathematical Practices

4 Apply Mathematics In this Launch the Lesson, students can see a real-world application of congruent chords and arcs.

Go Online to find additional teaching notes and questions to promote classroom discourse.

Today's Standards

Tell students that they will be addressing these content and practice standards in this lesson. You may wish to have a student volunteer read aloud *How can I meet these standards?* and *How can I use these practices?* and connect these to the standards.

See the Interactive Presentation for I Can statements that align with the standards covered in this lesson.

Explore Chords in Circles

Objective

Students use dynamic geometry software to identify and describe relationships between radii and chords.

 Teaching the Mathematical Practices

> **3 Make Conjectures** In this Explore, students will make conjectures and then build a logical progression of statements to validate the conjectures. Once students have made their conjectures, guide the students to validate them.

Ideas for Use

Recommended Use Present the Inquiry Question, or have a student volunteer read it aloud. Have students work in pairs to complete the Explore activity on their devices. Pairs should discuss each of the questions. Monitor student progress during the activity. Upon completion of the Explore activity, have student volunteers share their responses to the Inquiry Question.

What if my students don't have devices? You may choose to project the activity on a whiteboard. A printable worksheet for each Explore is available online. You may choose to print the worksheet so that individuals or pairs of students can use it to record their observations.

Summary of the Activity

Students will complete guiding exercises throughout the Explore activity. Students begin by using dynamic geometry software to construct a circle with a chord and the perpendicular bisector of the chord. They then move the figure to see what happens, and make a conjecture that the bisector passes through the center of the circle. They also observe that the perpendicular bisector also bisects the central angle of the chord and its corresponding arc.

Next, students construct a new circle with two congruent chords. They measure the distance from the midpoint of each chord to the center of the circle to find that the chords are equidistant from the center. Then, students will answer the Inquiry Question.

(continued on the next page)

Interactive Presentation

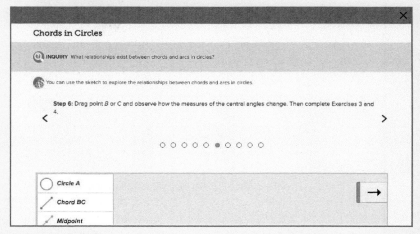

Explore

WEB SKETCHPAD

Students use a sketch to explore chords.

Interactive Presentation

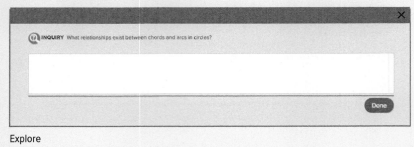

Explore

TYPE

| a| |

Students respond to the Inquiry Question and can view a sample answer.

---

1 **CONCEPTUAL UNDERSTANDING** | 2 FLUENCY | 3 APPLICATION

Explore Chords in Circles (*continued*)

ⓂⓅ Teaching the Mathematical Practices

5 Use Mathematical Tools Point out that to solve the problem in this Explore, students will need to use dynamic geometry software. Work with students to explore and deepen their understanding of relationships between radii and chords.

Questions

Have students complete the Explore activity.

Ask:

- Would it make sense for the perpendicular bisector of a chord to cut the arc into different sizes? Why or why not? Sample answer: If we look at the word *bisector*, it makes the most sense for the chord and the arc to be cut into two equal pieces.

- If you know that two chords are equidistant from the center of the circle, what do you think is true about the two chords? Sample answer: Based on the relationship we found, it would make sense for the two chords to be congruent.

ⓠ Inquiry

What relationships exist between chords and arcs in circles? Sample answer: The perpendicular bisector of a chord bisects the chord's arc. If two chords in a circle are congruent, then they are equidistant from the center of the circle.

🔎 **Go Online** to find additional teaching notes and sample answers for the guiding exercises.

1 CONCEPTUAL UNDERSTANDING | 2 FLUENCY | 3 APPLICATION

Learn Arcs and Chords

Objective
Students solve problems using the relationships between arcs, chords, and diameters.

Teaching the Mathematical Practices

6 Communicate Precisely Encourage students to routinely write or explain their solution methods. Point out that they should use clear definitions when they discuss their solutions with others.

Go Online

- Find additional teaching notes.
- View performance reports of the Checks.
- Assign or present an Extra Example.

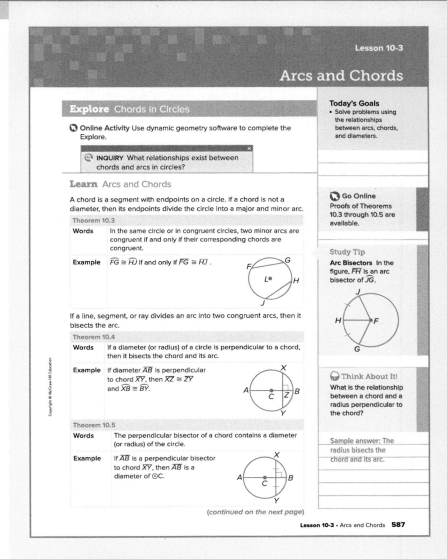

Lesson 10-3

Arcs and Chords

Explore Chords in Circles

Online Activity Use dynamic geometry software to complete the Explore.

INQUIRY What relationships exist between chords and arcs in circles?

Learn Arcs and Chords

A chord is a segment with endpoints on a circle. If a chord is not a diameter, then its endpoints divide the circle into a major and minor arc.

Theorem 10.3

Words	In the same circle or in congruent circles, two minor arcs are congruent if and only if their corresponding chords are congruent.
Example	$\overparen{FG} \cong \overparen{HJ}$ if and only if $\overline{FG} \cong \overline{HJ}$.

If a line, segment, or ray divides an arc into two congruent arcs, then it bisects the arc.

Theorem 10.4

Words	If a diameter (or radius) of a circle is perpendicular to a chord, then it bisects the chord and its arc.
Example	If diameter $\overline{AB}$ is perpendicular to chord $\overline{XY}$, then $\overline{XZ} \cong \overline{ZY}$ and $\overparen{XB} \cong \overparen{BY}$.

Theorem 10.5

Words	The perpendicular bisector of a chord contains a diameter (or radius) of the circle.
Example	If $\overline{AB}$ is a perpendicular bisector to chord $\overline{XY}$, then $\overline{AB}$ is a diameter of $\odot C$.

(continued on the next page)

Today's Goals
- Solve problems using the relationships between arcs, chords, and diameters.

Go Online
Proofs of Theorems 10.3 through 10.5 are available.

Study Tip
Arc Bisectors In the figure, $\overline{FH}$ is an arc bisector of $\overparen{JG}$.

Think About It!
What is the relationship between a chord and a radius perpendicular to the chord?

Sample answer: The radius bisects the chord and its arc.

Lesson 10-3 • Arcs and Chords **587**

Interactive Presentation

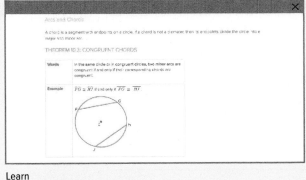

Learn

TAP

Students tap to reveal a Study Tip.

TYPE

Students answer a question to show they understand acrs and chords.

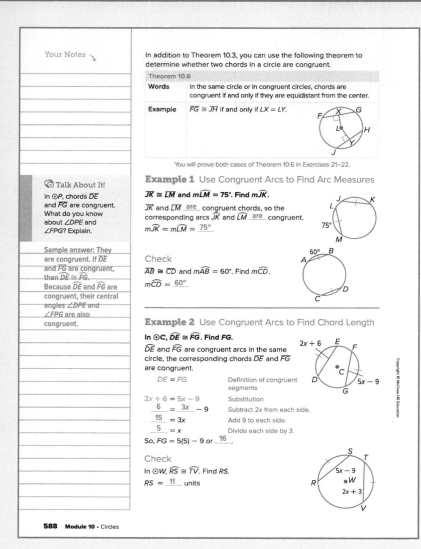

Your Notes

In addition to Theorem 10.3, you can use the following theorem to determine whether two chords in a circle are congruent.

Theorem 10.6

Words	In the same circle or in congruent circles, chords are congruent if and only if they are equidistant from the center.
Example	$\overline{FG} \cong \overline{JH}$ if and only if $LX = LY$.

You will prove both cases of Theorem 10.6 in Exercises 21–22.

Example 1 Use Congruent Arcs to Find Arc Measures

$\overline{JK} \cong \overline{LM}$ and $m\widehat{LM} = 75°$. Find $m\widehat{JK}$.

$\overline{JK}$ and $\overline{LM}$ __are__ congruent chords, so the corresponding arcs $\widehat{JK}$ and $\widehat{LM}$ __are__ congruent.

$m\widehat{JK} = m\widehat{LM} = $ __75°__

Check

$\overline{AB} \cong \overline{CD}$ and $m\widehat{AB} = 60°$. Find $m\widehat{CD}$.

$m\widehat{CD} = $ __60°__

Example 2 Use Congruent Arcs to Find Chord Length

In $\odot C$, $\widehat{DE} \cong \widehat{FG}$. Find FG.

$\widehat{DE}$ and $\widehat{FG}$ are congruent arcs in the same circle, the corresponding chords $\overline{DE}$ and $\overline{FG}$ are congruent.

$DE = FG$	Definition of congruent segments
$2x + 6 = 5x - 9$	Substitution
$\underline{6} = \underline{3x} - 9$	Subtract $2x$ from each side.
$\underline{15} = 3x$	Add 9 to each side.
$\underline{5} = x$	Divide each side by 3.

So, $FG = 5(5) - 9$ or __16__.

Check

In $\odot W$, $\overline{RS} \cong \overline{TV}$. Find RS.

$RS = $ __11__ units

📖 Talk About It!

In $\odot P$, chords $\overline{DE}$ and $\overline{FG}$ are congruent. What do you know about $\angle DPE$ and $\angle FPG$? Explain.

Sample answer: They are congruent. If $\overline{DE}$ and $\overline{FG}$ are congruent, then $\overline{DE} \cong \overline{FG}$. Because $\overline{DE}$ and $\overline{FG}$ are congruent, their central angles $\angle DPE$ and $\angle FPG$ are also congruent.

Interactive Presentation

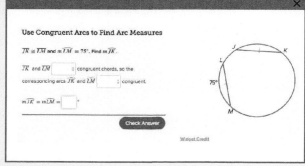

Use Congruent Arcs to Find Arc Measures

$\overline{JK} \cong \overline{LM}$ and $m\widehat{LM} = 75°$. Find $m\widehat{JK}$.

$\overline{JK}$ and $\overline{LM}$ ⬚ congruent chords, so the corresponding arcs $\widehat{JK}$ and $\widehat{LM}$ ⬚ congruent.

$m\widehat{JK} = m\widehat{LM} = $ ⬚ °

Check Answer

Widget Credit

Example 1

TYPE

Students complete the relationships to find arc measure.

Example 1 Use Congruent Arcs to Find Arc Measures

MP Teaching the Mathematical Practices

6 Communicate Precisely Encourage students to routinely write or explain their solution methods. Point out that they should use clear definitions when they discuss their solutions with others.

Questions for Mathematical Discourse

AL If $m\widehat{JK} = 55°$, what is $m\widehat{LM}$? 55°

OL What is $m\widehat{JK} + m\widehat{LM}$? 150°

BL Can we determine if the chords are parallel? No; sample answer: The chords could be anywhere on the circle and still be congruent, so we can't determine if they are parallel with the information given.

Example 2 Use Congruent Arcs to Find Chord Length

MP Teaching the Mathematical Practices

1 Check Answers Mathematically proficient students continually ask themselves, "Does this make sense?" Point out that in this example, students need to check their answer. Point out that they should ask themselves whether their answer makes sense and whether they have answered the problem question.

Questions for Mathematical Discourse

AL If $DE = 5$, what is FG? 5

OL If $DE = 2y + 7$ and $FG = 5y - 2$, what is y? 3

BL If an arc on one circle has the same measure as an arc on a second circle, are the two circles necessarily congruent? Explain. No; sample answer: A pair of arcs with the same measure is not enough to guarantee that two circles are congruent. The arcs could correspond to different chord lengths.

1 CONCEPTUAL UNDERSTANDING   **2 FLUENCY**   **3 APPLICATION**

Example 3 Use a Radius Perpendicular to a Chord

(MP) Teaching the Mathematical Practices

3 Construct Arguments In this example, students will use stated assumptions, definitions, and previously established results to construct an argument.

Questions for Mathematical Discourse

AL What is *HG*? 3.5

OL If $m\widehat{EF} = 65°$, what is $m\widehat{EG}$? 130°

BL If *HG* = 8, what is *EG*? 16

🌐 **Example 4** Use a Diameter Perpendicular to a Chord

(MP) Teaching the Mathematical Practices

4 Make Assumptions In the Study Tip, have students point out where an assumption or approximation was made in the solution.

Questions for Mathematical Discourse

AL What is *FG*? 5 in.

OL If the diameter of the record is decreased by 25%, what is *FG*?
3.75 in.

BL If the diameter of the record is decreased by 25%, what is *EG*?
2.49 in.

Example 3 Use a Radius Perpendicular to a Chord

In ⊙*D*, $m\widehat{EFG} = 120°$. Find $m\widehat{FG}$ and *EG*.

Radius $\overline{DF}$ is perpendicular to chord $\overline{EG}$. So, by Theorem 10.4, $\overline{DF}$ bisects $\widehat{EFG}$ and $\overline{EG}$.

Therefore, $m\widehat{EF} = m\widehat{FG}$ and *EH* = __HG__.

By substitution, $m\widehat{FG} = \frac{120}{2}$ or __60°__.

By the Segment Addition Postulate and substitution, *EG* = 2 · *EH*. So, *EG* = 2 · __3.5__ or __7__ units.

Check

In ⊙*S*, $m\widehat{PQR} = 90°$. Find $m\widehat{PQ}$ and *PR*.

$m\widehat{PQ}$ = __45°__

PR = __12__ units

🌐 **Example 4** Use a Diameter Perpendicular to a Chord

RECORDS The record shown can be modeled by a circle. Diameter $\overline{CD}$ is 12 inches long, and chord $\overline{FH}$ is 10 inches long. Find *EG*.

Step 1 Draw radius $\overline{EF}$.
Radius $\overline{EF}$ forms right △*EFG*.

Step 2 Find *EF* and *FG*.
Because *CD* = __12__ inches, *ED* = __6__ inches. All radii of a circle are congruent, so *EF* = __6__ inches. Because diameter $\overline{CD}$ is perpendicular to $\overline{FH}$, $\overline{CD}$ bisects chord $\overline{FH}$ by Theorem 10.4.
So *FG* = $\frac{1}{2}$(10) or __5__ inches.

Step 3 Use the Pythagorean Theorem to find *EG*.

$EG^2 + FG^2 = EF^2$	Pythagorean Theorem
$EG^2 + 5^2 = 6^2$	*FG* = __5__ and *EF* = __6__
$EG^2 + \underline{25} = \underline{36}$	Simplify.
$EG^2 = \underline{11}$	Subtract 25 from each side.
$EG = \sqrt{11}$	Take the positive square root of each side.

So, *EG* is $\sqrt{11}$ or about __3.32__ inches long.

> 🗨 **Think About It!**
> In a circle, $\overline{AB}$ is a diameter and $\overline{QR}$ is a chord that intersects $\overline{AB}$ at point *X*. Is it *sometimes*, *always*, or *never* true that *QX* = *XR*? Explain.
>
> Sometimes; sample answer: If the diameter is perpendicular to the chord, then it bisects the chord.

> **Study Tip**
> **Assumptions** Assuming that objects can be modeled by perfect circles allows you to find reasonable measures in objects.

Interactive Presentation

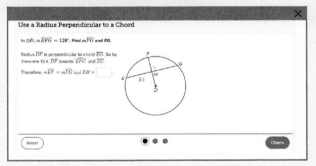

Example 3

TYPE

Students complete statements to find measures.

Check

DRIVING Steering devices provide drivers with more control and strength when turning a steering wheel. A technician is installing a steering device at point P on the steering wheel shown. The steering device extends to point T, and the diameter of the steering wheel is 15 inches long. If chord $\overline{SV}$ is 12 inches long and perpendicular to the diameter of the steering wheel, what is the length of the steering device?

___3 in.___

Example 5 Chords Equidistant from the Center

In $\odot H$, $PQ = 3x - 4$ and $RS = 14$. Find x.

Because chords $\overline{PQ}$ and $\overline{RS}$ are equidistant from H, they are congruent. So, $PQ = RS$.

$PQ = RS$	Definition of congruent segments
$3x - 4 = \underline{14}$	Substitution
$3x = \underline{18}$	Add 4 to each side.
$x = \underline{6}$	Divide each side by 3.

Check

In $\odot P$, $CE = FH = 48$. Find PG.

$PG = \underline{15}$ units

🔵 Go Online You can complete an Extra Example online.

Go Online
You may want to complete the construction activities for this lesson.

Example 5 Chords Equidistant from the Center

MP Teaching the Mathematical Practices ──────

2 Create Representations Guide students to write an equation that models the situation in this example. Then use the equation to solve the problem.

Questions for Mathematical Discourse

AL If $TH = 3$, what is UH? 3

OL If $TH = UH$, $PQ = 2z + 1$, and $RS = 3z - 7$, what is z? 8

BL Can we prove that $RU = US$? Explain. Yes; sample answer: If we draw $\overline{HR}$ and $\overline{HS}$, we know that $HR = HS$ because they are both radii. The triangles formed share $\overline{HU}$, therefore they are congruent by HL. Therefore $RU = US$.

Exit Ticket

Recommended Use

At the end of class, go online to display the Exit Ticket prompt and ask students to respond using a separate piece of paper. Have students hand you their responses as they leave the room.

Alternate Use

At the end of class, go online to display the Exit Ticket prompt and ask students to respond verbally or by using a mini-whiteboard. Have students hold up their whiteboards so that you can see all student responses. Tap to reveal the answer when most or all students have completed the Exit Ticket.

Interactive Presentation

Chords Equidistant from the Center ✕

In $\odot H$, $PQ = 3x - 4$ and $RS = 14$. Find x.

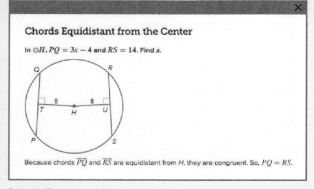

Because chords $\overline{PQ}$ and $\overline{RS}$ are equidistant from H, they are congruent. So, $PQ = RS$.

Example 5

TYPE

Students type to complete the solution.

CHECK

Students complete the Check online to determine whether they are ready to move on.

Practice and Homework

Suggested Assignments

Use the table below to select appropriate exercises.

DOK	Topic	Exercises
1, 2	exercises that mirror the examples	1–17
2	exercises that use a variety of skills from this lesson	18–20
2	exercises that extend concepts learned in this lesson to new contexts	21–22
3	exercises that emphasize higher-order and critical-thinking skills	23–26

ASSESS AND DIFFERENTIATE

📊 Use the data from the **Checks** to determine whether to provide resources for extension, remediation, or intervention.

IF students score 90% or more on the Checks,   `BL`
THEN assign:

- Practice, Exercises 1–21 odd, 23–26
- Extension: Patterns from Chords
- 🅐 **ALEKS** Chords and Arcs

IF students score 66%–89% on the Checks,   `OL`
THEN assign:

- Practice, Exercises 1–21 odd
- Remediation, Review Resources: Measuring Angles and Arcs
- Personal Tutors
- Extra Examples 1–5
- 🅐 **ALEKS** Comparing Angle Measures

IF students score 65% or less on the Checks,   `AL`
THEN assign:

- Practice, Exercises 1–17 odd
- Remediation, Review Resources: Measuring Angles and Arcs
- *Quick Review Math Handbook*: Arcs and Chords
- 🅐 **ALEKS** Comparing Angle Measures

Important to Know

Digital Exercise Alert Exercise 25 requires a construction and is not available online.

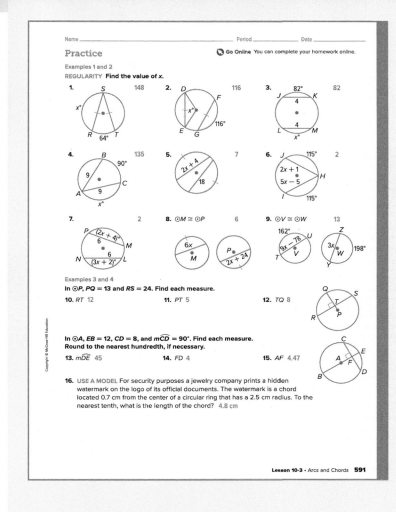

Name _____ Period _____ Date _____

Practice   🔵 **Go Online** You can complete your homework online.

Examples 1 and 2
REGULARITY Find the value of *x*.

1. 148
2. 116
3. 82

4. 135
5. 7
6. 2

7. 2
8. ⊙M ≅ ⊙P   6
9. ⊙V ≅ ⊙W   13

Examples 3 and 4
In ⊙*P*, *PQ* = 13 and *RS* = 24. Find each measure.

10. *RT* 12
11. *PT* 5
12. *TQ* 8

In ⊙*A*, *EB* = 12, *CD* = 8, and *mCD* = 90°. Find each measure. Round to the nearest hundredth, if necessary.

13. *mDE* 45
14. *FD* 4
15. *AF* 4.47

16. **USE A MODEL** For security purposes a jewelry company prints a hidden watermark on the logo of its official documents. The watermark is a chord located 0.7 cm from the center of a circular ring that has a 2.5 cm radius. To the nearest tenth, what is the length of the chord? 4.8 cm

Lesson 10-3 • Arcs and Chords   **591**

Example 5

17. In ⊙R, TS = 21 and UV = 3x. What is the value of x?
7

18. In ⊙Q, $\overline{CD} \cong \overline{CB}$, GQ = x + 5, and EQ = 3x − 6. What is the value of x?
5.5

Mixed Exercises

19. USE TOOLS A piece of a broken plate is found during an archaeological dig. Use the sketch of the pottery piece shown to demonstrate how constructions with chords and perpendicular bisectors can be used to draw the plate's original size. **See margin.**

20. REASONING A circular garden has paths around its edge that are identified by the given arc measures. It also has four straight paths, identified by segments $\overline{AC}$, $\overline{AD}$, $\overline{BE}$, and $\overline{DE}$, that cut through the garden's interior. Which two straight paths have the same length? $\overline{DE}$ **and** $\overline{AC}$

PROOF For Exercises 21 and 22, write a two-column proof of the indicated part of Theorem 10.6.

21. In a circle, if two chords are equidistant from the center, then they are congruent. **See margin.**

22. In a circle, if two chords are congruent, then they are equidistant from the center. **See Mod. 10 Answer Appendix.**

🧠 Higher-Order Thinking Skills

23. WRITE Neil draws a diameter of a circle and then marks its midpoint as the center. His teacher asks Neil how he knows that he drew the diameter of the circle and not a shorter chord. How can Neil determine whether he drew an actual diameter? **See margin.**

24. PERSEVERE Toshelle is following directions for a quilt pattern. The directions are intended to make a rectangle. They say "In a 10-inch diameter circle, measure 3 inches from the center of the circle and mark a chord $\overline{AB}$ perpendicular to the radius of the circle. Then cut along the chord." Toshelle is to repeat this for another chord, $\overline{CD}$. Finally, she is to cut along chord $\overline{DB}$ and $\overline{AC}$. The result should be four curved pieces and one quadrilateral. If Toshelle follows the directions, why might the resulting quadrilateral not be a rectangle? Explain how to adjust the directions.
Sample answer: The method will produce congruent chords $\overline{AB}$ and $\overline{CD}$, but the chords are not necessarily parallel. The directions should specify that $\overline{CD}$ should be parallel to $\overline{AB}$.

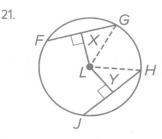

25. CREATE Construct a circle and draw a chord. Measure the chord and the distance that the chord is from the center. Find the length of the radius. **See margin.**

26. ANALYZE In a circle, $\overline{AB}$ is a diameter, and $\overline{HG}$ is a chord that intersects $\overline{AB}$ at point X. Is it *sometimes*, *always*, or *never* true that HX = GX? Justify your argument.
Sometimes; if the diameter is perpendicular to the chord, then it bisects the chord.

Copyright © McGraw-Hill Education

Answers

19. Sample answer: Draw two chords on the arc and find the perpendicular bisector of each chord. The perpendicular bisectors will intersect at the center of the original circle. Then use a compass and the radius to draw the circle for the original size plate.

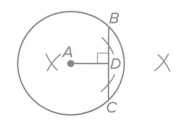

21.

Statements (Reasons)

1. $\overline{FG}$ and $\overline{JH}$ are equidistant from center L. (Given)
2. $\overline{LX} \cong \overline{LY}$ (Definition of equidistant)
3. $\overline{LG} \cong \overline{LH}$ (All radii of a circle are congruent.)
4. $\overline{LX} \perp \overline{FG}$, $\overline{LY} \perp \overline{JH}$ (Definition of equidistant)
5. ∠LXG and ∠LYH are right angles. (Definition of perpendicular lines)
6. △XGL ≅ △YHL (HL)
7. $\overline{XG} \cong \overline{YH}$ (CPCTC)
8. XG = YH (Definition of congruent segments)
9. 2(XG) = 2(YH) (Multiplication Property of Equality)
10. $\overline{LX}$ bisects $\overline{FG}$; $\overline{LY}$ bisects $\overline{JH}$ ($\overline{LX}$ and $\overline{LY}$ are contained in radii. A radius perpendicular to a chord bisects the chord.)
11. FG = 2(XG); JH = 2(YH) (Definition of segment bisector)
12. FG = JH (Substitution)
13. $\overline{FG} \cong \overline{JH}$ (Definition of congruent segments)

23. Sample answer: Neil can draw a line perpendicular to the chord he just drew through the mark he made. If the midpoint of the first chord is also the midpoint of the second line, it is a diameter.

25. Sample answer: BC = 4 centimeters and AD = 2 centimeters. Because $\overline{AD}$ is perpendicular to $\overline{BC}$, $\overline{AD}$ bisects $\overline{BC}$ and BD = 2. The Pythagorean Theorem can be used to find the length of the radius $\overline{AB}$.
$$AB^2 = AD^2 + BD^2$$
$$= 2^2 + 2^2$$
$$= 8$$
$AB = 2\sqrt{2}$ or about 2.83 cm

Inscribed Angles

LESSON GOAL

Students solve problems using inscribed angles.

1 LAUNCH

 Launch the lesson with a **Warm Up** and an introduction.

2 EXPLORE AND DEVELOP

Explore: Angles Inscribed in Circles

....

Develop:

Inscribed Angles
- Use Inscribed Angles to Find Measures
- Find Measures of Congruent Inscribed Angles
- Use Inscribed Angles in Proofs

Inscribed Polygons
- Find Angle Measures in Inscribed Triangles
- Find Angles Measures

....

 You may want your students to complete the **Checks** online.

3 REFLECT AND PRACTICE

Exit Ticket

....

Practice

....

Formative Assessment Math Probe

DIFFERENTIATE

View reports of student progress on the **Checks** after each example.

Resources	AL	OL	BL	ELL
Remediation: Arcs and Chords	●	●		●
Extension: Formulas for Regular Polygons		●	●	●

Language Development Handbook

Assign page 69 of the *Language Development Handbook* to help your students build mathematical language related to inscribed angles.

ELL You can use the tips and suggestions on page T69 of the handbook to support students who are building English proficiency.

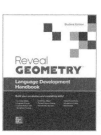

Suggested Pacing

90 min	0.5 day
45 min	1 day

Focus

Domain: Geometry

Standards for Mathematical Content:

G.C.2 Identify and describe relationships among inscribed angles, radii, and chords.

G.C.3 Construct the inscribed and circumscribed circles of a triangle, and prove properties of angles for a quadrilateral inscribed in a circle.

Standards for Mathematical Practice:

1 Make sense of problems and persevere in solving them.

3 Construct viable arguments and critique the reasoning of others.

5 Use appropriate tools strategically.

Coherence

Vertical Alignment

Previous
Students solved problems using the relationships between arcs, chords, and diameters.
G.C.2

Now
Students solve problems using inscribed angles.
G.C.2, G.C.3

Next
Students will solve problems using relationships between circles and tangents.
G.C.4

Rigor

The Three Pillars of Rigor

1 CONCEPTUAL UNDERSTANDING	2 FLUENCY	3 APPLICATION

Conceptual Bridge In this lesson, students develop understanding of inscribed angles. They build fluency by constructing inscribed and circumscribed circles, and they apply their understanding by solving real-world problems related to inscribed angles and polygons.

Mathematical Background

An *inscribed angle* is an angle that has its vertex on the circle and its sides contain chords of the circle. If an angle is inscribed in a circle, then the measure of the angle equals one-half of the measure of its *intercepted arc*. If an inscribed angle intercepts a semicircle, the angle is a right angle. If a quadrilateral is inscribed in a circle, then its opposite angles are supplementary.

Interactive Presentation

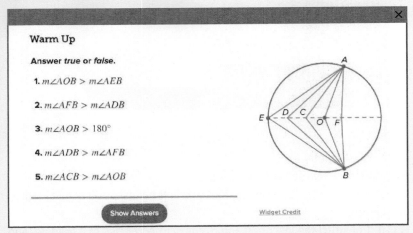

Warm Up

Answer *true* or *false*.

1. $m\angle AOB > m\angle AEB$
2. $m\angle AFB > m\angle ADB$
3. $m\angle AOB > 180°$
4. $m\angle ADB > m\angle AFB$
5. $m\angle ACB > m\angle AOB$

Show Answers   Widget Credit

Warm Up

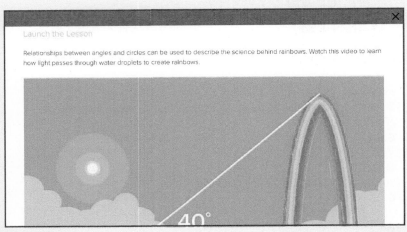

Launch the Lesson

Relationships between angles and circles can be used to describe the science behind rainbows. Watch this video to learn how light passes through water droplets to create rainbows.

40°

Launch the Lesson

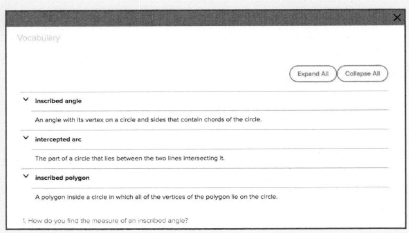

Vocabulary

Expand All   Collapse All

⌄ **inscribed angle**

An angle with its vertex on a circle and sides that contain chords of the circle.

⌄ **intercepted arc**

The part of a circle that lies between the two lines intersecting it.

⌄ **inscribed polygon**

A polygon inside a circle in which all of the vertices of the polygon lie on the circle.

1. How do you find the measure of an inscribed angle?

Today's Vocabulary

Warm Up

Prerequisite Skills

The Warm Up exercises address the following prerequisite skill for this lesson:

- comparing angle measures

Answers:

1. true
2. false
3. false
4. false
5. false

Launch the Lesson

Teaching the Mathematical Practices

4 Apply Mathematics In this Launch the Lesson, students can see a real-world application of relationships between angles and circles.

Go Online to find additional teaching notes and questions to promote classroom discourse.

Today's Standards

Tell students that they will be addressing these content and practice standards in this lesson. You may wish to have a student volunteer read aloud *How can I meet these standards?* and *How can I use these practices?* and connect these to the standards.

See the Interactive Presentation for I Can statements that align with the standards covered in this lesson.

Today's Vocabulary

Tell students that they will be using these vocabulary terms in this lesson. You can expand each row if you wish to share the definitions. Then, discuss the questions below with the class.

Explore Angles Inscribed in Circles

Objective
Students use dynamic geometry software to identify and describe relationships between inscribed angles and intercepted arcs.

 Teaching the Mathematical Practices

3 Reason Inductively In this Explore, students will use inductive reasoning to make plausible arguments.

Ideas for Use

Recommended Use Present the Inquiry Question, or have a student volunteer read it aloud. Have students work in pairs to complete the Explore activity on their devices. Pairs should discuss each of the questions. Monitor student progress during the activity. Upon completion of the Explore activity, have student volunteers share their responses to the Inquiry Question.

What if my students don't have devices? You may choose to project the activity on a whiteboard. A printable worksheet for each Explore is available online. You may choose to print the worksheet so that individuals or pairs of students can use it to record their observations.

Summary of the Activity

Students will complete guiding exercises throughout the Explore activity. Students begin by using dynamic geometry software to measure an angle inscribed in a circle and the arc that the angle intercepts. They move the vertex of the angle without changing the intercepted arc and observe that this does not change either measure. They change the arc in general and observe that the measure of the inscribed angle is always half that of the intercepted arc. Then students construct an angle that intercepts a diameter, and notice that it is always a right angle. Students write conjectures based on their observations. Then, students will answer the Inquiry Question.

(continued on the next page)

Interactive Presentation

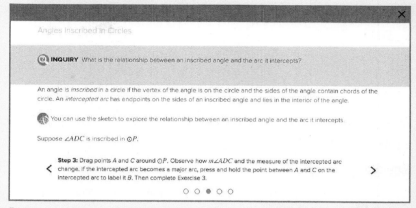

Explore

WEB SKETCHPAD

 Students use a sketch to explore inscribed angles.

G.C.2

Interactive Presentation

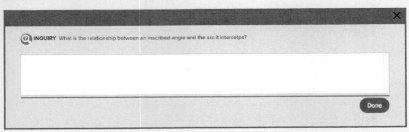

×

INQUIRY What is the relationship between an inscribed angle and the arc it intercetps?

Done

Explore

TYPE

Students respond to the Inquiry Question and can view a sample answer.

Explore Angles Inscribed in Circles (*continued*)

 Teaching the Mathematical Practices

3 Make Conjectures In this Explore, students will make conjectures and then build a logical progression of statements to validate the conjectures. Once students have made their conjectures, guide the students to validate them.

Questions
Have students complete the Explore activity.

Ask:
• How is an inscribed angle different than a central angle? Sample answer: The vertex of inscribed angles lie on the circle instead of at the center of the circle. This changes the relationship with the intercepted arcs.
• Would it be possible for an inscribed angle to be bigger than 90°? Bigger than 180°? Sample answer: It is possible for an inscribed angle to be bigger than 90°. For example, an inscribed angle could be 135° and the intercepted arc would measure 270° (or three-fourths of the circle). It would not be possible for the inscribed angle to be 180° or larger because the intercepted arc would be 360° or greater.

Inquiry
What is the relationship between an inscribed angle and the arc it intercepts? Sample answer: In a circle, the measure of an inscribed angle is equal to half the measure of its intercepted arc. Therefore, if an inscribed angle intercepts a semicircle or diameter, then the angle is a right angle.

Go Online to find additional teaching notes and sample answers for the guiding exercises.

---

1 CONCEPTUAL UNDERSTANDING | 2 FLUENCY | 3 APPLICATION

Learn Inscribed Angles

Objective
Students describe relationships between inscribed angles and use those relationships to solve problems.

(MP) Teaching the Mathematical Practices

3 Analyze Cases This learn guides students to examine the cases of inscribed angles in a circle for Theorem 10-7. Encourage students to familiarize themselves with all of the cases.

6 Communicate Precisely Encourage students to routinely write or explain their solution methods. Point out that they should use clear definitions when they discuss their solutions with others.

Important to Know
The three cases of inscribed angles for Theorem 10-7 are important, because each case requires a different proof. Once Case 1 is proved, it can be used with the angle addition and arc addition postulates to prove the other two cases. Work with students to prove the other two cases.

(e) Essential Question Follow-Up
Students learn about inscribed angles, chords, arcs, central angles, and their relationships.

Ask:

Why is it useful to be able to solve problems using angles, chords, and arcs in circles? Sample answer: There are many circular objects in the real world, and it is useful to solve problems relating to them.

DIFFERENTIATE

Enrichment Activity BL

Logical Learners Lesson 10-4 includes a proof using multiple cases. Locate some other examples using a college geometry text or the Internet that involve this type of proof to allow mathematically talented students to develop an understanding of why certain proofs require the consideration of multiple cases.

(→) Go Online

- Find additional teaching notes.
- View performance reports of the Checks.
- Assign or present an Extra Example.

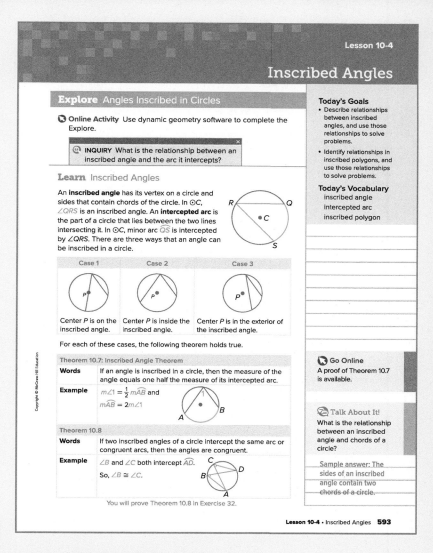

Lesson 10-4

Inscribed Angles

Explore Angles Inscribed in Circles

Online Activity Use dynamic geometry software to complete the Explore.

INQUIRY What is the relationship between an inscribed angle and the arc it intercepts?

Learn Inscribed Angles

An **inscribed angle** has its vertex on a circle and sides that contain chords of the circle. In ⊙C, ∠QRS is an inscribed angle. An **intercepted arc** is the part of a circle that lies between the two lines intersecting it. In ⊙C, minor arc QS is intercepted by ∠QRS. There are three ways that an angle can be inscribed in a circle.

Case 1	Case 2	Case 3
Center P is on the inscribed angle.	Center P is inside the inscribed angle.	Center P is in the exterior of the inscribed angle.

For each of these cases, the following theorem holds true.

Theorem 10.7: Inscribed Angle Theorem

Words	If an angle is inscribed in a circle, then the measure of the angle equals one half the measure of its intercepted arc.
Example	$m\angle 1 = \frac{1}{2} m\widehat{AB}$ and $m\widehat{AB} = 2m\angle 1$

Theorem 10.8

Words	If two inscribed angles of a circle intercept the same arc or congruent arcs, then the angles are congruent.
Example	∠B and ∠C both intercept $\widehat{AD}$. So, ∠B ≅ ∠C.

You will prove Theorem 10.8 in Exercise 32.

Today's Goals
- Describe relationships between inscribed angles, and use those relationships to solve problems.
- Identify relationships in inscribed polygons, and use those relationships to solve problems.

Today's Vocabulary
inscribed angle
intercepted arc
inscribed polygon

Go Online
A proof of Theorem 10.7 is available.

Talk About It!
What is the relationship between an inscribed angle and chords of a circle?

Sample answer: The sides of an inscribed angle contain two chords of a circle.

Lesson 10-4 • Inscribed Angles **593**

Interactive Presentation

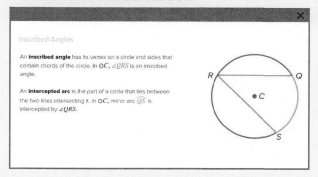

Inscribed Angles

An **inscribed angle** has its vertex on a circle and sides that contain chords of the circle. In ⊙C, ∠QRS is an inscribed angle.

An **intercepted arc** is the part of a circle that lies between the two lines intersecting it. In ⊙C, minor arc QS is intercepted by ∠QRS.

Learn

TAP

Students move through the steps to prove the Inscribed Angle Theorem.

TYPE

Students answer a question to show they understand inscribed angles.

G.C.2, G.C.3

1 CONCEPTUAL UNDERSTANDING | **2 FLUENCY** | 3 APPLICATION

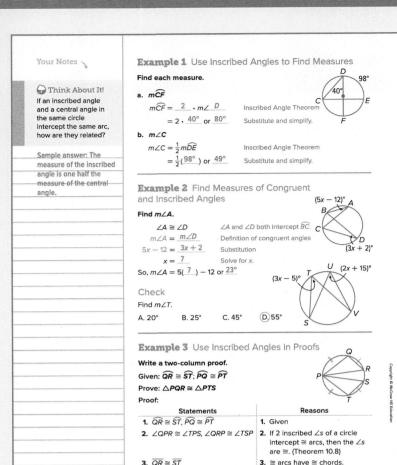

Your Notes

💭 Think About It!
If an inscribed angle and a central angle in the same circle intercept the same arc, how are they related?

Sample answer: The measure of the inscribed angle is one half the measure of the central angle.

Example 1 Use Inscribed Angles to Find Measures

Find each measure.

a. $m\overset{\frown}{CF}$

$m\overset{\frown}{CF} = \underline{2} \cdot m\angle \underline{D}$ Inscribed Angle Theorem

$= 2 \cdot \underline{40°}$ or $\underline{80°}$ Substitute and simplify.

b. $m\angle C$

$m\angle C = \frac{1}{2}m\overset{\frown}{DE}$ Inscribed Angle Theorem

$= \frac{1}{2}(\underline{98°})$ or $\underline{49°}$ Substitute and simplify.

Example 2 Find Measures of Congruent and Inscribed Angles

Find $m\angle A$.

$\angle A \cong \angle D$ $\angle A$ and $\angle D$ both intercept $\overset{\frown}{BC}$.

$m\angle A = \underline{m\angle D}$ Definition of congruent angles

$5x - 12 = \underline{3x + 2}$ Substitution

$x = \underline{7}$ Solve for x.

So, $m\angle A = 5(\underline{7}) - 12$ or $\underline{23°}$

Check

Find $m\angle T$.

A. 20°   B. 25°   C. 45°   (D.) 55°

Example 3 Use Inscribed Angles in Proofs

Write a two-column proof.

Given: $\overline{QR} \cong \overline{ST}$; $\overline{PQ} \cong \overline{PT}$

Prove: $\triangle PQR \cong \triangle PTS$

Proof:

Statements	Reasons
1. $\overline{QR} \cong \overline{ST}$, $\overline{PQ} \cong \overline{PT}$	1. Given
2. $\angle QPR \cong \angle TPS$, $\angle QRP \cong \angle TSP$	2. If 2 inscribed $\angle$s of a circle intercept $\cong$ arcs, then the $\angle$s are $\cong$. (Theorem 10.8)
3. $\overline{QR} \cong \overline{ST}$	3. $\cong$ arcs have $\cong$ chords.
4. $\triangle PQR \cong \triangle PTS$	4. $\underline{AAS}$

🔵 Go Online You can complete an Extra Example online.

Interactive Presentation

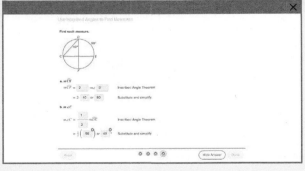

Example 1

TAP

Students move through the slides to use inscribed angles to find measures.

CHECK

Students complete the Check online to determine whether they are ready to move on.

Example 1 Use Inscribed Angles to Find Measures

🅜🅟 Teaching the Mathematical Practices

5 Use Estimation Point out that in this example, students need to include an estimate and check against the estimate at the end.

Questions for Mathematical Discourse

AL What are the two inscribed angles in this example? The intercepted arcs? $\angle C$ and $\angle D$; $\overset{\frown}{DE}$ and $\overset{\frown}{CF}$

OL If $m\overset{\frown}{DE} = 148°$, what is $m\angle C$? 74°

BL If an inscribed angle has endpoints on a diameter of a circle, what to you think the measure of the angle is? Explain. 90°; Sample answer: Because the measure of a semicircle is 180°, an inscribed angle that intercepts the arc would be half of that, or 90°.

Example 2 Find Measures of Congruent Inscribed Angles

🅜🅟 Teaching the Mathematical Practices

2 Create Representations Guide students to write an equation that models the situation in this example. Then use the equation to solve the problem.

Questions for Mathematical Discourse

AL How do we know that $\angle A$ is congruent to $\angle D$? Sample answer: They are both inscribed angles that intercept the same arc, so they are congruent.

OL If $m\overset{\frown}{BC} = 130°$, what is $m\angle A$? 65°

BL If $m\overset{\frown}{BC} = (14x - 4)°$ and $m\angle A = (3x + 6)°$, what is x? 2

Example 3 Use Inscribed Angles in Proofs

🅜🅟 Teaching the Mathematical Practices

3 Construct Arguments In this example, students will use stated assumptions, definitions, and previously established results to complete the given proof.

Questions for Mathematical Discourse

AL Why didn't we need to show that $\angle J$ is congruent to $\angle K$? Sample answer: We only needed to use two angles with AAS.

OL Can we prove that $\overline{PQ} \cong \overline{PT}$ without proving that the two triangles are congruent? Explain. Yes; sample answer: They are corresponding chords of congruent arcs.

BL If you draw in the extra segment, what do you know about $\triangle PQT$? Explain. Sample answer: The triangle is isosceles because $\overline{PQ} \cong \overline{PT}$

Common Error

Students may have difficulty determining the reasons for the steps in the proof. Encourage them to talk about what is happening in each step and which definitions or theorems may apply.

1 CONCEPTUAL UNDERSTANDING | **2 FLUENCY** | 3 APPLICATION

Learn Inscribed Polygons

Objective
Students identify relationships in inscribed polygons and use those relationships to solve problems.

MP Teaching the Mathematical Practices
3 Construct Arguments In this Learn, students will use stated assumptions, definitions, and previously established results to construct an argument.

Common Misconception
Because all triangles can be inscribed in a circle, students may assume this is true of all polygons. Sketch an example, such as a rhombus that is not a square, to help them remember that this is not the case.

Example 4 Find Angle Measures in Inscribed Triangles

MP Teaching the Mathematical Practices
6 Communicate Precisely Encourage students to routinely write or explain their solution methods. Point out that they should use clear definitions when they discuss their solutions with others.

Questions for Mathematical Discourse

AL What is $m\angle M$? 54°

OL What is $m\widehat{KL}$? 108°

BL If $m\widehat{KL} = 116°$, what is $m\angle K$? 32°

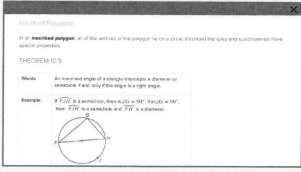

Learn Inscribed Polygons

In an **inscribed polygon**, all of the vertices of the polygon lie on a circle. Inscribed triangles and quadrilaterals have special properties.

Theorem 10.9

Words	An inscribed angle of a triangle intercepts a diameter or semicircle if and only if the angle is a right angle.
Example	If $\widehat{FJH}$ is a semicircle, then $m\angle G = 90°$. If $m\angle G = 90°$, then $\widehat{FJH}$ is a semicircle and $\overline{FH}$ is a diameter.

While many different types of triangles, including right triangles, can be inscribed in a circle, only certain quadrilaterals can be inscribed in a circle.

Theorem 10.10

Words	If a quadrilateral is inscribed in a circle, then its opposite angles are supplementary.
Example	If quadrilateral $KLMN$ is inscribed in $\odot A$, then $\angle L$ and $\angle N$ are supplementary and $\angle K$ and $\angle M$ are supplementary.

You will prove Theorems 10.9 and 10.10 in Exercises 34 and 33, respectively.

Example 4 Find Angle Measures in Inscribed Triangles

Find $m\angle K$.

$\triangle KLM$ is a right triangle because $\angle L$ inscribes a semicircle.

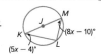

$m\angle K + m\angle M = \underline{90}$ — Acute $\angle$s of a right $\triangle$ are complementary.

$5x - 4 + 8x - 10 = \underline{90}$ — Substitution

$\underline{13}\ x - \underline{14} = 90$ — Simplify.

$13x = \underline{104}$ — Add $\underline{14}$ to each side.

$x = \underline{8}$ — Divide each side by 13.

So, $m\angle K = 5(8) - 4$ or $\underline{36}°$.

Check

Find $m\angle V$.

$m\angle V = \underline{18}°$

Go Online You can complete an Extra Example online.

Lesson 10-4 • Inscribed Angles   595

Think About It!
What special quadrilaterals can be inscribed in a circle? Justify your argument.

Sample answer: Squares and rectangles can be inscribed in circles because the opposite angles in these polygons are both right angles. Kites can be inscribed in circles if the angles that compose the congruent pair of opposite angles are right angles. All isosceles trapezoids can be inscribed in circles because the opposite angles are supplementary.

Go Online
You can watch a video to see how to solve problems involving inscribed triangles.

Think About It!
A 45°-45°-90° triangle is inscribed in a circle. What can you say about the arcs into which the circle is divided by the vertices of the triangles?

Sample answer: One arc is a semicircle and the other two arcs measure 90° and therefore are congruent.

Interactive Presentation

Inscribed Polygons

In an **inscribed polygon**, all of the vertices of the polygon lie on a circle. Inscribed triangles and quadrilaterals have special properties.

THEOREM 10.9

Words	An inscribed angle of a triangle intercepts a diameter or semicircle if and only if the angle is a right angle.
Example	If $\widehat{FJH}$ is a semicircle, then $m\angle G = 90°$. If $m\angle G = 90°$, then $\widehat{FJH}$ is a semicircle and $\overline{FH}$ is a diameter.

Learn

TYPE

a|

Students answer a question to show they understand incribed polygons.

1 CONCEPTUAL UNDERSTANDING | 2 FLUENCY | 3 APPLICATION

⊕ Example 5 Find Angle Measures

STAINED GLASS Luca is creating a collection of stained glass ornaments. The ornament shown uses a quadrilateral inscribed in a circle. Find $m\angle F$ and $m\angle G$.

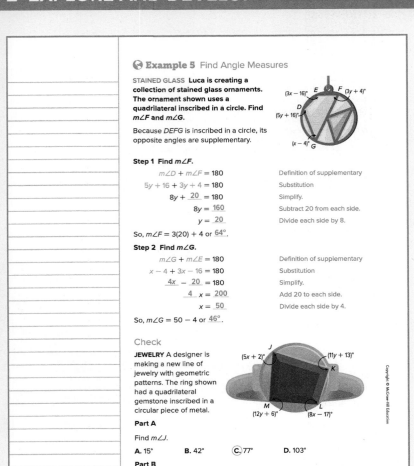

Because *DEFG* is inscribed in a circle, its opposite angles are supplementary.

Step 1 Find $m\angle F$.

$m\angle D + m\angle F = 180$	Definition of supplementary
$5y + 16 + 3y + 4 = 180$	Substitution
$8y + \underline{20} = 180$	Simplify.
$8y = \underline{160}$	Subtract 20 from each side.
$y = \underline{20}$	Divide each side by 8.

So, $m\angle F = 3(20) + 4$ or $\underline{64°}$.

Step 2 Find $m\angle G$.

$m\angle G + m\angle E = 180$	Definition of supplementary
$x - 4 + 3x - 16 = 180$	Substitution
$\underline{4x} - 20 = 180$	Simplify.
$\underline{4}\,x = \underline{200}$	Add 20 to each side.
$x = \underline{50}$	Divide each side by 4.

So, $m\angle G = 50 - 4$ or $\underline{46°}$.

Check

JEWELRY A designer is making a new line of jewelry with geometric patterns. The ring shown had a quadrilateral gemstone inscribed in a circular piece of metal.

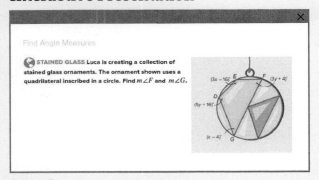

Part A

Find $m\angle J$.

A. 15°   B. 42°   C. 77°   D. 103°

Part B

Find $m\angle K$.

A. 7°   B. 46°   C. 64°   D. 90°

🔗 **Go Online** You can complete an Extra Example online.

Interactive Presentation

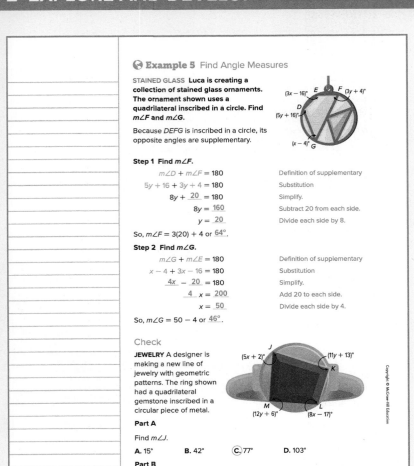

Example 5

TYPE

Students type to complete a solution.

CHECK

Students complete the Check online to determine whether they are ready to move on.

⊕ Example 5 Find Angle Measures

🆁🅿 Teaching the Mathematical Practices

4 Apply Mathematics In this example, students apply what they have learned about relationships in inscribed polygons to solving a real-world problem.

Questions for Mathematical Discourse

AL What is $m\angle D$? 116°

OL What is $m\widehat{DGF}$? 270°

BL If $m\angle D = 100°$, $m\angle E = (2x + 5)°$, and $m\angle G = (x + 25)°$, what is x? 50

Common Error

Students may try to set opposite angles of an inscribed quadrilateral equal to each other rather than using the fact that the angles are supplementary. Ask them what facts they know about the angles, and lead them to discover their error.

DIFFERENTIATE

Reteaching Activity **AL** **ELL**

Individual Learners Select or provide examples that cover each concept in the lesson so that students can sit quietly and work at their desks. Ask students to make a note if a particular type of problem gives them difficulty. Encourage students to reread and use the examples and theorems to work and understand the problems.

Exit Ticket

Recommended Use

At the end of class, go online to display the Exit Ticket prompt and ask students to respond using a separate piece of paper. Have students hand you their responses as they leave the room.

Alternate Use

At the end of class, go online to display the Exit Ticket prompt and ask students to respond verbally or by using a mini-whiteboard. Have students hold up their whiteboards so that you can see all student responses. Tap to reveal the answer when most or all students have completed the Exit Ticket.

Practice and Homework

Suggested Assignments

Use the table below to select appropriate exercises.

DOK	Topic	Exercises
1, 2	exercises that mirror the examples	1–25
2	exercises that use a variety of skills from this lesson	26–34
2	exercises that extend concepts learned in this lesson to new contexts	35–39
3	exercises that emphasize higher-order and critical-thinking skills	40–51

ASSESS AND DIFFERENTIATE

📊 Use the data from the **Checks** to determine whether to provide resources for extension, remediation, or intervention.

IF students score 90% or more on the Checks,   `BL`
THEN assign:

- Practice, Exercises 1–39 odd, 40–51
- Extension: Formulas for Regular Polygons
- 🔲 **ALEKS** Inscribed Angles and Polygons

IF students score 66%–89% on the Checks,   `OL`
THEN assign:

- Practice, Exercises 1–51 odd
- Remediation, Review Resources: Arcs and Chords
- Personal Tutors
- Extra Examples 1–5
- 🔲 **ALEKS** Comparing Angle Measures

IF students score 65% or less on the Checks,   `AL`
THEN assign:

- Practice, Exercises 1–25 odd
- Remediation, Review Resources: Arcs and Chords
- *Quick Review Math Handbook*: Inscribed Angles
- 🔲 **ALEKS** Comparing Angle Measures

Important to Know

Digital Exercise Alert Exercise 47 requires a construction and is not available online.

Answers

25c. Yes; sample answer: Because my estimate for the value of *x* is close to the exact value and ∠*J* appears to be a right angle, my answer is reasonable.

32. Proof: Statements (Reasons)

1. $\widehat{JL} \cong \widehat{RP}$; ∠*JKL* and ∠*RQP* are inscribed. (Given)

2. $m\angle JKL = \frac{1}{2}m\widehat{JL}$; $m\angle RQP = \frac{1}{2}m\widehat{RP}$ (The measure of an inscribed angle equals one half the measure of its intercepted arc.)

3. $m\widehat{JL} = m\widehat{RP}$ (Definition of congruent arcs)

4. $\frac{1}{2}m\widehat{JL} = \frac{1}{2}m\widehat{RP}$ (Multiplication Property of Equality)

5. $m\angle JKL = m\angle RQP$ (Substitution)

6. ∠*JKL* ≅ ∠*RQP* (Definition of congruent angles)

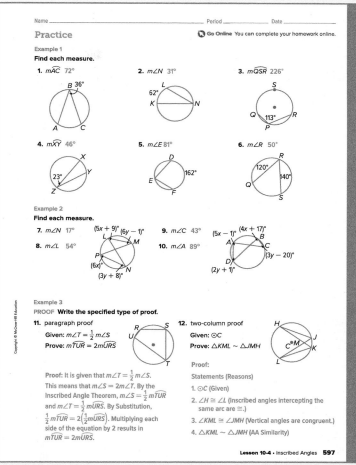

Name _____ Period _____ Date _____

Practice

🔵 **Go Online** You can complete your homework online.

Example 1
Find each measure.

1. $m\widehat{AC}$ 72°
2. $m\angle N$ 31°
3. $m\widehat{QSR}$ 226°

4. $m\widehat{XY}$ 46°
5. $m\angle E$ 81°
6. $m\angle R$ 50°

Example 2
Find each measure.

7. $m\angle N$ 17°
8. $m\angle L$ 54°
9. $m\angle C$ 43°
10. $m\angle A$ 89°

Example 3
PROOF Write the specified type of proof.

11. paragraph proof
Given: $m\angle T = \frac{1}{2}m\angle S$
Prove: $m\widehat{TUR} = 2m\widehat{URS}$

Proof: It is given that $m\angle T = \frac{1}{2}m\angle S$. This means that $m\angle S = 2m\angle T$. By the Inscribed Angle Theorem, $m\angle S = \frac{1}{2}m\widehat{TUR}$ and $m\angle T = \frac{1}{2}m\widehat{URS}$. By Substitution, $\frac{1}{2}m\widehat{TUR} = 2(\frac{1}{2}m\widehat{URS})$. Multiplying each side of the equation by 2 results in $m\widehat{TUR} = 2m\widehat{URS}$.

12. two-column proof
Given: ⊙*C*
Prove: △*KML* ~ △*JMH*

Proof:
Statements (Reasons)

1. ⊙*C* (Given)
2. ∠*H* ≅ ∠*L* (Inscribed angles intercepting the same arc are ≅.)
3. ∠*KML* ≅ ∠*JMH* (Vertical angles are congruent.)
4. △*KML* ~ △*JMH* (AA Similarity)

Lesson 10-4 • Inscribed Angles   **597**

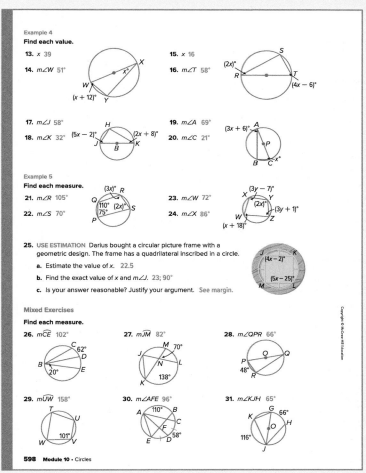

Example 4
Find each value.

13. *x*   39
14. $m\angle W$ 51°
15. *x*   16
16. $m\angle T$ 58°

17. $m\angle J$ 58°
18. $m\angle K$ 32°
19. $m\angle A$ 69°
20. $m\angle C$ 21°

Example 5
Find each measure.

21. $m\angle R$ 105°
22. $m\angle S$ 70°
23. $m\angle W$ 72°
24. $m\angle X$ 86°

25. **USE ESTIMATION** Darius bought a circular picture frame with a geometric design. The frame has a quadrilateral inscribed in a circle.

a. Estimate the value of *x*.   22.5

b. Find the exact value of *x* and $m\angle J$.   23; 90°

c. Is your answer reasonable? Justify your argument.   See margin.

Mixed Exercises
Find each measure.

26. $m\widehat{CE}$ 102°
27. $m\widehat{JM}$ 82°
28. $m\angle QPR$ 66°

29. $m\widehat{UW}$ 158°
30. $m\angle AFE$ 96°
31. $m\angle KJH$ 65°

598   Module 10 • Circles

| 1 CONCEPTUAL UNDERSTANDING | 2 FLUENCY | 3 APPLICATION |

Name _____ Period _____ Date _____

PROOF Write the specified type of proof to prove each theorem. 32–33. See margin.

32. two-column proof Theorem 10.8

Given: $\overline{JL} \cong \overline{RP}$; $\angle JKL$ and $\angle RQP$ are inscribed.

Prove: $\angle JKL \cong \angle RQP$

33. paragraph proof Theorem 10.10

Given: Quadrilateral DEFG is inscribed in ⊙C.

Prove: $\angle D$ and $\angle F$ are supplementary.
$\angle E$ and $\angle G$ are supplementary.

34. **PROOF** Write a paragraph proof to prove each part of Theorem 10.9. a–b. See margin.

a. Given: $\widehat{XWZ}$ is a semicircle.
   Prove: $\angle XYZ$ is a right angle.

b. Given: $\angle XYZ$ is a right angle.
   Prove: $\widehat{XWZ}$ is a semicircle.

35. **PROOF** Write a paragraph proof to prove that if PQRS is an inscribed quadrilateral and $\angle Q \cong \angle S$, then $\overline{PR}$ is a diameter of the circle. See margin.

36. **REASONING** A landscaping crew is installing a circular garden with three paths that form a triangle. The figure shows the plan for the garden and the paths. The leader of the crew wants to determine the radius they should use when they install the circular garden.

a. Find the measures of the angles in △ABD.
   $m\angle ABD = 90°$, $m\angle BAD = 41°$, and $m\angle BDA = 49°$

b. Use trigonometry to find the radius of the circular garden. Round to the nearest tenth meter, if necessary. 10.6 m

c. Given that the path will go along the outside of the garden, as well as along the three interior paths, find the total length of the path that will need to be installed. See margin.

Lesson 10-4 • Inscribed Angles **599**

---

37. **ARENA** A concert arena is lit by five lights equally spaced around the perimeter. What is $m\angle 1$? 72°

38. **JEWELRY** Alyssa makes earrings by bending wire into various shapes. She often bends the wire to form a circle with an inscribed quadrilateral as shown. She would like to know how she can find $m\widehat{ADC}$ if she knows $m\angle ADC$. Write a formula for finding $m\widehat{ADC}$ given that $m\angle ADC = x°$. $m\widehat{ADC} = 360° - 2(x°)$

39. **TAPESTRY** Helga is creating a design for a tapestry she is making for her art class. The design shown uses a kite inscribed in a circle. Find $m\angle SRU$ and the value of x. $m\angle SRU = 80°$; $x = 12$

Higher-Order Thinking Skills

ANALYZE Determine whether the quadrilateral can always, sometimes, or never be inscribed in a circle. Justify your argument. 40–44. See margin.

40. square   **41.** rectangle   **42.** parallelogram   **43.** rhombus   **44.** kite

45. **PERSEVERE** A square is inscribed in a circle. What is the ratio of the area of the circle to the area of the square? $\frac{\pi}{2}$

46. **WRITE** A 45°-45°-90° right triangle is inscribed in a circle. If the radius of the circle is given, explain how to find the lengths of the legs of the triangle. See margin.

47. **CREATE** Draw an inscribed polygon. Then find the measure of each intercepted arc. See Mod. 10 Answer Appendix.

48. **WRITE** Compare and contrast inscribed angles and central angles of a circle. If they intercept the same arc, how are they related? See margin.

ANALYZE Determine whether each statement is always, sometimes, or never true. Justify your argument.

49. If $\widehat{PQR}$ is a major arc of a circle, then $\angle PQR$ is obtuse. Never; sample answer: $\widehat{PR}$ is a minor arc, so $m\widehat{PR} < 180°$. By the Inscribed Angle Theorem, $m\angle PQR < 90°$.

50. If $\overline{AB}$ is a diameter of circle O, and X is any point on circle O other than A or B, then $\triangle AXB$ is a right triangle.
Always; sample answer: $\angle AXB$ is an inscribed angle that intercepts a diameter, so it is a right angle.

51. When an equilateral triangle is inscribed in a circle it partitions the circle into three minor arcs that each measure 120°. Always; sample answer: Each angle of the triangle measures 60°, so each intercepted arc measures 120°.

600 Module 10 • Circles

Answers

33. Proof: By arc addition and the definitions of arc measure and the sum of central angles, $m\widehat{EFG} + m\widehat{EDG} = 360°$. By Theorem 10.7, $m\angle D = \frac{1}{2}m\widehat{EFG}$ and $m\angle F = \frac{1}{2}m\widehat{EDG}$. So, $m\angle D + m\angle F = \frac{1}{2}m\widehat{EFG} + \frac{1}{2}m\widehat{EDG}$ or $\frac{1}{2}(m\widehat{EFG} + m\widehat{EDG})$. By substitution, $m\angle D + m\angle F = \frac{1}{2}(360)$ or $180°$. By the definition of supplementary angles, $\angle D$ and $\angle F$ are supplementary. Because the sum of the measures of the interior angles of a quadrilateral is 360°, $m\angle D + m\angle F + m\angle E + m\angle G = 360°$. By substitution, $180 + m\angle E + m\angle G = 360°$. By the Subtraction Property of Equality, $m\angle E + m\angle G = 180°$. Therefore, $\angle E$ and $\angle G$ are supplementary by the definition of supplementary angles.

34a. Because $\widehat{XWZ}$ is a semicircle, $m\widehat{XWZ} = 180°$. Then, $m\angle XYZ = \frac{1}{2}m\widehat{XWZ} = \frac{1}{2}(180°) = 90°$ because $\angle XYZ$ is an inscribed angle. So, $\angle XYZ$ is a right angle by definition.

34b. Because $\angle XYZ$ is an inscribed angle, $m\angle XYZ = \frac{1}{2}m\widehat{XWZ}$. By the Multiplication Property of Equality, $m\widehat{XWZ} = 2\,m\angle XYZ$. Because $\angle XYZ$ is a right angle, $m\angle XYZ = 90°$. So, $m\widehat{XWZ} = 2(90°) = 180°$. So, $m\widehat{XWZ}$ is a semicircle by definition.

35. Proof: Because PQRS is inscribed in a circle, $\angle Q$ is supplementary to $\angle S$ because they are opposite angles. Because $\angle Q \cong \angle S$, $\angle Q$ and $\angle S$ must be right angles. So, $\angle Q$ intercepts $\widehat{PSR}$, $m\angle Q = 90°$ and $m\widehat{PSR} = 180°$ by the Inscribed Angle Theorem. This means that $\widehat{PSR}$ is a semicircle, so $\overline{PR}$ must be a diameter.

36c. Sample answer: The circumference of the circle is $(2\pi)(10.6) = 66.6$ m. $AD = 2(10.6) = 21.2$ m. $AB = 16$ m. $BD = \sqrt{21.2^2 - 16^2} = 13.9$ m; the total is $66.6 + 21.2 + 16 + 13.9 = 117.7$ m.

40. Always; sample answer: Squares have right angles at each vertex, therefore each pair of opposite angles will be supplementary and inscribed in a circle.

41. Always; sample answer: Rectangles have right angles at each vertex, therefore each pair of opposite angles will be supplementary and inscribed in a circle.

42. Sometimes; sample answer: A parallelogram can be inscribed in a circle as long as it is a rectangle.

43. Sometimes; sample answer: A rhombus can be inscribed in a circle as long as it is a square. Because the opposite angles of rhombi that are not squares are not supplementary, they cannot be inscribed in a circle.

44. Sometimes; as long as the angles that compose the pair of congruent opposite angles are right angles.

46. Sample answer: According to Theorem 10.9, an inscribed angle of a triangle intercepts a diameter if the angle is a right angle. Therefore, the hypotenuse is a diameter and has a length of 2r. Using trigonometry, each leg $= \sin 45° \cdot 2r$ or $\sqrt{2}\,r$.

48. An inscribed angle has its vertex on the circle. A central angle has its vertex at the center of the circle. If an inscribed angle and a central angle intercept the same arc, then the measure of the inscribed angle is one-half the measure of the central angle.

Tangents

LESSON GOAL

Students solve problems using relationships between circles and tangents.

1 LAUNCH

 Launch the lesson with a **Warm Up** and an introduction.

2 EXPLORE AND DEVELOP

Develop:

Tangents
- Identify Common Tangents
- Identify a Tangent
- Use a Tangent to Find Missing Values
- Use Congruent Tangents to Find Measures

Explore: Tangents and Circumscribed Angles

Develop:

Circumscribed Angles
- Use Circumscribed Angles to Find Measures
- Find Measures in Circumscribed Polygons

 You may want your students to complete the **Checks** online.

3 REFLECT AND PRACTICE

Exit Ticket

Practice

DIFFERENTIATE

View reports of student progress on the **Checks** after each example.

Resources	AL	OL	BL	ELL
Remediation: Converse of the Pythagorean Theorem	●	●		●
Extension: Tangent Circles		●	●	●

Language Development Handbook

Assign page 70 of the *Language Development Handbook* to help your students build mathematical language related to the relationships between circles and tangents.

ELL You can use the tips and suggestions on page T70 of the handbook to support students who are building English proficiency.

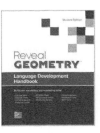

Suggested Pacing

90 min	**0.5 day**
45 min	**1 day**

Focus

Domain: Geometry

Standards for Mathematical Content:

G.C.4 Construct a tangent line from a point outside a given circle to the circle.
G.CO.13 Construct an equilateral triangle, a square, and a regular hexagon inscribed in a circle.

Standards for Mathematical Practice:

1 Make sense of problems and persevere in solving them.
3 Construct viable arguments and critique the reasoning of others.
8 Look for and express regularity in repeated reasoning.

Coherence

Vertical Alignment

Previous
Students solved problems using inscribed angles.
G.C.2, G.C.3

Now
Students solve problems using relationships between circles and tangents.
G.C.4, G.CO.13

Next
Students will solve problems using relationships between circles, tangents, and secants.
G.C.2

Rigor

The Three Pillars of Rigor

1 CONCEPTUAL UNDERSTANDING	2 FLUENCY	3 APPLICATION

🏛 **Conceptual Bridge** Working through the Explore and Learn activities can help students build a bridge to conceptual understanding. When students understand tangents of circles, they can move to procedural fluency and apply the math to real-world problems.

Mathematical Background

A tangent intersects a circle in exactly one point. This point is called the point of tangency. A line is tangent to a circle if and only if it is perpendicular to the radius drawn to the point of tangency. If two segments from the same exterior point are tangent to a circle, then they are congruent. Circles can be inscribed in polygons, just as polygons can be inscribed in circles. If a circle is inscribed in a polygon, then every side of the polygon is tangent to the circle.

Interactive Presentation

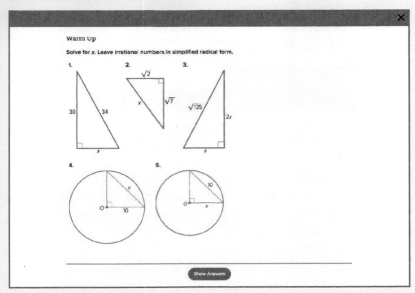

Warm Up

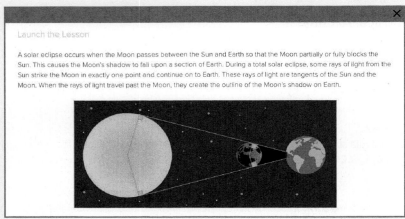

Launch the Lesson

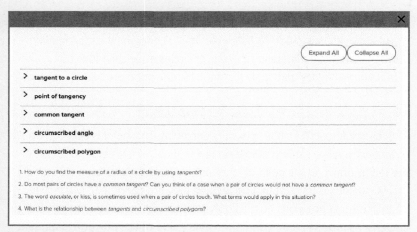

Today's Vocabulary

Warm Up

Prerequisite Skills

The Warm Up exercises address the following prerequisite skill for this lesson:

- using the Pythagorean Theorem

Answers:

1. 16
2. 3
3. 5
4. $10\sqrt{2}$
5. $5\sqrt{2}$

Launch the Lesson

 Teaching the Mathematical Practices

4 Apply Mathematics In this Launch the Lesson, students can see a real-world application of tangents.

Go Online to find additional teaching notes and questions to promote classroom discourse.

Today's Standards

Tell students that they will be addressing these content and practice standards in this lesson. You may wish to have a student volunteer read aloud *How can I meet these standards?* and *How can I use these practices?* and connect these to the standards.

See the Interactive Presentation for I Can statements that align with the standards covered in this lesson.

Today's Vocabulary

Tell students that they will be using these vocabulary terms in this lesson. You can expand each row if you wish to share the definitions. Then, discuss the questions below with the class.

Explore Tangents and Circumscribed Angles

Objective
Students use dynamic geometry software to identify and describe relationships among radii, tangents, and circumscribed angles.

 Teaching the Mathematical Practices

> **5 Use Mathematical Tools** Point out that to solve the problem in this Explore, students will need to use dynamic geometry software. Work with students to explore and deepen their understanding of relationships among radii, tangents, and circumscribed angles.

Ideas for Use

Recommended Use Present the Inquiry Question, or have a student volunteer read it aloud. Have students work in pairs to complete the Explore activity on their devices. Pairs should discuss each of the questions. Monitor student progress during the activity. Upon completion of the Explore activity, have student volunteers share their responses to the Inquiry Question.

What if my students don't have devices? You may choose to project the activity on a whiteboard. A printable worksheet for each Explore is available online. You may choose to print the worksheet so that individuals or pairs of students can use it to record their observations.

Summary of the Activity
Students will complete guiding exercises throughout the Explore activity. Students begin by using dynamic geometry software to construct two radii in the same circle and the line tangent to each radius such that the lines intersect. Students then measure the distance from the intersection point to the point of tangency on each line and notice that the distances are the same. Next students measure the angle between the tangent lines and the central angle and notice that they are supplementary. Students write conjectures based on their work. Then, students will answer the Inquiry Question.

(continued on the next page)

Interactive Presentation

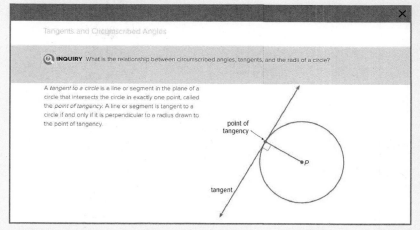

Explore

Explore

WEB SKETCHPAD

Students use the sketch to explore tangents of circles.

Interactive Presentation

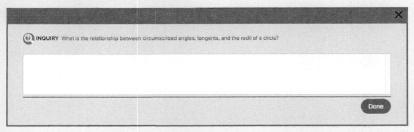

Explore

TYPE

Students respond to the Inquiry Question and can view a sample answer.

---

1 CONCEPTUAL UNDERSTANDING | 2 FLUENCY | 3 APPLICATION

Explore Tangents and Circumscribed Angles (*continued*)

Teaching the Mathematical Practices

3 Make Conjectures In the Explore, students will use stated assumptions, definitions, and previously established results to make a conjecture.

Questions
Have students complete the Explore activity.

Ask:
- How do the names *inscribed* and *circumscribed* help you remember where the angles are located? Sample answer: When a shape is inscribed, it is *inside* something. This helps me to remember that inscribed angles are *inside* the circle. When a shape is circumscribed, it is *outside* something. This helps me to remember that circumscribed angles are *outside* the circle.
- What sort of quadrilateral would be formed by the tangents and radii if the circumscribed angle measured 90°? Sample answer: If the circumscribed angle is 90°, then the tangent lines are perpendicular. Also, these segments are congruent because they are intersecting in a point exterior to the circle and are tangent to the circle. The circumscribed angle and central angle are supplementary, which means that both angles are 90°. A segment that is tangent to a circle is perpendicular to the radius at the point of tangency, so all angles are 90°. Lastly, all radii are congruent. The quadrilateral has 4 right angles, and two sets of adjacent sides congruent, so the quadrilateral is a square.

Inquiry
What is the relationship between circumscribed angles, tangents, and the radii of a circle? Sample answer: A tangent intersects a circle in a single point and is perpendicular to a radius of the circle at the point of intersection. If two segments are tangent to a circle and intersect in an exterior point of the circle, then the segments are congruent. These congruent segments form the sides of a circumscribed angle. The circumscribed angle and the central angle that intercept the same arc are supplementary.

Go Online to find additional teaching notes and sample answers for the guiding exercises.

1 CONCEPTUAL UNDERSTANDING | **2 FLUENCY** | 3 APPLICATION

Learn Tangents

Objective
Students describe relationships between radii and tangents, and use those relationships to solve problems.

 Teaching the Mathematical Practices

3 Analyze Cases The Concept Check guides students to examine the cases of tangents to a circle. Encourage students to familiarize themselves with all of the cases.

Example 1 Identify Common Tangents

 Teaching the Mathematical Practices

6 Communicate Precisely Encourage students to routinely write or explain their solution methods. Point out that they should use clear definitions when they discuss their solutions with others.

Questions for Mathematical Discourse

AL Do circles need to be touching in order to have common tangents? Explain. No; sample answer: Circles can have common tangents whether or not they are touching.

OL If two circles share a common center but are not the same size, do they have any common tangents? Explain. No; sample answer: If there was a tangent to the smaller circle, the point of tangency would be inside the larger circle, so they cannot share a common tangent.

BL Do you think three circles can share a common tangent? Explain. Yes; sample answer: If three congruent circles are placed so their centers are on one line, there will be tangents to both the top and bottom of all three circles.

Example 2 Identify a Tangent

 Teaching the Mathematical Practices

3 Construct Arguments In this example, students will use stated assumptions, definitions, and previously established results to construct an argument.

Questions for Mathematical Discourse

AL What is the point of tangency? B

OL If $AB = 7$, does B lie on the interior or exterior of the circle? interior

BL If you drew a second triangle with vertices A, B, and E, where E lies on $\overline{BC}$, would the triangle necessarily be a right triangle? Explain. Yes; sample answer: Because we know that $\overline{BC}$ is tangent to ⊙A, the radius drawn through B must be perpendicular, so the triangle would be right.

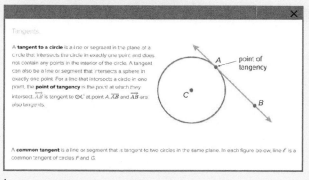

Interactive Presentation

Learn

TAP

Students select the number of tangents.

Your Notes

Problem-Solving Tip

Solve a Simpler Problem
You can *solve a simpler problem* by sketching and labeling the right triangle in the example without the circle. A drawing of the triangle is shown below.

Example 3 Use a Tangent to Find Missing Values

$\overline{QS}$ is tangent to $\odot R$ at Q. Find the value of x.

By Theorem 10.11, $\overline{RQ} \perp \overline{QS}$. So, $\triangle RQS$ is a right triangle.

$RQ^2 + QS^2 = \underline{RS^2}$ Pythagorean Theorem
$x^2 + \underline{4}^2 = (\underline{x} + 2)^2$ $RQ = x$, $QS = 4$, and $RS = \underline{x} + 2$
$x^2 + \underline{16} = x^2 + \underline{4x} + \underline{4}$ Multiply.
$12 = \underline{4x}$ Simplify.
$\underline{3} = x$ Divide each side by 4.

Check
$\overline{BC}$ is tangent to $\odot A$ at C. Find the value of x to the nearest hundredth.

$x = \underline{9.64}$

🌐 **Example 4** Use Congruent Tangents to Find Measures

PHOTOGRAPHY A photographer wants to take a picture of a local fountain. She positions herself at point A so that the fountain will be centered in the picture. $\overline{AB}$ and $\overline{AC}$ are tangent to the fountain as shown. If the lengths of the tangents are given in feet, find AB.

Because tangents $\overline{AB}$ and $\overline{AC}$ are from the same exterior point A, $\overline{AB} \cong \overline{AC}$.

$AB = AC$ Definition of congruent segments
$\underline{7x - 9} = 5x + 5$ Substitution
$x = \underline{7}$ Solve.

So, $AB = 7(\underline{7}) - 9$ or $\underline{40}$ feet.

Check

LANDSCAPING A landscape designer is creating a tiled patio with a circular design pattern. A corner of the patio is shown. $\overline{DE}$ and $\overline{FE}$ are tangent to $\odot G$, and the lengths of the tangents are given in feet. Find DE.

$DE = \underline{2.5}$ ft

🌐 **Go Online** You can complete an Extra Example online.

Interactive Presentation

Use a Tangent to Find Missing Values

$\overline{QS}$ is tangent to $\odot R$ at Q. Find the value of x.

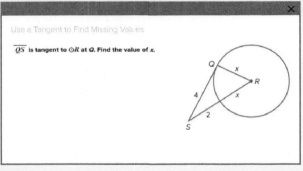

Example 3

TYPE

Students enter segment names and values to use a tangent to find the solution.

CHECK

Students complete the Check online to determine whether they are ready to move on.

Example 3 Use a Tangent to Find Missing Values

🅜🅟 **Teaching the Mathematical Practices**

2 Create Representations Guide students to write an equation that models the situation in this example. Then use the equation to solve the problem.

Questions for Mathematical Discourse

AL How do we know that the triangle is a right triangle? Sample answer: Because Q is a point of tangency, the radius from the center of the circle to Q must be perpendicular to the tangent, so it is a right triangle.

OL If $m\angle S = 45°$ and $QS = 7$, what is the radius of the circle? 7

BL If $m\angle S = 30°$ and $QS = 7$, what is the radius of the circle? $\frac{7\sqrt{3}}{3}$

Common Error

Students may have difficulty visualizing the right triangle with the circle in the diagram. Use the Problem-Solving Tip to help them draw a new diagram using just the triangle and its side lengths. Then help them write the equation needed to solve the problem.

🌐 Example 4 Use Congruent Tangents to Find Measures

🅜🅟 **Teaching the Mathematical Practices**

4 Apply Mathematics In this example, students apply what they have learned about relationships between radii and tangents to solving a real-world problem.

Questions for Mathematical Discourse

AL If $AB = 9$, what is CB? 9

OL If B lies in the interior of the circle, does the relationship still hold true? Explain. No; sample answer: If B lies in the interior of the circle, then $\overline{AB}$ and $\overline{CB}$ would no longer be tangents.

BL What type of triangle is $\triangle ABC$? isosceles

DIFFERENTIATE

Language Development Activity AL BL ELL
Social Learners Organize students into small groups. Explain that a company wants to market a new toy with a diameter of 5 in. Their task is to design a container for the toy that takes up the least amount of shelf space and has flat sides, and they are considering a square container and a hexagonal container. Have students draw and label the circular toy and the container surrounding it for each type of container. If the display shelf is 3 ft by 10 ft, how many toys will fit in a single layer on the shelf? Which shape will allow the maximum number of toys to be displayed on the shelf?

1 CONCEPTUAL UNDERSTANDING | **2 FLUENCY** | 3 APPLICATION

Learn Circumscribed Angles

Objective
Students describe relationships between central and circumscribed angles, and use those relationships to solve problems.

 Teaching the Mathematical Practices

> **7 Use Structure** Help students to explore the structure of circumscribed angles and polygons in this Learn.

Common Misconception
Students may confuse the relationship that a circumscribed angle has with its corresponding central angle, being supplementary, with the relationship that an inscribed angle has with its central angle, being half the measure of the central angle. Draw lots of diagrams to illustrate many different circumscribed, inscribed, and central angles and their relationships.

Example 5 Use Circumscribed Angles to Find Measures

 Teaching the Mathematical Practices

> **6 Communicate Precisely** Encourage students to routinely write or explain their solution methods. Point out that they should use clear definitions when they discuss their solutions with others.

Questions for Mathematical Discourse

AL What are the points of tangency? *E* and *F*

OL What kind of quadrilateral is *DEGF*? kite

BL If $m\angle G$ is twice $m\angle D$, what is $m\angle D$? 60°

Common Error
Students may set the sum of the angle measures of the circumscribed and central angles equal to 90° or 360°. Remind them that the angles are supplementary and ask them what that means.

 Go Online

- Find additional teaching notes.
- View performance reports of the Checks.
- Assign or present an Extra Example.

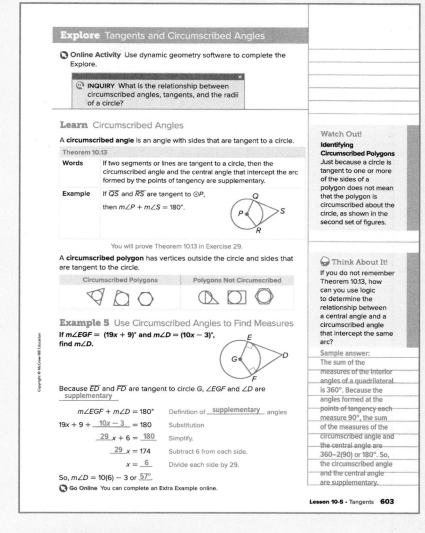

Explore Tangents and Circumscribed Angles

Online Activity Use dynamic geometry software to complete the Explore.

> **INQUIRY** What is the relationship between circumscribed angles, tangents, and the radii of a circle?

Learn Circumscribed Angles

A **circumscribed angle** is an angle with sides that are tangent to a circle.

Theorem 10.13

Words	If two segments or lines are tangent to a circle, then the circumscribed angle and the central angle that intercept the arc formed by the points of tangency are supplementary.
Example	If $\overline{QS}$ and $\overline{RS}$ are tangent to $\odot P$, then $m\angle P + m\angle S = 180°$.

You will prove Theorem 10.13 in Exercise 29.

A **circumscribed polygon** has vertices outside the circle and sides that are tangent to the circle.

Circumscribed Polygons	Polygons Not Circumscribed

Example 5 Use Circumscribed Angles to Find Measures

If $m\angle EGF = (19x + 9)°$ and $m\angle D = (10x - 3)°$, find $m\angle D$.

Because $\overline{ED}$ and $\overline{FD}$ are tangent to circle G, $\angle EGF$ and $\angle D$ are __supplementary__.

$m\angle EGF + m\angle D = 180°$ Definition of __supplementary__ angles

$19x + 9 + \underline{10x - 3} = 180$ Substitution

$\underline{29}x + 6 = \underline{180}$ Simplify.

$\underline{29}x = 174$ Subtract 6 from each side.

$x = \underline{6}$ Divide each side by 29.

So, $m\angle D = 10(6) - 3$ or $\underline{57°}$.

Go Online You can complete an Extra Example online.

Watch Out!
Identifying Circumscribed Polygons Just because a circle is tangent to one or more of the sides of a polygon does not mean that the polygon is circumscribed about the circle, as shown in the second set of figures.

Think About It!
If you do not remember Theorem 10.13, how can you use logic to determine the relationship between a central angle and a circumscribed angle that intercept the same arc?

Sample answer: The sum of the measures of the interior angles of a quadrilateral is 360°. Because the angles formed at the points of tangency each measure 90°, the sum of the measures of the circumscribed angle and the central angle are 360−2(90) or 180°. So, the circumscribed angle and the central angle are supplementary.

Interactive Presentation

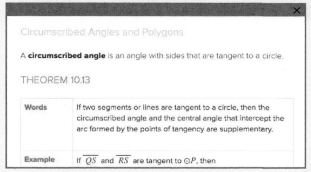

Circumscribed Angles and Polygons

A **circumscribed angle** is an angle with sides that are tangent to a circle.

THEOREM 10.13

Words	If two segments or lines are tangent to a circle, then the circumscribed angle and the central angle that intercept the arc formed by the points of tangency are supplementary.
Example	If $\overline{QS}$ and $\overline{RS}$ are tangent to $\odot P$, then

Learn

TAP

Students tap to reveal a reminder about tangents.

Check

If $m\angle XWZ = 7x + 10$ and $m\angle Y = 4x + 5$, find $m\angle Y$.

$m\angle Y =$ _65°_

Example 6 Find Measures in Circumscribed Polygons

$\triangle JKL$ is circumscribed about $\odot Q$.
Find the perimeter of $\triangle JKL$.

Step 1 Find the missing measures.

Because $\triangle JKL$ is circumscribed about $\odot Q$, $\overline{JM}$ and $\overline{JP}$ are tangent to $\odot Q$, as are $\overline{KM}$, $\overline{KN}$, $\overline{LN}$, and $\overline{LP}$. Therefore, $\overline{JM} \cong \overline{JP}$, $\overline{KM} \cong \overline{KN}$, and $\overline{LN} \cong \overline{LP}$.

So, $JM = JP = 14$ feet, $\underline{KM} = KN = \underline{7}$ feet, and $\underline{LN} = LP = \underline{11}$ feet.

Step 2 Find the perimeter of $\triangle JKL$.

By the Segment Addition Postulate, $JK = JM + KM = 14 + 7$ or $\underline{21}$ units,

$KL = KN + \underline{LN} = 7 + \underline{11}$ or $\underline{18}$ units, and
$JL = \underline{JP} + LP = \underline{14} + 11$ or $\underline{25}$ units.

$$\text{perimeter} = JK + KL + JL$$
$$= 21 + \underline{18} + 25 \text{ or } \underline{64} \text{ units}$$

So, the perimeter of $\triangle JKL$ is $\underline{64}$ units.

Check

Quadrilateral $RSTU$ is circumscribed about $\odot J$. If the perimeter is 18 units, find the value of x.

(A.) 1.5 units   **B.** 2 units   **C.** 3 units   **D.** 6 units

🔵 **Go Online** You can complete an Extra Example online.

Sidebar:

💭 **Think About It!**
How can you check your answer?

Sample answer: Because there are three pairs of congruent tangents that form the perimeter of $\triangle JKL$, I can check my answer by doubling each tangent length and finding the sum of the products. So, the perimeter of $\triangle JKL$ is equal to $2(14) + 2(7) + 2(11)$ or 64 units.

🔵 **Go Online**
You can watch a video to see how to solve problems involving circumscribed triangles.

🔵 **Go Online**
You may want to complete the construction activities for this lesson.

Example 6 Find Measures in Circumscribed Polygons

👥 **Teaching the Mathematical Practices**

8 Attend to Details Mathematically proficient students continually ask themselves, "Does this make sense?" Point out that in this example, students will evaluate the reasonableness of their answer.

Questions for Mathematical Discourse

AL What are the points of tangency? *M, N,* and *P*

OL What is the largest angle of the triangle? Explain. The largest is $\angle K$, because it is opposite the longest side of the triangle.

BL What type of triangle is $\triangle JKL$? Explain. Acute, because $KL^2 + JK^2 > JL^2$.

Exit Ticket

Recommended Use

At the end of class, go online to display the Exit Ticket prompt and ask students to respond using a separate piece of paper. Have students hand you their responses as they leave the room.

Alternate Use

At the end of class, go online to display the Exit Ticket prompt and ask students to respond verbally or by using a mini-whiteboard. Have students hold up their whiteboards so that you can see all student responses. Tap to reveal the answer when most or all students have completed the Exit Ticket.

Interactive Presentation

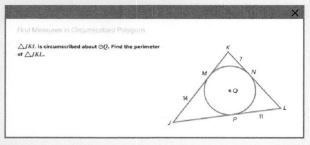

Example 6

TYPE

Students enter segment names and values to complete the solution.

CHECK

Students complete the Check online to determine whether they are ready to move on.

Practice and Homework

Suggested Assignments

Use the table below to select appropriate exercises.

DOK	Topic	Exercises
1, 2	exercises that mirror the examples	1–26
2	exercises that use a variety of skills from this lesson	27–31
2	exercises that extend concepts learned in this lesson to new contexts	32–37
3	exercises that emphasize higher-order and critical-thinking skills	38–42

ASSESS AND DIFFERENTIATE

📊 Use the data from the **Checks** to determine whether to provide resources for extension, remediation, or intervention.

IF students score 90% or more on the Checks, `BL`
THEN assign:
- Practice, Exercises 1–37 odd, 38–42
- Extension: Tangent Circles
- 🔵 **ALEKS** Segments in a Circle and Tangent Lines

IF students score 66%–89% on the Checks, `OL`
THEN assign:
- Practice, Exercises 1–41 odd
- Remediation, Review Resources: Converse of the Pythagorean Theorem
- Personal Tutors
- Extra Examples 1–6
- 🔵 **ALEKS** Using the Pythagorean Theorem

IF students score 65% or less on the Checks, `AL`
THEN assign:
- Practice, Exercises 1–25 odd
- Remediation, Review Resources: Converse of the Pythagorean Theorem
- *Quick Review Math Handbook*: Tangents
- 🔵 **ALEKS** Using the Pythagorean Theorem

Important to Know

Digital Exercise Alert Exercise 40 requires a construction and is not available online. To fully address G.C.3, have students complete this exercise using their books.

28. Proof: Statements (Reasons)
    1. $\overline{AC}$ is tangent to $\odot H$ at C, and $\overline{AB}$ is tangent to $\odot H$ at B. (Given)
    2. Draw $\overline{AH}$, $\overline{BH}$, and $\overline{CH}$. (Through any two points, there is one line.)
    3. $\overline{AC} \perp \overline{CH}$, $\overline{AB} \perp \overline{BH}$ (A line tangent to a circle is perpendicular to the radius at the point of tangency.)
    4. $\angle ACH$ and $\angle ABH$ are right angles. (Definition of perpendicular)
    5. $\overline{CH} \cong \overline{BH}$ (All radii of a circle are congruent.)
    6. $\overline{AH} \cong \overline{AH}$ (Reflexive Property of Congruence)
    7. $\triangle ACH \cong \triangle ABH$ (HL Congruence Theorem)
    8. $\overline{AC} \cong \overline{AB}$ (CPCTC)

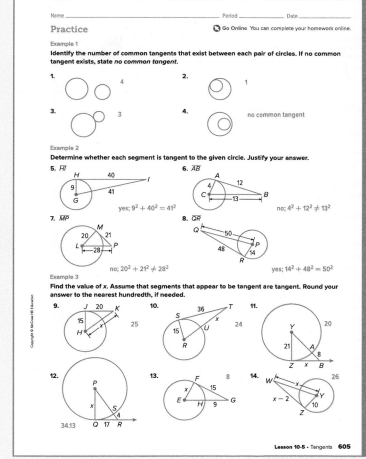

Name _____ Period _____ Date _____

Practice
🔵 Go Online You can complete your homework online.

Example 1
Identify the number of common tangents that exist between each pair of circles. If no common tangent exists, state *no common tangent*.

1. 4
2. 1
3. 3
4. no common tangent

Example 2
Determine whether each segment is tangent to the given circle. Justify your answer.

5. $\overline{HI}$ yes; $9^2 + 40^2 = 41^2$
6. $\overline{AB}$ no; $4^2 + 12^2 \neq 13^2$
7. $\overline{MP}$ no; $20^2 + 21^2 \neq 28^2$
8. $\overline{QR}$ yes; $14^2 + 48^2 = 50^2$

Example 3
Find the value of *x*. Assume that segments that appear to be tangent are tangent. Round your answer to the nearest hundredth, if needed.

9.
10.
11.
12. 34.13
13.
14.

Lesson 10-5 · Tangents **605**

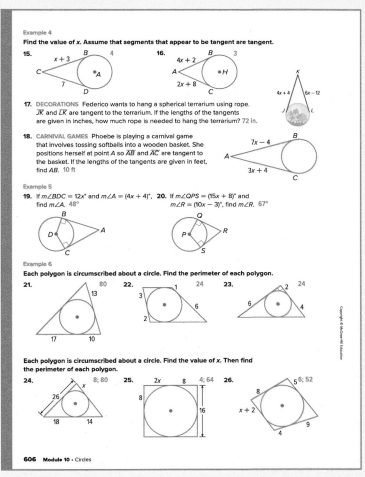

Example 4
Find the value of *x*. Assume that segments that appear to be tangent are tangent.

15.
16.
17. **DECORATIONS** Federico wants to hang a spherical terrarium using rope. $\overline{JK}$ and $\overline{LK}$ are tangent to the terrarium. If the lengths of the tangents are given in inches, how much rope is needed to hang the terrarium? 72 in.
18. **CARNIVAL GAMES** Phoebe is playing a carnival game that involves tossing softballs into a wooden basket. She positions herself at point *A* so $\overline{AB}$ and $\overline{AC}$ are tangent to the basket. If the lengths of the tangents are given in feet, find *AB*. 10 ft

Example 5
19. If $m\angle BDC = 12x°$ and $m\angle A = (4x + 4)°$, find $m\angle A$. 48°
20. If $m\angle QPS = (15x + 8)°$ and $m\angle R = (10x - 3)°$, find $m\angle R$. 67°

Example 6
Each polygon is circumscribed about a circle. Find the perimeter of each polygon.
21. 80
22. 24
23. 24

Each polygon is circumscribed about a circle. Find the value of *x*. Then find the perimeter of each polygon.
24. 8; 80
25. 4; 64
26. 6; 52

606 Module 10 · Circles

Lesson 10-5 · Tangents **605-606**

Mixed Exercises

27. REASONING The design shown in the figure is that of a circular clock face inscribed in a triangular base. *AF* and *FC* are equal.
a. Find *AB*. 9.5 in.
b. Find the perimeter of the clock. 34 in.

PROOF Write a two-column proof to prove each theorem. 28–29. See margin.

28. Theorem 10.12
Given: $\overline{AC}$ is tangent to ⊙*H* at *C*.
$\overline{AB}$ is tangent to ⊙*H* at *B*.
Prove: $\overline{AC} \cong \overline{AB}$

29. Theorem 10.13
Given: $\overline{RQ}$ is tangent to ⊙*P* at *Q*.
$\overline{RT}$ is tangent to ⊙*P* at *T*.
Prove: $m\angle P + m\angle R = 180°$

30. PROOF Write a two-column proof.
Given: Quadrilateral *ABCD* is circumscribed about ⊙*P*.
Prove: $AB + CD = AD + BC$
See Mod. 10 Answer Appendix.

31. JEWELRY Joan is designing a pendant with a circular gem inscribed in a triangle.
a. Find the values of *x*, *y*, and *z*. 5; 2; 10
b. Find the perimeter of the triangle. 68

PRECISION Find the value of *x* to the nearest hundredth. Assume that segments that appear to be tangent are tangent.

32. 9

33. 8.06

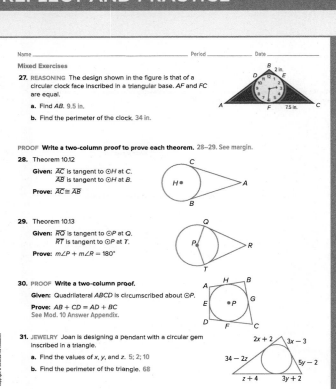

Lesson 10-5 · Tangents **607**

---

34. DESIGN Ignacio wants to make a design of circles inside an equilateral triangle as shown.
a. What is the radius of the large circle to the nearest hundredth of an inch? 2.89 in.
b. What are the radii of the smaller circles to the nearest hundredth of an inch? 0.96 in.

35. PERSEVERE A wheel is rolling down an incline as shown in the figure at the right. Twelve evenly spaced radii form spokes of the wheel. When spoke 2 is vertical, which spoke will be perpendicular to the incline? spoke 10

36. USE TOOLS Construct a line tangent to a circle through a point on the circle. Use a compass to draw ⊙*A*. Choose a point *P* on the circle and draw $\overrightarrow{AP}$. Then construct a segment through point *P* perpendicular to $\overrightarrow{AP}$. Label the tangent line *t*. Justify each step. See margin.

37. USE A MODEL NASA has procedures for limiting orbital debris to mitigate the risk to human life and space missions. *Orbital debris* refers to materials from space missions that still orbit Earth. Suppose an ammonia tank is accidentally discarded from a spacecraft at an altitude of 435 miles. What is the distance from the tank to the farthest point on Earth's surface from which the tank is visible? Assume that the radius of Earth is 4000 miles. Round your answer to the nearest mile. Draw a diagram to represent this situation. See margin.

Higher-Order Thinking Skills

38. PERSEVERE $\overline{PQ}$ is tangent to circles *R* and *S*. Find *PQ*. Explain your reasoning. See margin.

39. WHICH ONE DOESN'T BELONG? Which of the polygons shown below is not circumscribed? Justify your conclusion.

Figure A   Figure B   Figure C   Figure D

Figure B; because one of the sides of the quadrilateral is not tangent to the circle, the quadrilateral is not circumscribed about the circle.

40. CREATE Draw a circumscribed triangle and an inscribed triangle. See Mod. 10 Answer Appendix.

41. ANALYZE In the figure, $\overline{XY}$ and $\overline{XZ}$ are tangent to ⊙*A*. $\overline{XZ}$ and $\overline{XW}$ are tangent to ⊙*B*. Explain how segments $\overline{XY}$, $\overline{XZ}$, and $\overline{XW}$ can all be congruent if the circles have different radii. See Mod. 10 Answer Appendix.

42. WRITE Is it possible to draw a tangent from a point that is located anywhere outside, on, or inside a circle? Explain. See Mod. 10 Answer Appendix.

Answers

29. Proof:
Statements (Reasons)
1. $\overline{RQ}$ is tangent to ⊙*P* at *Q*; $\overline{RT}$ is tangent to ⊙*P* at *T*. (Given)
2. $\overline{PQ} \perp \overline{RQ}$, $\overline{PT} \perp \overline{RT}$ (A tangent is ⊥ to the radius drawn to the point of tangency.)
3. $\angle Q$ and $\angle T$ are rt. angles. (⊥ segments form right angles.)
4. $m\angle Q = 90°$, $m\angle T = 90°$ (Def. of right angle)
5. PQRT is a quadrilateral. (Def. of quadrilateral)
6. $m\angle P + m\angle Q + m\angle R + m\angle T = 360°$ (Polygon Interior Angles Sum Thm.)
7. $m\angle P + 90° + m\angle R + 90° = 360°$ (Substitution)
8. $m\angle P + m\angle R + 180° = 360°$ (Substitution)
9. $m\angle P + m\angle R = 180°$ (Subtraction Property of Equality)

36. Sample answer:
a. Draw $\overleftrightarrow{AP}$. (Two points determine a line.)
b. Construct a perpendicular at *P*. (The tangent is perpendicular to the radius at its endpoint.)

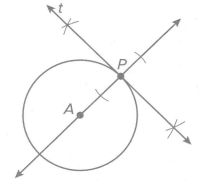

37. 1916 mi;

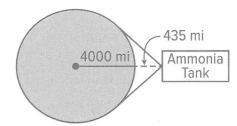

38. Sample answer:

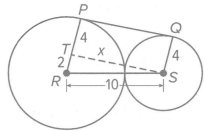

Construct $\overline{ST}$ such that *T* is between *P* and *R* on $\overline{PR}$ and $\overline{ST}$ is parallel to $\overline{PQ}$. Using the Pythagorean Theorem, $2^2 + x^2 = 10^2$, so $x \approx 9.8$. Because PQST is a rectangle, $PQ = x = 9.8$.

Tangents, Secants, and Angle Measures

LESSON GOAL

Students solve problems using relationships between circles, tangents, and secants.

1 LAUNCH

 Launch the lesson with a **Warm Up** and an introduction.

2 EXPLORE AND DEVELOP

 Explore: Relationships Between Tangents and Secants

 Develop:

Tangents, Secants, and Angle Measures
- Intersecting Chords of Secants
- Secants and Tangents Intersecting on a Circle
- Tangents and Secants Intersecting Outside a Circle

 You may want your students to complete the **Checks** online.

3 REFLECT AND PRACTICE

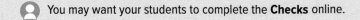 Exit Ticket

Practice

DIFFERENTIATE

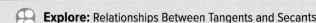 View reports of student progress on the **Checks** after each example.

Resources	AL	OL	BL	ELL
Remediation: Inscribed Angles	●	●		●
Extension: Orbiting Bodies		●	●	●

Language Development Handbook

Assign page 71 of the *Language Development Handbook* to help your students build mathematical language related to the relationships between circles, tangents, and secants.

ELL You can use the tips and suggestions on page T71 of the handbook to support students who are building English proficiency.

Suggested Pacing

90 min	**0.5 day**	
45 min		**1 day**

Focus

Domain: Geometry
Standards for Mathematical Content:
G.C.2 Identify and describe relationships among inscribed angles, radii, and chords.
Standards for Mathematical Practice:
3 Construct viable arguments and critique the reasoning of others.
4 Model with mathematics.
7 Look for and make use of structure.

Coherence

Vertical Alignment

Previous
Students solved problems using relationships between circles and tangents.
G.C.4, G.CO.13

Now
Students solve problems using relationships between circles, tangents, and secants.
G.C.2

Next
Students will write and graph the equations of circles.
G.GPE.1, G.GPE.4

Rigor

The Three Pillars of Rigor

1 CONCEPTUAL UNDERSTANDING	2 FLUENCY	3 APPLICATION

Conceptual Bridge In this lesson, students extend their understanding of lines related to circles to include secant lines. They build fluency and apply their understanding of tangent and secant lines by solving real-world problems.

Mathematical Background

A line that intersects a circle in exactly two points is called a secant. If two secants intersect in the interior of a circle, then the measure of an angle formed is one-half the sum of the measure of the arcs intercepted by the angle and its vertical angle. A secant can also intersect a tangent at the point of tangency. If this occurs, then the measure of each angle formed is one-half the measure of its intercepted arc. Secants and tangents can intersect outside a circle as well.

Interactive Presentation

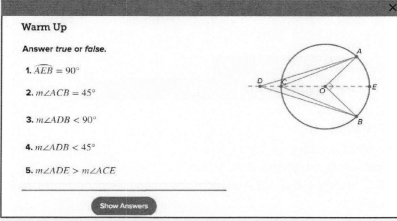

Warm Up

Answer *true* or *false*.

1. $\overset{\frown}{AEB} = 90°$

2. $m\angle ACB = 45°$

3. $m\angle ADB < 90°$

4. $m\angle ADB < 45°$

5. $m\angle ADE > m\angle ACE$

Show Answers

Warm Up

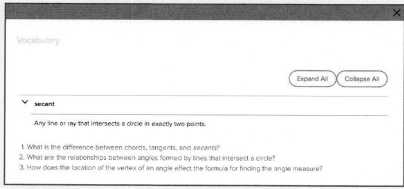

Launch the Lesson

Many satellites above the Earth are in a geostationary orbit, which means that that they remain stationary in relation to a fixed point on the planet. This allows the satellites to stay about 35,900 kilometers above Earth's equator. If space centers *A* and *B* are located on the equator, a two dimensional diagram using tangents could be used to represent the radar signals sent to the space centers from the satellite. If you know $m\overset{\frown}{AB}$, then you could use the relationship between tangents and angle measures to find the measure of the angle formed by the signals.

Launch the Lesson

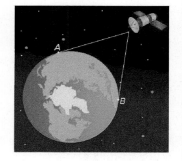

Vocabulary

Expand All | Collapse All

⌄ **secant**

Any line or ray that intersects a circle in exactly two points.

1. What is the difference between chords, tangents, and *secants*?
2. What are the relationships between angles formed by lines that intersect a circle?
3. How does the location of the vertex of an angle affect the formula for finding the angle measure?

Today's Vocabulary

Warm Up

Prerequisite Skills

The Warm Up exercises address the following prerequisite skill for this lesson:

- testing angle knowledge

Answers:

1. true
2. true
3. true
4. true
5. false

Launch the Lesson

MP Teaching the Mathematical Practices

4 Apply Mathematics In this Launch the Lesson, students can see a real-world application of tangents.

Go Online to find additional teaching notes and questions to promote classroom discourse.

Today's Standards

Tell students that they will be addressing these content and practice standards in this lesson. You may wish to have a student volunteer read aloud *How can I meet these standards?* and *How can I use these practices?* and connect these to the standards.

See the Interactive Presentation for I Can statements that align with the standards covered in this lesson.

Today's Vocabulary

Tell students that they will be using this vocabulary term in this lesson. You can expand the row if you wish to share the defintion. Then, discuss the questions below with the class.

Explore Relationships Between Tangents and Secants

Objective

Students use dynamic geometry software to discover and describe relationships between tangents, secants, and the angles formed by intersecting tangents and secants.

 Teaching the Mathematical Practices

> **5 Use Mathematical Tools** Point out that to solve the problem in this Explore, students will need to use dynamic geometry software. Work with students to explore and deepen their understanding of relationships between tangents, secants, and the angles formed by intersecting tangents and secants.

Ideas for Use

Recommended Use Present the Inquiry Question, or have a student volunteer read it aloud. Have students work in pairs to complete the Explore activity on their devices. Pairs should discuss each of the questions. Monitor student progress during the activity. Upon completion of the Explore activity, have student volunteers share their responses to the Inquiry Question.

What if my students don't have devices? You may choose to project the activity on a whiteboard. A printable worksheet for each Explore is available online. You may choose to print the worksheet so that individuals or pairs of students can use it to record their observations.

Summary of the Activity

Students will complete guiding exercises throughout the Explore activity. Students begin by constructing two secants that intersect inside a circle. They measure opposite arcs formed by the secants and an angle that intercepts one of them. Then they make a conjecture that the angle measure is half the sum of the arc measures. Next, students construct a tangent of a circle and a secant that intersects the point of tangency. They measure the angle formed between the tangent and the secant and the intercepted arc, and find that the measure of the angle is half that of the arc. Then, students will answer the Inquiry Question.

(continued on the next page)

Interactive Presentation

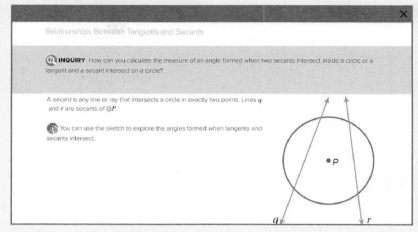

Explore

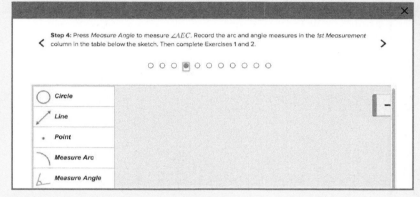

Explore

WEB SKETCHPAD

 Students use a sketch to explore intersecting tangents and secants.

G.C.2

Interactive Presentation

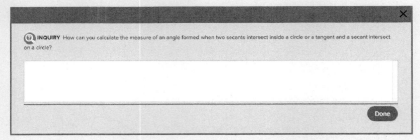

Explore

TYPE

a|

Students respond to the Inquiry Question and can view a sample answer.

Explore Relationships Between Tangents and Secants (*continued*)

MP Teaching the Mathematical Practices

5 Use Mathematical Tools Point out that to solve the problem in this Explore, students will need to use dynamic geometry software. Work with students to explore and deepen their understanding of relationships between tangents, secants, and the angles formed by intersecting tangents and secants.

Questions

Have students complete the Explore activity.

Ask:

- Why do you think the angle relationship for intersecting secants is more complicated than a central angle or an inscribed angle? Sample answer: Because the secants can intersect at some point inside the circle, that is not the center or a point on the circle, the relationship wouldn't be the same as a central angle or inscribed angle.

- If you knew $m\angle AEC$ and $m\widehat{AC}$, could you find $m\widehat{BD}$? Explain. Yes; sample answer: We know the measure of the angle formed by the secants is one half the sum of the intercepted arcs. We could substitute what we know and solve for the missing measure of the arc.

? Inquiry

How can you calculate the measure of an angle formed when two secants intersect inside a circle or when a tangent and a secant intersect on a circle? Sample answer: When two secants intersect in a circle, the measure of an angle formed by the secants is one half the sum of the arcs intercepted by the angle and its vertical angle. When a secant and a tangent intersect on a circle, the measure of an angle formed by the secant and tangent is one half the measure of the arc intercepted by the angle.

▶ **Go Online** to find additional teaching notes and sample answers for the guiding exercises.

1 CONCEPTUAL UNDERSTANDING | **2 FLUENCY** | 3 APPLICATION

Learn Tangents, Secants, and Angle Measures

Objective
Students use relationships between tangents and secants to solve problems.

Teaching the Mathematical Practices

7 Use Structure Help students to explore the structure of secants in this Learn.

3 Construct Arguments In this Learn, students will use stated assumptions, definitions, and previously established results to complete the given proof.

1 Explain Correspondences Encourage students to explain the relationships between tangents and secants in this Learn.

Common Misconception
Students may have difficulty keeping the conclusions from theorems 10.14, 10.15, and 10.16 straight. A way to help keep them straight is the direction the arcs curve. If the arcs curve away from the vertex of the angle, they are added, and if they curve toward the vertex, they are subtracted.

Essential Question Follow-Up
Students study tangents, secants, and circumscribed angles and polygons.
Ask:

Why is it important to understand objects that relate to the outside of circles? Sample answer: Tangents and other objects outside circles are important in the real world, like for bicycle chains and satellites.

Example 1 Intersecting Chords or Secants

Teaching the Mathematical Practices

3 Find the Error This example requires students to read the arguments of others, decide whether they make sense, and ask useful questions to clarify or improve the arguments.

Questions for Mathematical Discourse

AL What is $m\angle NKQ$? 65°

OL What is $m\angle PKQ$? 65°

BL If $x = 110$, what is $m\widehat{MP} + m\widehat{NQ}$? 220°

Common Error
Students may forget that x does not represent the measure of one of the angles that intercept the arcs with given measures, and stop before going on to find x. Ask them if they have reread the question to make sure they are finished.

Go Online

- Find additional teaching notes.
- View performance reports of the Checks.
- Assign or present an Extra Example.

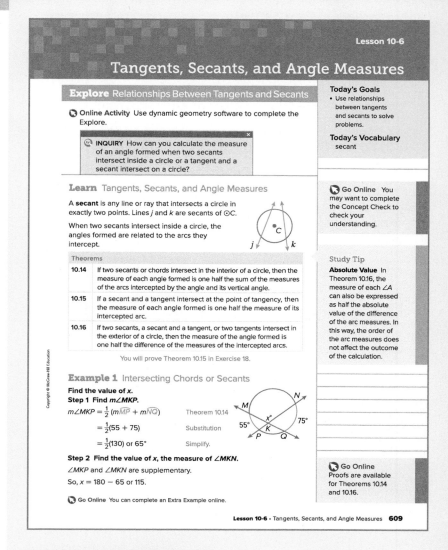

Lesson 10-6

Tangents, Secants, and Angle Measures

Explore Relationships Between Tangents and Secants

Online Activity Use dynamic geometry software to complete the Explore.

INQUIRY How can you calculate the measure of an angle formed when two secants intersect inside a circle or a tangent and a secant intersect on a circle?

Learn Tangents, Secants, and Angle Measures

A **secant** is any line or ray that intersects a circle in exactly two points. Lines j and k are secants of $\odot C$.

When two secants intersect inside a circle, the angles formed are related to the arcs they intercept.

Theorems	
10.14	If two secants or chords intersect in the interior of a circle, then the measure of each angle formed is one half the sum of the measures of the arcs intercepted by the angle and its vertical angle.
10.15	If a secant and a tangent intersect at the point of tangency, then the measure of each angle formed is one half the measure of its intercepted arc.
10.16	If two secants, a secant and a tangent, or two tangents intersect in the exterior of a circle, then the measure of the angle formed is one half the difference of the measures of the intercepted arcs.

You will prove Theorem 10.15 in Exercise 18.

Example 1 Intersecting Chords or Secants

Find the value of x.

Step 1 Find $m\angle MKP$.

$m\angle MKP = \frac{1}{2}(m\widehat{MP} + m\widehat{NQ})$ Theorem 10.14

$= \frac{1}{2}(55 + 75)$ Substitution

$= \frac{1}{2}(130)$ or 65°   Simplify.

Step 2 Find the value of x, the measure of $\angle MKN$.

$\angle MKP$ and $\angle MKN$ are supplementary.
So, $x = 180 - 65$ or 115.

Go Online You can complete an Extra Example online.

Today's Goals
- Use relationships between tangents and secants to solve problems.

Today's Vocabulary
secant

Go Online You may want to complete the Concept Check to check your understanding.

Study Tip
Absolute Value In Theorem 10.16, the measure of each $\angle A$ can also be expressed as half the absolute value of the difference of the arc measures. In this way, the order of the arc measures does not affect the outcome of the calculation.

Go Online
Proofs are available for Theorems 10.14 and 10.16.

Interactive Presentation

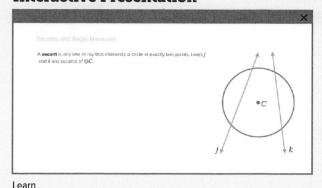

Secants and Angle Measures

A **secant** is any line or ray that intersects a circle in exactly two points. Lines j and k are secants of $\odot C$.

Learn

TAP

Students tap to move through the steps of a proof.

G.C.2

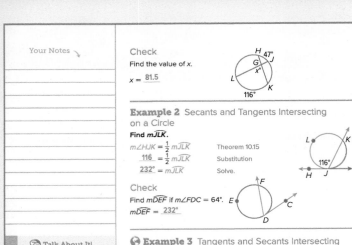

Your Notes

Check

Find the value of *x*.

x = __81.5__

Example 2 Secants and Tangents Intersecting on a Circle

Find *m$\widehat{JLK}$*.

$m\angle HJK = \frac{1}{2} m\widehat{JLK}$ Theorem 10.15

$\underline{116} = \frac{1}{2} m\widehat{JLK}$ Substitution

$\underline{232°} = m\widehat{JLK}$ Solve.

Check

Find *m$\widehat{DEF}$* if *m∠FDC* = 64°.

m$\widehat{DEF}$ = __232°__

☺ Example 3 Tangents and Secants Intersecting Outside a Circle

MEMORIALS A photographer is taking a photo of the Thomas Jefferson Memorial in Washington, D.C., from a boat in the Tidal Basin. The photographer's lines of sight are tangent to the memorial at points *Q* and *S*. If the camera's viewing angle measures 36°, what portion of the memorial will be visible in the photo?

Because the Thomas Jefferson Memorial can be modeled by a circle, the arc measure of the memorial is 360°. So, the portion of the memorial that will be visible in the photo is equal to $\frac{m\widehat{QS}}{360}$.

Let $m\widehat{QS} = x°$. So, $m\widehat{QRS} = 360 - x$.

$m\angle P = \frac{1}{2} m\widehat{QRS} - m\widehat{QS}$ Theorem 10.16

$\underline{36} = \frac{1}{2}[(360 - \underline{x}) - \underline{x}]$ Substitution

$\underline{36} = \frac{1}{2}(360 - \underline{2}x)$ Simplify.

$\underline{72} = 360 - \underline{2}x$ Multiply each side by 2.

$\underline{-288} = \underline{-2}x$ Subtract 360 from each side.

$\underline{144} = x$ Divide each side by −2.

So, $m\widehat{QS} = 144°$, and the portion of the memorial that will be visible in the photo is $\frac{144}{360}$ or 40%.

☁ Go Online You can complete an Extra Example online.

610   Module 10 · Circles

☑ Talk About It!

What is the difference between a tangent and a secant?

Sample answer: A tangent intersects a circle in exactly one point and does not pass through the interior of the circle. A secant intersects a circle in two different points and passes through the interior of the circle.

 Go Online to practice what you've learned about circles in the Put It All Together over Lessons 10-1 through 10-6.

Interactive Presentation

Secants and Tangents Intersecting on a Circle

Find *m$\widehat{JLK}$*.

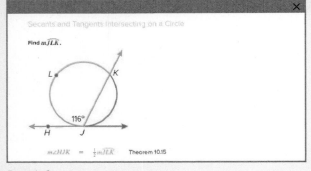

$m\angle HJK = \frac{1}{2} m\widehat{JLK}$ Theorem 10.15

Example 2

TYPE

| a| |

Students type to complete the solution.

CHECK

Students complete the Check online to determine whether they are ready to move on.

Example 2 Secants and Tangents Intersecting on a Circle

MP Teaching the Mathematical Practices

3 Compare Arguments Mathematically proficient students can compare arguments, determine which one is flawed, and explain the flaw. In this example, students have to identify the flawed argument and choose the correct one.

Questions for Mathematical Discourse

AL If you added point *X* to $\overleftrightarrow{HJ}$ to the right of *J*, what would *m∠KJX* be?   64°

OL What is the measure of minor arc $\widehat{JK}$?   128°

BL How is the angle formed by a secant and a tangent like an inscribed angle?   Sample answer: Both have measure equal to half of the arc they intercept.

☺ Example 3 Tangents and Secants Intersecting Outside a Circle

MP Teaching the Mathematical Practices

6 Communicate Precisely Encourage students to routinely write or explain their solution methods. Point out that they should use clear definitions when they discuss their solutions with others.

Questions for Mathematical Discourse

AL What is *m$\widehat{QRS}$*?   216°

OL If the camera moves to the side of the monument but the viewing angle remains the same, would the percentage of the monument visible in the photo change? Explain.   No; sample answer: The side of the monument would be in the figure instead of the front, but as long as the viewing angle remains the same, the percentage remains the same.

BL If the photographer narrows the camera angle to show only 30% of the monument, what is the measure of the arc visible in the photo?   108°

Exit Ticket

Recommended Use

At the end of class, go online to display the Exit Ticket prompt and ask students to respond using a separate piece of paper. Have students hand you their responses as they leave the room.

Alternate Use

At the end of class, go online to display the Exit Ticket prompt and ask students to respond verbally or by using a mini-whiteboard. Have students hold up their whiteboards so that you can see all student responses. Tap to reveal the answer when most or all students have completed the Exit Ticket.

Practice and Homework

Suggested Assignments

Use the table below to select appropriate exercises.

DOK	Topic	Exercises
1, 2	exercises that mirror the examples	1–16
2	exercises that use a variety of skills from this lesson	17–18
2	exercises that extend concepts learned in this lesson to new contexts	19–21
3	exercises that emphasize higher-order and critical-thinking skills	22–26

ASSESS AND DIFFERENTIATE

📊 Use the data from the **Checks** to determine whether to provide resources for extension, remediation, or intervention.

IF students score 90% or more on the Checks,   `BL`
THEN assign:

- Practice, Exercises 1–21 odd, 22–26
- Extension: Orbiting Bodies
- 🔵 **ALEKS'** Angle and Segment Relationships in Circles

IF students score 66%–89% on the Checks,   `OL`
THEN assign:

- Practice, Exercises 1–25 odd
- Remediation, Review Resources: Inscribed Angles
- Personal Tutors
- Extra Examples 1–3
- 🔵 **ALEKS'** Testing Angle Knowledge

IF students score 65% or less on the Checks,   `AL`
THEN assign:

- Practice, Exercises 1–15 odd
- Remediation, Review Resources: Inscribed Angles
- 🔵 **ALEKS'** Testing Angle Knowledge

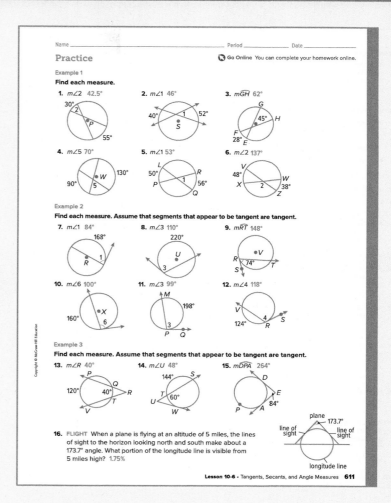

Name _____ Period _____ Date _____

Practice

🔵 Go Online You can complete your homework online.

Example 1

Find each measure.

1. $m\angle 2$ 42.5°

2. $m\angle 1$ 46°

3. $m\overarc{GH}$ 62°

4. $m\angle 5$ 70°

5. $m\angle 1$ 53°

6. $m\angle 2$ 137°

Example 2

Find each measure. Assume that segments that appear to be tangent are tangent.

7. $m\angle 1$ 84°

8. $m\angle 3$ 110°

9. $m\overarc{RT}$ 148°

10. $m\angle 6$ 100°

11. $m\angle 3$ 99°

12. $m\angle 4$ 118°

Example 3

Find each measure. Assume that segments that appear to be tangent are tangent.

13. $m\angle R$ 40°

14. $m\angle U$ 48°

15. $m\overarc{DPA}$ 264°

16. **FLIGHT** When a plane is flying at an altitude of 5 miles, the lines of sight to the horizon looking north and south make about a 173.7° angle. What portion of the longitude line is visible from 5 miles high? 1.75%

Lesson 10-6 • Tangents, Secants, and Angle Measures   **611**

Mixed Exercises

17. REASONING Salvador places a circular canvas on his A-frame easel and carefully centers it. The top of the easel forms a 30° angle and $m\widehat{BC} = 22°$. What is $m\widehat{AB}$? **128°**

18. PROOF Write a paragraph proof for each part of Theorem 10.15.

a. **Given:** $\overleftrightarrow{AB}$ is a tangent of $\odot O$.
$\overline{AC}$ is a secant of $\odot O$.
$\angle CAE$ is acute.
Prove: $m\angle CAE = \frac{1}{2}m\widehat{CA}$ See margin.

b. Prove that if $\angle CAB$ is obtuse, $m\angle CAB = \frac{1}{2}m\widehat{CDA}$. See margin.

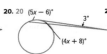

REASONING Find the value of x.

19. 9

$(9x + 26)°$ $35°$ $4x$

20. 20 $(5x - 6)°$

$3°$

$(4x + 8)°$

21. 19

$94°$ $(9x - 1)°$

$2x°$

Higher-Order Thinking Skills

22. ANALYZE Isosceles △ABC is inscribed in $\odot D$. What can you conclude about $m\widehat{AB}$ and $m\widehat{BC}$? Explain.
Sample answer: $m\widehat{AB} = m\widehat{BC}$; $m\angle BAC = m\angle BCA$ because the triangle is isosceles. Because $\angle BAC$ and $\angle BCA$ are inscribed angles by Theorem 10.6, $m\widehat{AB} = 2m\widehat{BCA}$ and $m\widehat{BC} = 2m\widehat{BAC}$. So, $m\widehat{AB} = m\widehat{BC}$.

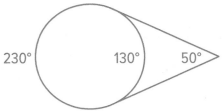

23. WRITE Explain how to find the measure of an angle formed by a secant and a tangent that intersect outside a circle.
Sample answer: Find the difference of the two intercepted arcs and divide by 2.

24. CREATE Draw a circle and two tangents that intersect outside the circle. Use a protractor to measure the angle that is formed. Find the measures of the minor and major arcs formed. Explain your reasoning. See margin.

25. PERSEVERE The circles shown are concentric. What is the measure of $\angle A$?
32°

$79°$ $118°$ $54°$ A

26. WRITE A circle is inscribed within △PQR. If $m\angle P = 50°$ and $m\angle Q = 60°$, describe how to find the measures of the three minor arcs formed by the points of tangency. Sample answer: Using Theorem 10.12, $60° = \frac{1}{2}[(360 - x) - x]$ or 120°; repeat for 50° to get 130°. The third arc can be found by adding 120° and 130° and subtracting from 360° to get 110°.

Answers

18a. Proof: By Theorem 10.11, $\overline{OA} \perp \overline{AB}$. So, $\angle FAE$ is a right angle with measure 90°, and $\widehat{FCA}$ is a semicircle with measure of 180°. Because $\angle CAE$ is acute, C is in the interior of $\angle FAE$. By the Angle and Arc Addition Postulates, $m\angle FAE = m\angle FAC + m\angle CAE$ and $m\widehat{FCA} = m\widehat{FC} + m\widehat{CA}$. By substitution, $90° = m\angle FAC + m\angle CAE$ and $180° = m\widehat{FC} + m\widehat{CA}$. So, $90° = \frac{1}{2}m\widehat{FC} + \frac{1}{2}m\widehat{CA}$ by the Division Property of Equality, and $m\angle FAC + m\angle CAE = \frac{1}{2}m\widehat{FC} + \frac{1}{2}m\widehat{CA}$ by substitution. $m\angle FAC = \frac{1}{2}m\widehat{FC}$ by the Inscribed Angle Theorem, so substitution yields $\frac{1}{2}m\widehat{FC} + m\angle CAE = \frac{1}{2}m\widehat{FC} + \frac{1}{2}m\widehat{CA}$. By the Subtraction Property of Equality, $m\angle CAE = \frac{1}{2}m\widehat{CA}$.

18b. Proof: Using the Angle and Arc Addition Postulates, $m\angle CAB = m\angle CAF + m\angle FAB$, and $m\widehat{CDA} = m\widehat{CF} + m\widehat{FDA}$. Because $\overline{OA} \perp \overline{AB}$ and $\overline{FA}$ is a diameter, $\angle FAB$ is a right angle with measure 90° and $\widehat{FDA}$ is a semicircle with a measure of 180°. By substitution, $m\angle CAB = m\angle CAF + 90°$ and $m\widehat{CDA} = m\widehat{CF} + 180°$. Because $\angle CAF$ is inscribed, $m\angle CAF = \frac{1}{2}m\widehat{CF}$, and by substitution, $m\angle CAB = \frac{1}{2}m\widehat{CF} + 90°$. Using the Division and Subtraction Properties on the Arc Addition equation yields $\frac{1}{2}m\widehat{CDA} - \frac{1}{2}m\widehat{CF} = 90°$. By substituting for 90°, $m\angle CAB = \frac{1}{2}m\widehat{CF} + \frac{1}{2}m\widehat{CDA} - \frac{1}{2}m\widehat{CF}$. By subtraction $m\angle CAB = \frac{1}{2}m\widehat{CDA}$.

24. Sample answer:

$230°$ $130°$ $50°$

By Theorem 10.15, $m\angle 1 = \frac{1}{2}(x - y)$. So, $50° = \frac{1}{2}[(360° - x) - x]$. Therefore, x (minor arc) $= 130°$, and y (major arc) $= 360° - 130°$ or 230°.

Equations of Circles

LESSON GOAL

Students write and graph the equations of circles.

1 LAUNCH

Launch the lesson with a **Warm Up** and an introduction.

2 EXPLORE AND DEVELOP

Explore:
Deriving Equations of Circles
Exploring Equations of Circles

Develop:

Equations of Circles
- Write an Equation by Using the Center and Radius
- Write an Equation by Using the Center and a Point
- Graph a Circle
- Use a Diameter to Write an Equation
- Intersections with Circles

You may want your students to complete the **Checks** online.

3 REFLECT AND PRACTICE

Exit Ticket

Practice

DIFFERENTIATE

View reports of student progress on the **Checks** after each example.

Resources	AL	OL	BL	ELL
Remediation: Distance	●	●		●
Extension: Equations of Circles and Tangents		●	●	●

Language Development Handbook

Assign page 72 of the *Language Development Handbook* to help your students build mathematical language related to writing and graphing the equations of circles.

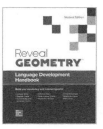

ELL You can use the tips and suggestions on page T72 of the handbook to support students who are building English proficiency.

Suggested Pacing

90 min	**0.5 day**	
45 min		**1 day**

Focus

Domain: Geometry

Standards for Mathematical Content:

G.GPE.1 Derive the equation of a circle of given center and radius using the Pythagorean Theorem; complete the square to find the center and radius of a circle given by an equation.

G.GPE.4 Use coordinates to prove simple geometric theorems algebraically.

Standards for Mathematical Practice:

1 Make sense of problems and persevere in solving them.

3 Construct viable arguments and critique the reasoning of others.

4 Model with mathematics.

6 Attend to precision.

Coherence

Vertical Alignment

Previous
Students solved problems using relationships between circles, tangents, and secants.
G.C.2

Now
Students write and graph the equations of circles.
G.GPE.1, G.GPE.4

Next
Students will write and graph equations of parabolas.
G.GPE.2

Rigor

The Three Pillars of Rigor

1 CONCEPTUAL UNDERSTANDING	2 FLUENCY	3 APPLICATION

Conceptual Bridge In this lesson, students build fluency by deriving equations of circles and finding centers and radii of circles when given the equations. They apply their understanding by deriving equations of circles in the real world.

Mathematical Background

Because a circle is the set of points on the plane equidistant from a common point, it is possible to use the Distance Formula to derive the equation of a circle on the coordinate plane. The standard form for the equation of a circle is $(x - h)^2 + (y - k)^2 = r^2$, where the coordinates of the center are (h, k) and the radius has length r. Given an equation, you can solve many problems such as determining the coordinates of the center, finding the length of the radius, graphing the circle, and finding intersecting points between the circle and other figures.

Interactive Presentation

Warm Up

Use the Distance Formula to determine whether each point is within 5 units of $(10, 8)$. Answer *within, not within, or exactly 5 units away.*

1. $(10, 14)$

2. $(8, 12)$

3. $(13, 12)$

4. $(7, 3)$

5. $(8, 4)$

Show Answers

Warm Up

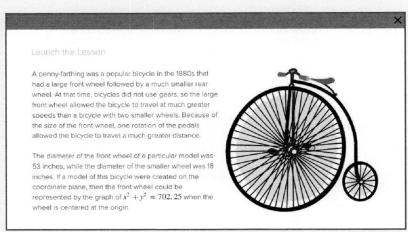

Launch the Lesson

A penny-farthing was a popular bicycle in the 1880s that had a large front wheel followed by a much smaller rear wheel. At that time, bicycles did not use gears, so the large front wheel allowed the bicycle to travel at much greater speeds than a bicycle with two smaller wheels. Because of the size of the front wheel, one rotation of the pedals allowed the bicycle to travel a much greater distance.

The diameter of the front wheel of a particular model was 53 inches, while the diameter of the smaller wheel was 18 inches. If a model of this bicycle were created on the coordinate plane, then the front wheel could be represented by the graph of $x^2 + y^2 = 702.25$ when the wheel is centered at the origin.

Launch the Lesson

Warm Up

Prerequisite Skills

The Warm Up exercises address the following prerequisite skill for this lesson:

- using the Distance Formula

Answers:

1. not within
2. within
3. exactly 5 units away
4. not within
5. within

Launch the Lesson

 Teaching the Mathematical Practices

4 Apply Mathematics In this Launch the Lesson, students can see a real-world application of equations of circles.

Go Online to find additional teaching notes and questions to promote classroom discourse.

Today's Standards

Tell students that they will be addressing these content and practice standards in this lesson. You may wish to have a student volunteer read aloud *How can I meet these standards?* and *How can I use these practices?* and connect these to the standards.

See the Interactive Presentation for I Can statements that align with the standards covered in this lesson.

Explore Deriving Equations of Circles

Objective
Students use coordinates and algebra to prove or disprove whether a point lies on a given circle.

 Teaching the Mathematical Practices

6 Communicate Precisely Encourage students to routinely write or explain their solution methods. Point out that they should use clear definitions when they discuss their solutions with others.

Ideas for Use

Recommended Use Present the Inquiry Question, or have a student volunteer read it aloud. Have students work in pairs to complete the Explore activity on their devices. Pairs should discuss each of the questions. Monitor student progress during the activity. Upon completion of the Explore activity, have student volunteers share their responses to the Inquiry Question.

What if my students don't have devices? You may choose to project the activity on a whiteboard. A printable worksheet for each Explore is available online. You may choose to print the worksheet so that individuals or pairs of students can use it to record their observations.

Summary of the Activity

Students will complete guiding exercises throughout the Explore activity. Students begin by considering a point (x, y) on a circle with radius r and center (h, k). They answer guiding questions to help them derive the equation of a circle with that center and radius by using the Distance Formula. Then students find an equation for a specific circle, and determine whether a given point falls on the circle. Then, students will answer the Inquiry Question.

(continued on the next page)

Interactive Presentation

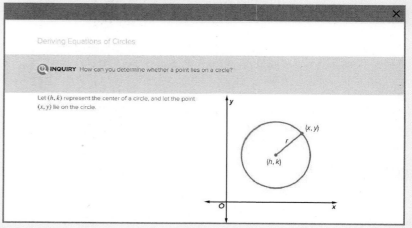

Explore

TAP

 Students tap to reveal guiding questions.

Interactive Presentation

INQUIRY How can you determine whether a point lies on a circle?

Done

Explore

TYPE

Students respond to the Inquiry Question and can view a sample answer.

Explore Deriving Equations of Circles (*continued*)

Teaching the Mathematical Practices

7 Use Structure Help students to use the structure of a circle's equation in this Explore to determine its center and radius.

Questions

Have students complete the Explore activity.

Ask:

- What happened to h and k in the equation of $\odot P$? Sample answer: The center of the circle is at the origin, so the values of h and k are both zero. The equation simplifies to $4 = \sqrt{(x^2 + y^2)}$.

- How could you use the equation of a circle to find a point on the circle for a chosen x-value? Sample answer: You could substitute the chosen value for x into the equation, then square both sides of the equation to remove the radical. Then, solve for y.

Inquiry

How can you determine whether a point lies on a circle? Sample answer: When given the center and radius of a circle, you can write the equation of the circle using the equation $r^2 = (x - h)^2 + (y - k)^2$ where (h, k) is the center of the circle and r is the radius. Then you can substitute the coordinates of the given point into the equation. If the equation is true, then the point lies on the circle.

 Go Online to find additional teaching notes and sample answers for the guiding exercises.

Explore Exploring Equations of Circles

Objective
Students use dynamic geometry software to determine the center and radius of circles and graph equations of circles.

🆄🅿 Teaching the Mathematical Practices

> **5 Use Mathematical Tools** Point out that to solve the problem in the Explore, students will need to use dynamic geometry software. Work with students to explore and deepen their understanding of equations of circles.

Ideas for Use

Recommended Use Present the Inquiry Question, or have a student volunteer read it aloud. Have students work in pairs to complete the Explore activity on their devices. Pairs should discuss each of the questions. Monitor student progress during the activity. Upon completion of the Explore activity, have student volunteers share their responses to the Inquiry Question.

What if my students don't have devices? You may choose to project the activity on a whiteboard. A printable worksheet for each Explore is available online. You may choose to print the worksheet so that individuals or pairs of students can use it to record their observations.

Summary of the Activity

Students will complete guiding exercises throughout the Explore activity. Students begin by using a construction of the equation of a circle and sliders for the number values in the equation to change the graph of the circle. Students drag h and determine that it represents the x-coordinate of the center. They drag the k slider and determine that k represents the y-coordinate of the center. They drag the r slider and determine that it represents the radius of the circle. Finally students use this information to determine the equation of a circle given its center and radius. Then, students will answer the Inquiry Question.

(continued on the next page)

Interactive Presentation

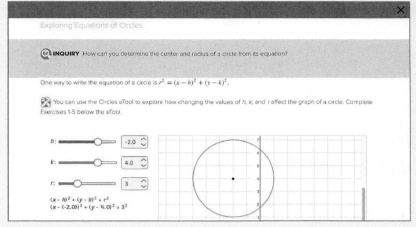

Exploring Equations of Circles

 INQUIRY How can you determine the center and radius of a circle from its equation?

One way to write the equation of a circle is $r^2 = (x - h)^2 + (y - k)^2$.

You can use the Circles eTool to explore how changing the values of h, k, and r affect the graph of a circle. Complete Exercises 1-5 below the eTool.

h: [-2.0]
k: [4.0]
r: [3]

$(x - h)^2 + (y - k)^2 = r^2$
$(x - (-2.0))^2 + (y - 4.0)^2 = 3^2$

Explore

SWIPE

Students move sliders to explore equations of circles.

Interactive Presentation

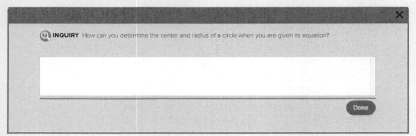

Explore

TYPE

| a| |

Students respond to the Inquiry Question and can view a sample answer.

---

1 CONCEPTUAL UNDERSTANDING   2 FLUENCY   3 APPLICATION

Explore Exploring Equations of Circles (*continued*)

Teaching the Mathematical Practices

8 Notice Regularity In this lesson, help students see the regularity in the way that changing values in the equation of a circle changes the graph of the circle.

Questions

Have students complete the Explore activity.

Ask:

- Do h and k perform the same transformations with circles as with other functions? Explain. Yes; sample answer: The variable h moves the circle left or right and k moves the circle up or down.
- What is the center and radius of the circle with equation $(x + 4)^2 + (y - 2)^2 = 9$? The center is $(-4, 2)$ and the radius is 3.

Inquiry

How can you determine the center and radius of a circle when you are given its equation? Sample answer: When the equation is presented as $r^2 = (x - h)^2 + (y - k)^2$, the center is located at (h, k), and the radius is r. If the equation is not shown in this form, then writing it in this form will allow you to easily find the center and radius.

Go Online to find additional teaching notes and sample answers for the guiding exercises.

Learn Equations of Circles

Objective
Students derive the equation of a circle using the Pythagorean Theorem and complete the square to find the center and radius of a circle.

 Teaching the Mathematical Practices

3 Justify Conclusions Mathematically proficient students can explain the conclusions drawn when solving a problem. This Learn asks students to respond to the arguments of others.

Important to Know
In most digital graphing aids, you cannot graph the equation of a circle in its standard form because it is not in the $y = f(x)$ form required. Solve the equation of the circle for y first, split it into two equations using the $\pm$ symbol that will occur, and then graph both equations in order to graph the circle.

Example 1 Write an Equation by Using the Center and Radius

 Teaching the Mathematical Practices

3 Construct Arguments In this example, students will use stated assumptions, definitions, and previously established results to construct an argument.

Questions for Mathematical Discourse

AL How do we know that the radius is 4? Sample answer: The radius is half the diameter. Count on the coordinate plane from one side of the circle to the other.

OL If the circle has center $(-4, -11)$ and radius $\sqrt{6}$, what is the equation for the circle? $(x + 4)^2 + (y + 11)^2 = 6$

BL What are the center and radius of the circle $x^2 + (y + 2)^2 = 9$? center: $(0, -2)$; radius: 3

🡢 Go Online

- Find additional teaching notes.
- View performance reports of the Checks.
- Assign or present an Extra Example.

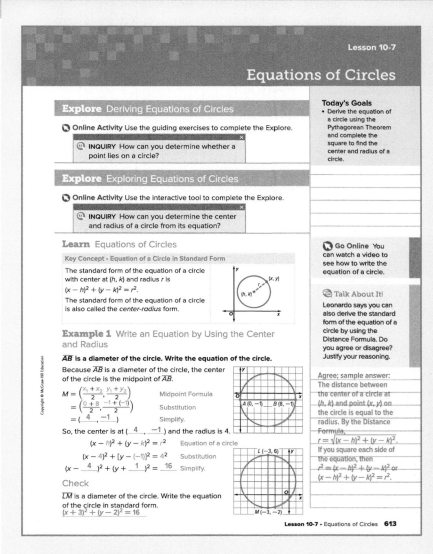

Lesson 10-7

Equations of Circles

Explore Deriving Equations of Circles

🡢 **Online Activity** Use the guiding exercises to complete the Explore.

INQUIRY How can you determine whether a point lies on a circle?

Explore Exploring Equations of Circles

🡢 **Online Activity** Use the interactive tool to complete the Explore.

INQUIRY How can you determine the center and radius of a circle from its equation?

Learn Equations of Circles

Key Concept · Equation of a Circle in Standard Form

The standard form of the equation of a circle with center at (h, k) and radius r is
$(x - h)^2 + (y - k)^2 = r^2$.
The standard form of the equation of a circle is also called the *center-radius* form.

Example 1 Write an Equation by Using the Center and Radius

$\overline{AB}$ is a diameter of the circle. Write the equation of the circle.

Because $\overline{AB}$ is a diameter of the circle, the center of the circle is the midpoint of $\overline{AB}$.

$M = \left(\frac{x_1 + x_2}{2}, \frac{y_1 + y_2}{2}\right)$ Midpoint Formula

$= \left(\frac{0 + 8}{2}, \frac{-1 + (-1)}{2}\right)$ Substitution

$= (\underline{4}, \underline{-1})$ Simplify.

So, the center is at $(\underline{4}, \underline{-1})$ and the radius is 4.

$(x - h)^2 + (y - k)^2 = r^2$ Equation of a circle

$(x - 4)^2 + [y - (-1)]^2 = 4^2$ Substitution

$(x - \underline{4})^2 + (y + \underline{1})^2 = \underline{16}$ Simplify.

Check

$\overline{LM}$ is a diameter of the circle. Write the equation of the circle in standard form.
$(x + 3)^2 + (y - 2)^2 = 16$

Today's Goals
- Derive the equation of a circle using the Pythagorean Theorem and complete the square to find the center and radius of a circle.

🡢 **Go Online** You can watch a video to see how to write the equation of a circle.

📌 **Talk About It!**
Leonardo says you can also derive the standard form of the equation of a circle by using the Distance Formula. Do you agree or disagree? Justify your reasoning.

Agree; sample answer: The distance between the center of a circle at (h, k) and point (x, y) on the circle is equal to the radius. By the Distance Formula, $r = \sqrt{(x - h)^2 + (y - k)^2}$. If you square each side of the equation, then $r^2 = (x - h)^2 + (y - k)^2$ or $(x - h)^2 + (y - k)^2 = r^2$.

Lesson 10-7 · Equations of Circles 613

Interactive Presentation

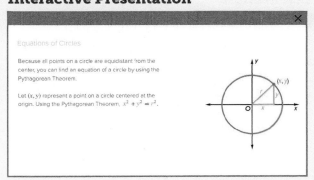

Equations of Circles

Because all points on a circle are equidistant from the center, you can find an equation of a circle by using the Pythagorean Theorem.

Let (x, y) represent a point on a circle centered at the origin. Using the Pythagorean Theorem, $x^2 + y^2 = r^2$.

Learn

TYPE

Students type to agree or disagree with someone's reasoning.

1 CONCEPTUAL UNDERSTANDING | **2 FLUENCY** | 3 APPLICATION

Example 2 Write an Equation by Using the Center and a Point

Write the equation of the circle with center at (−3, −5) that passes through (0, 0).

Step 1 Find the length of the radius.

Find the distance between the points to determine the radius.

$r = \sqrt{(x_2 - x_1)^2 + (y_2 - y_1)^2}$ Distance Formula

$= \sqrt{[0 - (-3)]^2 + [0 - (-5)]^2}$ $(x_1, y_1) = (-3, -5)$ and $(x_2, y_2) = (0, 0)$

$= \sqrt{34}$ Simplify.

Step 2 Write the equation of the circle.

Write the equation using $h = -3$, $k = -5$, and $r = \sqrt{34}$.

$(x - h)^2 + (y - k)^2 = r^2$ Equation of a circle

$[x - (\underline{-3})]^2 + [y - (\underline{-5})]^2 = (\sqrt{34})^2$ Substitution

$(x + \underline{3})^2 + (y + \underline{5})^2 = \underline{34}$ Simplify.

Example 3 Graph a Circle

The equation of a circle is $x^2 + y^2 + 8x - 14y + 40 = 0$. State the coordinates of the center and the measure of the radius. Then graph the equation.

Step 1 Complete the squares.

Write the equation in standard form by completing the squares.

$x^2 + y^2 + 8x - 14y + 40 = 0$ Original equation

$x^2 + y^2 + 8x - 14y = -40$ Subtract 40 from each side.

$x^2 + 8x + y^2 - 14y = -40$ Group terms.

$x^2 + 8x + 16 + y^2 - 14y + 49 = -40 + 16 + 49$ Complete the squares.

$(x + 4)^2 + (y - 7)^2 = 25$ Factor and simplify.

Step 2 Identify h, k, and r.

$(x + 4)^2 + (y - 7)^2 = 25$ can also be written as $[x - (-4)]^2 + (y - 7)^2 = 5^2$. Now you can identify h, k, and r.

$h = -4$, $k = 7$, and $r = 5$

The center is at $(-4, 7)$, and the radius is 5.

Step 3 Graph the circle.

Plot the center and four points that are 5 units from the center. Sketch the circle through these four points.

Your Notes

Think About It!
Does the graph of a circle represent a function? Justify your reasoning.

No; sample answer: The graph of a circle fails the vertical line test because an element of the domain is paired with more than one element of the range. Therefore, a circle represents a relation, not a function.

Think About It!
A circle has the equation $(x - 5)^2 + (y + 7)^2 = 16$. If the center of the circle is shifted 3 units right and 9 units up, what would be the equation of the new circle? Explain your reasoning.

$(x - 8)^2 + (y - 2)^2 = 16$; Sample answer: The first circle has its center at $(5, -7)$. If the circle is shifted 3 units right and 9 units up, then the new center is at $(8, 2)$. So, the new equation becomes $(x - 8)^2 + (y - 2)^2 = 16$.

Interactive Presentation

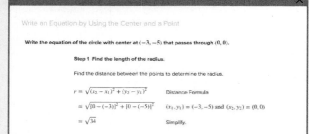

Example 2

TYPE

Students enter values to find the solution.

Example 2 Write an Equation by Using the Center and a Point

MP Teaching the Mathematical Practices

4 Use Tools Point out that to solve the problem in this example, students will need to use the general equation for a circle.

Questions for Mathematical Discourse

AL How can we check the reasonableness of this solution? Sample answer: Graph the circle and estimate.

OL If the circle has center $(-2, 4)$ and passes through $(-2, 7)$, what is the equation for the circle? $(x + 2)^2 + (y - 4)^2 = 9$

BL If you can't remember the Distance Formula is there another way to determine the radius of a circle? Explain. Yes; sample answer: Graph the circle on the coordinate plane and use the Pythagorean Theorem to find the radius.

Example 3 Graph a Circle

MP Teaching the Mathematical Practices

6 Communicate Precisely Encourage students to routinely write or explain their solution methods. Point out that they should use clear definitions when they discuss their solutions with others.

Questions for Mathematical Discourse

AL After you find the center and radius, why is it good to find other points on the circle before you sketch it? Sample answer: Finding points on each side of the center makes the graph more accurate.

OL Is it possible to draw a perfect circle using just 4 points? No; it is a sketch of the circle.

BL If you needed to know an exact point on a circle and it was not located at whole number coordinates, what is one way to find the coordinates? Sample answer: Use a graphing calculator or other graphing program.

Common Error

Students may tend to draw the graph of the circle through the four points almost as if it was a square. Remind them that circles are curved, and to take their time and draw a reasonable curve to the circle.

🌐 Apply Example 4   Use a Diameter to Write an Equation

Recommended Use

Have students work in pairs or small groups. You may wish to present the task, or have a volunteer read it aloud. Then allow students the time to make sure they understand the task, think of possible strategies, and work to solve the problem.

Encourage Productive Struggle

As students work, monitor their progress. Instead of instructing them on a particular strategy, encourage them to use their own strategies to solve the problem and to evaluate their progress along the way. They may or may not find that they need to change direction or try out several strategies.

Signs of Non-Productive Struggle

If students show signs of non-productive struggle, such as feeling overwhelmed, frustrated, or disengaged, intervene to encourage them to think of alternate approaches to the problem. Some sample questions are shown.

- How did we find the radius?
- If you know the endpoints of a line, what formula can you use to find the location of the center?

✒ Write About It!

Have students share their responses with another pair/group of students or the entire class. Have them clearly state or describe the mathematical reasoning they can use to defend their solution.

DIFFERENTIATE

Enrichment Activity BL ELL

Logical Learners Explain that students will rely heavily on their geometric knowledge and reasoning skills to solve the problems in this lesson. Allow students to explain how to explore and collaborate as they work through examples and exercises. Students need to recall definitions, concepts, and theorems to help explain why they use certain methods to solve problems.

🌐 Apply Example 4   Use a Diameter to Write an Equation

TRANSPORTATION The school board is determining the new boundary for Riverdale High School's bus transportation. The high school is at point H and is the center of the circle that represents the new boundary. The students that live on or within the circle will have to walk to school. Students that live at points $J(-5, 2)$, $K(5, 6)$, and $L(5, 2)$ lie on the boundary, and $\overline{JK}$ is a diameter of $\odot H$. Write the equation of $\odot H$ in standard form.

1 What is the task?

Describe the task in your own words. Then list any questions that you may have. How can you find answers to your questions?

Sample answer: I need to find the equation of the circle that describes the boundary for bus transportation. Where is the center of the circle located? What is the length of the radius of the circle?

2 How will you approach the task? What have you learned that you can use to help you complete the task?

Sample answer: Because I know the endpoints of the diameter of the circle, I can use the Midpoint Formula to find the location of the center of the circle. Then, I can use the Distance Formula to find the length of the radius of the circle. Using this information, I can write an equation of the circle in standard form.

3 What is your solution?

Use your strategy to solve the problem.

The coordinates of the center of the circle are (0, 4) .

What is the length of the radius of the circle?

$r = \underline{\sqrt{29}}$ units

Write the equation of the circle in standard form.

$(x - 0)^2 + (y - 4)^2 = 29$

4 How can you know that your solution is reasonable?

✒ **Write About It!** Write an argument that can be used to defend your solution.

Sample answer: If you graph the equation, the center of the circle is at (0, 4), and the circle passes through $J(-5, 2)$, $K(5, 6)$, and $L(5, 2)$. So, the answer is reasonable.

Interactive Presentation

Use a Diameter to Write an Equation

🌐 **TRANSPORTATION** The school board is determining the new boundary for Riverdale High School's bus transportation. The high school is at point H and is the center of the circle that represents the new boundary. The students that live on or within the circle will have to walk to school. Students that live at points $J(-5, 2)$, $K(5, 6)$, and $L(5, 2)$ lie on the boundary, and $\overline{JK}$ is a diameter of $\odot H$. Write the equation of $\odot H$ in standard form.

Apply Example 4

TAP

Students tap to see steps in the solution.

Check

NAVIGATION A mariner is using a GPS, or global positioning system, to create a nautical chart that documents underwater objects and hazards. The mariner has found three hazards positioned in a circular pattern at points $D(7, 1)$, $E(14, -4)$, and $F(2, -6)$. If $\overline{EF}$ is a diameter of the circle, what is the equation of the circle that contains the three hazards? Write your answer in standard form.

$(x - 8)^2 + (y + 5)^2 = 37$

Example 5 Intersections with Circles

Find the point(s) of intersection between $x^2 + y^2 = 9$ and $y = x - 2$.

Step 1 Graph the equations on the same coordinate plane.

The points of intersection are solutions of both equations, and can be estimated to be at about $(-0.9, -2.9)$ and $(2.9, 0.9)$.

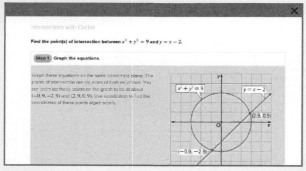

Step 2 Use substitution to find the points of intersection algebraically.

$$x^2 + y^2 = 9 \quad \text{Equation of circle}$$
$$x^2 + (x - 2)^2 = 9 \quad \text{Substitute}$$
$$x^2 + x^2 - 4x + 4 = 9 \quad \text{Multiply.}$$
$$2x^2 - 4x - 5 = 0 \quad \text{Subtract 9 from each side.}$$

Step 3 Use the Quadratic Formula.

Use $\dfrac{-b \pm \sqrt{b^2 - 4ac}}{2a}$ to solve $2x^2 - 4x - 5 = 0$, with $a = 2$, $b = -4$, and $c = -5$.

The solutions are $x = 1 + \dfrac{\sqrt{14}}{2}$ or $x = 1 - \dfrac{\sqrt{14}}{2}$.

Step 4 Find the points of intersection.

Use the equation $y = x - 2$ to find the corresponding y-values. The points of intersection are $\left(1 + \dfrac{\sqrt{14}}{2}, -1 + \dfrac{\sqrt{14}}{2}\right)$ and $\left(1 - \dfrac{\sqrt{14}}{2}, -1 - \dfrac{\sqrt{14}}{2}\right)$ or at about $(2.87, 0.87)$ and $(-0.87, -2.87)$.

Check

Find the point(s) of intersection between $x^2 + y^2 = 8$ and $y = -x$. If there are no points of intersection, select *no intersection points*.

A. $(2, -2)$ and $(-2, 2)$

B. $(2\sqrt{2}, -2\sqrt{2})$ and $(-2\sqrt{2}, 2\sqrt{2})$

C. $(2, 2)$ and $(-2, -2)$

D. $(2, -2)$

E. no intersection points

🔵 **Go Online** You can complete an Extra Example online.

Study Tip

Solving Quadratic Equations In addition to using the Quadratic Formula, you can also solve quadratic equations by taking square roots, completing the square, and factoring.

💭 Think About It!

Will a line always intersect a circle in two points? Justify your reasoning.

No; sample answer: Sometimes a line will not intersect a circle at all, or it will intersect the circle in only one point. If a line intersects a circle in one point, then the line is tangent to the circle.

Interactive Presentation

Example 5

TAP

 Students tap to see steps in the solution.

CHECK

 Students complete the Check online to determine whether they are ready to move on.

Example 5 Intersections with Circles

🎓 Teaching the Mathematical Practices

5 Use Estimation Point out that in this example, students need to include an estimate and check against the estimate at the end.

Questions for Mathematical Discourse

AL How many times can a line intersect a circle? Explain. 0, 1, or 2 times; A line can pass entirely outside a circle, be tangent to the circle, or cross through to the interior of the circle.

OL How many chords and radii are in a diameter? one chord; two radii

BL How can you tell if a chord is a diameter? A chord is a diameter if it contains the center of the circle.

Common Error

Students may forget how to solve quadratic equations from previous courses. Help them remember by doing a brief review of each solution method, such as using the Quadratic Formula taking square roots, factoring, and completing the square.

📧 Essential Question Follow-Up

Students have learned to write and graph equations of circles.

Ask:

Why are equations of circles important? Sample answer: So that we can graph circles in real-world settings.

Exit Ticket

Recommended Use

At the end of class, go online to display the Exit Ticket prompt and ask students to respond using a separate piece of paper. Have students hand you their responses as they leave the room.

Alternate Use

At the end of class, go online to display the Exit Ticket prompt and ask students to respond verbally or by using a mini-whiteboard. Have students hold up their whiteboards so that you can see all student responses. Tap to reveal the answer when most or all students have completed the Exit Ticket.

DIFFERENTIATE

Language Development Activity AL ELL

Verbal/Linguistic Learners List terms on the board such as center, radius, diameter, and chord. As you work through the examples with the class, point to the terms as you use them, or ask students what term applies to given figures in a problem. Guide students to use the terms correctly as they talk about solutions or answer questions.

Practice and Homework

Suggested Assignments

Use the table below to select appropriate exercises.

DOK	Topic	Exercises
1, 2	exercises that mirror the examples	1–18
2	exercises that use a variety of skills from this lesson	19–27
3	exercises that emphasize higher-order and critical-thinking skills	28–31

ASSESS AND DIFFERENTIATE

Use the data from the **Checks** to determine whether to provide resources for extension, remediation, or intervention.

IF students score 90% or more on the Checks, **THEN** assign: `BL`

- Practice, Exercises 1–27 odd, 28–31
- Extension: Equations of Circles and Tangents
- **ALEKS** Graphs and Equations of Circles

IF students score 66%–89% on the Checks, **THEN** assign: `OL`

- Practice, Exercises 1–31 odd
- Remediation, Review Resources: Distance
- Personal Tutors
- Extra Examples 1–5
- **ALEKS** Using the Distance Formula

IF students score 65% or less on the Checks, **THEN** assign: `AL`

- Practice, Exercises 1–17 odd
- Remediation, Review Resources: Distance
- *Quick Review Math Handbook*: Equations of Circles
- **ALEKS** Using the Distance Formula

Answers

9.
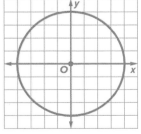

10.
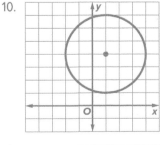

11.
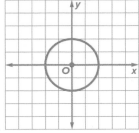

12.
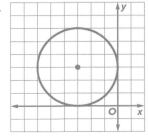

Name _____ Period _____ Date _____

Practice

Go Online You can complete your homework online.

Examples 1 and 2

Write the equation of each circle.

1. center at (0, 0), radius 8 $x^2 + y^2 = 64$

2. center at (−2, 6), diameter 8
   $(x + 2)^2 + (y − 6)^2 = 16$

3.

   $(x − 3)^2 + (y − 2)^2 = 4$

4.

   $x^2 + (y + 2)^2 = 9$

5. center at (3, −4), passes through (−1, −4)
   $(x − 3)^2 + (y + 4)^2 = 16$

6. center at (0, 3), passes through (2, 0)
   $x^2 + (y − 3)^2 = 13$

7. center at (−4, −1), passes through (−2, 3)
   $(x + 4)^2 + (y + 1)^2 = 20$

8. center at (5, −2), passes through (4, 0)
   $(x − 5)^2 + (y + 2)^2 = 5$

Example 3

State the coordinates of the center and the measure of the radius of the circle with the given equation. Then graph the equation. 9–12. See margin for graphs.

9. $x^2 + y^2 = 16$ (0, 0); $r = 4$

10. $(x − 1)^2 + (y − 4)^2 = 9$ (1, 4); $r = 3$

11. $x^2 + y^2 − 4 = 0$ (0, 0); $r = 2$

12. $x^2 + y^2 + 6x − 6y + 9 = 0$ (−3, 3); $r = 3$

Example 4

13. PETS The Villani family is placing a stake in the ground that is connected to a dog leash. The proposed location of the stake is at point Q and is the center of the circle that represents the circular boundary in which their dog will be able to roam. The points $R(−4, 1)$ and $S(8, 7)$ lie on the boundary, and $\overline{RS}$ is a diameter of $\odot Q$. Write the equation of $\odot Q$ in standard form. $(x − 2)^2 + (y − 4)^2 = 45$

14. DELIVERY A new pizza restaurant is determining the boundary for its delivery service. The pizza restaurant is at point P and is the center of the circle that represents the boundary. Customers who are on or within the circle will be eligible for delivery. Customers who live or work at points $A(−2, 2)$, $B(2, −2)$, and $C(6, 2)$ lie on the boundary, and $\overline{AC}$ is a diameter of $\odot P$. Write the equation of $\odot P$ in standard form. $(x − 2)^2 + (y − 2)^2 = 16$

Example 5

Find the point(s) of intersection, if any, between each circle and line with the equations given.

15. $x^2 + y^2 = 9$; $y = 2x + 3$
    (0, 3), (−2.4, −1.8)

16. $(x + 4)^2 + (y − 3)^2 = 25$; $y = x + 2$
    (−4, −2), (1, 3)

17. $(x − 5)^2 + (y − 2)^2 = 100$; $y = x − 1$
    (−3, −4), (11, 10)

18. $x^2 + y^2 = 25$; $y = x$
    $\left(\frac{5\sqrt{2}}{2}, \frac{5\sqrt{2}}{2}\right), \left(−\frac{5\sqrt{2}}{2}, −\frac{5\sqrt{2}}{2}\right)$

Mixed Exercises

For Exercises 19–20, write the equation of each circle.

19. a circle with a diameter having endpoints at (0, 4) and (6, −4)
$(x − 3)^2 + y^2 = 25$

20. a circle with $d = 22$ and a center translated 13 units left and 6 units up from the origin
$(x + 13)^2 + (y − 6)^2 = 121$

21. STRUCTURE Adam says that $x^2 + y^2 + 4x − 10y = k$ is the equation of a circle for any value of k because it is always possible to complete the square to find the center and the radius. Do you agree? Explain. Disagree; sample answer: Completing the square shows that the equation can be written as $x^2 + 4x + 4 + y^2 − 10y + 25 = k + 29$ or $(x + 2)^2 + (y − 5)^2 = k + 29$. The radius of the circle is $\sqrt{k + 29}$, and this expression results in a positive radius only when $k + 29 > 0$. So, the equation represents a circle only if $k > −29$.

22. STRUCTURE The design of a piece of wallpaper consists of circles that can be modeled by $(x − a)^2 + (y − b)^2 = 4$, for all even integers b. Sketch part of the wallpaper on a grid.
See margin.

23. PRECISION What is the equation of the circle that is inscribed in the square shown? $(x − 4)^2 + (y − 3)^2 = 4$

24. REASONING The design for a park is drawn on a coordinate graph. The perimeter of the park is modeled by the equation $(x − 3)^2 + (x − 7)^2 = 225$. Each unit on the graph represents 10 feet. What is the radius of the actual park? 150 ft

25. FIRE SAFETY A fire station responds to emergencies within a circular area. On a map of the city, the boundary for the area is given by the equation $(x − 8)^2 + (y + 2)^2 = 324$. Each unit on the map represents 1 mile. What is the radius of the boundary? 18 mi

Write an equation of a circle that contains each set of points with the given diameter. Then graph the circle. 26–27. See margin for graphs.

26. $A(−2, 3)$, $B(1, 0)$, $C(4, 3)$; $\overline{AC}$
$(x − 1)^2 + (y − 3)^2 = 9$

27. $F(3, 0)$, $G(5, −2)$, $H(1, −2)$; $\overline{GH}$
$(x − 3)^2 + (y + 2)^2 = 4$

🧠 **Higher-Order Thinking Skills**

28. FIND THE ERROR The points $P(−1, 2)$, $Q(5, 2)$, and $R(7, −2)$ lie on a circle. Rosalina says that the circle will not intersect $y = 3$. Is Rosalina correct? Explain your reasoning.
No; sample answer: The line will intersect the circle at (2, 3).

29. WRITE Describe how the equation for a circle changes if the circle is translated a units to the right and b units down. See margin.

30. CREATE Graph three noncollinear points and connect them to form a triangle. Then construct the circle that circumscribes it. What is the equation of the circle? See margin.

31. PERSEVERE The center of a circle is at (2, 3). The point (2, 1) lies on the circle. Find three other points with integer coordinates that lie on the circle. Explain how to do this without finding the equation of the circle.
Sample answer: (2, 1) falls exactly two units below the center point of (2, 3). This means that the radius of the circle is 2. If we count two units in any direction, the result will be a point on the circle. Up two units is (2, 5). To the left two units is (0, 3). To the right two units is (4, 3). These three points all have integer coordinates.

Answers

22.

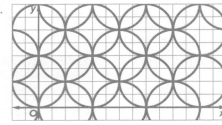

26.

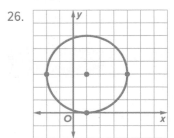

27.

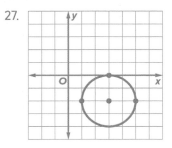

29. Sample answer: The equation for a circle is $(x − h)^2 + (y − k)^2 = r^2$. When the circle is translated a units to the right, the new x-coordinate of the center is $x + a$. When the circle is translated b units down, the new y-coordinate of the center is $y − b$. The new equation for the circle is $(x − (h + a))^2 + (y − (k − b))^2 = r^2$, or $(x − h − a)^2 + (y − k + b)^2 = r^2$.

30. Sample answer: $x^2 + y^2 = 16$

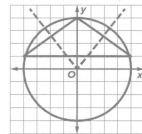

LESSON GOAL

Students write and graph the equations of parabolas using techniques for solving quadratic equations.

1 LAUNCH

👥 Launch the lesson with a **Warm Up** and an introduction.

2 EXPLORE AND DEVELOP

👥 **Explore:** Focus and Directrix of a Parabola

··

👥 **Develop:**

Equations of Parabolas
- Write an Equation for a Parabola
- Find Points of Intersection

👤 You may want your students to complete the **Checks** online.

3 REFLECT AND PRACTICE

👥 Exit Ticket

··

👥 Practice

DIFFERENTIATE

📊 View reports of student progress on the **Checks** after each example.

Resources	AL	OL	BL	ELL
Remediation: Distance	●	●		●
Extension: Parabolas and Associated Circles		●	●	●

Language Development Handbook

Assign page 73 of the *Language Development Handbook* to help your students build mathematical language related to writing and graphing the equations of parabolas.

ELL You can use the tips and suggestions on page T73 of the handbook to support students who are building English proficiency.

Suggested Pacing

90 min	**1 day**	
45 min		**2 days**

Focus

Domain: Geometry

Standards for Mathematical Content:

G.GPE.2 Derive the equation of a parabola given a focus and directrix.

Standards for Mathematical Practice:

4 Model with mathematics.

5 Use appropriate tools strategically.

6 Attend to precision.

Coherence

Vertical Alignment

Previous
Students wrote and graphed equations of circles.
G.GPE.1, G.GPE.4

Now
Students write and graph the equations of parabolas.
G.GPE.2

Next
Students will find areas of quadrilaterals by using the formulas they derive.
G.GPE.3

Rigor

The Three Pillars of Rigor

1 CONCEPTUAL UNDERSTANDING	2 FLUENCY	3 APPLICATION

🏛 **Conceptual Bridge** In this lesson, students build fluency by deriving equations of parabolas when given the focus and directrix. They apply their understanding by deriving equations of parabolas in the real world.

Mathematical Background

A *parabola* is the set of all points equidistant from a given point, called a *focus*, and a given line, called a *directrix*. It is a particular type of U-shaped curve with mirror symmetry along a line, called the *axis of symmetry*, that passes through the focus and is perpendicular to the directrix. It is also the curve of a cross section of a cone, so it is called a *conic section*.

On the coordinate plane, if the directrix is a horizontal line, the equation of the parabola can be written in the form $y = ax^2 + bx + c$. It is possible to find this equation using the coordinates of the focus and the equation of the directrix using the Distance Formula.

Interactive Presentation

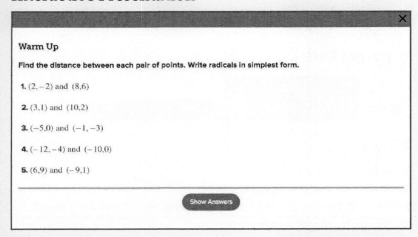

Warm Up

Find the distance between each pair of points. Write radicals in simplest form.

1. $(2, -2)$ and $(8, 6)$

2. $(3, 1)$ and $(10, 2)$

3. $(-5, 0)$ and $(-1, -3)$

4. $(-12, -4)$ and $(-10, 0)$

5. $(6, 9)$ and $(-9, 1)$

Show Answers

Warm Up

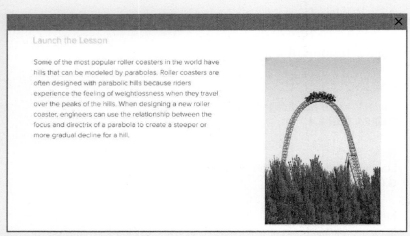

Launch the Lesson

Some of the most popular roller coasters in the world have hills that can be modeled by parabolas. Roller coasters are often designed with parabolic hills because riders experience the feeling of weightlessness when they travel over the peaks of the hills. When designing a new roller coaster, engineers can use the relationship between the focus and directrix of a parabola to create a steeper or more gradual decline for a hill.

Launch the Lesson

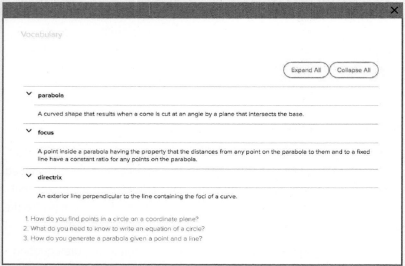

Vocabulary

Expand All   Collapse All

⌄ **parabola**

A curved shape that results when a cone is cut at an angle by a plane that intersects the base.

⌄ **focus**

A point inside a parabola having the property that the distances from any point on the parabola to them and to a fixed line have a constant ratio for any points on the parabola.

⌄ **directrix**

An exterior line perpendicular to the line containing the foci of a curve.

1. How do you find points in a circle on a coordinate plane?
2. What do you need to know to write an equation of a circle?
3. How do you generate a parabola given a point and a line?

Today's Vocabulary

Warm Up

Prerequisite Skills

The Warm Up exercises address the following prerequisite skill for this lesson:

- using the Distance Formula

Answers:

1. 10
2. $5\sqrt{2}$
3. 5
4. $2\sqrt{5}$
5. 17

Launch the Lesson

 Teaching the Mathematical Practices

4 Apply Mathematics In this Launch the Lesson, students can see a real-world application of parabolas.

🐦 **Go Online** to find additional teaching notes and questions to promote classroom discourse.

Today's Standards

Tell students that they will be addressing these content and practice standards in this lesson. You may wish to have a student volunteer read aloud *How can I meet this standard?* and *How can I use these practices?* and connect these to the standards.

See the Interactive Presentation for I Can statements that align to the standards covered in this lesson.

Today's Vocabulary

Tell students that they will be using these vocabulary terms in this lesson. You can expand each row if you wish to share the definitions. Then discuss the questions below with the class.

Explore Focus and Directrix of a Parabola

Objective
Students use dynamic geometry software to explore the relationship between the focus and directrix of a parabola.

 Teaching the Mathematical Practices

> **5 Use Mathematical Tools** Point out that to solve the problem in this Explore, students will need to use dynamic geometry software. Work with students to explore and deepen their understanding of relationship between the focus and directrix of a parabola.

Ideas for Use

Recommended Use Present the Inquiry Question, or have a student volunteer read it aloud. Have students work in pairs to complete the Explore activity on their devices. Pairs should discuss each of the questions. Monitor student progress during the activity. Upon completion of the Explore activity, have student volunteers share their responses to the Inquiry Question.

What if my students don't have devices? You may choose to project the activity on a whiteboard. A printable worksheet for each Explore is available online. You may choose to print the worksheet so that individuals or pairs of students can use it to record their observations.

Summary of the Activity

Students will complete guiding exercises throughout the Explore activity. Students begin by using dynamic geometry software to construct a point on a parabola and measuring its distance from the focus and its distance from the directrix. They move the point along the parabola and notice that the distances are always the same. Then students change the y-coordinate of the focus and notice that it makes the parabola narrower or wider, or, if on the other side of the directrix, changes whether the parabola opens up or down. Students also notice that the vertex is halfway between the focus and the directrix. Then, students will answer the Inquiry Question.

(continued on the next page)

Interactive Presentation

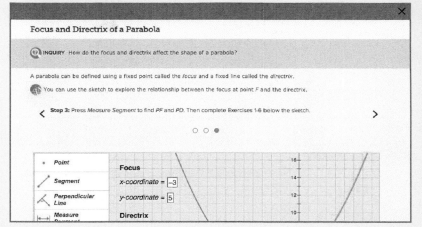

Explore

WEB SKETCHPAD

Students use a sketch to explore parabolas.

G.GPE.2

Interactive Presentation

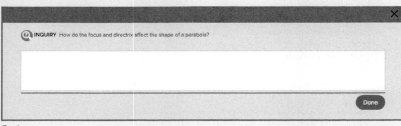

Explore

TYPE

Students respond to the Inquiry Question and can view a sample answer.

Explore Focus and Directrix of a Parabola (*continued*)

 Teaching the Mathematical Practices

7 Use Structure Help students to explore the structure of parabolas in the Explore to use the focus and directrix to find the equation of a parabola.

Questions

Have students complete the Explore activity.

Ask:

• What happens when the directrix is above the focus? Why do you think this happens? Sample answer: The parabola must be between the directrix and focus for *PD* and *PF* to be equal, so it makes sense that the parabola would have to open down.

• Is it possible for a parabola to have a focus at $(3, -2)$ and a directrix at $y = -2$? Why or why not? No; sample answer: The focus is on the directrix, so no parabola would be created.

Inquiry

How do the focus and directrix affect the shape of a parabola? Sample answer: The focus and directrix of a parabola can change how wide the parabola is compared to the parent function $y = x^2$ and whether the parabola opens up or down. Because every point on the parabola is equidistant from the focus and directrix, as the focus and directrix change, the parabola changes to maintain this relationship.

 Go Online to find additional teaching notes and sample answers for the guiding exercises.

1 CONCEPTUAL UNDERSTANDING | **2 FLUENCY** | 3 APPLICATION

Learn Equations of Parabolas

Objective
Students derive the equation of a parabola when given a focus and directrix and find the intersection points of linear and quadratic functions.

MP **Teaching the Mathematical Practices**

6 Communicate Precisely Encourage students to routinely write or explain their solution methods. Point out that they should use clear definitions when they discuss their solutions with others.

Common Misconception
Students may think that all parabolas are functions. Sketch some parabolas which open sideways or diagonally each along with its focus and directrix, so that students can see that there are other possible orientations for parabolas.

Example 1 Write an Equation for a Parabola

MP **Teaching the Mathematical Practices**

4 Use Tools Point out that to solve the problem in this example, students will need to use the Distance Formula.

Questions for Mathematical Discourse

AL Where is the vertex located in relationship to the focus and directrix? exactly halfway between them

OL Will the graph of a parabola ever intersect its directrix? Explain. No; sample answer: The parabola must stay on the same side of the directrix as the focus.

BL Previously you learned that a parabola is symmetric with respect to its axis of symmetry. What is the relationship between the directrix and the axis of symmetry? They are perpendicular.

Example 2 Use an Equation for a Parabola

MP **Teaching the Mathematical Practices**

4 Apply Mathematics In this example, students apply what they have learned about equations of parabolas to solve a real-world problem.

Questions for Mathematical Discourse

AL What is the relationship between the focus and directrix of a parabola? Sample answer: The focus and directrix are equidistant from the parabola.

OL How could you find the width of the tunnel floor without substituting 0 for y? Explain. Sample answer: I could graph the equation of the parabola and $y = 0$. Then I could find the intersection points of the two functions and calculate the distance between the intersection points.

BL If the focus was closer to the parabola, would the floor of the tunnel be wider or narrower? narrower

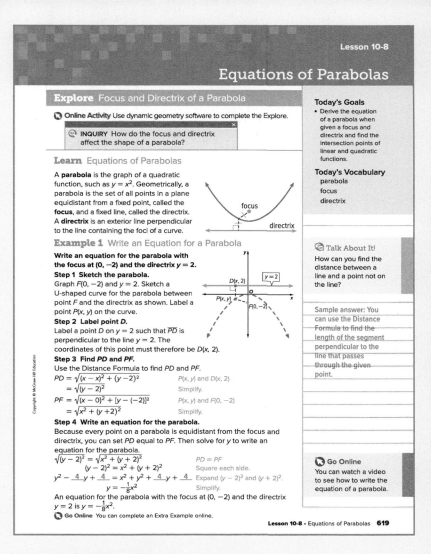

Interactive Presentation

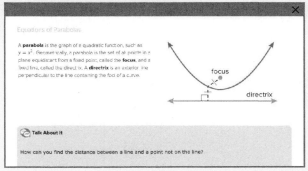

Learn

TYPE

Students describe how to find the distance between a line and a point not on the line.

Left panel

Your Notes

Check

Select the equation of the parabola with the focus at $\left(0, \frac{1}{2}\right)$ and the directrix $y = -\frac{1}{2}$.

A. $y = -\frac{1}{2}x^2$ **B.** $y = 2x^2$ **C.** $y = -\frac{1}{2}x^2 - \frac{1}{4}$ **(D.)** $y = \frac{1}{2}x^2$

🔵 **Go Online** to see Example 2.

Example 3 Find Points of Intersection

Find the point(s) of intersection, if any, between $y = 2x^2$ and $y = 4x - 2$.

Graph these equations on the same coordinate plane. The point of intersection is a solution of both equations. You can estimate the intersection point on the graph to be at about (1, 2). Use substitution to find the exact coordinates of the point algebraically.

Find the x-coordinate of the intersection point.

$y = 2x^2$	Quadratic Equation
$4x - 2 = 2x^2$	Substitute $4x - 2$ for y.
$-\underline{2} = 2x^2 - \underline{4x}$	Subtract $4x$ from each side.
$0 = 2x^2 - \underline{4x} + \underline{2}$	Add 2 to each side.
$0 = 2(\underline{x^2} - \underline{2x} + \underline{1})$	Factor out the GCF of $2x^2$, $4x$ and 2.
$0 = 2(x - \underline{1})(x - \underline{1})$	Factor $x^2 - 2x + 1$.
$0 = x - \underline{1}$	Set the repeated factor equal to zero.
$\underline{1} = x$	Add 1 to each side.

Because there is one solution of $4x - 2 = 2x^2$, the parabola and the line intersect in one point.

You can use $y = 4x - 2$ to find the corresponding y-value for $x = 1$.

$y = 4x - 2$	Equation of line
$y = 4(\underline{1}) - 2$	Substitute.
$y = \underline{2}$	Simplify.

So, $y = 2x^2$ and $y = 4x - 2$ intersect at $(\underline{1}, \underline{2})$.

Check

Find the point(s) of intersection, if any, between $y = -3x^2$ and $y = 6x$. If there are no points of intersection, select *no intersection points*.

A. $(-2, -12)$ **(B.)** $(0, 0)$ and $(-2, -12)$

C. $(2, 12)$ **D.** no intersection points

🔵 **Go Online** You can complete an Extra Example online.

Interactive Presentation

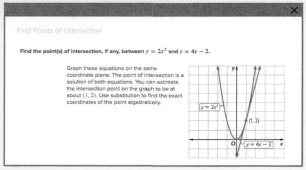

✕

Find Points of Intersection

Find the point(s) of intersection, if any, between $y = 2x^2$ and $y = 4x - 2$.

Example 3

TAP

Students tap to reveal steps in the solution.

CHECK

Students complete the Check online to determine whether they are ready to move on.

Right panel

Example 3 Find Points of Intersection

 Teaching the Mathematical Practices

5 Use Estimation In this example, students must choose an estimate and then find an exact answer.

Questions for Mathematical Discourse

AL How can you check your solution(s)? Plug them into each equation and make sure they satisfy both equations.

OL What types of graphs are these? a line and a parabola

BL Explain another way to solve this problem algebraically. You could solve the linear equation for x and substitute that expression into the Quadratic Equation.

Common Error

Students may try to stop when they have solved the equation. Remind them that they are looking for the coordinates of intersection points, so they need to continue until they have the coordinates.

DIFFERENTIATE

Reteaching Activity **AL** **ELL**

Kinesthetic Learners Have students plot the focus of a parabola in the middle of a sheet of paper, and the directrix on one long edge of the paper. Have students fold the paper so that the middle of the directrix edge touches the focus. Have them crease the fold so that it stays visible, then unfold the paper. Then, have them repeat this with a different point along the directrix until they have completed around 20 folds all along the directrix. Have them trace the parabola formed by the creases left from the folds. Have students estimate the location of the vertex. Have them measure the distance between the focus and vertex and the distance between the focus and directrix and compare the distances.

Exit Ticket

Recommended Use

At the end of class, go online to display the Exit Ticket prompt and ask students to respond using a separate piece of paper. Have students hand you their responses as they leave the room.

Alternate Use

At the end of class, go online to display the Exit Ticket prompt and ask students to respond verbally or by using a mini-whiteboard. Have students hold up their whiteboards so that you can see all student responses. Tap to reveal the answer when most or all students have completed the Exit Ticket.

Practice and Homework

Suggested Assignments

Use the table below to select appropriate exercises.

DOK	Topic	Exercises
1, 2	exercises that mirror the examples	1–14
2	exercises that extend concepts learned in this lesson to new contexts	15–17
3	exercises that emphasize higher-order and critical-thinking skills	18–21

ASSESS AND DIFFERENTIATE

 Use the data from the **Checks** to determine whether to provide resources for extension, remediation, or intervention.

IF students score 90% or more on the Checks, **THEN** assign: `BL`

- Practice, Exercises 1–17 odd, 18–21
- Extension: Parabolas and Associated Circles
- **ALEKS** Graphs and Equations of Parabolas

IF students score 66%–89% on the Checks, **THEN** assign: `OL`

- Practice, Exercises 1–21 odd
- Remediation, Review Resources: Distance
- Personal Tutors
- Extra Examples 1–3
- **ALEKS** Using the Distance Formula

IF students score 65% or less on the Checks, **THEN** assign: `AL`

- Practice, Exercises 1–13 odd
- Remediation, Review Resources: Distance
- *Quick Review Math Handbook*: Parabolas
- **ALEKS** Using the Distance Formula

Name _____ Period _____ Date _____

Practice

 Go Online You can complete your homework online.

Example 1

Write an equation of the parabola with the given focus and directrix.

1. focus (0, 3), directrix $y = -3$ $y = \frac{1}{12}x^2$

2. focus (0, 8), directrix $y = -8$ $y = \frac{1}{32}x^2$

3. focus (0, −5), directrix $y = 5$ $y = -\frac{1}{20}x^2$

4. focus (0, −9), directrix $y = 9$ $y = -\frac{1}{36}x^2$

5. focus (0, 4), directrix $y = -4$ $y = \frac{1}{16}x^2$

6. focus (0, 2), directrix $y = -2$ $y = \frac{1}{8}x^2$

Example 2

Write an equation of the parabola with the given focus and directrix.

7. focus (1, 7), directrix $y = -9$ $y = \frac{1}{32}(x-1)^2 - 1$

8. focus (8, 0), directrix $y = 4$ $y = -\frac{1}{8}(x-8)^2 + 2$

9. **USE A MODEL** A highway is level except for a section that passes through a valley. That section of the highway can be modeled by a parabola with the focus at (100, 55) and the directrix at $y = 5$.

   a. Write an equation for the parabola. $y = \frac{1}{100}(x-100)^2 + 30$

   b. If the level section of the highway is modeled by $y = 70$ and each unit represents a kilometer, what is the maximum width of the valley? Round your answer to the nearest hundredth.   126.49 km

10. **USE A MODEL** An engineer is using a coordinate plane to design a tunnel in the shape of a parabola. The focus of the tunnel will be at (4, −2.5), and the top of the wall that will contain the tunnel can be modeled by the directrix $y = 2.5$. The base of the tunnel is at ground level and represented by $y = -10$.

    a. Write an equation of the parabola. $y = -\frac{1}{10}(x-4)^2$

    b. Each unit of the coordinate plane represents one foot. Prove or disprove that the width of the tunnel at a height of 5 feet above the ground is exactly 14 feet.   Sample answer: The set of points 5 feet above the ground are represented by the line $y = -5$. Solving $-5 = -\frac{1}{10}(x-4)^2$ shows that $x = 4 \pm \sqrt{50}$. So, the width of the tunnel at this height is $2\sqrt{50}$. Because $2\sqrt{50} \neq 14$, the width of the tunnel at this height is not exactly 14 feet.

Example 3

Find the point(s) of intersection, if any, between each parabola and line with the given equations.

11. $y = x^2, y = x + 2$ (−1, 1), (2, 4)

12. $y = 2x^2, y = 4x - 2$ (1, 2)

13. $y = -3x^2, y = 6x$ (−2, −12), (0, 0)

14. $y = -(x+1)^2, y = -x$ no points of intersection

Lesson 10-8 · Equations of Parabolas   **621**

1 CONCEPTUAL UNDERSTANDING | 2 FLUENCY | 3 APPLICATION

Mixed Exercises

15. HEADLIGHTS The mirrored parabolic reflector plate of a car headlight has its bulb located at the focus of the parabola as shown. The focus of the parabola is at (2.5, 0) and the directrix is $x = -2.5$. Write an equation that represents the parabolic reflector plate. $x = \frac{1}{10}y^2$

16. CONSTRUCT ARGUMENTS Prove or disprove that the point $(\sqrt{3}, -4)$ lies on the parabola with the focus at $(0, -3)$ and the directrix $y = 3$. Justify your argument.
Sample answer: The equation of the parabola is $y = -\frac{1}{12}x^2$. Substituting $x = \sqrt{3}$ in the equation gives $y = -\frac{1}{12}(3) = -\frac{1}{4}$. So, $(\sqrt{3}, -4)$ is not a solution of the equation, and the parabola does not pass through this point.

17. FLASHLIGHTS The parabolic reflector plate of a flashlight has its bulb located at the focus of the parabola. The focus of the parabola is at $(-0.9, 0)$ and the directrix is $x = 0.9$. Write an equation that represents the reflector plate.
$x = -\frac{5}{18}y^2$

🧠 **Higher-Order Thinking Skills**

18. CREATE Identify the focus and directrix of a parabola if the focus does not lie on the x- or y- axis. Then write the equation of the parabola.
Sample answer: focus $(-4, 2)$; directrix $y = -2$; $y = \frac{1}{8}(x + 4)^2$

19. WRITE The focus of a parabola is at $\left(-\frac{3}{4}, 0\right)$ and the directrix is $x = \frac{3}{4}$. Explain how to determine whether the parabola opens upward, downward, left, or right.
Sample answer: Because the directrix is vertical, the parabola must open left or right. The focus is $\left(-\frac{3}{4}, 0\right)$, which is to the left of the directrix, so the parabola opens to the left.

20. PERSEVERE The equation of parabola A is $y = \frac{1}{24}x^2$. Parabola B has the same vertex as parabola A and opens in the same direction as parabola A. However, the focus and directrix for parabola B are twice as far apart as they are for parabola A. Write the equation for parabola B. Explain your steps.
Since the equation of parabola A is $y = \frac{1}{24}x^2$, the value of p must be 6. This means the focus and directrix for parabola A are 12 units apart. So, the focus and directrix for parabola B are 24 units apart, and $p = 12$. Therefore, the equation for parabola B is $y = \frac{1}{48}x^2$.

21. ANALYZE Determine whether the following statement is *sometimes*, *always*, or *never* true. The vertex of a parabola is closer to the focus than it is to the directrix.
Never; sample answer: Because the vertex is a point on the parabola, it is always equidistant from the focus and directrix.

Rate Yourself

Have students return to the Module Opener to rate their understanding of the concepts presented in this module. They should see that their knowledge and skills have increased. After completing the chart, have them respond to the prompts in their *Interactive Student Edition* and share their responses with a partner.

℮ Answering the Essential Question

Before answering the Essential Question, have students review their answers to the Essential Question Follow-Up questions found throughout the module.

- Why is it useful to be able to solve problems using angles, chords, and arcs in circles?
- Why is it important to understand objects that relate to the outside of circles?
- Why are equations of circles important?

Then, have them write their answer to the Essential Question in the space provided.

DINAH ZIKE FOLDABLES

ELL A completed Foldable for this module should include the key concepts related to circles.

LS LearnSmart Use LearnSmart as part of your test preparation plan to measure student topic retention. You can create a student assignment in LearnSmart for additional practice on these topics for **Circles** and **Connecting Algebra and Geometry Through Coordinates.**

- Understand and apply theorems about circles
- Determine circle measurements
- Understand circles on the coordinate plane
- Understand parabolas on the coordinate plane

℮ **Essential Question**

How can circles and parts of circles be used to model situations in the real world?

Sample answer: Anything round can be modeled by a circle. Engineers and architects use circles to model moving parts of models they build. Banquet managers use circles to model tables so they know how much room they have to set up an event.

Module Summary

Lessons 10-1 and 10-2

Circles, Arcs, and Angles

- The circumference, or distance around a circle, C equals diameter times pi ($C = \pi d$).
- All circles are similar. Circles with equal radii are congruent.
- To convert a degree measure to radians, multiply by $\frac{\pi \text{ radians}}{180°}$. To convert a radian measure to degrees, multiply by $\frac{180°}{\pi \text{ radians}}$.
- In the same circle or in congruent circles, two minor arcs are congruent if and only if their corresponding chords are congruent.
- If a diameter (or radius) of a circle is perpendicular to a chord, then it bisects the chord and its arc.
- In the same circle or in congruent circles, chords are congruent if and only if they are equidistant from the center.

Lessons 10-3 and 10-4

Inscribed Angles, Tangents, and Secants

- If an angle is inscribed in a circle, then the measure of the angle equals one half the measure of its intercepted arc.
- If two inscribed angles of a circle intercept the same arc or congruent arcs, then the angles are congruent.
- An inscribed angle of a triangle intercepts a diameter or semicircle if and only if the angle is a right angle.
- If a quadrilateral is inscribed in a circle, then its opposite angles are supplementary.

Lessons 10-5 and 10-6

Tangents, Secants, and Angle Measures

- If two segments from the same exterior point are tangent to a circle, then they are congruent.
- If two secants or chords intersect in the interior of a circle, then the measure of each angle formed is one half the sum of the measures of the arcs intercepted by the angle and its vertical angle.
- If a secant and a tangent intersect at the point of tangency, then the measure of each angle formed is one half the measure of its intercepted arc.
- If two secants, a secant and a tangent, or two tangents intersect in the exterior of a circle, then the measure of the angle formed is one half the difference of the measures of the intercepted arcs.

Lessons 10-7 and 10-8

Equations of Circles and Parabolas

- The equation of a circle with center at (h, k) and radius r is $(x - h)^2 + (y - k)^2 = r^2$.
- A parabola is the set of all points in a plane equidistant from a fixed point, called the focus, and a fixed line, called the directrix.

Study Organizer

📖 Foldables

Use your Foldable to review this module. Working with a partner can be helpful. Ask for clarification of concepts as needed.

Test Practice

Name _____ Period _____ Date _____

1. MULTIPLE CHOICE Kina is building a fence around the circular field used for barrel racing at the rodeo. If the radius of the field is 45 feet, about how many feet of fencing does she need? (Lesson 10-1)

- (A) 71 ft
- (B) 90 ft
- (C) 142 ft
- (D) 283 ft

2. OPEN RESPONSE The diameter of circle W is 48 centimeters, the diameter of circle Z is 72 centimeters, and YZ is 30 centimeters. What is the length of $\overline{WX}$ in centimeters? (Lesson 10-1)

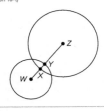

18

3. OPEN RESPONSE What is 240° in radians? Explain your solution process. (Lesson 10-2)

$\frac{4\pi}{3}$; Sample answer: I used the constant of proportionality $\frac{\pi}{180}$ multiplied by 240 to find the measure in radians.

4. OPEN RESPONSE $\overline{JK}$ is a diameter of ⊙C. What is the measure of $\widehat{BK}$? (Lesson 10-2)

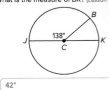

42°

5. OPEN RESPONSE Describe the steps to construct a regular hexagon inscribed in a circle. (Lesson 10-1)

Sample answer: Use a compass to construct a circle with center C. Place point P on the circle. Keeping the same compass setting that was used to construct circle C, place the point of the compass on P and construct an arc through the circle. Label the point of intersection Q. Without changing the compass setting, place the compass point on Q and intersect the circle again labeling the new point R. Repeat this step for points S, T, and U. Use a straightedge to connect each point to the next consecutive point. The result is a regular hexagon.

6. MULTIPLE CHOICE If $m\widehat{WXY} = 90°$, then what is $m\widehat{WX}$? (Lesson 10-3)

- (A) 45°
- (B) 90°
- (C) 135°
- (D) 180°

Review and Assessment Options

The following online review and assessment resources are available for you to assign to your students. These resources include technology-enhanced questions that are auto-scored, as well as essay questions.

Review Resources

Put It All Together: Lesson 10-6
Vocabulary Activity
Module Review

Assessment Resources

Vocabulary Test
AL Module Test Form B
OL Module Test Form A
BL Module Test Form C
Performance Task*

*The module-level performance task is available online as a printable document. A scoring rubric is included.

Test Practice

You can use these pages to help your students review module content and prepare for online assessments. Exercises 1–16 mirror the types of questions your students will see on online assessments.

Question Type	Description	Exercise(s)
Multiple Choice	Students select one correct answer.	1, 6–8, 11, 14
Multi-Select	Multiple answers may be correct. Students must select all correct answers.	12
Table Item	Students complete a table by entering in the correct values.	10
Open Response	Students construct their own response in the area provided.	2–5, 9, 13, 15–16

To ensure that students understand the standards, check students' success on individual exercises.

Standard	Lesson(s)	Exercise(s)
G.CO.1	10-1	1–2
G.CO.13	10-1	5
G.C.2	10-2, 10-3, 10-4, 10-6	4, 6–9, 11
G.C.4	10-5	10
G.C.5	10-2	3
G.GPE.1	10-7	12, 13
G.GPE.2	10-8	14, 15, 16

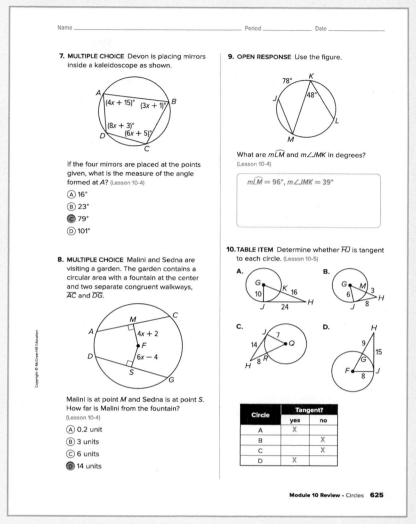

7. MULTIPLE CHOICE Devon is placing mirrors inside a kaleidoscope as shown.

If the four mirrors are placed at the points given, what is the measure of the angle formed at *A*? (Lesson 10-4)

Ⓐ 16°
Ⓑ 23°
Ⓒ 79°
Ⓓ 101°

8. MULTIPLE CHOICE Malini and Sedna are visiting a garden. The garden contains a circular area with a fountain at the center and two separate congruent walkways, $\overline{AC}$ and $\overline{DG}$.

Malini is at point *M* and Sedna is at point *S*. How far is Malini from the fountain? (Lesson 10-4)

Ⓐ 0.2 unit
Ⓑ 3 units
Ⓒ 6 units
Ⓓ 14 units

9. OPEN RESPONSE Use the figure.

What are $m\widehat{LM}$ and $m\angle JMK$ in degrees? (Lesson 10-4)

$m\widehat{LM} = 96°, m\angle JMK = 39°$

10. TABLE ITEM Determine whether $\overline{HJ}$ is tangent to each circle. (Lesson 10-5)

A.
B.
C.
D.

Circle	Tangent?	
	yes	no
A	X	
B		X
C		X
D	X	

Module 10 Review • Circles **625**

Name _____ Period _____ Date _____

11. **MULTIPLE CHOICE** What is the measure of $\overset{\frown}{JMK}$? (Lesson 10-6)

Ⓐ 128°

Ⓑ 308°

Ⓒ 334°

Ⓓ 347°

12. **MULTI-SELECT** A circle has a diameter with endpoints at $(-2, 5)$ and $(4, 1)$. What is the equation of the circle? Select all that apply. (Lesson 10-7)

Ⓐ $(x - 1)^2 + (y - 3)^2 = 13$

Ⓑ $(x - 3)^2 + (y - 3)^2 = 13$

Ⓒ $(x - 1)^2 + (y - 3)^2 = 52$

Ⓓ $x^2 + y^2 - 2x - 6y = 8$

Ⓔ $x^2 + y^2 - 6x - 6y = 34$

Ⓕ $x^2 + y^2 - 2x - 6y = 3$

13. **OPEN RESPONSE** A meteorologist is tracking a storm and has mapped it to a coordinate plane to make a forecast. At 3 PM, the eye of the storm will be located at $(1, 7)$ and will reach as far as a town located at $(10, -5)$.

What is the equation that could be used to describe this circle? Is the point $(16, 7)$ on the circle? (Lesson 10-7)

$(x - 1)^2 + (y - 7)^2 = 225$; yes

14. **MULTIPLE CHOICE** Which equation of a parabola has the focus at $\left(0, \frac{1}{5}\right)$ and the directrix $y = -\frac{1}{5}$? (Lesson 10-8)

Ⓐ $y = \frac{5}{4}x^2 - \frac{8}{25}$

Ⓑ $y = \frac{4}{5}x^2$

Ⓒ $y = -\frac{5}{4}x^2$

Ⓓ $y = \frac{5}{4}x^2$

15. **OPEN RESPONSE** What is the equation of a parabola with focus $(4, 5)$ and directrix $y = -1$? (Lesson 10-8)

$y = \frac{1}{12}(x - 4)^2 + 2$

16. **OPEN RESPONSE** A curve in a highway can be modeled using a parabola where the focus is $(0, 5)$ and the directrix is $y = -5$. Write the equation of the parabola in simplest form. (Lesson 10-8)

$y = \frac{1}{20}x^2$

Lesson 10-3

22. Proof:

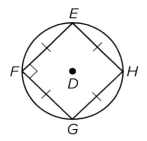

Statements (Reasons)

1. $\odot L$, $\overline{FG} \cong \overline{JH}$, $\overline{LG}$ and $\overline{LH}$ are radii (Given)

2. Construct $\overline{LX}$ perpendicular to $\overline{FG}$ and $\overline{LY}$ perpendicular to $\overline{JH}$. (Construction)

3. $\overline{LX}$ bisects $\overline{FG}$; $\overline{LY}$ bisects $\overline{JH}$ ($\overline{LX}$ and $\overline{LY}$ are contained in radii. A radius perpendicular to a chord bisects the chord.)

4. $XG = \frac{1}{2}FG$; $YH = \frac{1}{2}JH$ (Definition of segment bisector)

5. $FG = JH$ (Definition of congruent segments)

6. $\frac{1}{2}FG = \frac{1}{2}JH$ (Multiplication Property of Equality)

7. $XG = YH$ (Substitution Property)

8. $\overline{XG} \cong \overline{YH}$ (Definition of congruent segments)

9. $\overline{LG} \cong \overline{LH}$ (All radii of a circle are congruent.)

10. $\angle GXL$ and $\angle HYL$ are right angles. (Definition of perpendicular lines)

11. $\triangle XLG \cong \triangle YLH$ (HL)

12. $\overline{LX} \cong \overline{LY}$ (CPCTC)

Lesson 10-4

47. Sample Answer:

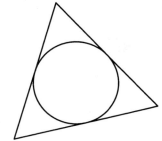

$m\widehat{EHG} = m\widehat{HGF} = m\widehat{GFE} = m\widehat{FEH} = 180°$

Lesson 10-5

30. Proof:

Statements (Reasons)

1. Quadrilateral $ABCD$ is circumscribed about $\odot P$. (Given)

2. Sides $\overline{AB}$, $\overline{BC}$, $\overline{CD}$, and $\overline{DA}$ are tangent to $\odot P$ at points H, G, F, and E, respectively. (Definition of circumscribed)

3. $\overline{EA} \cong \overline{AH}$; $\overline{HB} \cong \overline{BG}$; $\overline{GC} \cong \overline{CF}$; $\overline{FD} \cong \overline{DE}$ (Two segments tangent to a circle from the same exterior point are congruent.)

4. $AB = AH + HB$; $BC = BG + GC$; $CD = CF + FD$; $DA = DE + EA$ (Segment Addition Postulate)

5. $AB + CD = AH + HB + CF + FD$; $DA + BC = DE + EA + BG + GC$ (Substitution)

6. $AB + CD = AH + BG + GC + FD$; $DA + BC = FD + AH + BG + GC$ (Substitution)

7. $AB + CD = FD + AH + BG + GC$ (Commutative Property of Addition)

8. $AB + CD = DA + BC$ (Substitution)

40. Sample answer:

Circumscribed

Inscribed

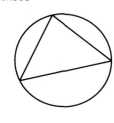

41. By Theorem 10.12, if two segments from the same exterior point are tangent to a circle, then they are congruent. So, $\overline{XY} \cong \overline{XZ}$ and $\overline{XZ} \cong \overline{XW}$. Thus, $\overline{XY} \cong \overline{XZ} \cong \overline{XW}$.

42. No; sample answer: Two tangents can be drawn from a point outside a circle and one tangent can be drawn from a point on a circle. However, no tangents can be drawn from a point inside the circle because a line would intersect the circle in two points.

Measurement

Module Goals

- Students give an informal argument for the formulas for the circumference of a circle, area of a circle, volume of a cylinder, pyramid, and cone.
- Students identify the shapes of two-dimensional cross sections of three-dimensional objects.
- Students use volume formulas for cylinders, pyramids, cones, and spheres to solve problems.

Focus

Domain: Geometry

Standards for Mathematical Content:

G.GMD.1 Give an informal argument for the formulas for the circumference of a circle, area of a circle, volume of a cylinder, pyramid, and cone.

G.GMD.3 Use volume formulas for cylinders, pyramids, cones, and spheres to solve problems.

Also addresses G.C.5, G.GMD.2, G.GMD.4, G.MG.2, and G.MG.3.

Standards for Mathematical Practice:

All Standards for Mathematical Practice will be addressed in this module.

Coherence

Vertical Alignment

Previous

Students used composing and decomposing to understand the area of polygons and circles and surface area and volume of three-dimensional figures.
6.G.1, 6.G.2, 7.G.4, 7.G.6, 8.G.9

Now

Students derive and use surface area and volume formulas for cylinders, pyramids, cones, and spheres.
G.GMD.1, G.GMD.3

Next

Students will understand and apply concepts of probability.
S.CP.1, S.MD.6

Rigor

The Three Pillars of Rigor

To help students meet standards, they need to illustrate their ability to use the three pillars of rigor. Students gain conceptual understanding as they move from the Explore to Learn sections within a lesson. Once they understand the concept, they practice procedural skills and fluency and apply their mathematical knowledge as they go through the Examples and Practice.

1 CONCEPTUAL UNDERSTANDING	2 FLUENCY	3 APPLICATION

EXPLORE 〉 LEARN 〉 EXAMPLE & PRACTICE

Suggested Pacing

Lessons	Standards	45-min classes	90-min classes
Module Pretest and Launch the Module Video		1	0.5
11-1 Areas of Quadrilaterals		2	1
11-2 Areas of Regular Polygons	G.MG.3	1	0.5
11-3 Areas of Circles and Sectors	G.C.5, G.GMD.1	1	0.5
Put It All Together: Lessons 11-1 through 11-3		1	0.5
11-4 Surface Area	G.MG.3	3	1.5
11-5 Cross Sections and Solids of Revolution	G.GMD.4	1	0.5
11-6 Volumes of Prisms and Pyramids	G.GMD.1, G.GMD.2, G.GMD.3	2	1
11-7 Volumes of Cylinders, Cones and Spheres	G.GMD.1, G.GMD.2, G.GMD.3	2	1
Put It All Together: Lessons 11-4 through 11-7		1	0.5
11-8 Applying Similarity to Solid Figures	G.GMD.3	1	0.5
11-9 Density	G.MG.2	1	0.5
Module Review		1	0.5
Module Assessment		1	0.5
Total Days		**19**	**9.5**

CHERYL TOBEY MATH PROBES

Formative Assessment Math Probe
Heights in Solids

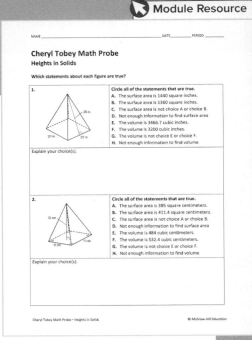

NAME _____ DATE _____ PERIOD _____

Cheryl Tobey Math Probe
Heights in Solids

Which statements about each figure are true?

1.	Circle all of the statements that are true.
	A. The surface area is 1440 square inches.
	B. The surface area is 1360 square inches.
	C. The surface area is not choice A or choice B.
	D. Not enough information to find surface area
	E. The volume is 3466.7 cubic inches.
	F. The volume is 3200 cubic inches.
	G. The volume is not choice E or choice F.
	H. Not enough information to find volume

Explain your choice(s).

2.	Circle all of the statements that are true.
	A. The surface area is 385 square centimeters.
	B. The surface area is 411.4 square centimeters.
	C. The surface area is not choice A or choice B.
	D. Not enough information to find surface area
	E. The volume is 484 cubic centimeters.
	F. The volume is 532.4 cubic centimeters.
	G. The volume is not choice E or choice F.
	H. Not enough information to find volume

Explain your choice(s).

Cheryl Tobey Math Probe • Heights in Solids   © McGraw-Hill Education

Answers: 1. A, F   2. B, E

Analyze the Probe

Review the probe prior to assigning it to your students.

In this probe, students will determine which statements about two pyramids are true and explain their choices.

Targeted Concepts Understand what information is needed to find surface areas and volumes of pyramids.

Targeted Misconceptions

- Students may incorrectly interchange the height of a pyramid with the slant height of the sides.
- Students may not realize that the slant height of a square pyramid can be found given the height and dimensions of the base and vice versa.

Use the Probe after Lesson 11-6.

Collect and Assess Student Answers

If the student selects these responses...	**Then** the student likely...
1. B, E **2.** A, F	is interchanging the height of the pyramids with the slant height and/or does not know which one to use when finding surface area and volume.
1. C, G **2.** C, G	does not know the formulas for surface area and volume of pyramids and/or how to use them accurately.
1. D, H **2.** D, H	does not know how to find a missing height and/or missing slant height using the given information and the Pythagorean Theorem.

Take Action

After the Probe Design a plan to address any possible misconceptions. You may wish to assign the following resources.

- **ALEKS** Volumes of Pyramids and Cones
- Lesson 11-6, Learns, Examples 4–5

Revisit the probe at the end of the module to be sure that your students no longer carry these misconceptions.

IGNITE!

The Ignite! activities, created by Dr. Raj Shah, cultivate curiosity and engage and challenge students. Use these open-ended, collaborative activities, located online in the module Launch section, to encourage your students to develop a growth mindset towards mathematics and problem solving. Use the teacher notes for implementation suggestions and support for encouraging productive struggle.

Ⓔ Essential Question

At the end of this module, students should be able to answer the Essential Question.

How are measurements of two- and three-dimensional figures useful for modeling situations in the real world? Sample answer: Two- and three-dimensional figures can allow you to visualize or estimate measurements of real-world objects.

What Will You Learn?

Prior to beginning this module, have your students rate their knowledge of each item listed. Then, at the end of the module, you will be reminded to have your students return to these pages to rate their knowledge again. They should see that their knowledge and skills have increased.

DINAH ZIKE FOLDABLES

Focus Students read about measurement of area and volume.

Teach Throughout the module, have students take notes under the tabs of their Foldables while working through each lesson. They should include definitions, terms, and key concepts. Encourage students to record examples of each area and volume formula from a lesson on the back of their Foldable.

When to Use It Use the appropriate tabs as students cover each lesson in this module. Students should add to the vocabulary tab during each lesson.

Launch the Module

For this module, the Launch the Module video uses a recreational park, and the processes used in planning and developing that park, to describe measuring two- and three-dimensional figures. Students learn what type of geometrical considerations are made when planning and developing a recreational park.

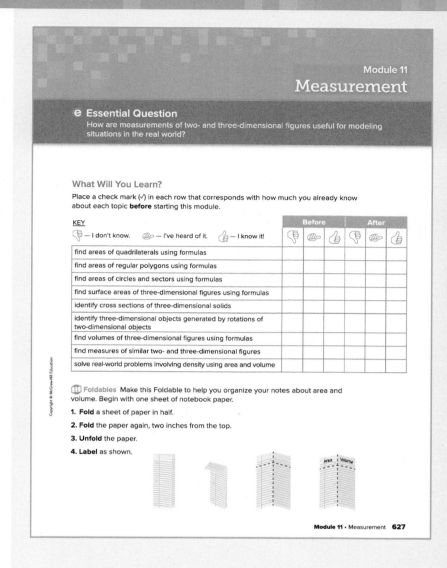

Interactive Presentation

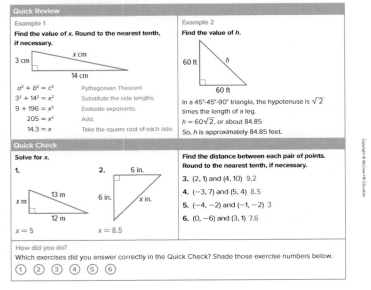
What Vocabulary Will You Learn?

ELL As you proceed through the module, introduce the key vocabulary by using the following routine.

Define The apothem is a segment drawn perpendicular to a side of a regular polygon from the center point.

Example apothem $= \overline{LM}$

Ask

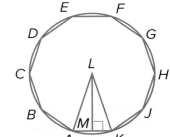

- How does the apothem relate to the central angle of a regular polygon? The apothem bisects the central angle of a regular polygon.
- How does the radius of a circle circumscribed about a regular polygon relate to the apothem? The radius of a circle circumscribed about a regular polygon forms the hypotenuse of a right triangle with the apothem and half the length of the side of the polygon bisected by the apothem.

Are You Ready?

Students may need to review the following prerequisite skills to succeed in this module.

- classifying trapezoids
- calculating interior angles of regular polygons
- calculating circumference and arc length
- finding areas
- identifying solids
- finding volumes by counting
- finding volumes of prisms, pyramids, and cones
- identifying similar figures
- finding volumes of quantities

◎ ALEKS®

ALEKS is an adaptive, personalized learning environment that identifies precisely what each student knows and is ready to learn, ensuring student success at all levels. You may want to use the **Area and Volume** section to ensure student success in this module.

🧠 Mindset Matters

Mistakes = Learning

When a student makes a mistake and goes on to learn from it, he or she can actually build new connections in their brain while figuring out a new path or process.

How Can I Apply It?

ALEKS is a great tool to not only individualize learning for each student, but to also help students understand that making mistakes and trying new problems will help them to learn and grow over the long run. Have students keep track of their ALEKS Pie Chart to see their progress.

Areas of Quadrilaterals

LESSON GOAL

Students find areas of quadrilaterals by using the formulas they derive.

1 LAUNCH

 Launch the lesson with a **Warm Up** and an introduction.

2 EXPLORE AND DEVELOP

 Explore: Deriving the Area Formulas

 Develop:

Areas of Parallelograms
- Area of a Parallelogram
- Use Trigonometry to Find the Area of a Parallelogram

Areas of Trapezoids
- Area of a Trapezoid
- Use Right Triangles to Find the Area of a Trapezoid

Areas of Kites and Rhombi
- Area of a Rhombus
- Area of a Kite
- Use Area to Find Missing Measures

 You may want your students to complete the **Checks** online.

3 REFLECT AND PRACTICE

 Exit Ticket

 Practice

DIFFERENTIATE

 View reports of student progress on the **Checks** after each example.

Resources	AL	OL	BL	ELL
Remediation: Area of Trapezoids	●	●		●
Extension: Area of a Parallelogram		●	●	●

Language Development Handbook

Assign page 74 of the *Language Development Handbook* to help your students build mathematical language related to finding the areas of quadrilaterals.

ELL You can use the tips and suggestions no page T74 of the handbook to support students who are building English proficiency.

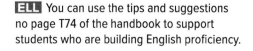

Suggested Pacing

| 90 min | 1 day |
| 45 min | 2 days |

Focus

Domain: Geometry
Standards for Mathematical Practice:
2 Reason abstractly and quantitatively.
3 Construct viable arguments and critique the reasoning of others.
4 Model with mathematics.
5 Use appropriate tools strategically.
6 Attend to precision.
7 Look for and make use of structure.

Coherence

Vertical Alignment

Previous
Students used composing and decomposing to understand the area of parallelograms and trapezoids.
6.G.1

Now
Students find the areas of quadrilaterals.

Next
Students will find areas of regular polygons.
G.MG.3

Rigor

The Three Pillars of Rigor

1 CONCEPTUAL UNDERSTANDING	2 FLUENCY	3 APPLICATION

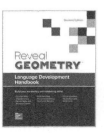 **Conceptual Bridge** In this lesson, students expand on their understanding of and fluency with finding area (which they have been studying since Grade 3) to prepare for finding volumes. They apply their understanding by using geometric models to find areas of real-world objects.

Mathematical Background

Any side of a parallelogram can be called a base, and for each base, there is a corresponding altitude that is perpendicular to the base. The altitude corresponds to the height of the parallelogram. If a parallelogram has an area A, a base b, and a height h, then $A = bh$. If a trapezoid has an area A, bases b_1 and b_2, and a height h, then $A = \frac{1}{2}h(b_1 + b_2)$. If a rhombus or kite has an area A and diagonals d_1 and d_2, then $A = \frac{1}{2}d_1d_2$.

Interactive Presentation

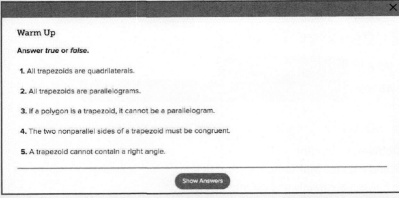

Warm Up

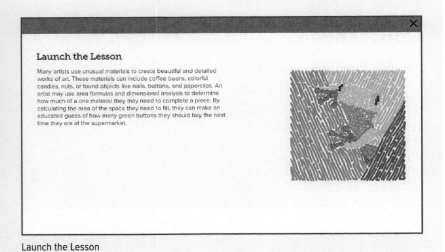

Launch the Lesson

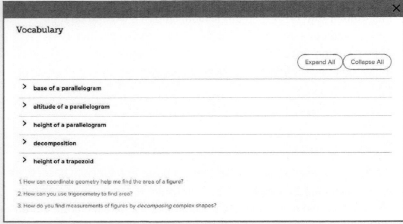

Today's Vocabulary

Warm Up

Prerequisite Skills

The Warm Up exercises address the following prerequisite skill for this lesson:

- classifying trapezoids

Answers:

1. true
2. false
3. true
4. false
5. false

Launch the Lesson

 Teaching the Mathematical Practices

4 Apply Mathematics In this Launch the Lesson, students can see a real-world application of area formulas.

Go Online to find additional teaching notes and questions to promote classroom discourse.

Today's Standards

Tell students that they will be addressing these content and practice standards in this lesson. You may wish to have a student volunteer read aloud *How can I meet these standards*? and *How can I use these practices*? and connect these to the standards.

See the Interactive Presentation for I Can statements that align with the standards covered in this lesson.

Today's Vocabulary

Tell students that they will be using these vocabulary terms in this lesson. You can expand each row if you wish to share the definitions. Then, discuss the questions below with the class.

Explore Deriving the Area Formulas

Objective

Students use dynamic geometry software to discover the formula for the area of a parallelogram.

 Teaching the Mathematical Practices

> **7 Interpret Complicated Expressions** Mathematically proficient students can see complicated expressions as single objects or as being composed of several objects. In this Explore, guide students to see what information they can gather about the expression just from looking at it.

Ideas for Use

Recommended Use Present the Inquiry Question, or have a student volunteer read it aloud. Have students work in pairs to complete the Explore activity on their devices. Pairs should discuss each of the questions. Monitor student progress during the activity. Upon completion of the Explore activity, have student volunteers share their responses to the Inquiry Question.

What if my students don't have devices? You may choose to project the activity on a whiteboard. A printable worksheet for each Explore is available online. You may choose to print the worksheet so that individuals or pairs of students can use it to record their observations.

Summary of the Activity

Students will complete guiding exercises throughout the Explore activity. Students first determine that a figure in a sketch is a parallelogram. Then they measure its area. Next, students change parts of the parallelogram and observe what changes occur in the area of the parallelogram. At this point students follow instructions to construct a rectangle with the same base and height measurements as the parallelogram. Students measure the area of the rectangle and observe that it is the same as the area of the parallelogram. Finally, students answer guiding exercises to write a formula for the area of a parallelogram. Then, students will answer the Inquiry Question.

 Go Online to find additional teaching notes and sample answers for the guiding exercises.

(continued on the next page)

Interactive Presentation

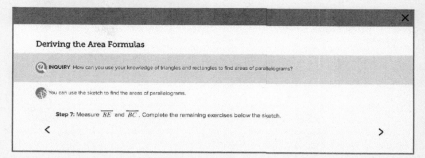

Explore

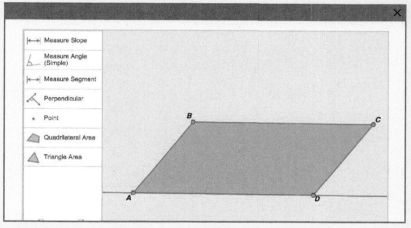

Explore

WEB SKETCHPAD

Students use a sketch to derive a formula for the area of a parallelogram.

Interactive Presentation

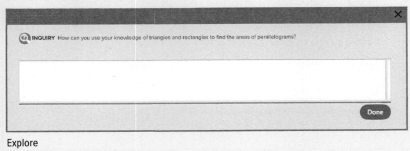

Explore

TYPE

a|

Students respond to the Inquiry Question and can view a sample answer.

Explore Deriving the Area Formulas (*continued*)

 Teaching the Mathematical Practices

> **6 Communicate Precisely** Encourage students to routinely write or explain their solution methods. Point out that they should use clear definitions when they discuss their solutions with others.

Questions
Have students complete the Explore activity.

Ask:

- Are all parallelograms rectangles? Are all rectangles parallelograms? Sample answer: Not all parallelograms are rectangles, but rectangles are a special type of parallelogram with all equal angles.

- How does the relationship between rectangles and parallelograms help your understanding of the area? Sample answer: Because all rectangles are parallelograms, and the area of a rectangle can be found by multiplying the base and height, it makes sense that the area of a parallelogram also uses those measures.

- What other shapes could you have used to find the area of the parallelogram? Sample answer: Every parallelogram can be divided into 2 congruent triangles by constructing a diagonal. To find the area of one triangle, you would find the height by constructing an altitude and then using the formula $A = \frac{1}{2}bh$. Because there are two congruent triangles, the area of the parallelogram is $2\left(\frac{1}{2}bh\right) = bh$.

Inquiry
How can you use your knowledge of triangles and rectangles to find the areas of parallelograms? Sample answer: The area of a parallelogram with height h and base b is the same as the area of a rectangle with height h and base b. When you construct the height of a parallelogram, you create a right triangle. If you translate the right triangle along the length of the parallelogram, you create a rectangle.

Go Online to find find additional teaching notes and sample answers for the guiding exercises.

Learn Areas of Parallelograms

Objective
Students find areas of parallelograms by using the formulas they derive.

Teaching the Mathematical Practices

6 Communicate Precisely Encourage students to routinely write or explain their solution methods. Point out that they should use clear definitions when they discuss their solutions with others.

Common Misconception
Students may think that they should use the lengths of consecutive sides of a parallelogram to find the area of the parallelogram. Remind them that this only works in parallelograms that are rectangles. Guide them to use the height, not the length of an adjacent side to the base.

Example 1 Area of a Parallelogram

Teaching the Mathematical Practices

4 Use Tools Point out that to solve the problem in this example, students will need to use the Pythagorean Theorem.

Questions for Mathematical Discourse

AL How are units of the given measurements different from units of area? The given units are units of length. Units of area are square units of length.

OL If the height is 10 feet, what is the area? 230 ft²

BL If the height changes, will the perimeter necessarily change? Explain. No; sample answer: The height affects the area. The area could be changed without changing the perimeter.

Common Error
Students may recognize 7 feet as the measure of the height because it is the height of the right triangle connected to the figure. Encourage students to recognize the difference between the height as a perpendicular to the base and the measurement of the extension of a base.

Go Online

- Find additional teaching notes.
- View performance reports of the Checks.
- Assign or present an Extra Example.

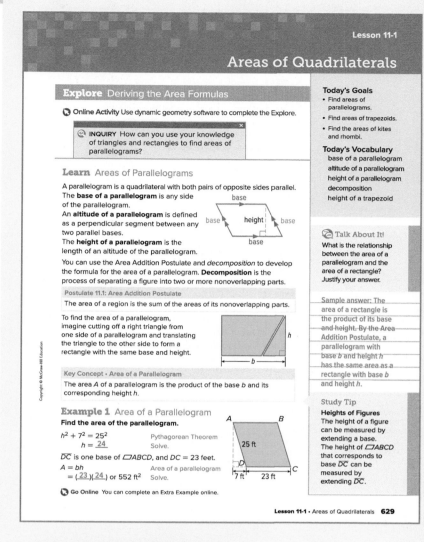

Interactive Presentation

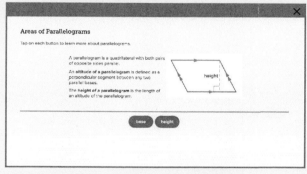

Learn

TAP	
	Students tap to reveal information about the area formula for a parallelogram.

TYPE	
	Students answer a question to show they understand the area of parallelograms.

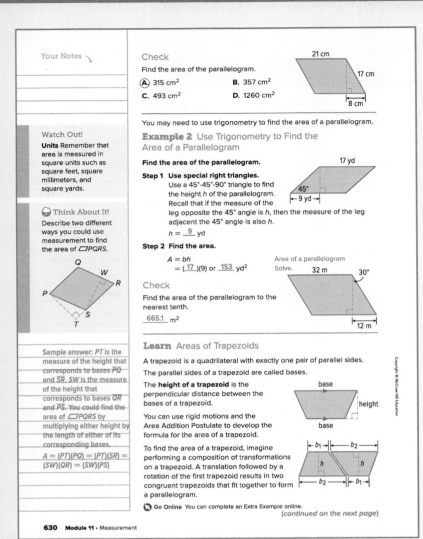

Your Notes

Check

Find the area of the parallelogram.

A. 315 cm²
B. 357 cm²
C. 493 cm²
D. 1260 cm²

21 cm
17 cm
8 cm

You may need to use trigonometry to find the area of a parallelogram.

Example 2 Use Trigonometry to Find the Area of a Parallelogram

Find the area of the parallelogram.

Step 1 Use special right triangles.
Use a 45°-45°-90° triangle to find the height h of the parallelogram. Recall that if the measure of the leg opposite the 45° angle is h, then the measure of the leg adjacent the 45° angle is also h.

$h = \underline{9}$ yd

17 yd
45°
9 yd

Step 2 Find the area.

$A = bh$
$= (\underline{17})(9)$ or $\underline{153}$ yd²

Area of a parallelogram
Solve.

32 m
30°
12 m

Check

Find the area of the parallelogram to the nearest tenth.

$\underline{665.1}$ m²

Watch Out!
Units Remember that area is measured in square units such as square feet, square millimeters, and square yards.

Think About It!
Describe two different ways you could use measurement to find the area of ▱PQRS.

Q
W
R
P
S
T

Sample answer: PT is the measure of the height that corresponds to bases $\overline{PQ}$ and $\overline{SR}$. SW is the measure of the height that corresponds to bases $\overline{QR}$ and $\overline{PS}$. You could find the area of ▱PQRS by multiplying either height by the length of either of its corresponding bases.

$A = (PT)(PQ) = (PT)(SR) = (SW)(QR) = (SW)(PS)$

Learn Areas of Trapezoids

A trapezoid is a quadrilateral with exactly one pair of parallel sides. The parallel sides of a trapezoid are called bases.

The **height of a trapezoid** is the perpendicular distance between the bases of a trapezoid.

base
height
base

You can use rigid motions and the Area Addition Postulate to develop the formula for the area of a trapezoid.

To find the area of a trapezoid, imagine performing a composition of transformations on a trapezoid. A translation followed by a rotation of the first trapezoid results in two congruent trapezoids that fit together to form a parallelogram.

b₁ b₂
h   h
b₂ b₁

Go Online You can complete an Extra Example online.

(continued on the next page)

Interactive Presentation

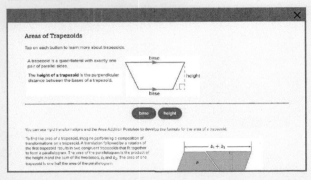

Areas of Trapezoids

Tap on each button to learn more about trapezoids.

A trapezoid is a quadrilateral with exactly one pair of parallel sides.

The **height of a trapezoid** is the perpendicular distance between the bases of a trapezoid.

base
height
base

base   height

b₁ + b₂
h

Learn

TAP
Students tap to display information about areas of trapezoids.

TYPE
a|
Students answer a question to show they understand areas of trapezoids.

CHECK

Students complete the Check online to determine whether they are ready to move on.

Example 2 Use Trigonometry to Find the Area of a Parallelogram

MP Teaching the Mathematical Practices
6 Use Quantities Use the Watch Out! to guide students to clarifying their use of quantities in this example. Ensure that they specify the units of measure used in the problem and label axes appropriately.

Questions for Mathematical Discourse

AL What do you know about 45°-45°-90° special triangles? Sample answer: the two legs are the same length and the hypotenuse is $\sqrt{2}$ times the length of a leg.

OL What is the perimeter of the rectangle? 59.5 yd

BL If the given angle measured 60°, what would the area be? 265.0 yd²

Common Error
Students may think that the solution from the special right triangle is too easy, and use the hypotenuse of a 45°-45°-90° right triangle rather than the leg. Remind students that some problems are easier than they think, and if they are uncertain of the answer they need to check their work.

DIFFERENTIATE

Language Development Activity AL BL ELL
Have students cut out a parallelogram from card stock. First, have students cut a right triangle from the end of the parallelogram and rearrange the pieces to form a rectangle. Then, ask students to find the area of the rectangle.

Learn Areas of Trapezoids

Objective
Students find areas of trapezoids by using the formulas they derive.

MP Teaching the Mathematical Practices
6 Communicate Precisely Encourage students to routinely write or explain their solution methods. Point out that they should use clear definitions when they discuss their solutions with others.

About the Key Concept
The formula for the area of a parallelogram is useful for deriving other area formulas such as the area of a trapezoid. Help students to see how two congruent trapezoids make a parallelogram.

🌐 Example 3 Area of a Trapezoid

MP Teaching the Mathematical Practices

4 Interpret Mathematical Results In this example, point out that to solve the problem, students should interpret their mathematical results in the context of the problem.

Questions for Mathematical Discourse

AL Define the height of a trapezoid in your own words. The height of a trapezoid is the perpendicular distance between the parallel bases.

OL Can you define different bases and heights for trapezoids in the way that you can parallelograms and triangles? Explain. No; the bases must be the two parallel sides, and the height must be the distance between them.

BL If the bases are the same but the area is 38 square feet, what is the height? 8 ft

---

The area of the parallelogram is the product of the height h and the sum of the two bases, b_1 and b_2. The area of one trapezoid is one half the area of the parallelogram.

Key Concept • Area of a Trapezoid

The area A of a trapezoid is one half the product of the height h and the sum of its bases, b_1 and b_2.

$$A = \frac{1}{2}h(b_1 + b_2)$$

🌐 **Example 3** Area of a Trapezoid

GARDENS Andrea needs enough mulch to cover the garden she planted in a raised bed constructed in the shape of a trapezoid. If one bag of mulch covers 12 square feet at the desired depth, how many bags of mulch does she need to buy?

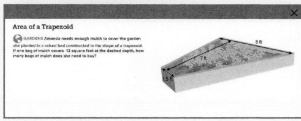

Step 1 Find the area of the garden.

$$A = \frac{1}{2}h(b_1 + b_2)$$ Area of a trapezoid

$$= \frac{1}{2}(7)(8 + 1.5)$$ $h = 7$, $b_1 = 8$, and $b_2 = 1.5$

$$= \underline{33.25}\ \text{ft}^2$$ Solve.

The area of the garden is 33.25 square feet.

Step 2 Calculate the number of bags needed.

Use unit analysis to determine how many bags of mulch Andrea should buy.

$$33.25\ \text{ft}^2 \cdot \frac{1\ \text{bag}}{12\ \text{ft}^2} = \underline{2.77}\ \text{bags}$$

Round the number of bags up so there is enough mulch. Andrea needs to buy 3 bags of mulch to cover her garden.

Check

ART Miguel wants to cover the top of his desk with butcher paper before working on a project for his art class. If one sheet of butcher paper covers a square meter of work space, how many sheets will Miguel need?

The top of the table has an area of 1.35 square meters. Miguel will need 2 sheets of butcher paper.

🌐 **Go Online** You can complete an Extra Example online.

Think About It!

What is the relationship between the area of a parallelogram and the area of a trapezoid? Justify your answer.

Sample answer: The area of a parallelogram is the product of its base and height. The area of a trapezoid with bases b_1 and b_2 and height h is one half the product of its height and the sum of its bases.

Interactive Presentation

Area of a Trapezoid

🌐 GARDENS Amanda needs enough mulch to cover the garden she planted in a raised bed constructed in the shape of a trapezoid. If one bag of mulch covers 12 square feet at the desired depth, how many bags of mulch does she need to buy?

Learn

TAP

Students move through the steps to find the area of a trapezoid.

TYPE

Students complete the calculations to find the area of a trapezoid.

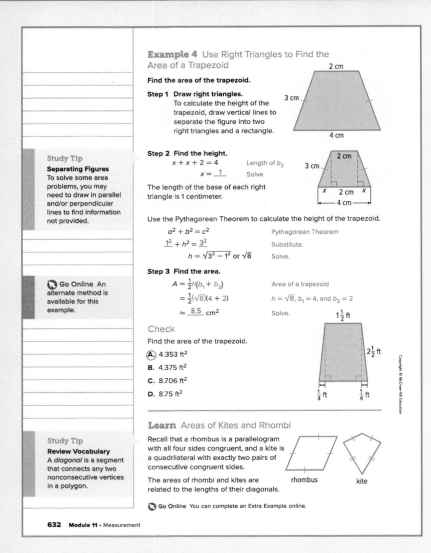

Study Tip

Separating Figures
To solve some area problems, you may need to draw in parallel and/or perpendicular lines to find information not provided.

Go Online An alternate method is available for this example.

Study Tip

Review Vocabulary
A *diagonal* is a segment that connects any two nonconsecutive vertices in a polygon.

Interactive Presentation

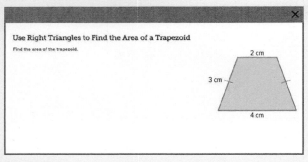

Example 4

Example 4 Use Right Triangles to Find the Area of a Trapezoid

 Teaching the Mathematical Practices

7 Interpret Complicated Expressions Mathematically proficient students can see complicated expressions as single objects or as being composed of several objects. In this example, guide students to see what information they can gather about the expression just from looking at it.

Questions for Mathematical Discourse

AL How do you know that the segments labeled x are the same length? because they are corresponding parts of congruent triangles

OL How do you know that the two triangles formed in Step 1 are congruent? Because the legs are congruent, this is an isosceles trapezoid, so the base angles are congruent. The right angles are also congruent, so the triangles are congruent by AAS.

BL What is another method you could use to find the area? You could draw a diagonal and divide the trapezoid into two triangles. If you find the areas of the triangles and add them, you will get the area of the trapezoid.

DIFFERENTIATE

Enrichment Activity AL BL ELL

Draw on students' prior knowledge by having them create a blueprint of their kitchen including the bases of all structures. Ask students to include a scale. Use these drawings to have students estimate the number of tiles that would be needed to cover the floor. Varying the size of the tile is an easy way to differentiate this task for different ability levels. This task enables students to view area as something that is not always neat and formulaic.

Learn Areas of Kites and Rhombi

Objective
Students find areas of kites and rhombi by using the formulas they derive.

 Teaching the Mathematical Practices

7 Use Structure Help students to explore the structure of areas of kites and rhombi in this Learn.

Example 5 Area of a Rhombus

 Teaching the Mathematical Practices

> **4 Use Tools** Point out that to solve the problem in this example, students will need to use the formula for the area of a rhombus.

Questions for Mathematical Discourse

AL What do you know about the diagonals of a rhombus? Sample answer: They are perpendicular bisectors of each other.

OL The diagonals of a rhombus are 5 inches and 9 inches. What is the area of the rhombus? 22.5 in^2

BL The area of a rhombus is 82.5 square centimeters. If the length of one diagonal is 11 centimeters, what is the length of the other? 15 cm

Common Error

Students may recognize that rhombi are parallelograms and may try to use the previous formula for the problem. While this can be done correctly, it is much more difficult than using the formula for kites and rhombi.

Example 6 Area of a Kite

 Teaching the Mathematical Practices

> **4 Use Tools** Point out that to solve the problem in this example, students will need to use the formula for the area of a kite.

Questions for Mathematical Discourse

AL How are rhombi and kites different? In a rhombus, all four sides are congruent, and the diagonals bisect each other. In a kite, two distinct pairs of consecutive sides are congruent, and only one diagonal bisects the other.

OL The diagonals of a kite are 5 inches and 9 inches long. What is the area of the kite? 22.5 in^2

BL The area of a kite is 52 square centimeters. If the length of one diagonal is 8 centimeters, what is the length of the other? 13 cm

---

DIFFERENTIATE

Language Development Activity ELL
Intermediate Instruct a small group of students to go online and consider the illustration of the development of the formula for the area of a trapezoid. Have them write a paragraph describing what is happening in the illustration. Their paragraphs should describe each part of the diagram in their own words. Ask for volunteers to read their paragraphs. Have students ask for clarification as needed.

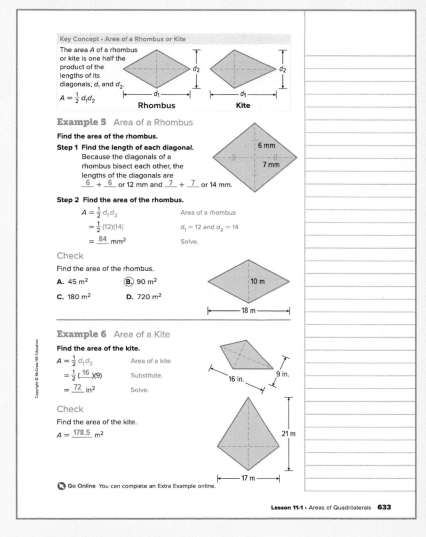

Key Concept · Area of a Rhombus or Kite

The area A of a rhombus or kite is one half the product of the lengths of its diagonals, d_1 and d_2.

$A = \frac{1}{2} d_1 d_2$

Rhombus   Kite

Example 5 Area of a Rhombus

Find the area of the rhombus.

Step 1 Find the length of each diagonal. Because the diagonals of a rhombus bisect each other, the lengths of the diagonals are $\underline{6} + \underline{6}$ or 12 mm and $\underline{7} + \underline{7}$ or 14 mm.

Step 2 Find the area of the rhombus.

$A = \frac{1}{2} d_1 d_2$ Area of a rhombus
$= \frac{1}{2}(12)(14)$ $d_1 = 12$ and $d_2 = 14$
$= \underline{84} \text{ mm}^2$ Solve.

Check
Find the area of the rhombus.
A. 45 m^2 (B.) 90 m^2
C. 180 m^2 D. 720 m^2

Example 6 Area of a Kite

Find the area of the kite.
$A = \frac{1}{2} d_1 d_2$ Area of a kite
$= \frac{1}{2}(\underline{16})(9)$ Substitute.
$= \underline{72} \text{ in}^2$ Solve.

Check
Find the area of the kite.
$A = \underline{178.5} \text{ m}^2$

Go Online You can complete an Extra Example online.

Lesson 11-1 · Areas of Quadrilaterals **633**

Interactive Presentation

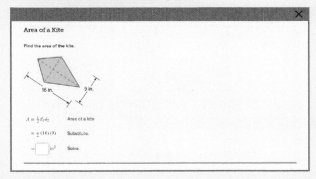

Area of a Kite

Find the area of the kite.

$A = \frac{1}{2} d_1 d_2$ Area of a kite
$= \frac{1}{2}(16)(9)$ Substitute.
$= \square \text{ in}^2$ Solve.

Example 6

TYPE

Students type to complete the solution.

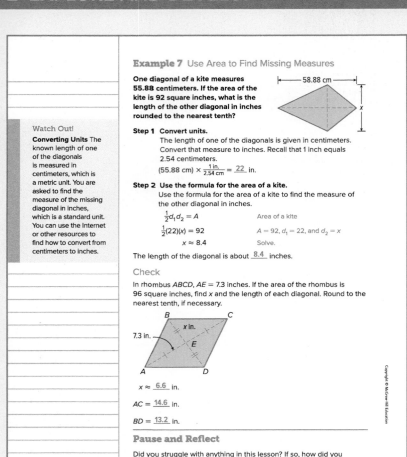

Example 7 Use Area to Find Missing Measures

One diagonal of a kite measures 55.88 centimeters. If the area of the kite is 92 square inches, what is the length of the other diagonal in inches rounded to the nearest tenth?

Watch Out!

Converting Units The known length of one of the diagonals is measured in centimeters, which is a metric unit. You are asked to find the measure of the missing diagonal in inches, which is a standard unit. You can use the Internet or other resources to find how to convert from centimeters to inches.

Step 1 Convert units.

The length of one of the diagonals is given in centimeters. Convert that measure to inches. Recall that 1 inch equals 2.54 centimeters.

$$(55.88 \text{ cm}) \times \frac{1 \text{ in.}}{2.54 \text{ cm}} = \underline{22} \text{ in.}$$

Step 2 Use the formula for the area of a kite.

Use the formula for the area of a kite to find the measure of the other diagonal in inches.

$\frac{1}{2}d_1d_2 = A$	Area of a kite
$\frac{1}{2}(22)(x) = 92$	$A = 92$, $d_1 = 22$, and $d_2 = x$
$x \approx 8.4$	Solve.

The length of the diagonal is about $\underline{8.4}$ inches.

Check

In rhombus $ABCD$, $AE = 7.3$ inches. If the area of the rhombus is 96 square inches, find x and the length of each diagonal. Round to the nearest tenth, if necessary.

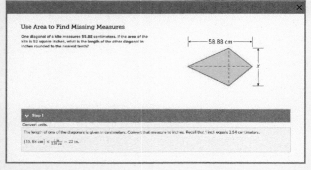

$x \approx \underline{6.6}$ in.

$AC = \underline{14.6}$ in.

$BD = \underline{13.2}$ in.

Pause and Reflect

Did you struggle with anything in this lesson? If so, how did you deal with it?

See students' observations.

🔄 **Go Online** You can complete an Extra Example online.

Interactive Presentation

Example 7

TAP

 Students tap to reveal steps in the solution.

CHECK

 Students complete the Check online to determine whether they are ready to move on.

Example 7 Use Area to Find Missing Measures

 Teaching the Mathematical Practices

6 Use Quantities Use the Watch Out! to guide students to clarifying their use of quantities in this example. Ensure that they specify the units of measure used in the problem and label axes appropriately.

Questions for Mathematical Discourse

AL How would you describe finding the area of a kite in words?
Sample answer: Multiply the diagonals and divide by 2.

OL One diagonal of a rhombus is 3 units longer than the length of the other diagonal. If the area of the rhombus is 44 square millimeters, what are the lengths of the diagonals? 8 mm; 11 mm

BL The diagonals of a rhombus are congruent. If the area of the rhombus is 50 square inches, what is the measure of each diagonal? 10 in.

Common Error

Students may not notice the difference in the given units and might try to solve the problem without converting units first. Remind them to check that the given units match.

Exit Ticket

Recommended Use

At the end of class, go online to display the Exit Ticket prompt and ask students to respond using a separate piece of paper. Have students hand you their responses as they leave the room.

Alternate Use

At the end of class, go online to display the Exit Ticket prompt and ask students to respond verbally or by using a mini-whiteboard. Have students hold up their whiteboards so that you can see all student responses. Tap to reveal the answer when most or all students have completed the Exit Ticket.

Practice and Homework

Suggested Assignments

Use the table below to select appropriate exercises.

DOK	Topic	Exercises
1, 2	exercises that mirror the examples	1–21
2	exercises that use a variety of skills from this lesson	22–31
2	exercises that extend concepts learned in this lesson to new contexts	32–34
3	exercises that emphasize higher-order and critical-thinking skills	35–40

ASSESS AND DIFFERENTIATE

.ıll Use the data from the **Checks** to determine whether to provide resources for extension, remediation, or intervention.

IF students score 90% or more on the Checks, `BL`
THEN assign:

- Practice, Exercises 1–33 odd, 35–40
- Extension: Area of a Parallelogram
- **⊙ ALEKS** Areas of Parallelograms and Triangles; Areas of Trapezoids, Rhombi, and Kites

---

IF students score 66%–89% on the Checks, `OL`
THEN assign:

- Practice, Exercises 1–39 odd
- Remediation, Review Resources: Area of Trapezoids
- Personal Tutors
- BrainPOP Video: Area of Polygons
- Extra Examples 1–7
- **⊙ ALEKS** Area of Parallelograms, Triangles, and Trapezoids

---

IF students score 65% or less on the Checks, `AL`
THEN assign:

- Practice, Exercises 1–21 odd
- Remediation, Review Resources: Area of Trapezoids
- *Quick Review Math Handbook*: Areas of Trapezoids, Rhombi, and Kites
- **⊙ ALEKS** Area of Parallelograms, Triangles, and Trapezoids

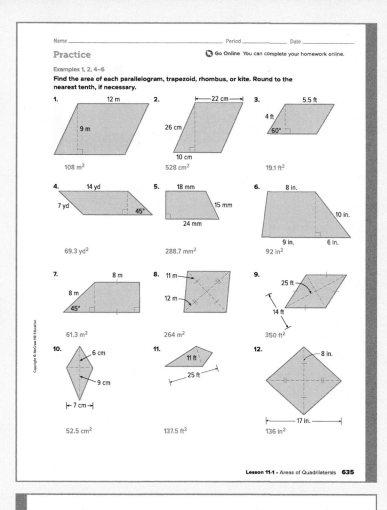

Name _____ Period _____ Date _____

Practice   ⓖ **Go Online** You can complete your homework online.

Examples 1, 2, 4–6

Find the area of each parallelogram, trapezoid, rhombus, or kite. Round to the nearest tenth, if necessary.

1. 12 m, 9 m — 108 m²
2. 22 cm, 26 cm, 10 cm — 528 cm²
3. 5.5 ft, 4 ft, 60° — 19.1 ft²
4. 14 yd, 7 yd, 45° — 69.3 yd²
5. 18 mm, 15 mm, 24 mm — 288.7 mm²
6. 8 in., 10 in., 9 in., 6 in. — 92 in²
7. 8 m, 8 m, 45° — 61.3 m²
8. 11 m, 12 m — 264 m²
9. 25 ft, 14 ft — 350 ft²
10. 6 cm, 9 cm, 7 cm — 52.5 cm²
11. 11 ft, 25 ft — 137.5 ft²
12. 8 in., 17 in. — 136 in²

Lesson 11-1 • Areas of Quadrilaterals **635**

Example 3

13. **CONSTRUCTION** A contractor is replacing a trapezoidal window on the front of a house.
    a. Find the area of the window. 13.5 ft²
    b. If the glass for the window costs $7 per square foot, about how much should the contractor expect to pay to replace the window? $94.50

14. **HOME IMPROVEMENT** Iker is building an island for his kitchen in the shape of a trapezoid as shown.
    a. What is the area of the top surface of the island? 24.75 ft²
    b. The island will be made of granite which costs $65 per square foot. Approximately how much will the granite cost? $1608.75

Example 7

15. The area of a rhombus is 168 square centimeters. If one diagonal is three times as long as the other, what are the lengths of the diagonals to the nearest tenth of a centimeter? 10.6 cm, 31.7 cm

16. A trapezoid has base lengths of 12 and 14 feet and an area of 322 square feet. What is the height of the trapezoid? 24.8 ft

17. A trapezoid has a height of 8 meters, a base length of 12 meters, and an area of 64 square meters. What is the length of the other base? 4 m

18. The height of a parallelogram is 10 feet more than the length of the base. If the area of the parallelogram is 1200 square feet, find the length of the base and the height. $b = 30$ ft; $h = 40$ ft

19. A trapezoid has base lengths of 4 feet and 19 feet, and an area of 115 square feet. What is the height of the trapezoid? 10 ft

20. One diagonal of a kite is twice as long as the other diagonal. If the area of the kite is 240 square inches, what are the lengths of the diagonals? 15.5 in., 31.0 in.

21. One diagonal of a kite is four times as long as the other diagonal. If the area of the kite is 72 square meters, what are the lengths of the diagonals? 6 m; 24 m

Mixed Exercises

22. **REASONING** Meghana is making a kite out of nylon. The material is sold for $5.99 per square yard. She needs enough material to cover her kite on both sides.
    a. What is the area of Meghana's kite? 36 ft² or 4 yd²
    b. How many yards of material will Meghana need to cover both sides of her kite? 8 yd²
    c. How much will the material cost before taxes? $47.92

23. **DESIGN** An architect is planning to build an office with a glass façade in the shape of a parallelogram using the given measurements. How much glass will be needed to cover this structure? 480 m²

636 Module 11 • Measurement

---

24. The diagonal of a square is $6\sqrt{2}$ inches. What is the area of the square?   36 in^2

25. SHADOWS A rectangular billboard casts a shadow on the ground in the shape of a parallelogram. What is the area of the ground covered by the shadow? Round your answer to the nearest tenth.   389.7 ft^2

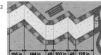

26. PATHS The concrete path shown is made by joining several parallelograms. What is the total area of the path?   58,548 in^2

Find the area of each quadrilateral with the given vertices.

27. $A(-8, 6)$, $B(-5, 8)$, $C(-2, 6)$, and $D(-5, 0)$ 24 units^2

28. $W(3, 0)$, $X(0, 3)$, $Y(-3, 0)$, and $Z(0, -3)$ 18 units^2

29. REGULARITY Given the area of a geometric figure, describe the method you use to solve for a missing dimension.
Sample answer: Using the area formula for the given figure, you can substitute the known area and all the other known dimensions into the formula. Use algebraic properties to solve for the missing dimension.

30. PRECISION Refer to parallelogram $PQRS$.

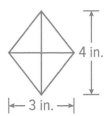

  a. Explain how a 30°-60°-90° triangle can be used to find the area of parallelogram $PQRS$.
A 30°-60°-90° triangle can be used to find the altitude, $x\sqrt{3}$, and PT, x. The hypotenuse of $\triangle PQT$ is $2x$ or 14. So, $x = 7$, the altitude is $7\sqrt{3}$, and $PT = 7$. Because the height and base of parallelogram $PQRS$ are known, the area can be calculated.
  b. Find the area of parallelogram $PQRS$ to the nearest tenth.
The base is $7 + 14$ or 21, and the height is $7\sqrt{3}$. $A = (21)(7\sqrt{3}) \approx 254.6$ in^2

31. STRUCTURE For Bruno's birthday, he got a cake shaped like a kite. He cuts the cake along the diagonals to form 4 pieces. The diagonals are 6 inches and 10 inches long. Which piece(s) is the largest? What is the area of the top of the cake?
Pieces 3 and 4 are the largest. The area of the top of the cake is 30 square inches.

32. GARDENS A square landscape plan is composed of three indoor gardens and one walkway that are all congruent. The gardens are centered around a square lounging area. If each side of the lounging area is 15 feet long, what is the area of one of the gardens?   43.75 ft^2

33. STRUCTURE A trapezoid is cut from a rectangle that is 6 inches long and 2 inches wide. The length of one base of the trapezoid is 6 inches. What is the area of the trapezoid?   8 in^2

34. REASONING Tile making often requires an artist to find clever ways of dividing a shape into several smaller, congruent shapes. Consider the isosceles trapezoid shown at the right. The trapezoid can be divided into 3 congruent triangles. What is the area of each triangle?
≈ 0.43 units^2

🌐 **Higher-Order Thinking Skills**

35. ANALYZE Will the perimeter of a nonrectangular parallelogram *sometimes*, *always*, or *never* be greater than the perimeter of a rectangle with the same area and the same height? Justify your argument.   See margin.

36. FIND THE ERROR Armando and Niran want to draw a trapezoid that has a height of 4 units and an area of 18 square units. Armando says that only one trapezoid will meet the criteria. Niran disagrees and thinks that she can draw several different trapezoids with a height of 4 units and an area of 18 square units. Who is correct? Explain your reasoning.   See margin.

37. PERSEVERE Find x in parallelogram $ABCD$.   7.2

38. CREATE Draw a kite and a rhombus with an area of 6 square inches. Label and justify your drawings.   See margin.

39. ANALYZE If the areas of two rhombi are equal, are the perimeters *sometimes*, *always*, or *never* equal? Justify your argument.
Sometimes; sample answer: If the areas are equal, it means that the products of the diagonals are equal. The only time that the perimeters will be equal is when the diagonals are also equal, or when the two rhombi are congruent.

40. WRITE How can you use trigonometry to find the area of a figure?
Sample answer: You can use trigonometry and known angle and side measures to find unknown triangular measures that are required to calculate the area.

Answers

35. Always; sample answer: If the areas are equal, the perimeter of the nonrectangular parallelogram will always be greater because the length of the side that is not perpendicular to the height forms a right triangle with the height. The height is a leg of the triangle and the side of the parallelogram is the hypotenuse of the triangle. Because the hypotenuse is always the longest side of a right triangle, the non-perpendicular side of the parallelogram is always greater than the height. The bases of the quadrilaterals must be the same because the areas and the heights are the same. Because the bases are the same and the height of the rectangles is also the length of a side, the perimeter of the parallelogram will always be greater.

36. Niran; sample answer: There is more than one trapezoid with a height of 4 units and an area of 18 square units. The sum of the bases of a trapezoid must be 9, so one possibility is a trapezoid with bases 4 and 5 units and a height of 4 units. Another is a trapezoid with bases 3 and 6 units and a height of 4 units.

38. Sample answer: Because the area formula for both a rhombus and a kite is one half the product of the lengths of two diagonals, if the area is 6 square inches, the product of the two diagonals must be 12. I used 3 and 4 inches for the diagonals of the rhombus and 2 and 6 inches for the diagonals of the kite.

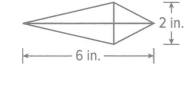

LESSON GOAL

Students find areas of regular polygons by using the formulas they derive.

1 LAUNCH

 Launch the lesson with a **Warm Up** and an introduction.

2 EXPLORE AND DEVELOP

 Explore: Regular Polygons

Develop:

Areas of Regular Polygons
- Identify Segments and Angles in Regular Polygons
- Area of a Regular Polygon

Areas of Composite Figures
- Find the Area of a Composite Figure by Adding
- Find the Area of a Composite Figure by Subtracting

 You may want your students to complete the **Checks** online.

3 REFLECT AND PRACTICE

Exit Ticket

Practice

DIFFERENTIATE

View reports of student progress on the **Checks** after each example.

Resources	AL	OL	BL	ELL
Remediation: Angles of Polygons	●	●		●
Extension: Areas of Inscribed Polygons		●	●	●

Language Development Handbook

Assign page 75 of the *Language Development Handbook* to help your students build mathematical language related to finding the areas of regular polygons.

ELL You can use the tips and suggestions on page T75 of the handbook to support students who are building English proficiency.

Suggested Pacing

| 90 min | 0.5 day |
| 45 min | 1 day |

Focus

Domain: Geometry
Standards for Mathematical Content:
G.MG.3 Apply geometric methods to solve design problems.
Standards for Mathematical Practice:
1 Make sense of problems and persevere in solving them.
3 Construct viable arguments and critique the reasoning of others.
4 Model with mathematics.
7 Look for and make use of structure.

Coherence

Vertical Alignment

Previous
Students used decomposing to find the area of regular polygons.
6.G.1

Now
Students find areas of regular polygons.
G.MG.3

Next
Students will find areas of circles and sectors.
G.C.5, G.GMD.1

Rigor

The Three Pillars of Rigor

1 CONCEPTUAL UNDERSTANDING	2 FLUENCY	3 APPLICATION

🏛 **Conceptual Bridge** In this lesson, students extend their understanding of area to regular polygons. They apply their understanding by using geometric models to find areas of real-world objects.

Mathematical Background

A regular polygon can be divided into congruent isosceles triangles. The area can be determined by adding the areas of the triangles. The area of a *composite figure* is the sum of the areas of its parts.

Interactive Presentation

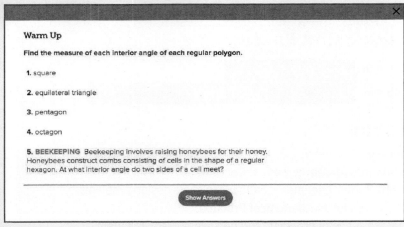

Warm Up

Find the measure of each interior angle of each regular polygon.

1. square
2. equilateral triangle
3. pentagon
4. octagon
5. **BEEKEEPING** Beekeeping involves raising honeybees for their honey. Honeybees construct combs consisting of cells in the shape of a regular hexagon. At what interior angle do two sides of a cell meet?

Show Answers

Warm Up

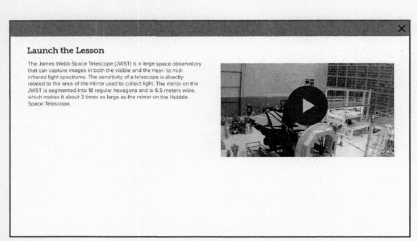

Launch the Lesson

The James Webb Space Telescope (JWST) is a large space observatory that can capture images in both the visible and the near- to mid-infrared light spectrums. The sensitivity of a telescope is directly related to the area of the mirror used to collect light. The mirror on the JWST is segmented into 18 regular hexagons and is 6.5 meters wide, which makes it about 3 times as large as the mirror on the Hubble Space Telescope.

Launch the Lesson

Vocabulary

Expand All   Collapse All

> center of a regular polygon
> radius of a regular polygon
> apothem
> central angle of a regular polygon
> composite figure

1. What is the *radius of a regular polygon*?
2. Are regular polygons the only polygons with *apothems*? Why or why not?
3. Some of the terms related to regular polygons are the same as those used with circles. Why do you think that is?

Today's Vocabulary

Warm Up

Prerequisite Skills

The Warm Up exercises address the following prerequisite skill for this lesson:

- calculating interior angles of regular polygons

Answers:

1. 90°
2. 60°
3. 108°
4. 135°
5. 120°

Launch the Lesson

MP **Teaching the Mathematical Practices**

4 Apply Mathematics In this Launch the Lesson, students can see a real-world application of area of regular polygons.

Go Online to find additional teaching notes and questions to promote classroom discourse.

Today's Standards

Tell students that they will be addressing these content and practice standards in this lesson. You may wish to have a student volunteer read aloud *How can I meet these standards*? and *How can I use these practices*? and connect these to the standards.

See the Interactive Presentation for I Can statements that align with the standards covered in this lesson.

Today's Vocabulary

Tell students that they will be using these vocabulary terms in this lesson. You can expand each row if you wish to share the definitions. Then, discuss the questions below with the class.

Explore Regular Polygons

Objective
Students use dynamic geometry software to discover the formula for the areas of regular polygons.

 Teaching the Mathematical Practices

2 Create Representations Guide students to write an equation that models the situation in this Explore. Then use the equation to solve the problem.

Ideas for Use

Recommended Use Present the Inquiry Question, or have a student volunteer read it aloud. Have students work in pairs to complete the Explore activity on their devices. Pairs should discuss each of the questions. Monitor student progress during the activity. Upon completion of the Explore activity, have student volunteers share their responses to the Inquiry Question.

What if my students don't have devices? You may choose to project the activity on a whiteboard. A printable worksheet for each Explore is available online. You may choose to print the worksheet so that individuals or pairs of students can use it to record their observations.

Summary of the Activity

Students will complete guiding exercises throughout the Explore activity. Students begin by answering guiding exercises to understand that a regular n-gon can be divided into n congruent isosceles triangles. Students then use the sketch to explore the area of regular polygons. Next, students answer more guiding exercises to discover formulas for the area of regular polygons using the side length or using the perimeter. Then, students will answer the Inquiry Question.

 Go Online to find additional teaching notes and sample answers for the guiding exercises.

(continued on the next page)

Interactive Presentation

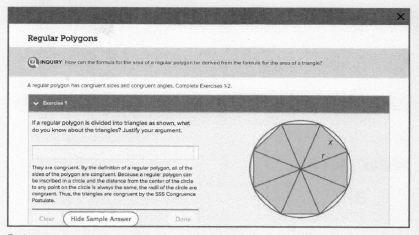

Explore

WEB SKETCHPAD

Students use a sketch to explore the area of regular polygons.

Interactive Presentation

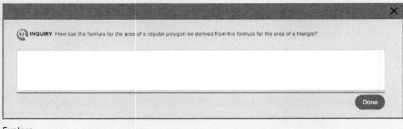

INQUIRY How can the formula for the area of a regular polygon be derived from the formula for the area of a triangle?

Done

Explore

TYPE

| a| |

Students respond to the Inquiry Question and can view a sample answer.

Explore Regular Polygons (*continued*)

MP Teaching the Mathematical Practices

2 Make Sense of Quantities Mathematically proficient students need to be able to make sense of quantities and their relationships. In the Explore, notice the relationship between the parts of regular polygons and the area of regular polygons.

Questions

Have students complete the Explore activity.

Ask:

• Why is it important to distinguish that the formula is for *regular* polygons? Sample answer: If a polygon is a regular polygon, then all sides are equal and all angles are equal. This also means you can divide it equally into congruent triangles. If the polygon were not regular, it could still be divided into triangles, but they wouldn't be congruent.

• How would you find the area of an octagon with side lengths of 10 units and an apothem of 12 units? Sample answer: Find the perimeter, knowing that there are 8 sides of length 10 units, so 80 units. Then substitute into the formula, $A = \frac{1}{2}aP = \frac{1}{2}(12)(80) = 480$ units^2.

⑦ Inquiry

How can the formula for the area of a regular polygon be derived from the formula for the area of a triangle? Sample answer: You can divide a regular *n*-gon into *n* congruent triangles. You can calculate the area of one triangle and then multiply the area by the number of triangles in the polygon.

🔖 **Go Online** to find additional teaching notes and sample answers for the guiding exercises.

1 CONCEPTUAL UNDERSTANDING   2 FLUENCY   3 APPLICATION

Learn Areas of Regular Polygons

Objective
Students find areas of regular polygons using the formulas they derive.

 Teaching the Mathematical Practices

7 Use Structure Help students to explore the structure of the parts of regular polygons in this Learn.

About the Key Concept
The length of an apothem of a regular polygon depends on the side length and the number of sides of the polygon. An apothem is one leg of a right triangle where the other leg is half of a side, and that includes an angle resulting from bisecting a central angle. Because the measure of the central angle depends on the number of sides, you can use trigonometry, the number of sides, and the side length to find the length of an apothem.

 Go Online

- Find additional teaching notes.
- View performance reports of the Checks.
- Assign or present an Extra Example.

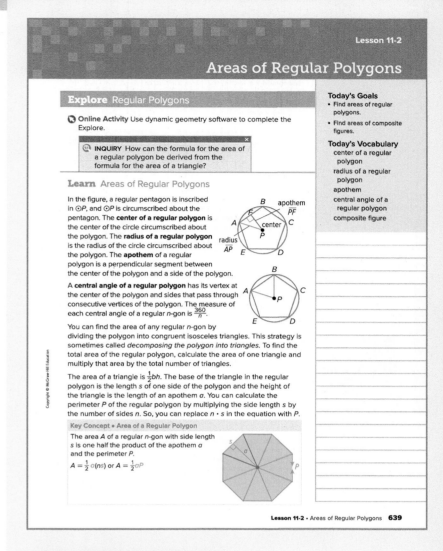

Lesson 11-2

Areas of Regular Polygons

Explore Regular Polygons

Online Activity Use dynamic geometry software to complete the Explore.

INQUIRY How can the formula for the area of a regular polygon be derived from the formula for the area of a triangle?

Learn Areas of Regular Polygons

In the figure, a regular pentagon is inscribed in ⊙P, and ⊙P is circumscribed about the pentagon. The **center of a regular polygon** is the center of the circle circumscribed about the polygon. The **radius of a regular polygon** is the radius of the circle circumscribed about the polygon. The **apothem** of a regular polygon is a perpendicular segment between the center of the polygon and a side of the polygon.

A **central angle of a regular polygon** has its vertex at the center of the polygon and sides that pass through consecutive vertices of the polygon. The measure of each central angle of a regular n-gon is $\frac{360}{n}$.

You can find the area of any regular n-gon by dividing the polygon into congruent isosceles triangles. This strategy is sometimes called *decomposing the polygon into triangles*. To find the total area of the regular polygon, calculate the area of one triangle and multiply that area by the total number of triangles.

The area of a triangle is $\frac{1}{2}bh$. The base of the triangle in the regular polygon is the length s of one side of the polygon and the height of the triangle is the length of an apothem a. You can calculate the perimeter P of the regular polygon by multiplying the side length s by the number of sides n. So, you can replace $n \cdot s$ in the equation with P.

Key Concept • Area of a Regular Polygon

The area A of a regular n-gon with side length s is one half the product of the apothem a and the perimeter P.

$A = \frac{1}{2}a(ns)$ or $A = \frac{1}{2}aP$

Today's Goals
- Find areas of regular polygons.
- Find areas of composite figures.

Today's Vocabulary
center of a regular polygon
radius of a regular polygon
apothem
central angle of a regular polygon
composite figure

Lesson 11-2 • Areas of Regular Polygons **639**

Interactive Presentation

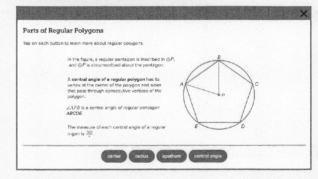

Parts of Regular Polygons

Tap on each button to learn more about regular polygons.

In the figure, a regular pentagon is inscribed in ⊙P, and ⊙P is circumscribed about the pentagon.

A central angle of a regular polygon has its vertex at the center of the polygon and sides that pass through consecutive vertices of the polygon.

∠APB is a central angle of regular pentagon ABCDE.

The measure of each central angle of a regular n-gon is $\frac{360}{n}$.

center   radius   apothem   central angle

Learn

 TAP

Students tap to reveal the parts of a regular polygon.

 SWIPE

Students move through the slides to find the area and perimeter of an octagon.

G.MG.3

1 CONCEPTUAL UNDERSTANDING | 2 FLUENCY | 3 APPLICATION

Your Notes

Example 1 Identify Segments and Angles in Regular Polygons

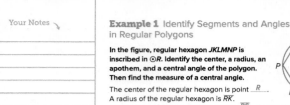

In the figure, regular hexagon *JKLMNP* is inscribed in ⊙*R*. Identify the center, a radius, an apothem, and a central angle of the polygon. Then find the measure of a central angle.

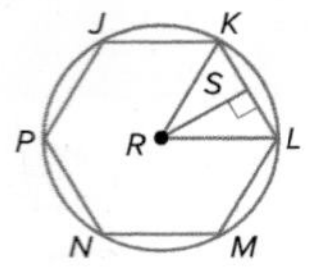

The center of the regular hexagon is point R.
A radius of the regular hexagon is $\overline{RK}$.
An apothem of the regular hexagon is $\overline{RS}$. A central angle of the regular hexagon is ∠*KRL*. A regular hexagon has 6 sides. Thus, the measure of each central angle is $\frac{360}{6}$ or 60°.

Example 2 Area of a Regular Polygon

PATCHES **Lindsay created a patch for the robotics club at her school. The patch is a regular octagon with a side length of 4 centimeters. Find the area covered by the patch. Round to the nearest tenth.**

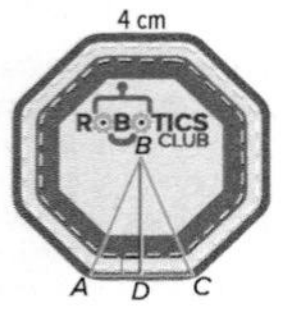

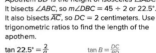

Step 1 Find the measure of a central angle.

A regular octagon has 8 congruent central angles, so $m\angle ABC = \frac{360}{8}$ or 45°.

Step 2 Find the length of the apothem.

Apothem $\overline{BD}$ is the height of isosceles △*ABC*. It bisects ∠*ABC*, so $m\angle DBC = 45 \div 2$ or 22.5°. It also bisects $\overline{AC}$, so $DC = 2$ centimeters. Use trigonometric ratios to find the length of the apothem.

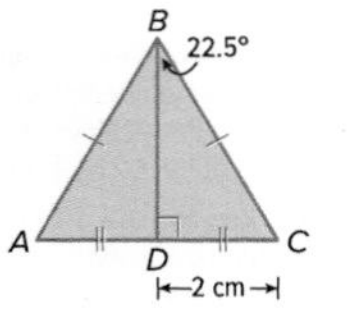

$\tan 22.5° = \frac{2}{a}$ — $\tan B = \frac{DC}{BD}$

$a = \frac{2}{\tan 22.5°}$ — Solve for *a*.

Step 3 Use the formula for the area of a regular polygon.

$A = \frac{1}{2}aP$ — Area of a regular polygon

$= \frac{1}{2}\left(\frac{2}{\tan 22.5°}\right)(32)$ — $a = \frac{2}{\tan 22.5°}$ and $P = 32$

≈ 77.25 — Solve.

The patch covers an area of about 77.25 square centimeters.

Think About It!

James calculated the area of the trampoline. His calculations are shown.

$A = \frac{1}{2}aP$

$\approx \frac{1}{2}(4)(27.3)$

≈ 54.6 ft

Do you agree? Justify your argument.

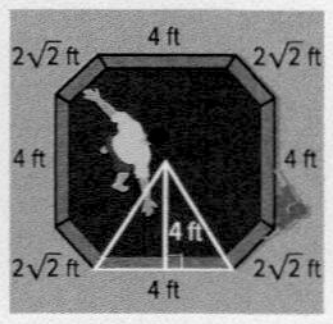

No; sample answer: James used the formula for the area of a regular polygon to calculate the area of the trampoline. But, the trampoline is an irregular octagon, so he cannot apply the formula.

Check

CERAMICS Imani is crafting coasters for a local craft fair. Each side measures 4 inches. Find the area of each coaster. Round your answer to the nearest tenth, if necessary.

$A \approx 27.5$ in^2

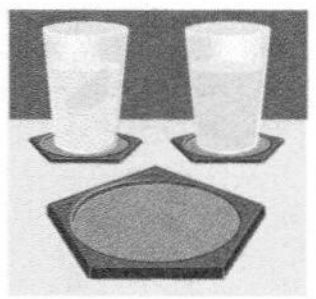

Go Online You can complete an Extra Example online.

640 Module 11 • Measurement

Interactive Presentation

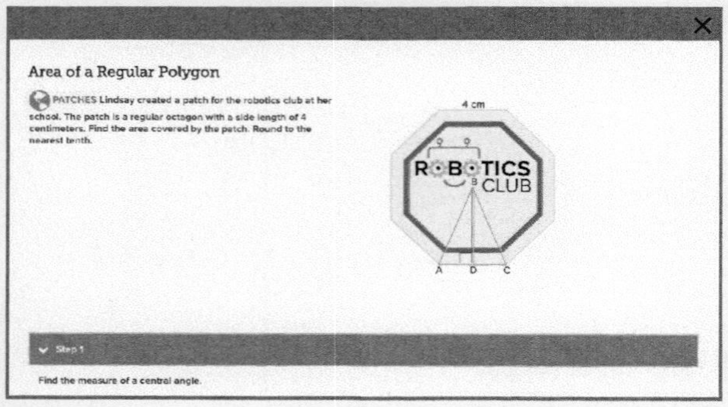

Example 2

TAP

Students move through the steps to find the area of a regular polygon.

CHECK

Students complete the Check online to determine whether they are ready to move on.

Example 1 Identify Segments and Angles in Regular Polygons

Teaching the Mathematical Practices

6 Communicate Precisely Encourage students to routinely write or explain their solution methods. Point out that they should use clear definitions when they discuss their solutions with others.

Questions for Mathematical Discourse

AL What is another radius that we could draw? Sample answer: $\overline{RJ}$

OL If we drew all possible radii, name another central angle that would be formed. Sample answer: ∠*KRJ*

BL If a polygon inscribed in a circle has 8 central angles, what is the polygon? an octagon

Example 2 Area of a Regular Polygon

Teaching the Mathematical Practices

4 Analyze Relationships Mathematically Point out that to solve the problem in this example, students will need to analyze the mathematical relationships in the problem to draw a conclusion.

Questions for Mathematical Discourse

AL When you find the area of a regular polygon, how is the number of triangles formed related to the number of sides of the polygon? They are the same.

OL If the radius of the octagonal badge is 15 millimeters and the side length is 11.5 millimeters, what is the area of the badge? 637.3 mm^2

BL If the badge is a hexagon with a side length of 4 centimeters, what would the area be? 41.57 cm^2

Common Error

Students may confuse an apothem with a radius or a side of the polygon. Make sure that they are trying to find the length of the correct segment.

DIFFERENTIATE

Language Development Activity AL ELL

Have students describe how to find the area of an inscribed polygon. Sample answer: First, find the apothem, or the distance from the center of the polygon perpendicular to the midpoint of a side of the polygon. Then, find half the product of the perimeter and the apothem.

1 CONCEPTUAL UNDERSTANDING | 2 FLUENCY | 3 APPLICATION

Learn Areas of Composite Figures

Objective
Students find areas of composite figures by using the formulas they derive.

 Teaching the Mathematical Practices

> **7 Use Structure** Help students to explore the structure of areas of composite figures in this Learn.

Common Misconception
Students may think that they must always break a composite figure into smaller figures. Remind them that they can also think of a composite figure as a larger figure with a smaller figure removed.

Example 3 Find the Area of a Composite Figure by Adding

 Teaching the Mathematical Practices

> **7 Interpret Complicated Expressions** Mathematically proficient students can see complicated expressions as single objects or as being composed of several objects. In this example, guide students to see what information they can gather about the expression just from looking at it.

Questions for Mathematical Discourse

AL How can we estimate the solution? The area would be less than the area of a rectangle 15 cm wide and $19 + 2(9) + 9$ cm long, or $15(19 + 2(9) + 9) = 690$ cm².

OL If the square portion of the figure is removed, what is the new area to the nearest tenth? 438.4 cm²

BL If the base of the trapezoid is increased to 20 centimeters, what is the new area of the figure? 566.5 cm²

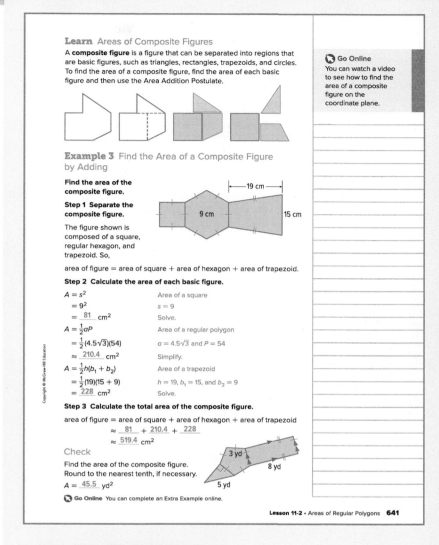

Learn Areas of Composite Figures

A **composite figure** is a figure that can be separated into regions that are basic figures, such as triangles, rectangles, trapezoids, and circles. To find the area of a composite figure, find the area of each basic figure and then use the Area Addition Postulate.

🔵 **Go Online**
You can watch a video to see how to find the area of a composite figure on the coordinate plane.

Example 3 Find the Area of a Composite Figure by Adding

Find the area of the composite figure.

Step 1 Separate the composite figure.

The figure shown is composed of a square, regular hexagon, and trapezoid. So,

area of figure = area of square + area of hexagon + area of trapezoid.

Step 2 Calculate the area of each basic figure.

$A = s^2$ Area of a square
$= 9^2$ $s = 9$
$= \underline{81}$ cm²   Solve.

$A = \frac{1}{2}aP$ Area of a regular polygon
$= \frac{1}{2}(4.5\sqrt{3})(54)$ $a = 4.5\sqrt{3}$ and $P = 54$
$\approx \underline{210.4}$ cm²   Simplify.

$A = \frac{1}{2}h(b_1 + b_2)$ Area of a trapezoid
$= \frac{1}{2}(19)(15 + 9)$ $h = 19$, $b_1 = 15$, and $b_2 = 9$
$= \underline{228}$ cm²   Solve.

Step 3 Calculate the total area of the composite figure.

area of figure = area of square + area of hexagon + area of trapezoid
$\approx \underline{81} + \underline{210.4} + \underline{228}$
$\approx \underline{519.4}$ cm²

Check

Find the area of the composite figure. Round to the nearest tenth, if necessary.

$A = \underline{45.5}$ yd²

🔵 **Go Online** You can complete an Extra Example online.

Interactive Presentation

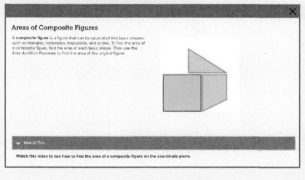

Areas of Composite Figures

A composite figure is a figure that can be separated into basic shapes, such as triangles, rectangles, trapezoids, and circles. To find the area of a composite figure, find the area of each basic shape. Then use the Area Addition Postulate to find the area of the original figure.

Watch this video to see how to find the area of a composite figure on the coordinate plane.

Learn

WATCH

 Watch a video to see how to find the area of a composite figure on the coordinate plane.

The areas of some figures can be found by subtracting the areas of basic figures.

Example 4 Find the Area of a Composite Figure by Subtracting

Find the area of the composite figure. Round to the nearest tenth, if necessary.

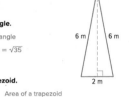

To find the area of the figure, subtract the area of the triangle from the area of the trapezoid.

Step 1 Find the height of the triangle.
You can use the Pythagorean Theorem and what you know about isosceles triangles to calculate the height of the triangle. The altitude of the isosceles triangle bisects the base of the triangle.

So, $1^2 + h^2 = 6^2$ or $h = \sqrt{35}$.

Step 2 Find the area of the triangle.

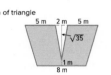

$A = \frac{1}{2}bh$ Area of a triangle

$= \frac{1}{2}(2)(\sqrt{35})$ $b = 2$ and $h = \sqrt{35}$

$= \sqrt{35}$ m²   Solve.

Step 3 Find the area of the trapezoid.

$A = \frac{1}{2}h(b_1 + b_2)$ Area of a trapezoid

$= \frac{1}{2}(\sqrt{35} + 1)(12 + 8)$ $b_1 = 12, b_2 = 8,$ and $h = \sqrt{35} + 1$

$= 10\sqrt{35} + 10$ m²   Solve.

Step 4 Find the area of the figure.

area of figure = area of trapezoid − area of triangle

$= 10\sqrt{35} + 10 - \sqrt{35}$

$\approx$ ___63.2___ m²

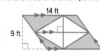

Check

Select the area of the composite figure.

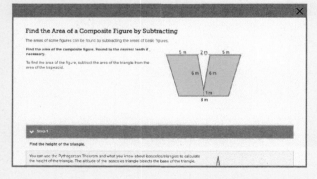

A. 31.5 ft²   B. 63 ft²   C. 94.5 ft²   D. 126 ft²

 Go Online You can complete an Extra Example online.

Copyright © McGraw-Hill Education

Study Tip

Drawing Figures
To solve some area problems by subtracting, you may need to draw figures to represent the basic shapes that are being removed from the composite figure. You can use the figures you draw to help you visualize the situation and calculate missing measures.

Interactive Presentation

Example 4

TAP

Students move through the steps to find the area of a composite figure.

CHECK

Students complete the Check online to determine whether they are ready to move on.

Example 4 Find the Area of a Composite Figure by Subtracting

MP Teaching the Mathematical Practices

1 Explain Correspondences Guide students as they use the information in this example to draw diagrams to represent the situation.

Questions for Mathematical Discourse

AL Why can't we find the area of the figure by adding the areas of two parallelograms? Sample answer: The parallelograms overlap.

OL If the removed triangle is equilateral with a base 6 meters long and legs 5 meters long, what is the area of the figure? 40.5 m²

BL If a triangle of the same size was removed from the other side of the trapezoid, would a composite figure be formed? Explain. No; sample answer: Because the height of each triangle is greater than one-half the height of the trapezoid, two figures would be formed.

Common Error

Students may not notice that the triangle cut out of the trapezoid has a height 1 cm less than the height of the trapezoid. Make sure that students are determining the dimensions of the figure accurately.

DIFFERENTIATE

Enrichment Activity AL BL ELL

Have the students find the area of the white stars on the United States Flag. Assume that the regular pentagon in the center of each star has an apothem of 0.69 centimeter. The five triangles of each star have bases of 1 centimeter and height of 1.5 centimeters. The area of each star is 5.475 cm². So, the area of all the stars is 273.75 cm².

Exit Ticket

Recommended Use

At the end of class, go online to display the Exit Ticket prompt and ask students to respond using a separate piece of paper. Have students hand you their responses as they leave the room.

Alternate Use

At the end of class, go online to display the Exit Ticket prompt and ask students to respond verbally or by using a mini-whiteboard. Have students hold up their whiteboards so that you can see all student responses. Tap to reveal the answer when most or all students have completed the Exit Ticket.

1 CONCEPTUAL UNDERSTANDING   **2 FLUENCY**   3 APPLICATION

Practice and Homework

Suggested Assignments

Use the table below to select appropriate exercises.

DOK	Topic	Exercises
1, 2	exercises that mirror the examples	1–13
2	exercises that use a variety of skills from this lesson	14–32
3	exercises that emphasize higher-order and critical-thinking skills	33–38

ASSESS AND DIFFERENTIATE

📊 Use the data from the **Checks** to determine whether to provide resources for extension, remediation, or intervention.

IF students score 90% or more on the Checks, **BL**
THEN assign:

- Practice, Exercises 1–31 odd, 33–38
- Extension: Areas of Inscribed Polygons
- ⊙ **ALEKS** Areas of Regular Polygons and Similar Polygons

IF students score 66%–89% on the Checks, **OL**
THEN assign:

- Practice, Exercises 1–37 odd
- Remediation, Review Resources: Angles of Polygons
- Personal Tutors
- BrainPOP Video: Area of Polygons
- Extra Examples 1–4
- ⊙ **ALEKS** Angles of Polygons

IF students score 65% or less on the Checks, **AL**
THEN assign:

- Practice, Exercises 1–13 odd
- Remediation, Review Resources: Angles of Polygons
- *Quick Review Math Handbook*: Areas of Regular Polygons and Composite Figures
- ⊙ **ALEKS** Angles of Polygons

Answers

1. Sample answer: center: point *Z*, radius: $\overline{ZY}$, apothem: $\overline{ZQ}$, central angle: ∠*YZR*, 45°

2. Sample answer: center: point *L*, radius: $\overline{LK}$, apothem: $\overline{LM}$, central angle: ∠*ALK*, 36°

17. Sample answer:

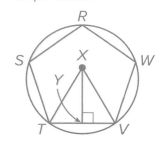

Name _____   Period _____ Date _____

Practice   🌐 **Go Online** You can complete your homework online.

Example 1

In each figure, a regular polygon is inscribed in a circle. Identify the center, a radius, an apothem, and a central angle of each polygon. Then find the measure of a central angle. See margin.

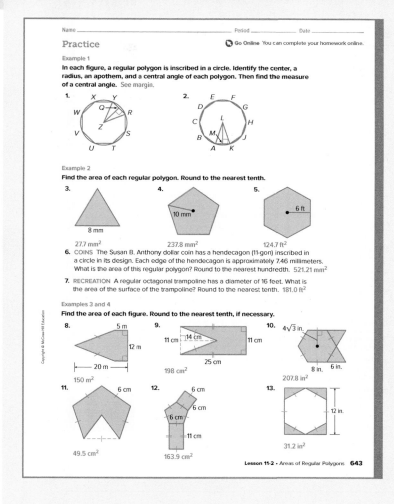

Example 2

Find the area of each regular polygon. Round to the nearest tenth.

3.

8 mm

27.7 mm²

4.

10 mm

237.8 mm²

5.

6 ft

124.7 ft²

6. COINS The Susan B. Anthony dollar coin has a hendecagon (11-gon) inscribed in a circle in its design. Each edge of the hendecagon is approximately 7.46 millimeters. What is the area of this regular polygon? Round to the nearest hundredth. 521.21 mm²

7. RECREATION A regular octagonal trampoline has a diameter of 16 feet. What is the area of the surface of the trampoline? Round to the nearest tenth. 181.0 ft²

Examples 3 and 4

Find the area of each figure. Round to the nearest tenth, if necessary.

8.
5 m
12 m
20 m
150 m²

9.
11 cm 14 cm 11 cm
25 cm
198 cm²

10.
$4\sqrt{3}$ in.
8 in. 6 in.
207.8 in²

11.
6 cm
49.5 cm²

12.
6 cm
6 cm
6 cm
11 cm
163.9 cm²

13.
12 in.
31.2 in²

Lesson 11-2 • Areas of Regular Polygons **643**

Mixed Exercises

14. LAWN Lalita has to buy grass seed for her lawn. Her lawn is in the shape of the composite figure shown. What is the area of the lawn? 295 ft²
2.5 ft
5 ft
10 ft
2.5 ft
6 ft
20 ft
15 ft

15. PATIO Chenoa is building a patio to surround his fire pit. The patio is in the shape of the composite figure shown. If each side of the fire pit is 2 feet long, how many square feet of patio pavers will Chenoa need to buy to complete the patio? 128.1 ft²
15 feet
9 feet
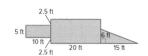

16. Find the area of a regular hexagon with a perimeter of 72 inches. Round to the nearest square inch. 374 in²

17. USE TOOLS Draw a regular pentagon inscribed in a circle with center of *X*, a radius of $\overline{XV}$, an apothem of $\overline{XY}$, and a central angle of ∠*VXT* that measures 72°. See margin.

18. Find the perimeter and area of a regular hexagon with a side length of 12 centimeters. Round to the nearest tenth, if necessary. 72 cm; 374.1 cm²

19. Find the total area of the shaded regions. Round to the nearest tenth, if necessary. 52.0 in²

6 in.

20. HOME IMPROVEMENT Pilar is putting a backsplash in her kitchen made up of octagon and square tiles. The pattern she has chosen is sold in sheets of 4 × 3 octagons as shown. The side length of both the squares and the octagons is 3 centimeters.

  a. Draw one octagon and one square. Label the side length and area of each and the apothem of the octagon. Find the area of one tile sheet to the nearest whole number. See margin.

  b. Small square tiles will be placed to fill the nooks around the edges of the tile sheet. How many complete squares will be needed? What is the additional area of these tiles? 6 squares; 54 cm²

  c. If Pilar's backsplash measures 42 centimeters by 84 centimeters, approximately how many sheets of tile will Pilar need to purchase? How many extra square tiles will need to be purchased? 6 sheets of tile; between 30 and 35 extra squares

644 Module 11 • Measurement

Name _____ Period _____ Date _____

21. REASONING Miguel is planning to renovate his living room. Refer to the given floor plan. a–b. See margin.

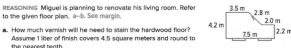

  a. How much varnish will he need to stain the hardwood floor? Assume 1 liter of finish covers 4.5 square meters and round to the nearest tenth.

  b. The height of the room is 2.6 meters. Approximate how much paint is needed for the walls. Assume that 1 liter of paint covers 7.5 square meters and round to the nearest tenth.

  c. Why might Miguel adjust your estimates when he purchases materials? Sample answer: Miguel may need to adjust the estimate because I did not account for the area taken up by doors and windows. So, the original estimate is too high.

22. STATE YOUR ASSUMPTION Chilam is going to build a shelf for his 15 homerun baseballs. He wants the shelf to be in the shape of a regular triangle. Find the area of the shelf he must create. State any assumptions you make. Round your answer to the nearest tenth. See margin.

23. USE A SOURCE Research the shape and dimensions of the Pentagon building in Arlington, Virginia.

  a. Draw and label a diagram of the Pentagon including the courtyard. See margin.

  b. Use your diagram in part **a** to find the area in square feet of the Pentagon. Round your answer to the nearest tenth. 1,233,238.2 ft²

24. REGULARITY Explain how using the formula for the area of a regular polygon is related to finding the area of a triangle. See margin.

25. SIGNS A stop sign has side lengths of approximately 12.5 inches. What is the area of a regular octagonal stop sign? Round your answer to the nearest tenth. 754.4 in²

26. DIAMONDS Mr. Figueroa has bought his wife an anniversary ring with a regular heptagon diamond as shown. If each side of the diamond is 6 millimeters long, what is the area of the face of the diamond? 130.8 mm²

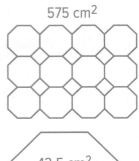

27. ARCHITECTURE Fort Jefferson in the Florida Keys is the largest brick masonry building in the Americas. The Fort was built in the shape of a hexagon with side lengths of 477 feet. What is the area of the hexagon formed by the exterior walls of the fort? Round your answer to the nearest tenth. 591,137.7 ft²

28. FRAME Darren is hanging a picture frame that is shaped like a regular pentagon with outside lengths of 9 inches. What is the area this picture frame will take up on Darren's wall? Round your answer to the nearest tenth. 139.4 in²

29. FLOWER Delfina photographed a triangular flower for a photo contest. The flower was approximately regular and had side lengths measuring about 4 centimeters. What is the area of the flower? Round your answer to the nearest tenth. 6.9 cm²

30. STAINED GLASS Kenia makes regular octagonal-shaped stained glass windows. If the apothem of the window is 14 inches, what is the area of the window? Round your answer to the nearest tenth. 649.5 in²

Lesson 11-2 · Areas of Regular Polygons   **645**

31. GAMING A 12-sided gaming die is made up of 12 regular pentagons, each with a side length of 1.5 centimeters. What is the area of one face of the gaming die? Round your answer to the nearest hundredth. 3.87 cm²

32. HONEYCOMB A honeycomb is a structure bees make of hexagonal wax cells to contain honey, larvae, and pollen. The height of one hexagon in a honeycomb is approximately 5 millimeters. What is the area of one hexagon? Round your answer to the nearest tenth. 21.7 mm²

Higher-Order Thinking Skills

33. FIND THE ERROR Chenglei and Flavio want to find the area of the hexagon shown. Who is correct? Explain your reasoning. See Mod. 11 Answer Appendix.

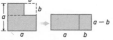

34. ANALYZE Is the measure of an apothem of a regular polygon *sometimes, always,* or *never* $\frac{\sqrt{3}}{2}s$ where s is a side length of the polygon? Justify your argument. See Mod. 11 Answer Appendix.

35. CREATE Draw a pair of composite figures that have the same area. Make one composite figure out of a rectangle and a trapezoid, and make the other composite figure out of a triangle and a rectangle. Show the area of each basic figure. See Mod. 11 Answer Appendix.

36. PERSEVERE Consider the sequence of area diagrams shown. What algebraic theorem do the diagrams prove? Explain your reasoning. See Mod. 11 Answer Appendix.

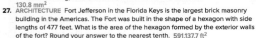

37. WRITE How can you find the area of any figure? See Mod. 11 Answer Appendix.

38. WHICH ONE DOESN'T BELONG? Alden drew the following diagrams to find the area of 4 regular polygons. Which drawing is incorrect? Justify your conclusion.

The drawing for the octagon is incorrect because Alden did not divide the measure of the central angle by two.

646   Module 11 · Measurement

Answers

20a.

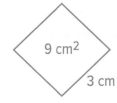

575 cm²

43.5 cm²

3.621 cm

3 cm

9 cm²

3 cm

21a. Sample answer: Floor area $= (7.5)(2.2) + (3.5)(4.2 - 2.2) + \frac{1}{2}(7.5 - 3.5 - 2.0)(4.2 - 2.2) = 25.5$ m²; $\frac{x}{1.0\,L} = \frac{25.5\,m^2}{4.5\,m^2}$, so $x = \frac{25.5\,m^2}{4.5\,m^2}(1.0\,L) \approx 5.7$ L.

21b. Sample answer: Perimeter $= 7.5 + 2.2 + 2.0 + 2.8 + 3.5 + 4.2 = 22.2$ m. Area to be painted (ignoring door and windows) $= (22.2)(2.6) = 57.72$ m². $\frac{x}{1.0}L = \frac{52.72\,m^2}{7.5\,m^2}$, so $x = \frac{52.72\,m^2}{7.5\,m^2} \approx 7.7$ L.

22. Sample answer: I assumed that the diameter of each baseball is 2.85 inches, that there will be 0.25 inches between each ball, and that the baseballs will be displayed in a 5, 4, 3, 2, 1 pyramid. The area of the regular triangle with side lengths 15.25 inches is 100.7 square inches.

23a. Sample answer:

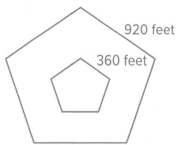

920 feet

360 feet

24. Sample answer: Every regular polygon can be broken down into isosceles triangles equal to the number of sides of the polygon. The height of each of those triangles will be the same and the base is equal to the side length of the polygon. So, to find the area of the polygon, add up the areas of each of the triangles. The formula, $A = \frac{1}{2}ap$, is related to the process of adding up the area of the triangles because the $\frac{1}{2}$ is the same in both, the apothem represents the heights of the triangles, and the perimeter is all the triangle bases added together.

Areas of Circles and Sectors

LESSON GOAL

Students find areas of circles and sectors by using the formulas they derive.

1 LAUNCH

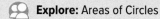 Launch the lesson with a **Warm Up** and an introduction.

2 EXPLORE AND DEVELOP

Explore: Areas of Circles

....

Develop:

Areas of Circles
- Area of a Circle
- Use the Area of a Circle to Find a Missing Measure

Areas of Sectors
- Area of a Sector
- Use the Area of a Sector to Find the Area of a Circle

....

You may want your students to complete the **Checks** online.

3 REFLECT AND PRACTICE

Exit Ticket

....

Practice

DIFFERENTIATE

 View reports of student progress on the **Checks** after each example.

Resources	AL	OL	BL	ELL
Remediation: Circles and Circumference	●	●		●
Extension: Circular Regions		●	●	●

Language Development Handbook

Assign page 76 of the *Language Development Handbook* to help your students build mathematical language related to finding the areas of circles and sectors.

ELL You can use the tips and suggestions on page T76 of the handbook to support students who are building English proficiency.

Reveal
GEOMETRY
Language Development Handbook

Suggested Pacing

90 min	0.5 day
45 min	1 day

Focus

Domain: Geometry

Standards for Mathematical Content:

G.C.5 Derive using similarity the fact that the length of the arc intercepted by an angle is proportional to the radius, and define the radian measure of the angle as the constant of proportionality; derive the formula for the area of a sector.

G.GMD.1 Give an informal argument for the formulas for the circumference of a circle, area of a circle, volume of a cylinder, pyramid, and cone.

Standards for Mathematical Practice:

1 Make sense of problems and persevere in solving them.

2 Reason abstractly and quantitatively.

5 Use appropriate tools strategically.

Coherence

Vertical Alignment

Previous
Students found areas of regular polygons.
7.G.6, G.MG.3

Now
Students find areas of circles and sectors.
G.C.5, G.GMD.1

Next
Students will find surface areas of three-dimensional figures.
G.MG.3

Rigor

The Three Pillars of Rigor

1 CONCEPTUAL UNDERSTANDING	2 FLUENCY	3 APPLICATION

Conceptual Bridge In this lesson, students extend their understanding of the area of parallelograms to the area of circles. They build fluency by finding areas of circles and sectors, and they apply their understanding by finding area of circles and sectors in the real world.

Interactive Presentation

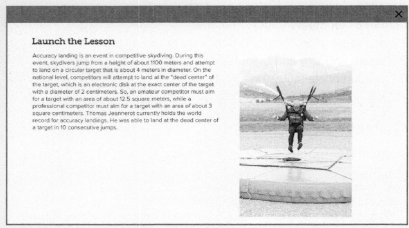

Warm Up

Answer each question.

1. A circle has a diameter of 12 inches. What is the circumference of the circle in terms of π?

2. A circle has a circumference of 15π feet. Find the length of its diameter.

3. The diameter of a circle is 25 meters. Find the length of an arc of the circle with a central angle of 180°. Round to the nearest foot.

4. A circle has a circumference of 312 centimeters. What is the length of an arc of this circle if the arc has a measure of 90°?

5. An arc of a circle has a length of 10 feet and a measure of 45°. What is the circumference of the circle?

Show Answers

Warm Up

Launch the Lesson

Accuracy landing is an event in competitive skydiving. During this event, skydivers jump from a height of about 1100 meters and attempt to land on a circular target that is about 4 meters in diameter. On the national level, competitors will attempt to land at the "dead center" of the target, which is an electronic disk at the exact center of the target with a diameter of 2 centimeters. So, an amateur competitor must aim for a target with an area of about 12.5 square meters, while a professional competitor must aim for a target with an area of about 3 square centimeters. Thomas Jeannerot currently holds the world record for accuracy landings. He was able to land at the dead center of a target in 10 consecutive jumps.

Launch the Lesson

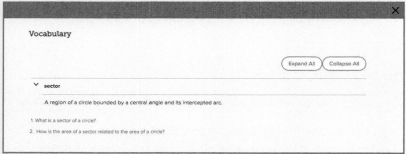

Vocabulary

Expand All   Collapse All

⌄ sector

A region of a circle bounded by a central angle and its intercepted arc.

1. What is a sector of a circle?
2. How is the area of a sector related to the area of a circle?

Today's Vocabulary

Warm Up

Prerequisite Skills

The Warm Up exercises address the following prerequisite skill for this lesson:

• calculating circumference and arc length

Answers:

1. 12π in.
2. 15 ft
3. 39 m
4. 78 cm
5. 80 ft

Launch the Lesson

MP **Teaching the Mathematical Practices**

> **4 Apply Mathematics** In this Launch the Lesson, students can see a real-world application of area of circles.

Go Online to find additional teaching notes and questions to promote classroom discourse.

Today's Standards

Tell students that they will be addressing these content and practice standards in this lesson. You may wish to have a student volunteer read aloud *How can I meet these standards?* and *How can I use these practices?* and connect these to the standards.

See the Interactive Presentation for I Can statements that align with the standards covered in this lesson.

Today's Vocabulary

Tell students that they will be using this vocabulary term in this lesson. You can expand the row if you wish to share the definition. Then, discuss the questions below with the class.

Mathematical Background

If a circle has an area A and a radius r, then $A = \pi r^2$. A sector of a circle is a region of a circle bounded by a central angle and its intercepted arc. If a sector of a circle has an area A, a central angle measuring $N°$, and a radius r, then $A = \frac{N}{360}\pi r^2$.

Explore Areas of Circles

Objective
Students use dynamic geometry software to discover the formula for the area of a circle.

Teaching the Mathematical Practices

5 Use Mathematical Tools Point out that to solve the problem in this Explore, students will need to use dynamic geometry software. Work with students to explore and deepen their understanding of the formula for the area of a circle.

Ideas for Use

Recommended Use Present the Inquiry Question, or have a student volunteer read it aloud. Have students work in pairs to complete the Explore activity on their devices. Pairs should discuss each of the questions. Monitor student progress during the activity. Upon completion of the Explore activity, have student volunteers share their responses to the Inquiry Question.

What if my students don't have devices? You may choose to project the activity on a whiteboard. A printable worksheet for each Explore is available online. You may choose to print the worksheet so that individuals or pairs of students can use it to record their observations.

Summary of the Activity

Students will complete guiding exercises throughout the Explore activity. Students begin by using a sketch to explore the relationship between the areas of regular polygons inscribed in a circle and the area of that circle. They compare the lengths of the radius and apothems and compare the perimeters and circumference. Students then complete guiding exercises on what happens as the number of sides increases. The students then use the formula for the area of a regular polygon to derive the formula for the area of a circle. Then, students will answer the Inquiry Question.

Go Online to find additional teaching notes and sample answers for the guiding exercises.

(continued on the next page)

Interactive Presentation

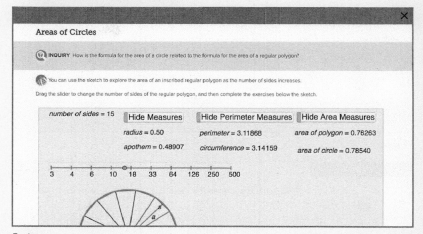

Explore

WEB SKETCHPAD

Students use a sketch to explore the areas of circles.

G.GMD.1

Interactive Presentation

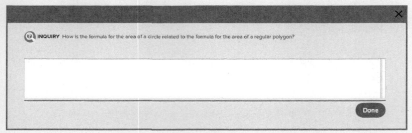

Explore

TYPE

a| Students respond to the Inquiry Question and can view a sample answer.

Explore Areas of Circles (*continued*)

MP Teaching the Mathematical Practices

3 Construct Arguments In the Explore, students will use stated assumptions, definitions, and previously established results to construct an argument.

Questions

Have students complete the Explore activity.

Ask:

- Why does the measure of the apothem approach the measure of the radius as the number of sides increases? Sample answer: The side lengths will decrease as the number of sides increases, so the distance between the apothem and radius gets closer. The closer these get, the more similar the measures become.

- Is the area of a circle more closely related to the area of a 20-gon or a 100-gon? Why? Sample answer: More closely related to the 100-gon, because there are more sides making it appear closer to a circle.

Inquiry

How is the formula for the area of a circle related to the formula of the area of a regular polygon? Sample answer: You can derive the formula for a circle by using the formula for the area of a regular polygon. The length of the apothem can be replaced with the length of the radius, and the measure of the perimeter of the polygon can be replaced with the measure of the circumference of the circle. By substituting the known formula for the circumference of a circle and simplifying, you can derive the formula for the area of a circle.

Go Online to find additional teaching notes and sample answers for the guiding exercises.

1 CONCEPTUAL UNDERSTANDING | **2 FLUENCY** | **3 APPLICATION**

Learn Areas of Circles

Objective
Students find areas of circles by using the formulas they derive.

Ⓜ️ Teaching the Mathematical Practices

2 Different Properties Mathematically proficient students look for different ways to solve problems. Encourage them to examine both ways to derive the formula for the area of a circle and to choose the derivation that makes the most sense for them.

Common Misconception
Students often think that π is just a symbol that needs to be included in answers dealing with circles. Remind them that π is a number approximately equal to 3.14159, and that an answer like 2π is a shorter way to write an exact number that is approximately equal to 6.28.

Ⓔ Essential Question Follow-Up
Students find areas of two-dimensional figures.
Ask:
Why is it important to be able to find the area of two-dimensional figures? Sample answer: Knowing the area of a two-dimensional figure is useful in many situations such as tiling a floor or shingling a roof.

🌐 Example 1 Area of a Circle

Ⓜ️ Teaching the Mathematical Practices

6 Use Precision In this example, students learn how to calculate accurately and efficiently and to express numerical answers with a degree of precision appropriate to the problem context.

Questions for Mathematical Discourse

AL If the radius is 10 feet, what is the area of the patio? about 314 ft^2

OL If the diameter is 25 feet, what is the area of the patio? about 491 ft^2

BL If you double the radius of the patio, what happens to the area? The area multiplies by 4.

🔵 Go Online

- Find additional teaching notes.
- View performance reports of the Checks.
- Assign or present an Extra Example.

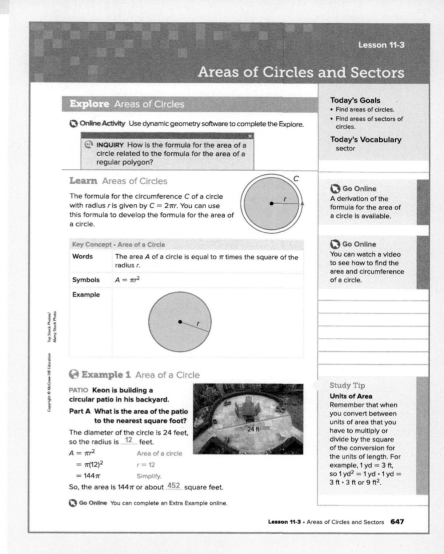

Lesson 11-3

Areas of Circles and Sectors

Explore Areas of Circles

🔵 **Online Activity** Use dynamic geometry software to complete the Explore.

❓ **INQUIRY** How is the formula for the area of a circle related to the formula for the area of a regular polygon?

Learn Areas of Circles

The formula for the circumference C of a circle with radius r is given by $C = 2\pi r$. You can use this formula to develop the formula for the area of a circle.

Key Concept · Area of a Circle

Words	The area A of a circle is equal to π times the square of the radius r.
Symbols	$A = \pi r^2$
Example	

🔵 **Example 1** Area of a Circle

PATIO Keon is building a circular patio in his backyard.

Part A What is the area of the patio to the nearest square foot?

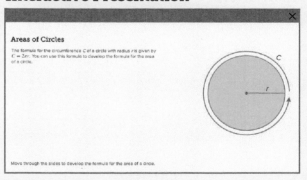

The diameter of the circle is 24 feet, so the radius is __12__ feet.

$A = \pi r^2$ Area of a circle
$= \pi(12)^2$ $r = 12$
$= 144\pi$ Simplify.

So, the area is 144π or about __452__ square feet.

🔵 **Go Online** You can complete an Extra Example online.

Today's Goals
- Find areas of circles.
- Find areas of sectors of circles.

Today's Vocabulary
sector

🔵 **Go Online**
A derivation of the formula for the area of a circle is available.

🔵 **Go Online**
You can watch a video to see how to find the area and circumference of a circle.

Study Tip
Units of Area
Remember that when you convert between units of area that you have to multiply or divide by the square of the conversion for the units of length. For example, 1 yd = 3 ft, so 1 yd^2 = 1 yd · 1 yd = 3 ft · 3 ft or 9 ft^2.

Interactive Presentation

Areas of Circles

The formula for the circumference C of a circle with radius r is given by $C = 2\pi r$. You can use this formula to develop the formula for the area of a circle.

Move through the slides to develop the formula for the area of a circle.

Learn

TAP

Students move through the slides to develop the formula for the area of a circle.

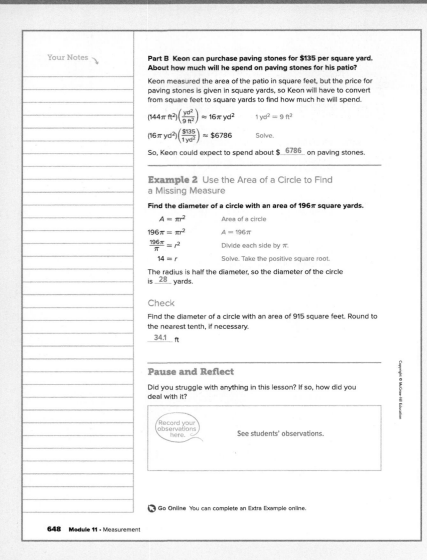

Example 2 Use the Area of a Circle to Find a Missing Measure

MP Teaching the Mathematical Practices

2 Attend to Quantities Point out that it is important to note the meaning of the quantities used in this problem.

Questions for Mathematical Discourse

AL The formula for area does not use the diameter, so how can we find it? The diameter is twice the radius, so find the radius and double it.

OL If the area of a circle is 755 square centimeters, what is the diameter of the circle? about 31 cm

BL The area of a circle is 144π square centimeters. If the radius of the circle is $x + 3$, what is the value of x? 9

Common Error

Students may stop once they have found the radius of the circle. Remind students that they should find the diameter.

Interactive Presentation

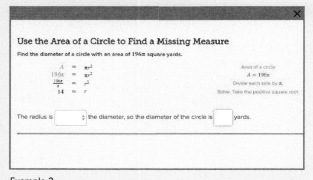

Example 2

TYPE

Students complete the calculations to find the diameter of a circle.

CHECK

Students complete the Check online to determine whether they are ready to move on.

1 CONCEPTUAL UNDERSTANDING | **2 FLUENCY** | **3 APPLICATION**

Learn Areas of Sectors

Objective
Students find areas of sectors of circles by using the formulas they derive.

 Teaching the Mathematical Practices

3 Construct Arguments In this Learn, students will use stated assumptions, definitions, and previously established results to construct an argument.

🌐 **Example 3** Area of a Sector

Teaching the Mathematical Practices

4 Apply Mathematics In this example, students apply what they have learned about sector area to solving a real-world problem.

Questions for Mathematical Discourse

AL What is a sector of a circle in your own words? Sample answer: It is an area that is made up of the area of a circle between two radii, like a slice of pie.

OL On a pie graph, a sector represents 20% of the graph. What is the central angle measure of the sector? 72°

BL The area of a sector of a circle with radius 8 inches is 68 square inches. What is the measure of the central angle of the sector? about 122°

Common Error
Students using a proportion rather than the formula to find the area of a sector may multiply by the inverse of the correct proportion. Guide them to use the formula or help them use the proportion correctly.

Learn Areas of Sectors

A **sector** is a region of a circle bounded by a central angle and its intercepted arc. The formula for the area of a sector is similar to the formula for arc length.

 Go Online
A derivation of the formula for the area of a sector is available.

Key Concept • Area of a Sector

The ratio of the area A of a sector to the area of the whole circle πr^2, is equal to the ratio of the degree measure of the intercepted arc x to 360°.

Proportion: $\frac{A}{\pi r^2} = \frac{x°}{360°}$

Equation: $A = \frac{x°}{360°} \cdot \pi r^2$

 Go Online
You can watch a video to see how to find the area of a sector of a circle.

🌐 **Example 3** Area of a Sector

GAMES Malaya is playing a game where she must track her progress using sectors of a circle and a circular game piece. The game piece has a diameter of 3.5 centimeters and is divided into 6 congruent sectors. What is the area of one sector to the nearest hundredth?

Step 1 Find the arc measure.

Because the game piece is equally divided into 6 pieces, each piece will have an arc measure of 360 ÷ __6__ = 60°.

Step 2 Find the area.

$A = \frac{x°}{360°} \cdot \pi r^2$ Area of a sector

$= \frac{60°}{360°} \cdot \pi(1.75)^2$ $x = 60$ and $r = 1.75$

$\approx$ __1.60__   Solve.

So, the area of one sector of this game piece is about 1.60 square centimeters.

Check

ART Jorrie is crafting a wall clock using paint and a set of battery-operated clock hands. The clock will have a diameter of 3 feet. What is the area of each sector to the nearest hundredth?

$A =$ __0.59__ ft²

💡 **Think About It!**
What assumptions did you make?

Sample answer: I assumed that the dividers and the outside wall of the game piece did not contribute to the area of the circle. I assumed that each sector was congruent and that the sum of the areas of the 6 sectors created the total area of the game piece.

🌐 **Go Online** You can complete an Extra Example online.

Interactive Presentation

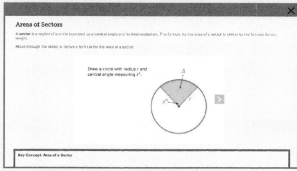

Areas of Sectors

A sector is a region of a circle bounded by a central angle and its intercepted arc. The formula for the area of a sector is similar to the formula for arc length.

Move through the slides to derive a formula for the area of a sector.

Draw a circle with radius r and central angle measuring $x°$.

Key Concept: Area of a Sector

Learn

TAP
Students move through the slides to derive a formula for the area of a sector.

TYPE
Students answer a question to show they understand how to find the area of a sector.

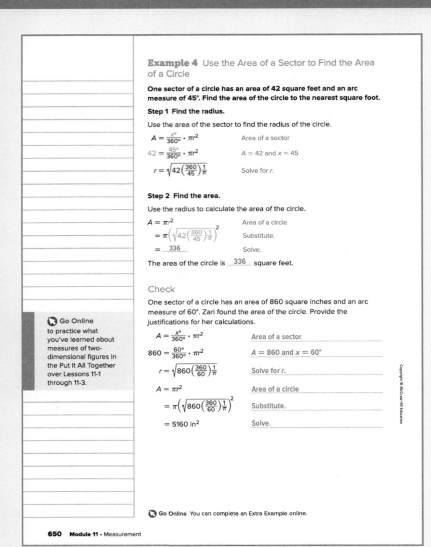

Example 4 Use the Area of a Sector to Find the Area of a Circle

One sector of a circle has an area of 42 square feet and an arc measure of 45°. Find the area of the circle to the nearest square foot.

Step 1 Find the radius.

Use the area of the sector to find the radius of the circle.

$$A = \frac{x°}{360°} \cdot \pi r^2 \qquad \text{Area of a sector}$$

$$42 = \frac{45°}{360°} \cdot \pi r^2 \qquad A = 42 \text{ and } x = 45$$

$$r = \sqrt{42\left(\frac{360}{45}\right)\frac{1}{\pi}} \qquad \text{Solve for } r.$$

Step 2 Find the area.

Use the radius to calculate the area of the circle.

$$A = \pi r^2 \qquad \text{Area of a circle}$$

$$= \pi\left(\sqrt{42\left(\frac{360}{45}\right)\frac{1}{\pi}}\right)^2 \qquad \text{Substitute.}$$

$$= \underline{\ 336\ } \qquad \text{Solve.}$$

The area of the circle is ___336___ square feet.

Check

One sector of a circle has an area of 860 square inches and an arc measure of 60°. Zari found the area of the circle. Provide the justifications for her calculations.

$$A = \frac{x°}{360°} \cdot \pi r^2 \qquad \underline{\text{Area of a sector}}$$

$$860 = \frac{60°}{360°} \cdot \pi r^2 \qquad \underline{A = 860 \text{ and } x = 60°}$$

$$r = \sqrt{860\left(\frac{360}{60}\right)\frac{1}{\pi}} \qquad \underline{\text{Solve for } r.}$$

$$A = \pi r^2 \qquad \underline{\text{Area of a circle}}$$

$$= \pi\left(\sqrt{860\left(\frac{360}{60}\right)\frac{1}{\pi}}\right)^2 \qquad \underline{\text{Substitute.}}$$

$$= 5160 \text{ in}^2 \qquad \underline{\text{Solve.}}$$

🔵 **Go Online** to practice what you've learned about measures of two-dimensional figures in the Put It All Together over Lessons 11-1 through 11-3.

🔵 **Go Online** You can complete an Extra Example online.

Example 4 Use the Area of a Sector to Find the Area of a Circle

Ⓜ️ Teaching the Mathematical Practices

6 Use Precision In this example, students learn how to calculate accurately and efficiently and to express numerical answers with a degree of precision appropriate to the problem context.

Questions for Mathematical Discourse

AL If you know the area of a sector, how can you find the area of its circle? Sample answer: Substitute the area of the sector into the proportion and solve for the total area.

OL What fraction of the circle contains a central angle of 45°? $\frac{1}{8}$

BL How would the answer change if the arc measure was 60°? Sample answer: The fraction would become $\frac{60°}{360°}$, which makes the area 252 square feet.

DIFFERENTIATE

Language Development Activity AL BL ELL

Have students discuss how the area of a sector relates to the area of the entire circle. Have them write how the formula of a sector logically represents a portion of the circle.

Exit Ticket

Recommended Use

At the end of class, go online to display the Exit Ticket prompt and ask students to respond using a separate piece of paper. Have students hand you their responses as they leave the room.

Alternate Use

At the end of class, go online to display the Exit Ticket prompt and ask students to respond verbally or by using a mini-whiteboard. Have students hold up their whiteboards so that you can see all student responses. Tap to reveal the answer when most or all students have completed the Exit Ticket.

Interactive Presentation

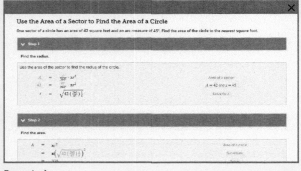

Example 4

TAP

Students tap to reveal steps in the solution.

CHECK

Students complete the Check online to determine whether they are ready to move on.

Practice and Homework

Suggested Assignments

Use the table below to select appropriate exercises.

DOK	Topic	Exercises
1, 2	exercises that mirror the examples	1–22
2	exercises that use a variety of skills from this lesson	23–30
2	exercises that extend concepts learned in this lesson to new contexts	31
3	exercises that emphasize higher-order and critical-thinking skills	32–37

ASSESS AND DIFFERENTIATE

📊 Use the data from the **Checks** to determine whether to provide resources for extension, remediation, or intervention.

IF students score 90% or more on the Checks, **BL**
THEN assign:

- Practice, Exercises 1–31 odd, 32–37
- Extension: Circular Regions
- 🅐 **ALEKS** Circumferences and Areas of Circles

IF students score 66%–89% on the Checks, **OL**
THEN assign:

- Practice, Exercises 1–37 odd
- Remediation, Review Resources: Circles and Circumference
- Personal Tutors
- Extra Examples 1–4
- 🅐 **ALEKS** Circumferences and Areas of Circles; Segments in a Circle and Tangent Lines

IF students score 65% or less on the Checks, **AL**
THEN assign:

- Practice, Exercises 1–21 odd
- Remediation, Review Resources: Circles and Circumference
- *Quick Review Math Handbook:* Areas of Circles and Sectors
- 🅐 **ALEKS** Circumferences and Areas of Circles; Segments in a Circle and Tangent Lines

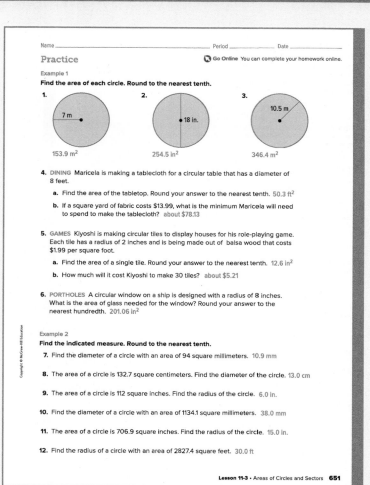

Name _____ Period _____ Date _____

Practice 🔵 **Go Online** You can complete your homework online.

Example 1

Find the area of each circle. Round to the nearest tenth.

1. 7 m
153.9 m²

2. 18 in.
254.5 in²

3. 10.5 m
346.4 m²

4. **DINING** Maricela is making a tablecloth for a circular table that has a diameter of 8 feet.
   a. Find the area of the tabletop. Round your answer to the nearest tenth. 50.3 ft²
   b. If a square yard of fabric costs $13.99, what is the minimum Maricela will need to spend to make the tablecloth? about $78.13

5. **GAMES** Kiyoshi is making circular tiles to display houses for his role-playing game. Each tile has a radius of 2 inches and is being made out of balsa wood that costs $1.99 per square foot.
   a. Find the area of a single tile. Round your answer to the nearest tenth. 12.6 in²
   b. How much will it cost Kiyoshi to make 30 tiles? about $5.21

6. **PORTHOLES** A circular window on a ship is designed with a radius of 8 inches. What is the area of glass needed for the window? Round your answer to the nearest hundredth. 201.06 in²

Example 2

Find the indicated measure. Round to the nearest tenth.

7. Find the diameter of a circle with an area of 94 square millimeters. 10.9 mm

8. The area of a circle is 132.7 square centimeters. Find the diameter of the circle. 13.0 cm

9. The area of a circle is 112 square inches. Find the radius of the circle. 6.0 in.

10. Find the diameter of a circle with an area of 1134.1 square millimeters. 38.0 mm

11. The area of a circle is 706.9 square inches. Find the radius of the circle. 15.0 in.

12. Find the radius of a circle with an area of 2827.4 square feet. 30.0 ft

Lesson 11-3 • Areas of Circles and Sectors **651**

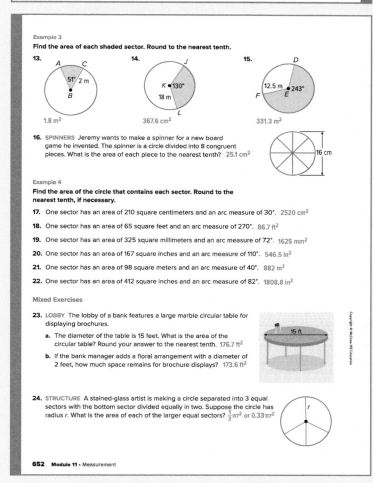

Example 3

Find the area of each shaded sector. Round to the nearest tenth.

13. A C 51° 2 m B
1.8 m²

14. J K ●130° 18 m L
367.6 cm²

15. D 12.5 m 243° F E
331.3 m²

16. **SPINNERS** Jeremy wants to make a spinner for a new board game he invented. The spinner is a circle divided into 8 congruent pieces. What is the area of each piece to the nearest tenth? 25.1 cm²
16 cm

Example 4

Find the area of the circle that contains each sector. Round to the nearest tenth, if necessary.

17. One sector has an area of 210 square centimeters and an arc measure of 30°. 2520 cm²

18. One sector has an area of 65 square feet and an arc measure of 270°. 86.7 ft²

19. One sector has an area of 325 square millimeters and an arc measure of 72°. 1625 mm²

20. One sector has an area of 167 square inches and an arc measure of 110°. 546.5 in²

21. One sector has an area of 98 square meters and an arc measure of 40°. 882 m²

22. One sector has an area of 412 square inches and an arc measure of 82°. 1808.8 in²

Mixed Exercises

23. **LOBBY** The lobby of a bank features a large marble circular table for displaying brochures.
    a. The diameter of the table is 15 feet. What is the area of the circular table? Round your answer to the nearest tenth. 176.7 ft²
    b. If the bank manager adds a floral arrangement with a diameter of 2 feet, how much space remains for brochure displays? 173.6 ft²
15 ft

24. **STRUCTURE** A stained-glass artist is making a circle separated into 3 equal sectors with the bottom sector divided equally in two. Suppose the circle has radius r. What is the area of each of the larger equal sectors? $\frac{1}{3}\pi r^2$ or $0.33\pi r^2$
r

652 Module 11 • Measurement

Name _____ Period _____ Date _____

25. SOUP CAN Jaclynn needs to cover the top and bottom of a can of soup with construction paper to include in her art project. Each circle has a diameter of 7.5 centimeters. What is the total area of the can that Jaclynn must cover? **88.4 cm²**

26. POOL A circular pool is surrounded by a circular sidewalk. The circular sidewalk is 3 feet wide. The diameter of the sidewalk and the pool is 26 feet.

a. What is the diameter of the pool? **20 ft**

b. What is the area of the sidewalk and the pool? **169π ≈ 530.9 ft²**

c. What is the area of the pool? **100π ≈ 314.2 ft²**

27. REASONING Explain how to find the area of the shaded region. Then find the area of the shaded region. Round to the nearest tenth, if necessary. **See margin.**

28. REGULARITY A sector of a circle has an area A and a central angle that measures $x°$. Explain how you can find the area of the whole circle. Multiply the area of the sector by $\frac{360}{x}$. The area of the circle is $\frac{360A}{x}$.

29. PIE One sector of an apple pie has an area of 8 square inches and an arc measure of 45°. Find the area of the pie. **64 in²**

30. USE ESTIMATION A lawn sprinkler sprays water in an arc as shown in the picture. The area of the sector covered by the spray is approximately 235.6 square feet.

a. Estimate the area of the yard that can be covered by the sprinkler if the sprinkler is set to water a complete circle. **690 ft²**

b. Find the exact area covered by the sprinkler. **706.8 ft²**

c. Is your answer reasonable? Justify your argument. **Yes; sample answer: Because my estimate is close to the exact area covered, my answer is reasonable.**

---

31. PRECISION Luciano wants to use sectors of different circles as part of a mural he is painting. The specifications for each sector are shown.

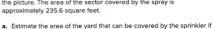

Red: radius: 14 ft, central angle: 60°
Purple: radius: 12 ft, central angle: 75°
Green: radius: 18 ft, central angle: 30°

a. Find the area of each sector to the nearest tenth.
red: 102.6 ft², purple: 94.2 ft², green: 84.8 ft²

b. Was the sector with the largest area the one with the longest radius? Was it the one with the largest central angle? What can you conclude from this? The largest sector was neither the one with the largest radius nor the one with the largest central angle. We can conclude that *both* factors affect the area of the sector.

c. Luciano plans to paint 235 stars on each of the purple sectors and 153 stars on each of the green sectors. To the nearest tenth, how many stars are there per square foot for sectors of each color? purple: 2.5 stars per square foot; green: 1.8 stars per square foot

d. Luciano also plans to paint stars on the red sectors. He wants there to be twice as many stars per square foot in the red sectors as there are in the green sectors. How many stars should he paint on each red sector? Round to the nearest whole star. 2 × 1.8 = 3.6; 3.6(area of the red sector) ≈ 370 stars

Higher-Order Thinking Skills

32. FIND THE ERROR Ketria and Colton want to find the area of a shaded region in the circle shown. Who is correct? Explain your reasoning. Colton; sample answer: Ketria used the diameter in the area formula instead of the radius.

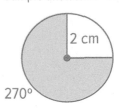

Ketria	Colton
$A = \frac{x}{360} \cdot \pi r^2$	$A = \frac{x}{360} \cdot \pi r^2$
$= \frac{58}{360} \cdot \pi(8)^2$	$= \frac{58}{360} \cdot \pi(4)^2$
$= 32.4\ in^2$	$= 8.1\ in^2$

33. PERSEVERE Find the area of the shaded region. Round to the nearest tenth. **30.1 cm²**

34. ANALYZE A **segment of a circle** is the region bounded by an arc and a chord. Is the area of a sector of a circle *sometimes*, *always*, or *never* greater than the area of its corresponding segment? Justify your argument. Sometimes; when the arc is a semicircle, the areas are the same.

35. WRITE Describe two methods you could use to find the area of the shaded region of the circle. Which method do you think is more efficient? Explain your reasoning. **See margin.**

36. PERSEVERE Derive the formula for the area of a sector of a circle using the formula for arc length. **See margin.**

37. CREATE Draw a circle with a shaded sector. Label the length of the radius and the measure of the arc intercepted by the sector. Then find the area of the shaded sector. **See margin.**

Answers

27. Sample answer: The area of the circle is 36π. The area of the hexagon is $A = \frac{1}{2}aP$. Because a regular hexagon can be divided into six equilateral triangles, use the 30°-60°-90° triangle ratios to find a and the length of one side of the hexagon. So, $a = 3\sqrt{3}$ in., each side is 6 in., and $P = 36$ in. By substitution, the area of the hexagon is 93.5 in². The area of the shaded region is $36\pi - 93.5 \approx 19.6$ in².

35. Sample answer: You can find the shaded area of the circle by subtracting x from 360° and using the resulting measure in the formula for the area of a sector. You could also find the shaded area by finding the area of the entire circle, finding the area of the unshaded sector using the formula for the area of a sector, and subtracting the area of the unshaded sector from the area of the entire circle. The first method is more efficient. It requires less steps, is faster, and there is a lower probability for error.

36. The ratio of the area of a sector to the area of a whole circle is equal to the ratio of the corresponding arc length to the circumference of the circle. Let A represent the area of the sector.

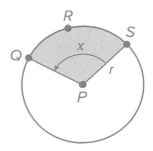

$$\frac{\text{area of sector}}{\text{area of circle}} = \frac{\text{arc length}}{\text{circumference}}$$

$$\frac{A}{\pi r^2} = \frac{\text{length of arc } QRS}{2\pi r}$$

$$\frac{A}{\pi r^2} = \frac{\frac{\pi r x}{180}}{2\pi r}$$

$$A = \frac{\frac{\pi r x}{180}}{2\pi r} \cdot \pi r^2$$

$$A = \frac{\frac{\pi r x}{180}}{2} \cdot r$$

$$A = \frac{\pi r x}{360} \cdot r$$

$$A = \frac{\pi r^2 x}{360}$$

37. Sample answer: $A \approx 9.42$ cm²

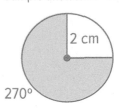

Surface Area

LESSON GOAL

Students find surface areas of prisms, cylinders, pyramids, cones, and spheres and composites of these shapes using the formulas they derive.

1 LAUNCH

 Launch the lesson with a **Warm Up** and an introduction.

2 EXPLORE AND DEVELOP

 Develop:

Surface Areas of Prisms and Cylinders
- Lateral Area and Surface Area of a Prism
- Lateral Area and Surface Area of a Cylinder
- Approximate Surface Areas of Prisms and Cylinders (online only)

 Explore: Cone Patterns

 Develop:

Surface Areas of Pyramids and Cones
- Lateral Area and Surface Area of a Regular Pyramid
- Lateral Area and Surface Area of a Right Cone
- Approximate Surface Areas of Pyramids and Cones

Surface Areas of Spheres
- Surface Area of a Sphere
- Use Formulas to Find the Surface Area of a Sphere
- Surface Area of a Composite Solid

 You may want your students to complete the **Checks** online.

3 REFLECT AND PRACTICE

 Exit Ticket

 Practice

DIFFERENTIATE

 View reports of student progress on the **Checks** after each example.

Resources	AL	OL	BL	ELL
Remediation: Area of Circles	●	●		●
Extension: Minimizing Cost in Manufacturing		●	●	●

Language Development Handbook

Assign page 77 of the *Language Development Handbook* to help your students build mathematical language related to finding surface areas.

ELL You can use the tips and suggestions on page T77 of the handbook to support students who are building English proficiency.

Suggested Pacing

| 90 min | **1.5 days** |
| 45 min | **3 days** |

Focus

Domain: Geometry
Standards for Mathematical Content:
G.MG.3 Apply geometric methods to solve design problems.
Standards for Mathematical Practice:
1 Make sense of problems and persevere in solving them.
4 Model with mathematics.

Coherence

Vertical Alignment

Previous
Students found areas of circles and sectors.
7.G.4, G.C.5, G.GMD.1

Now
Students find surface areas of three-dimensional figures.
G.MG.3

Next
Students will determine cross sections of three-dimensional figures.
G.GMD.4

Rigor

The Three Pillars of Rigor

1 CONCEPTUAL UNDERSTANDING	2 FLUENCY	3 APPLICATION

Conceptual Bridge In this lesson, students extend their understanding of area to surface area. They apply their understanding by using geometric models to find surface areas of real-world objects.

Mathematical Background

The bases of a prism are congruent faces in parallel planes. The surface area is the lateral area plus the area of the bases. A cylinder is a solid with bases that are congruent circles that lie in parallel planes. A cylinder has surface area $S = 2\pi rh + 2\pi r^2$.

A pyramid is a solid with lateral faces that intersect at one point called the vertex and are triangles. The surface area is given by $S = \frac{1}{2}P\ell + B$, where B is the area and P is the perimeter of the base and ℓ is the slant height. A cone is a solid that tapers from a circular base to a point and has surface area $S = \pi r\ell + \pi r^2$.

Interactive Presentation

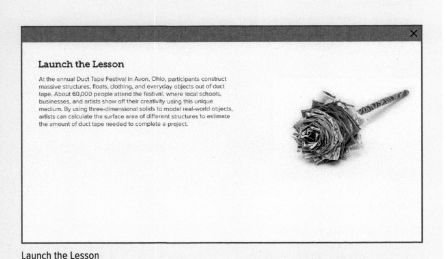

Warm Up

Answer each question.

1. What is the area of a square with a side length of 12 inches?

2. A rectangle has a length of 10 feet and an area of 330 square feet. What is the width of the rectangle?

3. A circle has a diameter of 12 meters. A square has a side length of 12 meters. Which has the greater area?

4. A circle has an area of 12 square feet. What is the area of half of the circle?

5. A circle has a diameter of 30 centimeters. What is the circumference of the circle to the nearest tenth?

Show Answers

Warm Up

Launch the Lesson

At the annual Duct Tape Festival in Avon, Ohio, participants construct massive structures, floats, clothing, and everyday objects out of duct tape. About 60,000 people attend the festival, where local schools, businesses, and artists show off their creativity using this unique medium. By using three-dimensional solids to model real-world objects, artists can calculate the surface area of different structures to estimate the amount of duct tape needed to complete a project.

Launch the Lesson

Vocabulary

Expand All   Collapse All

> lateral faces

> lateral edges

> base edge

> height of a solid

> composite solid

1. What is the difference between the area and the *surface area* of a geometric figure?

2. What is the shape of each face of a cylinder? a square pyramid?

3. How does knowing the parts of polyhedron help you find the *surface area*?

4. What steps might you follow to find the volume of a composite solid?

Today's Vocabulary

Warm Up

Prerequisite Skills

The Warm Up exercises address the following prerequisite skill for this lesson:

- finding areas

Answers:

1. 144 in²
2. 33 ft
3. square
4. 6 ft²
5. 94.2 cm

Launch the Lesson

MP **Teaching the Mathematical Practices**

> **4 Apply Mathematics** In this Launch the Lesson, students can see a real-world object whose surface area can be calculated by modeling with three-dimensional solids.

Go Online to find additional teaching notes and questions to promote classroom discourse.

Today's Standards

Tell students that they will be addressing these content and practice standards in this lesson. You may wish to have a student volunteer read aloud *How can I meet these standards?* and *How can I use these practices?* and connect these to the standards.

See the Interactive Presentation for I Can statements that align with the standards covered in this lesson.

Today's Vocabulary

Tell students that they will be using these vocabulary terms in this lesson. You can expand each row if you wish to share the definitions. Then, discuss the questions below with the class.

Explore Cone Patterns

Objective
Students use manipulatives to explore the surface area of a cone.

 Teaching the Mathematical Practices

3 Reason Inductively In this Explore, students will use inductive reasoning to make plausible arguments.

Ideas for Use

Recommended Use Present the Inquiry Question, or have a student volunteer read it aloud. Have students work in pairs to complete the Explore activity on their devices. Pairs should discuss each of the questions. Monitor student progress during the activity. Upon completion of the Explore activity, have student volunteers share their responses to the Inquiry Question.

What if my students don't have devices? You may choose to project the activity on a whiteboard. A printable worksheet for each Explore is available online. You may choose to print the worksheet so that individuals or pairs of students can use it to record their observations.

Summary of the Activity
Students will complete guiding exercises throughout the Explore activity. Students begin by drawing a sector of a circle. Students then answer some questions about the measurements of the whole circle and the sector. Next, students cut out and tape the sector into a cone without a base. Students answer guiding exercises about the measurements of this cone. Then students answer more guiding exercises leading them to derive a formula for the surface area of a cone. Then, students will answer the Inquiry Question.

🔘 **Go Online** to find additional teaching notes and sample answers for the guiding exercises.

(continued on the next page)

Interactive Presentation

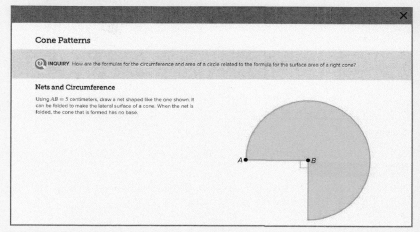

Cone Patterns

🔍 **INQUIRY** How are the formulas for the circumference and area of a circle related to the formula for the surface area of a right cone?

Nets and Circumference

Using $AB = 5$ centimeters, draw a net shaped like the one shown. It can be folded to make the lateral surface of a cone. When the net is folded, the cone that is formed has no base.

Explore

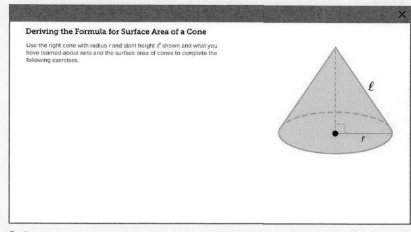

Deriving the Formula for Surface Area of a Cone

Use the right cone with radius r and slant height ℓ shown and what you have learned about nets and the surface area of cones to complete the following exercises.

Explore

TYPE

Students answer the questions to show they understand cone patterns.

Interactive Presentation

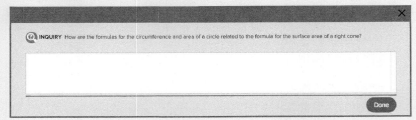

Explore

Explore Cone Patterns (*continued*)

 Teaching the Mathematical Practices

2 Represent a Situation Symbolically Guide students to define variables to solve the problem in this Explore. Help students to identify the independent and dependent variables. Then work with them to find the other relationships in the problem.

DRAG

Students drag terms and expressions to their correct locations in diagrams and formulas.

TYPE

a|

Students respond to the Inquiry Question and can view a sample answer.

Questions

Have students complete the Explore activity.

Ask:

- Explain why the net of the lateral area of a cone is a circle with a missing section. Sample answer: In order to fold the net into a shape that has a vertex and a circle for the base, it makes sense that you would use part of a circle.

- If you know the radius and height of a cone, can you find the total surface area? Sample answer: Yes, but you must first find the slant height using the Pythagorean Theorem. Then you can substitute all values into the formula.

Inquiry

How are the formulas for the circumference and area of a circle related to the formula for the surface area of a right cone? Sample answer: You can use the formulas for the area and circumference of a circle to develop a formula for the lateral area of a cone. Then, the total surface area is equal to the sum of the lateral area and the area of the circular base.

Go Online to find additional teaching notes and sample answers for the guiding exercises.

1 CONCEPTUAL UNDERSTANDING | 2 FLUENCY | 3 APPLICATION

Learn Surface Areas of Prisms and Cylinders

Objective
Students find surface areas of prisms and cylinders by using the formulas they derive.

 Teaching the Mathematical Practices

> **7 Use Structure** Help students to explore the structure of prisms in this Learn.

Things to Remember
The lateral faces of all prisms are parallelograms. Sometimes, as in right prisms, those parallelograms will also be rectangles, but this is not always the case. In right prisms, all lateral faces have the same height as the prism. In oblique prisms, different lateral faces may have heights that are different from each other and different from the height of the prism.

Go Online

- Find additional teaching notes.
- View performance reports of the Checks.
- Assign or present an Extra Example.

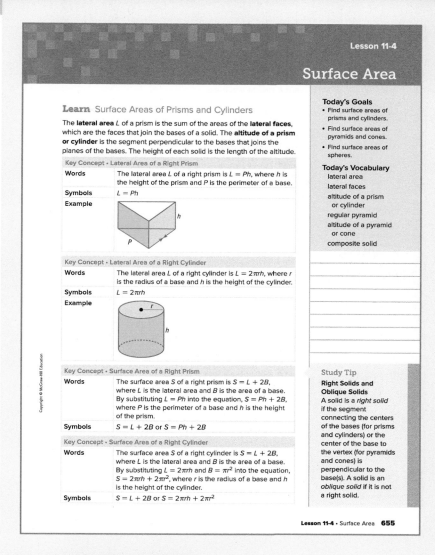

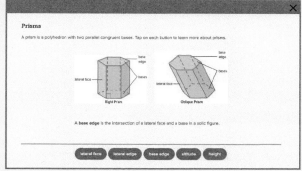

Learn

TAP

 Students tap to reveal information about prisms and cylinders.

1 CONCEPTUAL UNDERSTANDING | **2 FLUENCY** | 3 APPLICATION

Left Panel (Student Notes)

Your Notes

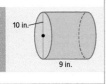

Example 1 Lateral Area and Surface Area of a Prism

Find the lateral area and surface area of the prism. Round to the nearest tenth, if necessary.

Part A Find the lateral area.

$L = Ph$ Lateral area of a prism

$= (8 \times 6)11$ The base has 8 sides.

$= 528$ Solve.

So, the lateral area of the prism is 528 square inches.

Part B Find the surface area.

Step 1 Find the area of the base. A central angle of the octagon is $\frac{360°}{8}$ or $\underline{45}$°, so the angle formed in the triangle is 22.5°.

$\tan 22.5° = \frac{3}{a}$ Write a trigonometric ratio to find a.

$a = \frac{3}{\tan 22.5°}$ Solve for a.

$A = \frac{1}{2}Pa$ Area of a regular polygon.

$\approx \frac{1}{2}(48)\left(\frac{3}{\tan 22.5}\right)$ $P = 48$ and $a = \frac{3}{\tan 22.5}$

$\approx \underline{173.8}$ Multiply.

So, the area of the base B is approximately $\underline{173.8}$ square inches.

Step 2 Find the surface area of the prism.

$S = L + 2B$ Surface area of a right prism

$\approx 528 + 2(173.8)$ $L = 528$ and $B \approx 173.8$

≈ 875.6 Simplify.

The surface area of the prism is about $\underline{875.6}$ square inches.

Example 2 Lateral Area and Surface Area of a Cylinder

Find the lateral area and surface area of the cylinder. Round to the nearest tenth.

Part A Find the lateral area.

$L = 2\pi rh$ Lateral area of a cylinder

$= 2\pi(5)(9)$ Substitution

$\approx \underline{282.7}$ Solve.

So, the lateral area of the cylinder is 282.7 square inches.

Part B Find the surface area.

$S = 2\pi rh + 2\pi r^2$ Surface area of a cylinder

$\approx 282.7 + 2\pi(5)^2$ Substitute.

≈ 439.8 Solve.

The surface area of the cylinder is about $\underline{439.8}$ square inches.

Problem-Solving Tip

Use Your Skills To find the lateral area or surface area of a solid, you may have to use other skills to find missing measures. Remember that you can use trigonometric ratios or the Pythagorean Theorem to solve for missing measures in right triangles.

Go Online You can complete an Extra Example online.

 Go Online to see Example 3.

656 Module 11 · Measurement

Interactive Presentation

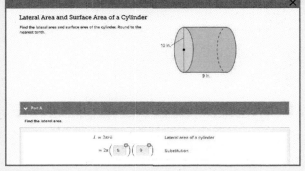

Lateral Area and Surface Area of a Cylinder

Find the lateral area and surface area of the cylinder. Round to the nearest tenth.

Part A

Find the lateral area.

$L = 2\pi rh$ Lateral area of a cylinder

$= 2\pi\left(\boxed{5}\right)\left(\boxed{9}\right)$ Substitution

Example 2

TAP

Students tap to reveal the steps of a solution.

CHECK

Students complete the Check online to determine whether they are ready to move on.

Right Panel

Example 1 Lateral Area and Surface Area of a Prism

MP Teaching the Mathematical Practices

4 Use Tools Point out that to solve the problem in this example, students will need to use the formulas for lateral area and surface area of a prism.

Questions for Mathematical Discourse

AL If the height of the prism is decreased to 5 in., what is the lateral surface area of the prism? 240 in²

OL If the base was a regular hexagon with the same side length, what is the lateral surface area of the prism? 396 in²

BL If the height of the prism is changed and the new lateral surface area is 552 in², what is the new height? 11.5 in.

Example 2 Lateral Area and Surface Area of a Cylinder

MP Teaching the Mathematical Practices

6 Use Precision Students must calculate accurately and efficiently and express numerical answers with a degree of precision appropriate to the problem context.

Questions for Mathematical Discourse

AL What is the shape of the lateral area of a cylinder? a rectangle

OL If the diameter of the cylinder is 20 in., what are the new lateral and surface areas? 565.5 in²; 1193.8 in²

BL If the diameter of the cylinder is changed and the new lateral area is 424 in², what is the new diameter? about 15 in.

Common Error

Students may forget to multiply the area of the base by 2 in order to obtain the surface area. Remind them that there are two bases, and they need to include both.

1 CONCEPTUAL UNDERSTANDING | **2 FLUENCY** | 3 APPLICATION

Learn Surface Areas of Pyramids and Cones

Objective
Students find surface areas of pyramids and cones by using the formulas they derive.

MP Teaching the Mathematical Practices

7 Use Structure Help students to explore the structure of pyramids in this Learn.

Common Misconception
Students may confuse the height of a prism or a cone with the slant height of a lateral face. Remind them to be careful with the two terms as both use the word "height."

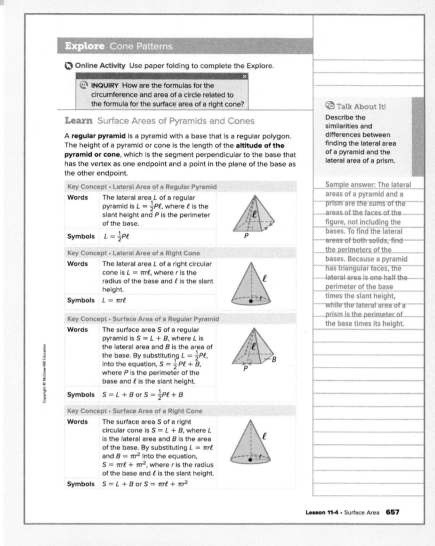

Explore Cone Patterns

Online Activity Use paper folding to complete the Explore.

INQUIRY How are the formulas for the circumference and area of a circle related to the formula for the surface area of a right cone?

Learn Surface Areas of Pyramids and Cones

A **regular pyramid** is a pyramid with a base that is a regular polygon. The height of a pyramid or cone is the length of the **altitude of the pyramid or cone**, which is the segment perpendicular to the base that has the vertex as one endpoint and a point in the plane of the base as the other endpoint.

Key Concept · Lateral Area of a Regular Pyramid

| Words | The lateral area L of a regular pyramid is $L = \frac{1}{2}P\ell$, where ℓ is the slant height and P is the perimeter of the base. |

Symbols $L = \frac{1}{2}P\ell$

Key Concept · Lateral Area of a Right Cone

| Words | The lateral area L of a right circular cone is $L = \pi r\ell$, where r is the radius of the base and ℓ is the slant height. |

Symbols $L = \pi r\ell$

Key Concept · Surface Area of a Regular Pyramid

| Words | The surface area S of a regular pyramid is $S = L + B$, where L is the lateral area and B is the area of the base. By substituting $L = \frac{1}{2}P\ell$, into the equation, $S = \frac{1}{2}P\ell + B$, where P is the perimeter of the base and ℓ is the slant height. |

Symbols $S = L + B$ or $S = \frac{1}{2}P\ell + B$

Key Concept · Surface Area of a Right Cone

| Words | The surface area S of a right circular cone is $S = L + B$, where L is the lateral area and B is the area of the base. By substituting $L = \pi r\ell$ and $B = \pi r^2$ into the equation, $S = \pi r\ell + \pi r^2$, where r is the radius of the base and ℓ is the slant height. |

Symbols $S = L + B$ or $S = \pi r\ell + \pi r^2$

Lesson 11-4 · Surface Area **657**

Talk About It!
Describe the similarities and differences between finding the lateral area of a pyramid and the lateral area of a prism.

Sample answer: The lateral areas of a pyramid and a prism are the sums of the areas of the faces of the figure, not including the bases. To find the lateral areas of both solids, find the perimeters of the bases. Because a pyramid has triangular faces, the lateral area is one half the perimeter of the base times the slant height, while the lateral area of a prism is the perimeter of the base times its height.

Interactive Presentation

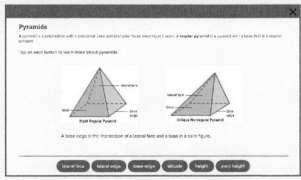

Pyramids

A pyramid is a polyhedron with a polygonal base and triangular faces meeting at a point. A regular pyramid is a pyramid with a base that is a regular polygon.

Tap on each button to learn more about pyramids.

A base edge is the intersection of a lateral face and a base in a solid figure.

lateral face | lateral edge | base edge | altitude | height | slant height

Learn

TAP

Students tap to reveal information about pyramids and cones.

DIFFERENTIATE

Language Development Activity ELL

Beginning Before reading the lesson, use images or objects to introduce regular pyramids, right cones, and oblique cones. Have students repeat each term and point to the visual representation as you review the vocabulary.

Intermediate Have partners make and use flashcards to check each other's pronunciation and understanding of each term.

Advanced Have students scan the lesson for content vocabulary words in context. Help them pronounce the vocabulary words correctly. Discuss vocabulary meanings with them.

Advanced High Allow students to use a search engine to find images of regular pyramids, right cones, and oblique cones. Have pairs of students choose a representative image for each term to share with the class. Ask them to explain why their image represents the term.

1 CONCEPTUAL UNDERSTANDING   **2 FLUENCY**   3 APPLICATION

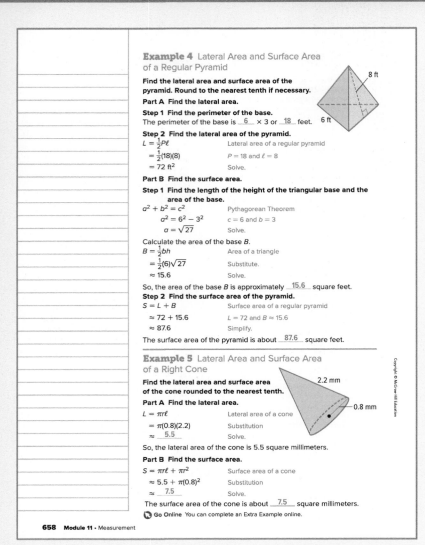

Example 4 Lateral Area and Surface Area
of a Regular Pyramid

Find the lateral area and surface area of the
pyramid. Round to the nearest tenth if necessary.

Part A Find the lateral area.

Step 1 Find the perimeter of the base.
The perimeter of the base is __6__ × 3 or __18__ feet.

Step 2 Find the lateral area of the pyramid.

$L = \frac{1}{2}P\ell$ Lateral area of a regular pyramid

$= \frac{1}{2}(18)(8)$ $P = 18$ and $\ell = 8$

$= 72$ ft²   Solve.

Part B Find the surface area.

Step 1 Find the length of the height of the triangular base and the
area of the base.

$a^2 + b^2 = c^2$ Pythagorean Theorem

$a^2 = 6^2 - 3^2$ $c = 6$ and $b = 3$

$a = \sqrt{27}$ Solve.

Calculate the area of the base B.

$B = \frac{1}{2}bh$ Area of a triangle

$= \frac{1}{2}(6)\sqrt{27}$ Substitute.

≈ 15.6 Solve.

So, the area of the base B is approximately __15.6__ square feet.

Step 2 Find the surface area of the pyramid.

$S = L + B$ Surface area of a regular pyramid

$\approx 72 + 15.6$ $L = 72$ and $B \approx 15.6$

≈ 87.6 Simplify.

The surface area of the pyramid is about __87.6__ square feet.

Example 5 Lateral Area and Surface Area
of a Right Cone

Find the lateral area and surface area
of the cone rounded to the nearest tenth.

Part A Find the lateral area.

$L = \pi r\ell$ Lateral area of a cone

$= \pi(0.8)(2.2)$ Substitution

≈ 5.5 Solve.

So, the lateral area of the cone is 5.5 square millimeters.

Part B Find the surface area.

$S = \pi r\ell + \pi r^2$ Surface area of a cone

$\approx 5.5 + \pi(0.8)^2$ Substitution

≈ 7.5 Solve.

The surface area of the cone is about __7.5__ square millimeters.

🔵 **Go Online** You can complete an Extra Example online.

Copyright © McGraw-Hill Education

Interactive Presentation

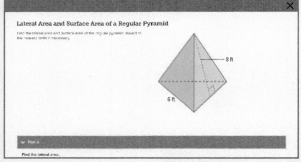

Example 4

TAP

Students tap to reveal steps in the
solution.

Example 4 Lateral Area and Surface Area of a Regular Pyramid

MP **Teaching the Mathematical Practices**

6 Use Precision In this example, students must calculate
accurately and efficiently and express numerical answers with a
degree of precision appropriate to the problem context.

Questions for Mathematical Discourse

AL What other method could we use to find the lateral area of the
pyramid? Find the area of the triangle that makes up one lateral
face and multiply by 3.

OL If the side of the base is increased to 7 feet, what would the new
lateral surface area be? 84 ft²

BL If instead of a slant height of 8 ft you were given a pyramid height
of 5 ft, what would the new surface area be? 51.6 ft²

Common Error

Students may forget to add the area of the base after finding the lateral
surface area. Remind students to persevere until they have completed
the problem.

DIFFERENTIATE

Language Development Activity ELL

Ask students to name a similarity and a difference between finding the
lateral area of a pyramid and the lateral area of a prism. The similarity is
that both lateral areas use the perimeter of the base in their formulas. The
difference is that the lateral area of a pyramid is one-half the perimeter
of the base times its slant height, while the lateral area of a prism is the
perimeter of the base times its regular height.

Example 5 Lateral Area and Surface Area of a Right Cone

MP **Teaching the Mathematical Practices**

4 Use Tools Point out that to solve the problem in this example,
students will need to use the formulas for lateral area and surface
area of a right cone.

Questions for Mathematical Discourse

AL What is the base of a cone? What part makes up the lateral surface
area? a circle; the surface from the circle to the vertex

OL If the slant height is changed to 3 mm, what is the new lateral
surface area? The new surface area? 7.5 mm²; 9.5 mm²

BL If the slant height is changed and the new lateral surface area is
3.4 mm², what is the new surface area? 5.4 mm²

1 CONCEPTUAL UNDERSTANDING | **2 FLUENCY** | **3 APPLICATION**

⊕ Example 6 Approximate Surface Areas of Pyramids and Cones

Ⓜ Teaching the Mathematical Practices

4 Use Tools Point out that to solve the problem in this example, students will need to use surface area formulas.

Questions for Mathematical Discourse

AL What is the approximate shape of the base of the pyramid?
an equilateral triangle

OL What kind of triangle can be used to find the height of the triangular base? a 30°-60°-90° triangle

BL If the slant height is changed to $3x + 6$, what would the approximate surface area of the watermelon be? about 494.4 in²

Learn Surface Area of Spheres

Objective

Students find surface areas of spheres by using the formulas they derive.

Ⓜ Teaching the Mathematical Practices

7 Use Structure Help students to explore the structure of spheres in this Learn.

About the Key Concept

The formula for the surface area of a sphere is difficult to derive without the use of calculus, so the formula is presented here with a plausible explanation of where it comes from.

Example 7 Surface Area of a Sphere

Ⓜ Teaching the Mathematical Practices

6 Use Precision In this example, students must calculate accurately and efficiently and express numerical answers with a degree of precision appropriate to the problem context.

Questions for Mathematical Discourse

AL If the radius of the sphere is 3 cm, what is the surface area? 113.1 cm²

OL If the surface area of a sphere is 804 in², what is the radius of the sphere? about 8 in.

BL The radius of one sphere is three times greater than the radius of the second sphere. How many times greater is the surface area of the first sphere than the surface area of the second? 9 times

---

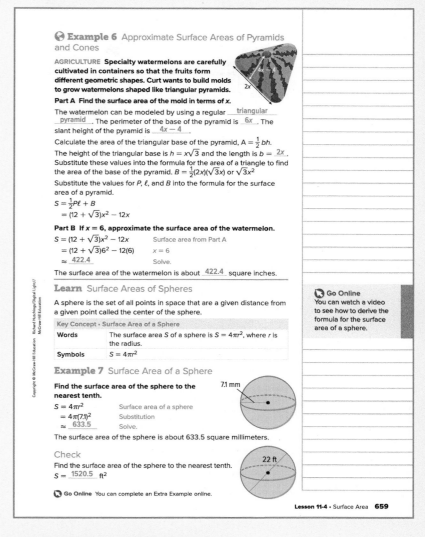

⊕ Example 6 Approximate Surface Areas of Pyramids and Cones

AGRICULTURE Specialty watermelons are carefully cultivated in containers so that the fruits form different geometric shapes. Curt wants to build molds to grow watermelons shaped like triangular pyramids.

Part A Find the surface area of the mold in terms of x.

The watermelon can be modeled by using a regular __triangular pyramid__. The perimeter of the base of the pyramid is __6x__. The slant height of the pyramid is __4x − 4__.

Calculate the area of the triangular base of the pyramid, $A = \frac{1}{2}bh$.

The height of the triangular base is $h = x\sqrt{3}$ and the length is $b = $ __2x__. Substitute these values into the formula for the area of a triangle to find the area of the base of the pyramid. $B = \frac{1}{2}(2x)(\sqrt{3}x)$ or $\sqrt{3}x^2$

Substitute the values for P, ℓ, and B into the formula for the surface area of a pyramid.

$S = \frac{1}{2}P\ell + B$

$= (12 + \sqrt{3})x^2 − 12x$

Part B If $x = 6$, approximate the surface area of the watermelon.

$S = (12 + \sqrt{3})x^2 − 12x$ Surface area from Part A

$= (12 + \sqrt{3})6^2 − 12(6)$ $x = 6$

$\approx$ __422.4__   Solve.

The surface area of the watermelon is about __422.4__ square inches.

Learn Surface Areas of Spheres

A sphere is the set of all points in space that are a given distance from a given point called the center of the sphere.

Key Concept • Surface Area of a Sphere

Words	The surface area S of a sphere is $S = 4\pi r^2$, where r is the radius.
Symbols	$S = 4\pi r^2$

Example 7 Surface Area of a Sphere

Find the surface area of the sphere to the nearest tenth.

$S = 4\pi r^2$ Surface area of a sphere

$= 4\pi(7.1)^2$ Substitution

$\approx$ __633.5__   Solve.

The surface area of the sphere is about 633.5 square millimeters.

7.1 mm

Check

Find the surface area of the sphere to the nearest tenth.

$S =$ __1520.5__ ft²

22 ft

⟳ **Go Online** You can complete an Extra Example online.

> 🎬 **Go Online** You can watch a video to see how to derive the formula for the surface area of a sphere.

Lesson 11-4 • Surface Area **659**

Interactive Presentation

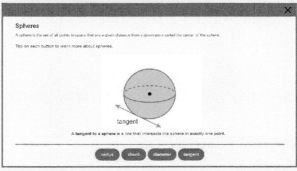

Spheres

A sphere is the set of all points in space that are a given distance from a given point called the center of the sphere.

Tap on each button to learn more about spheres.

tangent

A tangent to a sphere is a line that intersects the sphere in exactly one point.

radius   chord   diameter   tangent

Learn

TAP

Students tap to reveal information about surface area of a sphere.

CHECK

Students complete the Check online to determine whether they are ready to move on.

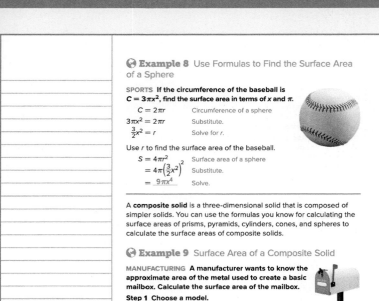

Example 8 Use Formulas to Find the Surface Area of a Sphere

SPORTS If the circumference of the baseball is $C = 3\pi x^2$, find the surface area in terms of x and π.

$C = 2\pi r$	Circumference of a sphere
$3\pi x^2 = 2\pi r$	Substitute.
$\frac{3}{2}x^2 = r$	Solve for r.

Use r to find the surface area of the baseball.

$S = 4\pi r^2$	Surface area of a sphere
$= 4\pi\left(\frac{3}{2}x^2\right)^2$	Substitute.
$= 9\pi x^4$	Solve.

A **composite solid** is a three-dimensional solid that is composed of simpler solids. You can use the formulas you know for calculating the surface areas of prisms, pyramids, cylinders, cones, and spheres to calculate the surface areas of composite solids.

Example 9 Surface Area of a Composite Solid

MANUFACTURING A manufacturer wants to know the approximate area of the metal used to create a basic mailbox. Calculate the surface area of the mailbox.

Step 1 Choose a model.

The mailbox can be modeled by a ___square prism___ without a top face and one half of a ___cylinder___.

Step 2 Draw a net of the composite solid.

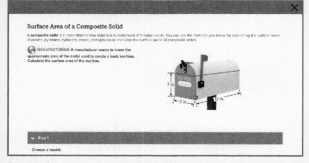

Step 3 Calculate the surface area.

The surface area of the square prism is made up of three rectangles measuring 12 inches by 7 inches and two squares measuring 7 inches by 7 inches. The surface area of the half cylinder is made up of a rectangle measuring 12 inches by 3.5π inches and two half circles with a radius measuring 3.5 inches.

$S = 3(12 \times 7) + 2(7 \times 7) + (12 \times 3.5\pi) + \pi(3.5)^2$ or about 520.4 square inches.

The surface area of the mailbox is about ___520.4___ square inches.

Go Online You can complete an Extra Example online.

Interactive Presentation

Surface Area of a Composite Solid

A composite solid is a three-dimensional solid that is composed of simpler solids. You can use the formulas you know for calculating the surface areas of prisms, pyramids, cylinders, cones, and spheres to calculate the surface areas of composite solids.

MANUFACTURING A manufacturer wants to know the approximate area of the metal used to create a basic mailbox. Calculate the surface area of the mailbox.

Step 1
Choose a model.

Example 9

TAP

Students tap to reveal parts of the solution.

CHECK

Students complete the Check online to determine whether they are ready to move on.

🌐 **Example 8** Use Formulas to Find the Surface Area of a Sphere

MP Teaching the Mathematical Practices

4 Use Tools Point out that to solve the problem in this example, students will need to use surface area formulas.

Questions for Mathematical Discourse

AL What information can you easily get from the circumference of the sphere? the radius or the diameter

OL If the circumference is 10π, what is the surface area of the sphere? 100π

BL If you sliced a sphere in half, how would the area of the circular cross section relate to the surface area of a sphere? The surface area of the sphere is four times the area of the cross section.

DIFFERENTIATE

Language Development Activity AL BL ELL

Have students research the diameters of planets and moons in our solar system. Ask them to compute the surface areas, and check their work based on research on surface areas.

🌐 **Example 9** Surface Area of a Composite Solid

MP Teaching the Mathematical Practices

4 Apply Mathematics In this example, students apply what they have learned about surface areas of composite solids to solving a real-world problem.

Questions for Mathematical Discourse

AL What two figures make up the composite figure? a prism and half a cylinder

OL If the mailbox were 15 inches long, what would the surface area be? 616.4 in²

BL If the width of the mailbox increased to 8 inches, what is the new surface area? 617.1 in²

Exit Ticket

Recommended Use

At the end of class, go online to display the Exit Ticket prompt and ask students to respond using a separate piece of paper. Have students hand you their responses as they leave the room.

Alternate Use

At the end of class, go online to display the Exit Ticket prompt and ask students to respond verbally or by using a mini-whiteboard. Have students hold up their whiteboards so that you can see all student responses. Tap to reveal the answer when most or all students have completed the Exit Ticket.

Practice and Homework

Suggested Assignments

Use the table below to select appropriate exercises.

DOK	Topic	Exercises
1, 2	exercises that mirror the examples	1–25
2	exercises that use a variety of skills from this lesson	26–32
2	exercises that extend concepts learned in this lesson to new contexts	33–41
3	exercises that emphasize higher-order and critical-thinking skills	42–46

ASSESS AND DIFFERENTIATE

📊 Use the data from the **Checks** to determine whether to provide resources for extension, remediation, or intervention.

IF students score 90% or more on the Checks,   `BL`
THEN assign:

- Practice, Exercises 1–41 odd, 42–46
- Extension: Minimizing Cost in Manufacturing
- 🅐 **ALEKS·** Surface Areas of Prisms and Cylinders; Surface Areas and Volumes of Spheres

---

IF students score 66%–89% on the Checks,   `OL`
THEN assign:

- Practice, Exercises 1–46 odd
- Remediation, Review Resources: Area of Circles
- Personal Tutors
- Extra Examples 1–9
- 🅐 **ALEKS·** Circumference and Area of Circles

IF students score 65% or less on the Checks,   `AL`
THEN assign:

- Practice, Exercises 1–25 odd
- Remediation, Review Resources: Area of Circles
- 🅐 **ALEKS·** Circumference and Area of Circles

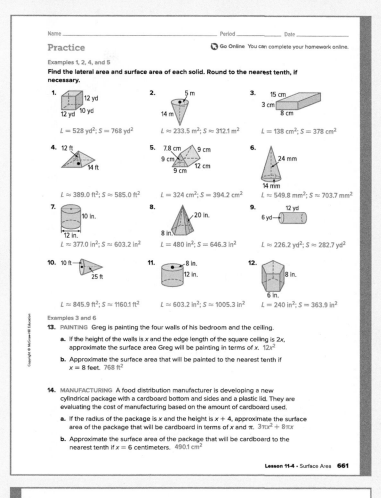

Name _____ Period _____ Date _____

Practice

🖥 Go Online You can complete your homework online.

Examples 1, 2, 4, and 5

Find the lateral area and surface area of each solid. Round to the nearest tenth, if necessary.

1. 12 yd, 12 yd, 10 yd
   $L = 528$ yd^2; $S \approx 768$ yd^2

2. 5 m, 14 m
   $L \approx 233.5$ m^2; $S \approx 312.1$ m^2

3. 15 cm, 3 cm, 8 cm
   $L = 138$ cm^2; $S = 378$ cm^2

4. 12 ft, 14 ft
   $L \approx 389.0$ ft^2; $S \approx 585.0$ ft^2

5. 7.8 cm, 9 cm, 9 cm, 9 cm, 12 cm
   $L = 324$ cm^2; $S \approx 394.2$ cm^2

6. 24 mm, 14 mm
   $L \approx 549.8$ mm^2; $S \approx 703.7$ mm^2

7. 10 in., 12 in.
   $L \approx 377.0$ in^2; $S \approx 603.2$ in^2

8. 20 in., 8 in.
   $L = 480$ in^2; $S \approx 646.3$ in^2

9. 12 yd, 6 yd
   $L \approx 226.2$ yd^2; $S \approx 282.7$ yd^2

10. 10 ft, 25 ft
    $L \approx 845.9$ ft^2; $S \approx 1160.1$ ft^2

11. 8 in., 12 in.
    $L \approx 603.2$ in^2; $S \approx 1005.3$ in^2

12. 8 in., 6 in.
    $L = 240$ in^2; $S \approx 363.9$ in^2

Examples 3 and 6

13. **PAINTING** Greg is painting the four walls of his bedroom and the ceiling.
    a. If the height of the walls is x and the edge length of the square ceiling is $2x$, approximate the surface area Greg will be painting in terms of x. $12x^2$
    b. Approximate the surface area that will be painted to the nearest tenth if $x = 8$ feet. 768 ft^2

14. **MANUFACTURING** A food distribution manufacturer is developing a new cylindrical package with a cardboard bottom and sides and a plastic lid. They are evaluating the cost of manufacturing based on the amount of cardboard used.
    a. If the radius of the package is x and the height is $x + 4$, approximate the surface area of the package that will be cardboard in terms of x and π. $3\pi x^2 + 8\pi x$
    b. Approximate the surface area of the package that will be cardboard to the nearest tenth if $x = 6$ centimeters. 490.1 cm^2

Lesson 11-4 · Surface Area   **661**

---

15. **CAMPING** A company that manufactures camping gear is designing a new tent shaped like a square pyramid with sidewalls made of a waterproof material.
    a. If the base of the tent is x units long and the slant height of the walls is 1.5x units, approximate the surface area of the sidewalls in terms of x. $3x^2$
    b. Approximate the amount of material needed to manufacture the sidewalls if $x = 9$ feet. 243 ft^2

16. **TOPIARY** Davea is planning to prune her landscaping bushes into topiaries shaped like cones.
    a. The radius of a bush is $\frac{1}{2}x$ units and the slant height is $4x$ units. Approximate the lateral area of one topiary in terms of x and π. $2\pi x^2$
    b. A frost is expected, and Davea is making plastic slipcovers to protect her new topiaries. Approximate the surface area of one slipcover to the nearest tenth if the slipcover does not cover the base of the topiary and $x = 0.75$ meter. 3.5 m^2

Example 7
Find the surface area of each sphere to the nearest tenth.

17. 7 in.
    $S \approx 615.8$ in^2

18. 32 m
    $S \approx 3217.0$ m^2

19. 4.8 mm
    $S \approx 289.5$ mm^2

20. **MOONS OF SATURN** The planet Saturn has several moons, and they can be modeled accurately by spheres. Saturn's largest moon, Titan, has a radius of about 2575 kilometers. What is the approximate surface area of Titan? Round your answer to the nearest tenth. $83{,}322{,}891.2$ km^2

Example 8

21. **AMUSEMENT PARK** Spaceship Earth at Disney's Epcot Center is a sphere. If the circumference of Spaceship Earth is $C = 7\pi x^2$, find the surface area in terms of x and π. $49\pi x^4$

22. **BILLIARDS** If the circumference of an eight-ball is $C = 4\pi x$, find the surface area in terms of x and π. $16\pi x^2$

Example 9
Find the surface area of each figure to the nearest tenth.

23. 8 cm, 4 cm, 6 cm
    $S \approx 301.6$ cm^2

24. 24 mm, 18 mm
    $S \approx 5768.0$ mm^2

25. **THEATER** Carlos is building a prop for the school play, and he needs to calculate the amount of lumber needed to make it. The prop is shaped like a tower and the radius of the base of the tower is 2.5 feet. If the tower is hollow and has no base, what is the approximate surface area of the tower? Round your answer to the nearest tenth. 156.3 ft^2

662   Module 11 · Measurement

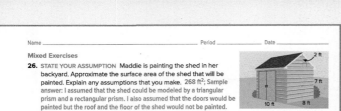

Name _____ **Period** _____ **Date** _____

Mixed Exercises

26. STATE YOUR ASSUMPTION Maddie is painting the shed in her backyard. Approximate the surface area of the shed that will be painted. Explain any assumptions that you make. 268 ft²; Sample answer: I assumed that the shed could be modeled by a triangular prism and a rectangular prism. I also assumed that the doors would be painted but the roof and the floor of the shed would not be painted.

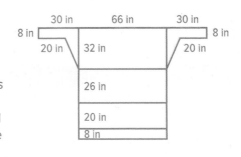

27. STRUCTURE A cylinder has a lateral area of 120π square meters and a height of 7 meters. Find the radius of the cylinder. Round to the nearest tenth. 8.6 m

For Exercises 28–32, find the lateral area and surface area of each solid. Round to the nearest tenth, if necessary.

28. a triangular prism with height of 6 inches, right triangular base with legs of 9 inches and 12 inches $L = 216$ in²; $S = 324$ in²

29. a square pyramid with an altitude of 12 inches and a slant height of 18 inches $L \approx 966.0$ in²; $S \approx 1686.0$ in²

30. a hexagonal pyramid with a base edge of 6 millimeters and a slant height of 9 millimeters $L \approx 162$ mm²; $S \approx 255.5$ mm²

31. a cone with a diameter of 3.4 centimeters and a slant height of 6.5 centimeters $L \approx 34.7$ cm²; $S \approx 43.8$ cm²

32. a cone with an altitude of 5 feet and a slant height of $9\frac{1}{2}$ feet $L \approx 241.1$ ft²; $S \approx 446.1$ ft²

33. The *great circle* of a sphere lies on a plane that passes through the center of the circle. The diameter of a sphere's great circle is the *diameter of the sphere*.
  a. Find the surface area of a sphere with a great circle that has a circumference of 2π centimeters. Round to the nearest tenth, if necessary. $S = 12.6$ cm²
  b. Find the surface area of a sphere with a great circle that has an area of about 32 square feet. Round to the nearest tenth, if necessary. $S = 128$ ft²

34. GREENHOUSE Reina's greenhouse is shaped like a square pyramid with four congruent equilateral triangles for its sides. All of the edges are 6 feet long. What is the total surface area of the greenhouse including the floor? Round your answer to the nearest hundredth. 98.35 ft²

35. PAPER MODELS Prevan is making a paper model of a castle. Part of the model involves cutting out the net shown and folding it into a pyramid. The pyramid has a square base. What is the surface area of the resulting pyramid? 825 cm²

20 cm   20 cm
15 cm

36. CAKES A cake is a rectangular prism with a height of 4 inches and a base that is 12 inches by 15 inches. Wallace wants to apply frosting to the sides and the top of the cake. What is the surface area of the part of the cake that will have frosting? 396 in²

37. CONSTRUCTION A metal pipe is shaped like a cylinder with a height of 50 inches and a radius of 6 inches. What is the surface area of the pipe? Round your answer to the nearest tenth. 1885.0 in²

Lesson 11-4 · Surface Area **663**

---

38. INSTRUMENTS A mute for a brass instrument is formed by taking a solid cone with a radius of 10 centimeters and an altitude of 20 centimeters and cutting off the top. The cut is made along a plane that is perpendicular to the altitude of the cone and intersects the altitude 6 centimeters from the vertex. Round your answers to the nearest hundredth.
  a. What is the surface area of the original cone? 1016.64 cm²
  b. What is the surface area of the cone that is removed? 91.50 cm²
  c. What is the surface area of the mute? 953.42 cm²

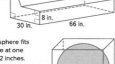

39. USE A MODEL The model shows the dimensions of a sofa. a–b. See margin.
  a. Draw a diagram to show how to calculate the total surface area of the sofa that would be covered by a fitted cover. Explain your technique.
  b. How much fabric is needed for a fitted sofa cover?

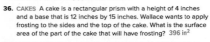

26 in.
32 in.   20 in.
8 in.
30 in.   66 in.

40. REASONING Jaylen builds a sphere inside of a cube. The sphere fits snugly inside the cube so that the sphere touches the cube at one point on each face. The length of each edge of the cube is 2 inches.
  a. What is the surface area of the cube? 24 in²
  b. What is the surface area of the sphere? Round your answers to the nearest hundredth. 12.57 in²
  c. What is the ratio of the surface area of the cube to the surface area of the sphere? Round your answer to the nearest hundredth. 1.91

41. CONSTRUCT ARGUMENTS A cone and a square pyramid have the same surface area. If the areas of their bases are also equal, do they have the same slant height as well? Justify your argument. See margin.

🕒 **Higher-Order Thinking Skills**

42. ANALYZE Classify the following statement as *sometimes*, *always*, or *never* true. Justify your argument. See margin.
   The surface area of a cone of radius *r* and height *h* is less than the surface area of a cylinder of radius *r* and height *h*.

43. WRITE Compare and contrast finding the surface area of a prism and finding the surface area of a cylinder. See margin.

44. CREATE Give an example of two cylinders that have the same lateral area and different surface areas. Find the lateral area and surface areas of each cylinder. See margin.

45. PERSEVERE A right prism has a height of *h* units and a base that is an equilateral triangle with a side length of ℓ units. Find the general formula for the total surface area of the prism. Explain your reasoning. See margin.

46. WRITE A square prism and a triangular prism are the same height. The base of the triangular prism is an equilateral triangle, with an altitude equal in length to the side of the square. Compare the lateral areas of the prisms. See margin.

Answers

39a. Sample answer: I drew a figure showing all of the surfaces of the sofa, using simple geometric figures with the dimensions labeled. To find the total surface area, I can find and add the areas of the simple figures.

30 in   66 in   30 in
8 in [   ] 8 in
20 in | 32 in | 20 in
        26 in
        20 in
        8 in

39b. Sample answer: Area $= (66)(8 + 20 + 26 + 32) + 2(30)(8) + 2\left[\frac{1}{2}(30 - 20)(32 - 8)\right] = 6396$ in²; I did not include the base in my calculation.

41. No; sample answer: The slant height of the cone is $\frac{2\sqrt{\pi}}{\pi}$ or about 1.13 times greater than the slant height of the square pyramid.

42. Always; if the heights and radii are the same, the surface area of the cylinder will be greater because it has two circular bases and additional lateral area.

43. Sample answer: To find the surface area of any solid figure, find the area of the base (or bases) and add the area of the lateral faces of the figure. The lateral bases of a rectangular prism are rectangles. Because the bases of a cylinder are circles, the lateral face of a cylinder is a rectangle.

44. Sample answer: A cylinder with a height 8 units and radius of 3 units has a lateral area of 48π square units and a surface area of 66π square units; a cylinder a with height of 6 units and radius of 4 units has a lateral area of 48π square units and a surface area of 80π square units.

45. $\frac{\sqrt{3}}{2}\ell^2 + 3\ell h$; Sample answer: The area of an equilateral triangle with side length ℓ is $\frac{\sqrt{3}}{4}\ell^2$, and the perimeter of the triangle is 3ℓ. So, the total surface area is $\frac{\sqrt{3}}{2}\ell^2 + 3\ell h$.

46. The lateral area of the square-based prism is greater than that of the triangular prism. The square has a perimeter of $4s$ and the triangle has a perimeter of $2s\sqrt{3}$ and $4s > 2s\sqrt{3}$.

Cross Sections and Solids of Revolution

LESSON GOAL

Students identify the shapes of cross sections formed by cuts to a solid, the three-dimensional objects generated by rotations of two-dimensional objects, and the three-dimensional symmetries of solids.

1 LAUNCH

Launch the lesson with a **Warm Up** and an introduction.

2 EXPLORE AND DEVELOP

Explore: Cross Sections

Develop:

Cross Sections
- Plane Symmetry
- Identify Cross Sections

Solids of Revolution
- Identify Solids of Revolution
- Axis Symmetry

You may want your students to complete the **Checks** online.

3 REFLECT AND PRACTICE

Exit Ticket

Practice

DIFFERENTIATE

View reports of student progress on the **Checks** after each example.

Resources	AL	OL	BL	ELL
Remediation: Three-Dimensional Figures	●	●		●
Extension: Solids Formed by Translation		●	●	●

Language Development Handbook

Assign page 78 of the *Language Development Handbook* to help your students build mathematical language related to finding the volumes of prisms and pyramids.

ELL You can use the tips and suggestions on page T78 of the handbook to support students who are building English proficiency.

Suggested Pacing

90 min	**0.5 day**	
45 min	**1 day**	

Focus

Domain: Geometry

Standards for Mathematical Content:

G.GMD.4 Identify the shapes of two-dimensional cross-sections of three-dimensional objects, and identify three-dimensional objects generated by rotations of two-dimensional objects.

Standards for Mathematical Practice:

3 Construct viable arguments and critique the reasoning of others.

7 Look for and make use of structure.

8 Look for and express regularity in repeated reasoning.

Coherence

Vertical Alignment

Previous
Students identified two-dimensional cross setcions of three-dimensional figures.
7.G.3

Now
Students determine cross sections of three-dimensional figures.
G.GMD.4

Next
Students will find volumes of prisms and pyramids.
G.GMD.3

Rigor

The Three Pillars of Rigor

1 CONCEPTUAL UNDERSTANDING	2 FLUENCY	3 APPLICATION

Conceptual Bridge In this lesson, students extend their understanding of two-dimensional figures to three dimensions. They build fluency and apply their understanding by finding cross sections of solid figures in the real world.

Mathematical Background

A *cross section* is the intersection of a solid figure and a plane. The shape of the cross section formed by the intersection of the plane and the figure depends on the angle of the plane.

A *solid of revolution* is a solid figure obtained by rotating a plane figure or curve around an axis. The shape of the solid of revolution depends on the location of the axis and the shape of the plane figure or curve being rotated.

Interactive Presentation

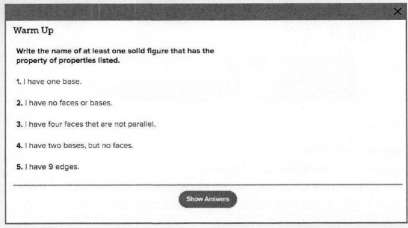

Warm Up

Write the name of at least one solid figure that has the property of properties listed.

1. I have one base.

2. I have no faces or bases.

3. I have four faces that are not parallel.

4. I have two bases, but no faces.

5. I have 9 edges.

Show Answers

Warm Up

Launch the Lesson

Cross sections are often used in science to show the interior of real-world objects. Circular cross sections of Earth show the different layers that make up the interior. Circular cross sections of a tree trunk can be used to determine the age of a tree by counting the growth rings. A rectangular cross section of a cylindrical camera lens shows the intricate mechanisms that go into making the lens work.

Launch the Lesson

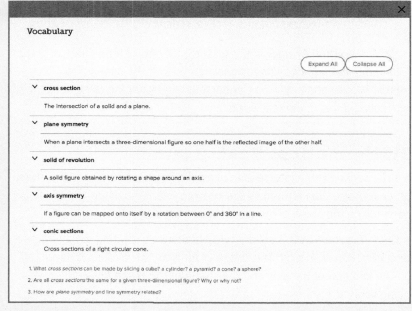

Vocabulary

Expand All   Collapse All

⌄ **cross section**

The intersection of a solid and a plane.

⌄ **plane symmetry**

When a plane intersects a three-dimensional figure so one half is the reflected image of the other half.

⌄ **solid of revolution**

A solid figure obtained by rotating a shape around an axis.

⌄ **axis symmetry**

If a figure can be mapped onto itself by a rotation between 0° and 360° in a line.

⌄ **conic sections**

Cross sections of a right circular cone.

1. What *cross sections* can be made by slicing a cube? a cylinder? a pyramid? a cone? a sphere?

2. Are all *cross sections* the same for a given three-dimensional figure? Why or why not?

3. How are *plane symmetry* and line symmetry related?

Today's Vocabulary

Warm Up

Prerequisite Skills

The Warm Up exercises address the following prerequisite skill for this lesson:

• identifying solids

Answers:

1-5. Sample answers are given.

1. pyramid, cone

2. sphere

3. square pyramid

4. cylinder

5. triangular prism

Launch the Lesson

(MP) Teaching the Mathematical Practices

4 Apply Mathematics In this Launch the Lesson, students can see a real-world application of cross sections.

Go Online to find additional teaching notes and questions to promote classroom discourse.

Today's Standards

Tell students that they will be addressing these content and practice standards in this lesson. You may wish to have a student volunteer read aloud *How can I meet these standards?* and *How can I use these practices?* and connect these to the standards.

See the Interactive Presentation for I Can statements that align with the standards covered in this lesson.

Today's Vocabulary

Tell students that they will be using these vocabulary terms in this lesson. You can expand each row if you wish to share the definitions. Then, discuss the questions below with the class.

Explore Cross Sections

Objective
Students use three-dimensional solids to explore cross sections.

Teaching the Mathematical Practices

5 Use Mathematical Tools Point out that to solve the problem in this Explore, students will need to use concrete models. Work with students to explore and deepen their understanding of cross sections.

Ideas for Use
Recommended Use Present the Inquiry Question, or have a student volunteer read it aloud. Have students work in pairs to complete the Explore activity on their devices. Pairs should discuss each of the questions. Monitor student progress during the activity. Upon completion of the Explore activity, have student volunteers share their responses to the Inquiry Question.

What if my students don't have devices? You may choose to project the activity on a whiteboard. A printable worksheet for each Explore is available online. You may choose to print the worksheet so that individuals or pairs of students can use it to record their observations.

Summary of the Activity
Students will complete guiding exercises throughout the Explore activity. Students first consider a cube and answer guiding exercises about cross sections of the cube. Students then consider a square pyramid and answer guiding exercises about cross sections of the pyramid. The questions guide students to discover that the number of faces a plane intersects determines the number of sides of the cross section. Then, students will answer the Inquiry Question.

Go Online to find additional teaching notes and sample answers for the guiding exercises.

(continued on the next page)

Interactive Presentation

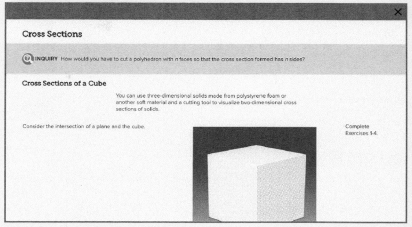

Explore

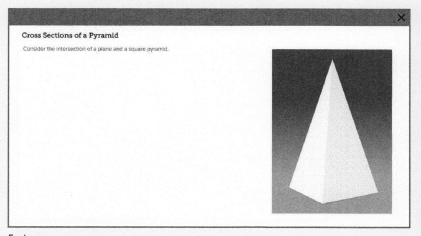

Explore

TYPE

Students type to answer guiding exercises.

1 CONCEPTUAL UNDERSTANDING | 2 FLUENCY | 3 APPLICATION

Interactive Presentation

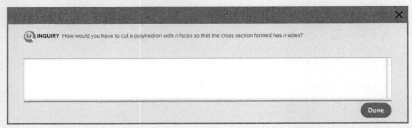

INQUIRY How would you have to cut a polyhedron with *n* faces so that the cross section formed has *n* sides?

Done

Explore

TYPE

Students respond to the Inquiry Question and can view a sample answer.

Explore Cross Sections (*continued*)

MP Teaching the Mathematical Practices

5 Use Mathematical Tools Point out that to solve the problem in this Explore, students will need to use concrete models. Work with students to explore and deepen their understanding of cross sections.

Questions
Have students complete the Explore activity.

Ask:
- Why does changing the angle of the cut affect the shape of the cross section? Sample answer: If the plane that is cutting the polyhedron is at an angle, it is possible to intersect with more or fewer faces of the polyhedron.

- Is it possible to cut the square pyramid so that the cross section forms a hexagon? Why or why not? No; sample answer: You would need to intersect with 6 faces in order to make a hexagon, but the square pyramid only has 5 faces.

Inquiry
How would you have to cut a polyhedron with *n* faces so that the cross section formed has *n* sides? Sample answer: Whenever a plane intersects the face of a solid, it forms the edge of a cross section. To form a cross section with *n* sides, the plane should intersect *n* faces of the polyhedron.

Go Online to find additional teaching notes and sample answers for the guiding exercises.

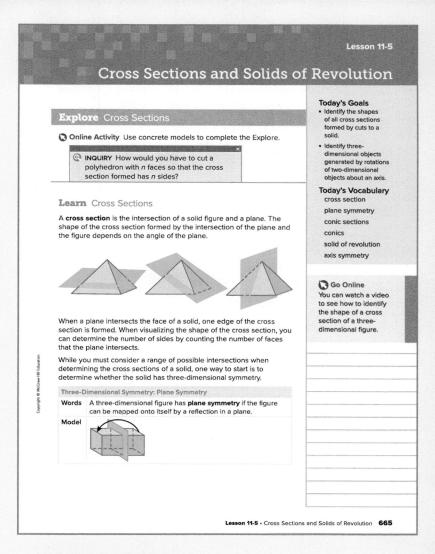

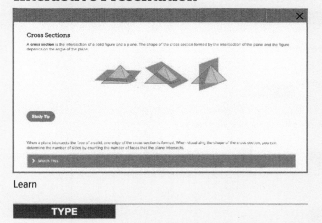

1 CONCEPTUAL UNDERSTANDING | **2 FLUENCY** | **3 APPLICATION**

Learn Cross Sections

Objective
Students identify the shapes of all cross sections formed by cuts to a solid.

MP Teaching the Mathematical Practices

6 Communicate Precisely Encourage students to routinely write or explain their solution methods. Point out that they should use clear definitions when they discuss their solutions with others.

Common Misconception
Students may think that cross sections must be congruent or similar to faces of the solid from which they are cut. Remind students that they can get a triangular cross-section by cutting off a corner of a cube, so the shape of the faces of a solid may be very different from the shapes of cross sections.

e Essential Question Follow-Up
Students find areas of two-dimensional figures.

Ask:

Why is it important to be able to identify cross sections of solid figures?
Sample answer: The cross sections of many real-world objects are useful.

Go Online

- Find additional teaching notes.
- View performance reports of the Checks.
- Assign or present an Extra Example.

Interactive Presentation

Learn

TYPE

Students type to answer the Talk About It! question.

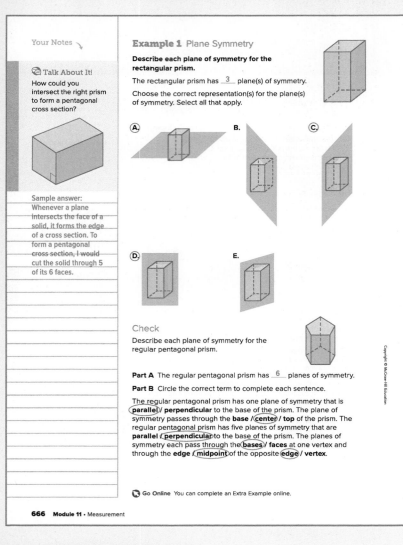

Your Notes

Talk About It!
How could you intersect the right prism to form a pentagonal cross section?

Sample answer: Whenever a plane intersects the face of a solid, it forms the edge of a cross section. To form a pentagonal cross section, I would cut the solid through 5 of its 6 faces.

Example 1 Plane Symmetry

Describe each plane of symmetry for the rectangular prism.

The rectangular prism has __3__ plane(s) of symmetry.

Choose the correct representation(s) for the plane(s) of symmetry. Select all that apply.

Ⓐ   B.   Ⓒ

Ⓓ   E.

Check

Describe each plane of symmetry for the regular pentagonal prism.

Part A The regular pentagonal prism has __6__ planes of symmetry.

Part B Circle the correct term to complete each sentence.

The regular pentagonal prism has one plane of symmetry that is **parallel** / perpendicular to the base of the prism. The plane of symmetry passes through the base / **center** / top of the prism. The regular pentagonal prism has five planes of symmetry that are parallel / **perpendicular** to the base of the prism. The planes of symmetry each pass through the **bases** / faces at one vertex and through the **edge** / midpoint of the opposite **edge** / vertex.

Go Online You can complete an Extra Example online.

666   Module 11 · Measurement

Example 1 Plane Symmetry

Teaching the Mathematical Practices

4 Analyze Relationships Mathematically Point out that to solve the problem in this example, students will need to analyze the mathematical relationships in the problem to draw a conclusion.

Questions for Mathematical Discourse

AL For each rectangular face of the prism, how many lines of symmetry does the face have? 2

OL How does a plane of symmetry intersect a face of the figure? It intersects at a line of symmetry of the face.

BL If exactly two faces of the rectangular prism are square, how many planes of symmetry would the figure have? 5

Common Error

Students may not notice that the rectangular prism has no square faces. If it had a square face, there would be more planes of symmetry that would pass through the diagonals of the square face. Help students to see that the faces are all rectangles.

DIFFERENTIATE

Reteaching Activity AL ELL
Divide the students into groups and give each group half a stick of room temperature butter and a butter knife. Ask students to slice the butter several times. Each cut should show a given shape in the cross section, such as a triangle, rectangle, quadrilateral that is not a rectangle, or a pentagon.

Interactive Presentation

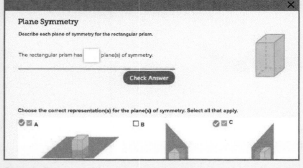

Plane Symmetry

Describe each plane of symmetry for the rectangular prism.

The rectangular prism has ☐ plane(s) of symmetry.

Check Answer

Choose the correct representation(s) for the plane(s) of symmetry. Select all that apply.

☑A   ☐B   ☑C

Example 1

SELECT

Students select which figures have plane symmetry.

1 CONCEPTUAL UNDERSTANDING | **2 FLUENCY** | 3 APPLICATION

Example 2 Identify Cross Sections

 Teaching the Mathematical Practices

3 Analyze Cases The Concept Check guides students to examine the cases of a plane intersecting a cone. Encourage students to familiarize themselves with all of the cases.

Questions for Mathematical Discourse

AL What shape would a horizontal cut of a cone produce? a circle

OL What shape would an angled cut of a cone produce? an ellipse or a parabola

BL Give an example of a solid and a cross section that would produce a rectangle. Sample answer: a diagonal cut of a cube

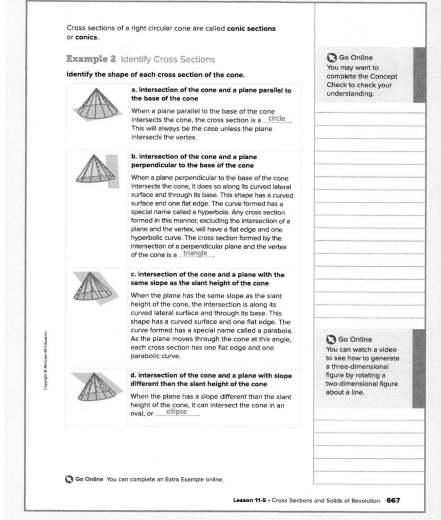

Cross sections of a right circular cone are called **conic sections** or **conics**.

Example 2 Identify Cross Sections

Identify the shape of each cross section of the cone.

a. intersection of the cone and a plane parallel to the base of the cone

When a plane parallel to the base of the cone intersects the cone, the cross section is a ___circle___. This will always be the case unless the plane intersects the vertex.

b. intersection of the cone and a plane perpendicular to the base of the cone

When a plane perpendicular to the base of the cone intersects the cone, it does so along its curved lateral surface and through its base. This shape has a curved surface and one flat edge. The curve formed has a special name called a hyperbola. Any cross section formed in this manner, excluding the intersection of a plane and the vertex, will have a flat edge and one hyperbolic curve. The cross section formed by the intersection of a perpendicular plane and the vertex of the cone is a ___triangle___.

c. intersection of the cone and a plane with the same slope as the slant height of the cone

When the plane has the same slope as the slant height of the cone, the intersection is along its curved lateral surface and through its base. This shape has a curved surface and one flat edge. The curve formed has a special name called a parabola. As the plane moves through the cone at this angle, each cross section has one flat edge and one parabolic curve.

d. intersection of the cone and a plane with slope different than the slant height of the cone

When the plane has a slope different than the slant height of the cone, it can intersect the cone in an oval, or ___ellipse___.

Go Online You can complete an Extra Example online.

Go Online
You may want to complete the Concept Check to check your understanding.

Go Online
You can watch a video to see how to generate a three-dimensional figure by rotating a two-dimensional figure about a line.

Copyright © McGraw-Hill Education

Lesson 11-5 · Cross Sections and Solids of Revolution **667**

Interactive Presentation

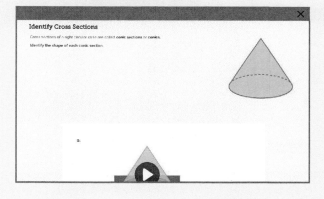

Identify Cross Sections

Cross sections of a right circular cone are called **conic sections** or **conics**.
Identify the shape of each conic section.

a.

Example 2

TAP

Students tap to reveal parts of the problem.

CHECK

Students complete the Check online to determine whether they are ready to move on.

1 CONCEPTUAL UNDERSTANDING | 2 FLUENCY | 3 APPLICATION

Learn Solids of Revolution

A **solid of revolution** is a solid figure obtained by rotating a plane figure or curve around an axis. The shape of the solid of revolution depends on the location of the axis and the shape of the plane figure or curve being rotated.

You can determine whether a three-dimensional figure could have been created by rotation by identifying whether the solid figure has axis symmetry.

Three-Dimensional Symmetry: Axis Symmetry

Words	A three-dimensional figure has **axis symmetry** if the figure can be mapped onto itself by a rotation between 0° and 360° in a line.
Model	

Example 3 Identify Solids of Revolution

Identify the solid formed by rotating the two-dimensional shape about line ℓ.

Imagine rotating the two-dimensional figure about line ℓ.

The solid of revolution is a ___cylinder___.

Check

Identify the solid formed by rotating the two-dimensional shape about line ℓ.

The solid of revolution is a ___cone___.

⟳ Example 4 Axis Symmetry

Circle each item with axis symmetry.

Check

Select all of the images that demonstrate axis symmetry.

A. **B.** **C.** **D.** **E.**

🖥 **Go Online** You can complete an Extra Example online.

Math History Minute

Russian **Sofia Kovalevskaya** (1850–1891) was a great mathematician, writer, and passionate advocate for women's rights. In 1888, she entered a paper, "On the Rotation of a Solid Body about a Fixed Point," in a competition for the Prix Bordin by the French Academy of Science, and she won. Sofia considered it her greatest personal triumph.

Study Tip

Use Tools You can use many different tools to help you visualize the solids of revolution. Straws or dowel rods could be used to represent the axis of rotation. Card stock or heavy construction paper can be attached to the straws or dowel rods to represent the two-dimensional figures. You could also sketch the figure using dynamic geometry software or graph paper.

Interactive Presentation

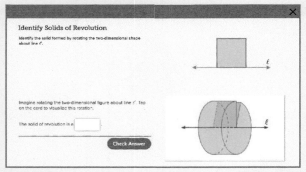

Example 3

TYPE

 a|

Students complete the calculations to identify solids of revolution.

CHECK

Students complete the Check online to determine whether they are ready to move on.

Learn Solids of Revolution

Objective

Students identify three-dimensional objects generated by rotations of two-dimensional objects about an axis.

MP Teaching the Mathematical Practices

7 Use Structure Help students to explore the structure of solids of revolution in this Learn.

DIFFERENTIATE

Reteaching Activity AL BL

Have students cut out many copies of a two-dimensional figure from cardstock, then use modeling clay to form the figures into a solid of revolution.

Example 3 Identify Solids of Revolution

Questions for Mathematical Discourse

AL What two-dimensional shape is used to form the solid of revolution? a square

OL How does a cross section containing line ℓ compare to the two-dimensional shape given? The cross section is two copies of the shape joined together.

BL If the two-dimensional figure was a triangle, what three-dimensional shape would it make? a cone

---

Example 4 Axis Symmetry

Questions for Mathematical Discourse

AL What shape is a cross section perpendicular to a line of axis symmetry? a circle or multiple concentric circles

OL Does a cone have axis symmetry? Explain. Yes; sample answer: A cone has axis symmetry around the line perpendicular to the center of its base.

BL Can an object have axis symmetry around more than one line? Explain. Yes; sample answer: A sphere has axis symmetry around every line through its center.

Exit Ticket

Recommended Use

At the end of class, go online to display the Exit Ticket prompt and ask students to respond using a separate piece of paper. Have students hand you their responses as they leave the room.

Alternate Use

At the end of class, go online to display the Exit Ticket prompt and ask students to respond verbally or by using a mini-whiteboard. Have students hold up their whiteboards so that you can see all student responses. Tap to reveal the answer when most or all students have completed the Exit Ticket.

Practice and Homework

Suggested Assignments

Use the table below to select appropriate exercises.

DOK	Topic	Exercises
1, 2	exercises that mirror the examples	1–17
2	exercises that use a variety of skills from this lesson	18–26
2	exercises that extend concepts learned in this lesson to new contexts	27–31
3	exercises that emphasize higher-order and critical-thinking skills	32–35

ASSESS AND DIFFERENTIATE

📊 Use the data from the **Checks** to determine whether to provide resources for extension, remediation, or intervention.

IF students score 90% or more on the Checks, **THEN** assign:　　　BL

- Practice, Exercises 1–31 odd, 32–35
- Extension: Solids Formed by Translation
- ⊙ **ALEKS** Solids and Cross Sections

IF students score 66%–89% on the Checks, **THEN** assign:　　　OL

- Practice, Exercises 1–35 odd
- Remediation, Review Resources: Three-Dimensional Figures
- Personal Tutors
- Extra Examples 1–4
- ⊙ **ALEKS** Three–Dimensional Figures

IF students score 65% or less on the Checks, **THEN** assign:　　　AL

- Practice, Exercises 1–17 odd
- Remediation, Review Resources: Three-Dimensional Figures
- *Quick Review Math Handbook*: Cross Sections of Three-Dimensional Figures
- ⊙ **ALEKS** Three–Dimensional Figures

Answers

1. The square pyramid has 2 planes of symmetry. One plane of symmetry is perpendicular to the base of the pyramid and passes through the vertex. Another plane of symmetry is perpendicular to the base of the pyramid, perpendicular to the first plane of symmetry, and passes through the vertex.

2. The regular hexagonal prism has 7 planes of symmetry. One plane of symmetry is parallel to the base of the prism and passes through the center of the prism. The regular hexagonal prism has six planes of symmetry that are perpendicular to the base of the prism. Three planes of symmetry each pass through the bases at opposite vertices. Three planes of symmetry each pass through the bases at midpoints of the opposite edges.

3. The triangular prism has 1 plane of symmetry. The plane of symmetry is parallel to the base of the prism and passes through the center of the prism.

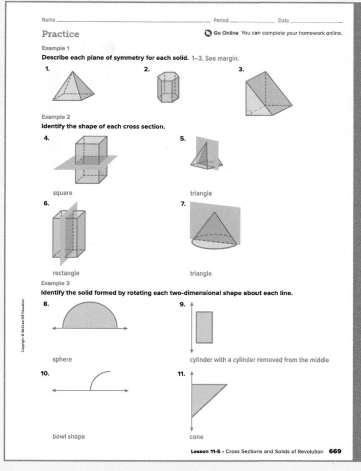

Name _____ Period _____ Date _____

Practice　　　⊙ **Go Online** You can complete your homework online.

Example 1
Describe each plane of symmetry for each solid. 1–3. See margin.

1.　　　2.　　　3.

Example 2
Identify the shape of each cross section.

4.　　　5.

square　　　triangle

6.　　　7.

rectangle　　　triangle

Example 3
Identify the solid formed by rotating each two-dimensional shape about each line.

8.　　　9.

sphere　　　cylinder with a cylinder removed from the middle

10.　　　11.

bowl shape　　　cone

Lesson 11-5 • Cross Sections and Solids of Revolution　**669**

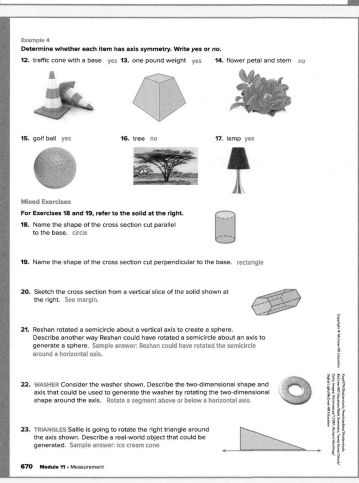

Example 4
Determine whether each item has axis symmetry. Write *yes* or *no*.

12. traffic cone with a base　yes　13. one pound weight　yes　14. flower petal and stem　no

15. golf ball　yes　16. tree　no　17. lamp　yes

Mixed Exercises

For Exercises 18 and 19, refer to the solid at the right.

18. Name the shape of the cross section cut parallel to the base.　circle

19. Name the shape of the cross section cut perpendicular to the base.　rectangle

20. Sketch the cross section from a vertical slice of the solid shown at the right.　See margin.

21. Reshan rotated a semicircle about a vertical axis to create a sphere. Describe another way Reshan could have rotated a semicircle about an axis to generate a sphere.　Sample answer: Reshan could have rotated the semicircle around a horizontal axis.

22. **WASHER** Consider the washer shown. Describe the two-dimensional shape and axis that could be used to generate the washer by rotating the two-dimensional shape around the axis.　Rotate a segment above or below a horizontal axis.

23. **TRIANGLES** Sallie is going to rotate the right triangle around the axis shown. Describe a real-world object that could be generated.　Sample answer: ice cream cone

670　**Module 11** • Measurement

1 CONCEPTUAL UNDERSTANDING | **2 FLUENCY** | **3 APPLICATION**

Name _____ Period _____ Date _____

24. REASONING The rectangle shown will be rotated about the *x*-axis.

a. Describe the three-dimensional shape that is generated. cylinder

b. What is the length of the radius and height of the figure generated? radius = 2 units; height = 8 units

25. USE TOOLS Determine whether each cross section can be made from a cube. If so, sketch the cube and its cross section.

a. triangle   b. square   c. rectangle

d. pentagon   e. hexagon   f. octagon

a. yes   b. yes   c. yes

d. yes   e. yes   f. no

26. USE A SOURCE Research the shape and dimensions of the Washington Monument.

a. Describe each plane of symmetry of the Washington Monument. See margin.

b. Describe the cross section of the Washington Monument from a vertical slice perpendicular to the base through the vertex. pentagon

c. Determine if the Washington Monument has axis symmetry. Write *yes* or *no*. yes

Lesson 11-5 • Cross Sections and Solids of Revolution **671**

For Exericses 27 and 28, identify and sketch the cross section of an object made by each cut described. 27–28. See margin.

27. square pyramid cut perpendicular to base but not through the vertex

28. rectangular prism cut diagonally from a top edge to a bottom edge on the opposite side

29. You want to cut each geometric object so that the cross section is a circle. Give the name for each object. Then describe the cut that results in a circle.

a.   b.   c.

sphere; any cut   cylinder; cut parallel to bases   cone; cut parallel to base

30. USE TOOLS Sketch and describe the object that is created by rotating each shape around the indicated axis of rotation. a–c. See margin.

a.   b.   c.

  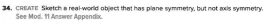

31. CONSTRUCT ARGUMENTS A regular polyhedron has axis symmetry of order 3, but does not have plane symmetry. What is the figure? Justify your argument. See margin.

🎧 Higher-Order Thinking Skills

32. PERSEVERE The figure at the right is a cross section of a geometric solid. Describe a solid and how the cross section was made. See margin.

33. WRITE A hexagonal pyramid is sliced through the vertex and the base so that the prism is separated into two congruent parts. Describe the cross section. Is there more than one way to separate the figure into two congruent parts? Will the shape of the cross section change? Explain. See margin.

34. CREATE Sketch a real-world object that has plane symmetry, but not axis symmetry. See Mod. 11 Answer Appendix.

35. ANALYZE Determine whether the statement below is *true* or *false*. Justify your argument. The only two shapes formed by the cross sections of a square pyramid are a triangle and a square. See Mod. 11 Answer Appendix.

672 Module 11 • Measurement

Answers

20.

26a. The Washington Monument has 4 planes of symmetry. Two planes of symmetry are perpendicular to the base of the monument and pass through opposite vertices. Two other planes of symmetry are perpendicular to the base of the monument and pass through the base at midpoint of the opposite edges.

27. trapezoid   28. rectangle

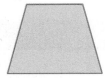 

30a. two cones together   30b. ring

 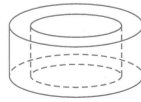

30c. two cones joined by a cylinder

31. Equilateral triangular pyramid; sample answer: Because the figure has axis symmetry of order 3, the base has to be an equilateral triangle. Because it does not have plane symmetry, you know that it is a pyramid instead of a prism. Therefore, the figure must be an equilateral triangular pyramid.

32. Sample answer: A cone is sliced at an angle through its lateral side and base.

33. Sample answer: The cross section is a triangle. There are six different ways to slice the pyramid so that two equal parts are formed because the figure has six planes of symmetry. In each case, the cross section is an isosceles triangle. Only the side lengths of the triangles change.

Volumes of Prisms and Pyramids

LESSON GOAL

Students find volumes of prisms and pyramids by using the formulas they derive.

1 LAUNCH

 Launch the lesson with a **Warm Up** and an introduction.

2 EXPLORE AND DEVELOP

 Develop:

Volumes of Prisms
- Volume of a Prism
- Volume of an Oblique Prism
- Volume of a Prism Using Algebraic Expressions

 Explore: Volumes of Square Pyramids

 Develop:

Volumes of Pyramids
- Volume of a Pyramid
- Volume of a Pyramid Using Algebraic Expressions
- Volume of a Composite Solid
- Approximate the Volume of a Composite Solid

 You may want your students to complete the **Checks** online.

3 REFLECT AND PRACTICE

 Exit Ticket

 Practice

Formative Assessment Math Probe

DIFFERENTIATE

View reports of student progress on the **Checks** after each example.

Resources	AL	OL	BL	ELL
Remediation: Volume	●	●		●
Extension: Frustums		●	●	●

Language Development Handbook

Assign page 75 of the *Language Development Handbook* to help your students build mathematical language related to finding the volumes of prisms and pyramids.

ELL You can use the tips and suggestions on page T75 of the handbook to support students who are building English proficiency.

Suggested Pacing

90 min — 1 day
45 min — 2 days

Focus

Domain: Geometry

Standards for Mathematical Content:

G.GMD.1 Give an informal argument for the formulas for the circumference of a circle, area of a circle, volume of a cylinder, pyramid, and cone.

G.GMD.2 Give an informal argument using Cavalieri's principle for the formulas for the volume of a sphere and other solid figures.

G.GMD.3 Use volume formulas for cylinders, pyramids, cones, and spheres to solve problems.

Standards for Mathematical Practice:

1 Make sense of problems and persevere in solving them.

4 Model with mathematics.

7 Look for and make use of structure.

Coherence

Vertical Alignment

Previous
Students understood volume of prisms and pyramids.
6.G.2, 7.G.6

Now
Students find volumes of prisms and pyramids.
G.GMD.3

Next
Students will find volumes of cylinders, cones, and spheres.
G.GMD.3

Rigor

The Three Pillars of Rigor

1 CONCEPTUAL UNDERSTANDING	2 FLUENCY	3 APPLICATION

Conceptual Bridge In this lesson, students extend their understanding of area to volume. They build fluency by finding areas of prisms and pyramids, and they apply their understanding by finding volumes of solid figures in the real world.

Mathematical Background

If a prism has a volume V cubic units, a height of h units, and each base has an area of B units, then $V = Bh$. If a pyramid has a volume V, a height h, and a base with an area B, then $V = \frac{1}{3}Bh$.

Interactive Presentation

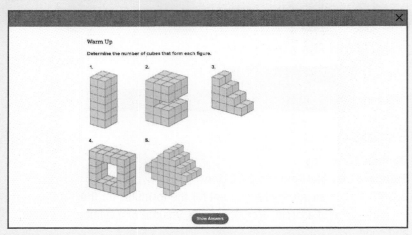

Warm Up

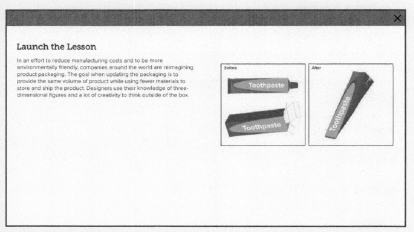

Launch the Lesson

Warm Up

Prerequisite Skills

The Warm Up exercises address the following prerequisite skill for this lesson:

• finding volumes by counting

Answers:

1. 24
2. 39
3. 20
4. 32
5. 75

Launch the Lesson

 Teaching the Mathematical Practices

> **4 Apply Mathematics** In this Launch the Lesson, students can see a real-world application of three-dimensional figures.

🔽 **Go Online** to find additional teaching notes and questions to promote classroom discourse.

Today's Standards

Tell students that they will be addressing these content and practice standards in this lesson. You may wish to have a student volunteer read aloud *How can I meet these standards?* and *How can I use these practices?* and connect these to the standards.

See the Interactive Presentation for I Can statements that align with the standards covered in this lesson.

Explore Volumes of Square Pyramids

Objective
Students derive the formula for the volume of a square pyramid using informal limit arguments.

 Teaching the Mathematical Practices

6 Communicate Precisely Encourage students to routinely write or explain their solution methods. Point out that they should use clear definitions when they discuss their solutions with others.

Ideas for Use

Recommended Use Present the Inquiry Question, or have a student volunteer read it aloud. Have students work in pairs to complete the Explore activity on their devices. Pairs should discuss each of the questions. Monitor student progress during the activity. Upon completion of the Explore activity, have student volunteers share their responses to the Inquiry Question.

What if my students don't have devices? You may choose to project the activity on a whiteboard. A printable worksheet for each Explore is available online. You may choose to print the worksheet so that individuals or pairs of students can use it to record their observations.

Summary of the Activity
Students will complete guiding exercises throughout the Explore activity. Students begin by considering a step pyramid with the same base and height as a square pyramid, and determine that as the number of steps gets larger, the volume gets closer to the volume of the square pyramid. Then they compute the volume of an individual step based on its side length and height. Next they find the volume of each step based on the dimensions of the original pyramid and the number of steps. Students add them together to get the total volume of the step pyramid. Finally, they use some algebra to determine what happens to this formula as the number of steps increases to find a formula for the volume of the square pyramid. Then, students will answer the Inquiry Question.

Go Online to find additional teaching notes and sample answers for the guiding exercises.

(continued on the next page)

Interactive Presentation

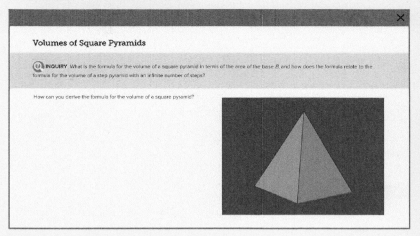

Explore

WATCH

Students watch videos illustrating the derivation of the volume formula.

Interactive Presentation

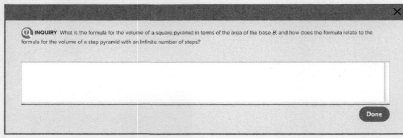

Explore

TYPE

| a| | Students respond to the Inquiry Question and can view a sample answer. |

Explore Volumes of Square Pyramids (*continued*)

Teaching the Mathematical Practices

8 Look for a Pattern Help students to see the pattern in the Explore.

Questions
Have students complete the Explore activity.

Ask:
- Why should each step be the same height? Sample answer: If you use equal heights for each step, you are more accurately approximating a pyramid.
- Could you have found the formula if we started with a different shape for the base of the pyramid? Sample answer: Yes, because we could still use a formula for the area of the base. It's also possible to use the variable B for the area of the base, and let it represent any shape.

Inquiry
What is the formula for the volume of a square pyramid in terms of the area of the base B, and how does the formula relate to the formula for the volume of a step pyramid with an infinite number of steps? Sample answer: $V = \frac{1}{3}Bh$; the formula for the volume of a square pyramid is the same as the formula for the volume of a step pyramid as the number of steps approaches infinity.

Go Online to find additional teaching notes and sample answers for the guiding exercises.

1 CONCEPTUAL UNDERSTANDING | **2 FLUENCY** | 3 APPLICATION

Learn Volumes of Prisms

Objective
Students find volumes of prisms by using the formulas they derive.

 Teaching the Mathematical Practices

7 Use Structure Help students to explore the structure of volumes of prisms in this Learn.

Important to Know
Cavalieri's Principle is very important, because it shows that finding the volume of an oblique solid just requires finding the volume of the corresponding right solid.

Essential Question Follow-Up
Students learn about volume of three-dimensional solids.

Ask:

Why is it important to be able to compute the volume of solids? Sample answer: It is important to know how much can fit into containers or how much material is needed to make an object.

Example 1 Volume of a Prism

 Teaching the Mathematical Practices

6 Use Precision In this example, students must calculate accurately and efficiently and express numerical answers with a degree of precision appropriate to the problem context.

Questions for Mathematical Discourse

AL What is the shape of the base? The base is a regular pentagon.

OL What is the volume of a square prism with side length 7 cm and height 4 cm? 196 cm³

BL What is the height of a square prism with side length 5 cm and volume 225 cm³? 9 cm

Go Online
- Find additional teaching notes.
- View performance reports of the Checks.
- Assign or present an Extra Example.

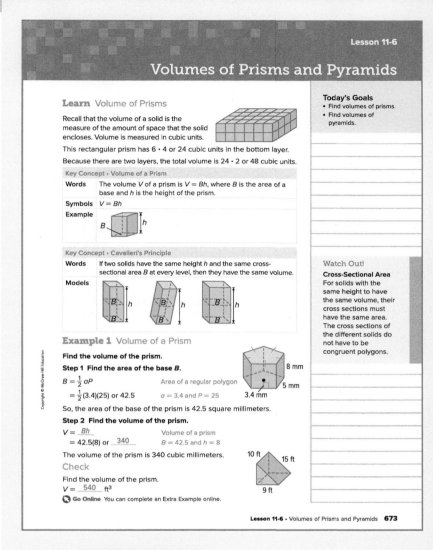

Lesson 11-6

Volumes of Prisms and Pyramids

Learn Volume of Prisms

Recall that the volume of a solid is the measure of the amount of space that the solid encloses. Volume is measured in cubic units.

This rectangular prism has 6 · 4 or 24 cubic units in the bottom layer. Because there are two layers, the total volume is 24 · 2 or 48 cubic units.

Key Concept · Volume of a Prism

Words	The volume V of a prism is $V = Bh$, where B is the area of a base and h is the height of the prism.
Symbols	$V = Bh$
Example	

Key Concept · Cavalieri's Principle

Words	If two solids have the same height h and the same cross-sectional area B at every level, then they have the same volume.
Models	

Example 1 Volume of a Prism

Find the volume of the prism.

Step 1 Find the area of the base B.

$B = \frac{1}{2} aP$ Area of a regular polygon

$= \frac{1}{2}(3.4)(25)$ or 42.5 $a = 3.4$ and $P = 25$

So, the area of the base of the prism is 42.5 square millimeters.

Step 2 Find the volume of the prism.

$V = \underline{Bh}$ Volume of a prism

$= 42.5(8)$ or $\underline{340}$ $B = 42.5$ and $h = 8$

The volume of the prism is 340 cubic millimeters.

Check

Find the volume of the prism.

$V = \underline{540}$ ft³

Go Online You can complete an Extra Example online.

Today's Goals
- Find volumes of prisms.
- Find volumes of pyramids.

Watch Out!
Cross-Sectional Area For solids with the same volume, their cross sections must have the same area. The cross sections of the different solids do not have to be congruent polygons.

Lesson 11-6 · Volumes of Prisms and Pyramids **673**

Interactive Presentation

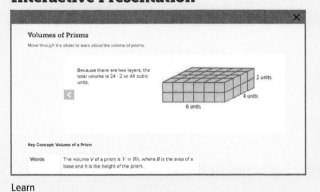

Volumes of Prisms
Move through the slides to learn about the volume of prisms.

Because there are two layers, the total volume is 24 · 2 or 48 cubic units.

2 units
4 units
6 units

Key Concept: Volume of a Prism

Words	The volume V of a prism is $V = Bh$, where B is the area of a base and h is the height of the prism.

Learn

TAP

Students move through the slides to learn about the volume of a prism.

1 CONCEPTUAL UNDERSTANDING | **2 FLUENCY** | **3 APPLICATION**

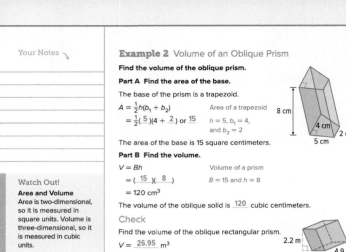

Your Notes

Example 2 Volume of an Oblique Prism

Find the volume of the oblique prism.

Part A Find the area of the base.

The base of the prism is a trapezoid.

$A = \frac{1}{2}h(b_1 + b_2)$ Area of a trapezoid

$= \frac{1}{2}(\underline{5})(4 + \underline{2})$ or $\underline{15}$ $h = 5, b_1 = 4,$ and $b_2 = 2$

The area of the base is 15 square centimeters.

Part B Find the volume.

$V = Bh$ Volume of a prism

$= (\underline{15})(\underline{8})$ $B = 15$ and $h = 8$

$= 120$ cm^3

The volume of the oblique solid is $\underline{120}$ cubic centimeters.

Watch Out!
Area and Volume
Area is two-dimensional, so it is measured in square units. Volume is three-dimensional, so it is measured in cubic units.

Check

Find the volume of the oblique rectangular prism.

$V = \underline{26.95}$ m^3

Example 3 Volume of a Prism Using Algebraic Expressions

SNACKS Gustavo wants to calculate the volume of juice in his juice box in cubic inches.

Part A Find the volume of the juice box in terms of x.

Step 1 Find the area of the base.

The base of the juice box is a rectangle.

$A = \ell w$ Area of a rectangle

$= (\underline{4x})x$ Substitution

$= \underline{4x^2}$ Solve.

Step 2 Find the volume.

$V = Bh$ Volume of a prism

$= (4x^2)(4x + 3)$ Substitute.

$= 16x^3 + 12x^2$ Simplify.

Part B Find the volume of the juice box if $x = 2$.

$V = 16x^3 + 12x^2$ Surface area of a cylinder with one base

$= 16(2)^3 + 12(2)^2$ Substitute.

$= \underline{176}$ in^3 Simplify.

Go Online You can complete an Extra Example online.

674   Module 11 • Measurement

Interactive Presentation

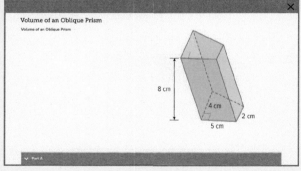

Volume of an Oblique Prism

Example 2

TAP

Students tap through the steps to find the volume of an oblique prism.

CHECK

Students complete the Check online to determine whether they are ready to move on.

Example 2 Volume of an Oblique Prism

MP Teaching the Mathematical Practices

2 Make Sense of Quantities Mathematically proficient students need to be able to make sense of quantities and their relationships. In this example, notice the relationship between the variables and their units.

Questions for Mathematical Discourse

AL Why is the height outside of the prism?   Sample answer: This is one way of visualizing the perpendicular height of the prism. If it were drawn from a different vertex, it could show up inside the prism.

OL If the height of the prism is 10 cm, what is the volume?   150 cm^3

BL If the volume of a prism with the same height is 136 cm^3, what is the area of the base of the prism?   17 cm^2

Common Error

Students may try to find and use the length of the lateral faces of the prism. Remind them that to find volume they need to use the height, not the length of a lateral face.

DIFFERENTIATE

Reteaching Activity **AL**

Students should reason that an oblique square prism can be likened to a stack of squares that has been shifted so that they make an oblique angle with the base. If a line segment is drawn connecting the center of each base (called the axis), then the axis is also an altitude for a right cylinder, but the axis is not an altitude for an oblique cylinder.

Example 3 Volume of a Prism Using Algebraic Expressions

MP Teaching the Mathematical Practices

4 Apply Mathematics In this example, students apply what they have learned about volumes of prisms to solving a real-world problem.

Questions for Mathematical Discourse

AL If $x = 5$, what is the length of the box?   20 units

OL If $x = 3$, what is the volume of the box?   540 units^3

BL If the box is changed so the length is 2 units shorter, what is the expression for the volume in terms of x? $16x^3 + 4x^2 - 6x$

Common Error

Students may forget to multiply by the width x after multiplying the binomials for the length and height together. Remind them that they need to multiply all three dimensions to find volume.

1 CONCEPTUAL UNDERSTANDING | **2 FLUENCY** | **3 APPLICATION**

Learn Volumes of Pyramids

Objective
Students find volumes of pyramids using the formulas they derive.

MP Teaching the Mathematical Practices

2 Make Sense of Quantities Mathematically proficient students need to be able to make sense of quantities and their relationships. In the Learn, notice the relationship between the base, height, and volume of a pyramid and the base, height, and volume of a prism with the same base.

Example 4 Volume of a Pyramid

MP Teaching the Mathematical Practices

4 Use Tools Point out that to solve the problem in this example, students will need to use the formula for the volume of a pyramid.

Questions for Mathematical Discourse

AL How does the volume of a pyramid compare to the volume of a prism with the same base and height? The volume of a pyramid is one-third of the volume of the prism with the same base and height.

OL If the height is changed to 6 cm, what is the new volume? 44 cm³

BL If the base stays the same but the height is changed so that the volume is now 55 cm³, what is the new height? 7.5 cm

⊕ Example 5 Volume of a Pyramid Using Algebraic Expressions

MP Teaching the Mathematical Practices

2 Represent a Situation Symbolically Guide students to define variables to solve the problem in this example. Help students to identify the independent and dependent variables. Then work with them to find the other relationships in the problem.

Questions for Mathematical Discourse

AL If $x = 5$, what is the length of the base of the pyramid? 40

OL If $x = 3$, what is the volume of the pyramid? 1728

BL If the height is changed so it is 3 units shorter, what is the expression for the volume in terms of x? $64x^3 - 64x^2$

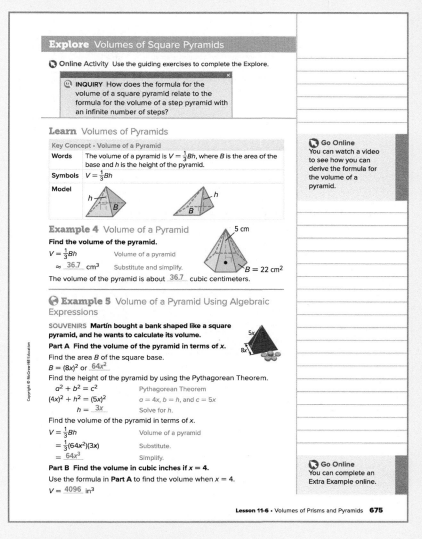

Explore Volumes of Square Pyramids

🔵 **Online Activity** Use the guiding exercises to complete the Explore.

> **INQUIRY** How does the formula for the volume of a square pyramid relate to the formula for the volume of a step pyramid with an infinite number of steps?

Learn Volumes of Pyramids

Key Concept · Volume of a Pyramid

Words	The volume of a pyramid is $V = \frac{1}{3}Bh$, where B is the area of the base and h is the height of the pyramid.
Symbols	$V = \frac{1}{3}Bh$
Model	

Example 4 Volume of a Pyramid

Find the volume of the pyramid.

$V = \frac{1}{3}Bh$ Volume of a pyramid

$\approx$ __36.7__ cm³   Substitute and simplify.

The volume of the pyramid is about __36.7__ cubic centimeters.

5 cm
$B = 22$ cm²

⊕ **Example 5** Volume of a Pyramid Using Algebraic Expressions

SOUVENIRS Martín bought a bank shaped like a square pyramid, and he wants to calculate its volume.

Part A Find the volume of the pyramid in terms of x.

Find the area B of the square base.

$B = (8x)^2$ or __$64x^2$__

Find the height of the pyramid by using the Pythagorean Theorem.

$a^2 + b^2 = c^2$ Pythagorean Theorem

$(4x)^2 + h^2 = (5x)^2$ $a = 4x, b = h,$ and $c = 5x$

$h = $ __$3x$__   Solve for h.

Find the volume of the pyramid in terms of x.

$V = \frac{1}{3}Bh$ Volume of a pyramid

$= \frac{1}{3}(64x^2)(3x)$ Substitute.

$= $ __$64x^3$__   Simplify.

Part B Find the volume in cubic inches if $x = 4$.

Use the formula in **Part A** to find the volume when $x = 4$.

$V = $ __4096__ in³

🔵 **Go Online** You can watch a video to see how you can derive the formula for the volume of a pyramid.

🔵 **Go Online** You can complete an Extra Example online.

Lesson 11-6 · Volumes of Prisms and Pyramids **675**

Interactive Presentation

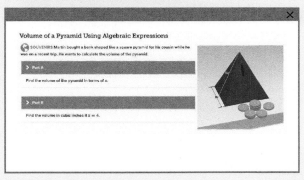

Volume of a Pyramid Using Algebraic Expressions

⊕ SOUVENIRS Martin bought a bank shaped like a square pyramid for his cousin while he was on a recent trip. He wants to calculate the volume of the pyramid.

> Part A

Find the volume of the pyramid in terms of x.

> Part B

Find the volume in cubic inches if x = 4.

Example 5

TYPE

Students type to solve for the volume of a pyramid.

CHECK

Students complete the Check online to determine whether they are ready to move on.

Example 6 Volume of a Composite Solid

Find the volume of the composite solid.

The composite solid is a combination of a prism and a square pyramid.

Part A Find the volume of the prism.

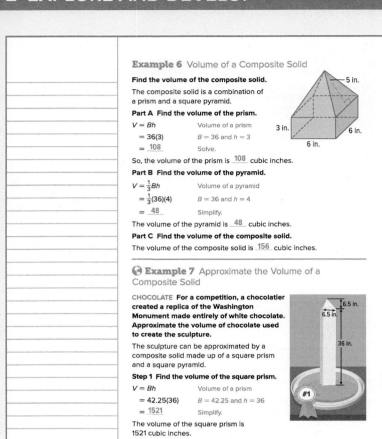

$V = Bh$ Volume of a prism

$= 36(3)$ $B = 36$ and $h = 3$

$= \underline{108}$ Solve.

So, the volume of the prism is $\underline{108}$ cubic inches.

Part B Find the volume of the pyramid.

$V = \frac{1}{3}Bh$ Volume of a pyramid

$= \frac{1}{3}(36)(4)$ $B = 36$ and $h = 4$

$= \underline{48}$ Simplify.

The volume of the pyramid is $\underline{48}$ cubic inches.

Part C Find the volume of the composite solid.

The volume of the composite solid is $\underline{156}$ cubic inches.

🌐 Example 7 Approximate the Volume of a Composite Solid

CHOCOLATE **For a competition, a chocolatier created a replica of the Washington Monument made entirely of white chocolate. Approximate the volume of chocolate used to create the sculpture.**

The sculpture can be approximated by a composite solid made up of a square prism and a square pyramid.

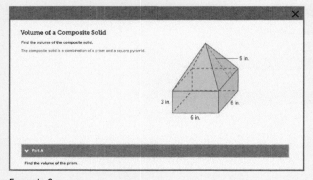

Step 1 Find the volume of the square prism.

$V = Bh$ Volume of a prism

$= 42.25(36)$ $B = 42.25$ and $h = 36$

$= \underline{1521}$ Simplify.

The volume of the square prism is 1521 cubic inches.

Step 2 Find the volume of the square pyramid. Round to the nearest tenth, if necessary.

$V = \frac{1}{3}Bh$ Volume of a pyramid

$= \frac{1}{3}(42.25)(6.5)$ $B = 42.25$ and $h = 6.5$

$\approx \underline{91.5}$ Simplify.

Step 3 Find the volume of the sculpture.

The volume of the sculpture is $\underline{1612.5}$ cubic inches.

🌐 **Go Online**
You can complete an Extra Example online.

Interactive Presentation

Example 6

TAP

Students tap to reveal parts of the solution.

CHECK

📊

Students complete the Check online to determine whether they are ready to move on.

Example 6 Volume of a Composite Solid

MP Teaching the Mathematical Practices

6 Communicate Precisely Encourage students to routinely write or explain their solution methods. Point out that they should use clear definitions when they discuss their solutions with others.

Questions for Mathematical Discourse

AL How can you determine the side length of the base of the pyramid part of the solid? Sample answer: It is the same as the length and width of the prism part of the solid.

OL If the height of the prism is changed to 2 inches, what is the volume of the solid? 120 in³

BL If the sides of the prism and pyramid are changed to 8 inches but the slant height remains the same, what is the height of the pyramid and the volume of the pyramid? 3 in.; 228 in³

🌐 Example 7 Approximate the Volume of a Composite Solid

MP Teaching the Mathematical Practices

4 Apply Mathematics In this example, students will apply what they have learned about volumes of composite solids to solving a real-world problem.

Questions for Mathematical Discourse

AL Do you need to compute the height of the pyramid part in this example? Explain. No; the height is given.

OL The width and height of the prism part of the solid are given. How can you find the length? The length is the same as the width because it is a square prism.

BL If the height of the prism is changed to 30 inches, what is the volume? 1359 in³

Exit Ticket

Recommended Use

At the end of class, go online to display the Exit Ticket prompt and ask students to respond using a separate piece of paper. Have students hand you their responses as they leave the room.

Alternate Use

At the end of class, go online to display the Exit Ticket prompt and ask students to respond verbally or by using a mini-whiteboard. Have students hold up their whiteboards so that you can see all student responses. Tap to reveal the answer when most or all students have completed the Exit Ticket.

Practice and Homework

Suggested Assignments

Use the table below to select appropriate exercises.

DOK	Topic	Exercises
1, 2	exercises that mirror the examples	1–21
2	exercises that use a variety of skills from this lesson	22–30
2	exercises that extend concepts learned in this lesson to new contexts	31, 32
3	exercises that emphasize higher-order and critical-thinking skills	33–36

ASSESS AND DIFFERENTIATE

📊 Use the data from the **Checks** to determine whether to provide resources for extension, remediation, or intervention.

IF students score 90% or more on the Checks,   BL
THEN assign:

- Practice, Exercises 1–31 odd, 33–36
- Extension: Frustums
- 🔵 **ALEKS·** Volumes of Prisms and Cylinders; Volumes of Pyramids and Cones

IF students score 66%–89% on the Checks,   OL
THEN assign:

- Practice, Exercises 1–35 odd
- Remediation, Review Resources: Volume
- Personal Tutors
- Extra Examples 1–7
- 🔵 **ALEKS·** Volume of Prisms and Cylinders; Other Topics Available: Perimeter, Area, and Volume

IF students score 65% or less on the Checks,   AL
THEN assign:

- Practice, Exercises 1–21 odd
- Remediation, Review Resources: Volume
- *Quick Review Math Handbook*: Volumes of Prisms and Cylinders
- 🔵 **ALEKS·** Volume of Prisms and Cylinders; Other Topics Available: Perimeter, Area, and Volume

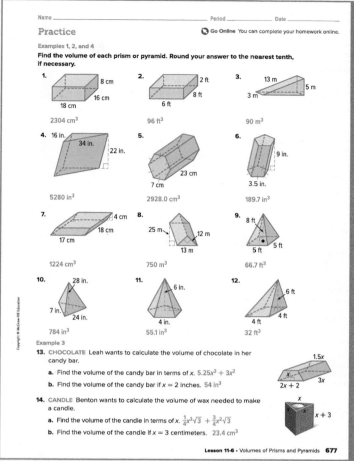

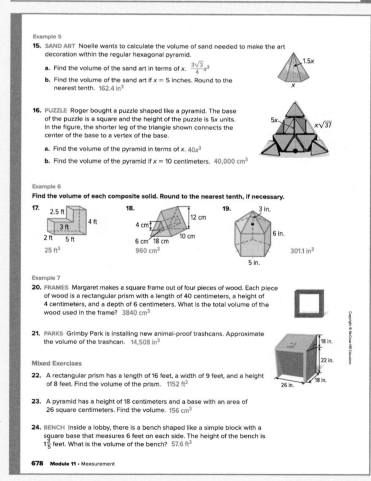

1 CONCEPTUAL UNDERSTANDING | 2 FLUENCY | 3 APPLICATION

Name _____ Period _____ Date _____

25. TUNNELS Construction workers are digging a tunnel through a mountain. The space inside the tunnel is going to be shaped like a rectangular prism. The mouth of the tunnel will be a rectangle 20 feet high and 50 feet wide, and the length of the tunnel will be 900 feet. What volume of rock must be removed to make the tunnel? **900,000 ft³**

26. GREENHOUSES A greenhouse has the shape of a square pyramid. The base has a side length of 30 yards. The height of the greenhouse is 18 yards. What is the volume of the greenhouse? **5400 yd³**

27. STAGES A solid wooden stage is made out of oak, which has a weight of about 45 pounds per cubic foot. The stage has the form of a square pyramid with the top sliced off along a plane parallel to the base. The side length of the top square is 12 feet, and the side length of the bottom square is 16 feet. The height of the stage is 3 feet.

a. What is the volume of the entire square pyramid from which the stage is made? **1024 ft³**
b. What is the volume of the top of the pyramid that is removed to create the stage? **432 ft³**
c. What is the volume of the stage? **592 ft³**
d. What is the weight of the stage? **about 26,640 pounds**

28. PRECISION Refer to the prisms.

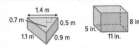

a. What is the volume of the triangular prism? **0.245 m³**
b. What is the volume of the rectangular prism? **440 in³**
c. Discuss how the formulas that you used to find the volume of each prism are similar. **See margin.**

29. USE A MODEL Benjamin finds that baking soda has a mass of 2.2 grams per cubic centimeter, and corn flakes have a mass of 0.12 gram per cubic centimeter. A box of baking soda is 8 centimeters long by 4 centimeters wide by 12 centimeters high. The dimensions for a box of corn flakes are 30 centimeters long by 6 centimeters wide by 35 centimeters high. Benjamin wants to find the mass of the contents of each box if each box is filled to within 2 centimeters of the top. **a–b. See margin.**

a. How can Benjamin determine the mass of the contents of each box?
b. Find the mass of the contents of each box.

Lesson 11-6 · Volumes of Prisms and Pyramids 679

---

30. STRUCTURE A model pyramid has a volume of 270 cubic feet and a base area of 90 square feet. What is the height if the pyramid is a right pyramid? What is the height if the pyramid is an oblique pyramid? Explain your reasoning.
Sample answer: The height is 9 feet whether the pyramid is right or oblique. The same formula is used for both: $V = \frac{1}{3}Bh$; so, $270 = \frac{1}{3}(90)(h)$ and $h = \frac{270}{30}$ or 9 feet.

31. REASONING Tristan makes and sells sugar-free candies. He packages them in square pyramid-shaped boxes with a height of 3 inches and a base that has a side length of 2 inches. He sells each box for $2.00. **a–c. See margin.**

a. What is the volume of the sugar-free candies in each box? What is the price per cubic inch?
b. Tristan wants to make a bigger package by doubling the lengths of the sides of the square base. How can he figure out how much to charge if he wants to keep the price per cubic inch the same?
c. Tristan wants to design a box in the shape of a square pyramid that holds between 7 and 8 cubic inches of sugar-free candies. He wants the height to be within $1\frac{1}{4}$ inches of the length of each side of the base. What is one possible set of dimensions that he can use?

32. STRUCTURE Anisa is building a box in the shape of a right triangular prism for her magic act. She is making a secret compartment inside the box. The compartment will be a pyramid with base $\triangle ABE$ and vertex at point C. After the secret compartment has been made, how is the volume of the space remaining inside the box related to the volume of the secret compartment? Explain your reasoning. **See margin.**

🧠 **Higher-Order Thinking Skills**

33. FIND THE ERROR Francisco and Valerie each calculated the volume of an equilateral triangular prism with a height of 5 units and a base that has an apothem of 4 units. Who is correct? Explain your reasoning. **See margin.**

Francisco	Valerie
$V = Bh$	$V = Bh$
$= \frac{1}{2}aP \cdot h$	$= \frac{\sqrt{3}}{2}s^2 \cdot h$
$= \frac{1}{2}(4)(24\sqrt{3}) \cdot 5$	$= \frac{\sqrt{3}}{2}(4\sqrt{3})^2 \cdot 5$
$= 240\sqrt{3}$ cubic units	$= 120\sqrt{3}$ cubic units

34. CREATE Give an example of a pyramid and a prism that have the same base and the same volume. Explain your reasoning. **See margin.**

35. ANALYZE Make a conjecture about how many pentagonal pyramids will fit inside a pentagonal prism of the same height. Justify your answer. **See margin.**

36. PERSEVERE Write an equation to find the dimensions of a composite solid composed of a cube with a square pyramid on top of equal height. If the volume is equal to 36 cubic inches, what are the dimensions of the solid? $\frac{4}{3}x^3$; The length, width, and height of both the cube and the square pyramid are 3 inches.

680 Module 11 · Measurement

Answers

28c. Each volume is found by multiplying the area of a two-dimensional base by a height. For part **a**, a triangle with area 0.49 m² is the base, multiplied by a height of 0.5 m. In part **b**, the base is a rectangle with an area of 55 in² multiplied by a height of 8 in.

29a. Sample answer: He can find the volume of the contents of each box by multiplying the length times the width times 2 less than the height of the box and then multiply by the mass per cubic centimeter of the contents.

29b. baking soda: volume = 8 · 4 · 10 = 320 cm³, weight = 320 · 2.2 = 704 grams; corn flakes: volume = 30 · 6 · 33 = 5940 cm³, weight = 5940 · 0.12 = 712.8 grams

31a. $V = \frac{1}{3} \cdot 2^2 \cdot 3 = 4$; the volume is 4 in³, and the price per cubic inch is $0.50.

31b. Sample answer: Doubling the length and the width multiplies the volume by 4. He would need to multiply the price by 4 and charge $8.00 for the larger box.

31c. Sample answer: base has sides of 3 inches, and the height is 2.5 inches; $V = \frac{1}{3} \cdot 3^2 \cdot 2.5 = 7.5$; the volume is 7.5 in³.

32. The volume of the remaining space is twice as great as the volume of the secret compartment; the secret compartment is one of three pyramids of equal volume that make up the triangular prism. So, the secret compartment has $\frac{1}{3}$ the volume of the prism, and the remaining space has $\frac{2}{3}$ the volume of the prism, or twice as much space as the secret compartment.

33. Francisco; sample answer: Valerie incorrectly used $4\sqrt{3}$ as the length of one side of the triangular base. Francisco used a different approach, but his solution is correct.

34. Sample answer: a square pyramid with a base area of 16 and a height of 12, a prism with a square base area of 16 and a height of 4; if a pyramid and prism have the same base, then in order to have the same volume, the height of the pyramid must be 3 times as great as the height of the prism.

35. 3; Sample answer: Because the volume of a pyramid is one-third the volume of the same prism, 3 of the pentagonal pyramids would fit in a prism of the same height.

Volumes of Cylinders, Cones, and Spheres

LESSON GOAL

Students find volumes of cylinders, cones, and spheres by using the formulas they derive.

1 LAUNCH

 Launch the lesson with a **Warm Up** and an introduction.

2 EXPLORE AND DEVELOP

 Develop:

Volumes of Cylinders
- Approximate the Volume of a Cylinder
- Volume of a Cylinder

Volumes of Cones
- Volume of a Cone
- Approximate the Volume of a Cone

 Explore: Volumes of Spheres

 Develop:

Volumes of Spheres
- Approximate the Volume of a Sphere
- Volume of a Sphere
- Volume of a Composite Solid
- Approximate the Volume of a Composite Solid

 You may want your students to complete the **Checks** online.

3 REFLECT AND PRACTICE

 Exit Ticket

 Practice

DIFFERENTIATE

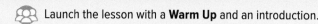 View reports of student progress on the **Checks** after each example.

Resources	AL	OL	BL	ELL
Remediation: Volume of Cones	●	●		●
Extension: Cavalieri's Principle		●	●	●

Language Development Handbook

Assign page 80 of the *Language Development Handbook* to help your students build mathematical language related to finding the volumes of cylinders, cones, and spheres.

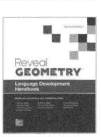

ELL You can use the tips and suggestions on page T80 of the handbook to support students who are building English proficiency.

Suggested Pacing

90 min	**1 day**
45 min	**2 days**

Focus

Domain: Geometry

Standards for Mathematical Content:

G.GMD.1 Give an informal argument for the formulas for the circumference of a circle, area of a circle, volume of a cylinder, pyramid, and cone.

G.GMD.2 Give an informal argument using Cavalieri's principle for the formulas for the volume of a sphere and other solid figures.

G.GMD.3 Use volume formulas for cylinders, pyramids, cones, and spheres to solve problems.

Standards for Mathematical Practice:

3 Construct viable arguments and critique the reasoning of others.

4 Model with mathematics.

6 Attend to precision.

Coherence

Vertical Alignment

Previous
Students understood volume of cylinders, cones, and spheres.
8.G.9

Now
Students find volumes of cylinders, cones, and spheres.
G.GMD.3

Next
Students will find measures of similar figures and solids by using scale factors.
G.GMD.3

Rigor

The Three Pillars of Rigor

1 CONCEPTUAL UNDERSTANDING	2 FLUENCY	3 APPLICATION

Conceptual Bridge In this lesson, students continue to expand their understanding of volume. They build fluency by finding areas of cylinders, cones, and spheres, and they apply their understanding by finding volumes of solid figures in the real world.

Interactive Presentation

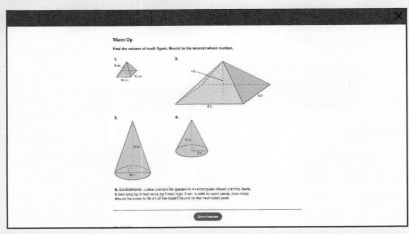

Warm Up

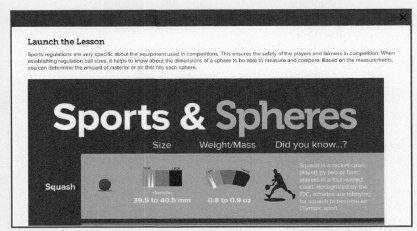

Launch the Lesson

Warm Up

Prerequisite Skills

The Warm Up exercises address the following prerequisite skill for this lesson:

- finding volumes of prisms, pyramids, and cones

Answers:

1. 300 cm³
2. 64 ft³
3. 393 in³
4. 85 in³
5. 3 yd³

Launch the Lesson

 Teaching the Mathematical Practices

> **4 Apply Mathematics** In this Launch the Lesson, students can see real-world applications of volumes of spheres.

Go Online to find additional teaching notes and questions to promote classroom discourse.

Today's Standards

Tell students that they will be addressing these content and practice standards in this lesson. You may wish to have a student volunteer read aloud *How can I meet these standards?* and *How can I use these practices?* and connect these to the standards.

See the Interactive Presentation for I Can statements that align with the standards covered in this lesson.

Mathematical Background

Like the volume of a prism, the volume of a cylinder has a volume of V cubic units, a height of h units, and the bases have radii of r units, then $V = \pi r^2 h$. Similarly, if a cone has a volume V, a height h, and the base has a radius r, then $V = \frac{1}{3}\pi r^2 h$. If a sphere has a volume of V cubic units and a radius of r units, then $V = \frac{4}{3}\pi r^3$.

Explore Volumes of Spheres

Objective
Students derive the formula of a sphere by using Cavalieri's Principle.

 Teaching the Mathematical Practices

3 Justify Conclusions Mathematically proficient students can explain the conclusions drawn when solving a problem. This Explore asks students to justify their conclusions.

Ideas for Use

Recommended Use Present the Inquiry Question, or have a student volunteer read it aloud. Have students work in pairs to complete the Explore activity on their devices. Pairs should discuss each of the questions. Monitor student progress during the activity. Upon completion of the Explore activity, have student volunteers share their responses to the Inquiry Question.

What if my students don't have devices? You may choose to project the activity on a whiteboard. A printable worksheet for each Explore is available online. You may choose to print the worksheet so that individuals or pairs of students can use it to record their observations.

Summary of the Activity

Students will complete guiding exercises throughout the Explore activity. Students begin by examining a cylinder with height equal to its radius and a cone of the same base and height removed. Students determine the volume of this solid in terms of its radius. Students then determine the area of a cross section of the solid in terms of the overall radius and the distance the cross section is from the vertex of the cone. Next, students examine a hemisphere with the same radius. They determine the area of a cross section in the same terms, and find that the cross sections have the same area. Finally, students use Cavalieri's Principle to determine that the first solid and the hemisphere have the same volume, giving them a formula for the volume of a sphere. Then, students will answer the Inquiry Question.

Go Online to find additional teaching notes and sample answers for the guiding exercises.

(continued on the next page)

Interactive Presentation

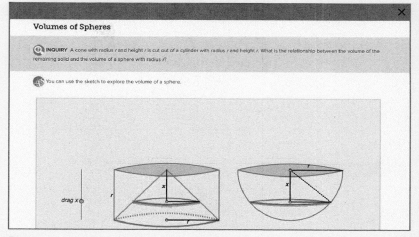

Explore

WEB SKETCHPAD

Students use a sketch to explore the volume of a sphere.

G.GMD.1, G.GMD.2

Interactive Presentation

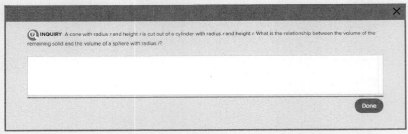

Explore

TYPE

a|

Students respond to the Inquiry Question and can view a sample answer.

Explore Volumes of Spheres (*continued*)

 Teaching the Mathematical Practices

3 Analyze Cases The Explore guides students to examine the cases of the cross sections of two solids. Encourage students to familiarize themselves with all of the cases.

Questions

Have students complete the Explore activity.

Ask:

- Why does the cross section of the cone grow as the cross section of the hemisphere shrinks? Sample answer: The hemisphere is created by removing the cone from the cylinder, so it makes sense that when you are removing more from the cylinder, there will be less to make up the new solid.

- Why did the cylinder need to have a height and radius of r? Sample answer: A hemisphere has only a single dimension, which is the radius. All points on the surface of the hemisphere are at an equal distance from the center. So, in order to create the hemisphere with the new solid, the height should be equal to the radius.

Inquiry

A cone with radius r and height r is cut out of a cylinder with radius r and height r. What is the relationship between the volume of the remaining solid and the volume of a sphere with radius r? Sample answer: The volume of the sphere is equal to twice the volume of a solid created by removing a cone of height and radius r from a cylinder with height and radius r.

Go Online to find additional teaching notes and sample answers for the guiding exercises.

1 CONCEPTUAL UNDERSTANDING | **2 FLUENCY** | **3 APPLICATION**

Learn Volumes of Cylinders

Objective
Students find volumes of cylinders by using the formulas they derive.

MP Teaching the Mathematical Practices

8 Look for a Pattern Help students to see the pattern in this Learn.

🌐 Example 1 Approximate the Volume of a Cylinder

MP Teaching the Mathematical Practices

4 Apply Mathematics In this example, students apply what they have learned about volumes of cylinders to solving a real-world problem.

Questions for Mathematical Discourse

AL How do we know that the equations $V = Bh$ and $V = \pi r^2 h$ are equivalent for a cylinder? The base of a cylinder is a circle, and the area of the base is $B = \pi r^2$.

OL If the height of the cylinder is increased to 12 in., what is the volume? 58.9 in³

BL If the height is changed and the volume is now 39.3 in³, what is the new height? about 8 in.

Example 2 Volume of a Cylinder

MP Teaching the Mathematical Practices

5 Use Mathematical Tools Point out that to solve the problem in this example, students will need to use pencil and paper. Work with students to explore and deepen their understanding of volumes of cylinders.

Questions for Mathematical Discourse

AL If $x = 8$, what is the radius of the cylinder? 3 cm

OL If $x = 10$, what is the volume of the cylinder? 785.4 cm³

BL If the cylinder is changed so the radius is 2 units longer, what is the expression for the volume in terms of x? $\pi(x - 3)^2 x$

Common Error
Students may confuse the dimensions they are given. Encourage them to draw a well-labeled diagram.

🖱 Go Online
- Find additional teaching notes.
- View performance reports of the Checks.
- Assign or present an Extra Example.

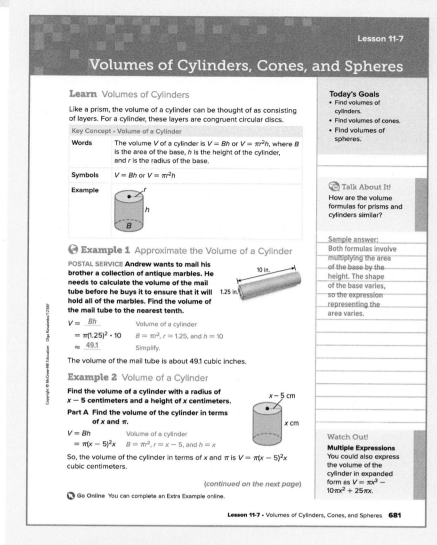

Volumes of Cylinders, Cones, and Spheres

Learn Volumes of Cylinders

Like a prism, the volume of a cylinder can be thought of as consisting of layers. For a cylinder, these layers are congruent circular discs.

Key Concept · Volume of a Cylinder

Words	The volume V of a cylinder is $V = Bh$ or $V = \pi r^2 h$, where B is the area of the base, h is the height of the cylinder, and r is the radius of the base.
Symbols	$V = Bh$ or $V = \pi r^2 h$
Example	

Today's Goals
- Find volumes of cylinders.
- Find volumes of cones.
- Find volumes of spheres.

🗨 Talk About It!
How are the volume formulas for prisms and cylinders similar?

Sample answer: Both formulas involve multiplying the area of the base by the height. The shape of the base varies, so the expression representing the area varies.

🌐 Example 1 Approximate the Volume of a Cylinder

POSTAL SERVICE Andrew wants to mail his brother a collection of antique marbles. He needs to calculate the volume of the mail tube before he buys it to ensure that it will hold all of the marbles. Find the volume of the mail tube to the nearest tenth.

10 in.
1.25 in.

$V = \underline{Bh}$ Volume of a cylinder
$= \pi(1.25)^2 \cdot 10$ $B = \pi r^2, r = 1.25,$ and $h = 10$
$\approx \underline{49.1}$ Simplify.

The volume of the mail tube is about 49.1 cubic inches.

Example 2 Volume of a Cylinder

Find the volume of a cylinder with a radius of $x - 5$ centimeters and a height of x centimeters.

Part A Find the volume of the cylinder in terms of x and π.

$x - 5$ cm
x cm

$V = Bh$ Volume of a cylinder
$= \pi(x - 5)^2 x$ $B = \pi r^2, r = x - 5,$ and $h = x$

So, the volume of the cylinder in terms of x and π is $V = \pi(x - 5)^2 x$ cubic centimeters.

Watch Out!
Multiple Expressions You could also express the volume of the cylinder in expanded form as $V = \pi x^3 - 10\pi x^2 + 25\pi x$.

(continued on the next page)

🔵 **Go Online** You can complete an Extra Example online.

Interactive Presentation

Volumes of Cylinders

Like a prism, the volume of a cylinder can be thought of as consisting of layers. For a cylinder, these layers are congruent circular discs, similar to the coins in the roll shown. If we interpret the area of the base as the volume of a one-unit high layer and the height of the cylinder as the number of layers, then the volume of the cylinder is equal to the volume of a layer times the number of layers or the area of the base times the height.

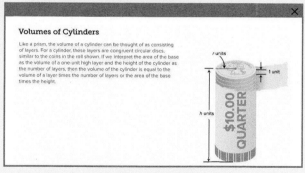

Learn

TYPE

Students type to answer the Talk About It! question.

CHECK

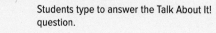

Students complete the Check online to determine whether they are ready to move on.

1 CONCEPTUAL UNDERSTANDING | **2 FLUENCY** | 3 APPLICATION

Left panel

Your Notes

Part B Find the volume.

Find the volume of the cylinder rounded to the nearest tenth if $x = 8$.

Substitute the value of x into the expression you found in **Part A**.

$V = \pi(x - 5)^2 x$ Expression from Part A

$= \pi(8 - 5)^2 \cdot 8$ Substitute.

$\approx \underline{226.2}$ Simplify.

The volume of the cylinder is about ___226.2___ cubic centimeters.

Watch Out!

Volumes of Cones The formula for the surface area of a cone only applies to right cones. However, the formula for the volume applies to oblique cones as well as right cones.

 Think About It!

Determine whether the following statement is *sometimes, always,* or *never* true. Justify your reasoning. The volume of a cone with radius r and height h equals the volume of a prism with height h.

~~Sometimes; sample answer: The statement is true if the base area of the cone is 3 times as great as the base area of the prism. For example, if the base of the prism has an area of 10 square units, then its volume is $10h$ cubic units. So, the cone must have a base area of 30 square units so that its volume is $\frac{1}{3}(30)h$ or $10h$ cubic units.~~

Learn Volumes of Cones

The pyramid and prism shown have the same base area B and height h as the cylinder and cone. You can use Cavalieri's Principle and similar triangles to show that the volume of the cone is equal to the volume of the pyramid.

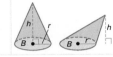

Key Concept • Volume of a Cone

Words	The volume of a circular cone is $V = \frac{1}{3}Bh$, or $V = \frac{1}{3}\pi r^2 h$, where B is the area of the base, h is the height of the cone, and r is the radius of the base.
Symbols	$V = \frac{1}{3}Bh$ or $V = \frac{1}{3}\pi r^2 h$
Model	

Example 3 Volume of a Cone

Examine the cone.

Part A Find the volume of a cone in terms of x and π.

$V = \frac{1}{3}Bh$ Volume of a cone

$= \frac{1}{3}\pi r^2 h$ $B = \pi r^2$

$= \frac{1}{3}\pi(x - 1)^2(3x - 5)$ $r = x - 1$ and $h = 3x - 5$

So, the volume of the cone in terms of x and π is

$V = \frac{1}{3}\pi(x - 1)^2(3x - 5)$ cubic feet.

(continued on the next page)

 Go Online You can complete an Extra Example online.

Interactive Presentation

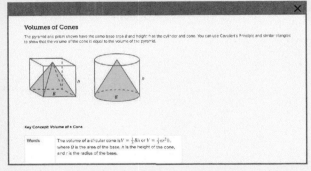

Learn

TYPE

a|

Students type to answer the Think About It! question.

Right panel

Learn Volumes of Cones

Objective

Students find volumes of cones by using the formulas they derive.

MP Teaching the Mathematical Practices

3 Construct Arguments In this Learn, students use stated assumptions, definitions, and previously established results to construct an argument.

Things to Remember

Notice the connections between the various volume formulas; the volume formulas of prisms and cylinders are basically the same, and the volume formulas of pyramids and cones are basically the same.

Example 3 Volume of a Cone

MP Teaching the Mathematical Practices

6 Communicate Precisely Encourage students to routinely write and explain their solution methods. Point out that they should use clear definitions when they discuss their solutions with others.

Questions for Mathematical Discourse

AL If $x = 5$, what is the height of the cone? 10 ft

OL If $x = 3$, what is the volume of the cone? 16.8 ft^3

BL If the cone is changed so the height is 4 units longer, what is the expression for the volume in terms of x? $\frac{1}{3}\pi(x - 1)^2(3x - 1)$

Common Error

Students may incorrectly square the binomial when computing the volume. Remind them of the formula for the square of a binomial, or remind them that a square means that the binomial is multiplied by itself and they can then use FOIL.

1 CONCEPTUAL UNDERSTANDING | **2 FLUENCY** | **3 APPLICATION**

🌐 Example 4 Approximate the Volume of a Cone

🔵 Teaching the Mathematical Practices

6 Use Precision In this example, students learn how to calculate accurately and efficiently and to express numerical answers with a degree of precision appropriate to the problem context.

Questions for Mathematical Discourse

AL What does the measurement 15 cm represent? the slant height

OL How can you use the given information to find the height? Use the Pythagorean Theorem with half the diameter and the slant height to find the height.

BL How would you find the angle formed by the slant height and the radius? Sample answer: I would use the inverse cosine of half the diameter divided by the slant height.

DIFFERENTIATE

AL **BL**

Reteaching Activity When you discuss the volume of cones, show students that 3 cones fit into a cylinder with the same corresponding base and height by filling a cone with water, rice, or beans and pouring it into the corresponding cylinder.

Part B Find the volume of the cone to the nearest tenth if $x = 4$.

Substitute the value of x into the expression you found in **Part A**.

$V = \frac{1}{3}\pi(x-1)^2(3x-5)$ Expression from Part A

$= \frac{1}{3}\pi(4-1)^2[3(4)-5]$ Substitute.

$\approx \underline{66.0}$ Simplify.

The volume of the cone is about __66.0__ cubic feet.

🌐 Example 4 Approximate the Volume of a Cone

TREATS Alyssa serves ice cream in paper cones with plastic lids. What is the volume of the paper cone?

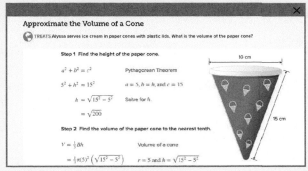

Step 1 Find the height of the paper cone.

$a^2 + b^2 = c^2$ Pythagorean Theorem

$5^2 + h^2 = \underline{15^2}$ $a = 5$, $b = h$, and $c = 15$

$h = \sqrt{200}$ Solve for h.

Step 2 Find the volume of the paper cone to the nearest tenth.

$V = \frac{1}{3}Bh$ Volume of a cone

$= \frac{1}{3}\pi(5)^2(\sqrt{200})$ $r = 5$ and $h = \sqrt{200}$

$\approx \underline{370.2}$ Simplify.

The volume of the paper cone is about 370.2 cubic centimeters.

Check

DÉCOR A soap dispenser can be modeled by a cone with a height of 15 centimeters and a radius of 4 centimeters. What is the approximate volume of soap that the dispenser can hold? Round your answer to the nearest tenth.

$V \approx \underline{251.3}$ cm³

> **Watch Out!**
> **Rounding** When you find the height of the ice cream container, you may be tempted to round that measure to the nearest tenth. However, rounding at that stage in the calculation will change the final calculation of the volume. Whenever possible, avoid rounding at intermediate steps. Wait to round until you have calculated the final answer.

🔄 **Go Online** You can complete an Extra Example online.

Interactive Presentation

Approximate the Volume of a Cone

🌐 **TREATS** Alyssa serves ice cream in paper cones with plastic lids. What is the volume of the paper cone?

Step 1 Find the height of the paper cone.

$a^2 + b^2 = c^2$ Pythagorean Theorem

$5^2 + h^2 = 15^2$ $a = 5$, $b = h$, and $c = 15$

$h = \sqrt{15^2 - 5^2}$ Solve for h.

$= \sqrt{200}$

Step 2 Find the volume of the paper cone to the nearest tenth.

$V = \frac{1}{3}Bh$ Volume of a cone

$= \frac{1}{3}\pi(5)^2\left(\sqrt{15^2 - 5^2}\right)$ $r = 5$ and $h = \sqrt{15^2 - 5^2}$

Example 4

TAP

Students tap to reveal parts of the solution.

CHECK

Students complete the Check online to determine whether they are ready to move on.

Explore Volumes of Spheres

Online Activity Use dynamic geometry software to complete the Explore.

INQUIRY A cone with radius r and height r is cut out of a cylinder with radius r and height r. What is the relationship between the volume of the remaining solid and the volume of a sphere with radius r?

Learn Volumes of Spheres

Go Online A derivation of the formula for the volume of a sphere is available.

Suppose a sphere with radius r contains infinitely many pyramids with vertices at the center of the sphere. Each pyramid has height r. The sum of the volumes of all the pyramids equals the volume of the sphere.

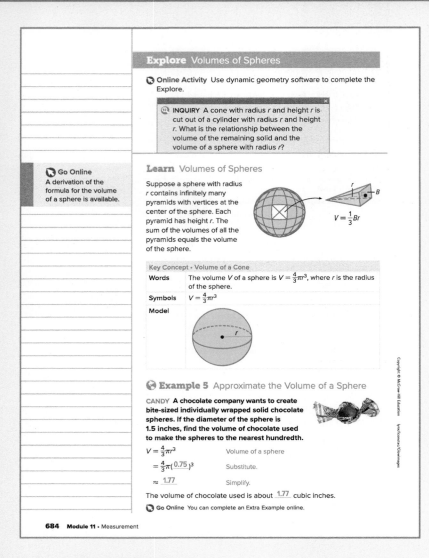

$V = \frac{1}{3}Br$

Key Concept • Volume of a Cone

Words	The volume V of a sphere is $V = \frac{4}{3}\pi r^3$, where r is the radius of the sphere.
Symbols	$V = \frac{4}{3}\pi r^3$
Model	

Example 5 Approximate the Volume of a Sphere

CANDY A chocolate company wants to create bite-sized individually wrapped solid chocolate spheres. If the diameter of the sphere is 1.5 inches, find the volume of chocolate used to make the spheres to the nearest hundredth.

$V = \frac{4}{3}\pi r^3$ Volume of a sphere

$ = \frac{4}{3}\pi(\underline{0.75})^3$ Substitute.

$ \approx \underline{1.77}$ Simplify.

The volume of chocolate used is about __1.77__ cubic inches.

Go Online You can complete an Extra Example online.

Interactive Presentation

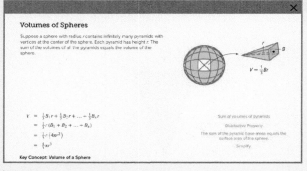

Volumes of Spheres

Suppose a sphere with radius r contains infinitely many pyramids with vertices at the center of the sphere. Each pyramid has height r. The sum of the volumes of all the pyramids equals the volume of the sphere.

Key Concept: Volume of a Sphere

Learn

TAP

Students tap to reveal steps in the solution.

Learn Volumes of Spheres

Objective
Students find volumes of spheres by using the formulas they derive.

MP Teaching the Mathematical Practices

7 Interpret Complicated Expressions Mathematically proficient students can see complicated expressions as single objects or as being composed of several objects. In this Learn, guide students to see what information they can gather about the expression just from looking at it.

Common Misconception
Students may have difficulty remembering the formulas for the surface area and volume of a sphere. Remind students that area requires only two dimensions, and so contains the square of the radius, and volume requires three dimensions, and so contains the cube of the radius.

Example 5 Approximate the Volume of a Sphere

MP Teaching the Mathematical Practices

4 Apply Mathematics In this example, students apply what they have learned about volumes of spheres to solving a real-world problem.

Questions for Mathematical Discourse

AL Can you substitute 1.5 into the formula for the volume of a sphere? Explain. No; 1.5 in. represents the diameter of the candy, and the formula uses the radius.

OL What is the volume of a hemisphere with diameter 15 cm? 883.6 cm³

BL What is the radius of a sphere with a volume of 180 cm³? about 3.5 cm

DIFFERENTIATE

Language Development Activity AL BL ELL
Have students research the diameters of planets and moons in our solar system. Ask them to compute the volume of those astronomical objects, and check their work based on research on the objects' volumes.

Example 6 Volume of a Sphere

Teaching the Mathematical Practices

2 Represent a Situation Symbolically Guide students to define variables to solve the problem in this example. Help students to identify the independent and dependent variables. Then work with them to find the other relationships in the problem.

Questions for Mathematical Discourse

AL What do you need to know to determine the radius of the sphere? *the value of x*

OL If $x = 5$, what is the volume of the sphere? *9202.8 in³*

BL If the sphere is changed so the radius is doubled, what is the expression for the volume in terms of x? $\frac{4}{3}\pi(4x + 6)^3$

Example 7 Volume of a Composite Solid

Teaching the Mathematical Practices

4 Use Tools Point out that to solve the problem in this example, students will need to use the formulas for the volumes of cones and hemispheres.

Questions for Mathematical Discourse

AL How are the hemisphere and cone related? *They have the same radius.*

OL If the radius is changed to 5 mm, what is the volume? *706.9 mm³*

BL If the radius changes and the volume is now 1590.7 mm³, what is the new radius? *approximately 7 mm*

Example 6 Volume of a Sphere

Examine the sphere.

Part A Find the volume of the sphere in terms of x and π.

$V = \frac{4}{3}\pi r^3$ Volume of a sphere

$= \frac{4}{3}\pi(2x + 3)^3$ $r = 2x + 3$

So, the volume of the sphere in terms of x and π is $V = \frac{4}{3}\pi(2x + 3)^3$ cubic inches.

Part B Find the volume of the sphere if $x = 2.2$.

Substitute the value of x into the expression you found in **Part A**.

$V = \frac{4}{3}\pi(2x + 3)^3$ Expression from Part A

$= \frac{4}{3}\pi[2(\underline{2.2}) + 3]^3$ Substitute.

$\approx \underline{1697.4}$ Simplify.

The volume of the sphere is about $\underline{1697.4}$ cubic inches.

Example 7 Volume of a Composite Solid

Find the volume of the composite solid.

The composite solid is a combination of a cone and a hemisphere.

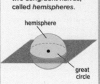

Step 1 Find the volume of the cone to the nearest tenth.

$V = \frac{1}{3}Bh$ Volume of a cone

$= \frac{1}{3}\pi r^2 h$ $B = \pi r^2$

$= \frac{1}{3}\pi(8)^2(17)$ $r = 8$ and $h = 17$

$\approx \underline{1139.4}$ Simplify.

The volume of the paper cone is about $\underline{1139.4}$ mm³.

Step 2 Find the volume of the hemisphere to the nearest tenth.

$V = \frac{1}{2}\left(\frac{4}{3}\pi r^3\right)$ Volume of a hemisphere

$= \frac{2}{3}\pi(8)^3$ $r = 8$

$\approx \underline{1072.3}$ Simplify.

The volume of the hemisphere is about $\underline{1072.3}$ mm³.

Step 3 Find the volume of the composite solid.

The volume of the composite solid is the sum of the volumes of the cone and the hemisphere.

$V \approx \underline{2211.7}$ mm³

 Go Online You can complete an Extra Example online.

Watch Out!

Multiple Expressions You could also express the volume of the sphere in expanded form as

$V = \frac{32\pi x^3 + 144\pi x^2 + 216\pi x + 108\pi}{3}$

cubic inches.

Study Tip

Hemispheres A plane can intersect a sphere in a point or in a circle. If the circle contains the center of the sphere, the intersection is called a *great circle*. A great circle separates a sphere into two congruent halves, called *hemispheres*.

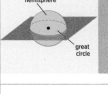

Interactive Presentation

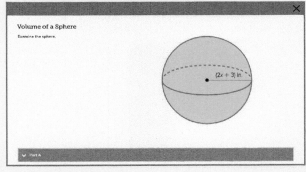

Example 6

TAP

 Students tap to reveal steps in the solution.

CHECK

Students complete the Check online to determine whether they are ready to move on.

1 CONCEPTUAL UNDERSTANDING | **2 FLUENCY** | 3 APPLICATION

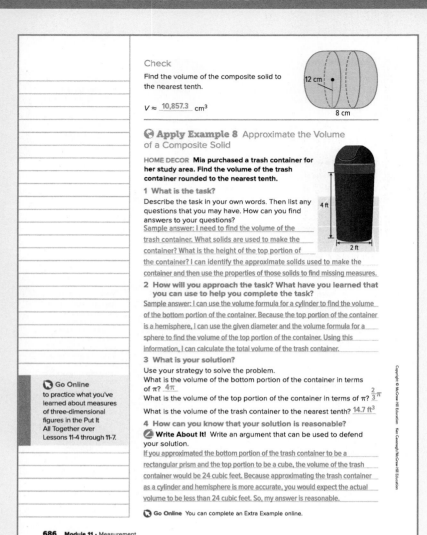

Check

Find the volume of the composite solid to the nearest tenth.

$V \approx \underline{10,857.3}$ cm³

12 cm

8 cm

Apply Example 8 Approximate the Volume of a Composite Solid

HOME DECOR **Mia purchased a trash container for her study area. Find the volume of the trash container rounded to the nearest tenth.**

1 What is the task?

Describe the task in your own words. Then list any questions that you may have. How can you find answers to your questions?

Sample answer: I need to find the volume of the trash container. What solids are used to make the container? What is the height of the top portion of the container? I can identify the approximate solids used to make the container and then use the properties of those solids to find missing measures.

2 How will you approach the task? What have you learned that you can use to help you complete the task?

Sample answer: I can use the volume formula for a cylinder to find the volume of the bottom portion of the container. Because the top portion of the container is a hemisphere, I can use the given diameter and the volume formula for a sphere to find the volume of the top portion of the container. Using this information, I can calculate the total volume of the trash container.

3 What is your solution?

Use your strategy to solve the problem.

What is the volume of the bottom portion of the container in terms of π? 4π

What is the volume of the top portion of the container in terms of π? $\frac{2}{3}\pi$

What is the volume of the trash container to the nearest tenth? 14.7 ft³

4 How can you know that your solution is reasonable?

✎ **Write About It!** Write an argument that can be used to defend your solution.

If you approximated the bottom portion of the trash container to be a rectangular prism and the top portion to be a cube, the volume of the trash container would be 24 cubic feet. Because approximating the trash container as a cylinder and hemisphere is more accurate, you would expect the actual volume to be less than 24 cubic feet. So, my answer is reasonable.

Go Online You can complete an Extra Example online.

 Go Online
to practice what you've learned about measures of three-dimensional figures in the Put It All Together over Lessons 11-4 through 11-7.

Interactive Presentation

Approximate the Volume of a Composite Solid

HOME DECOR Mia purchased a trash container for her study area. Find the volume of the trash container rounded to the nearest tenth.

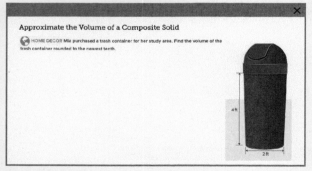

Apply Example 8

TAP

Students tap to reveal steps in the solution.

CHECK

Students complete the Check online to determine whether they are ready to move on.

Apply Example 8 Approximate the Volume of a Composite Solid

Recommended Use

Have students work in pairs or small groups. You may wish to present the task, or have a volunteer read it aloud. Then allow students the time to make sure they understand the task, think of possible strategies, and work to solve the problem.

Encourage Productive Struggle

As students work, monitor their progress. Instead of instructing them on a particular strategy, encourage them to use their own strategies to solve the problem and to evaluate their progress along the way. They may or may not find that they need to change direction or try out several strategies.

Signs of Non-Productive Struggle

If students show signs of non-productive struggle, such as feeling overwhelmed, frustrated, or disengaged, intervene to encourage them to think of alternate approaches to the problem. Some sample questions are shown.

- If you were to build a scale model of the trash can, what would be the shape of the base?

- If you were to take the trash can apart, what solids would model each piece?

✎ Write About It!

Have students share their responses with another pair/group of students or the entire class. Have them clearly state or describe the mathematical reasoning they can use to defend their solution.

Exit Ticket

Recommended Use

At the end of class, go online to display the Exit Ticket prompt and ask students to respond using a separate piece of paper. Have students hand you their responses as they leave the room.

Alternate Use

At the end of class, go online to display the Exit Ticket prompt and ask students to respond verbally or by using a mini-whiteboard. Have students hold up their whiteboards so that you can see all student responses. Tap to reveal the answer when most or all students have completed the Exit Ticket.

Practice and Homework

Suggested Assignments

Use the table below to select appropriate exercises.

DOK	Topic	Exercises
1, 2	exercises that mirror the examples	1–20
2	exercises that use a variety of skills from this lesson	21–24
2	exercises that extend concepts learned in this lesson to new contexts	25–29
3	exercises that emphasize higher-order and critical-thinking skills	30–35

ASSESS AND DIFFERENTIATE

📊 Use the data from the **Checks** to determine whether to provide resources for extension, remediation, or intervention.

IF students score 90% or more on the Checks, `BL`
THEN assign:

- Practice, Exercises 1–29 odd, 30–35
- Extension: Cavalieri's Principle
- 🖥 **ALEKS** Volumes of Prisms and Cylinders; Volumes of Pyramids and Cones; Surface Areas and Volumes of Spheres

IF students score 66%–89% on the Checks, `OL`
THEN assign:

- Practice, Exercises 1–35 odd
- Remediation, Review Resources: Volume of Cones
- Personal Tutors
- Extra Examples 1–8
- 🖥 **ALEKS** Volume of Pyramids, Cones, and Spheres

IF students score 65% or less on the Checks, `AL`
THEN assign:

- Practice, Exercises 1–19 odd
- Remediation, Review Resources: Volume of Cones
- *Quick Review Math Handbook*: Volumes of Pyramids and Cones
- 🖥 **ALEKS** Volume of Pyramids, Cones, and Spheres

Name _____ Period _____ Date _____

Practice
🖥 Go Online You can complete your homework online.

Example 1

1. DISPOSAL The Meyer family uses a kitchen trash can shaped like a cylinder. It has a height of 18 inches and a base diameter of 12 inches. What is the approximate volume of the trash can? Round your answer to the nearest tenth of a cubic inch. 2035.8 in³

2. COFFEE A roasting company sells their coffee in canisters shaped like a cylinder. The radius of the canister is 1.5 inches and the height is 7.5 inches. What is the approximate volume of a coffee canister? Round your answer to the nearest cubic inch. 53 in³

Example 2

3. Find the volume of a cylinder with a radius of $2x$ millimeters and a height of $x - 2$ millimeters.
   a. Find the volume of the cylinder in terms of x and π. $4\pi x^3 - 8\pi x^2$ mm³
   b. Find the volume of the cylinder if $x = 10$. Round your answer to the nearest tenth. 10,053.1 mm³

4. Find the volume of a cylinder with a diameter that is 6 centimeters shorter than the height x.
   a. Find the volume of the cylinder in terms of x and π. $\pi\left(\frac{x-6}{2}\right)^2(x)$ cm³
   b Find the volume of the cylinder if the height is 14 centimeters. Round your answer to the nearest tenth. 703.7 cm³

5. Find the volume of a cylinder with a radius of x feet and a height of $3x + 4$ feet.
   a. Find the volume of the cylinder in terms of x and π. $3\pi x^3 + 4\pi x^2$ ft³
   b. Find the volume of the cylinder if $x = 3$. Round your answer to the nearest tenth. 367.6 ft³

Examples 3 and 4

6. Examine the cone.
   a. Find the volume of the cone in terms of x and π. $\frac{1}{3}\pi(x+1)^2(2x+3)$ cubic units
   b. Find the volume of the cone if $x = 4$ feet. Round your answer to the nearest tenth. 288.0 ft³

7. Examine the cone.
   a. Find the volume of the cone in terms of x and π. $\frac{1}{3}\pi(2x)^2(5x-5)$ cubic units
   b. Find the volume of the cone if $x = 6$ meters. Round your answer to the nearest tenth. 3769.9 m³

8. Examine the cone.
   a. Find the volume of the cone in terms of x and π. $\frac{1}{3}\pi(3x-1)^2(4x+1)$ cubic units
   b. Find the volume of the cone if $x = 3$ inches. Round your answer to the nearest tenth. 871.3 in³

9. DINING The part of a dish designed for ice cream is shaped like a cone. The base of the cone has a radius of 2 inches and the height is 1.2 inches. What is the volume of the cone? Round your answer to the nearest hundredth. 5.03 in³

---

10. AUTOMOBILE Don uses a funnel to pour oil into his car engine. The funnel has a radius of 6 centimeters and a slant height of 10 centimeters. How much oil, to the nearest cubic centimeter, will the funnel hold? 301.6 cm³

Examples 5 and 6

11. ORANGES Moesha cuts a spherical orange in half along a great circle. The radius of the orange is 2 inches. Find the approximate volume of the orange to the nearest tenth of a cubic inch. 33.5 in³

12. DESIGN A spherical fountain has a radius of 1.5 feet. Find the volume of the fountain to the nearest tenth of a cubic foot. 14.1 ft³

13. Examine the sphere.
    a. Find the volume of the sphere in terms of x and π. $\frac{4}{3}\pi(4x)^3$ cubic units
    b. Find the volume of the sphere if $x = 1$ centimeter. Round your answer to the nearest tenth. 268.1 cm³

14. Examine the sphere.
    a. Find the volume of the sphere in terms of x and π. $\frac{4}{3}\pi(2x)^3$ cubic units
    b. Find the volume of the sphere if $x = 4.3$ inches. Round your answer to the nearest tenth. 2664.3 in³

15. Examine the sphere.
    a. Find the volume of the sphere in terms x and π. $\frac{4}{3}\pi(5x-0.5)^3$ cubic units
    b. Find the volume of the sphere if $x = 0.25$ yards. Round your answer to the nearest tenth. 1.8 yd³

16. Examine the sphere.
    a. Find the volume of the sphere in terms of x and π. $\frac{4}{3}\pi\left(\frac{3x+1.2}{2}\right)^3$ cubic units
    b. Find the volume of the sphere if $x = 5$ centimeters. Round your answer to the nearest tenth. 2226.1 cm³

Examples 7 and 8

Find the volume of each composite solid. Round to the nearest tenth, if necessary.

17. 9 m 1102.7 m³ — 14 m, 24 m

18. 5 in. 497.4 in³ — 14 in.

19. CELEBRATION Emilia is having a three-tiered cake made for her quinceañera party. Each tier of the cake will have a height of 4 inches. The diameters of the top, middle, and bottom tiers will measure 6 inches, 10 inches, and 14 inches, respectively. Find the total volume of the cake to the nearest cubic inch. 1043 in³

20. SCULPTING A sculptor wants to remove stone from a cylindrical block that has a height of 3 feet to create a cone. The diameter of the base of the cone and cylinder is 2 feet. What is the volume of the stone that the sculptor must remove? Round your answer to the nearest hundredth. 6.28 ft³

| 1 CONCEPTUAL UNDERSTANDING | 2 FLUENCY | 3 APPLICATION |

Name _____ Period _____ Date _____

Mixed Exercises

For Exercises 21 and 22, refer to the composite solid shown at the right.

21. STRUCTURE Write a formula for the volume of this solid in terms of the radius r.
$2\pi r^3 + \frac{2\pi r^3}{3} + \frac{\pi r^3}{3}$ or $3\pi r^3$ cubic units

22. PRECISION Explain how you wrote a formula for the volume of this solid. See margin.

23. Find the volume of the cone. Round to the nearest tenth. 1210.6 mm³

24. REASONING A hemisphere has a base with an area that is 25π square centimeters. Find the volume of the hemisphere. Round to the nearest tenth. 261.8 cm³

25. TEEPEE Cathy made a teepee for a class project. Her teepee had a diameter of 6 feet. The angle that the side of the teepee made with the ground was 65°. What was the volume of the teepee? Round your answer to the nearest hundredth. 60.63 ft³

26. SCHOOL SUPPLIES A pencil grip is shaped like a triangular prism with a cylinder removed from the middle. The base of the prism is a right isosceles triangle with leg lengths of 2 centimeters. The diameter of the base of the removed cylinder is 1 centimeter. The heights of the prism and the cylinder are the same and equal to 4 centimeters. What is the exact volume of the pencil grip? $8 - \pi$ cm³

27. CONSTRUCT ARGUMENTS A wooden sphere is carved from a solid cube of wood so that the least amount of wood is carved away. a–b. See margin.

a. If the block of wood had a volume of 729 cubic inches, what is the volume of the sphere? Explain.

b. Devon says that he can multiply the volume of any cube by $\frac{\pi}{6}$ to find the volume of the sphere that shares the same diameter as the cube's side. Is he correct? Justify your argument.

28. REASONING Reginald is creating a scale model of a building using a scale of 4 feet = 3 inches. The building is in the shape of a cube topped with a hemisphere so that the circular base of the hemisphere is inscribed in the square base of the cube. At its highest point, the building has a height of 30 feet. Find the volume of his scale model to the nearest cubic inch. Explain. See margin.

---

29. REGULARITY A container company manufactures cylindrical containers with a radius of 3 inches and a height of 10 inches. The company decided to produce a different cylindrical container that has a height of 8 inches and the same volume as the original container. What steps would you use to find the radius of the new container? What is the radius of the new container to the nearest tenth? Sample answer: I would find the volume of the original container. Then, I would substitute that volume and the 8-inch height in the volume formula and solve for r; 3.4 inches.

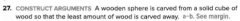

Higher-Order Thinking Skills

30. PERSEVERE The cylindrical can shown is used to fill a container with liquid. It takes three full cans to fill the container. Describe possible dimensions of the container if it is each of the following shapes.

a. rectangular prism base 3 in. by 5 in., height 4π in.

b. square prism base 5 in. per side, height $\frac{12}{5}\pi$ in.

c. triangular prism with a right triangle as the base base with legs measuring 3 in. and 4 in., height 10π in.

31. CREATE Sketch a composite solid made of a cylinder and cone that has an approximate volume of 7698.5 cubic centimeters. See margin.

32. WRITE How are the volume formulas for prisms and cylinders similar? How are they different? Sample answer: Both formulas involve multiplying the area of the base by the height. The base of a prism is a polygon, so the expression representing the area varies depending on the type of polygon it is. The base of a cylinder is a circle, so its area is πr^2.

33. ANALYZE Determine whether the following statement is *sometimes, always,* or *never* true. Justify your argument. See margin.

The volume of a cone with radius r and height h equals the volume of a prism with height h.

34. FIND THE ERROR Alexandra and Cornelio are calculating the volume of the cone at the right. Who is correct? Explain your reasoning.
Cornelio; sample answer: Alexandra incorrectly used the slant height.

Alexandra	Cornelio
$V = \frac{1}{3}Bh$	$5^2 + 12^2 = 13^2$
$= \frac{1}{3}\pi(5)^2(13)$	$V = \frac{1}{3}Bh$
$= 340.3$ cm³	$= \frac{1}{3}\pi(5)^2(12)$
	$= 314.2$ cm³

35. ANALYZE Determine whether the following statement is *true* or *false*. If true, explain your reasoning. If false, provide a counterexample.

If a sphere has radius r, there exists a cone with radius r having the same volume.
True; sample answer: A cone of radius r and height $4r$ has the same volume, $\frac{4}{3}\pi r^3$, as a sphere with radius r.

Answers

22. The volume of the cylinder is $\pi r^2 \cdot 2r$. The volume of the hemisphere is $\frac{2\pi r^3}{3}$. The volume of the cone is $\pi r^2 \cdot \frac{r}{3}$. Therefore, the total volume is $2\pi r^3 + \frac{2\pi r^3}{3} + \frac{\pi r^3}{3}$ or $3\pi r^3$ cubic units.

27a. About 382 in³; sample answer: The cube root of 729 is 9, so the side length of the cube of wood in 9 inches. The largest sphere that could be carved has a radius of 4.5 inches. So, $V = \frac{4}{3}\pi (4.5)^3$ or about 382 in³.

27b. Yes; sample answer: The radius of the sphere is exactly one half of the side of the cube. If the cube has a side s, then the volume of the sphere is $\frac{4}{3}\pi\left(\frac{s}{2}\right)^3 = \frac{4}{3}\pi \frac{s^3}{8} = \frac{s^3\pi}{6} = s^3 \frac{\pi}{6}$. Therefore, the volume of a sphere that shares a diameter with the side of a cube is always $\frac{\pi}{6}$ times the volume of the cube.

28. 4259 in³; In the actual building, the diameter of the hemisphere is the same length as a side s of the cube, and the radius r is half the length. So, $s = 20$ ft and $r = 10$ ft. In the scale model, $s = 15$ in. and $r = 7.5$ in. The volume of the cube is $V = 15^3$ or 3375 in³. The volume of the hemisphere is $V = \frac{1}{2} \cdot \frac{4}{3}\pi (7.5)^3$ or ≈ 884 in³. So, the volume is about $3375 + 884$ or 4259 in³.

31. Sample answer:

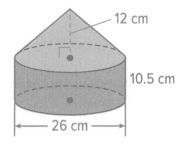

33. Sometimes; sample answer: The statement is true if the base area of the cone is 3 times as great as the base area of the prism. For example, if the base of the prism has an area of 10 square units, then its volume is $10h$ cubic units. So, the cone must have a base area of 30 square units so that its volume is $\frac{1}{3}(30)h$ or $10h$ cubic units.

Applying Similarity to Solid Figures

LESSON GOAL

Students find measures of similar figures and solids by using scale factors.

1 LAUNCH

 Launch the lesson with a **Warm Up** and an introduction.

2 EXPLORE AND DEVELOP

 Explore: Similar Solids

 Develop:

Similar Two-Dimensional Figures
- Use Similar Figures to Find Area
- Use Areas of Similar Figures
- Use Similar Figures to Solve Problems

Similar Three-Dimensional Solids
- Use Similar Solids to Find Volume
- Use Similar Solids to Solve Problems

 You may want your students to complete the **Checks** online.

3 REFLECT AND PRACTICE

 Exit Ticket

 Practice

DIFFERENTIATE

 View reports of student progress on the **Checks** after each example.

Resources	AL	OL	BL	ELL
Remediation: Similarity and Transformations	●	●		●
Extension: The Scale of the Solar System		●	●	●

Language Development Handbook

Assign page 81 of the *Language Development Handbook* to help your students build mathematical language related to finding the measures of similar figures and solids.

ELL You can use the tips and suggestions on page T81 of the handbook to support students who are building English proficiency.

Suggested Pacing

| 90 min | 0.5 day |
| 45 min | 1 day |

Focus

Domain: Geometry

Standards for Mathematical Content:

G.GMD.3 Use volume formulas for cylinders, pyramids, cones, and spheres to solve problems.

Standards for Mathematical Practice:

3 Construct viable arguments and critique the reasoning of others.
6 Attend to precision.
7 Look for and make use of structure.

Coherence

Vertical Alignment

Previous
Students understood similarity in terms of similarity transformations.
8.G.4, G.SRT.1, G.SRT.2

Now
Students find measures of similar figures and solids by using scale factors.
G.GMD.3

Next
Students will solve real-world problems involving density by using area and volume.
G.MG.2

Rigor

The Three Pillars of Rigor

1 CONCEPTUAL UNDERSTANDING	2 FLUENCY	3 APPLICATION

🏛 **Conceptual Bridge** In this lesson, students extend their understanding of volume to the relationships between similar figures. They build fluency and apply their understanding by comparing measures of similar real-world objects.

Mathematical Background

If two polygons are similar, then the perimeters are proportional to the scale factor between them. The areas of two similar polygons are proportional to the square of the scale factor between them. Similar solids are solids that have exactly the same shape but not necessarily the same size. The ratio of the measures of two similar figures is the scale factor. Congruent solids are exactly the same shape and exactly the same size. Two solids are congruent when the corresponding angles, faces, and edges are congruent. The volumes of two congruent solids are equal.

Interactive Presentation

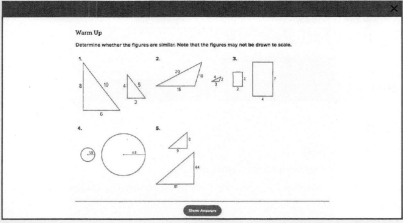

Warm Up

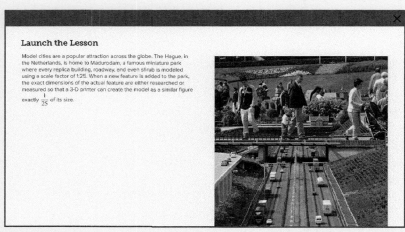

Launch the Lesson

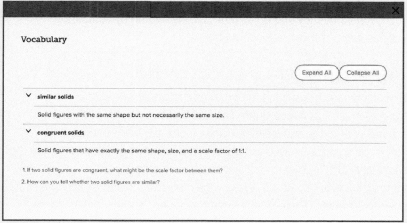

Today's Vocabulary

Warm Up

Prerequisite Skills

The Warm Up exercises address the following prerequisite skill for this lesson:

- identifying similar figures

Answers:

1. yes
2. yes
3. no
4. yes
5. no

Launch the Lesson

MP Teaching the Mathematical Practices

4 Apply Mathematics In this Launch the Lesson, students can see a real-world application of similar figures and solids.

Go Online to find additional teaching notes and questions to promote classroom discourse.

Today's Standards

Tell students that they will be addressing these content and practice standards in this lesson. You may wish to have a student volunteer read aloud *How can I meet these standards?* and *How can I use these practices?* and connect these to the standards.

See the Interactive Presentation for I Can statements that align with the standards covered in this lesson.

Today's Vocabulary

Tell students that they will be using these vocabulary terms in this lesson. You can expand each row if you wish to share the definitions. Then, discuss the questions below with the class.

Explore Similar Solids

Objective

Students derive relationships in similar figures and solids by using dynamic geometry software.

 Teaching the Mathematical Practices

2 Create Representations Guide students to write an equation that models the situation in this Explore. Then use the equation to solve the problem.

Ideas for Use

Recommended Use Present the Inquiry Question, or have a student volunteer read it aloud. Have students work in pairs to complete the Explore activity on their devices. Pairs should discuss each of the questions. Monitor student progress during the activity. Upon completion of the Explore activity, have student volunteers share their responses to the Inquiry Question.

What if my students don't have devices? You may choose to project the activity on a whiteboard. A printable worksheet for each Explore is available online. You may choose to print the worksheet so that individuals or pairs of students can use it to record their observations.

Summary of the Activity

Students will complete guiding exercises throughout the Explore activity. Students begin by computing the surface area of each solid and the ratio between the surface areas. Next students change the shape of the similar solids and the scale factor and observe what happens to the ratio between the surface areas. They then do the same with the volumes of the similar solids. Finally students observe that the ratio between the surface areas is the square of the scale factor, and the ratio between the volumes is the cube of the scale factor. Then, students will answer the Inquiry Question.

 Go Online to find additional teaching notes and sample answers for the guiding exercises.

(continued on the next page)

Interactive Presentation

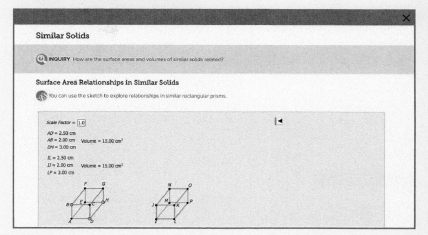

Explore

WEB SKETCHPAD

Students use the sketch to explore similar solids.

Interactive Presentation

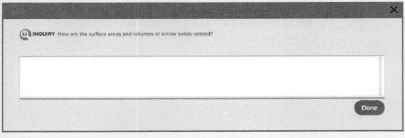

INQUIRY How are the surface areas and volumes of similar solids related?

Done

Explore

TYPE

| a| |

Students respond to the Inquiry Question and can view a sample answer.

Explore Similar Solids (*continued*)

MP Teaching the Mathematical Practices

2 Attend to Quantities Point out that it is important to note the meaning of the quantities used in this Explore.

Questions

Have students complete the Explore activity.

Ask:

- How is the surface area of similar solids related to the area of similar polygons? Sample answer: Both are related by the square of the scale factor. This makes sense for the solids because you are finding areas of similar polygons that are on each face of the solid.

- If you have the ratio of the surface areas and the volume of one solid, can you find the volume of the similar solid? If so, how? Yes; sample answer: If you know the solids are similar, then you know the ratio of the surface areas is the square of the scale factor. You can take the square root to find the scale factor, then cube this to find the ratio of the volumes and set up a proportion.

Inquiry

How are the surface areas and volumes of similar solids related? Sample answer: When two solids are similar, there is an associated scale factor between them. The square of this scale factor is equivalent to the scale factor of the corresponding surface areas, and the cube of this scale factor is equivalent to the scale factor of the corresponding volumes. If you know the surface area or volume of one solid, you can use the associated scale factor to find the surface area or volume of the other.

Go Online to find additional teaching notes and sample answers for the guiding exercises.

1 CONCEPTUAL UNDERSTANDING | **2 FLUENCY** | 3 APPLICATION

Learn Similar Two-Dimensional Figures

Objective
Students find measures of similar figures by using scale factors.

Teaching the Mathematical Practices

2 Represent a Situation Symbolically Guide students to define variables to solve the problem in this Learn. Help students to identify the independent and dependent variables. Then work with them to find the other relationships in the problem.

About the Key Concept
Because area involves two dimensions, not just one, the ratio between the areas of similar figures is the square of the scale factor. For example, both the length and width of similar rectangles are affected by the scale factor, so the area is multiplied by the scale factor once for the length and once for the width.

Example 1 Use Similar Figures to Find Area

Teaching the Mathematical Practices

6 Communicate Precisely Encourage students to routinely write and explain their solution methods. Point out that they should use clear definitions when they discuss their solutions with others.

Questions for Mathematical Discourse

AL Why is the scale factor less than 1? *JKLM* is smaller than *ABCD*.

OL How can we check our solution? Sample answer: Use the area of *ABCD* to find *CD*, use the scale factor to find *LM*, and compute the area of *JKLM* directly.

BL If the scale factor is 2, what is the area of *JKLM*? 128 cm²

Go Online
- Find additional teaching notes.
- View performance reports of the Checks.
- Assign or present an Extra Example.

DIFFERENTIATE

Enrichment Activity AL BL

Have students prove Theorem 11.1 for rectangles. Sample answer: Let the scale factor between two rectangles be k, and the length and width of the first rectangle be ℓ and w respectively. Then the length of the second rectangle is $k\ell$ and the width is kw. The area of the first rectangle is ℓw, and the area of the second rectangle is $(k\ell)(kw) = k^2\ell w$, so the ratio of the areas is $\frac{k^2\ell w}{\ell w} = k^2$.

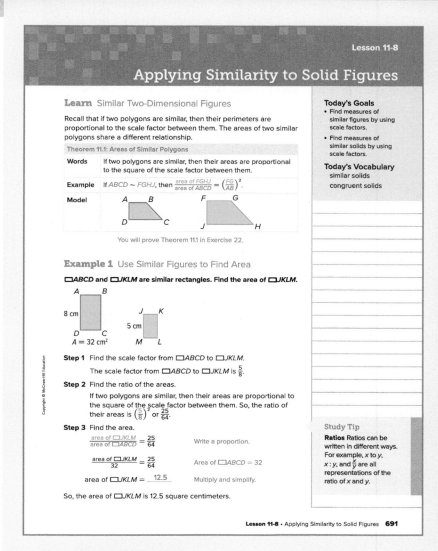

Lesson 11-8

Applying Similarity to Solid Figures

Learn Similar Two-Dimensional Figures

Recall that if two polygons are similar, then their perimeters are proportional to the scale factor between them. The areas of two similar polygons share a different relationship.

Theorem 11.1: Areas of Similar Polygons

Words If two polygons are similar, then their areas are proportional to the square of the scale factor between them.

Example If $ABCD \sim FGHJ$, then $\frac{\text{area of } FGHJ}{\text{area of } ABCD} = \left(\frac{FG}{AB}\right)^2$.

Model

You will prove Theorem 11.1 in Exercise 22.

Example 1 Use Similar Figures to Find Area

▢*ABCD* and ▢*JKLM* are similar rectangles. Find the area of ▢*JKLM*.

$A = 32$ cm²

Step 1 Find the scale factor from ▢*ABCD* to ▢*JKLM*.
The scale factor from ▢*ABCD* to ▢*JKLM* is $\frac{5}{8}$.

Step 2 Find the ratio of the areas.
If two polygons are similar, then their areas are proportional to the square of the scale factor between them. So, the ratio of their areas is $\left(\frac{5}{8}\right)^2$ or $\frac{25}{64}$.

Step 3 Find the area.

$\frac{\text{area of } ▢JKLM}{\text{area of } ▢ABCD} = \frac{25}{64}$ Write a proportion.

$\frac{\text{area of } ▢JKLM}{32} = \frac{25}{64}$ Area of ▢*ABCD* = 32

area of ▢*JKLM* = ___12.5___   Multiply and simplify.

So, the area of ▢*JKLM* is 12.5 square centimeters.

Today's Goals
- Find measures of similar figures by using scale factors.
- Find measures of similar solids by using scale factors.

Today's Vocabulary
similar solids
congruent solids

Study Tip
Ratios Ratios can be written in different ways. For example, x to y, $x : y$, and $\frac{x}{y}$ are all representations of the ratio of x and y.

Interactive Presentation

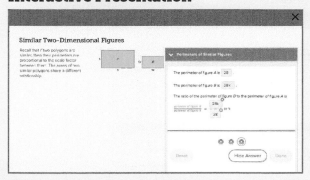

Similar Two-Dimensional Figures

Learn

TAP

Students tap to reveal information about the perimeter and area of similar figures.

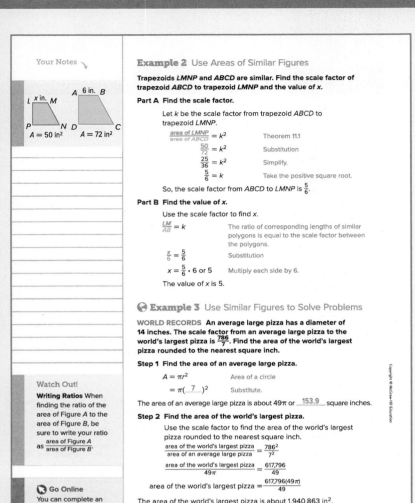

Your Notes

Example 2 Use Areas of Similar Figures

Trapezoids *LMNP* and *ABCD* are similar. Find the scale factor of trapezoid *ABCD* to trapezoid *LMNP* and the value of *x*.

Part A Find the scale factor.

Let *k* be the scale factor from trapezoid *ABCD* to trapezoid *LMNP*.

$$\frac{\text{area of } LMNP}{\text{area of } ABCD} = k^2 \qquad \text{Theorem 11.1}$$

$$\frac{50}{72} = k^2 \qquad \text{Substitution}$$

$$\frac{25}{36} = k^2 \qquad \text{Simplify.}$$

$$\frac{5}{6} = k \qquad \text{Take the positive square root.}$$

So, the scale factor from *ABCD* to *LMNP* is $\frac{5}{6}$.

Part B Find the value of *x*.

Use the scale factor to find *x*.

$$\frac{LM}{AB} = k \qquad \text{The ratio of corresponding lengths of similar polygons is equal to the scale factor between the polygons.}$$

$$\frac{x}{6} = \frac{5}{6} \qquad \text{Substitution}$$

$$x = \frac{5}{6} \cdot 6 \text{ or } 5 \qquad \text{Multiply each side by 6.}$$

The value of *x* is 5.

🌐 Example 3 Use Similar Figures to Solve Problems

WORLD RECORDS An average large pizza has a diameter of 14 inches. The scale factor from an average large pizza to the world's largest pizza is $\frac{786}{7}$. Find the area of the world's largest pizza rounded to the nearest square inch.

Step 1 Find the area of an average large pizza.

$$A = \pi r^2 \qquad \text{Area of a circle}$$

$$= \pi(\underline{7})^2 \qquad \text{Substitute.}$$

The area of an average large pizza is about 49π or $\underline{153.9}$ square inches.

Step 2 Find the area of the world's largest pizza.

Use the scale factor to find the area of the world's largest pizza rounded to the nearest square inch.

$$\frac{\text{area of the world's largest pizza}}{\text{area of an average large pizza}} = \frac{786^2}{7^2}$$

$$\frac{\text{area of the world's largest pizza}}{49\pi} = \frac{617,796}{49}$$

$$\text{area of the world's largest pizza} = \frac{617,796(49\pi)}{49}$$

The area of the world's largest pizza is about 1,940,863 in².

Watch Out!
Writing Ratios When finding the ratio of the area of Figure *A* to the area of Figure *B*, be sure to write your ratio as $\frac{\text{area of Figure } A}{\text{area of Figure } B}$.

 Go Online
You can complete an Extra Example online.

Interactive Presentation

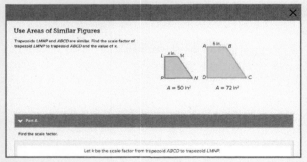

Example 2

TAP

Students tap to find the area of similar figures.

CHECK

Students complete the Check online to determine whether they are ready to move on.

Example 2 Use Areas of Similar Figures

MP Teaching the Mathematical Practices

1 Check Answers Mathematically proficient students continually ask themselves, "Does this make sense?" Point out that in this example, students need to check their answer. They should ask themselves whether their answer makes sense and whether they have answered the problem question.

Questions for Mathematical Discourse

AL The ratio of two areas is $\frac{25}{49}$. What is the scale factor of the two figures? $\frac{5}{7}$

OL If the ratio of the area of Figure A to Figure B is $\frac{25}{4}$, what is the ratio of the perimeter of Figure A to Figure B? $\frac{5}{2}$

BL If the area of Trapezoid A is 108 cm² and the area of Trapezoid B is 300 cm², what is the scale factor of Trapezoid B to Trapezoid A? $\frac{5}{3}$

Common Error

Students may try to use the ratio of the areas as the scale factor. Remind them that the areas are proportional by the square of the scale factor.

🌐 Example 3 Use Similar Figures to Solve Problems

MP Teaching the Mathematical Practices

4 Apply Mathematics In this example, students apply what they have learned about similar figures to solving a real-world problem.

Questions for Mathematical Discourse

AL What does it mean to have a scale factor from an average pizza to the world's largest pizza of $\frac{786}{7}$? It means that the world's largest pizza is $\frac{786}{7}$ times larger than the average pizza.

OL Describe how the circumference of the average pizza relates to the circumference of the world's largest pizza. The circumference of the world's largest pizza is $\frac{786}{7}$ times larger than the circumference of the average pizza.

BL The scale factor from an average pizza to a personal size pizza is one-half. What is the approximate area of a personal size pizza? 38.5 in²

1 CONCEPTUAL UNDERSTANDING | 2 FLUENCY | 3 APPLICATION

Learn Similar Three-Dimensional Solids

Objective
Students find measures of similar solids by using scale factors.

 Teaching the Mathematical Practices

3 Construct Arguments In this Learn, students will use stated assumptions, definitions, and previously established results to construct an argument.

Common Misconception
Students may confuse when they should use the scale factor, its square, or its cube when solving problems. Help them to remember that: when they are dealing with a single dimension like a side length or perimeter, they should use the scale factor; when they are dealing with two dimensions as in area or surface area, they should use the square; and when they are dealing with three dimensions like with volume, they should use the cube.

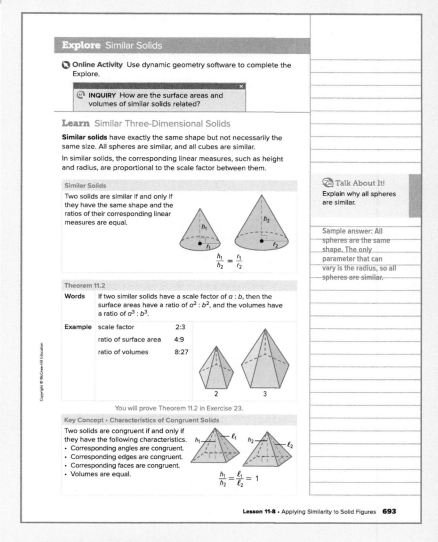

Explore Similar Solids

Online Activity Use dynamic geometry software to complete the Explore.

INQUIRY How are the surface areas and volumes of similar solids related?

Learn Similar Three-Dimensional Solids

Similar solids have exactly the same shape but not necessarily the same size. All spheres are similar, and all cubes are similar.

In similar solids, the corresponding linear measures, such as height and radius, are proportional to the scale factor between them.

Similar Solids

Two solids are similar if and only if they have the same shape and the ratios of their corresponding linear measures are equal.

$$\frac{h_1}{h_2} = \frac{r_1}{r_2}$$

Theorem 11.2

Words If two similar solids have a scale factor of $a : b$, then the surface areas have a ratio of $a^2 : b^2$, and the volumes have a ratio of $a^3 : b^3$.

Example
scale factor	2:3
ratio of surface area	4:9
ratio of volumes	8:27

You will prove Theorem 11.2 in Exercise 23.

Key Concept • Characteristics of Congruent Solids

Two solids are congruent if and only if they have the following characteristics.
- Corresponding angles are congruent.
- Corresponding edges are congruent.
- Corresponding faces are congruent.
- Volumes are equal.

$$\frac{h_1}{h_2} = \frac{\ell_1}{\ell_2} = 1$$

Talk About It!
Explain why all spheres are similar.

Sample answer: All spheres are the same shape. The only parameter that can vary is the radius, so all spheres are similar.

Lesson 11-8 • Applying Similarity to Solid Figures **693**

Interactive Presentation

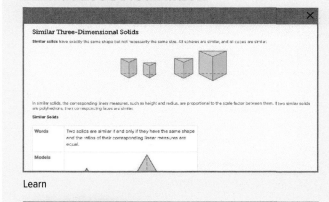

Similar Three-Dimensional Solids

Similar solids have exactly the same shape but not necessarily the same size. All spheres are similar, and all cubes are similar.

In similar solids, the corresponding linear measures, such as height and radius, are proportional to the scale factor between them. If two similar solids are polyhedrons, their corresponding faces are similar.

Similar Solids

Words Two solids are similar if and only if they have the same shape and the ratios of their corresponding linear measures are equal.

Models

Learn

TAP

 Students tap to reveal information about similar three-dimensional solids.

TYPE

 Students answer a question to show they understand similar three-dimensional solids.

Example 4 Use Similar Solids to Find Volume

The three cones are similar. Find the volume of each cone.

Cone 1   Cone 2   Cone 3

Step 1 Find the volume of Cone 1

$V = \frac{1}{3}Bh$ Volume of a cone

$= \frac{1}{3}\pi(5)^2 \cdot \sqrt{119}$ $B = \pi r^2, r = 5$, and $h = \sqrt{12^2 - 5^2}$

$= \frac{25\pi\sqrt{119}}{3}$ Simplify.

Step 2 Find the volume of Cone 2.

Cone 2 is similar to Cone 1. The scale factor from Cone 2 to Cone 1 is 5 : 6. Find the volume of Cone 2.

$\frac{\text{volume of Cone 1}}{\text{volume of Cone 2}} = \left(\frac{5}{6}\right)^3$ Theorem 11.2

volume of Cone 2 $= \left(\frac{6}{5}\right)^3 \times \frac{25\pi\sqrt{119}}{3}$ Substitute, then solve for the volume of Cone 2.

$= \frac{72\pi\sqrt{119}}{5}$ Simplify.

Step 3 Find the volume of Cone 3.

Cone 3 is similar to Cone 1. The scale factor from Cone 3 to Cone 1 is 5 : 5 or 1 : 1. Because the two solids are similar and have a scale factor of 1 : 1, we know that the two solids are congruent. Congruent solids have the same volume, so the volume of Cone 3 is $\frac{25\pi\sqrt{119}}{3}$ cubic inches.

Example 5 Use Similar Solids to Solve Problems

Two similar rectangular prisms with square bases have surface areas of 98 square centimeters and 18 square centimeters. If one base edge of the larger rectangular prism measures 9 centimeters, what is the perimeter of one base of the smaller prism?

First, find the scale factor. $\frac{\text{surface area of larger prism}}{\text{surface area of smaller prism}} = \frac{98}{18} = \frac{49}{9} = \left(\frac{7}{3}\right)^2$ The scale factor is $\frac{7}{3}$.

Then, find the length of the base edge of the small prism.

$\frac{\text{base edge of larger prism}}{\text{base edge of smaller prism}} = \frac{7}{3}$ The scale factor is $\frac{7}{3}$.

$\frac{9}{\text{base edge of smaller prism}} = \frac{7}{3}$ Substitute.

base edge of small prism $= \frac{27}{7}$ Use a proportion

The base edge of the smaller prism is $\frac{27}{7}$ centimeters.

Find the perimeter of the base of the smaller prism to the nearest tenth.

$P = 4s$ Perimeter of square

$= 4 \cdot \frac{27}{7} \approx 15.4$ Substitute and simplify.

The perimeter of the base of the smaller prism is about 15.4 centimeters.

Check

Two similar cylinders have volumes of 270π and 640π cubic inches, respectively. If the height of the larger cylinder is 10 inches, what is the area of the base of the smaller cylinder? $36\pi\ \text{in}^2$

Study Tip

Similar and Congruent Solids If two solids are similar, then their corresponding linear measures are proportional. If two solids are congruent, then their corresponding linear measures are equal.

 Go Online
You can complete an Extra Example online.

694   **Module 11 ·** Measurement

Copyright © McGraw-Hill Education

Example 4 Use Similar Solids to Find Volume

🎓 **Teaching the Mathematical Practices**

6 Use Precision In this example, students learn how to calculate accurately and efficiently and to express numerical answers with a degree of precision appropriate to the problem context.

Questions for Mathematical Discourse

AL Why did we cube the scale factor to find the volume of Cone 2?
Volume is a cubic length, so we need to cube the scale factor to find volume.

OL What is the ratio of the surface area of Cone 1 to Cone 2? $\frac{25}{36}$

BL The ratio of the volumes of two similar cones is $\frac{27}{64}$. If the volume of the smaller cone is about 29.3 in³, what is the volume of the larger cone?   69.5 in³

Example 5 Use Similar Solids to Solve Problems

Questions for Mathematical Discourse

AL Why did we rewrite the ratio of the surface areas as a square?
The ratio of the surface areas is the square of the scale factor.

OL What is the ratio of the volume of the larger prism to the smaller prism? $\frac{343}{27}$

BL The ratio of the volumes of two similar cones is $\frac{8}{125}$. If the volume of the larger cone is about 785.4 in³, and the height of the smaller cone is 4 inches, what is the diameter of the larger cone?   17.3 in.

DIFFERENTIATE

Reteaching Activity AL BL

Tell students that for the two-dimensional measurement of surface area, the ratio involves the power of two. For the three-dimensional measurement of volume, the ratio involves the power of three.

Exit Ticket

Recommended Use

At the end of class, go online to display the Exit Ticket prompt and ask students to respond using a separate piece of paper. Have students hand you their responses as they leave the room.

Alternate Use

At the end of class, go online to display the Exit Ticket prompt and ask students to respond verbally or by using a mini-whiteboard. Have students hold up their whiteboards so that you can see all student responses. Tap to reveal the answer when most or all students have completed the Exit Ticket.

Interactive Presentation

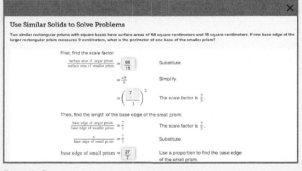

Example 5

TAP

Students tap to reveal steps in the solution.

CHECK

Students complete the Check online to determine whether they are ready to move on.

Practice and Homework

Suggested Assignments

Use the table below to select appropriate exercises.

DOK	Topic	Exercises
1, 2	exercises that mirror the examples	1–17
2	exercises that use a variety of skills from this lesson	18–24
2	exercises that extend concepts learned in this lesson to new contexts	25–28
3	exercises that emphasize higher-order and critical-thinking skills	29–33

ASSESS AND DIFFERENTIATE

📊 Use the data from the **Checks** to determine whether to provide resources for extension, remediation, or intervention.

IF students score 90% or more on the Checks,   `BL`
THEN assign:

- Practice, Exercises 1–27 odd, 29–33
- Extension: The Scale of the Solar System
- 🔲 **ALEKS** Areas of Regular Polygons and Similar Polygons; Similar Polygons

IF students score 66%–89% on the Checks,   `OL`
THEN assign:

- Practice, Exercises 1–33 odd
- Remediation, Review Resources: Similarity and Transformations
- Personal Tutors
- Extra Examples 1–5
- 🔲 **ALEKS** Congruence and Similarity

IF students score 65% or less on the Checks,   `AL`
THEN assign:

- Practice, Exercises 1–17 odd
- Remediation, Review Resources: Similarity and Transformations
- *Quick Review Math Handbook*: Measures of Transformed Solids
- 🔲 **ALEKS** Congruence and Similarity

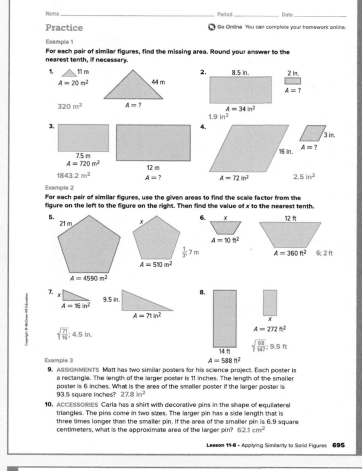

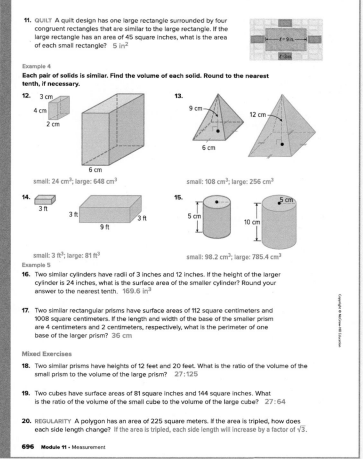

Name _____ Period _____ Date _____

21. REASONING Smith's Bakery is baking several cakes for a community festival. The cakes consist of two geometrically similar shapes as shown. If 50 pieces of cake can be cut from the small cake, how many pieces of the same size can be cut from the large cake? Round to the nearest piece of cake. **313 pieces of cake**

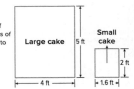

Large cake — 5 ft — 4 ft

Small cake — 2 ft — 1.6 ft

PROOF Write a paragraph proof to prove each theorem. **22–23. See margin.**

22. Theorem 11.1

Given: $\triangle DEF \sim \triangle PQR$

Prove: $\dfrac{\text{area of } \triangle DEF}{\text{area of } \triangle PQR} = \left(\dfrac{d}{p}\right)^2$

23. Theorem 11.2

Given: rectangular prisms with scale factor $a : b$

Prove: The surface areas have a ratio of $a^2 : b^2$, and the volumes have a ratio of $a^3 : b^3$.

24. ATMOSPHERE About 99% of Earth's atmosphere is contained in a 31-kilometer thick layer that surrounds the planet. The Earth itself is approximately a sphere with a radius of 6378 kilometers. What is the ratio of the volume of the atmosphere to the volume of Earth? Round your answer to the nearest thousandth. **0.015 : 1**

25. SCULPTURE An artist creates metal sculptures in the shapes of regular octagons. The length of each side of the larger sculpture is 7 inches, and the area of the base of the smaller sculpture is 19.28 square inches.
 a. What is the length of each side of the smaller sculpture? **2 in.**
 b. The artist is going to pack the sculptures in a circular box to take them to an art show. Will the larger sculpture fit in a circular box with a 15-inch diameter? Explain your reasoning. **See margin.**

26. SPORTS Major League Baseball, or MLB, rules state that baseballs must have a circumference of 9 inches. The National Softball Association, or NSA, rules state that softballs must have a circumference not exceeding 12 inches.
 a. Find the ratio of the circumference of an MLB baseball to the circumference of a 12-inch NSA softball. **3 : 4**
 b. Find the ratio of the volume of the MLB baseball to the volume of the NSA softball. Round your answer to the nearest tenth. **27 : 64**

Lesson 11-8 • Applying Similarity to Solid Figures   **697**

27. STRUCTURE At a pet store, toy tennis balls for pets are sold in 3 different sizes. Complete the table by calculating the volume for each size ball. Record the volume of each tennis ball in terms of π. What pattern do you notice as the diameter increases? **See margin.**

Size	Diameter (cm)	Volume (cm³)
Small	3	
Medium	4.5	
Large	6.75	

28. Describe the dimensions of a similar trapezoid that has an area four times the area of the one shown. Explain how you found your answer.
Sample answer: A similar trapezoid with an area four times the area of the one shown will increase the lengths of the sides by the same factor. For the area to quadruple, the length of the sides must double. Therefore, the height of the new trapezoid and one of the bases must become $2x$, while the length of the other base must become $2(x + 1)$ or $2x + 2$.

$x + 1$

x

x

🔲 **Higher-Order Thinking Skills**

29. FIND THE ERROR Violeta and Gerald are trying to come up with a formula that can be used to find the area of a circle with a radius r after it has been enlarged by a scale factor k. Is either of them correct? Explain your reasoning.

Violeta	Gerald
$A = k\pi r^2$	$A = \pi (r^2)^k$

Neither: sample answer: To find the area of the enlarged circle, you can multiply the radius by the scale factor and substitute it into the area formula, or you can multiply the area formula by the scale factor squared. The formula for the area of the enlargement is $A = \pi(kr)^2$ or $A = k^2\pi r^2$.

30. PERSEVERE If you want the area of a polygon to be $x\%$ of its original area, by what scale factor should you multiply each side length? $\sqrt{\dfrac{x}{100}}$ or $\dfrac{1}{10}\sqrt{x}$

31. CREATE Draw a pair of similar figures with areas that have a ratio of 4:1. Explain. **See margin.**

32. WRITE Explain how to find the area of an enlarged polygon if you know the area of the original polygon and the scale factor of the enlargement.
Sample answer: If you know the area of the original polygon and the scale factor of the enlargement, you can find the area of the enlarged polygon by multiplying the original area by the scale factor squared.

33. PERSEVERE The ratio of the volume of Cylinder A to the volume of Cylinder B is 5:1. Cylinder A is similar to Cylinder C with a scale factor of 2:1, and Cylinder B is similar to Cylinder D with a scale factor of 3:1. What is the ratio of the volume of Cylinder C to the volume of Cylinder D? Explain your reasoning.
8 : 135; Sample answer: The volume of Cylinder C is 8 times the volume of Cylinder A, and the volume of Cylinder D is 27 times the volume of Cylinder B. If the original ratio of volumes was $1x : 5x$, the new ratio is $8x : 135x$. So, the ratio of volumes is 8 : 135.

Answers

22. Proof: It is given that $\triangle DEF \sim \triangle PQR$. The area of $\triangle DEF$ is $\frac{1}{2}eh_1$ and the area of $\triangle PQR$ is $\frac{1}{2}qh_2$. The ratio of the area of $\triangle DEF$ to the area of $\triangle PQR$ is $\dfrac{h_1 e}{h_2 q} = \dfrac{h_1}{h_2} \cdot \dfrac{e}{q}$. By the definition of similar triangles, the ratio of the corresponding measures are $\dfrac{d}{p} = \dfrac{e}{q} = \dfrac{h_1}{h_2}$. By substitution, $\dfrac{\text{area of } \triangle DEF}{\text{area of } \triangle PQR} = \left(\dfrac{d}{p}\right)\left(\dfrac{d}{p}\right) = \left(\dfrac{d}{p}\right)^2$.

23. Proof: We are given rectangular prisms with a scale factor of $a : b$. By the definition of similar solids, $\dfrac{f}{t} = \dfrac{g}{u} = \dfrac{h}{v} = \dfrac{a}{b}$, so $t = f \cdot \dfrac{b}{a}$, $u = g \cdot \dfrac{b}{a}$, and $v = h \cdot \dfrac{b}{a}$.

Then, $\dfrac{\text{surface area of smaller prism}}{\text{surface area of larger prism}} = \dfrac{2fg + 2fh + 2gh}{2tu + 2tv + 2uv}$.

By substitution, the right side of the equation becomes

$$\dfrac{2fg + 2fh + 2gh}{2\left(f \cdot \frac{b}{a}\right)\left(g \cdot \frac{b}{a}\right) + 2\left(f \cdot \frac{b}{a}\right)\left(h \cdot \frac{b}{a}\right) + 2\left(g \cdot \frac{b}{a}\right)\left(h \cdot \frac{b}{a}\right)}$$ · Simplify this fraction to get

$$\dfrac{2fg + 2fh + 2gh}{2fg \cdot \frac{b^2}{a^2} + 2fh \cdot \frac{b^2}{a^2} + 2gh \cdot \frac{b^2}{a^2}}$$ · By using the Distributive Property, this

becomes $\dfrac{2fg + 2fh + 2gh}{(2fg + 2fh + 2gh) \cdot \frac{b^2}{a^2}} = \dfrac{a^2}{b^2}$. Also, the ratio of the

volume is $\dfrac{\text{volume of smaller prism}}{\text{volume of larger prism}} = \dfrac{fgh}{tuv}$. Using the definition of similar solids, we can rewrite the right side of the equation above as

$\dfrac{fgh}{\left(f \cdot \frac{b}{a}\right)\left(g \cdot \frac{b}{a}\right)\left(h \cdot \frac{b}{a}\right)}$. After multiplying, this becomes $\dfrac{fgh}{fgh \cdot \frac{b^3}{a^3}}$, which

simplifies to $\dfrac{a^3}{b^3}$. Thus, the surface areas have a ratio of $a^2 : b^2$, and the volumes have a ratio of $a^3 : b^3$.

25b. No; sample answer: The larger sculpture has an apothem of about 8.5 inches. This means that the octagonal shape of the larger sculpture is about 17 inches across. This is greater than the diameter of the box.

27. Sample answer: As the diameter increases, the volume increases by the cube of the ratio of the diameters. For example, from size Small to Medium, the ratio of the diameters is $\dfrac{4.5}{3}$ or 1.5. The volume of the Medium is $4.5\pi(1.5)^3$ or 15.1875π.

Size	Diameter (cm)	Volume (cm³)
Small	3	**4.5π**
Medium	4.5	**15.1875π**
Large	6.75	**51.2578125π**

31. Sample answer: Because the ratio of the areas should be 4:1, the ratio of the lengths of the sides will be $\sqrt{4} : \sqrt{1}$ or 2:1. Thus, a 0.5-inch by 1-inch rectangle and a 1-inch by 2-inch rectangle are similar, and the ratio of their areas is 4:1.

$A = 0.5$ in.²
0.5 in.
1 in.

$A = 2$ in.²
1 in.
2 in.

Density

LESSON GOAL

Students solve real-world problems involving density by using area and volume.

1 LAUNCH

 Launch the lesson with a **Warm Up** and an introduction.

2 EXPLORE AND DEVELOP

 Explore: Strategies Based on Density

....

Develop:

Density Based on Area
- Find the Density of an Area
- Use the Density of an Area

Density Based on Volume
- Find the Density of a Solid

....

You may want your students to complete the **Checks** online.

3 REFLECT AND PRACTICE

Exit Ticket

....

Practice

DIFFERENTIATE

View reports of student progress on the **Checks** after each example.

Resources	AL	OL	BL	ELL
Remediation: Volume of Cylinders	●	●		●
Extension: Density and Bouyancy		●	●	●

Language Development Handbook

Assign page 82 of the *Language Development Handbook* to help your students build mathematical language related to density.

ELL You can use the tips and suggestions on page T82 of the handbook to support students who are building English proficiency.

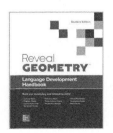

Suggested Pacing

90 min	0.5 day
45 min	1 day

Focus

Domain: Geometry

Standards for Mathematical Content:

G.MG.2 Apply concepts of density based on area and volume in modeling situations.

Standards for Mathematical Practice:

1 Make sense of problems and persevere in solving them.

4 Model with mathematics.

5 Use appropriate tools strategically.

6 Attend to precision.

Coherence

Vertical Alignment

Previous
Students found area, surface area, and volume of figures.
G.MD.1, G.MD.2, G.MD.3

Now
Students compute density in real-world problems.
G.MG.2

Next
Students will describe events as subsets of sample spaces.
S.CP.1

Rigor

The Three Pillars of Rigor

1 CONCEPTUAL UNDERSTANDING	2 FLUENCY	3 APPLICATION

Conceptual Bridge In this lesson, students extend their understanding of area and volume to density. They develop fluency and apply their understanding by finding densities in the real world.

Mathematical Background

Density is a measure of the quantity of some physical property per unit of length, area, or volume. One example of density is population density, which is the measurement of population per unit of area. If two objects have the same volume but different masses, the object with the greater mass will be denser.

Interactive Presentation

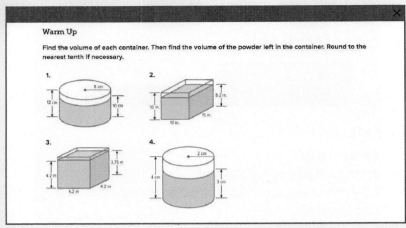

Warm Up

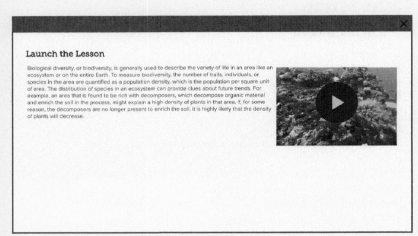

Launch the Lesson

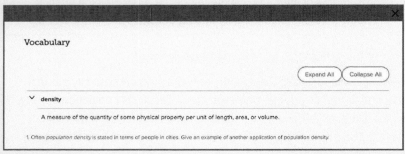

Today's Vocabulary

Warm Up

Prerequisite Skills

The Warm Up exercises address the following prerequisite skill for this lesson:

- finding volumes of quantities

Answers:

1. 2412.7 cm³; 2010.6 cm³
2. 1500 in³; 1230 in³
3. 74.1 m³; 66.2 m³
4. 50.3 cm³; 37.8 cm³
5. 156 ft³

Launch the Lesson

Teaching the Mathematical Practices

4 Apply Mathematics In this Launch the Lesson, students can see a real-world application of density.

Go Online to find additional teaching notes and questions to promote classroom discourse.

Today's Standards

Tell students that they will be addressing these content and practice standards in this lesson. You may wish to have a student volunteer read aloud *How can I meet these standards?* and *How can I use these practices?* and connect these to the standards.

See the Interactive Presentation for I Can statements that align with the standards covered in this lesson.

Today's Vocabulary

Tell students that they will be using this vocabulary term in this lesson. You can expand the row if you wish to share the definition. Then, discuss the question below with the class.

Explore Strategies Based on Density

Objective
Students use density to evaluate situations and make decisions.

 Teaching the Mathematical Practices

> **3 Justify Conclusions** Mathematically proficient students can explain the conclusions drawn when solving a problem. This Explore asks students to justify their conclusions.

Ideas for Use

Recommended Use Present the Inquiry Question, or have a student volunteer read it aloud. Have students work in pairs to complete the Explore activity on their devices. Pairs should discuss each of the questions. Monitor student progress during the activity. Upon completion of the Explore activity, have student volunteers share their responses to the Inquiry Question.

What if my students don't have devices? You may choose to project the activity on a whiteboard. A printable worksheet for each Explore is available online. You may choose to print the worksheet so that individuals or pairs of students can use it to record their observations.

Summary of the Activity

Students will complete guiding exercises throughout the Explore activity. Students begin by watching a video about a computer game. Then students answer guiding exercises to help them analyze the density of hazards to avoid and targets to hit in the game, and determine how to use density to create strategies to get better scores and win the game. Then, students will answer the Inquiry Question.

Go Online to find additional teaching notes and sample answers for the guiding exercises.

(continued on the next page)

Interactive Presentation

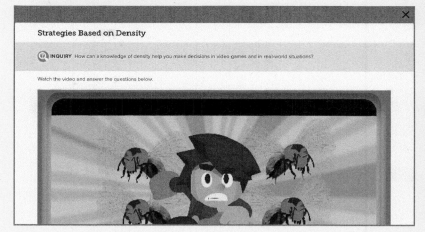

Explore

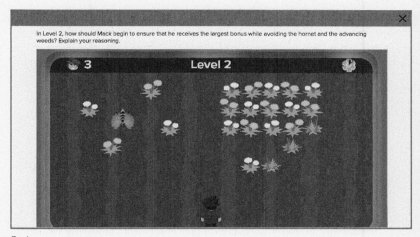

Explore

WATCH

Students watch videos to explore strategies based on density.

Interactive Presentation

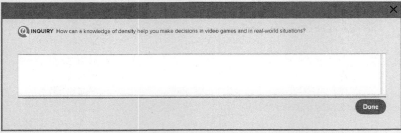

Explore

TYPE

Students respond to the Inquiry Question and can view a sample answer.

Explore Strategies Based on Density (*continued*)

MP Teaching the Mathematical Practices

6 Communicate Precisely Encourage students to routinely write or explain their solution methods. Point out that they should use clear definitions when they discuss their solutions with others.

Questions

Have students complete the Explore activity.

Ask:

- How does the density of the weeds help you make a decision about what Mack should do? Sample answer: The more weeds, or higher density of weeds, means that he has more to do in one area. This means you are able to get a higher score.

- How could you use population density to make decisions about buildings or transportation? Sample answer: A higher density means that there will be more people in a specific area that need buildings and transportation. You could decide to make more housing or offer a wider variety of transportation options in areas with larger densities than areas with smaller densities.

Inquiry

How can a knowledge of density help you make decisions in video games and real-world situations? Sample answer: In the video game, Mack made decisions on where to concentrate his efforts based on the density of weeds, brambles, and hornets. In the real-world, you can use density to make decisions about where to advertise or build new attractions, where to take a vacation, or even where to go to college.

Go Online to find additional teaching notes and sample answers for the guiding exercises.

Learn Density Based on Area

Objective
Students solve real-world problems involving density by using area.

 Teaching the Mathematical Practices

6 Use Quantities Use the Study Tip to guide students to clarifying their use of quantities in this Learn. Ensure that they specify the units of measure used in the problem and label axes appropriately.

Things to Remember
Another important use of density based on area is the crop yield for a field. Farmers can use the amount of food produced by a particular crop per unit of area to determine how much they will need to store and ship.

🌐 **Example 1** Find the Density of an Area

 Teaching the Mathematical Practices

5 Use a Source Guide students to find external information to answer the questions posed in the Use a Source feature.

Questions for Mathematical Discourse

AL What are the "objects" for which you are finding the density? people or population

OL Why is the very low result not surprising? The number of people is very low compared to the size of the area.

BL If a city has a population of 8 million in an area of 300 square miles, what is the population density? 26,667 persons per square mile

🔗 Go Online
- Find additional teaching notes.
- View performance reports of the Checks.
- Assign or present an Extra Example.

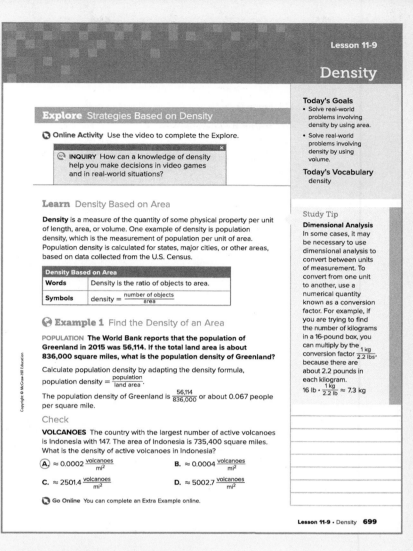

Interactive Presentation

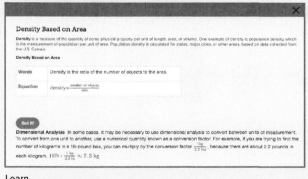

Learn

TAP

Students tap to reveal a Study Tip.

G.MG.2

🌐 **Example 2** Use the Density of an Area

GREENHOUSE GASES Masha has a farm with 220 milking cows that produce 286 pounds per acre for a total of 1,412,840 pounds of milk. Due to recent regulations, Masha must pay a fee if she has more than 30 cows per square mile on her farm. Determine whether Masha will have to pay the fee. (*Hint:* There are 640 acres in 1 square mile.)

Step 1 Find the area of the farm.

$\frac{1{,}412{,}840 \text{ lb}}{286 \text{ lb/acre}} = \underline{4940}$ acres on Masha's farm

Step 2 Convert to square miles.
Use a conversion factor.

4940 acres $\cdot \frac{1 \text{ mi}^2}{640 \text{ acres}} = \frac{247}{32} \approx \underline{7.7}$ mi^2

There are about 7.7 square miles on Masha's farm.

Step 3 Find the density of cows per acre.

Calculate population density by adapting the density formula.

population density $= \frac{\text{population}}{\text{land area}}$ Population Density Formula

$= \frac{220}{\frac{247}{32}}$ 220 cows on $\frac{247}{32}$ square miles

$= 220 \cdot \frac{32}{247}$ Multiply by the reciprocal.

$\approx \underline{28.50}$ Simplify.

Because 28.50 is <u>fewer</u> than 30, Masha <u>will not</u> have to pay the fee.

Check

DUCK POND For a school carnival game, Adalynn is planning to fill a pool with water and float a layer of numbered rubber ducks on top. She knows that it takes 25 rubber ducks to fill 1 square foot of area. The pool used for the carnival has an area of about 7 square feet. How many rubber ducks should she buy to fill the pool?

Adalynn should buy <u>175</u> rubber ducks.

POPULATION DENSITY The city of Manila, Philippines, is one of the most densely populated cities on Earth. Its 1,650,000 residents share a space that can be approximated by a rectangle 5.1 miles long by 2.9 miles wide. To the nearest person, what is the approximate density of Manila?

<u>111,562</u> people per square mile

🌐 **Go Online** You can complete an Extra Example online.

Your Notes

 Think About It!
Why do we multiply 4940 by $\frac{1}{640}$ in Step 2?

Sample answer: Because we are looking for the number of cows per square mile, we need to calculate the population density in square mileage. Multiply by the conversion factor to convert acres to square miles.

🌐 **Example 2** Use the Density of an Area

MP Teaching the Mathematical Practices

> **1 Analyze Givens and Constraints** In this example, guide students to identify the meaning of the problem and look for entry points to its solution.

Questions for Mathematical Discourse

AL How can you tell that you need to find area in this problem? The problem uses square miles and acres, which are measurements of area.

OL If Masha has 250 cows, does she need to pay the fee? Explain. Yes; if she has 250 cows she has 32 cows per square mile.

BL What is the largest number of cows Masha can have and not pay the fee? 230

Common Error

Students may have difficulty determining whether they should multiply or divide the numbers given, and in what order. Help them to examine the units and determine what would happen in combining the units as if they were variables in each option. Guide them in choosing the one where the units combine into the units they are seeking for an answer.

DIFFERENTIATE

Reteaching Activity AL
Mark off areas in your classroom of different sizes. Have different numbers of students stand in each area and calculate the density of students per square foot or students per floor tile. Ask students how crowded or spacious each density felt.

Interactive Presentation

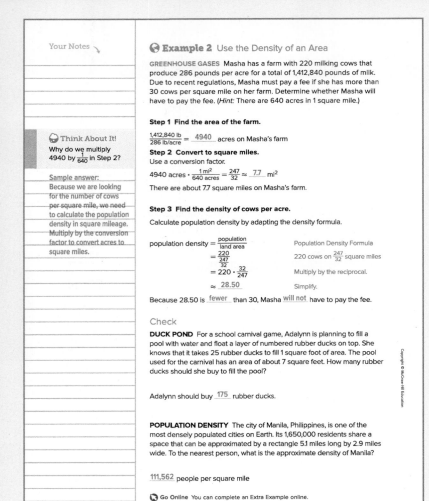

Use the Density of an Area

GREENHOUSE GASES Masha has a farm with 220 milking cows that produce 286 pounds per acre for a total of 1,412,840 pounds of milk. Due to recent regulations, Masha must pay a fee if she has more than 30 cows per square mile on her farm. Determine whether Masha will have to pay the fee. (*Hint:* There are 640 acres in 1 square mile.)

Move through the steps to determine whether Masha will have to pay the fee.

Step 3 Find the density of cows per acre.
Calculate population density by adapting the density formula.

Example 2

TAP

 Students move through steps to find the density of an area.

TYPE

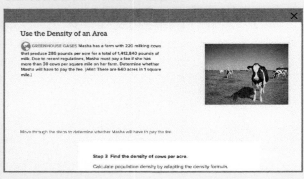 Students answer a question to show they understand the density of an area.

CHECK

 Students complete the Check online to determine whether they are ready to move on.

Learn Density Based on Volume

Objective
Students solve real-world problems involving density by using volume.

 Teaching the Mathematical Practices

7 Use Structure Help students to explore the structure of density based on volume in this Learn.

Common Misconception

Students may have learned about density in a science class and may think that this is the only possible kind of density. Remind them that terms can have multiple meanings based on the subject that they are used in, and those meanings may also be different from how those terms are used in everyday life. In mathematics, both density based on area and density based on volume are useful concepts, and either can be meant by the word *density*.

🌐 Example 3 Find the Density of a Solid

 Teaching the Mathematical Practices

6 Communicate Precisely Encourage students to routinely write and explain their solution methods. Point out that they should use clear definitions when they discuss their solutions with others.

Questions for Mathematical Discourse

AL What do you know about the dimensions of a cube? Length, width, and height are all the same.

OL If the cube weighs 2.6 pounds, what would the dimensions of the cube be? each about 7.5 in.

BL If the cube is 2 inches on a side, what would it weigh? about 0.4 pounds

---

Learn Density Based on Volume

Density is the measure of the quantity of some physical property per unit of length, area, or volume. If two objects have the same volume but different masses, the object with the greater mass will be denser.

Density Based on Volume	
Words	Density is the ratio of mass (or weight) to volume.
Symbols	$\text{density} = \frac{\text{mass (or weight)}}{\text{volume}}$

🌐 Example 3 Find the Density of a Solid

ART Antonio opens a new brick of clay that weighs 25 pounds.

a. What is the density of the brick of clay?

First find the volume of the clay, which can be approximated by using the formula for the volume of a rectangular prism.

$$V = \ell wh \qquad \text{Volume of a rectangular prism}$$
$$V = 6(\underline{9})(\underline{10}) \qquad \ell = 6, w = 9, \text{ and } h = 10$$
$$= \underline{540} \text{ in}^3 \qquad \text{Simplify.}$$

Next, use the density formula to calculate the density.

$$\text{density} = \frac{\text{weight}}{\text{volume}} \qquad \text{Density Formula}$$
$$d = \frac{25}{540} \qquad \text{mass} = 25 \text{ lb and volume} = 540 \text{ in}^3$$

The density of the clay is about _0.046_ pounds per cubic inch.

b. Antonio uses the same clay to make a foundational cube for a sculpture. If the cube weighs 1.3 pounds, what are the dimensions of the cube?

Use the density formula to find the volume of the clay Antonio is using given the weight and the density of the clay.

$$\text{density} = \frac{\text{weight}}{\text{volume}} \qquad \text{Density Formula}$$
$$\frac{25}{540} = \frac{1.3}{V} \qquad \text{density} = \frac{25}{540} \text{ and weight} = 1.3$$
$$V = \underline{28.08} \qquad \text{Simplify.}$$

Because the foundation is a cube, each edge s must be the same length. Therefore, $s^3 = 28.08$ and $s \approx \underline{3.04}$.

Each side of Antonio's cube will be about 3.04 inches long.

🌐 **Go Online** You can complete an Extra Example online.

> **💭 Think About It!**
> If Antonio decides to change the size of the cube so that its weight is greater than 1.3 pounds, how will this change affect the density? Explain.
>
> Sample answer: The density of the clay will remain the same no matter what amount of it is used to make the cube.

Interactive Presentation

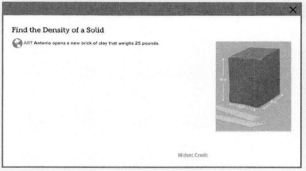

Find the Density of a Solid

🌐 ART Antonio opens a new brick of clay that weighs 25 pounds.

Widget Credit

Example 3

TAP

Students tap to reveal steps in the solution.

Check

GARDENING When Kimani filled her planter with soil, the weight of the planter increased by 90 pounds.

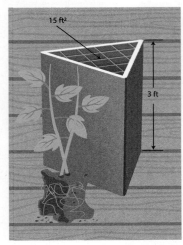

15 ft²

3 ft

The density of the soil is ___2___ pounds per cubic foot.

Kimani uses the same soil to fill another planter, and the weight increased by 154 pounds. The volume of the other planter is ___77___ cubic feet.

Pause and Reflect

Did you struggle with anything in this lesson? If so, how did you deal with it?

  See students' observations.

Copyright © McGraw-Hill Education

DIFFERENTIATE

Reteaching Activity AL ELL
Have students weigh a cup of various food or drink such as rice, beans, water, and popcorn. Have them compute the density of each item. Ask how the density might affect how full they make students feel when they eat them.

Exit Ticket

Recommended Use
At the end of class, go online to display the Exit Ticket prompt and ask students to respond using a separate piece of paper. Have students hand you their responses as they leave the room.

Alternate Use
At the end of class, go online to display the Exit Ticket prompt and ask students to respond verbally or by using a mini-whiteboard. Have students hold up their whiteboards so that you can see all student responses. Tap to reveal the answer when most or all students have completed the Exit Ticket.

Interactive Presentation

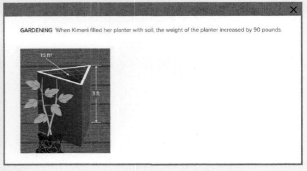

GARDENING When Kimani filled her planter with soil, the weight of the planter increased by 90 pounds.

15 ft²

3 ft

Check

CHECK

Students complete the Check online to determine whether they are ready to move on.

Practice and Homework

Suggested Assignments

Use the table below to select appropriate exercises.

DOK	Topic	Exercises
1, 2	exercises that mirror the examples	1–8
2	exercises that use a variety of skills from this lesson	9–10
2	exercises that extend concepts learned in this lesson to new contexts	11–12
3	exercises that emphasize higher-order and critical-thinking skills	13–16

ASSESS AND DIFFERENTIATE

📊 Use the data from the **Checks** to determine whether to provide resources for extension, remediation, or intervention.

IF students score 90% or more on the Checks, **BL**
THEN assign:

- Practice, Exercises 1–11 odd, 13–16
- Extension: Density and Buoyancy
- 🔲 **ALEKS** Areas of Parallelograms and Triangles; Volumes of Prisms and Cylinders

IF students score 66%–89% on the Checks, **OL**
THEN assign:

- Practice, Exercises 1–15 odd
- Remediation, Review Resources: Volume of Cylinders
- Personal Tutors
- Extra Examples 1–3
- 🔲 **ALEKS** Volume of Prisms and Cylinders

IF students score 65% or less on the Checks, **AL**
THEN assign:

- Practice, Exercises 1–7 odd
- Remediation, Review Resources: Volume of Cylinders
- *Quick Review Math Handbook*: Population Density
- 🔲 **ALEKS** Volume of Prisms and Cylinders

Name _____ Period _____ Date _____

Practice

🔵 **Go Online** You can complete your homework online.

Example 1

POPULATION **Use the data in the table to find the population density of each city.**

1. London, England ≈ 14,290.0 people/mi^2
2. Paris, France ≈ 54,643.7 people/mi^2
3. Madrid, Spain ≈ 13,525.6 people/mi^2
4. Sydney, Australia ≈ 899.1 people/mi^2

City	Population	Area (mi^2)
London	8,674,000	607
Paris	2,224,000	40.7
Madrid	3,165,000	234
Sydney	4,293,000	4775

Example 2

5. WILDLIFE A town is installing bat boxes to reduce the number of mosquitos in the area. Each bat box will house 150 bats. The town officials approximate that 300 bats per square mile can control the mosquito population. If the area of the town is 12 square miles, how many bat boxes are needed? 24

6. OCCUPANCY Jamero is planning to open a new restaurant. Safety regulations recommend that a restaurant allows for 15 square feet of floor space per person. If Jamero wants his restaurant to be able to accommodate 50 people, what is the smallest area of floor space he will need? 750 ft^2

Example 3

7. FESTIVALS Every year the Ohio State Fair features sculptures made of butter. While the sculptures vary from year to year, every year a new rendition of a cow and calf are created. In 2017, the sculptures of the cow and calf weighed 2000 pounds.

5 in. 1.25 in. 1.25 in.

   a. If a stick of butter weighs 4 ounces, what is its approximate density? 0.512 oz/in^3
   b. What was the total volume of the cow and calf sculptures that were made in 2017? (*Hint:* 1 pound = 16 ounces) 62,500 in^3
   c. Approximately how many sticks of butter were used to create the sculptures? 8000

8. ENERGY A British Thermal Unit (BTU) is equal to the amount of energy used to raise the temperature of one pound of water 1°F. A house is shaped like a rectangular prism with a length, width, and height of 80 feet, 25 feet, and 8 feet, respectively. Approximately 60,000 BTUs are required to heat the house properly.
   a. What is the density of the house in BTUs? 3.75 BTUs/ft^3
   b. A nearby house requires approximately 52,000 BTUs for heating. If the house is 31 feet long and 25 feet wide, what is the height of the house? Round your answer to the nearest foot. 18 ft

Mixed Exercises

9. REGULATIONS A rectangular national sight-seeing park with a length of 2 miles and a width of 3 miles has a maximum capacity of 250 people. Find the population density of people to the nearest hundredth. 41.67 people/mi^2

10. REASONING A city is divided by a river. The portion of the city east of the river covers 25% of the city and has a population density of 28 people/km^2. The portion on the west side of the river has a population density of 17 people/km^2. Find the population density of the city as a whole. 19.75 people/km^2

11. CONSTRUCT ARGUMENTS The cargo of a semi-trailer can weigh no more than 34,000 pounds. The interior dimensions of a semi-trailer are shown. Suppose a freight company wants to haul a shipment that will completely fill the entire interior of the trailer, and the freight has a known density of 0.006 pounds/in³. Will this proposed load meet the weight restrictions? Justify your argument. See margin.

12. PAPER WEIGHTS The cylindrical paper weight with dimensions shown has a mass of 606.7 grams.

a. Find the density of the paperweight. 8.05 g/cm³

b. Use the table to determine which, if any, of the materials listed may have been used to make the paperweight. steel

Material	Density
Silver	10.5 g/cm³
Copper	8.96 g/cm³
Steel	8.05 g/cm³

🌐 **Higher-Order Thinking Skills**

13. WHICH ONE DOESN'T BELONG? Jonathan is building his own terrarium for 18 plants, and he wants 120 cubic inches of space per plant. Which of the following proposed structures will not allow Jonathan to meet his requirement? Justify your conclusion. pentagonal prism; The pentagonal prism would only allow for 105.4 cubic inches per plant.

14. WRITE Explain why a cubic foot of gas and a cubic foot of gold do not have the same density. See margin.

15. ANALYZE Determine whether the following statement is *true* or *false*. Justify your argument. Block A has a greater density than block B.

Block A   **Block B**

3.5 kg   4200 g

False; Block B has a density of 0.79 g/cm³, and Block A has a density of 0.66 g/cm³. So, Block B has a greater density.

16. PERSEVERE An engineer is designing a marble fountain for the lobby of a museum. Before the engineer can finalize the design, she must choose a type of marble to use for the fountain. The marble samples that are available for viewing are rectangular prisms. The width, length, and height of each sample is 4 inches, 6 inches, and 1 inch, respectively. The mass of each sample is 1066.32 grams.

a. What is the density of each marble sample? 44.43 g/in³

b. The main feature of the fountain will be a marble sphere that has a radius of 2 feet. What will be the mass of the sphere? Round your answer to the nearest kilogram. 2573 kg

Answers

11. No; sample answer: Because the load will weigh 42,411.6 pounds, which exceeds the limit of 34,000 pounds, it will not meet the weight restrictions.

14. Sample answer: Density based on volume is calculated by dividing the mass of an object by its volume. While the gas and the gold both have the same volume, the gold has a greater mass, so it's density will be greater.

Module 11 · Measurement
Review

Rate Yourself!

Have students return to the Module Opener to rate their understanding of the concepts presented in this module. They should see that their knowledge and skills have increased. After completing the chart, have them respond to the prompts in their *Interactive Student Edition* and share their responses with a partner.

ⓔ Answering the Essential Question

Before answering the Essential Question, have students review their answers to the Essential Question Follow-Up questions found throughout the module.

- Why is it important to be able to find the area of two-dimensional figures?
- Why is it important to be able to identify cross sections of solid figures?
- Why is it important to be able to compute the volume of solids?

Then have them write their answer to the Essential Question in the space provided.

DINAH ZIKE FOLDABLES

ELL A completed Foldable for this module should include the key concepts related to measurement.

LS **LearnSmart** Use LearnSmart as part of your test preparation plan to measure student topic retention. You can create a student assignment in LearnSmart for additional practice on these topics for **Extend to Three Dimensions**.

- Explain volume formulas and use them to solve problems

Module 11 · Measurement
Review

ⓔ **Essential Question**

How are measurements of two- and three-dimensional figures useful for modeling situations in the real world?

Sample answer: Two- and three-dimensional figures can allow you to visualize or estimate measurements of real-world objects.

Module Summary

Lessons 11-1 through 11-3

Two-Dimensional Areas
- parallelogram: $A = bh$
- trapezoid: $A = \frac{1}{2}h(b_1 + b_2)$
- rhombus or kite: $A = \frac{1}{2}d_1d_2$
- regular n-gon: $A = \frac{1}{2}aP$
- circle: $A = \pi r^2$
- sector: $A = \frac{x°}{360°} \cdot \pi r^2$

Lessons 11-4 and 11-7

Surface Area
- right prism: $S = Ph + 2B$, where P is the perimeter of a base and h is the height
- right cylinder: $S = 2\pi rh + 2\pi r^2$, where r is the radius of a base and h is the height
- regular pyramid: $S = \frac{1}{2}P\ell + B$, where P is perimeter of the base and ℓ is slant height
- right circular cone: $S = \pi r\ell + \pi r^2$, where r is radius of the base and ℓ is slant height
- sphere: $S = 4\pi r^2$, where r is the radius of the sphere

Lessons 11-6 and 11-7

Volume
- prism: $V = Bh$, where B is the area of a base and h is the height of the prism
- pyramid: $V = \frac{1}{3}Bh$, where B is the area of the base and h is the height of the pyramid
- cylinder: $V = Bh$ or $V = \pi r^2h$, where B is the area of the base, h is the height of the cylinder, and r is the radius of the base
- circular cone: $V = \frac{1}{3}Bh$ or $V = \frac{1}{3}\pi r^2h$, where B is the area of the base, h is the height of the cone, and r is the radius of the base.
- sphere: is $V = \frac{4}{3}\pi r^3$, where r is the radius

Lessons 11-5, 11-8, and 11-9

Other Measurement Topics
- A cross section is the intersection of a solid figure and a plane.
- A solid of revolution is obtained by rotating a plane figure or curve around an axis.
- If two similar solids have a scale factor of $a : b$, then the surface areas have a ratio of $a^2 : b^2$, and the volumes have a ratio of $a^3 : b^3$.
- Density is the ratio of objects to area
- Density is the ratio of mass (or weight) to volume.

Study Organizer

📖 Foldables
Use your Foldable to review this module. Working with a partner can be helpful. Ask for clarification of concepts as needed.

Name _____ Period _____ Date _____

Test Practice

1. MULTIPLE CHOICE The diagram below is a blueprint for the head of a shovel. If the shovel head is cut from a square piece of aluminum that has a side length of 8 inches. What is the area of the wasted aluminum? (Lesson 11-2)

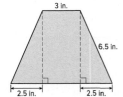

3 in.

6.5 in.

2.5 in.   2.5 in.

Ⓐ 12 in²   Ⓑ 16 in²   Ⓒ 31 in²   Ⓓ 40 in²

2. OPEN RESPONSE A company is using the figure below as the background for its logo. A designer at the company wants to know the area the logo will cover on a document. Find the area, in square centimeters, of the composite figure. (Lesson 11-2)

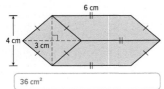

6 cm

4 cm   3 cm

| 36 cm² |

3. MULTIPLE CHOICE A sign-making company wants to know the minimum amount of metal needed to make a stop sign. A stop sign is shaped like a regular octagon. The distance between opposite sides of a stop sign is 30 inches. One side of the stop sign measures approximately 12.4 inches. What is the approximate area of the stop sign to the nearest square inch? (Lesson 11-2)

Ⓐ 372 in²   Ⓑ 588 in²

Ⓒ 744 in²   Ⓓ 1488 in²

4. OPEN RESPONSE Describe how you can derive the formula for the area of a sector by using the area of a circle. (Lesson 11-3)

> Sample answer: First, set up a proportion that relates the area of the sector to the area of a circle; $\frac{A}{\pi r^2}$. Then set the proportion equal to the ratio of the central angle of the sector to 360°; $\frac{A}{\pi r^2} = \frac{x}{360}$. Then solve for the area of the sector; $A = \frac{x}{360}\pi r^2$.

5. MULTI-SELECT Given a circle with radius r and circumference, $C = 2\pi r$, which of the following steps would be included in an informal argument for the formula for area of a circle? Select all that apply. (Lesson 11-3)

Ⓐ As the number of congruent pieces increases, the figure approaches a circle.

Ⓑ Divide the circle into equal wedge-shaped pieces.

Ⓒ Divide the circle into 4 pieces.

Ⓓ As the number of congruent pieces increases, the figure approaches a sector.

Ⓔ The wedge-shaped pieces form a regular polygon.

Ⓕ The area formula for a regular polygon is $A = \frac{1}{2}aP$.

Ⓖ Use the area of each of the 4 sectors to derive the formula for the area of a circle.

6. OPEN RESPONSE A pharmaceutical company is developing a new medicine and needs a capsule in the shape of a sphere to hold the medicine. The company wants to find the amount of material needed to make the capsule. What is the surface area of the capsule if the diameter is 10 millimeters? (Lesson 11-4)

| 314 mm² |

Review and Assessment Options

The following online review and assessment resources are available for you to assign to your students. These resources include technology-enhanced questions that are auto-scored, as well as essay questions.

Review Resources

Put It All Together: Lessons 11-1 through 11-3

Put It All Together: Lessons 11-4 through 11-7

Vocabulary Activity

Module Review

Assessment Resources

Vocabulary Test

AL Module Test Form B

OL Module Test Form A

BL Module Test Form C

Performance Task*

*The module-level performance task is available online as a printable document. A scoring rubric is included.

Test Practice

You can use these pages to help your students review module content and prepare for online assessments. Exercises 1–18 mirror the types of questions your students will see on online assessments.

Question Type	Description	Exercise(s)
Multiple Choice	Students select one correct answer.	1, 3, 7, 10, 12, 14, 16, 17
Multi-Select	Multiple answers may be correct. Students must select all correct answers.	5, 8, 9
Open Response	Students construct their own response in the area provided.	2, 4, 6, 11, 13, 15, 18

To ensure that students understand the standards, check students' success on individual exercises.

Standard(s)	Lesson(s)	Exercise(s)
G.C.5	11-3	4, 5
G.GMD.1	11-3, 11-6, 11-7	4, 5, 8, 9, 10, 11, 12, 13
G.GMD.3	11-6, 11-7, 11-8	8, 9, 10, 11, 12, 13, 14, 15, 16
G.GMD.4	11-5	7
G.MG.2	11-9	17, 18
G.MG.3	11-1, 11-2, 11-4	1, 2, 3, 6

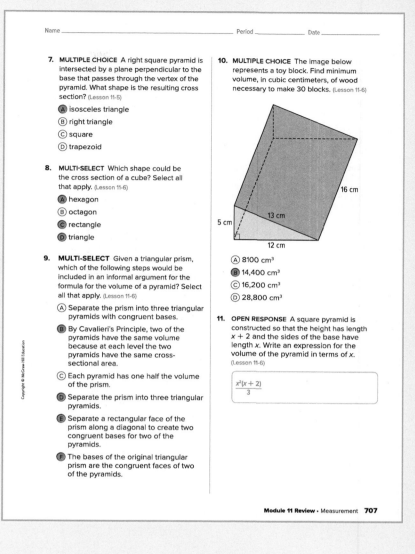

Name _____ Period _____ Date _____

7. MULTIPLE CHOICE A right square pyramid is intersected by a plane perpendicular to the base that passes through the vertex of the pyramid. What shape is the resulting cross section? (Lesson 11-5)

Ⓐ isosceles triangle

Ⓑ right triangle

Ⓒ square

Ⓓ trapezoid

8. MULTI-SELECT Which shape could be the cross section of a cube? Select all that apply. (Lesson 11-6)

Ⓐ hexagon

Ⓑ octagon

Ⓒ rectangle

Ⓓ triangle

9. MULTI-SELECT Given a triangular prism, which of the following steps would be included in an informal argument for the formula for the volume of a pyramid? Select all that apply. (Lesson 11-6)

Ⓐ Separate the prism into three triangular pyramids with congruent bases.

Ⓑ By Cavalieri's Principle, two of the pyramids have the same volume because at each level the two pyramids have the same cross-sectional area.

Ⓒ Each pyramid has one half the volume of the prism.

Ⓓ Separate the prism into three triangular pyramids.

Ⓔ Separate a rectangular face of the prism along a diagonal to create two congruent bases for two of the pyramids.

Ⓕ The bases of the original triangular prism are the congruent faces of two of the pyramids.

10. MULTIPLE CHOICE The image below represents a toy block. Find minimum volume, in cubic centimeters, of wood necessary to make 30 blocks. (Lesson 11-6)

Ⓐ 8100 cm³

Ⓑ 14,400 cm³

Ⓒ 16,200 cm³

Ⓓ 28,800 cm³

11. OPEN RESPONSE A square pyramid is constructed so that the height has length $x + 2$ and the sides of the base have length x. Write an expression for the volume of the pyramid in terms of x. (Lesson 11-6)

$$\frac{x^2(x + 2)}{3}$$

12. MULTIPLE CHOICE The height of a cylinder is 1 inch less than the diameter of the cylinder. Which expression represents the volume of the cylinder in terms of its radius, x? (Lesson 11-7)

Ⓐ $2\pi x^3 - \pi x^2$

Ⓑ $\pi x^3 - \pi x^2$

Ⓒ $2\pi x^3 - 1$

Ⓓ $2\pi x^3 + \pi x^2$

13. OPEN RESPONSE At the center of a baseball is a sphere called the pill that has an approximate volume of 1.32 cubic inches. The pill is wrapped with 3 types of string to form the center of the baseball. The center of the baseball is covered with a leather casing and sewn together to make the final product. If the radius of the center of the baseball is 2.9 inches, what is the approximate volume of string, to the nearest cubic inch, that is used to wrap the pill? (Lesson 11-7)

101 in³

14. MULTIPLE CHOICE An artist has made a scale model of a sculpture shaped like a cone. The ratio of the scale model to the final sculpture is 2 : 5. If the volume of the scale model is approximately 75.4 cubic inches, what is the volume of the final sculpture? (Lesson 11-8)

Ⓐ 188.5 in³

Ⓑ 226.2 in³

Ⓒ 471.3 in³

Ⓓ 1178.1 in³

15. OPEN RESPONSE A candle maker sells sets of candles in the shape of square pyramids. The volume of a smaller candle is 125 cubic centimeters. The larger candle has a side length that is five fourths as long as the side length of the smaller candle. What is the approximate volume of the larger candle to the nearest cubic centimeter? (Lesson 11-8)

244 cm³

16. MULTIPLE CHOICE These cylinders are similar.

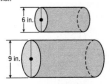

Find the volume of the smaller cylinder given that the larger cylinder has a volume of 190.85 cubic inches. (Lesson 11-8)

Ⓐ 28.3 in³   Ⓑ 56.5 in³

Ⓒ 84.8 in³   Ⓓ 91.1 in³

17. MULTIPLE CHOICE A pile of sand forms a cone with a diameter of 2 meters and a height of 0.7 meter. The mass of the pile is 1170 kilograms. What is the approximate density of the sand in kilograms per cubic meter? (Lesson 11-9)

Ⓐ 399 kg/m³   Ⓑ 532 kg/m³

Ⓒ 1140 kg/m³   Ⓓ 1596 kg/m³

18. OPEN RESPONSE Jacksonville, Florida, has a land area of 875 square miles and a population of 880,619. What is the approximate population density of Jacksonville to the nearest whole number? (Lesson 11-9)

1006 people/mi²

708 Module 11 Review • Measurement

33. Chenglei; sample answer: The measure of each angle of a regular hexagon is 120°, so the segments from the center of each vertex form 60°-angles. The triangles formed by the segments from the center to each vertex are equilateral, so each side of the hexagon is 11 in. The perimeter of the hexagon is 66 in. Using technology, the length of the apothem is about 9.5 in. Substituting the values into the formula for the area of a regular polygon and simplifying, the area is about 313.5 in².

34. Sometimes; if the polygon is a hexagon, then the apothem bisects a central angle of the polygon and forms a 30°-60°-90° right triangle. Thus, the length of the apothem is $\sqrt{3} \cdot \frac{1}{2}$ or $\frac{\sqrt{3}}{2} s$.

35. Sample answer:

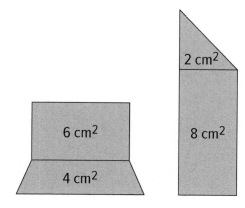

36. $a^2 - b^2 = (a + b)(a - b)$; Sample answer: The area of the first figure is equal to the area of the larger square a^2 minus the area of the smaller square b^2 or $a^2 - b^2$. The area of the second figure is the area of a rectangle with side lengths $a + b$ and $a - b$ or $(a + b)(a - b)$. Because the figures are composed of congruent shapes, the areas are equal so $a^2 - b^2 = (a + b)(a - b)$.

37. Sample answer: You can decompose the figure into shapes of which you know the area formulas. Then, you can add all of the areas to find the total area of the figure.

34. Sample answer:

35. False; sample answer: If a plane has a slope different than the slant height of the pyramid and intersects a lateral face of the pyramid, then the cross section is a trapezoid.

Probability

Module Goals

- Students represent sample spaces.
- Students use permutations and combinations with probability.
- Students find probabilities of compound events.
- Students solve real-world problems involving probability.

Focus

Domain: Statistics & Probability

Standards for Mathematical Content:

S.CP.1 Describe events as subsets of a sample space (the set of outcomes) using characteristics (or categories) of the outcomes, or as unions, intersections, or complements of other events ("or," "and," "not").

S.CP.6 Find the conditional probability of *A* given *B* as the fraction of *B*'s outcomes that also belong to *A*, and interpret the answer in terms of the model.

Also addresses S.CP.2, S.CP.3, S.CP.4, S.CP.5, S.CP.7, S.CP.8, S.CP.9, S.MD.6, and S.MD.7.

Standards for Mathematical Practice:

All Standards for Mathematical Practice will be addressed in this module.

✪ Be Sure to Cover

To completely cover S.MD.6, go online to assign the following activity:

- Making Fair Decisions (Expand, Lesson 12-3)

Coherence

Vertical Alignment

Previous
Students found experimental and theoretical probabilities of simple and compound events.
7.SP.7

Now
Students solve probability problems, including those involving conditional probability.
S.CP.1, S.CP.6

Rigor

The Three Pillars of Rigor

To help students meet standards, they need to illustrate their ability to use the three pillars of rigor. Students gain conceptual understanding as they move from the Explore to Learn sections within a lesson. Once they understand the concept, they practice procedural skills and fluency and apply their mathematical knowledge as they go through the Examples and Practice.

1 CONCEPTUAL UNDERSTANDING	2 FLUENCY	3 APPLICATION
EXPLORE	LEARN	EXAMPLE & PRACTICE

Suggested Pacing

Lessons	Standards	45-min classes	90-min classes
Module Pretest and Launch the Module Video		1	0.5
12-1 Sample Spaces		1	0.5
12-2 Probability and Counting	S.CP.1	1	0.5
12-3 Geometric Probability	S.MD.6, S.MD.7	1	0.5
12-4 Probability with Permutations and Combinations	S.CP.9	1	0.5
12-5 Probability and the Multiplication Rule	S.CP.2, S.CP.8	1	0.5
12-6 Probability and the Addition Rule	S.CP.7	2	1
12-7 Conditional Probability	S.CP.3, S.CP.5	1	0.5
Put It All Together: Lessons 12-2 and 12-5 through 12-7		1	0.5
12-8 Two-Way Frequency Tables	S.CP.4, S.CP.6	2	1
Module Review		1	0.5
Module Assessment		1	0.5
Total Days		**14**	**7**

Formative Assessment Math Probe
Probability

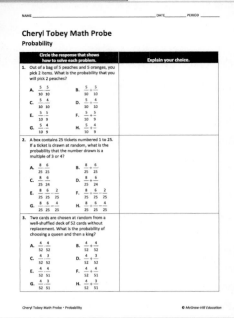

□ **A**nalyze the Probe

Review the probe prior to assigning it to your students.

In this probe, students will determine which solution method correctly represents the situation described and explain their choices.

Targeted Concepts Understand events and how to assign probabilities to them.

Targeted Misconceptions

- Students may misinterpret descriptors distinguishing between the intersection of events (*A* and *B*) and the union of events (*A* or *B*).

- Students cannot distinguish between independent and dependent events when the description is not explicit.

- Students cannot distinguish between mutually exclusive and not mutually exclusive events.

Use the Probe after Lesson 12-6.

Answers: 1. D; 2. G; 3. C

□ **C**ollect and Assess Student Answers

If the student selects these responses...	**Then** the student likely...
1. E, F, G, H **2.** A, B, C, D **3.** E, F, G, H	does not use the correct operation for calculating the probability (does not use multiplication for intersection and addition for union).
1. E, F, G, H **3.** E, F, G, H	does not distinguish between the intersection of events (*A* and *B*) and the union of events (*A* or *B*) when the descriptors *and* and *or* are not used.
1. A, B, C **2.** E, F **3.** A, B, D	does not understand that events are dependent, and/or does not know how to translate this correctly into a fraction.

□ **T**ake Action

After the Probe Design a plan to address any possible misconceptions. You may wish to assign the following resources.

- **ALEKS** Probability of Independent and Dependent Events, Probabilities of the Union of Two Events
- Lessons 12-5 and 12-6, all Learns, all Examples

Revisit the Probe at the end of the module to be sure that your students no longer carry these misconceptions.

IGNITE!

The Ignite! activities, created by Dr. Raj Shah, cultivate curiosity and engage and challenge students. Use these open-ended, collaborative activities, located online in the module Launch section, to encourage your students to develop a growth mindset towards mathematics and problem solving. Use the teacher notes for implementation suggestions and support for encouraging productive struggle.

℮ Essential Question

At the end of this module, students should be able to answer the Essential Question.

How can you use measurements to find probabilities? Sample answer: You can find the number of favorable outcomes for an experiment and also find the total number of possible outcomes for an experiment and then find probabilities using a ratio. That ratio can be used to predict how many times a certain event may occur.

What Will You Learn?

Prior to beginning this module, have your students rate their knowledge of each item listed. Then, at the end of the module, you will be reminded to have your students return to these pages to rate their knowledge again. They should see that their knowledge and skills have increased.

DINAH ZIKE FOLDABLES

Focus Students write the names of methods of counting and types of probabilities.

Teach After students make their Foldables, have them label the tabs to correspond to the eight lessons in this module. Instruct students to take notes while reading each lesson and listening to instruction. They should include definitions of terms and key concepts, as well as diagrams and examples related to the lesson.

📖 **When to Use It** Use the appropriate tabs as students cover each lesson in this module. Students can add to the vocabulary tab during each lesson.

Launch the Module

For this module, the Launch the Module video uses tossing a coin to introduce simple probability models, and expands that into the modeling of more elaborate situations using probability. Students learn about geometric and conditional probability, as well as how different types of probability can be used to analyze decisions and choose a strategy in a real-world situation.

Interactive Presentation

What Vocabulary Will You Learn?

ELL As you proceed through the module, introduce the key vocabulary by using the following routine.

Define The complement of an event A consists of all of the outcomes of a sample space that are not included as outcomes of event A.

Example If A consists of rolling a 1 or a 5 on a die, then the complement of A is rolling a 2, 3, 4, or 6.

Ask What is the probability that A or its complement occurs? 1

Are You Ready?

Students may need to review the following prerequisite skills to succeed in this module.

- die rolling
- using Venn diagrams
- sample spaces
- using tree diagrams
- theoretical probabilities
- experimental probabilities
- finding probabilities of independent and dependent events
- two-way tables

 ALEKS

ALEKS is an adaptive, personalized learning environment that identifies precisely what each student knows and is ready to learn, ensuring student success at all levels.

You may want to use the **Probability** section to ensure student success in this module.

Mindset Matters

Promote Process Over Results

The process that a student takes as he or she encounters a new problem is just as important—if not more important—than the result.

How Can I Apply It?

Encourage students to consider the **Think About It!** prompts in their Interactive Student Edition. Have students discuss their problem-solving strategies with a partner. Be sure to support the process and reward effort as students explore and work through problems.

LESSON GOAL

Students describe events using subsets.

1 LAUNCH

 Launch the lesson with a **Warm Up** and an introduction.

2 EXPLORE AND DEVELOP

Develop:

Sample Spaces
- Define a Sample Space
- Represent a Sample Space
- Finite and Infinite Sample Spaces

Fundamental Counting Principle
- Use the Fundamental Counting Principle

· ·

You may want your students to complete the **Checks** online.

3 REFLECT AND PRACTICE

Exit Ticket

· ·

Practice

DIFFERENTIATE

View reports of student progress on the **Checks** after each example.

Resources	AL	OL	BL	ELL
Remediation: Relative Frequency of Simple Events	●	●		●
Extension: Traveling Salesman Problem		●	●	●

Language Development Handbook

Assign page 83 of the *Language Development Handbook* to help your students build mathematical language related to describing events using subsets.

ELL You can use the tips and suggestions on page T83 of the handbook to support students who are building English proficiency.

Suggested Pacing

| 90 min | 0.5 day |
| 45 min | 1 day |

Focus

Standards for Mathematical Practice:
5 Use appropriate tools strategically

Coherence

Vertical Alignment

Previous
Students used tree diagrams, tables, and organized lists to find sample spaces.
7.G.8

Now
Students describe and count events using subsets.

Next
Students will solve problems using the rule for the probability of complementary events.
S.CP.1

Rigor

The Three Pillars of Rigor

1 CONCEPTUAL UNDERSTANDING	2 FLUENCY	3 APPLICATION

Conceptual Bridge In this lesson, students expand on their understanding of and fluency with sample spaces (first studied in Grade 7) to prepare for identifying unions, intersections, and complements. They apply their understanding of sample spaces by solving real-world problems.

Mathematical Background

A sample space of an experiment is the set of all possible outcomes. The sample space can be finite or infinite, depending whether or not the possible outcomes can be counted. The Fundamental Counting Principle says that in an experiment with multiple stages, the number of possible outcomes can be found by multiplying the number of possible outcomes from each stage.

Interactive Presentation

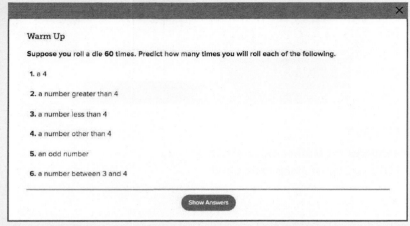

Warm Up

Launch the Lesson

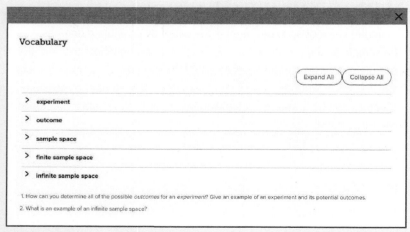

Today's Vocabulary

Warm Up

Prerequisite Skills

The Warm Up exercises address the following prerequisite skill for this lesson:

- rolling die

Answers:

1. 10 times
2. 20 times
3. 30 times
4. 50 times
5. 30 times
6. 0 times

Launch the Lesson

MP Teaching the Mathematical Practices

4 Apply Mathematics In this Launch the Lesson, students can see a real-world application of experiments.

Go Online to find additional teaching notes and questions to promote classroom discourse.

Today's Standards

Tell students that they will be addressing these content and practice standards in this lesson. You may wish to have a student volunteer read aloud *How can I meet this standard*? and *How can I use this practice*? and connect these to the standards.

See the Interactive Presentation for I Can statements that align with the standards covered in this lesson.

Today's Vocabulary

Tell students that they will be using these vocabulary terms in this lesson. You can expand each row if you wish to share the definitions. Then, discuss the questions below with the class.

Learn Sample Spaces

Objective
Students define sample spaces and describe subsets of sample spaces.

 Teaching the Mathematical Practices

> **7 Use Structure** Help students to explore the structure of sample spaces in this Learn.

Common Misconception
Remind students that even though a sample space contains a finite number of outcomes, the outcomes are not necessarily equally likely. You can represent this visually with an unequal spinner, such as the one represented in the Finite column of the table in the Learn.

DIFFERENTIATE

Enrichment Activity **AL** **BL**
Organize students in groups of three or four. Provide each group with a handful of four to six different manipulatives. Challenge each group to make as many unique groups of items as possible. Have students draw and record the total number of unique groups they can make by using one item, two items, three items, and so on. Challenge some groups to find the total number of unique groups if order is important (ABC and BCA are considered two separate groups) and if order is not important (ABC and BCA are considered the same group). Have groups share with the class their drawings and the total number of groups made.

Example 1 Define a Sample Space

 Teaching the Mathematical Practices

> **2 Create Representations** Guide students to write sample spaces that model the situations in this example.

Questions for Mathematical Discourse

AL What is the geometric shape of a fair die? cube

OL What is S(even number on a die)? S(even number on a die) = {2, 4, 6}

BL What is S(odd prime number on a die)?
S(odd prime number on a die) = {3, 5}

Go Online
- Find additional teaching notes.
- View performance reports of the Checks.
- Assign or present an Extra Example.

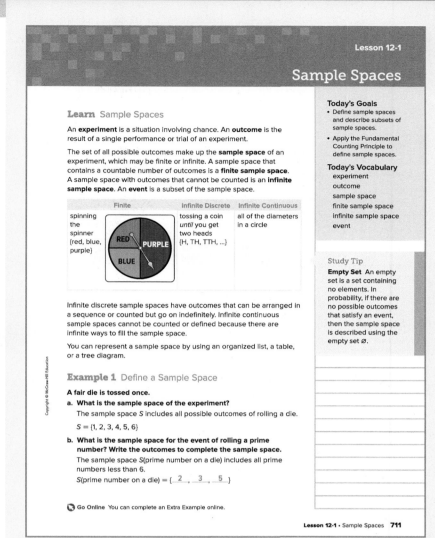

Interactive Presentation

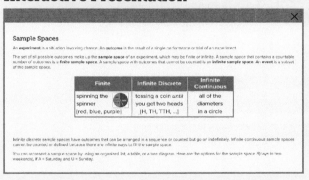

Learn

TAP

Students tap to see different ways to represent sample spaces.

🌐 Example 2 Represent a Sample Space

CLOTHING Kembe has a black hat and a red hat. He chooses one hat for each day, Saturday and Sunday. Represent the sample space for this experiment by making an organized list, a table, and a tree diagram.

For each day, Saturday and Sunday, there are two possibilities: the red hat (R) or the black hat (B).

Organized List
Pair each possible outcome from the Saturday's hat choice with the possible outcomes from Sunday's hat choice using coordinates.

$S = \{(R, R), (R, B), (B, B), (\underline{\,B\,}, \underline{\,R\,})\}$

Table
Saturday's hat choices are represented vertically, and Sunday's hat choices are represented horizontally.

Saturday	Sunday	
	R	B
R	R, R	R, B
B	B, R	B, B

Tree Diagram
Each event is represented by a different stage of the tree diagram.

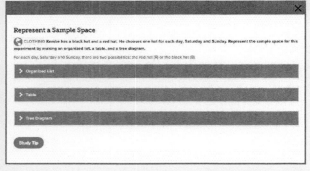

Outcomes

Saturday's Hat Choices	R	B
Sunday's Hat Choices	R B	R B
Sample Space	R, R R, B	B, R B, B

Check

GROUP WORK A geometry teacher always breaks her class up into the red, yellow, and blue groups for class projects. Represent the sample space for the next two class projects by making an organized list.

Enter the outcomes to complete the organized list.

$S = \{(R, R), (R, Y), \underline{(R, B)}, (Y, R), \underline{(Y, Y)}, \underline{(R, B)}, (B, R), \underline{(B, Y)}, \underline{(B, B)}\}$

🌐 **Go Online** You can complete an Extra Example online.

Your Notes

💬 Talk About It!
Why are R, B and B, R not the same outcome?

Sample answer: Because a red or black hat is chosen on Saturday and then again on Sunday, R, B means he wears the red hat on Saturday and the black hat on Sunday. B, R means he wears the black hat on Saturday and the red hat on Sunday.

Study Tip
Tree Diagram Notation Choose notation for outcomes in your tree diagrams that will eliminate confusion. In the example, R stands for red hat and B stands for black hat.

Interactive Presentation

Represent a Sample Space

🌐 CLOTHING Kembe has a black hat and a red hat. He chooses one hat for each day, Saturday and Sunday. Represent the sample space for this experiment by making an organized list, a table, and a tree diagram.

For each day, Saturday and Sunday, there are two possibilities: the red hat (R) or the black hat (B).

> Organized List

> Table

> Tree Diagram

Study Tip

Example 2

TAP

Students tap to see the sample space represented in different forms.

TYPE

Students answer a question to show that they understand how to represent a sample space.

🌐 **Example 2** Represent a Sample Space

MP Teaching the Mathematical Practices

4 Apply Mathematics In this example, students apply what they have learned about sample spaces to solving a real-world problem.

Questions for Mathematical Discourse

AL Which outcome means that Kembe wore the black hat on both Saturday and Sunday? B, B

OL How many outcomes would be in the sample space if Kembe also wore one of the hats on Monday? 8

BL What is another situation that would have the same number of outcomes as the sample space in Example 2? Sample answer: flipping a coin two times

℮ Essential Question Follow-Up

Students have begun to quantify outcomes of events as sample spaces.

Ask:

How can we predict the outcomes of events? Sample answer: You can conduct an experiment to determine the chance that the event will occur; you can use the information from previous events; you can use new information that you've gathered.

DIFFERENTIATE

Language Development Activity AL BL ELL
Write the following menu choices on the board: 1. What size sundae would you like: small, medium, or large? 2. Would you like chocolate or vanilla ice cream? 3. Would you like caramel sauce, chocolate sauce, or strawberry sauce? 4. Would you like whipped cream? Ask students to create a tree diagram to show all of the possible sundae combinations.

Example 3 Finite and Infinite Sample Spaces

(MP) Teaching the Mathematical Practices

1 Explain Correspondences Encourage students to explain the relationships between the sample spaces and the situations they represent in this example.

Questions for Mathematical Discourse

AL What type of sample space is represented by a spinner with four equal parts of green, blue, red, and yellow that is spun twice? Finite discrete

OL A random number generator generates an amount of money, down to the nearest cent, from $1 to $1,000,000. How is the sample space classified? Explain. Finite discrete; sample answer: Even though there are many possible outcomes from $1 to $1,000,000, these outcomes are not continuous because they are to the nearest cent. They are finite because the exact number of options is a finite number.

BL Is it possible to have a finite continuous sample space? Explain. No; sample answer: If a sample space is continuous, then between any two different outcomes there are an infinite number of other outcomes.

Common Error

In practice, an experiment usually has a constraint on the measurement that means that the results will be discrete. For example, in part **c** of Example 3, the measuring tool used will put a constraint on how continuous the height measurements can actually be. It is still continuous, though, because those heights actually exist, even though they cannot be measured.

Learn Fundamental Counting Principle

(MP) Teaching the Mathematical Practices

7 Look for a Pattern Help students to see the pattern in this Learn.

Objective

Students apply the Fundamental Counting Principle to define sample spaces.

Things to Remember

The Fundamental Counting Principle can be used to check whether all possible outcomes have been considered in the sample space of a given event.

Common Misconception

Remind students that if they are considering a situation where they do not need to choose an option at a certain stage, they should include that lack of choice as one of the options, both when explicitly listing out the sample space or using the Fundamental Counting Principle to calculate them.

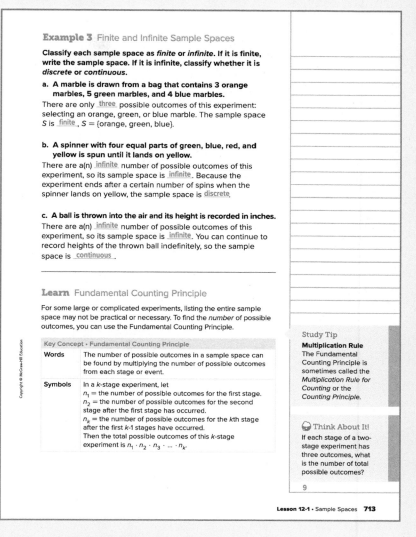

Example 3 Finite and Infinite Sample Spaces

Classify each sample space as *finite* or *infinite*. If it is finite, write the sample space. If it is infinite, classify whether it is *discrete* or *continuous*.

a. A marble is drawn from a bag that contains 3 orange marbles, 5 green marbles, and 4 blue marbles.

There are only __three__ possible outcomes of this experiment: selecting an orange, green, or blue marble. The sample space S is __finite__ , $S = \{\text{orange, green, blue}\}$.

b. A spinner with four equal parts of green, blue, red, and yellow is spun until it lands on yellow.

There are a(n) __infinite__ number of possible outcomes of this experiment, so its sample space is __infinite__. Because the experiment ends after a certain number of spins when the spinner lands on yellow, the sample space is __discrete__.

c. A ball is thrown into the air and its height is recorded in inches.

There are a(n) __infinite__ number of possible outcomes of this experiment, so its sample space is __infinite__. You can continue to record heights of the thrown ball indefinitely, so the sample space is __continuous__ .

Learn Fundamental Counting Principle

For some large or complicated experiments, listing the entire sample space may not be practical or necessary. To find the *number* of possible outcomes, you can use the Fundamental Counting Principle.

Key Concept · Fundamental Counting Principle	
Words	The number of possible outcomes in a sample space can be found by multiplying the number of possible outcomes from each stage or event.
Symbols	In a k-stage experiment, let n_1 = the number of possible outcomes for the first stage. n_2 = the number of possible outcomes for the second stage after the first stage has occurred. n_k = the number of possible outcomes for the kth stage after the first k-1 stages have occurred. Then the total possible outcomes of this k-stage experiment is $n_1 \cdot n_2 \cdot n_3 \cdot \ldots \cdot n_k$.

Study Tip

Multiplication Rule The Fundamental Counting Principle is sometimes called the *Multiplication Rule for Counting* or the *Counting Principle*.

Think About It! If each stage of a two-stage experiment has three outcomes, what is the number of total possible outcomes?

9

Lesson 12-1 · Sample Spaces **713**

Interactive Presentation

Finite and Infinite Sample Spaces

Classify each sample space as *finite* or *infinite*. If it is finite, write the sample space. If it is infinite, classify whether it is *discrete* or *continuous*. Expand to see each classification.

(Expand All) (Collapse All)

> a. A marble is drawn from a bag that contains 3 orange marbles, 5 green marbles, and 4 blue marbles.
> b. A spinner with four equal parts of green, blue, red, and yellow is spun until it lands on yellow.
> c. A ball is thrown into the air and its height is recorded in inches.

Example 3

EXPAND

Students expand to see problems about finite and infinite sample spaces.

CHECK

Students complete the Check online to determine whether they are ready to move on.

🌐 Example 4 Use the Fundamental Counting Principle

COLLEGE Santiago lists the number of sections available for the courses he will take in his first semester at college. How many different schedules could Santiago create for this semester?

Course	Sections Offered
Art History	6
French	5
Mathematics	9
Art	4
English	6

You can estimate the total number of different schedules he can make. There are about 10 sections of the __mathematics__ course offered. For each of the other four courses, there are about __5__ sections offered. Multiply to estimate that Santiago can create about __6250__ schedules.

Find the number of possible outcomes by using the Fundamental Counting Principle to complete the equation.

Art History	French	Mathematics	Art	English	Possible Outcomes
6 ×	5 ×	9 ×	4 ×	6 =	6480

Santiago could create 6480 different schedules. Because 6480 is close to the estimate of 6250, the answer is reasonable.

Check

CLOTHING A sneaker company lets you customize your own sneaker on their Web site. Using their most popular sneaker as the base, you have the option to customize the color of each part of the sneaker.

• Customize Your Shoes

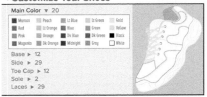

Main Color ▼ 20

Base ▶ 12
Side ▶ 29
Toe Cap ▶ 12
Sole ▶ 2
Laces ▶ 29

Part A Which is the best estimate for the number of possible customizations? __B__

A. 100
B. 3,600,000
C. 5,062,500
D. 36,000,000

Part B How many different customizations can be created? __4,844,160__

🌐 **Go Online** You can complete an Extra Example online.

714 Module 12 · Probability

Use a Source

Colleges typically assign general studies courses to freshman undergraduates who haven't yet selected a major. Use available resources to find the freshman curriculum for a college of your choice and determine the number of possible schedules that can be created.

Sample answer: The University of Connecticut offers 67 Arts and Humanities courses, 36 Social Sciences courses, 22 Science and Technology courses, 16 Laboratory Courses, and 26 Diversity and Multiculturalism courses to freshmen. From these courses, 22,074,624 different schedules are possible.

🌐 Example 4 Use the Fundamental Counting Principle

🅜🅟 Teaching the Mathematical Practices

5 Use a Source Guide students to find external information to answer the questions posed in the Use a Source feature.

Questions for Mathematical Discourse

AL How many sections of French are available? 5

OL If the college adds a seventh English section, how many different schedules could be created? 7,560

BL At an ice cream store, there are three cone options and five topping options. The total number of possible combinations of cone, ice cream, and a single topping is 270. How many ice cream flavors are offered? 18

DIFFERENTIATE

Enrichment Activity 🅑🅛

Have students write a multi-stage experiment involving marketing, such as mix-and-match outfits, special-of-the-day dinner choices at a restaurant, or pizzas with a selection of toppings. Have students create a table listing all the choice options and then use the Fundamental Counting Principle to determine the number of possible outcomes. Then have students create a tree diagram to identify the sample space. Finally, have students create a marketing flyer highlighting the number of choices available for their product.

Exit Ticket

Recommended Use

At the end of class, go online to display the Exit Ticket prompt and ask students to respond using a separate piece of paper. Have students hand you their responses as they leave the room.

Alternate Use

At the end of class, go online to display the Exit Ticket prompt and ask students to respond verbally or by using a mini-whiteboard. Have students hold up their whiteboards so that you can see all student responses. Tap to reveal the answer when most or all students have completed the Exit Ticket.

Interactive Presentation

Use the Fundamental Counting Principle

🌐 COLLEGE Santiago lists the number of sections available for the courses he will take in his first semester at college. How many different schedules could Santiago create for this semester?

Example 4

TYPE

Students complete the calculations to use the fundamental counting principle.

DRAG

Students drag the values to find the total number of possible outcomes.

CHECK

Students complete the Check online to determine whether they are ready to move on.

Practice and Homework

Suggested Assignments

Use the table below to select appropriate exercises.

DOK	Topic	Exercises
1, 2	exercises that mirror the examples	1–14
2	exercises that use a variety of skills from this lesson	15–27
3	exercises that emphasize higher-order and critical-thinking skills	28–31

ASSESS AND DIFFERENTIATE

📊 Use the data from the **Checks** to determine whether to provide resources for extension, remediation, or intervention.

IF students score 90% or more on the Checks, **BL**
THEN assign:

- Practice, Exercises 1–27 odd, 28–31
- Extension: Traveling Salesman Problem
- ☑ **ALEKS** Theoretical and Experimental Probability

IF students score 66%-89% on the Checks, **OL**
THEN assign:

- Practice, Exercises 1–31 odd
- Remediation, Review Resources: Sample Spaces
- Personal Tutors
- Extra Examples 1–4
- ☑ **ALEKS** Die Rolling

IF students score 65% or less on the Checks, **AL**
THEN assign:

- Practice, Exercises 1–13 odd
- Remediation, Review Resources: Sample Spaces
- *Quick Review Math Handbook*: Representing Sample Spaces
- ☑ **ALEKS** Die Rolling

Answers

18.

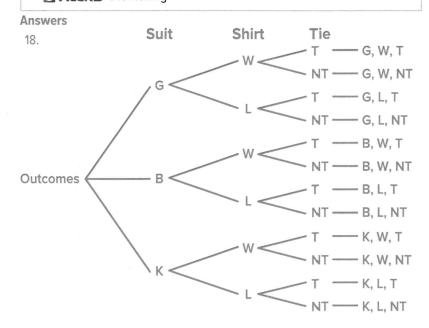

Name _____ Period _____ Date _____

Practice 🔵 Go Online You can complete your homework online.

Example 1

1. Define the sample space, *S*, of a fair coin being tossed once. $S = \{H, T\}$

2. A numbered spinner with six equal parts is spun once.
   a. What is the sample space of the experiment?
      $S = \{1, 2, 3, 4, 5, 6\}$
   b. What is the sample space for the event of landing on a prime number?
      $S(\text{prime number}) = \{2, 3, 5\}$

3. **DODECAGON** A regular, 12-sided dodecagon is rolled once.
   a. What is the sample space of the experiment?
      $S = \{1, 2, 3, 4, 5, 6, 7, 8, 9, 10, 11, 12\}$
   b. What is the sample space for the event of rolling an even number?
      $S(\text{even number}) = \{2, 4, 6, 8, 10, 12\}$

4. **SPINNERS** A lettered spinner with five equal parts is spun once.
   a. What is the sample space of the experiment?
      $S = \{A, B, C, D, E\}$
   b. What is the sample space for landing on a vowel?
      $S(\text{vowel}) = \{A, E\}$

Example 2

5. **UNIFORMS** For away games, the baseball team can wear blue or white shirts with blue or white pants. Represent the sample space for each experiment by completing the table and tree diagram, and by making an organized list.
   BB, BW, WB, WW

	Blue Pants	White Pants
Blue Shirts	B, B	B, W
White Shirts	W, B	W, W

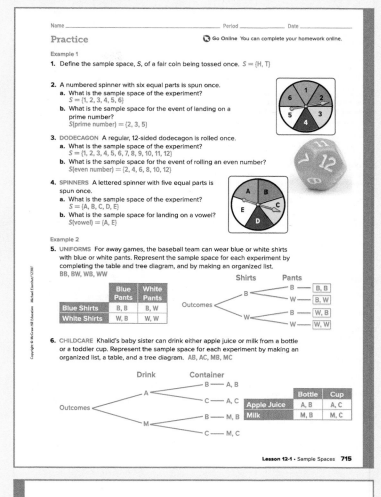

6. **CHILDCARE** Khalid's baby sister can drink either apple juice or milk from a bottle or a toddler cup. Represent the sample space for each experiment by making an organized list, a table, and a tree diagram. AB, AC, MB, MC

	Bottle	Cup
Apple Juice	A, B	A, C
Milk	M, B	M, C

Example 3

Classify each sample space as *finite* or *infinite*. If it is finite, write the sample space. If it is infinite, classify whether it is *discrete* or *continuous*.

7. A color tile is drawn from a cup that contains 1 yellow, 2 blue, 3 green, and 4 red color tiles.
   finite; $S = \{\text{yellow, blue, green, red}\}$

8. A numbered spinner with eight equal parts is spun until it lands on 2.
   infinite; discrete

9. An angler casts a fishing line into a body of water and its distance is recorded in centimeters. infinite; continuous

10. A letter is randomly chosen from the alphabet. finite; $S = \{A, B, C, D, E, F, G, H, I, J, K, L, M, N, O, P, Q, R, S, T, U, V, W, X, Y, Z\}$

Example 4

Find the number of possible outcomes for each situation.

11. A video game lets you decorate a bedroom using one choice from each category. 28,800

Bedroom Décor	Number of Choices
Paint color	8
Comforter set	6
Sheet set	8
Throw rug	5
Lamp	3
Wall hanging	5

12. A cafeteria meal at Angela's work includes one choice from each category. 864

Cafeteria Meal	Number of Choices
Main dish	3
Side dish	4
Vegetable	2
Salad	2
Salad Dressing	3
Dessert	2
Drink	3

13. **SHOPPING** On a website showcasing outdoor patio plans, there are 4 types of stone, 3 types of edging, 5 dining sets, and 6 grills. Kamar plans to order one item from each category. How many different patio sets can Kamar order? 360

14. **AUDITIONS** The drama club held tryouts for 6 roles in a one-act play. Five people auditioned for lead female, 3 for lead male, 8 for the best friend, 4 for the mother, 2 for the father, and 3 for the humorous aunt. How many different casts can be created from those who auditioned? 2880

Mixed Exercises

15. **BOARD GAMES** The spinner shown is used in a board game. If the spinner is spun 4 times, how many different possible outcomes are there? 1296

Name _____ Period _____ Date _____

16. BASKETBALL In a city basketball league there must be a minimum of 14 players on a team's roster. One 14-player team has three centers, four power forwards, two small forwards, three shooting guards, and the rest of the players are point guards. How many different 5-player teams are possible if one player is selected from each position? 144

17. VACATION RENTAL Angelica is comparing vacation prices in Boulder, Colorado, and Sarasota, Florida. In Boulder, she can choose a 1- or 2-week stay in a 1- or 2-bedroom suite. In Sarasota, she can choose a 1-, 2-, or 3-week stay in a 2- or 3-bedroom suite, on the beach or not.

   a. How many outcomes are available in Boulder? 4

   b. How many outcomes are available in Sarasota? 12

   c. How many total outcomes are available? 16

18. TRAVEL Maurice packs suits, shirts, and ties that can be mixed and matched. Use his packing list to draw a tree diagram to represent the sample space for possible suit combinations using one article from each category. See margin.

> **Maurice's Packing List**
> 1. Suits: Gray, black, khaki
> 2. Shirts: White, light blue
> 3. Ties: Striped (But optional)

Find the number of possible outcomes for each situation.

19. SCHOOL Tala wears a school uniform that consists of a skirt or pants, a white shirt, a blue jacket or sweater, white socks, and black shoes. She has 3 pairs of pants, 3 skirts, 6 white shirts, 2 jackets, 2 sweaters, 6 pairs of white socks, and 3 pairs of black shoes. 2592

20. FOOD A sandwich shop provides its customers with a number of choices for bread, meats, and cheeses. Provided one item from each category is selected, how many different sandwiches can be made? 60

Bread	Meats	Cheeses
White	Turkey	American
Wheat	Ham	Swiss
Whole Grain	Roast Beef	Provolone
	Chicken	Colby-Jack
		Muenster

21. List six different expressions that could be used to evaluate the area of the composite figure. See margin.

22. LICENSE PLATES One state requires license plates to consist of three letters followed by three numbers. The letter "O" and the number "0" may not be used, but any other combination of letters or numbers is allowed. How many different license plates can be created? 11,390,625 license plates

23. COLLEGE Jack has been offered a number of internships that could occur in 3 different months, in 4 different departments, and for 3 different companies. Jack is only available to complete his internship in July. How many different outcomes are there for his internship? 12

24. BIKING Talula got a new bicycle lock that has a four-number combination. Each number in the combination is from 0 to 9.

   a. How many combinations are possible if there are no restriction on the number of times Talula can use each number? 10,000

   b. How many combinations are possible if Talula can use each number only once? Explain. See margin.

25. BOARD GAMES Hugo and Monette are playing a board game in which the player rolls two fair dice per turn.

   a. In one turn, how many outcomes result in a sum of 8? 5

   b. How many outcomes in one turn result in an odd sum? 18

26. WRITING Explain when it is necessary to show all the possible outcomes of an experiment by using a tree diagram and when using the Fundamental Counting Principle is sufficient. See margin.

27. REASONING A multistage experiment has n possible outcomes at each stage. If the experiment is performed with k stages, write an equation for the total number of possible outcomes P. Explain. See margin.

💡 **Higher-Order Thinking Skills**

28. PERSEVERE A box contains n different objects. If you remove three objects from the box, one at a time, without putting the previous object back, how many possible outcomes exist? Explain your reasoning. See margin.

29. CREATE Sometimes a tree diagram for an experiment is not symmetrical. Describe a two-stage experiment where the tree diagram is asymmetrical. Include a sketch of the tree diagram. Explain. See margin.

30. WRITE Explain why it is not possible to represent the sample space for a multi-stage experiment by using a table. See margin.

31. ANALYZE Determine if the following statement is *sometimes*, *always*, or *never* true. Justify your argument. See margin.

   When an outcome falls outside the sample space, it is a failure.

Answers

21. Sample answer: 6 different ways
$2(x + 4) + 4(x + 6) + 2(3)$;
$2(x + 4) + 2(x + 6) + 2(x + 6) + 2(3)$;
$2(x) + 2(4) + 4(x + 6) + 2(3)$;
$2(x) + 2(4) + 2(x + 6) + 2(x + 6) + 2(3)$;
$2(x) + 2(2) + 2(2) + 4(x + 6) + 2(3)$;
$2(x) + 2(2) + 2(2) + 2(x + 6) + 2(x + 6) + 2(3)$

24b. 5040; Sample answer: There are 10 possibilities for the first number in the combination. Because Talula can use each number only once, there are only 9 possibilities for the second number in the combination, 8 possibilities for the third number in the combination, and 7 possibilities for the fourth number in the combination. The number of possible combinations is $10 \times 9 \times 8 \times 7$ or 5040.

26. Sample answer: Drawing a tree diagram is necessary if you want to show the sample space for an experiment or if you want to know the number of times a certain outcome occurs. The Fundamental Counting Principle is sufficient when the number of outcomes is too large to show with a tree diagram.

27. $P = n^k$; Sample answer: The total number of possible outcomes is the product of the number of outcomes for each of the stages 1 through k. Because there are k stages, you are multiplying n by itself k times which is n^k.

28. $n^3 - 3n^2 + 2n$; Sample answer: There are n objects in the box when you remove the first object, so after you remove one object, there are $n - 1$ possible outcomes. After you remove the second object, there are $n - 2$ possible outcomes. The number of possible outcomes is the product of the number of outcomes of each experiment or $n(n - 1)(n - 2)$.

29. Sample answer: In an experiment, you choose between a blue box and a red box. You then remove a ball from the box that you chose without looking into the box. The blue box contains a red ball, a purple ball, and a green ball. The red box contains a yellow ball and an orange ball.

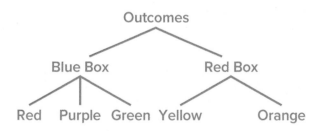

30. Sample answer: You can list the possible outcomes for one stage of an experiment in the columns and the possible outcomes for the other stage of the experiment in the rows. Because a table is two dimensional, it would be impossible to list the possible outcomes for three or more stages of an experiment. Therefore, tables can only be used to represent the sample space for a two-stage experiment.

31. Never; sample answer: The sample space is the set of all possible outcomes. An outcome cannot fall outside the sample space. A failure occurs when the outcome is in the sample space, but is not a favorable outcome.

Probability and Counting

LESSON GOAL

Students solve problems involving using the rule for the probability of complementary events.

1 LAUNCH

 Launch the lesson with a **Warm Up** and an introduction.

2 EXPLORE AND DEVELOP

 Explore: Venn Diagrams

 Develop:

Intersections and Unions
- Find Intersections
- Find Probability of Intersections
- Find Unions

Complements
- Complementary Events

 You may want your students to complete the **Checks** online.

3 REFLECT AND PRACTICE

 Exit Ticket

 Practice

DIFFERENTIATE

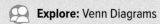 View reports of student progress on the **Checks** after each example.

Resources	AL	OL	BL	ELL
Extension: Probability in Genetics		●	●	●

Language Development Handbook

Assign page 84 of the *Language Development Handbook* to help your students build mathematical language related to the rule for the probability of complementary events.

ELL You can use the tips and suggestions on page T84 of the handbook to support students who are building English proficiency.

Suggested Pacing

| 90 min | 0.5 day |
| 45 min | 1 day |

Focus

Domain: Statistics & Probability

Standards for Mathematical Content:

S.CP.1 Describe events as subsets of a sample space (the set of outcomes) using characteristics (or categories) of the outcomes, or as unions, intersections, or complements of other events ("or," "and," "not").

Standards for Mathematical Practice:

3 Construct viable arguments and critique the reasoning of others.

4 Model with mathematics.

Coherence

Vertical Alignment

Previous
Students found experimental and theoretical probabilities.
7.SP.7

Now
Students solve problems involving using the rule for the probability of complementary events.
S.CP.1

Next
Students will find the probability of events by using lengths of segments and areas.
S.MD.6, S.MD.7

Rigor

The Three Pillars of Rigor

1 CONCEPTUAL UNDERSTANDING	2 FLUENCY	3 APPLICATION

🏛 **Conceptual Bridge** In this lesson, students draw on their work in the previous lesson to develop an understanding of independence with sample spaces. They apply their understanding by solving real-world problems.

Mathematical Background

Sample spaces represent a set of possible outcomes. An intersection of sample spaces A and B represents all the outcomes that are contained in both A and B. A union of two samples spaces A and B represents all the outcomes that are in either A or B. A complement of a sample space A, noted as A', represents all outcomes not included in A.

Interactive Presentation

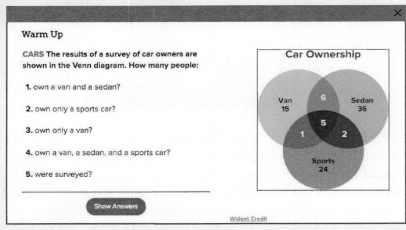

Warp Up

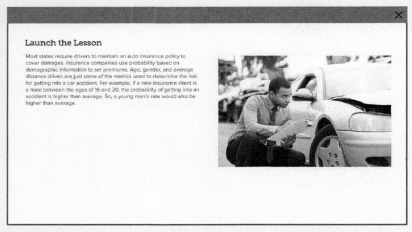

Launch the Lesson

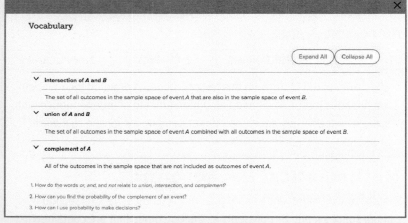

Today's Vocabulary

Warm Up

Prerequisite Skills

The Warm Up exercises address the following prerequisite skill for this lesson:

- using Venn diagrams

Answers:

1. 11
2. 24
3. 15
4. 5
5. 89

Launch the Lesson

MP Teaching the Mathematical Practices

4 Apply Mathematics In this Launch the Lesson, students can see a real-world application of probability.

Go Online to find additional teaching notes and questions to promote classroom discourse.

Today's Standards

Tell students that they will be addressing these content and practice standards in this lesson. You may wish to have a student volunteer read aloud *How can I meet this standard*? and *How can I use these practices?* and connect these to the standards.

See the Interactive Presentation for I Can statements that align with the standards covered in this lesson.

Today's Vocabulary

Tell students that they will be using these vocabulary terms in this lesson. You can expand each row if you wish to share the definitions. Then, discuss the questions below with the class.

Explore Venn Diagrams

Objective
Students use Venn diagrams to describe the intersection, union, and complement of sets.

Ideas for Use
Recommended Use Present the Inquiry Question, or have a student volunteer read it aloud. Have students work in pairs to complete the Explore activity on their devices. Pairs should discuss each of the questions. Monitor student progress during the activity. Upon completion of the Explore activity, have student volunteers share their responses to the Inquiry Question.

What if my students don't have devices? You may choose to project the activity on a whiteboard. A printable worksheet for each Explore is available online. You may choose to print the worksheet so that individuals or pairs of students can use it to record their observations.

Summary of the Activity
Students will complete guiding exercises throughout the Explore activity. They will use two sets, A and B, to analyze the ways that different elements relate to the sets as presented in a Venn diagram. Then, students will answer the Inquiry Question.

(continued on the next page)

Interactive Presentation

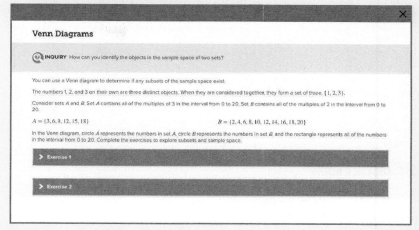

Explore

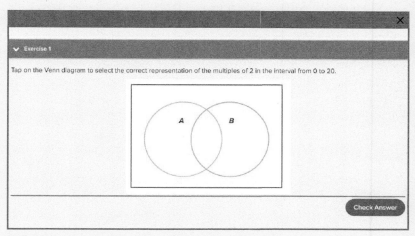

Explore

TAP

 Students tap to select the correct Venn diagram.

Interactive Presentation

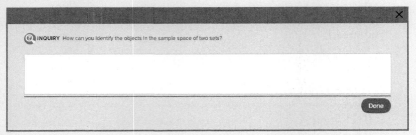

Explore

TYPE

a|

Students respond to the Inquiry Question and can view a sample answer.

Explore Venn Diagrams (*continued*)

Teaching the Mathematical Practices

6 Communicate Precisely Encourage students to routinely write or explain their solution methods. Point out that they should use clear definitions when they discuss their solutions with others.

Questions

Have students complete the Explore activity.

Ask:

- Why does it make sense for the circles in the Venn diagram to overlap for sets *A* and *B*? Sample answer: Because there are values that are the same in both sets. These would be located in the region that overlaps.

- What does it mean for the Venn diagram to have everything outside of *B* shaded? Sample answer: This means everything that is not in set *B*, so the set of numbers that are not multiples of 2.

Inquiry

How can you identify the objects in the sample space of the two sets? Sample answer: I can use the properties of a Venn diagram to visualize the subsets of the sample space.

Go Online to find additional teaching notes and sample answers for the guiding exercises.

Learn Intersections and Unions

Objective

Students describe events as subsets of sample spaces by using intersections and unions.

MP Teaching the Mathematical Practices

7 Use Structure Help students to explore the structure of intersections in this Learn.

3 Analyze Cases The Concept Check guides students to examine the cases of intersections and unions. Encourage students to familiarize themselves with all of the cases.

About the Key Concept

Point out to students that not all sets have intersections, though any set that contains elements will have a union. Ask them to come up with examples of two sample spaces that would have no intersection, such as the event of rolling an odd number and the event of rolling an even number on a fair die.

Common Misconception

It is easy for students to confuse the notation symbols for intersection (∩) and union (∪). Remind the students to take care in distinguishing between the symbols. Point out that the symbol for union looks like a U as a way of remembering which is which.

Example 1 Find Intersections

MP Teaching the Mathematical Practices

3 Justify Conclusions Mathematically proficient students can explain the conclusions drawn when solving a problem. This example asks students to justify their conclusions.

Questions for Mathematical Discourse

AL What would be the sample space of the event of rolling a number greater than or equal to 3? {3, 4, 5, 6}

OL What is the sample space of outcomes that are not part of *A*? {2, 4, 6}

BL Let *C* be the event of rolling an even number. What is *B* ∩ *C*? Explain. {4, 6}; Because *C* = {2, 4, 6} and *B* = {4, 5, 6}, the intersection would be all of the outcomes that are in both *C* and *B*, which is {4, 6}.

Common Error

Because $P(A \cap B)$ is read as "the probability of *A* and *B*," it is possible for students to think that it is the probability of the whole combined sample space (the union). Point out to the students that the intersection is the probability of both *A* and *B* being simultaneously true.

Lesson 12-2

Probability and Counting

Learn Intersections and Unions

When two events *A* and *B* occur, the **intersection of *A* and *B*** is the set of all outcomes in the sample space of event *A* that are also in the sample space of event *B*. In the Venn diagram, the shaded portion represents the intersection.

A ∩ B

To determine the probability of an outcome from the intersection of two or more events, find the ratio of the number of outcomes in both events to the total number of possible outcomes.

Key Concept • Probability Rule for Intersections

The probability of the intersection of two events *A* and *B* occurring is the ratio of the number of outcomes in both *A* and *B* to the total number of possible outcomes.

$$P(A \cap B) = \frac{\text{number of outcomes in } A \text{ and } B}{\text{total number of possible outcomes}}$$

When two events *A* and *B* occur, the **union of *A* and *B*** is the set of all outcomes in the sample space of event *A* combined with all outcomes in the sample space of event *B*. In the Venn diagram, the shaded portion represents the union.

Key Concept • Union of Two Events

The number of elements in the union of two events *A* and *B* is the number of outcomes in both event *A* and *B* minus the number of outcomes in their intersection.

$$n(A \cup B) = n(A) + n(B) - n(A \cap B)$$

Example 1 Find Intersections

A fair die is rolled once. Let *A* be the event of rolling an odd number, and let *B* be the event of rolling a number greater than 3. Find *A ∩ B*.

The possible outcomes for event ___*A*___ are all the numbers on a die that are odd, or {1, 3, 5}.

The possible outcomes for event ___*B*___ are all the numbers on a die that are greater than 3, or {4, 5, 6}.

A ∩ B contains ___all___ of the outcomes that are in both sample space *A* and *B*.

A ∩ B = ___{5}___

Go Online You can complete an Extra Example online.

Today's Goals
- Describe events as subsets of sample spaces by using intersections and unions.
- Describe events as subsets of sample spaces by using complements.

Today's Vocabulary
intersection of *A* and *B*
union of *A* and *B*
complement of *A*

Study Tip
Intersection The symbol for intersection is ∩, and it is associated with the word *and*.
$P(A \cap B)$ is read as *the probability of A and B*.

Study Tip
Union The symbol for union is ∪, and it is associated with the word *or*.
$n(A \cup B)$ is read as, *the number of elements in A or B*.

Think About It!
Is the sample space for *A ∩ B* finite or infinite? Justify your reasoning.

Sample answer: Because both sample spaces for *A* and *B* have a finite number of outcomes, the intersection of the sample spaces must also be finite.

Interactive Presentation

Intersections

When two events *A* and *B* occur, the **intersection of *A* and *B*** is the set of all outcomes in the sample space of event *A* that are also in the sample space of event *B*. In the Venn diagram, the shaded portion represents the intersection.

To determine the probability of an outcome from the intersection of two or more events, find the ratio of the number of outcomes in both events to the total number of possible outcomes.

A ∩ B

Learn

DRAG & DROP

Students drag outcomes to complete subsets of the sample space.

Your Notes

Go Online
You may want to complete the Concept Check to check your understanding.

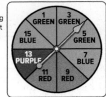

Math History Minute

Scottish physician **John Arbuthnot (1667–1735)** published *Of the Laws of Chance* anonymously in 1692, the first work on probability published in English. This appears to be the first time the word "probability" is used in print. In a 1710 paper, Arbuthnot discusses the first application of probability to social statistics.

Check

Let *A* be the event of the spinner landing on a blue section, and let *B* be the event of the spinner landing on a section with a number divisible by 3. What are the possible outcomes of each event?

$A = \{7, \underline{15}\}$

$B = \{3, \underline{9}, 15\}$

$A \cap B = \{\underline{15}\}$

Example 2 Find Probability of Intersections

PLAYING CARDS A card is selected from a standard deck of cards. What is the probability that the card is a queen and is red?

Let *A* be the event of choosing a queen, and let *B* be the event of choosing a red card. The total number of outcomes is the total number of cards in a deck, or 52.

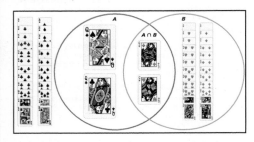

From the diagram, there are only $\underline{2}$ red cards that are also queens.

$$P(A \cap B) = \frac{\text{number of outcomes in } A \text{ and } B}{\text{total number of possible outcomes}} \quad \text{Probability Rule for Intersections}$$

$$= \frac{2}{52} \qquad \text{Substitution}$$

$$= \frac{1}{26} \qquad \text{Simplify.}$$

The probability that the card is both a queen and is red is $\frac{1}{26}$, or about $\underline{3.8\%}$.

Go Online You can complete an Extra Example online.

Example 2 Find Probability of Intersections

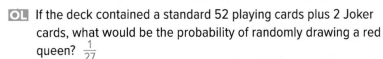

Teaching the Mathematical Practices

4 Apply Mathematics In this example, students apply what they have learned about finding probabilities of intersections to solving a real-world problem.

Questions for Mathematical Discourse

AL In a standard deck of 52 cards, how many cards are red? 26

OL If the deck contained a standard 52 playing cards plus 2 Joker cards, what would be the probability of randomly drawing a red queen? $\frac{1}{27}$

BL What is another intersection that would have the same probability as drawing two red queens? Sample answer: drawing two red kings

Common Error

Though playing cards are common, not all students will have equal familiarity with them. Many students may have familiarity with more modern card games, such as trading card games, where decks of cards are not standardized.

Go Online

- Find additional teaching notes.
- View performance reports of the Checks.
- Assign or present an Extra Example.

Interactive Presentation

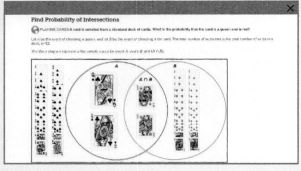

Example 2

TYPE

Students complete the calculations to find the probability of intersections.

1 CONCEPTUAL UNDERSTANDING | **2 FLUENCY** | 3 APPLICATION

Example 3 Find Unions

MP Teaching the Mathematical Practices

6 Communicate Precisely Encourage students to routinely write and explain their solution methods. Point out that they should use clear definitions when they discuss their solutions with others.

Questions for Mathematical Discourse

AL How many outcomes are in the sample space for the event of rolling less than 5? 4

OL Let C be the event of rolling an odd number. What is $A \cup C$? $A \cup C = \{1, 2, 3, 4, 5\}$

BL If L contains 5 events and M contains 8 events, what is the fewest number of events that $L \cup M$ could contain? Explain. 8; Sample answer: Because $L \cup M$ contains all of the events from both L and M, then it has to contain the 8 events from M. If there are events in L that are not in M, then it would have more than 8 (up to 13), but the fewest number will happen if all of the events from L are in M. In that case, there would be just 8 events in the intersection.

Learn Complements

Objective
Students describe events as subsets of sample spaces by using complements.

MP Teaching the Mathematical Practices

7 Use Structure Help students to explore the structure of complements in this Learn.

About the Key Concept
Ask the students to rewrite $P(A') = 1 - P(A)$ in an equivalent form that does not include a minus, resulting in $P(A) + P(A') = 1$. Encourage the students to explain what this equation represents in terms of the probability of the two events A and A', to elicit the understanding that it is certain that A either will happen or will not happen.

Common Misconception
Remind students that probabilities of events cannot be negative. Students may be inclined to think that the probability of an event not happening is the opposite of the probability of it happening.

Example 3 Find Unions

A fair die is rolled once. Let A be the event of rolling a number less than 5, and let B be the event of rolling a multiple of 2. Find $A \cup B$.

The possible outcomes for event A are all the numbers on a die that are less than 5, or (_1_ , _2_ , _3_ , _4_).

The possible outcomes for event B are all the numbers on a die that are multiples of _2_ , or (2, 4, 6).

$A \cup B$ contains all of the outcomes that are in _either_ sample space(s) A or B.

$A \cup B = \{$ _1_ , _2_ , _3_ , _4_ , _6_ $\}$

> **Think About It!**
> Why are 2 and 4 only listed once in $A \cup B$? Explain?
>
> Sample answer: Although 2 and 4 are outcomes for both events A and B, the union does not include the outcomes in the intersection of A and B.

Check
Let A be the event of the spinner landing on a blue section, and let B be the event of the spinner landing on a section with a number divisible by 3. What are the possible outcomes of each event?

$A = \{7,$ _15_ $\}$
$B = \{3,$ _9_ , 15$\}$
$A \cup B = \{3, 7, 9,$ _15_ $\}$

Learn Complements

The **complement of A** consists of all the outcomes in the sample space that are not included as outcomes of event A. The complement of event A can be noted as A', as shown in the Venn diagram.

The probability of rolling a die and getting a 3 is $\frac{1}{6}$. What is the probability of *not* getting a 3? There are 5 possible outcomes for this event: 1, 2, 4, 5, or 6. So, $P(\text{not } 3) = \frac{5}{6}$. Notice that this probability is also $1 - \frac{1}{6}$ or $1 - P(3)$.

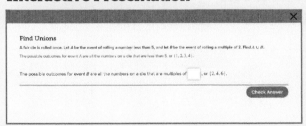

Key Concept • Probability of the Complement of an Event	
Words	The probability that an event will not occur is equal to 1 minus the probability that the event will occur.
Symbols	For an event A, $P(A') = 1 - P(A)$.

Interactive Presentation

Find Unions

A fair die is rolled once. Let A be the event of rolling a number less than 5, and let B be the event of rolling a multiple of 2. Find $A \cup B$.

The possible outcomes for event A are all the numbers on a die that are less than 5, or {1, 2, 3, 4}.

The possible outcomes for event B are all the numbers on a die that are multiples of ⬚ , or {2, 4, 6}.

[Check Answer]

Example 3

TYPE

Students complete the calculations to find unions.

CHECK

Students complete the Check online to determine whether they are ready to move on.

⊕ Example 4 Complementary Events

DIGITAL MEDIA Panju subscribes to a movie streaming service. For movie night, he is going to let the program randomly pick a movie from his list of favorites. What is the probability that a comedy movie will not be chosen?

🌳 My Movie Queue 🌳	
GENRES	
▶ Action	44
▶ Anime	109
▶ Children's	8
▶ Comedies	112
▶ Documentaries	13
▶ Dramas	30
▶ Foreign	5
▶ Horror	29

Let event A represent selecting a comedy movie from Panju's favorites. Then find the probability of the complement of A.

There are __112__ comedy movies in Panju's favorites list.

There are __350__ total movies in Panju's favorites list.

The probability of the complement of A is $P(A') = $ __1__ $ - P($ __A__ $)$.

$$P(A') = 1 - P(A) \qquad \text{Probability of a complement}$$
$$= 1 - \frac{112}{350} \qquad \text{Substitution}$$
$$= \frac{238}{350} \text{ or } \frac{17}{25} \qquad \text{Subtract and simplify.}$$

The probability that a comedy movie will not be chosen is $\frac{17}{25}$ or __68__ %.

Check

RAFFLE The Harvest Fair sold 967 raffle tickets for a chance to win a new TV. Complete the table to find each probability of not winning the TV with the given number of tickets.

Number of Tickets	Probability of Not Winning
20	98%
200	79%
100	90%
1	99.9%

🔵 **Go Online** You can complete an Extra Example online.

📱 Talk About It!

Why do you think the probability of the complement of an event is found by subtracting from 1?

Sample answer: A probability of 1 represents a 100% chance of an event happening. Subtracting the probability of an event happening from 1 will result in the probability of the event not happening.

Interactive Presentation

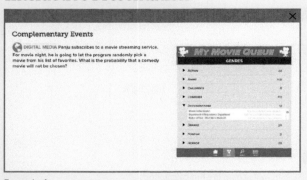

Example 4

| a| |

Students complete the calculations to find complementary events and answer a question to show they understand.

CHECK

Students complete the Check online to determine whether they are ready to move on.

⊕ **Example 4** Complementary Events

🅜🅟 Teaching the Mathematical Practices

4 Apply Mathematics In this example, students apply what they have learned about complements to solving a real-world problem.

Questions for Mathematical Discourse

AL What does the number 238 represent? the number of movies in Panju's favorites list that are not comedies

OL What is $P(A)$? $\frac{8}{25}$ or 32%

BL What is the probability that the movie chosen will be from Panju's list of favorites? Explain. 1; Sample answer: Because Panju is letting the program randomly pick a movie from his list of favorites, the movie picked is guaranteed to be from the list of favorites. If an outcome is certain, it has a probability of 1.

Exit Ticket

Recommended Use

At the end of class, go online to display the Exit Ticket prompt and ask students to respond using a separate piece of paper. Have students hand you their responses as they leave the room.

Alternate Use

At the end of class, go online to display the Exit Ticket prompt and ask students to respond verbally or by using a mini-whiteboard. Have students hold up their whiteboards so that you can see all student responses. Tap to reveal the answer when most or all students have completed the Exit Ticket.

Practice and Homework

Suggested Assignments

Use the table below to select appropriate exercises.

DOK	Topic	Exercises
1, 2	exercises that mirror the examples	1–14
2	exercises that use a variety of skills from this lesson	15–18
2	exercises that extend concepts learned in this lesson to new contexts	19–21
3	exercises that emphasize higher-order and critical-thinking skills	22–26

ASSESS AND DIFFERENTIATE

Use the data from the **Checks** to determine whether to provide resources for extension, remediation, or intervention.

IF students score 90% or more on the Checks,   `BL`
THEN assign:

- Practice, Exercises 1–21 odd, 22–26
- Extension: Probability in Genetics
- ⊙ **ALEKS** Counting

IF students score 66%–89% on the Checks,   `OL`
THEN assign:

- Practice, Exercises 1–25 odd
- Remediation, Review Resources: Probability and Counting
- Personal Tutors
- Extra Examples 1–3
- ⊙ **ALEKS** Using Venn Diagrams

IF students score 65% or less on the Checks,   `AL`
THEN assign:

- Practice, Exercises 1–13 odd
- Remediation, Review Resources: Probability and Counting
- *Quick Review Math Handbook*: Simple Probability
- ⊙ **ALEKS** Using Venn Diagrams

Name _____ Period _____ Date _____

Practice

⊙ **Go Online** You can complete your homework online.

Example 1

1. A fair die is rolled once. Let A be the event of rolling an even number, and let B be the event of rolling a number greater than 4. Find $A \cap B$. $A \cap B = \{6\}$

2. A fair die is rolled once. Let A be the event of rolling an even number, and let B be the event of rolling an odd number. Find $A \cap B$. $A \cap B = \varnothing$

Use the spinner.

3. Let A be the event of the spinner landing on 4 or 10, and let B be the event of the spinner landing on a section with a number divisible by 4. What are the possible outcomes of each event?

   a. $A = \{\_\_\_\}$ 4, 10

   b. $B = \{\_\_\_\}$ 4, 8, 12

   c. $A \cap B = \{\_\_\_\}$ 4

4. Let P be the event of the spinner landing on a section with a prime number, and let Q be the event of the spinner landing on a section with a number that is a multiple of 3. What are the possible outcomes of each event?

   a. $P = \{\_\_\_\}$ 2, 3, 5, 7, 11

   b. $Q = \{\_\_\_\}$ 3, 6, 9, 12

   c. $P \cap Q = \{\_\_\_\}$ 3

Example 2

5. A card is selected from a standard deck of cards. What is the probability that the card is a diamond and is a seven? $\frac{1}{52}$ or 1.92%

6. A card is selected from a standard deck of cards. What is the probability that the card has a number on it that is divisible by 2 and is black? $\frac{10}{52}$ or 19.23%

Example 3

Use the spinner.

7. Let A be the event that the spinner lands on a vowel. Let B be the event that it lands on the letter J. What are the possible outcomes of each event?

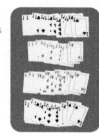

   a. $A = \{\_\_\_\}$ A, E, O, U

   b. $B = \{\_\_\_\}$ J

   c. $A \cup B = \{\_\_\_\}$ A, E, O, U, J

8. Let X be the event that the spinner lands on a consonant. Let Y be the event that it lands on the letter K. What are the possible outcomes of each event?

   a. $X = \{\_\_\_\}$ K, H, S, J

   b. $Y = \{\_\_\_\}$ K

   c. $X \cup Y = \{\_\_\_\}$ K, H, S, J

9. A random number generator is used to generate one integer between 1 and 20. Let C be the event of generating a multiple of 5, and let D be the event of generating a number less than 12. What are the possible outcomes of each event?

   a. $C = \{\_\_\_\}$ 5, 10, 15, 20

   b. $D = \{\_\_\_\}$ 1, 2, 3, 4, 5, 6, 7, 8, 9, 10, 11

   c. $C \cup D = \{\_\_\_\}$ 1, 2, 3, 4, 5, 6, 7, 8, 9, 10, 11, 15, 20

10. A random number generator is used to generate one integer between 1 and 100. Let A be the event of generating a multiple of 10, and let B be the event of generating a factor of 30. What are the possible outcomes of each event?

   a. $A = \{\_\_\_\}$ 10, 20, 30, 40, 50, 60, 70, 80, 90, 100

   b. $B = \{\_\_\_\}$ 1, 2, 3, 5, 6, 10, 15, 30

   c. $A \cup B = \{\_\_\_\}$ 1, 2, 3, 5, 6, 10, 15, 20, 30, 40, 50, 60, 70, 80, 90, 100

Example 4

Determine the probability of each event. Round to the nearest hundredth, if necessary.

11. What is the probability of drawing a card from a standard deck and not getting a spade? $\frac{39}{52}$ or $\frac{3}{4}$ or 0.75

12. What is the probability of flipping a coin and not landing on tails? $\frac{1}{2}$ or 0.5

13. Carmela purchased 10 raffle tickets. If 250 were sold, what is the probability that one of Carmela's tickets will not be drawn? $\frac{240}{250}$ or 0.96

14. What is the probability of spinning a spinner numbered 1 to 6 and not landing on 5? $\frac{5}{6}$ or about 0.83

| 1 CONCEPTUAL UNDERSTANDING | 2 FLUENCY | 3 APPLICATION |

Mixed Exercises

15. STATISTICS A survey found that about 90% of the junior class is right-handed. If 1 junior is chosen at random out of 100 juniors, what is the probability that he or she is left-handed? $\frac{10}{100}$ or $\frac{1}{10}$ or 0.10

16. RAFFLE Raul bought 24 raffle tickets out of 1545 tickets sold. What is the probability that Raul will not win the grand prize of the raffle? $\frac{507}{515}$ or 0.98

17. MASCOT At Riverview High School, 120 students were asked whether they prefer a lion or a timber wolf as the new school mascot. What is the probability that a randomly-selected student will have voted for a lion as the new school mascot? $\frac{13}{20}$ or 0.65

	Votes
Lion	78
Timber Wolf	42
Total	120

18. COLLEGE In Evan's senior class of 240 students, 85% are planning to attend college after graduation. What is the probability that a senior chosen at random is not planning to attend college after graduation? $\frac{36}{240}$ or $\frac{3}{20}$ or 0.15

19. DRAMA CLUB The Venn diagram shows the cast members who are in Acts I and II of a school play. One of the students will be chosen at random to attend a statewide performing arts conference. Let A be the event that a cast member is in Act I of the play and let B be the event that a cast member is in Act II of the play.

a. Find $A \cap B$. {Amy, Alex}

b. What is the probability that the student who is chosen to attend the conference is a cast member in only one of the two Acts of the play.
P(one musical) $= 1 - P$(both)
$= 1 - \frac{2}{9} = \frac{7}{9}$ or about 0.78

20. GAMES LaRae is playing a game that uses a spinner. What is the probability that the spinner will land on a prime number on her next spin? 1

21. SHOPPING Raya asks 40 people outside the mall whether or not they visited for shopping or dining. She records the results in a Venn diagram. One person will be chosen at random to be interviewed on the local evening news. Find the probability that the person chosen will be someone who visited the mall for shopping and dining. 0.275

🧠 **Higher-Order Thinking Skills**

22. PERSEVERE Let A be the possible integer side measures of the rectangle with perimeter $P = 52$. Let B represent the possible integer measures of $\overline{XY}$ in $\triangle XYZ$.

a. Find $A \cap B$. $A \cap B = \{10\}$

b. Find $A \cup B$. $A \cup B = \{4, 5, 6, 7, 8, 9, 10, 11, 12, 13, 14\}$

23. CREATE Let A be the months of the year with 31 days and let B be the months of the year that begin with the letter J. Create a Venn diagram to display this data.

24. WRITE Suppose you need to explain the concept of *intersections* and *unions* to someone with no knowledge of the topic. Write a brief description of your explanation.
Sample answer: When two events occur, their *intersection* consists of all the outcomes in their sample spaces that they have in common; whereas their *union* consists of all of the outcomes in their sample spaces combined.

25. ANALYZE Determine if the following statement is *sometimes, always,* or *never* true. Justify your argument.
        The union of two sets has more elements than the intersection of two sets.
Sometimes; sample answer: While it is usually the case that the union of two sets will consist of more elements than their intersection, there are exceptions. For example, let A be the days of the week that end in *day*, and let B be the days of the week that begin with the letters *F, M, S, T,* or *W*. Because the two sets have the same list of items, their intersection and union will also be this same list.

26. FIND THE ERROR Let A be the event that the spinner lands on a vowel. Let B be the event that it lands on the letter J. Truc says $A \cup B$ is {A, E, O, U, J}, and Alan says $A \cup B$ is ∅. Who is correct? Explain.
Truc; sample answer: The set that Truc listed is the union of sets A and B. Alan is probably stating the empty set because he mistakenly found the intersection of the two sets.

Geometric Probability

LESSON GOAL

Students find the probability of an event by using lengths of segments and areas.

1 LAUNCH

 Launch the lesson with a **Warm Up** and an introduction.

2 EXPLORE AND DEVELOP

 Explore: Probability Using Lengths of Segments

 Develop:

Probability with Length
• Use Length to Find Geometric Probability
• Model Real-World Probabilities

 Explore: Probability and Decision Making

Probability with Area
• Use Area to Find Geometric Probability
• Use Angle Measures to Find Geometric Probability
• Use Probability to Make Decisions

 You may want your students to complete the **Checks** online.

3 REFLECT AND PRACTICE

 Exit Ticket

 Practice

DIFFERENTIATE

 View reports of student progress on the **Checks** after each example.

Resources	AL	OL	BL	ELL
Remediation: Probability of Compound Events	●	●		●
Extension: Polygon Probability		●	●	●

Language Development Handbook

Assign page 85 of the *Language Development Handbook* to help your students build mathematical language related to finding the probability of an event by using lengths of segments and areas.

ELL You can use the tips and suggestions on page T85 of the handbook to support students who are building English proficiency.

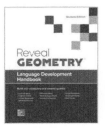
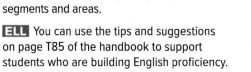

Suggested Pacing

90 min	0.5 day
45 min	1 day

Focus

Domain: Statistics & Probability
Standards for Mathematical Content:
S.MD.6 Use probabilities to make fair decisions (e.g., drawing by lots, using a random number generator).
S.MD.7 Analyze decisions and strategies using probability concepts (e.g., product testing, medical testing, pulling a hockey goalie at the end of a game).
Standards for Mathematical Practice:
4 Model with mathematics.
5 Use appropriate tools strategically.

Coherence

Vertical Alignment

Previous
Students found experimental and theoretical probabilities and found area of figures.
6.G.1, 7.G.4, 7.G.6, 7.SP.7, G.MD.1

Now
Students find the probability of events by using lengths of segments and areas.
S.MD.6, S.MD.7

Next
Students will solve problems involving probabilities of compound events using permutations and combinations.
S.CP.9

Rigor

The Three Pillars of Rigor

1 CONCEPTUAL UNDERSTANDING	2 FLUENCY	3 APPLICATION

🏛 **Conceptual Bridge** In this lesson, students apply what they have learned about probability to making decisions. They use real-world problems to illustrate how probabilities influence decision making.

Mathematical Background

Probability that involves a geometric measure such as length or area is called a geometric probability. You can find the probability that a point lies in part of a figure by comparing the length or area of the part to the length or area of the whole figure.

Interactive Presentation

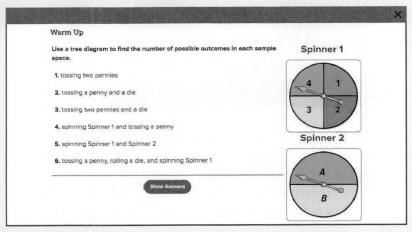

Warm Up

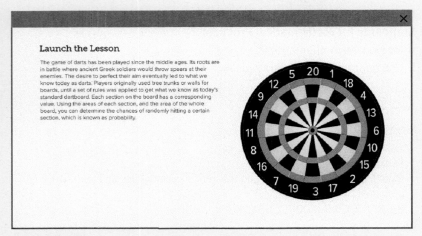

Launch the Lesson

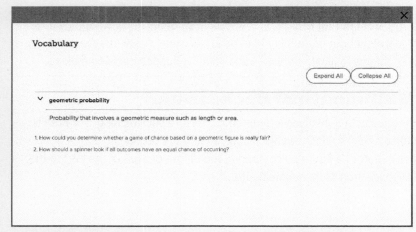

Today's Vocabulary

Warm Up

Prerequisite Skills

The Warm Up exercises address the following prerequisite skill for this lesson:

- defining sample spaces

Answers:

1. 4
2. 12
3. 24
4. 8
5. 8
6. 48

Launch the Lesson

 **Teaching the Mathematical Practices**

> **4 Apply Mathematics** In this Launch the Lesson, students can see a real-world application of probability using area.

Go Online to find additional teaching notes and questions to promote classroom discourse.

Today's Standards

Tell students that they will be addressing these content and practice standards in this lesson. You may wish to have a student volunteer read aloud *How can I meet these standards?* and *How can I use these practices?* and connect these to the standards.

See the Interactive Presentation for I Can statements that align with the standards covered in this lesson.

Today's Vocabulary

Tell students that they will be using this vocabulary term in this lesson. You can expand the row if you wish to share the definition. Then, discuss the questions below with the class.

Explore Probability Using Lengths of Segments

Objective
Students use dynamic geometry software to discover geometric probability with length.

Ideas for Use
Recommended Use Present the Inquiry Question, or have a student volunteer read it aloud. Have students work in pairs to complete the Explore activity on their devices. Pairs should discuss each of the questions. Monitor student progress during the activity. Upon completion of the Explore activity, have student volunteers share their responses to the Inquiry Question.

What if my students don't have devices? You may choose to project the activity on a whiteboard. A printable worksheet for each Explore is available online. You may choose to print the worksheet so that individuals or pairs of students can use it to record their observations.

Summary of the Activity
Students will complete guiding exercises throughout the Explore activity. They will use geometric tools to sketch and explore a geometric model of probability. Then, students will answer the Inquiry Question.

Go Online to find additional teaching notes and sample answers for the guiding exercises.

(continued on the next page)

Interactive Presentation

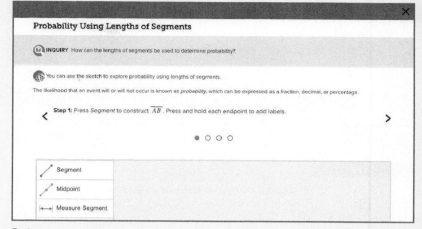

Probability Using Lengths of Segments

INQUIRY How can the lengths of segments be used to determine probability?

You can use the sketch to explore probability using lengths of segments.

The likelihood that an event will or will not occur is known as *probability*, which can be expressed as a fraction, decimal, or percentage.

Step 1: Press *Segment* to construct $\overline{AB}$. Press and hold each endpoint to add labels.

Segment

Midpoint

Measure Segment

Explore

WEB SKETCHPAD

Students will use a sketch to explore probability using lengths of segments.

TYPE

Students complete the calculations to find geometric probability.

Interactive Presentation

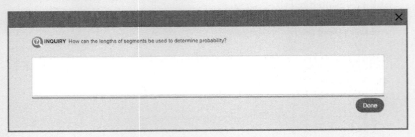

Explore

TYPE

Students will respond to the Inquiry Question and can view a sample answer.

1 **CONCEPTUAL UNDERSTANDING**   2 FLUENCY   3 APPLICATION

Explore Probability Using Lengths of Segments (*continued*)

MP Teaching the Mathematical Practices

3 Construct Arguments In this Explore, students will use stated assumptions, definitions, and previously established results to construct an argument.

Questions

Have students complete the Explore activity.

Ask:

- Why is it easier to find the probability when the segments are the same length? Sample answer: You can divide by the number of segments to find the probability of a point being in any one segment. Otherwise, you need to calculate the length of the segment and divide by the length of the larger segment.
- Would it make more sense to use lengths of segments to find the probability of drawing one of 6 marbles out of a bag or drawing a card from a full deck of 52? Why? Sample answer: While you could use either, it would make more sense to use the lengths of segments to simulate marbles because you are dividing the segment into fewer segments.

Inquiry

How can the lengths of segments be used to determine probability?
Sample answer: If a segment is contained within a longer segment, divide the length of the shorter segment by the length of the longer segment to determine the probability of a randomly chosen point being on the shorter segment.

Go Online to find additional teaching notes and sample answers for the guiding exercises.

Explore Probability and Decision Making

Objective
Students use dynamic geometry software to discover decision making with geometric probability.

Ideas for Use

Recommended Use Present the Inquiry Question, or have a student volunteer read it aloud. Have students work in pairs to complete the Explore activity on their devices. Pairs should discuss each of the questions. Monitor student progress during the activity. Upon completion of the Explore activity, have student volunteers share their responses to the Inquiry Question.

What if my students don't have devices? You may choose to project the activity on a whiteboard. A printable worksheet for each Explore is available online. You may choose to print the worksheet so that individuals or pairs of students can use it to record their observations.

Summary of the Activity
Students will complete guiding exercises throughout the Explore activity. They will proceed through a series of questions about a gambling scenario, relating the probability of outcomes to a decision-making process. Then, students will answer the Inquiry Question.

 Go Online to find additional teaching notes and sample answers for the guiding exercises.

(continued on the next page)

Interactive Presentation

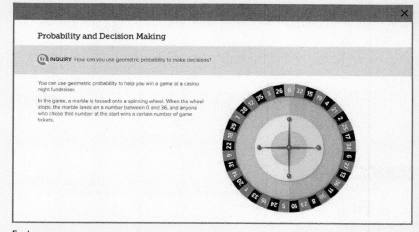

Probability and Decision Making

 INQUIRY How can you use geometric probability to make decisions?

You can use geometric probability to help you win a game at a casino night fundraiser.

In the game, a marble is tossed onto a spinning wheel. When the wheel stops, the marble lands on a number between 0 and 36, and anyone who chose that number at the start wins a certain number of game tickets.

Explore

TYPE

Students complete calculations to make a decision using geometric probability.

Interactive Presentation

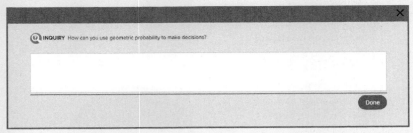

Explore

TYPE

Students will respond to the Inquiry Question and can view a sample answer.

---

1 CONCEPTUAL UNDERSTANDING | 2 FLUENCY | 3 APPLICATION

Explore Probability and Decision Making (*continued*)

MP Teaching the Mathematical Practices

> **2 Make Sense of Quantities** Mathematically proficient students need to be able to make sense of quantities and their relationships. In this Explore, notice the relationship between the problem variables and geometric properties.

Questions
Have students complete the Explore activity.

Ask:
- Why isn't the probability of red or black 50%? Sample answer: Because the spinning wheel includes a green 0, there is one other option besides red or black.
- What other games could be decided based on geometric probability? Sample answer: Finding the odds of throwing a dart or shooting an arrow involve geometric regions on a board.

? Inquiry
How can you use geometric probability to make decisions? Sample answer: I can apply geometric properties to solve probability problems and make decisions based on the results.

Go Online to find additional teaching notes and sample answers for the guiding exercises.

1 CONCEPTUAL UNDERSTANDING | **2 FLUENCY** | **3 APPLICATION**

Learn Probability with Length

Objective
Students find the probability of an event by using lengths of segments.

 Teaching the Mathematical Practices

> **4 Make Assumptions** Have students explain the assumptions that are needed to create geometric probability models.

DIFFERENTIATE

Reteaching Activity AL ELL

Have students model simple sample spaces by using geometric probabilities. Each event can be represented by a line segment whose length is proportional to the probability of the event. For example, flipping a coin can be represented by two lines of equal length, and the probability that a point is on either segment is 50%.

Example 1 Use Length to Find Geometric Probability

 Teaching the Mathematical Practices

> **4 Analyze Relationships Mathematically** Point out that to solve the problem in this example, students will need to analyze the mathematical relationships in the problem to draw a conclusion.

Questions for Mathematical Discourse

AL What is the probability that X is on $\overline{PQ}$? $\frac{4}{25}$, 0.16, or 16%

OL What is the probability that X is on $\overline{PR}$? $\frac{15}{25}$, 0.6, or 60%

BL What is the probability that X is *not* on $\overline{PQ}$? $\frac{21}{25}$, 0.84, or 84%

Go Online

- Find additional teaching notes.
- View performance reports of the Checks.
- Assign or present an Extra Example.

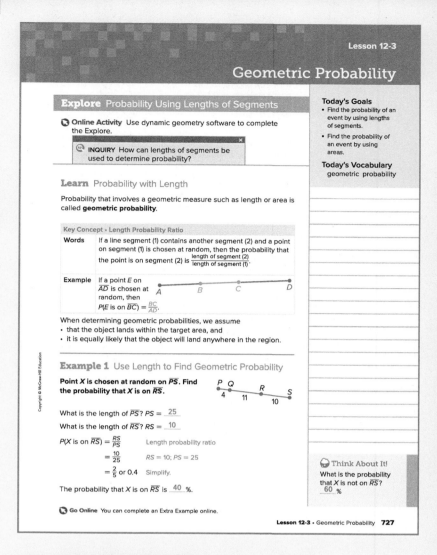

Lesson 12-3

Geometric Probability

Explore Probability Using Lengths of Segments

Online Activity Use dynamic geometry software to complete the Explore.

> **INQUIRY** How can lengths of segments be used to determine probability?

Learn Probability with Length

Probability that involves a geometric measure such as length or area is called **geometric probability**.

Key Concept • Length Probability Ratio

Words	If a line segment (1) contains another segment (2) and a point on segment (1) is chosen at random, then the probability that the point is on segment (2) is $\frac{\text{length of segment (2)}}{\text{length of segment (1)}}$.
Example	If a point E on $\overline{AD}$ is chosen at random, then $P(E$ is on $\overline{BC}) = \frac{BC}{AD}$.

When determining geometric probabilities, we assume
- that the object lands within the target area, and
- it is equally likely that the object will land anywhere in the region.

Example 1 Use Length to Find Geometric Probability

Point X is chosen at random on $\overline{PS}$. Find the probability that X is on $\overline{RS}$.

What is the length of $\overline{PS}$? $PS = \underline{25}$

What is the length of $\overline{RS}$? $RS = \underline{10}$

$P(X$ is on $\overline{RS}) = \frac{RS}{PS}$ Length probability ratio

$= \frac{10}{25}$ $RS = 10; PS = 25$

$= \frac{2}{5}$ or 0.4   Simplify.

The probability that X is on $\overline{RS}$ is $\underline{40}$ %.

Go Online You can complete an Extra Example online.

Today's Goals
- Find the probability of an event by using lengths of segments.
- Find the probability of an event by using areas.

Today's Vocabulary
geometric probability

💭 **Think About It!**
What is the probability that X is not on $\overline{RS}$?
$\underline{60}$ %

Interactive Presentation

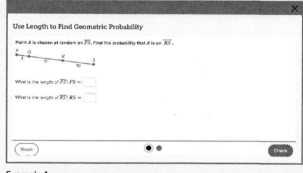

Use Length to Find Geometric Probability

Point X is chosen at random on $\overline{PS}$. Find the probability that X is on $\overline{RS}$.

What is the length of $\overline{PS}$? $PS =$ ▢

What is the length of $\overline{RS}$? $RS =$ ▢

Reset   Check

Example 1

TYPE

a|

Students complete the calculations to find geometric probability with length.

TYPE

a|

Students answer a question to show they understand geometric probability with length.

1 CONCEPTUAL UNDERSTANDING | 2 FLUENCY | 3 APPLICATION

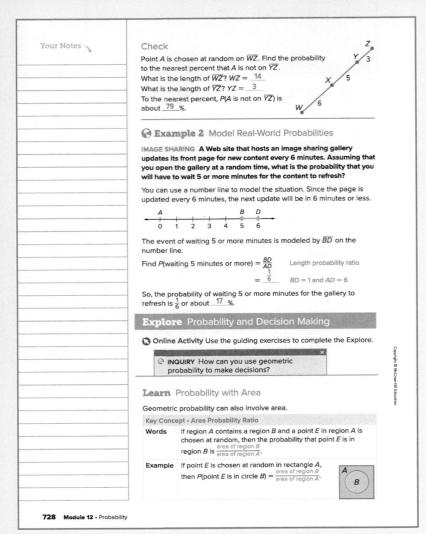

Your Notes

Check

Point A is chosen at random on $\overline{WZ}$. Find the probability to the nearest percent that A is not on $\overline{YZ}$.

What is the length of $\overline{WZ}$? $WZ = $ __14__

What is the length of $\overline{YZ}$? $YZ = $ __3__

To the nearest percent, $P(A$ is not on $\overline{YZ})$ is about __79__ %.

Example 2 Model Real-World Probabilities

IMAGE SHARING A Web site that hosts an image sharing gallery updates its front page for new content every 6 minutes. Assuming that you open the gallery at a random time, what is the probability that you will have to wait 5 or more minutes for the content to refresh?

You can use a number line to model the situation. Since the page is updated every 6 minutes, the next update will be in 6 minutes or less.

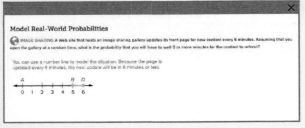

The event of waiting 5 or more minutes is modeled by $\overline{BD}$ on the number line.

Find P(waiting 5 minutes or more) $= \dfrac{BD}{AD}$ Length probability ratio

$= \dfrac{1}{6}$ $BD = 1$ and $AD = 6$

So, the probability of waiting 5 or more minutes for the gallery to refresh is $\frac{1}{6}$ or about __17__ %.

Explore Probability and Decision Making

 Online Activity Use the guiding exercises to complete the Explore.

> **INQUIRY** How can you use geometric probability to make decisions?

Learn Probability with Area

Geometric probability can also involve area.

Key Concept • Area Probability Ratio

Words	If region A contains a region B and a point E in region A is chosen at random, then the probability that point E is in region B is $\dfrac{\text{area of region } B}{\text{area of region } A}$.
Example	If point E is chosen at random in rectangle A, then P(point E is in circle B) $= \dfrac{\text{area of region } B}{\text{area of region } A}$.

728   Module 12 • Probability

Interactive Presentation

Model Real-World Probabilities

IMAGE SHARING A Web site that hosts an image sharing gallery updates its front page for new content every 6 minutes. Assuming that you open the gallery at a random time, what is the probability that you will have to wait 5 or more minutes for the content to refresh?

You can use a number line to model the situation. Because the page is updated every 6 minutes, this next update will be in 6 minutes or less.

Example 2

 TAP

Students tap to see the steps in finding the probability.

 CHECK

Students complete the Check online to determine whether they are ready to move on.

Example 2 Model Real-World Probabilities

MP Teaching the Mathematical Practices

4 Apply Mathematics In this example, students apply what they have learned about probability and geometric probability models to solving a real-world problem.

Questions for Mathematical Discourse

AL What is the probability that you will wait less than one minute? $\frac{1}{6}$, or about 16.7%

OL What is the probability that you will wait more than one minute? $\frac{5}{6}$, or about 83.3%

BL What is the probability that you will wait less than one minute or more than 5 minutes? $\frac{2}{6}$, or $\frac{1}{3}$, or about 33.3%

Common Error

Remind students that the interval of the probability being considered is not necessarily equal to the entire interval of the event. Caution students to use only the units equal to the interval being considered.

Learn Probability with Area

Objective

Students find the probability of an event by using areas.

MP Teaching the Mathematical Practices

2 Different Properties Mathematically proficient students look for different ways to solve problems. Encourage them to work through multiple approaches to solving probability problems and choose the method that works best for them.

7 Use Structure Help students to use the structure of geometric models to represent and solve probability problems.

Essential Question Follow-Up

Students have explored geometric probability.

Ask:

How can geometry be used to make predictions? Sample answer: You can find the probability of an event occurring by replacing the variables used for success and failure with measures of length or area. For example, you could find the probability of an event occurring in a specific sector of a circle by finding the ratio of the area of that sector to the area of the entire circle.

DIFFERENTIATE

Enrichment Activity AL BL

Have students create a game that applies the concepts of probability using area. Students should write clear directions for playing and winning the game. Directions should also include the probability of scoring for all possible events of the game. Allow students to play one another's games, checking to see whether the mathematical probabilities correspond to the experimental probabilities. Have students design games that are fair, very hard to win, or very easy to win.

🌐 Example 3   Use Area to Find Geometric Probability

🔵 Teaching the Mathematical Practices

4 Make Assumptions In the Study Tip, have students point out where an assumption or approximation was made in the solution.

Questions for Mathematical Discourse

AL What is the radius of the circular board, in inches?   12 inches

OL What is the probability that the bean bag will land on the board but not touch the target? $\frac{140}{144}$, or $\frac{35}{36}$, or about 97%

BL If the radius of the target is doubled and the radius of entire board is 24 inches, do you think the probability of the bean bag touching the target is the same? Explain.   Yes; sample answer: Because the measures all change proportionally, the probability will be the same.

Common Error

Encourage students to review the Study Tip related to units of measure, and make sure that they are aware of the need to pay attention to the units of measure when they encounter a description of a problem situation.

🌐 Example 3   Use Area to Find Geometric Probability

LAWN GAMES Haruko Games is designing a new lawn game where each player will attempt to hit a circular target by tossing a beanbag onto a larger, circular board.

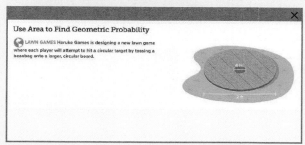

Part A What is the probability that a toss will land on the target?

Find the ratio of the area of the circular target to the area of the board.

$P(\text{toss lands on target}) = \dfrac{\text{area of target}}{\text{area of game board}}$ Area probability ratio

$\qquad = \dfrac{\pi(2)^2}{\pi(12)^2}$ Area $= \pi r^2$

$\qquad = \dfrac{4}{144}$ or $\dfrac{1}{36}$ Simplify.

The probability that the toss lands on the target is $\frac{1}{36}$ or about __3__ %.

Part B To make the game more enjoyable, the company wants to increase the probability of hitting the target. What diameter should they use for the circle so that the probability of a toss landing on the target is 10%? Round to the nearest hundredth of an inch.

Find the diameter of a circle so that the geometric probability of a toss landing in the circle is 10% or 0.1.

$P(\text{toss lands on target}) = \dfrac{\text{area of target}}{\text{area of game board}}$ Area probability ratio

$0.1 = \dfrac{\pi\left(\frac{d}{2}\right)^2}{\pi(12)^2}$ Substitution

$0.1 = \dfrac{d^2}{576}$ Simplify.

$\underline{576}\,(0.1) = d^2$ Multiply each side by 576.

$\underline{57.6} = d^2$ Simplify.

$\underline{7.59} \approx d$ Take the square root of each side.

To increase the probability of a toss landing on the target, the diameter of the target should be about 7.59 inches.

🌐 **Go Online** You can complete an Extra Example online.

Study Tip

Assumptions When determining the probability that a toss will land on the target, we are assuming that the toss must land on the game board, and not on the ground surrounding the board.

Study Tip

Units of Measure Notice that the diameter of the target is given in inches, while the diameter of the game board is given in feet. When finding geometric probabilities, be sure to check that all measurements are in the same unit, in order to avoid miscalculations.

Interactive Presentation

Use Area to Find Geometric Probability ✕

🌐 LAWN GAMES Haruko Games is designing a new lawn game where each player will attempt to hit a circular target by tossing a beanbag onto a larger, circular board.

Example 3

TAP

 Students tap to see the steps in finding geometric probability with area.

TYPE

 Students complete calculations to find the probability on a target.

1 CONCEPTUAL UNDERSTANDING   **2 FLUENCY**   3 APPLICATION

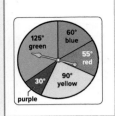

Example 4 Use Angle Measures to Find Geometric Probability

Use the spinner to find the probability of landing in each section.

a. *P*(pointer landing on purple): The angle measure of the purple region is 30°.
P(pointer landing on purple) = $\frac{30}{360}$ or 8.3%.

b. *P*(pointer landing on green):
The angle measure of the green region is 125 °.
P(pointer landing on green) = $\frac{125}{360}$ or 34.7 %.

c. *P*(pointer landing on neither yellow nor red):
Combine the angle measures of the yellow and red regions: 90 + 55.
P(pointer landing on neither yellow nor red) = $\frac{360 - 145}{360}$ or $\frac{215}{360}$
or 59.7 %.

🌐 **Example 5** Use Probability to Make Decisions

DECISION MAKING **Jayla is visiting the museum and wants to take a guided tour. A friend suggested that she do the tour with Demarcus, rather than Cody, because Demarcus' tour was more informative. Tours with Demarcus depart every 45 minutes, while tours with Cody depart every 30 minutes.**

a. What is the probability that Jayla will have to wait 20 minutes or less for each tour guide? Explain your reasoning.

The region below *y* = 45 represents the possible wait time for Demarcus' tour. The region to the left of *x* = 30 represents the possible wait time for Cody's tour. The area formed by the intersection is 45 · 30 or 1350 units².

The region to the left of *x* = 20 and below *y* = 20 represents the possible waiting times of 20 minutes or less for both tour guides. The area of the square is 400 units².
The geometric probability is $\frac{400}{1350}$ or about 30 %.

b. What is the probability that Jayla will have to wait 20 minutes or less for one tour guide? Explain your reasoning.

The region representing the possible wait times for Demarcus' and Cody's tour is the same as in part **a**.

The region bounded by the lines *x* = 30 and *y* = 20 represents the possibility of waiting 20 minutes or less for Cody's tour. The area of this rectangle is 600 units².

The region bounded by the lines *x* = 20 and *y* = 45 represents the possibility of waiting 20 minutes or less for Demarcus' tour. The area of this rectangle is 900 units².

Because the rectangles that describe Cody and Demarcus' tour times overlap, the waiting time of 20 minutes or less is counted twice. So, the geometric probability is $\frac{600}{1350} + \frac{900}{1350} - \frac{400}{1350} = \frac{1100}{1350}$, or about 81 %.

730 Module 12 · Probability

 Go Online
You can complete an Extra Example online.

💭 **Think About It!**
Jayla can wait no more than 20 minutes without risking her favorite exhibit closing. If Cody's tour should depart first, should she wait for Demarcus' tour or go on a tour with Cody? Explain your reasoning.
Sample answer:
Because the chance of Jayla waiting 20 minutes or less for both tour guides is only 30%, Jayla should go on the tour with Cody.

 Go Online
to learn how to use probability tools to make fair decisions in Expand 12-2.

Example 4 Use Angle Measures to Find Geometric Probability

🎓 **Teaching the Mathematical Practices**

1 Check Answers Mathematically proficient students continually ask themselves, "Does this make sense?" Point out that they should ask themselves whether their answer makes sense and whether they have answered the problem question.

5 Use Estimation Point out that in Example 4, students will sometimes get exact solutions and will sometimes arrive at solutions that require estimates.

Questions for Mathematical Discourse

AL What is the probability of the pointer landing on red? $\frac{11}{72}$, or about 15%

OL What is the probability of the pointer not landing on purple or yellow? $\frac{2}{3}$, or about 67%

BL What is the probability of the pointer landing on a multiple of 10 degree measure? $\frac{1}{2}$, or 50%

🌐 Example 5 Use Probability to Make Decisions

🎓 **Teaching the Mathematical Practices**

4 Apply Mathematics In this example, students apply what they have learned about finding probabilities of events by using areas to solving a real-world problem.

Questions for Mathematical Discourse

AL What are the dimensions of the rectangle formed by the area model in **Part A**? 45 units by 30 units

OL What other equations can be used to represent the maximum wait times for Cody's tour and Demarcus' tour? Sample answer: Cody: *y* = 30; Demarcus: *x* = 45

BL What is the probability that Jayla will have to wait 25 minutes or less for one tour guide? about 93%

Exit Ticket

Recommended Use

At the end of class, go online to display the Exit Ticket prompt and ask students to respond using a separate piece of paper. Have students hand you their responses as they leave the room.

Alternate Use

At the end of class, go online to display the Exit Ticket prompt and ask students to respond verbally or by using a mini-whiteboard. Have students hold up their whiteboards so that you can see all student responses. Tap to reveal the answer when most or all students have completed the Exit Ticket.

Interactive Presentation

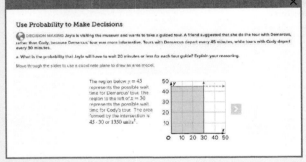

Example 5

TAP

Students tap to see how the coordinate plane is used to draw an area model.

CHECK

Students complete the Check online to determine whether they are ready to move on.

Practice and Homework

Suggested Assignments

Use the table below to select appropriate exercises.

DOK	Topic	Exercises
1, 2	exercises that mirror the examples	1–20
2	exercises that use a variety of skills from this lesson	21–28
2	exercises that extend concepts learned in this lesson to new contexts	29–30
3	exercises that emphasize higher-order and critical-thinking skills	31–35

ASSESS AND DIFFERENTIATE

📊 Use the data from the **Checks** to determine whether to provide resources for extension, remediation, or intervention.

IF students score 90% or more on the Checks,   `BL`
THEN assign:

- Practice, Exercises 1–29 odd, 31–35
- Extension: Polygon Probability
- 🔲 **ALEKS** Sample Spaces

IF students score 66%–89% on the Checks,   `OL`
THEN assign:

- Practice, Exercises 1–35 odd
- Remediation, Review Resources: Geometric Probability
- Personal Tutors
- Extra Examples 1–4
- 🔲 **ALEKS** Sample Spaces

IF students score 65% or less on the Checks,   `AL`
THEN assign:

- Practice, Exercises 1–19 odd
- Remediation, Review Resources: Geometric Probability
- *Quick Review Math Handbook*: Geometric Probability and Simulations
- 🔲 **ALEKS** Sample Spaces

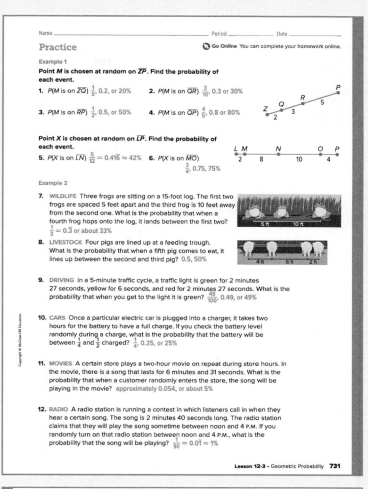

Name _____ Period _____ Date _____

Practice
🔴 **Go Online** You can complete your homework online.

Example 1
Point *M* is chosen at random on $\overline{ZP}$. Find the probability of each event.

1. $P(M$ is on $\overline{ZQ})$ $\frac{1}{5}$, 0.2, or 20%
2. $P(M$ is on $\overline{QR})$ $\frac{3}{10}$, 0.3 or 30%
3. $P(M$ is on $\overline{RP})$ $\frac{1}{2}$, 0.5, or 50%
4. $P(M$ is on $\overline{QP})$ $\frac{4}{5}$, 0.8 or 80%

Point *X* is chosen at random on $\overline{LP}$. Find the probability of each event.

5. $P(X$ is on $\overline{LN})$ $\frac{5}{12} = 0.41\overline{6} \approx 42\%$
6. $P(X$ is on $\overline{MO})$ $\frac{3}{4}$, 0.75, 75%

Example 2

7. WILDLIFE Three frogs are sitting on a 15-foot log. The first two frogs are spaced 5 feet apart and the third frog is 10 feet away from the second one. What is the probability that when a fourth frog hops onto the log, it lands between the first two? $\frac{1}{3} = 0.\overline{3}$ or about 33%

8. LIVESTOCK Four pigs are lined up at a feeding trough. What is the probability that when a fifth pig comes to eat, it lines up between the second and third pig? 0.5, 50%

9. DRIVING In a 5-minute traffic cycle, a traffic light is green for 2 minutes 27 seconds, yellow for 6 seconds, and red for 2 minutes 27 seconds. What is the probability that when you get to the light it is green? $\frac{49}{100}$, 0.49, or 49%

10. CARS Once a particular electric car is plugged into a charger, it takes two hours for the battery to have a full charge. If you check the battery level randomly during a charge, what is the probability that the battery will be between $\frac{1}{4}$ and $\frac{1}{2}$ charged? $\frac{1}{4}$, 0.25, or 25%

11. MOVIES A certain store plays a two-hour movie on repeat during store hours. In the movie, there is a song that lasts for 6 minutes and 31 seconds. What is the probability that when a customer randomly enters the store, the song will be playing in the movie? approximately 0.054, or about 5%

12. RADIO A radio station is running a contest in which listeners call in when they hear a certain song. The song is 2 minutes 40 seconds long. The radio station claims that they will play the song sometime between noon and 4 P.M. If you randomly turn on that radio station between noon and 4 P.M., what is the probability that the song will be playing? $\frac{1}{90} = 0.0\overline{1} \approx 1\%$

Example 3

13. GAMES One carnival game tasks players with launching a fish charm onto a circular landing pad. The largest prize is awarded if the charm lands in the center circle with a 4-foot diameter. What is the probability the charm lands in the center circle? $\frac{1}{9} = 0.\overline{1}$ or about 11%

14. RECREATION A parachutist is aiming to land in a circular target with a 10-yard radius. The target is in a rectangular field that is 120 yards long and 30 yards wide. Given that the parachutist will land in the field, what is the probability he will land in the target? $\frac{\pi}{36} \approx 0.09$ or about 9%

Example 4
Use the spinner to find each probability. If the spinner lands on a line it is spun again.

15. P(pointer landing on red) $\frac{1}{9} = 0.\overline{1}$ or about 11%

16. P(pointer landing on blue) $\frac{1}{12} = 0.08\overline{3}$ or about 8%

17. P(pointer landing on green) $\frac{2}{9} = 0.\overline{2}$ or about 22%

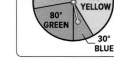

18. P(pointer landing on either green or blue) $\frac{11}{36} = 0.305$ or about 31%

19. P(pointer landing on neither red nor yellow) $\frac{7}{12} = 0.58\overline{3}$ or about 58%

Example 5

20. STATE YOUR ASSUMPTION Deangelo is planning a bus ride to the airport. He can choose between the Crimson bus, which arrives at the bus stop every 8 minutes, or the Gold bus, which arrives at the bus stop every 15 minutes. He would prefer to take the Gold bus because the bus makes fewer stops. In order to get to the airport by a certain time, Deangelo cannot wait more than 5 minutes without risking being late for his flight.

   a. What assumption do you have to make to solve this problem? Sample answer: Both buses leave from the same bus stop and would not require any additional travel time between them.
   b. To the nearest percent, what is the probability that Deangelo will have to wait 5 minutes or less to see both buses? 21%

   c. To the nearest percent, what is the probability that Deangelo will have to wait 5 minutes or less to see only one of the buses? 75%

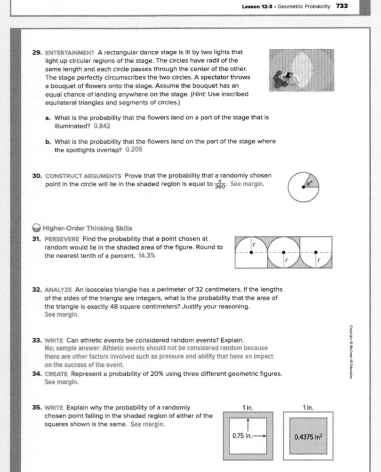

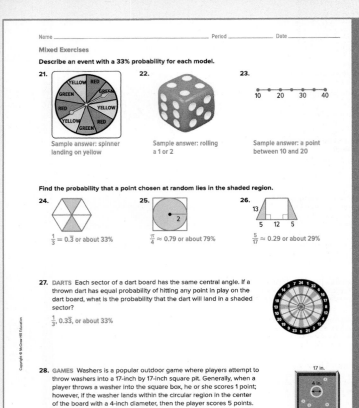

Answers

30. Sample answer: The probability that a randomly chosen point will lie in the shaded region is the ratio of the area of the sector to the area of the circle.

$$P(\text{lies in sector}) = \frac{\text{area of sector}}{\text{area of circle}}$$

$$\frac{x}{360} \overset{?}{=} \frac{\frac{x}{360}\pi r^2}{\pi r^2}$$

$$\frac{x}{360} = \frac{x}{360} \checkmark$$

32. $\frac{1}{7}$; Sample answer: Using the Triangle Inequality Theorem, there are 7 isosceles triangles with integer side lengths and a perimeter of 32 centimeters. Of those triangles, only the one with side lengths 10, 10, and 12 has an area of exactly 48 square centimeters. Therefore, the probability is 1 in 7.

34. Sample answer: The probability that a randomly chosen point on $\overline{AC}$ lies between A and B is 20%.

The probability that a randomly chosen point in the circle will lie in the shaded area is 20%.

The probability that a randomly chosen point in the square will lie in the unshaded area is 20%.

35. Sample answer: The probability of a randomly chosen point lying in the shaded region of the square on the left is found by subtracting the area of the unshaded square from the area of the larger square and finding the ratio of the difference of the areas to the area of the larger square. The probability is $\frac{1^2 - 0.75^2}{1^2}$ or 43.75%. The probability of a randomly chosen point lying in the shaded region of the square on the right is the ratio of the area of the shaded square to the area of the larger square, which is $\frac{0.4375}{1}$ or 43.75%. Therefore, the probability of a randomly chosen point lying in the shaded area of either square is the same.

Probability with Permutations and Combinations

LESSON GOAL

Students solve problems involving probabilities of compound events using permutations and combinations.

1 LAUNCH

 Launch the lesson with a **Warm Up** and an introduction.

2 EXPLORE AND DEVELOP

 Explore: Permutations and Combinations

 Develop:

Probability Using Permutations
- Probability and Permutations of *n* Objects
- Probability and Permutations with No Repetition
- Probability and Permutations with Repetition

Probability Using Combinations
- Probability and Combinations

 You may want your students to complete the **Checks** online.

3 REFLECT AND PRACTICE

 Exit Ticket

 Practice

DIFFERENTIATE

View reports of student progress on the **Checks** after each example.

Resources	AL	OL	BL	ELL
Remediation: Theoretical Probability of Simple Events	●	●		●
Extension: Finding Combinations by Using Pascal's Triangle		●	●	●

Language Development Handbook

Assign page 86 of the *Language Development Handbook* to help your students build mathematical language related to solving problems involving probabilities of compound events using permutations and combinations.

ELL You can use the tips and suggestions on page T86 of the handbook to support students who are building English proficiency.

Suggested Pacing

| 90 min | 0.5 day |
| 45 min | 1 day |

Focus

Domain: Statistics & Probability

Standards for Mathematical Content:

S.CP.9 Use permutations and combinations to compute probabilities of compound events and solve problems.

Standards for Mathematical Practice:

5 Use appropriate tools strategically.

8 Look for and express regularity in repeated reasoning.

Coherence

Vertical Alignment

Previous
Students found experimental and theoretical probabilities.
7.SP.7

Now
Students solve probability problems using permutations and combinations.
S.CP.9

Next
Students will solve probability problems using the Multiplication Rule.
S.CP.2, S.CP.8

Rigor

The Three Pillars of Rigor

1 CONCEPTUAL UNDERSTANDING	2 FLUENCY	3 APPLICATION

Conceptual Bridge In this lesson, students develop understanding of permutations and combinations, and they build fluency by using them to find probabilities. They apply their understanding by solving real-world problems.

Mathematical Background

A *permutation* is a selection of objects where order is important. A *combination* is a selection of objects in which order is not important. Factorials are used to count arrangements of objects.

Interactive Presentation

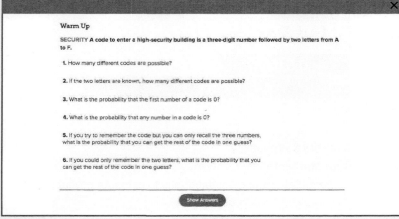

Warm Up

SECURITY A code to enter a high-security building is a three-digit number followed by two letters from A to F.

1. How many different codes are possible?

2. If the two letters are known, how many different codes are possible?

3. What is the probability that the first number of a code is 0?

4. What is the probability that any number in a code is 0?

5. If you try to remember the code but you can only recall the three numbers, what is the probability that you can get the rest of the code in one guess?

6. If you could only remember the two letters, what is the probability that you can get the rest of the code in one guess?

 Show Answers

Warm Up

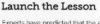

Launch the Lesson

Experts have predicted that the amount of digital data produced will exceed 40 zettabytes, or 40 trillion gigabytes, by 2020. That is about 5200 GB for every living human today. So far, we have only produced a fraction of this amount of data, and the majority is stored in data clouds. When considering highly sensitive materials, people also turn to external hard drives for storage. Lockable hard drives are now on the rise in popularity, due to their ability to lock out any user who does not enter the correct numbers. To access the files, the user needs to enter the correct permutation, or arrangement, of numbers.

Launch the Lesson

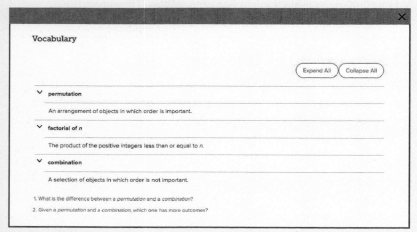

Vocabulary

Expand All   Collapse All

⌄ **permutation**

An arrangement of objects in which order is important.

⌄ **factorial of *n***

The product of the positive integers less than or equal to *n*.

⌄ **combination**

A selection of objects in which order is not important.

1. What is the difference between a *permutation* and a *combination*?

2. Given a *permutation* and a *combination*, which one has more outcomes?

Today's Vocabulary

Warm Up

Prerequisite Skills

The Warm Up exercises address the following prerequisite skill for this lesson:

- using tree diagrams

Answers:

1. 36,000
2. 1000
3. $\frac{1}{10}$
4. $\frac{3}{10}$
5. $\frac{1}{36}$
6. $\frac{1}{1000}$

Launch the Lesson

🅜🅟 **Teaching the Mathematical Practices**

4 Apply Mathematics In this Launch the Lesson, students can see a real-world application of permutations.

🔎 **Go Online** to find additional teaching notes and questions to promote classroom discourse.

Today's Standards

Tell students that they will be addressing these content and practice standards in this lesson. You may wish to have a student volunteer read aloud *How can I meet this standards?* and *How can I use these practices?* and connect these to the standards.

See the Interactive Presentation for I Can statements that align with the standards covered in this lesson.

Today's Vocabulary

Tell students that they will be using these vocabulary terms in this lesson. You can expand each row if you wish to share the definitions. Then, discuss the questions below with the class.

Explore Permutations and Combinations

Objective

Students use dynamic geometry software to discover permutations and combinations.

Ideas for Use

Recommended Use Present the Inquiry Question, or have a student volunteer read it aloud. Have students work in pairs to complete the Explore activity on their devices. Pairs should discuss each of the questions. Monitor student progress during the activity. Upon completion of the Explore activity, have student volunteers share their responses to the Inquiry Question.

What if my students don't have devices? You may choose to project the activity on a whiteboard. A printable worksheet for each Explore is available online. You may choose to print the worksheet so that individuals or pairs of students can use it to record their observations.

Summary of the Activity

Students will complete guiding exercises throughout the Explore activity. They will work with experiments involving permutations and combinations. Then, students will answer the Inquiry Question.

 Go Online to find additional teaching notes and sample answers for the guiding exercises.

(continued on the next page)

Interactive Presentation

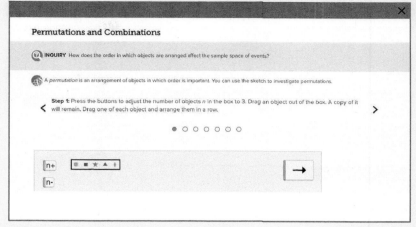

Explore

WEB SKETCHPAD

Students use a sketch to explore permutations and combinations.

TYPE

| a|

Students complete the calculations to find permutations and combinations

Interactive Presentation

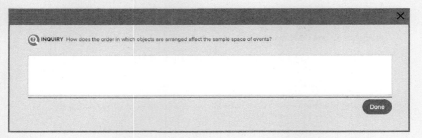

INQUIRY How does the order in which objects are arranged affect the sample space of events?

Done

Explore

TYPE

Students will respond to the Inquiry Question and can view a sample answer.

---

1 CONCEPTUAL UNDERSTANDING | 2 FLUENCY | 3 APPLICATION

Explore Permutations and Combinations (*continued*)

 Teaching the Mathematical Practices

8 Look for a Pattern Help students to see the pattern in this Explore.

Questions
Have students complete the Explore activity.

Ask:
- Why does it help to list the permutations in a specific order? Sample answer: Because you are arranging several of the same shapes in different orders, it helps to list them by keeping the first shape the same.

- When choosing 3 out of 5 objects, there were 6 ways to choose a circle, a square and a star. How many combinations of these three shapes are there? Sample answer: There is only one combination for these shapes because for a combination the order of the shapes does not matter. All variations are considered the same.

Inquiry
How does the order in which objects are arranged affect the sample space of events? Sample answer: When finding permutations, the order of the objects matters, so each arrangement of objects is counted. When finding combinations, the order of the objects does not matter, so arrangements that have the same objects in a different order are only counted once.

Go Online to find additional teaching notes and sample answers for the guiding exercises.

1 CONCEPTUAL UNDERSTANDING | 2 FLUENCY | 3 APPLICATION

Learn Probability Using Permutations

Objective
Students use permutations to compute probabilities.

Teaching the Mathematical Practices

4 Apply Mathematics In this Learn, students can see real-world applications of permutations and combinations.

Common Misconception
Students may confuse the use of *n* and *r* in the formula for calculating permutations. Remind students that the factorial $n > r$, and that the numbers for the factorial will always be possible. Point out to students that a permutation will always result in an integer value, because you cannot have a partial permutation.

@ Essential Question Follow-Up
Students have used probability to make predictions of outcomes.

Ask:

How can we quantify predictions? Sample answer: We can calculate or estimate the probability of the outcome occurring.

🖰 Go Online

- Find additional teaching notes.
- View performance reports of the Checks.
- Assign or present an Extra Example.

DIFFERENTIATE

Language Development Activity ELL

Beginning Before students read the lesson, use pattern blocks to illustrate how to categorize objects. Use color and shape to differentiate the blocks.

Intermediate Have partners make and use flashcards to check each other's pronunciation and understanding of vocabulary.

Advanced Have students scan the lesson for content vocabulary words in context. Help them pronounce the vocabulary words correctly. Discuss vocabulary meanings with them.

Advanced High After reading each example of the lesson, use an Interactive Question-Response to discuss it. Have students record the main idea and details of the paragraphs in their notes.

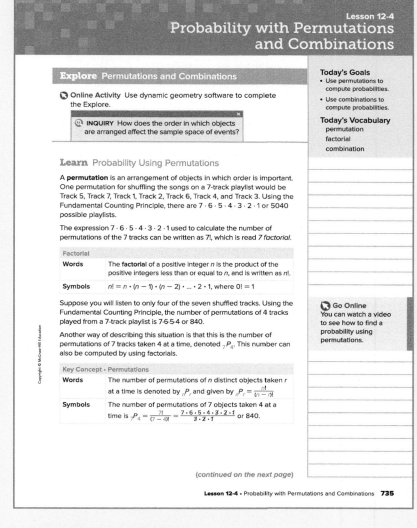

Lesson 12-4
Probability with Permutations and Combinations

Explore Permutations and Combinations

🖰 Online Activity Use dynamic geometry software to complete the Explore.

INQUIRY How does the order in which objects are arranged affect the sample space of events?

Learn Probability Using Permutations

A **permutation** is an arrangement of objects in which order is important. One permutation for shuffling the songs on a 7-track playlist would be Track 5, Track 7, Track 1, Track 2, Track 6, Track 4, and Track 3. Using the Fundamental Counting Principle, there are $7 \cdot 6 \cdot 5 \cdot 4 \cdot 3 \cdot 2 \cdot 1$ or 5040 possible playlists.

The expression $7 \cdot 6 \cdot 5 \cdot 4 \cdot 3 \cdot 2 \cdot 1$ used to calculate the number of permutations of the 7 tracks can be written as 7!, which is read *7 factorial*.

Factorial

Words	The **factorial** of a positive integer *n* is the product of the positive integers less than or equal to *n*, and is written as *n*!.
Symbols	$n! = n \cdot (n-1) \cdot (n-2) \cdot \ldots \cdot 2 \cdot 1$, where $0! = 1$

Suppose you will listen to only four of the seven shuffled tracks. Using the Fundamental Counting Principle, the number of permutations of 4 tracks played from a 7-track playlist is $7 \cdot 6 \cdot 5 \cdot 4$ or 840.

Another way of describing this situation is that this is the number of permutations of 7 tracks taken 4 at a time, denoted $_7P_4$. This number can also be computed by using factorials.

Key Concept • Permutations

Words	The number of permutations of *n* distinct objects taken *r* at a time is denoted $_nP_r$ and given by $_nP_r = \dfrac{n!}{(n-r)!}$.
Symbols	The number of permutations of 7 objects taken 4 at a time is $_7P_4 = \dfrac{7!}{(7-4)!} = \dfrac{7 \cdot 6 \cdot 5 \cdot 4 \cdot 3 \cdot 2 \cdot 1}{3 \cdot 2 \cdot 1}$ or 840.

(continued on the next page)

Today's Goals
- Use permutations to compute probabilities.
- Use combinations to compute probabilities.

Today's Vocabulary
permutation
factorial
combination

🖰 Go Online
You can watch a video to see how to find a probability using permutations.

Interactive Presentation

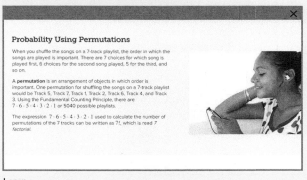

Probability Using Permutations

When you shuffle the songs on a 7-track playlist, the order in which the songs are played is important. There are 7 choices for which song is played first, 6 choices for the second song played, 5 for the third, and so on.

A **permutation** is an arrangement of objects in which order is important. One permutation for shuffling the songs on a 7-track playlist would be Track 5, Track 7, Track 1, Track 2, Track 6, Track 4, and Track 3. Using the Fundamental Counting Principle, there are $7 \cdot 6 \cdot 5 \cdot 4 \cdot 3 \cdot 2 \cdot 1$ or 5040 possible playlists.

The expression $7 \cdot 6 \cdot 5 \cdot 4 \cdot 3 \cdot 2 \cdot 1$ used to calculate the number of permutations of the 7 tracks can be written as 7!, which is read *7 factorial*.

Learn

WATCH

▶ Students can watch a video that explains probabilities using permuations.

Your Notes

Recall that the probability of an event is the ratio of the number of favorable outcomes to the number of total outcomes. To find probabilities with permutations, the number of favorable outcomes and the number of total outcomes can be written as a permutation.

Key Concept • Permutations with Repetition

The number of distinguishable permutations of n objects in which one object is repeated r_1 times, another is repeated r_2 times, and so on,

is $\dfrac{n!}{r_1! \cdot r_2! \cdot \ldots \cdot r_j!}$.

⊕ Example 1 Probability and Permutations of n Objects

PERFORMING ARTS Tyesha and Liam sign up for an open mic night with 32 available slots that are filled at random. What is the probability that Tyesha will perform first and Liam will perform second?

Step 1 Find the number of possible outcomes.

The number of possible outcomes in the sample space is the number of permutations of the __32__ performers' order, or 32!.

Step 2 Find the number of favorable outcomes.

The number of favorable outcomes is the number of permutations of the other performers' order given that Tyesha performs first and Liam performs second: $(32 - 2)!$ or __30__ !.

Step 3 Calculate the probability.

$P(\text{Tyesha 1, Liam 2}) = \dfrac{30!}{32!}$ ←number of favorable outcomes
                     ←number of possible outcomes

$= \dfrac{\overset{1}{30!}}{32 \cdot 31 \cdot \underset{1}{30!}}$ Expand 32! and divide out common factors.

$= \dfrac{1}{992}$ Simplify.

The probability that Tyesha will perform first and Liam will perform second is $\frac{1}{992}$, or about __0.1__ %.

Check

Five geometry students are asked to randomly choose a polygon and describe its properties. What is the probability that the first three students choose the hexagon, the pentagon, and the triangle, in that order? $\frac{1}{60}$

💭 Think About It!

How would the probability differ, if at all, of Liam performing first and Tyesha performing second?

Sample answer: Because neither the number of favorable outcomes nor the number of total possible outcomes has changed, the probability would remain unchanged.

 Go Online You can complete an Extra Example online.

⊕ Example 1 Probability and Permutations of n Objects

Ⓜ️ Teaching the Mathematical Practices

6 Communicate Precisely Encourage students to routinely write and explain their solution methods. Point out that they should use clear definitions when they discuss their solutions with others.

Questions for Mathematical Discourse

AL What would be the probability that Liam will perform first and Tyesha will perform second? $\frac{1}{992}$

OL If the organizers add 8 available slots to the open mic night, what division problem would give the probability that Tyesha will perform first and Liam will perform second? $\frac{38!}{40!}$

BL Tyesha and Liam are invited to a special performance by the organizers, where they are randomly assigned available slots. If the probability that Tyesha will perform first and Liam will perform second is $\frac{1}{132}$, how many available slots are there? 12

DIFFERENTIATE

Enrichment Activity BL

Organize students in groups of three or four. Provide each group with a handful of four different objects such as a variety of dry beans, color counters, or plastic beads. Have one group make as many unique combinations of two objects as possible. Have groups complete the same activity for permutations. Other groups can find combinations and permutations for groups of three or four objects. Have each group label a piece of paper and record all the different ways they arranged the objects. Allow groups to share their results with the class. Direct students to pay particular attention to the difference between the number of combinations and permutations made with the same number of objects.

Interactive Presentation

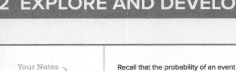

Probability and Permutations of n Objects

⊕ PERFORMING ARTS Tyesha and Liam sign up for an open mic night with 32 available slots that are filled at random. What is the probability that Tyesha will perform first and Liam will perform second?

Example 1

TYPE

`a|` Students complete the calculations to find probability and permutations of n objects.

TYPE

`a|` Student answer a question to show they understand probability and permutations of n objects.

1 CONCEPTUAL UNDERSTANDING | **2 FLUENCY** | **3 APPLICATION**

🌐 Example 2 Probability and Permutations with No Repetition

Ⓜ️ Teaching the Mathematical Practices

3 Construct Arguments In this example, students will use stated assumptions, definitions, and previously established results to construct an argument.

Questions for Mathematical Discourse

AL What factorial represents the total number of permutations of 12 photographs? 12!

OL Would it be more probable, less probable, or equally probable for the first two photos to be of only Rami's brother? more probable

BL What is the probability that the first 3 pictures will be the photos of the entire family? Show your work. $\frac{1}{220}$; Sample answer: $\frac{12!}{(12-3)!} = \frac{12 \cdot 11 \cdot 10 \cdot 9!}{9!} = 12 \cdot 11 \cdot 10 = 1,320$ total outcomes. $\frac{3!}{1,320} = \frac{6}{1,320} = \frac{1}{220}$

Common Error

Remind students that a factorial represents a series of products, so they can be eliminated as common factors from the numerator and denominator of a fraction just like any other common factors. Do some examples where you write out and cancel all of the individual factors, and prompt the students to explain that it is easier to eliminate the whole factorial in one step rather than writing it out entirely.

🌐 Example 3 Probability and Permutations with Repetition

Ⓜ️ Teaching the Mathematical Practices

4 Apply Mathematics In this example, students apply what they have learned about permutations and probability to solving a real-world problem.

Questions for Mathematical Discourse

AL If you have the numbers 1, 1, and 0 and you selected a permutation of those numbers at random, what is the probably that the result would be 101? $\frac{1}{3}$

OL Does the probability that we found mean that it is likely the numbers will equal the price of $25,852? Explain. No; sample answer: There are 30 distinguishable outcomes and only 1 is favorable, which is about 3%. So it is possible, but not likely that the numbers will equal 25,852.

BL What is the probability that the numbers would *not* equal 25,852? $\frac{29}{30}$

Common Error

Remind students to re-read the question they are asked to answer, and to check the reasonableness of their answer. For Instance, in Example 3 students may calculate the number of permutations and write an answer of 30. If they re-read the problem, they will see that the question is asking for the probability of a specific permutation, or $\frac{1}{30}$.

🌐 Example 2 Probability and Permutations with No Repetition

SLIDESHOW For a project, Rami selects 12 family photographs that will randomly play in a slideshow. The slideshow will not show repeat photos until all 12 photos have been shown. Three photos are of Rami's entire family, two photos are of his brother, three photos are just of him, and four photos are of his sister. What is the probability that the first four pictures in the slideshow will be of Rami's sister?

Step 1 Find the number of possible outcomes.
Because the photos will not repeat, order in this situation is important. The number of possible outcomes in the sample space is the number of permutations of __12__ photos taken 4 at a time, $_{12}P_4$.

$_{12}P_4 = \frac{(12!)}{(12-4)!} = \frac{12 \cdot 11 \cdot 10 \cdot 9 \cdot 8!}{8!}$ or 11,880

Step 2 Find the number of favorable outcomes.
The number of favorable outcomes is the number of permutations of the __4__ photos of Rami's sister, or 4!.

Step 3 Calculate the probability.
The probability of the four photos of Rami's sister appearing as the first four in the slideshow is $\frac{4!}{11,880}$, or $\frac{1}{495}$.

🌐 Example 3 Probability and Permutations with Repetition

GAME SHOW One game show has contestants arrange five number tiles to build their guess at the price of a prize. Mishka is given five tiles with the numbers 2, 2, 5, 5, and 8. If Mishka arranges the tiles randomly, what is the probability that she arranges them as the correct price of $25,852?

Step 1 There is a total of five numbers. Of these numbers, 2 occurs 2 times, 5 occurs 2 times, and 8 occurs 1 time. So, the number of distinguishable permutations of these numbers is
$\frac{5!}{(2! \cdot 2!)} = \frac{120}{4}$, or __30__   Simplify.

Step 2 There is only 1 favorable arrangement, the actual price, __25,852__.

Step 3 The probability that a permutation of these numbers selected at random results in the correct price of 25,852, is $\frac{1}{30}$.

Check

GAMES The physics team is holding a game night fundraiser. To win a grand prize in a particular game, you must spin the spinner four times and land on blue, red, green, and yellow, in that order. What is the probability that you will spin the winning sequence? $\frac{1}{110,880}$

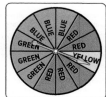

🔵 **Go Online** You can complete an Extra Example online.

💭 **Think About It!**
If the price of the prize were changed to $85,225, would the probability that Mishka arranges the tiles as the correct price increase, decrease, or stay the same? Justify your reasoning.
Sample answer: Because only the order of the numbers in the price of the prize is changing, the probability that she arranges the tiles as the correct price will stay the same. There are still $\frac{5!}{(2! \cdot 2!)}$, or 30, possible arrangements.

Study Tip
Randomness When outcomes are decided at random, they are equally likely to occur and their probabilities can be calculated using permutations and combinations.

Interactive Presentation

Probability and Permutations with Repetition

🌐 GAME SHOW One game show has contestants reach into a bag of 13 number tiles. Tiles are randomly selected from the bag by the contestant. Each number tile can be used or discarded as the contestant sees fit, but the order of the numbers cannot change. If you select a permutation of four numbers at random, what is the probability that they will result in the correct price of $1500?

Example 3

TYPE

Students answer a question to show they understand probability and permutations with repetition.

CHECK

Students complete the Check online to determine whether they are ready to move on.

1 CONCEPTUAL UNDERSTANDING | **2 FLUENCY** | 3 APPLICATION

Learn Probability Using Combinations

A **combination** is a selection of objects in which order is *not* important.

A combination of *n* objects taken *r* at a time, or $_nC_r$, is calculated by dividing the number of permutations $_nP_r$ by the number of arrangements containing the same elements, *r*!.

Key Concept · Combinations

Symbols	The number of combinations of *n* distinct objects taken *r* at a time is denoted by $_nC_r$, and is given by $_nC_r = \frac{n!}{(n-r)!r!}$.
Example	The number of combinations of 7 objects taken 3 at a time is $_7C_3 = \frac{7!}{(7-3)!3!} = \frac{7!}{4!3!} = \frac{7 \cdot 6 \cdot 5 \cdot 4!}{4! \cdot 6}$ or 35.

Recall that the probability of an event is the ratio of the number of favorable outcomes to the number of total outcomes. To find probabilities with combinations, the number of favorable outcomes and the number of total outcomes can each be written as a combination.

Example 4 Probability and Combinations

If three points are randomly chosen from those named on pentagon *ACEGJ*, what is the probability that they all lie on the same line segment?

Step 1 Find the number of possible outcomes.

Because the order in which the points are chosen does not matter, the number of possible outcomes in the sample space is the number of combinations of ___10___ points taken ___3___ at a time, $_{10}C_3$.

$_{10}C_3 = \frac{10!}{(10-3)!3!} = \frac{10 \cdot 9 \cdot 8 \cdot 7!}{7! \cdot 3!}$ or ___120___

Step 2 Find the number of favorable outcomes.

There are ___5___ favorable outcomes. The points could lie on $\overline{AC}$, $\overline{CE}$, $\overline{EG}$, $\overline{GJ}$, or $\overline{JA}$.

Step 3 Calculate the probability.

The probability of three randomly chosen points lying on the same segment is $\frac{5}{120}$, or $\frac{1}{24}$.

Check

A *lattice* is a point at the intersection of two or more grid lines in a coordinate plane.

If two lattice points are chosen randomly in rectangle *ABCD*, including its sides, the probability that they are in rectangle *WXYZ*, including its sides, is $\frac{4}{21}$ or 19%.

If four lattice points are chosen randomly in rectangle *ABCD*, including its sides, the probability that they are *W*, *X*, *Y*, and *Z* is $\frac{1}{58,905}$.

Go Online
You can watch a video to see how to find a probability using combinations.

Study Tip
Permutations and Combinations
Use permutations when the order of an arrangement is important, and use combinations when the order is not important.

Talk About It!
If you pull letter tiles from a bag containing all 26 letters, and you want to pull 3 vowels and 6 consonants, should you calculate the probability using a *permutation* or a *combination*? Explain.

Combination; sample answer: Because the order in which the tiles are drawn is not important.

Go Online
You can complete an Extra Example online.

Interactive Presentation

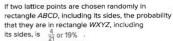

Probability and Combinations

If three points are randomly chosen from those named on pentagon *ACEGJ*, what is the probability that they all lie on the same line segment?

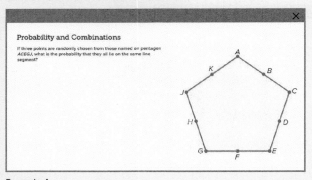

Example 4

TYPE

Students complete calculations using probability and combinations.

CHECK

Students complete the Check online to determine whether they are ready to move on.

Learn Probability Using Combinations

Objective
Students use combinations to compute probabilities.

MP Teaching the Mathematical Practices

1 Special Cases Work with students to evaluate the cases of permutations versus combinations. Encourage students to familiarize themselves with both cases, and to know the best time to use each one.

About the Key Concept
Review the Study Tip with the students, so they can clearly differentiate between when to apply permutations and combinations.

Example 4 Probability and Combinations

MP Teaching the Mathematical Practices

6 Communicate Precisely Encourage students to routinely write and explain their solution methods. Point out that they should use clear definitions when they discuss their solutions with others.

Questions for Mathematical Discourse

AL How are permutations and combinations different? For permutations, order is important. For combinations, order is not important.

OL If you were randomly choosing 2 points from the vertices *ACEGJ*, what is the probability that the two points would be on the same line? $\frac{5}{20}$ or $\frac{1}{4}$

BL How would you have to change the situation to require permutations instead of combinations? Sample answer: If the question were about the probability of selecting the points on the same line in alphabetical order, it would require permutations.

Exit Ticket

Recommended Use
At the end of class, go online to display the Exit Ticket prompt and ask students to respond using a separate piece of paper. Have students hand you their responses as they leave the room.

Alternate Use
At the end of class, go online to display the Exit Ticket prompt and ask students to respond verbally or by using a mini-whiteboard. Have students hold up their whiteboards so that you can see all student responses. Tap to reveal the answer when most or all students have completed the Exit Ticket.

Practice and Homework

Suggested Assignments

Use the table below to select appropriate exercises.

DOK	Topic	Exercises
1, 2	exercises that mirror the examples	1–13
2	exercises that use a variety of skills from this lesson	14–24
3	exercises that emphasize higher-order and critical-thinking skills	25–30

ASSESS AND DIFFERENTIATE

📊 Use the data from the **Checks** to determine whether to provide resources for extension, remediation, or intervention.

IF students score 90% or more on the Checks, **BL**
THEN assign:

- Practice, Exercises 1–23 odd, 25–30
- Extension: Finding Combinations by Using Pascal's Triangle
- 🔲 **ALEKS** Counting; Theoretical and Experimental Probability

IF students score 66%–89% on the Checks, **OL**
THEN assign:

- Practice, Exercises 1–29 odd
- Remediation, Review Resources: Theoretical Probability of Simple Events
- Personal Tutors
- Extra Examples 1–4
- 🔲 **ALEKS** Using Tree Diagrams

IF students score 65% or less on the Checks, **AL**
THEN assign:

- Practice, Exercises 1–13 odd
- Remediation, Review Resources: Theoretical Probability of Simple Events
- *Quick Review Math Handbook*: Probability with Permutations and Combinations
- 🔲 **ALEKS** Using Tree Diagrams

Name _____ **Period** _____ **Date** _____

Practice

🔲 **Go Online** You can complete your homework online.

Example 1

1. **CHEERLEADING** The cheerleading squad is made up of 12 girls. A captain and a co-captain are selected at random. What is the probability that Chantel and Clover are chosen as leaders? $\frac{1}{66}$

2. **BOOKS** You have a textbook for each of the following subjects: Spanish, English, Chemistry, Geometry, History, and Psychology. If you choose 4 of these books at random to arrange on a shelf, what is the probability that the Geometry textbook will be first from the left and the Chemistry textbook will be second from the left? $\frac{1}{30}$

3. **RAFFLE** Alfonso and Cordell each bought one raffle ticket at the state fair. If 50 tickets were randomly sold, what is the probability that Alfonso got ticket 14 and Cordell got ticket 23? $\frac{1}{2450}$

4. **CONCERT** Nia and Ciro are going to a concert with their high school's key club. If they choose a seat in the row below at random, what is the probability that Ciro will be in seat C11 and Nia will be in C12? $\frac{1}{132}$

Examples 2 and 3

5. **PHONE NUMBERS** What is the probability that a 7-digit telephone number generated using the digits 2, 3, 2, 5, 2, 7, and 3 is the number 222-3357? $\frac{1}{420}$

6. **IDENTIFICATION** A store randomly assigns their employees work identification numbers to track productivity. Each number consists of 5 digits ranging from 1–9. If the digits cannot repeat, find the probability that a randomly generated number is 25938. $\frac{1}{15,120}$

7. **STUDENT COUNCIL** The table shows the finalists for class president. The order in which they will give their speeches will be chosen randomly.

   a. What is the probability that Denny, Kelli, and Chaminade are the first 3 speakers, in any order? $\frac{1}{35}$

   b. What is the probability that Denny is first, Kelli is second, and Chaminade is third? $\frac{1}{210}$

Class President Finalists
Alan Shepherd
Chaminade Hudson
Denny Murano
Kelli Baker
Tanika Johnson
Jerome Murdock
Marlene Lindeman

Example 4

8. **TROPHIES** Taryn has 15 soccer trophies but she only has room to display 9 of them on a shelf. If she chooses them at random, what is the probability that each of the trophies from the school invitational from the 1st through 9th grades will be chosen? $\frac{1}{5005}$

9. **FROZEN YOGURT** Kali has a choice of 20 flavors for her triple scoop cone. If she chooses the flavors at random, what is the probability that the 3 flavors she chooses will be vanilla, chocolate, and strawberry? $\frac{1}{1140}$

10. **BUSINESS** Kaja has a dog walking business that serves 9 dogs. If she chooses 4 of the dogs at random to take an extra trip to the dog park, what is the probability that Cherish, Taffy, Haunter, and Maverick are chosen? $\frac{1}{126}$

11. **FOOD TRUCKS** A restaurant critic has 10 new food trucks to try. If she tries half of them this week, what is the probability that she will choose Nacho Best Tacos, Creme Bruleezin, Fre Sha Vaca Do's, You Can't Get Naan, and Grillarious? $\frac{1}{252}$

12. **DONATIONS** Emily has 20 collectible dolls from different countries that she will donate. If she selects 10 of them at random, what is the probability that she chooses the dolls from Ecuador, Paraguay, Chile, France, Spain, Sweden, Switzerland, Germany, Greece, and Italy? $\frac{1}{184,756}$

13. **AMUSEMENT PARK** An amusement park has 12 major attractions: four roller coasters, two carousels, two drop towers, and two dark rides. The park's app will randomly select attractions for you to visit in order. What is the probability that the four roller coasters are the first four suggested attractions? $\frac{1}{495}$

Mixed Exercises

14. **BUSINESS TRAVEL** A department manager is selecting team members at random to attend one of four conferences in Los Angeles, Atlanta, Chicago, and New York. If there are 20 team members, what is the probability that Jariah, Sherry, Emilio, and Lavon are chosen for the conferences? $\frac{1}{4845}$

15. **DINING** You are handed 5 pieces of silverware for the formal place setting shown. If you guess their placement at random, what is the probability that the knife and spoon are placed correctly? $\frac{1}{20}$

16. **CARDS** What is the probability in a line of these five cards that the ace would be first from the left and the 10 would be second from the left? $\frac{1}{20}$

Name _____ Period ___ Date ___

17. Points *A*, *B*, *C*, *D*, and *E* are coplanar, but no 3 are collinear.

  a. What is the total number of lines that can be determined by these points? 10

  b. What is the probability that $\overleftrightarrow{AB}$ would be chosen at random from all of the possible lines formed? $\frac{1}{10}$

18. CRAFTING Jaclyn bought some decorative letters for a scrapbook project. If she randomly selected a permutation of the letters shown, what is the probability that they would form the word "photography"? $\frac{1}{4,989,600}$

19. BUSINESS Andres sent emails to 20 of his contacts advertising his new lawn services. If 6 contacts responded to the email, what is the probability that the Michaelsons, the Rodriquezes, the Farooqis, the Salahis, the Kryceks, and the Waltons responded? $\frac{1}{38,760}$

20. GAME SHOW The people on the list at the right will be considered to participate in a game show. What is the probability that Wyatt, Gabe, and Isaac will be chosen as the first three contestants? $\frac{1}{56}$

DAY 1 STANDINGS
MCAFEE, DAVID
FORD, GABE
STANDISH, TRISTAN
NOCHOLS, WYATT
PURCELL, JACK
ANDERSON, BILL
WRIGHT, ISAAC
FILBERT, MITCH

21. SALES The owner of a hair salon advertises that on the first day of each month, the first 6 customers will receive one of the coupons shown at the right for a discount off their total bill. Each coupon is given at random to a different customer.

5% OFF	10% OFF
15% OFF	20% OFF
25% OFF	50% OFF

  a. What is the probability that the first customer on May 1 gets the 10% discount and the second customer gets the 25% discount? Explain your answer using favorable and possible outcomes. See margin.

  b. How many different groups of two coupons can the first two customers on August 1 receive regardless of order? $_6C_2 = 15$

22. DONATIONS As part of a school beautification project, 12 alumni each donated a tree to be planted on the school grounds. The types of trees are shown in the table. There will be a sign next to each tree with the donor's name.

Donated Trees	
Type	Number of Trees
Cherry	5
Dogwood	4
Crabapple	2
Redbud	1

  a. If the trees are planted in a row at random, what is the probability that they will be in alphabetical order by donor name? Explain. See margin.

  b. If 4 trees are randomly selected and planted near the school entrance, what is the probability that they will all be dogwood trees? Explain. See margin.

Lesson 12-4 · Probability with Permutations and Combinations **741**

---

23. PARKING STICKERS Parking stickers contain randomly generated numbers with 5 digits ranging from 1 to 9. No digits are repeated. What is the probability that a randomly generated number is 54321? $\frac{1}{15,120}$

24. CONSTRUCT ARGUMENTS Prove that $_nC_{n-r} = {}_nC_r$.

$$_nC_{n-r} \overset{?}{=} {}_nC_r$$
$$\frac{n!}{[n-(n-r)]![(n-r)!} \overset{?}{=} \frac{n!}{(n-r)!r!}$$
$$\frac{n!}{r![(n-r)!} \overset{?}{=} \frac{n!}{(n-r)!r!}$$
$$\frac{n!}{(n-r)!r!} = \frac{n!}{(n-r)!r!}$$
$$_nC_{n-r} = {}_nC_r \checkmark$$

Higher-Order Thinking Skills

25. PERSEVERE Fifteen boys and fifteen girls entered a drawing for four free movie tickets. What is the probability that all four tickets were won by girls? $\frac{13}{261}$

26. ANALYZE Is the following statement *sometimes*, *always*, or *never* true? Justify your reasoning.

$$_nP_r = {}_nC_r$$ Sometimes; sample answer: The statement is true when *r* is 1.

27. WRITE Compare and contrast permutations and combinations. Sample answer: Both permutations and combinations are used to find the number of possible arrangements of a group of objects. The order of the objects is important in permutations, but not in combinations.

28. CREATE Describe a situation in which the probability is given by $\frac{1}{7C_3}$. Sample answer: A bag contains seven marbles that are red, orange, yellow, green, blue, purple, and black. The probability that the orange, blue, and black marbles will be chosen if three marbles are drawn at random can be calculated using a combination.

29. PERSEVERE A student claimed that permutations and combinations were related by $r! \cdot {}_nC_r = {}_nP_r$. Use algebra to show that this is true. Then explain why $_nC_r$ and $_nP_r$ differ by the factor $r!$.

Sample answer:
$$r! \cdot {}_nC_r = r! \cdot \frac{n!}{(n-r)!r!}$$
$$= \frac{n!r!}{(n-r)!r!}$$
$$= \frac{n!}{(n-r)!}$$
$$= {}_nP_r$$

$_nC_r$ and $_nP_r$ differ by the factor $r!$ because there are always $r!$ ways to order the groups that are selected. Therefore, there are $r!$ permutations of each combination.

30. FIND THE ERROR Charlie claims that the number of ways *n* objects can be arranged if order matters is equal to the number of permutations of *n* objects taken $n-1$ at a time. Do you agree with Charlie? Explain your reasoning. Yes; sample answer: The number of ways *n* objects can be arranged if order matters is *n*!. The number of permutations of *n* objects taken $n-1$ at a time is $_nP_{n-1} = \frac{n!}{[n-(n-1)]!} = \frac{n!}{1!} = n!$.

742 Module 12 · Probability

Answers

21a. $\frac{1}{30}$; Sample answer: There are 6 possible coupons for the first customer, 5 possible for the second customer, and so forth, so the total number of possible outcomes is 6! = 720. If the first customer gets the 10% coupon and the second customer gets the 25% coupon, then there are 4! = 24 ways the remaining four customers can get coupons so the total number of favorable outcomes is 24. The probability is

$$\frac{\text{number of favorable outcomes}}{\text{number of possible outcomes}} = \frac{24}{720} = \frac{1}{30}.$$

22a. $\frac{1}{479,001,600}$; Sample answer: It is not necessary to consider repetition because the donor names are included. Order matters, so the number of possible outcomes is the number of permutations of 12 trees with names: 12! = 479, 001, 600. There is only 1 favorable outcome: the trees in order alphabetically by donor name. So,

$$\frac{\text{number of favorable outcomes}}{\text{number of possible outcomes}} = \frac{1}{479,001,600}.$$

22b. $\frac{1}{495}$; Sample answer: Order does not matter, so the number of possible outcomes is the number of combination of 12 trees taken 4 trees at a time: $\frac{12!}{(12-4)!4!}$ or 495. There is only 1 favorable outcome — that the 4 dogwood trees are chosen, in any order.

Probability and the Multiplication Rule

LESSON GOAL

Students solve problems involving probability of independent and dependent events using the Multiplication Rule.

1 LAUNCH

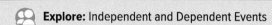 Launch the lesson with a **Warm Up** and an introduction.

2 EXPLORE AND DEVELOP

Explore: Independent and Dependent Events

Develop:

Probability of Independent Events
• Probability of Independent Events

Probability of Dependent Events
• Independent and Dependent Events
• Probability of Dependent Events

 You may want your students to complete the **Checks** online.

3 REFLECT AND PRACTICE

 Exit Ticket

Practice

DIFFERENTIATE

View reports of student progress on the **Checks** after each example.

Resources	AL	OL	BL	ELL
Remediation: Theoretical Probabilities of Simple Events	●	●		●
Extension: Weather Forecasting		●	●	●

Language Development Handbook

Assign page 87 of the *Language Development Handbook* to help your students build mathematical language related to solving problems involving probability of independent and dependent events using the Multiplication Rule.

ELL You can use the tips and suggestions on page T87 of the handbook to support students who are building English proficiency.

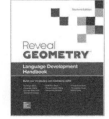

Suggested Pacing

| 90 min | 0.5 day |
| 45 min | 1 day |

Focus

Domain: Statistics & Probability

Standards for Mathematical Content:

S.CP.2 Understand that two events *A* and *B* are independent if the probability of *A* and *B* occurring together is the product of their probabilities, and use this characterization to determine if they are independent.

S.CP.8 Apply the general Multiplication Rule in a uniform probability model, $P(A \text{ and } B) = P(A)P(B|A) = P(B)P(A|B)$, and interpret the answer in terms of the model.

Standards for Mathematical Practice:

1 Make sense of problems and persevere in solving them.

4 Model with mathematics.

Coherence

Vertical Alignment

Previous
Students solved probability problems using permutations and combinations.
S.CP.9

Now
Students solve probability problems using the Multiplication Rule.
S.CP.2, S.CP.8

Next
Students will solve problems using the Addition Rule.
S.CP.7

Rigor

The Three Pillars of Rigor

1 CONCEPTUAL UNDERSTANDING	2 FLUENCY	3 APPLICATION

Conceptual Bridge In this lesson, students draw on their understanding of independence and build fluency by using the Multiplication Rule to find probabilities of independent and dependent events. They apply their understanding by solving real-world problems related to independent and dependent events.

Interactive Presentation

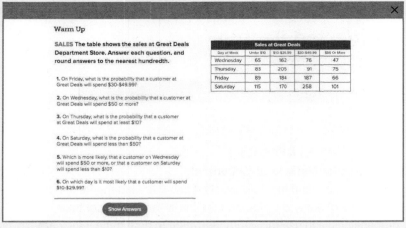

Warm Up

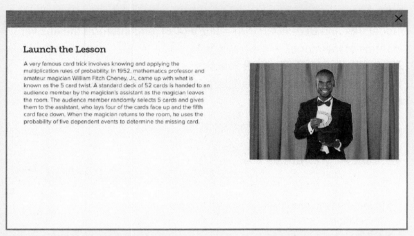

Launch the Lesson

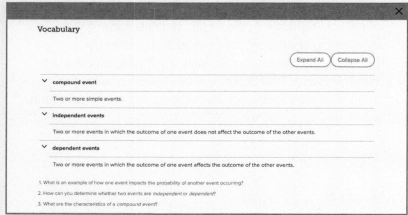

Today's Vocabulary

Warm Up

Prerequisite Skills

The Warm Up exercises address the following prerequisite skill for this lesson:

- finding theoretical probabilities

Answers:

1. 0.36
2. 0.13
3. 0.82
4. 0.84
5. less than $10 on Saturday
6. Wednesday

Launch the Lesson

 Teaching the Mathematical Practices

> **4 Apply Mathematics** In this Launch the Lesson, students can see a real-world application of probability of dependent events.

Go Online to find additional teaching notes and questions to promote classroom discourse.

Today's Standards

Tell students that they will be addressing these content and practice standards in this lesson. You may wish to have a student volunteer read aloud *How can I meet these standards?* and *How can I use these practices?* and connect these to the standards.

See the Interactive Presentation for I Can statements that align with the standards covered in this lesson.

Mathematical Background

A compound event consists of two or more simple events. Events A and B are independent if the probability that A occurs does not affect the probability that B occurs. The probability of independent events A and B can be calculated with $P(A \text{ and } B) = P(A)P(B)$. Events A and B are dependent if the probability that A occurs in some way changes the probability that B occurs. The probability of dependent events A and B can be calculated with $P(A \text{ and } B) = P(A)P(B|A)$.

Today's Vocabulary

Tell students that they will be using these vocabulary terms in this lesson. You can expand each row if you wish to share the definitions. Then, discuss the questions below with the class.

Explore Independent and Dependent Events

Objective

Students find the probabilities of dependent and independent events of various strategy games.

Ideas for Use

Recommended Use Present the Inquiry Question, or have a student volunteer read it aloud. Have students work in pairs to complete the Explore activity on their devices. Pairs should discuss each of the questions. Monitor student progress during the activity. Upon completion of the Explore activity, have student volunteers share their responses to the Inquiry Question.

What if my students don't have devices? You may choose to project the activity on a whiteboard. A printable worksheet for each Explore is available online. You may choose to print the worksheet so that individuals or pairs of students can use it to record their observations.

Summary of the Activity

Students will complete guiding exercises throughout the Explore activity. They will watch a video, then complete a series of exercises related to independent and dependent events. Then, students will answer the Inquiry Question.

Go Online to find additional teaching notes and sample answers for the guiding exercises.

(continued on the next page)

Interactive Presentation

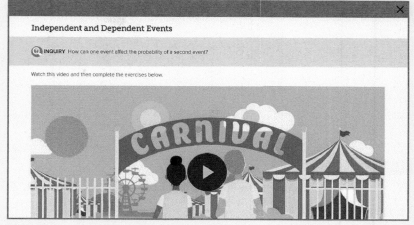

Explore

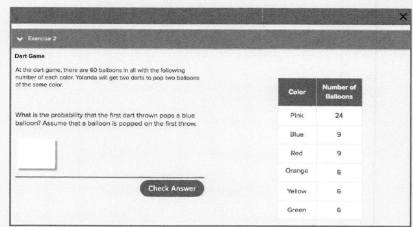

Explore

WATCH

Students can watch a video that models probability in the real-world.

TAP

Students tap to see examples of various probabilities.

S.CP.2

Interactive Presentation

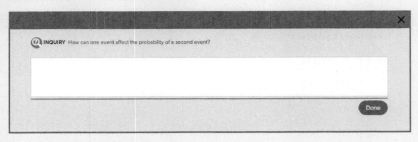

Explore

TYPE

Students will respond to the Inquiry Question and can view a sample answer.

---

1 **CONCEPTUAL UNDERSTANDING** | 2 FLUENCY | 3 APPLICATION

Explore Independent and Dependent Events (*continued*)

MP Teaching the Mathematical Practices

6 Communicate Precisely Encourage students to routinely write or explain their solution methods. Point out that they should use clear definitions when they discuss their solutions with others.

Questions

Have students complete the Explore activity.

Ask:

- How is the Dart Game different than the Duck Pond? Sample answer: For the Dart Game, once a balloon is popped, it is not replaced with a new balloon, so the probabilities change between events. In the Duck Pond, the duck is replaced, so the probabilities are the same for every event.

- What key words can help you determine if events are independent or dependent? Sample answer: If the situation mentions "replacement", then you know the events are independent.

Inquiry

How can one event affect the probability of a second event? Sample answer: If the sample space is changed in any way after the first event has occurred, then the events are dependent and the probability of the second event occurring depends on the outcome of the first event. If the sample space is not changed in any way after the first event has occurred, then the events are independent and the probability of the first event has no effect on the second event.

Go Online to find additional teaching notes and sample answers for the guiding exercises.

1 CONCEPTUAL UNDERSTANDING | 2 FLUENCY | 3 APPLICATION

Learn Independent Events

Objective
Students apply the multiplication rule to situations involving independent events.

 Teaching the Mathematical Practices

7 Use Structure Help students to explore the structure of independent events in this Learn.

About the Key Concept
Point out to the students that the formula for the probability of two independent events can be extended to any number of events. Encourage students to consider how they could use that formula to expand to the proof of the probability of three events, $P(A$ and B and $C)$.

DIFFERENTIATE

Language Development Activity AL ELL

Ask students to determine the probability of rolling a die five times and getting two each time. Have them use paper, pencils, and manipulatives to solve this problem with a partner. Ask them to explain their reasoning.

 Go Online

- Find additional teaching notes.
- View performance reports of the Checks.
- Assign or present an Extra Example.

Lesson 12-5

Probability and the Multiplication Rule

Explore Independent and Dependent Events

Online Activity Use the video to complete the Explore.

> **INQUIRY** How can one event affect the probability of a second event?

Learn Independent Events

A **compound event** or *composite event* consists of two or more simple events. **Independent events** are two or more events in which the outcome of one event does not affect the outcome of the other events.

Suppose a coin is tossed and the spinner shown is spun. The sample space for this experiment is {(H, 1), (H, 2), (H, 3), (T, 1), (T, 2), (T, 3)}.

Using the sample space, the probability of the coin landing on heads and the spinner on 2 is $P(H$ and $2) = \frac{1}{6}$.

Notice that the same probability can be found by multiplying the probabilities of each simple event.

$$P(H) = \frac{1}{2} \qquad P(2) = \frac{1}{3} \qquad P(H \text{ and } 2) = \frac{1}{2} \cdot \frac{1}{3} \text{ or } \frac{1}{6}$$

This example illustrates the first of two Multiplication Rules for Probability.

Key Concept • Probability of Two Independent Events	
Words	The probability that two independent events both occur is the product of the probabilities of each individual event.
Symbols	If two events A and B are independent, then $P(A$ and $B) = P(A) \cdot P(B)$.

This rule can be extended to any number of events.

Consider choosing objects from a group of objects. If you replace the object each time, choosing additional objects are independent events.

Today's Goals
- Apply the multiplication rule to situations involving independent events.
- Apply the multiplication rule to situations involving dependent events.

Today's Vocabulary
compound event
independent events
dependent events

Study Tip
and The word *and* often illustrates compound events. For example, if you roll a die, finding the probability of getting an odd number *and* getting a number greater than 5 indicates that the probabilities of the individual events should be multiplied.

Lesson 12-5 • Probability and the Multiplication Rule **743**

Interactive Presentation

Probability of Independent Events

A **compound event** or *composite event* consists of two or more simple events. **Independent events** are two or more events in which the outcome of one event does not affect the outcome of the other events.

Suppose a coin is tossed and the spinner shown is spun. The sample space for this experiment is {(H, 1), (H, 2), (H, 3), (T, 1), (T, 2), (T, 3)}.

Using the sample space, the probability of the coin landing on heads and the spinner on 2 is $P(H$ and $2) = \frac{1}{6}$.

Notice that the same probability can be found by multiplying the probabilities of each simple event.

$$P(H) = \frac{1}{2} \qquad P(2) = \frac{1}{3} \qquad P(H \text{ and } 2) = \frac{1}{2} \cdot \frac{1}{3} \text{ or } \frac{1}{6}$$

This example illustrates the first of two Multiplication Rules for Probability.

Learn

TAP

Students tap to reveal a study tip.

1 CONCEPTUAL UNDERSTANDING | **2 FLUENCY** | **3 APPLICATION**

Your Notes

Example 1 Probability of Independent Events

GAMING Ana is a member of a gaming Web site that randomly pairs users together to solve puzzles. Of the 50 other players currently online, Ana is friends with 10 of them. Suppose Ana is paired with a player for a game. Not liking the outcome, she disconnects and is paired with another player.

a. What is the probability that neither player that Ana is paired with is a friend of hers?

These events are independent because the set of possible matches is reset to 50 once Ana disconnects. Let F represent a player who is Ana's friend and NF represent a player who is not Ana's friend.

Complete the equation to determine the probability of independent events.

$$\begin{aligned} &\quad\quad\quad\quad\text{User 1}\quad\text{User 2}\\ P(NF \text{ and } NF) &= P(\underline{NF}) \cdot P(\underline{NF})\\ &= \frac{40}{50} \cdot \frac{40}{50} \quad\quad P(NF) = \frac{40}{50}\\ &= \frac{1600}{2500} \text{ or } \frac{16}{25} \quad \text{Simplify.} \end{aligned}$$

So, the probability that neither of the two players is Ana's friend is $\frac{16}{25}$ or $\underline{64}$%.

b. What assumption do you have to make in order to solve this problem?

We assume that the same 50 players remain in the set for both selections. If the number of available players <u>changes</u>, or the number of available players who are friends with Ana <u>changes</u>, the probability will change.

Alternate Method

You can also use an area model to calculate the probability that neither player is a friend of Ana's.

The probability that a player is not a friend of Ana's is $\frac{40}{50}$ or $\frac{4}{5}$.

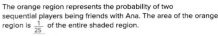

The blue region represents the probability of two sequential players not being friends with Ana. The area of the blue region is $\frac{16}{25}$ of the entire shaded region.

The orange region represents the probability of two sequential players being friends with Ana. The area of the orange region is $\frac{1}{25}$ of the entire shaded region.

Check

WEATHER Paola's weather app tells her that there is a 20% chance of rain on Tuesday and a 50% chance of rain on Wednesday. What is the probability that it will rain on both Tuesday and Wednesday? $\underline{10}$% or $\frac{1}{10}$

Go Online You can complete an Extra Example online.

744 **Module 12 · Probability**

Interactive Presentation

Probability of Independent Events

GAMING Ana is a member of a gaming Web site that randomly pairs users together to solve puzzles. Of the 50 other players currently online, Ana is friends with 10 of them. Suppose Ana is paired with a player for a game. Not liking the outcome, she disconnects and is paired with another player. What is the probability that neither player that Ana is paired with is a friend of hers?

These events are independent because the set of possible matches is reset to 50 once Ana disconnects. Let F represent a player who is Ana's friend and NF represent a player who is not Ana's friend.

Example 1

TYPE

Students complete the calculations to find the probability of independent events.

TAP

Students tap to see an alternate method.

CHECK

Students complete the Check online to determine whether they are ready to move on.

🌐 **Example 1** Probability of Independent Events

MP Teaching the Mathematical Practices

1 Understand the Approaches of Others Work with students to look at the Alternate Method. Ask students to compare and contrast the original method and the alternate method.

Questions for Mathematical Discourse

AL What is the probability that when Ana connects to the site one time, she is paired with someone who is not a friend of hers? $\frac{40}{50}$ or $\frac{4}{5}$

OL Why are Ana's two pairings independent events? Sample answer: Because each time Ana connects to the site, she has the same possible outcomes each time, they are independent events.

BL What is the probability that if Ana logs on twice, she will be paired with friends both times? $\frac{1}{25}$

DIFFERENTIATE

Enrichment Activity BL

Have students calculate the probability of simple independent events, such as tossing a coin, using the formula for dependent probabilities. Students should see that the formula produces the same probabilities for independent events as the formula for calculating independent events.

1 CONCEPTUAL UNDERSTANDING | **2 FLUENCY** | **3 APPLICATION**

Learn Dependent Events

Objective
Students apply the multiplication rule to situations involving dependent events.

 Teaching the Mathematical Practices

> **7 Use Structure** Help students to explore the structure of dependent events in this Learn.

Common Misconception
Encourage students to review the Study Tip, to be sure they do not confuse the conditional "given" symbol to be a division symbol. Also, consider some examples to convince the students that $P(B|A)$ and $P(A|B)$ are not equivalent if A and B are dependent.

Example 2 Independent and Dependent Events

 Teaching the Mathematical Practices

> **6 Communicate Precisely** Encourage students to routinely write or explain their solution methods. Point out that they should use clear definitions when they discuss their solutions with others.

Questions for Mathematical Discourse

AL If one coin is tossed, then a second coin is tossed, are they independent or dependent events? Explain. Independent; the first coin flip does not affect the possible outcomes of the second one.

OL What is an example of a dependent event? Sample answer: choosing teams for softball

BL What is an example of a series of four independent events? Sample answer: A marble is chosen from a bag, then replaced. The experiment is repeated three more times.

Learn Probability of Dependent Events

Dependent events are two or more events in which the outcome of one event affects the outcome of the other events.

Suppose a marble is chosen from the bag and placed on the table. Then, another marble is chosen from the bag. The sample space for this experiment is {(R, B), (R, R), (B, R), (B, B)}.

When choosing the first marble, there are 7 possible outcomes. The probability of choosing a red marble on the first draw is $\frac{5}{7}$. Because that marble is not returned to the bag, there are only 6 possible outcomes for second drawing. If a red marble has already been chosen, the probability of choosing a red marble on the second draw is $\frac{4}{6}$.

The second of the Multiplication Rules of Probability addresses the probability of two dependent events.

Key Concept · Probability of Two Dependent Events

Words	The probability that two dependent events both occur is the product of the probability that the first event occurs and the probability that the second event occurs *after* the first event has already occurred.
Symbols	If two events A and B are dependent, then $P(A \text{ and } B) = P(A) \cdot P(B|A)$.

This rule can be extended to any number of events.

Example 2 Independent and Dependent Events
Determine whether the events are *independent* or *dependent*. Explain your reasoning.

a. One spinner is spun twice.
The outcome of the first spin in no way changes the probability of the outcome of the second spin. Therefore, these two events are _independent_

b. In a raffle, one ticket is drawn for the first place prize, and then another ticket is drawn for the second place prize.
After the first place prize ticket is drawn, the ticket is removed and cannot be chosen again. This affects the probability of the second place prize winning ticket, because the sample space is reduced by one ticket. Therefore, these two events are _dependent_

c. A random number generator generates two numbers.
The number for the first generation has no bearing on the number for the second generation. Therefore, these two events are _independent_

 Go Online You can complete an Extra Example online.

Study Tip
Conditional Notation
The notation $P(B|A)$ is read *the probability that event B occurs given that event A has already occurred.* The "|" symbol should not be interpreted as a division symbol.

Go Online
You can watch a video to see how to use the Multiplication Rule to find the probability of two independent events.

Think About It!
Write an example of a series of three dependent events.

Sample answer: The first three numbers at a bingo game are chosen from a bag of bingo balls.

Copyright © McGraw-Hill Education

Interactive Presentation

Probability of Dependent Events

Dependent events are two or more events in which the outcome of one event affects the outcome of the other events.

Suppose a marble is chosen from the bag and placed on the table. Then, another marble is chosen from the bag. The sample space for this experiment is {(R, B) (R, R) (B, R) (B, B)}.

When choosing the first marble, there are 7 possible outcomes. The probability of choosing a red marble on the first draw is $\frac{5}{7}$. Because that marble is not returned to the bag, there are only 6 possible outcomes for the second drawing. If a red marble has already been chosen, the probability of choosing a red marble on the second draw is $\frac{4}{6}$.

Learn

WATCH

Students can watch a video that explains finding probability of dependent events.

Check

Determine whether the events are *independent* or *dependent*.

	Independent	Dependent
Of the $100 that Rei has to spend, she wants to spend $59 on a blouse and $44 on some jeans.		X
Rei asks each of three store associates which handbag they prefer.	X	
Rei purchases a handbag and a belt.	X	

Example 3 Probability of Dependent Events

FOOD The pizza that José and Tessa are eating has 10 slices and is half cheese, half mushroom. Tessa spins the pizza around and randomly selects a slice of mushroom pizza. If José spins the pizza and selects a slice after that, what is the probability that both he and Tessa select a slice of mushroom pizza?

These events are dependent because Tessa does not replace the slice she selected. Let M represent a slice of mushroom pizza and C represent a slice of cheese pizza.

$P(M \text{ and } M) = P(M) \cdot P(M|C)$ Probability of dependent events

$= \frac{5}{10} \cdot \frac{4}{9}$ or $\frac{2}{9}$ After the first slice of mushroom pizza is selected, 9 total pieces remain, and 4 of those slices have mushrooms.

So, the probability that both friends randomly select slices with mushrooms is $\frac{2}{9}$ or about __22__ %.

Check

SCHOOL On a math test, 5 out of 20 students got all the questions correct. If three students are chosen at random without replacement, what is the probability that all three got all the questions correct on the test?

__0.9% or $\frac{1}{114}$__

Pause and Reflect

Did you struggle with anything in this lesson? If so, how did you deal with it?

   See students' observations.

 Go Online You can complete an Extra Example online.

Interactive Presentation

Probability of Dependent Events

FOOD The pizza that José and Tessa are eating is half cheese, half mushroom. Tessa spins the pizza around and randomly selects a slice of mushroom pizza. If José spins the pizza and selects a slice after that, what is the probability that both he and Tessa select a slice of mushroom pizza?

Example 3

DRAG AND DROP

 Students drag events to complete a probability tree that allows them to check the solution.

CHECK

Students complete the Check online to determine whether they are ready to move on.

Example 3 Probability of Dependent Events

MP Teaching the Mathematical Practices

3 Compare Arguments Mathematically proficient students can compare arguments, determine which one is flawed, and explain the flaw. In this example, students have to identify the flawed argument and choose the correct one.

Questions for Mathematical Discourse

AL On the first spin, what is the probability of Tessa selecting a slice of mushroom pizza? $\frac{5}{10}$ or $\frac{1}{2}$ or 50%

OL Why are Tessa and José's pizza selections dependent events? Sample answer: Because Tessa does not replace her slice of pizza, the possible outcomes for José's pizza selection are different than Tessa's. Therefore, they are dependent events.

BL What is the probability that Tessa selects a slice with mushroom and José selects a slice without mushroom? $\frac{5}{18}$ or about 28%

Exit Ticket

Recommended Use

At the end of class, go online to display the Exit Ticket prompt and ask students to respond using a separate piece of paper. Have students hand you their responses as they leave the room.

Alternate Use

At the end of class, go online to display the Exit Ticket prompt and ask students to respond verbally or by using a mini-whiteboard. Have students hold up their whiteboards so that you can see all student responses. Tap to reveal the answer when most or all students have completed the Exit Ticket.

Practice and Homework

Suggested Assignments

Use the table below to select appropriate exercises.

DOK	Topic	Exercises
1, 2	exercises that mirror the examples	1–12
2	exercises that use a variety of skills from this lesson	13–25
3	exercises that emphasize higher-order and critical-thinking skills	26–29

ASSESS AND DIFFERENTIATE

📊 Use the data from the **Checks** to determine whether to provide resources for extension, remediation, or intervention.

IF students score 90% or more on the Checks,   `BL`
THEN assign:

- Practice, Exercises 1–25 odd, 26–29
- Extension: Weather Forecasting
- 🅐 ALEKS˙ Probability of Independent and Dependent Events

IF students score 66%–89% on the Checks,   `OL`
THEN assign:

- Practice, Exercises 1–29 odd
- Remediation, Review Resources: Theoretical Probabilities of Simple Events
- Personal Tutors
- Extra Examples 1-3
- 🅐 ALEKS˙ Theoretical Probabilities

IF students score 65% or less on the Checks,   `AL`
THEN assign:

- Practice, Exercises 1–11 odd
- Remediation, Review Resources: Theoretical Probabilities of Simple Events
- *Quick Review Math Handbook*: Probabilities of Independent and Dependent Events
- 🅐 ALEKS˙ Theoretical Probabilities

Name _____ Period _____ Date _____

Practice

🔁 **Go Online** You can complete your homework online.

Example 1

1. CLOTHING Omari has two pairs of red socks and two pairs of white socks in a drawer. He has a drawer with 2 red T-shirts and 1 white T-shirt. If he randomly chooses a pair of socks from the sock drawer and a T-shirt from the T-shirt drawer, what is the probability that he gets a pair of red socks and a white T-shirt? $\frac{1}{6}$ or about 17%

2. Phyllis drops a penny in a pond, and then she drops a nickel in the pond. What is the probability that both coins land with tails showing? $\frac{1}{4}$ or 25%

3. A die is rolled and a penny is flipped. Find the probability of rolling a two and landing on a tail. $\frac{1}{12}$ or about 8%

4. A bag contains 3 red marbles, 2 green marbles, and 4 blue marbles. A marble is drawn randomly from the bag and replaced before a second marble is chosen. Find the probability that both marbles are blue. $\frac{16}{81}$ or about 20%

5. The forecast predicts a 40% chance of rain on Tuesday and a 60% chance on Wednesday. If these probabilities are independent, what is the chance that it will rain on both days? $\frac{6}{25}$ or 24%

Example 2

Determine whether the events are *independent* or *dependent*. Explain your reasoning.

6. You roll an even number on a fair die, and then spin a spinner numbered 1 through 5 and it lands on an odd number. Independent; sample answer: These two events have no bearing on each other.

7. An ace is drawn from a standard deck of 52 cards, and is not replaced. Then, a second ace is drawn. Dependent; sample answer: Because the first ace drawn was not replaced, the probability of drawing the second card is affected.

8. In a bag of 3 green and 4 blue marbles, a blue marble is drawn and not replaced. Then, a second blue marble is drawn. Dependent; sample answer: Because the first blue marble drawn was not replaced, the probability of the drawing the second marble is affected.

9. You roll two fair dice and roll a 5 on each. Independent; sample answer: These two rolls have no bearing on each other.

Example 3

10. LOTTERY Mr. Hanes places the names of four of his students, Joe, Sofia, Hayden, and Bonita, on slips of paper. From these, he intends to randomly select two students to represent his class at the robotics convention. He draws the name of the first student, sets it aside, then draws the name of the second student. What is the probability he draws Sofia, then Joe? $\frac{1}{12}$ or about 8%

---

11. CARDS A card is drawn from a standard deck of playing cards and is not replaced. Then a second card is drawn. Find the probability the first card is a jack of spades and the second card is black. $\frac{25}{2652}$ or about 1%

12. INTRAMURAL SPORTS The table shows the color and number of jerseys available for the intramural volleyball tournament. If each jersey is given away randomly, what is the probability that the first and second jerseys given away are both red? $\frac{20}{161}$ or about 12%

Jersey Color	Amount
blue	20
white	15
red	25
black	10

Mixed Exercises

13. SPORTS The format used to determine an overall champion varies by sport. One type of format used is the *best-of-seven series*, where up to seven games are played and four wins determine a champion. If you assume that each team has an equal chance of winning each game, what is the probability of a team winning the first four games in a best-of-seven series? $\frac{1}{16}$ or about 6.25%

14. BUSINESS A sales management team consists of three directors and three assistant directors. To ensure that each team member has an equal chance to be chosen to represent the team at a national conference, all 6 names are placed into a hat and four names are drawn at random. What is the probability that those chosen will consist of 3 directors and 1 assistant director? $\frac{1}{5}$, 0.2, or 20%

15. MAGIC Iris performs a magic trick in which she holds a standard deck of cards and has each of three people randomly choose a card from the deck. Each person keeps his or her card as the next person draws. What is the probability that all three people will draw a heart? $\frac{11}{850}$ or about 1.29%

16. SCHOOL The probability that a student takes geometry and French at Saul's school is 0.064. The probability that a student takes French is 0.45. If taking geometry and taking French are dependent events, what is the probability that a student takes geometry if the student takes French? 0.14

17. EXTRACURRICULAR ACTIVITIES At Bell High School, 43% of the students are in an after-school club and 28% play sports. What is the probability that a student is in an after-school club if he or she also plays a sport if being in a club and playing sports are independent events? 0.43

Name _____ Period _____ Date _____

Sunita and Derek work for a company that produces microchips. Part of their job is to estimate the number of defective chips given the total number produced. The table shows the estimated contents of 2 boxes of microchips. Use this information for Exercises 18 and 19.

18. Derek randomly selects one chip from Box B, does not put it back, and then randomly selects another chip from Box B. What is the probability that both chips are defective? Explain.

	Number of Chips	Defective
Box A	100	4%
Box B	150	2%

$\frac{1}{3725}$; Sample answer: The probability that the first chip is defective is $\frac{3}{150}$. After that chip has been removed, the probability that the second chip is defective is $\frac{2}{149}$. So, the probability is $\frac{3}{150} \cdot \frac{2}{149}$ or $\frac{3}{3725}$.

19. Sunita randomly selects one chip from Box A, and then she randomly selects another chip from Box A. The probability that both chips are defective is $\frac{1}{625}$. Did Sunita replace the first chip before selecting the second one? Explain.
Yes; sample answer: The probability of selecting a defective chip from Box A is $\frac{1}{25}$. Because $\frac{1}{625} = \frac{1}{25} \cdot \frac{1}{25}$, $P(A \text{ and } B) = P(A) \cdot P(B)$ and the events are independent.

20. TRAVEL A travel agency conducts a survey to determine whether people drive (D) or fly (F) to their vacation destinations. The results indicated that $P(D) = 0.6$, $P(D \cap F) = 0.2$, and the probability that a family did not vacation is 0.1.

Fly F   Drive D

  a. What is the probability that a family reached their vacation destination by flying? 0.3

  b. What is the probability that a family that drives will also fly? 0.33

21. BUSINESS TRENDS You are trying to decide whether you should expand a business. If you do not expand and the economy remains good, you expect $2 million in revenue. If the economy is bad, you expect $0.5 million. The cost to expand is $1 million, but the expected revenue after the expansion is $4 million in a good economy and $1 million in a bad economy. You assume that the chances of a good and a bad economy are 30% and 70%, respectively. Create a tree diagram to represent the situation. See margin.

22. REASONING If Fred spins the spinner twice, determine the probability that he lands on sections labeled "orange" and "green." Show that $P(\text{orange}) \cdot P(\text{green} \mid \text{orange}) = P(\text{green}) \cdot P(\text{orange} \mid \text{green})$ in this situation and explain why this is true in terms of the model. Justify your answer. See margin.

23. TRICKS Sam is doing a trick with a standard deck of 52 playing cards where she begins each trick with a fresh deck of cards. Her friend Tracy randomly selects a card, looks at it, and puts it back in the deck. Then Sam randomly selects the same card. Are the events independent? What is the probability that they both pick the queen of spades? Explain.
$\frac{1}{2704}$; Sample answer: The card is replaced, so the events are independent; the probability of each picking the queen of spades is $\frac{1}{52}$, so the probability of them both picking it is $\frac{1}{52} \cdot \frac{1}{52} = \frac{1}{2704}$.

24. CONSTRUCT ARGUMENTS Use the formula for the probability of two dependent events $P(A \text{ and } B)$ to derive the conditional probability formula for $P(B \mid A)$.

$P(A \text{ and } B) = P(A) \cdot P(B \mid A)$ Formula for $P(A \text{ and } B)$
$\frac{P(A \text{ and } B)}{P(A)} = P(B \mid A)$ Divide each side by $P(A)$.

25. USE A MODEL A double fault in tennis is when the serving player fails to land their serve "in" without stepping on or over the service line in two chances. Kelly's first serve percentage is 40%, while her second serve percentage is 70%.

  a. Draw a probability tree that shows each outcome. See margin.

  b. What is the probability that Kelly will double fault? A double fault is back-to-back faults, or $P(F, F)$, which equals 0.18 or 18%.

🧠 Higher-Order Thinking Skills

26. ANALYZE There are n different objects in a bag. The probability of drawing object A and then object B without replacement is about 2.4%. What is the value of n? Explain.
7; Sample answer: The probability of drawing object A is $\frac{1}{n}$, and the probability of drawing object B when object A is not replaced is $\frac{1}{n-1}$. Because we know that the probability is 2.4%, $\frac{1}{n} \cdot \frac{1}{n-1} = \frac{2.4}{100}$ or 0.024. Solve this equation to determine that n is 7.

27. WRITE An article states the chance that a person is left-handed given that his or her parent is left-handed. Explain how you could determine the likelihood that a person being left-handed and their parent being left-handed are independent events.
Sample answer: In order for the events to be independent, two things must be true: 1) the chance that a person is left-handed is the same as the chance that a person is left-handed given that the person's parent is left-handed, and 2) the chance that a person's parent is left-handed is the same as the chance that a person's parent is left-handed given that the person is left-handed.

28. CREATE Describe a pair of independent events and a pair of dependent events. Explain your reasoning.
Sample answer: Flipping a coin two times represents a pair of independent events. Regardless of the outcome of the first flip, the probability of getting heads and tails on the second flip does not change. Drawing two colored marbles out of a bag without replacing the first marble represents a pair of dependent events. Based on the color of the first marble, the probability that the second marble will be a specific color will change.

29. PERSEVERE If $P(A \mid B)$ is the same as $P(A)$, and $P(B \mid A)$ is the same as $P(B)$, what can be said about the relationship between events A and B? A and B are independent events.

Answers

21.

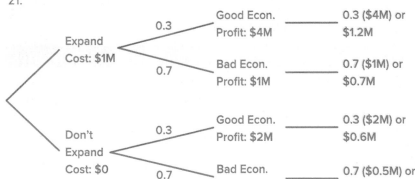

Expand Cost: $1M
0.3 — Good Econ. Profit: $4M — 0.3 ($4M) or $1.2M
0.7 — Bad Econ. Profit: $1M — 0.7 ($1M) or $0.7M

Don't Expand Cost: $0
0.3 — Good Econ. Profit: $2M — 0.3 ($2M) or $0.6M
0.7 — Bad Econ. Profit: $0.5M — 0.7 ($0.5M) or $0.35M

22. $\frac{3}{32}$; Sample answer: Events are independent so $P(\text{orange and green}) = P(\text{orange}) \cdot P(\text{green}) = \frac{2}{8} \cdot \frac{3}{8} = \frac{6}{64} = \frac{3}{32}$. Because events are independent, $P(\text{green} \mid \text{orange}) = P(\text{green})$ and $P(\text{orange} \mid \text{green}) = P(\text{orange})$ so $P(\text{orange}) \cdot P(\text{green} \mid \text{orange}) = P(\text{orange}) \cdot P(\text{green}) = P(\text{orange} \mid \text{green}) \cdot P(\text{green})$. This means that the probability of landing on green and orange does not depend on which color is landed on first.

25a. The first branch of the tree should be the first serve, while the second set of branches should be the second serve. The second serve only occurs when the first serve is a fault.

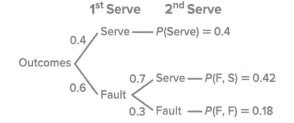

1st Serve   2nd Serve
Outcomes
0.4 — Serve — $P(\text{Serve}) = 0.4$
0.6 — Fault
  0.7 — Serve — $P(F, S) = 0.42$
  0.3 — Fault — $P(F, F) = 0.18$

Probability and the Addition Rule

LESSON GOAL

Students solve problems involving events that are and are not mutually exclusive using the Addition Rule.

1 LAUNCH

 Launch the lesson with a **Warm Up** and an introduction.

2 EXPLORE AND DEVELOP

 Explore: Mutually Exclusive Events

 Develop:

Probability of Mutually Exclusive Events
- Identify Mutually Exclusive Events
- Probability of Mutually Exclusive Events

Probability of Events that Are Not Mutually Exclusive
- Events That Are Not Mutually Exclusive

 You may want your students to complete the **Checks** online.

3 REFLECT AND PRACTICE

 Exit Ticket

 Practice

 Formative Assessment Math Probe

DIFFERENTIATE

View reports of student progress on the **Checks** after each example.

Resources	AL	OL	BL	ELL
Remediation: Compare Probabilities of Simple Events	●	●		●
Extension: Demographics		●	●	●

Language Development Handbook

Assign page 88 of the *Language Development Handbook* to help your students build mathematical language related to solving problems involving events that are and are not mutually exclusive using the Addition Rule.

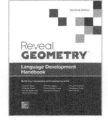

ELL You can use the tips and suggestions on page T88 of the handbook to support students who are building English proficiency.

Suggested Pacing

| 90 min | 1 day |
| 45 min | 2 days |

Focus

Domain: Statistics & Probability

Standards for Mathematical Content:

S.CP.7 Apply the Addition Rule, $P(A \text{ or } B) = P(A) + P(B) - P(A \text{ and } B)$, and interpret the answer in terms of the model.

Standards for Mathematical Practice:

3 Construct viable arguments and critique the reasoning of others.

4 Model with mathematics.

Coherence

Vertical Alignment

Previous
Students solved probability problems using the Multiplication Rule.
S.CP.2, S.CP.8

Now
Students solve problems using the Addition Rule.
S.CP.7

Next
Students will solve probability problems involving conditional probability.
S.CP.3, S.CP.5

Rigor

The Three Pillars of Rigor

1 CONCEPTUAL UNDERSTANDING	2 FLUENCY	3 APPLICATION

Conceptual Bridge In this lesson, students develop understanding of mutually exclusive events and build fluency by using the Addition Rule to find probabilities of mutually exclusive events and of events that are not mutually exclusive. They apply their understanding by solving real-world problems related to mutually exclusive events and of events that are not mutually exclusive.

Mathematical Background

Mutually exclusive events, A and B, cannot occur at the same time. The probability that A or B occurs is the sum of the probabilities of each individual event, $P(A \text{ or } B) = P(A) + P(B)$. If A and B are not mutually exclusive then their probability is the sum of the individual probabilities minus the probability that both A and B occur, $P(A \text{ or } B) = P(A) + P(B) - P(A \text{ and } B)$.

Interactive Presentation

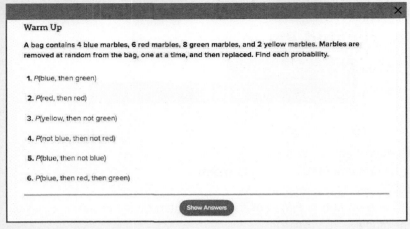

Warm Up

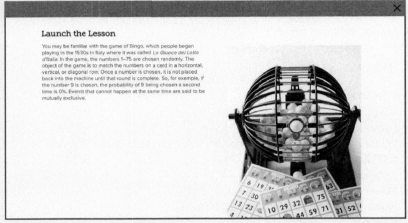

Launch the Lesson

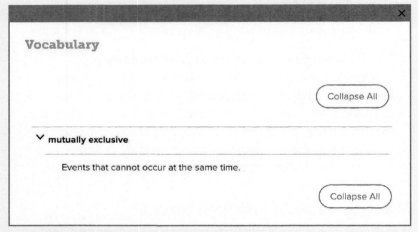

Today's Vocabulary

Warm Up

Prerequisite Skills

The Warm Up exercises address the following prerequisite skill for this lesson:

- finding experimental probabilities

Answers:

1. $\frac{2}{25}$ 2. $\frac{9}{100}$

3. $\frac{3}{50}$ 4. $\frac{14}{25}$

5. $\frac{4}{25}$ 6. $\frac{3}{125}$

Launch the Lesson

MP **Teaching the Mathematical Practices**

4 Apply Mathematics In this Launch the Lesson, students can see a real-world application of probability of mutually exclusive events.

Go Online to find additional teaching notes and questions to promote classroom discourse.

Today's Standards

Tell students that they will be addressing these content and practice standards in this lesson. You may wish to have a student volunteer read aloud *How can I meet this standard?* and *How can I use these practices?* and connect these to the standards.

See the Interactive Presentation for I Can statements that align with the standards covered in this lesson.

Today's Vocabulary

Tell students that they will be using this vocabulary term in this lesson. You can expand the row if you wish to share the definition. Then, discuss the question below with the class.

Explore Mutually Exclusive Events

Objective
Students find the probabilities of and distinguish between events that are mutually exclusive and events that are not mutually exclusive.

Ideas for Use
Recommended Use Present the Inquiry Question, or have a student volunteer read it aloud. Have students work in pairs to complete the Explore activity on their devices. Pairs should discuss each of the questions. Monitor student progress during the activity. Upon completion of the Explore activity, have student volunteers share their responses to the Inquiry Question.

What if my students don't have devices? You may choose to project the activity on a whiteboard. A printable worksheet for each Explore is available online. You may choose to print the worksheet so that individuals or pairs of students can use it to record their observations.

Summary of the Activity
Students will complete guiding exercises throughout the Explore activity. They will work through a series of questions and problems related to distinguishing events that are mutually exclusive to each other. Then, students will answer the Inquiry Question.

Go Online to find additional teaching notes and sample answers for the guiding exercises.

(continued on the next page)

Interactive Presentation

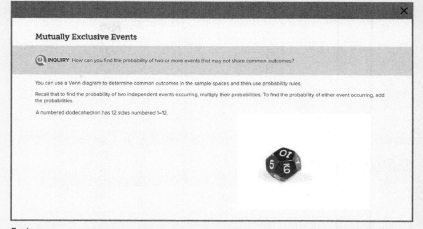

Explore

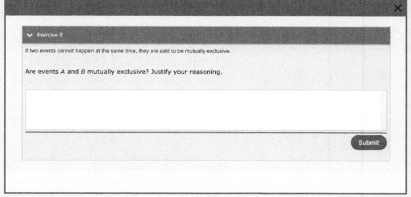

Explore

TAP

Students tap to move through the exercises.

DRAG & DROP

Students drag possible outcomes to complete the Venn diagrams.

Interactive Presentation

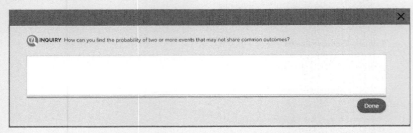

Explore

TYPE	
	Students will respond to the Inquiry Question and can view a sample answer.

Explore Mutually Exclusive Events (*continued*)

MP Teaching the Mathematical Practices

7 Look for a Pattern Help students to see the pattern in this Explore.

Questions

Have students complete the Explore activity.

Ask:

- Why does it help to know if events are mutually exclusive? Sample answer: It helps to know that events are mutually exclusive so that when you find the probability, you are not counting something twice.

- Are the events of rolling an even number or a 12 mutually exclusive? No, 12 is an even number so the events are not mutually exclusive.

Inquiry

How can you find the probability of two or more events that may not share common outcomes? Sample answer: If there are no common outcomes, add their probabilities. If there are common outcomes, add their probabilities and subtract the probability that both or all events occur.

Go Online to find additional teaching notes and sample answers for the guiding exercises.

1 CONCEPTUAL UNDERSTANDING　　2 FLUENCY　|　3 APPLICATION

Learn Probability of Mutually Exclusive Events

Objective
Students apply the addition rule to situations involving mutually exclusive events.

Teaching the Mathematical Practices
2 Attend to Quantities Point out that it is important to note the meaning of the quantities used in this Learn.

What Students Are Learning
Remind students about complement sample spaces A and A', and what they discovered about the probability relationship of these complements. Point out to students that complements are mutually exclusive, such that $P(A \text{ or } A') = 1$. Encourage the students to consider how the probability of mutually exclusive events relates to the probability of complement sets.

Essential Question Follow-Up
Students have explored probability of independent and dependent events.

Ask:

How can the probabilities of independent and dependent events be used to make predictions? Sample answer: Identifying events as dependent or independent can help you calculate the probability of an event's success or failure.

DIFFERENTIATE

Enrichment Activity BL
The game show *Let's Make a Deal* has created controversy in the study of probability with the question: Switch or stay? Contestants on the show were asked to choose one door out of three. They were then shown one of the remaining doors that did not contain the one grand prize. The question was then asked, "Do you want to stay with your original choice, or switch to the remaining door?" Students can create a simulation or use an online applet to explore this question. Students should be able to explain why repeating an experiment many times forces the experimental and theoretical probabilities closer together.

Go Online
- Find additional teaching notes.
- View performance reports of the Checks.
- Assign or present an Extra Example.

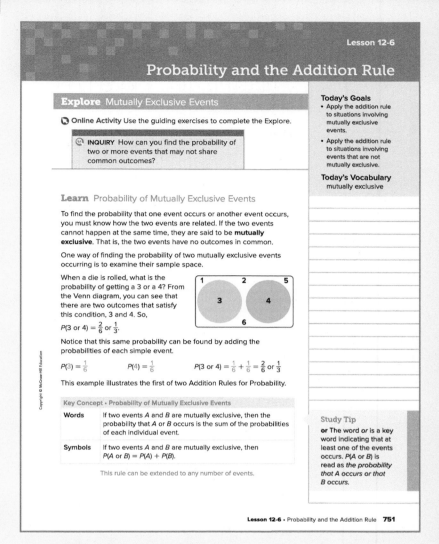

Lesson 12-6

Probability and the Addition Rule

Explore Mutually Exclusive Events

Online Activity Use the guiding exercises to complete the Explore.

INQUIRY How can you find the probability of two or more events that may not share common outcomes?

Today's Goals
- Apply the addition rule to situations involving mutually exclusive events.
- Apply the addition rule to situations involving events that are not mutually exclusive.

Today's Vocabulary
mutually exclusive

Learn Probability of Mutually Exclusive Events

To find the probability that one event occurs or another event occurs, you must know how the two events are related. If the two events cannot happen at the same time, they are said to be **mutually exclusive**. That is, the two events have no outcomes in common.

One way of finding the probability of two mutually exclusive events occurring is to examine their sample space.

When a die is rolled, what is the probability of getting a 3 or a 4? From the Venn diagram, you can see that there are two outcomes that satisfy this condition, 3 and 4. So,
$P(3 \text{ or } 4) = \frac{2}{6} \text{ or } \frac{1}{3}$.

Notice that this same probability can be found by adding the probabilities of each simple event.

$P(3) = \frac{1}{6}$　　　$P(4) = \frac{1}{6}$　　　$P(3 \text{ or } 4) = \frac{1}{6} + \frac{1}{6} = \frac{2}{6} \text{ or } \frac{1}{3}$

This example illustrates the first of two Addition Rules for Probability.

Key Concept • Probability of Mutually Exclusive Events

Words	If two events A and B are mutually exclusive, then the probability that A or B occurs is the sum of the probabilities of each individual event.
Symbols	If two events A and B are mutually exclusive, then $P(A \text{ or } B) = P(A) + P(B)$.

This rule can be extended to any number of events.

Study Tip
or The word *or* is a key word indicating that at least one of the events occurs. $P(A \text{ or } B)$ is read as *the probability that A occurs or that B occurs.*

Lesson 12-6 • Probability and the Addition Rule　**751**

Interactive Presentation

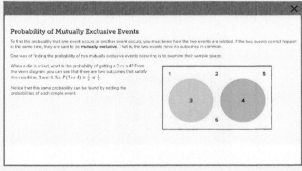

Probability of Mutually Exclusive Events

Learn

TAP

Students tap to see a study tip.

1 CONCEPTUAL UNDERSTANDING | **2 FLUENCY** | **3 APPLICATION**

Your Notes

Example 1 Identify Mutually Exclusive Events

A card is drawn from a standard deck of 52 cards. Determine whether the events are *mutually exclusive* or *not mutually exclusive*. Explain your reasoning.

a. drawing a 3 or a 2

There are no common outcomes — a card cannot be both a 2 and a 3. These events __are__ mutually exclusive.

b. drawing a 7 or a red card

The 7 of diamonds is an outcome that both events have in common. These events __are not__ mutually exclusive.

c. drawing a queen or a spade

Because the queen of spades represents both events, they __are not__ mutually exclusive.

 Talk About It!
Describe a pair of events that are mutually exclusive.

Sample answer: I can eat my lunch in the cafeteria or I can eat my lunch on the picnic benches.

Example 2 Probability of Mutually Exclusive Events

SOCIAL MEDIA **Daniel organizes all of his social media contacts into three groups. If the program sends Daniel an update from a randomly chosen contact, what is the probability that the contact is either a close friend or acquaintance?**

These are mutually exclusive events, because the contacts selected cannot be a close friend and an acquaintance.

Let event F represent selecting a close friend. Let event A represent selecting an acquaintance. There are a total of $10 + 68 + 24$ or 102 contacts.

Because the events are mutually exclusive, you know that

$$P(F \text{ or } A) = \underline{P(F)} + \underline{P(A)}.$$

$$P(F \text{ or } A) = P(F) + P(A) \qquad \text{Probability of mutually exclusive events}$$

$$= \frac{68}{102} + \frac{24}{102} \qquad P(F) = \frac{68}{102} \text{ and } P(A) = \frac{24}{102}$$

$$= \frac{92}{102} \text{ or } \frac{46}{51} \qquad \text{Add.}$$

So the probability that the update is from a close friend or acquaintance is $\frac{46}{51}$ or about __90__ %.

 Go Online You can complete an Extra Example online.

 Think About It!
What assumption did you make in order to solve this problem?

Sample answer: I assumed that Daniel doesn't add or remove any contacts. Any change to the sample space would affect the probability.

752 **Module 12** • Probability

Example 1 Identify Mutually Exclusive Events

Teaching the Mathematical Practices

> **6 Communicate Precisely** Encourage students to routinely write or explain their solution methods. Point out that they should use clear definitions when they discuss their solutions with others.

Questions for Mathematical Discourse

AL Is drawing a red card or drawing a black card mutually exclusive? yes

OL A theater has seats divided into three sections, Left, Center, and Right. How would you describe the probability of getting a Center Section ticket or a Right Section ticket? mutually exclusive

BL Describe a pair of events that are not mutually exclusive? Sample answer: rolling a fair die and getting a multiple of 3 or an even number

Example 2 Probability of Mutually Exclusive Events

Teaching the Mathematical Practices

> **4 Make Assumptions** In the Think About It, have students point out where an assumption or approximation was made in the solution.

Questions for Mathematical Discourse

AL How many contacts are in Daniel's Close Friends group? 68

OL What is the probability that the update from a randomly chosen contact is from the Acquaintances group? $\frac{24}{102}$ or $\frac{12}{51}$

BL What is the probability that the update is from the Restricted group? Explain. $\frac{5}{51}$; Sample answer: Any outcome other than F or A is going to be the restricted group, R, so R is the complement of F or A. This means that $P(R) = 1 - P(F \text{ or } A) = 1 - \frac{46}{51} = \frac{5}{51}$.

Interactive Presentation

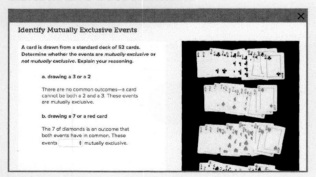

Example 1

TAP

Students select phrases to identify mutually exclusive events.

TYPE

Students answer a question to show they understand mutually exclusive events.

1 CONCEPTUAL UNDERSTANDING | **2 FLUENCY** | **3 APPLICATION**

Learn Probability of Events that Are Not Mutually Exclusive

Objective
Students apply the Addition Rule to situations involving events that are not mutually exclusive.

 Teaching the Mathematical Practices

> **7 Use Structure** Help students to explore the structure of events that are not mutually exclusive in this Learn.

About the Key Concept
Encourage the students to consider a case where A and B are mutually exclusive, and therefore $P(A \text{ and } B) = 0$, to show that the earlier Addition Rule for Probability is a simplified special case of this more general form of the Addition Rule for Probability.

Common Misconception
Emphasize to students the importance of remembering to include the step where they remove the probability $P(A \text{ and } B)$ when calculating the probability of events that are not mutually exclusive.

DIFFERENTIATE

Enrichment Activity BL

Have students write about how understanding and applying the principles of probability might influence their decision making in some situations. Encourage students to use specific and detailed examples of situations that support their thought processes.

Check

BIODIVERSITY Of the more than 79,800 species on a Red List of Threatened Species, seabirds are of particular interest because they are indicators of broader marine health issues. The circle graph shows the proportion of seabird species in each Red List category. What is the probability that a randomly selected species of seabird is on the critically endangered list or the endangered list?

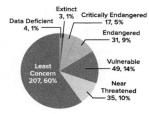

$\frac{14}{100}, \frac{7}{50}$, 14%, or 0.14

Learn Probability of Events that are Not Mutually Exclusive

If two events can happen at the same time, they are not mutually exclusive.

When a die is rolled, what is the probability of getting a number greater than 2 or an even number? From the Venn diagram, you can see that there are 5 numbers on a die that are either greater than 2 or are an even number: 2, 3, 4, 5, and 6. So, $P(\text{greater than 2 or even}) = \frac{5}{6}$.

Because it is possible to roll a number that is greater than 2 and an even number, these events are not mutually exclusive. Consider the probability of each individual event.

$$P(\text{greater than 2}) = \frac{4}{6} \qquad P(\text{even}) = \frac{3}{6}$$

Adding these probabilities results in a number greater than 1 because two of the outcomes, 4 and 6, are in the intersection of the sample spaces—they are both greater than 2 and even. To account for the intersection, subtract the probability of the common outcomes.

$P(\text{greater than 2 or even}) = P(\text{greater than 2}) + P(\text{even}) - P(\text{greater than 2 and even}) \frac{4}{6} + \frac{3}{6} - \frac{2}{6}$ or $\frac{5}{6}$

This leads to the second of the Addition Rules for Probability.

Key Concept • Probability of Events That Are Not Mutually Exclusive	
Words	If two events A and B are not mutually exclusive, then the probability that A or B occurs is the sum of their individual probabilities minus the probability that both A and B occur.
Symbols	If two events A and B are not mutually exclusive, then $P(A \text{ or } B) = P(A) + P(B) - P(A \text{ and } B)$.

This rule can be extended to any number of events.

Go Online You can complete an Extra Example online.

Go Online
You can watch a video to see how to use the Addition Rule to find the probability of two events that are not mutually exclusive.

Interactive Presentation

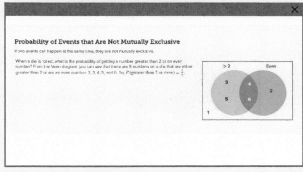

Probability of Events that Are Not Mutually Exclusive

Learn

WATCH
Students watch a video to learn more about events that are not mutually exclusive.

CHECK
Students complete the Check online to determine whether they are ready to move on.

Example 3 Events That Are Not Mutually Exclusive

A game piece is selected at random from the plate at the right. What is the probability that the game piece is round or orange?

Because some of the game pieces are both round and orange, these events are not mutually exclusive. Use the rule for two events that are not mutually exclusive. The total number of game pieces from which to choose is 10.

$P(\text{round or orange}) = P(\text{round}) + P(\text{orange}) - P(\text{round and orange})$

$$= \frac{5}{10} + \frac{4}{10} - \frac{2}{10}$$

$$= \frac{7}{10}$$

The probability that a game piece will be round or orange is $\frac{7}{10}$ or __70__ %.

Check

A polygon is chosen at random. Find the probability of each set of events.

choosing a figure that has more than 4 lines of symmetry or more than 7 sides	↔	75%
choosing a figure that has more than 15 diagonals or a total interior angle measure greater than 900°	↔	37.5%
choosing a figure that has more than 2 pairs of parallel sides or at least 1 diagonal	↔	87.5%

Pause and Reflect

Did you struggle with anything in this lesson? If so, how did you deal with it?

See students' observations.

Record your observations here.

Go Online You can complete an Extra Example online.

Think About It!

Why is $\frac{2}{10}$ subtracted from the sum of the probabilities $P(\text{round})$ and $P(\text{orange})$?

Sample answer: If we don't account for when both of the events occur, such as a game piece that is both round and orange in this example, we double count them and the probability is higher than it should be.

Copyright © McGraw-Hill Education

Interactive Presentation

Events That Are Not Mutually Exclusive

A game piece is selected at random from the plate at the right. What is the probability that the game piece is round and orange?

Because some of the game pieces are both round and orange, these events are not mutually exclusive. Use the rule for two events that are not mutually exclusive. The total number of game pieces from which to choose is 10.

Example 3

TYPE

Students answer a question to show they understand events that are not mutually exclusive.

CHECK

Students complete the Check online to determine whether they are ready to move on.

Example 3 Events That Are Not Mutually Exclusive

 Teaching the Mathematical Practices

6 Communicate Precisely Encourage students to routinely write and explain their solution methods. Point out that they should use clear definitions when they discuss their solutions with others.

Questions for Mathematical Discourse

AL How many game pieces are on the plate? 10

OL How many game pieces on the plate are neither round nor orange? 3

BL What is the probability that the game piece is an orange pentagon? 0

Exit Ticket

Recommended Use

At the end of class, go online to display the Exit Ticket prompt and ask students to respond using a separate piece of paper. Have students hand you their responses as they leave the room.

Alternate Use

At the end of class, go online to display the Exit Ticket prompt and ask students to respond verbally or by using a mini-whiteboard. Have students hold up their whiteboards so that you can see all student responses. Tap to reveal the answer when most or all students have completed the Exit Ticket.

Practice and Homework

Suggested Assignments

Use the table below to select appropriate exercises.

DOK	Topic	Exercises
1, 2	exercises that mirror the examples	1–6
2	exercises that use a variety of skills from this lesson	7–24
3	exercises that emphasize higher-order and critical-thinking skills	25–30

ASSESS AND DIFFERENTIATE

📊 Use the data from the **Checks** to determine whether to provide resources for extension, remediation, or intervention.

IF students score 90% or more on the Checks,   `BL`
THEN assign:

- Practice, Exercises 1–23 odd, 25–30
- Extension: Demographics
- Ⓐ **ALEKS** Probability of Independent and Dependent Events, Probabilities of the Union of Two Events

---

IF students score 66%–89% on the Checks,   `OL`
THEN assign:

- Practice, Exercises 1–29 odd
- Remediation, Review Resources: Probability and the Addition Rule
- Personal Tutors
- Extra Examples 1–3
- Ⓐ **ALEKS** Experimental Probabilities

IF students score 65% or less on the Checks,   `AL`
THEN assign:

- Practice, Exercises 1–5 odd
- Remediation, Review Resources: Probability and the Addition Rule
- *Quick Review Math Handbook*: Probabilities of Mutually Exclusive Events
- Ⓐ **ALEKS** Experimental Probabilities

Name _____ Period _____ Date _____

Practice

🖥 **Go Online** You can complete your homework online.

Example 1

Determine whether the events are *mutually exclusive* or *not mutually exclusive*. Explain your reasoning.

1. A die is rolled while a game is being played. The result of the next roll is a 6 or an even number.

Not mutually exclusive; sample answer: These are not mutually exclusive events because a 6 is also an even number.

2. SALES A street vendor is selling T-shirts outside of a concert arena. The colors and sizes of the available T-shirts are shown in the table. The vendor selects a T-shirt that is blue or large.

	Red	Blue	White
Small	1	2	2
Medium	3	2	4
Large	4	5	6
Extra Large	7	6	3

Not mutually exclusive; sample answer: These are not mutually exclusive events because there are T-shirts that are both blue and large.

Examples 2 and 3

3. AWARDS The student of the month gets to choose one award from 9 gift certificates to area restaurants, 8 T-shirts, 6 water bottles, or 5 gift cards to the mall. What is the probability that the student of the month chooses a T-shirt or a water bottle?

$\frac{1}{2}$ or 0.50

4. SALES PROMOTIONS At a grand opening event, a store allows customers to choose an envelope from a bag. Ten of the envelopes contain store coupons, 8 envelopes contain gift cards, and 2 envelopes contain $100. What is the probability that a customer selects an envelope with a gift card or an envelope with $100?

$\frac{1}{2}$ or 0.5

5. TRAFFIC If the chance of making a green light at a certain intersection is 35%, what is the probability of arriving when the light is yellow or red?

0.65

6. STUDENTS In a group of graduate students, 4 out of the 5 females are international students, and 2 out of the 3 men are international students. What is the probability of selecting a graduate student from this group that is a male or an international student?

0.88

Lesson 12-6 • Probability and the Addition Rule   **755**

Mixed Exercises

CARDS **Suppose you pull a card from a standard 52-card deck. Find the probability of each event.**

7. The card is a 4.
$\frac{1}{13}$ or 7.7%

8. The card is red.
$\frac{1}{2}$ or 50%

9. The card is a face card.
$\frac{3}{13}$ or 23.1%

10. The card is not a face card.
$\frac{10}{13}$ or 76.9%

11. P(queen or heart)
$\frac{4}{13}$ or about 31%

12. P(jack or spade)
$\frac{4}{13}$ or about 31%

13. P(five or prime number)
$\frac{4}{13}$ or about 31%

14. P(ace or black)
$\frac{7}{13}$ or about 54%

15. A drawing will take place where one ticket is to be drawn from a set of 80 tickets numbered 1 to 80. If a ticket is drawn at random, what is the probability that the number drawn is a multiple of 4 or a factor of 12?

0.30

16. SCHOOL The Venn diagram shows the extracurricular activities enjoyed by the senior class at Valley View High School.

a. How many students are in the senior class? 345

b. How many students participate in athletics? 159

c. If a student is randomly chosen, what is the probability that the student participates in athletics or drama? $\frac{227}{345}$ or about 66%

d. If a student is randomly chosen, what is the probability that the student participates in only drama and band? $\frac{2}{23}$ or about 9%

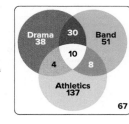

17. BOWLING Cindy's bowling records indicate that for any frame, the probability that she will bowl a strike is 30%, a spare 45%, and neither 25%. What is the probability that she will bowl either a spare or a strike for any given frame?

$\frac{3}{4}$ or 75%

18. SPORTS CARDS Dario owns 145 baseball cards, 102 football cards, and 48 basketball cards. What is the probability that he randomly selects a baseball or a football card?

$\frac{247}{295}$ or about 84%

756 Module 12 • Probability

Name _____ Period _____ Date _____

19. SCHOLARSHIPS A review committee read 3000 application essays for one $5000 college scholarship. Of the applications reviewed, 2865 essays were the required length, 2577 of the applicants had the minimum required grade-point average, and 2486 had the required length and minimum grade-point average. What is the probability that an application essay selected at random will have the required length or the required gradepoint average? $\frac{739}{750}$ or about 98.5%

20. PETS Ruby's cat had 8 kittens. The litter included 2 orange females, 3 mixed-color females, 1 orange male, and 2 mixed-color males. Ruby wants to keep one kitten. What is the probability that she randomly chooses a kitten that is female or orange? $\frac{3}{4}$ or 75%

21. SPORTS The table shows the age and number of participants in each sport at a sporting complex. What is the probability that a player is 14 or plays basketball? 56%

Mason Sports Complex			
Age	Soccer	Volleyball	Basketball
14	28	36	42
15	30	26	33
16	35	41	29

22. USE A MODEL Vicente and Kelly are designing a board game. They decide that the game will use a pair of dice and the players will have to find the sum of the numbers rolled. Vicente and Kelly created the table shown to help determine probabilities. Each player will roll the pair of dice twice during that player's turn.

1,1	1,2	1,3	1,4	1,5	1,6
2,1	2,2	2,3	2,4	2,5	2,6
3,1	3,2	3,3	3,4	3,5	3,6
4,1	4,2	4,3	4,4	4,5	4,6
5,1	5,2	5,3	5,4	5,5	5,6
6,1	6,2	6,3	6,4	6,5	6,6

  a. What is the probability of rolling a pair or two numbers that have a sum of seven? 0.333

  b. What is the probability of rolling two numbers whose sum is an even number or not rolling a 2? Round to the nearest thousandth. 0.833

23. PARKS The table shows Parks and Recreation Department classes and the number of participants ages 7–9. What is the probability that a participant chosen at random is in drama or is an 8-year-old? 0.6

Age	Swimming	Drama	Art
7	40	35	25
8	30	21	14
9	20	44	11

24. FLOWER GARDEN Erin is planning her summer garden. The table shows the number of bulbs she has according to type and color of flower. If Erin randomly selects one of the bulbs, what is the probability that she selects a bulb for a yellow flower or a dahlia? about 52.8%

Flower	Orange	Yellow	White
Dahlia	5	4	3
Lily	3	1	2
Gladiolus	2	5	6
Iris	0	1	4

Lesson 12-6 • Probability and the Addition Rule **757**

Higher-Order Thinking Skills

25. PERSEVERE You roll 3 dice. What is the probability that the outcome of at least two of the dice will be less than or equal to 4? Explain your reasoning.

0.74; Sample answer: There are three outcomes in which the values of two or more of the dice are less than or equal to 4 and one outcome where the values of all three of the dice are less than or equal to 4. You have to find the probability of each of the four scenarios and add them together.

26. FIND THE ERROR Teo and Mason want to determine the probability that a red marble will be chosen out of a bag of 4 red, 7 blue, 5 green, and 2 purple marbles. Is either of them correct? Explain your reasoning.

Teo	Mason
$P(R) = \frac{4}{17}$	$P(R) = 1 - \frac{4}{18}$

Neither; sample answer: The probability that a red marble will be chosen is $\frac{4}{18}$ or $1 - \frac{14}{18}$.

ANALYZE Determine whether the following are mutually exclusive. Explain.

27. choosing a quadrilateral that is a square and a quadrilateral that is a rectangle

Not mutually exclusive; sample answer: Because squares are rectangles, but rectangles are not necessarily squares, a quadrilateral can be both a square and a rectangle, and a quadrilateral can be a rectangle but not a square.

28. choosing a triangle that is equilateral and a triangle that is equiangular

Not mutually exclusive; sample answer: If a triangle is equilateral, it is also equiangular. The two can never be mutually exclusive.

29. choosing a complex number and choosing a natural number

Not mutually exclusive; sample answer: A natural number is also a complex number.

30. WRITE Explain why the sum of the probabilities of two mutually exclusive events is not always 1.

Sample answer: When two events are mutually exclusive, it means that they can't both happen, but it does not mean that one or the other of the events must happen. The sum of all possible outcomes in a sample space must be 1. For example, if Event A and Event B are mutually exclusive, the sample space includes the probability of Event A, the probability of Event B, and the probability of neither Event A nor Event B, which must all sum to 1. The sum of the probabilities of Event A and Event B may be 1, but not necessarily.

758 Module 12 • Probability

Lesson 12-7
Conditional Probability

S.CP.3, S.CP.5

LESSON GOAL

Students solve problems involving conditional probability using the Multiplication Rule.

1 LAUNCH

Launch the lesson with a **Warm Up** and an introduction.

2 EXPLORE AND DEVELOP

Explore: Conditional Probability

Develop:

Conditional Probabilities
• Conditional Probability

You may want your students to complete the **Checks** online.

3 REFLECT AND PRACTICE

Exit Ticket

Practice

DIFFERENTIATE

View reports of student progress on the **Checks** after each example.

Resources	AL	OL	BL	ELL
Remediation: Probability of Compound Events	●	●		●
Extension: Probability and Tic-Tac-Toe		●	●	●

Language Development Handbook

Assign page 89 of the *Language Development Handbook* to help your students build mathematical language related to solving problems involving conditional probability using the Multiplication Rule.

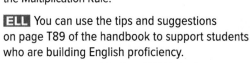

ELL You can use the tips and suggestions on page T89 of the handbook to support students who are building English proficiency.

Suggested Pacing

90 min	0.5 day
45 min	1 day

Focus

Domain: Statistics & Probability
Standards for Mathematical Content:
S.CP.3 Understand the conditional probability of A given B as $P(A \text{ and } B)/P(B)$, and interpret independence of A and B as saying that the conditional probability of A given B is the same as the probability of A, and the conditional probability of B given A is the same as the probability of B.
S.CP.5 Recognize and explain the concepts of conditional probability and independence in everyday language and everyday situations.
Standards for Mathematical Practice:
1 Make sense of problems and persevere in solving them.
4 Model with mathematics.

Coherence

Vertical Alignment

Previous
Students solved problems using the Addition Rule.
S.CP.7

Now
Students solve problems involving conditional probability.
S.CP.3, S.CP.5

Next
Students will use two-way frequency tables in probability situations.
S.CP.4, S.CP.6

Rigor

The Three Pillars of Rigor

1 CONCEPTUAL UNDERSTANDING	2 FLUENCY	3 APPLICATION

Conceptual Bridge In this lesson, students extend their understanding of the probability of independent and dependent events to conditional probability. They apply their understanding by solving real-world problems related to conditional probability.

Mathematical Background

The conditional probability of event B given event A, $P(B|A)$, can be used when additional information is known about two events. If the probability of event A and of both events A and B are known, the conditional probability can be calculated from $P(B|A) = \frac{P(A \text{ and } B)}{P(A)}$, where $P(A) \neq 0$.

Lesson 12-7 • Conditional Probability 759a

Interactive Presentation

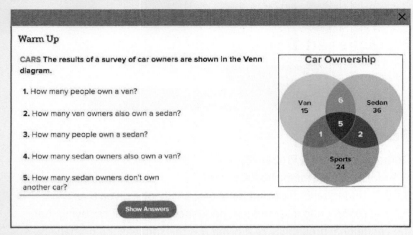

Warm Up

CARS The results of a survey of car owners are shown in the Venn diagram.

1. How many people own a van?

2. How many van owners also own a sedan?

3. How many people own a sedan?

4. How many sedan owners also own a van?

5. How many sedan owners don't own another car?

Show Answers

Warm Up

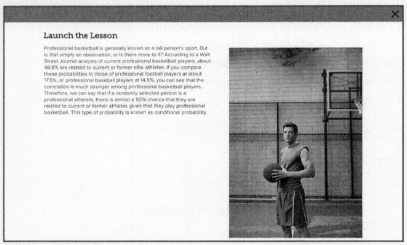

Launch the Lesson

Professional basketball is generally known as a tall person's sport. But is that simply an observation, or is there more to it? According to a Wall Street Journal analysis of current professional basketball players, about 48.8% are related to current or former elite athletes. If you compare these probabilities to those of professional football players at about 17.5%, or professional baseball players at 14.5%, you can see that the correlation is much stronger among professional basketball players. Therefore, we can say that if a randomly selected person is a professional athlete, there is almost a 50% chance that they are related to current or former athletes given that they play professional basketball. This type of probability is known as conditional probability.

Launch the Lesson

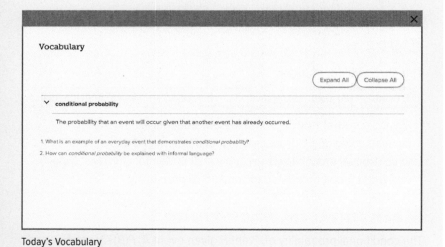

Vocabulary

Expand All   Collapse All

⌄ **conditional probability**

The probability that an event will occur given that another event has already occurred.

1. What is an example of an everyday event that demonstrates *conditional probability*?

2. How can *conditional probability* be explained with informal language?

Today's Vocabulary

Warm Up

Prerequisite Skills

The Warm Up exercises address the following prerequisite skill for this lesson:

- finding probabilities of independent and dependent events

Answers:

1. 27
2. 11
3. 49
4. 11
5. 36

Launch the Lesson

 Teaching the Mathematical Practices

> **4 Apply Mathematics** In this Launch the Lesson, students can see a real-world application of conditional probability.

🔎 **Go Online** to find additional teaching notes and questions to promote classroom discourse.

Today's Standards

Tell students that they will be addressing these content and practice standards in this lesson. You may wish to have a student volunteer read aloud *How can I meet these standards?* and *How can I use these practices?* and connect these to the standards.

See the Interactive Presentation for I Can statements that align with the standards covered in this lesson.

Today's Vocabulary

Tell students that they will be using this vocabulary term in this lesson. You can expand the row if you wish to share the defintion. Then, discuss the questions below with the class.

Explore Conditional Probability

Objective
Students use probability trees to determine conditional probability.

Ideas for Use
Recommended Use Present the Inquiry Question, or have a student volunteer read it aloud. Have students work in pairs to complete the Explore activity on their devices. Pairs should discuss each of the questions. Monitor student progress during the activity. Upon completion of the Explore activity, have student volunteers share their responses to the Inquiry Question.

What if my students don't have devices? You may choose to project the activity on a whiteboard. A printable worksheet for each Explore is available online. You may choose to print the worksheet so that individuals or pairs of students can use it to record their observations.

Summary of the Activity
Students will complete guiding exercises throughout the Explore activity. They will investigate a series of experimental outcomes to investigate conditional probability relationships. Then, students will answer the Inquiry Question.

Go Online to find additional teaching notes and sample answers for the guiding exercises.

(continued on the next page)

Interactive Presentation

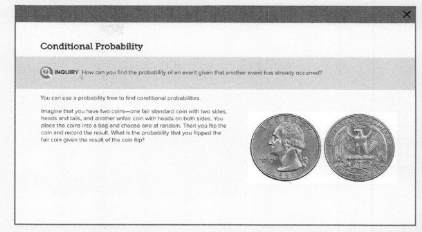

Conditional Probability

INQUIRY How can you find the probability of an event given that another event has already occurred?

You can use a probability tree to find conditional probabilities.

Imagine that you have two coins—one fair standard coin with two sides, heads and tails, and another unfair coin with heads on both sides. You place the coins into a bag and choose one at random. Then you flip the coin and record the result. What is the probability that you flipped the fair coin given the result of the coin flip?

Explore

DRAG & DROP

Students complete the probability tree for flipping a coin.

Interactive Presentation

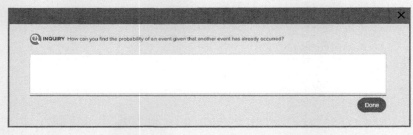

INQUIRY How can you find the probability of an event given that another event has already occurred?

Done

Explore

TYPE

a|

Students will respond to the Inquiry Question and can view a sample answer.

Explore Conditional Probability (*continued*)

Teaching the Mathematical Practices

6 Communicate Precisely Encourage students to routinely write or explain their solution methods. Point out that they should use clear definitions when they discuss their solutions with others.

Questions

Have students complete the Explore activity.

Ask:

- Why does flipping tails tell you more than flipping heads? Sample answer: Because only one coin has tails on it, so you can rule out the unfair coin, whereas flipping heads could be on either coin.

- Would it be possible to find the conditional probability if both coins were fair? Sample answer: It would be possible, but more difficult if both coins were fair. When one coin was unfair, it was easier to tell that it had not been chosen.

Inquiry

How can you find the probability of an event given that another event has already occurred? Sample answer: I can determine if knowing the outcome of an event affects the probability of the preceding event and determine the number of total outcomes and favorable outcomes.

Go Online to find additional teaching notes and sample answers for the guiding exercises.

---

1 CONCEPTUAL UNDERSTANDING | 2 FLUENCY | 3 APPLICATION

Learn Conditional Probabilities

Objective
Students recognize and explain the concepts of conditional probability and independence in everyday situations.

Teaching the Mathematical Practices

7 Use Structure Help students to explore the structure of conditional probabilities in this Learn.

What Students Are Learning
Encourage the students to discuss how conditional probability relates to the idea of mutually exclusive events. Have them investigate the outcome of calculating a conditional probability $P(B|A)$ when $P(A \text{ and } B) = 0$.

About the Key Concept
Have the students consider the meaning, in terms of probability, of the restriction $P(A) \neq 0$ on the Conditional Probability equation. Try to get them to articulate that if this constraint were false, it would mean that A could not possibly happen, so the $P(B|A)$ is impossible to determine, because A itself is impossible.

Common Misconception
Review the Study Tip with the students, to be sure that they know how to read the conditional probability notation.

DIFFERENTIATE

Language Development Activity AL ELL

Have students discuss the differences between finding probabilities for independent and dependent events and for conditional probabilities. This should include that the formulas for independent and dependent events calculate the probability of two or more events occurring, whereas conditional probability calculates the probability of one event given that another has occurred.

Go Online

- Find additional teaching notes.
- View performance reports of the Checks.
- Assign or present an Extra Example.

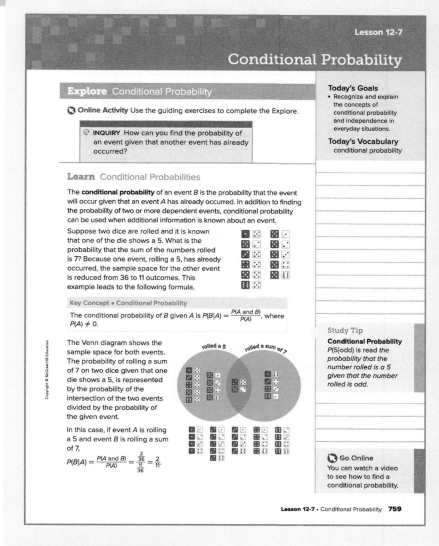

Lesson 12-7

Conditional Probability

Explore Conditional Probability

Online Activity Use the guiding exercises to complete the Explore.

INQUIRY How can you find the probability of an event given that another event has already occurred?

Learn Conditional Probabilities

The **conditional probability** of an event B is the probability that the event will occur given that an event A has already occurred. In addition to finding the probability of two or more dependent events, conditional probability can be used when additional information is known about an event.

Suppose two dice are rolled and it is known that one of the die shows a 5. What is the probability that the sum of the numbers rolled is 7? Because one event, rolling a 5, has already occurred, the sample space for the other event is reduced from 36 to 11 outcomes. This example leads to the following formula.

Key Concept • Conditional Probability

The conditional probability of B given A is $P(B|A) = \dfrac{P(A \text{ and } B)}{P(A)}$, where $P(A) \neq 0$.

The Venn diagram shows the sample space for both events. The probability of rolling a sum of 7 on two dice given that one die shows a 5, is represented by the probability of the intersection of the two events divided by the probability of the given event.

In this case, if event A is rolling a 5 and event B is rolling a sum of 7,

$$P(B|A) = \frac{P(A \text{ and } B)}{P(A)} = \frac{\frac{2}{36}}{\frac{11}{36}} = \frac{2}{11}.$$

Today's Goals
- Recognize and explain the concepts of conditional probability and independence in everyday situations.

Today's Vocabulary
conditional probability

Study Tip

Conditional Probability $P(5|\text{odd})$ is read *the probability that the number rolled is a 5 given that the number rolled is odd.*

Go Online
You can watch a video to see how to find a conditional probability.

Lesson 12-7 • Conditional Probability **759**

Interactive Presentation

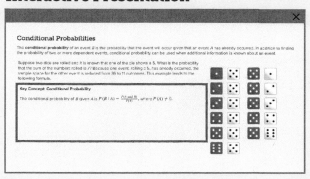

Learn

WATCH

Students can watch a video to learn more about conditional probability.

1 CONCEPTUAL UNDERSTANDING | **2 FLUENCY** | **3 APPLICATION**

🌐 **Example 1** Conditional Probability

GROCERY SHOPPING There are currently 16 customers in line at the deli counter, each holding a numbered ticket from 179 to 194. Naveen will help customers holding tickets with even numbers, and Ellie will help customers holding tickets with odd numbers. If a customer is helped by Naveen, what is the probability that the customer is holding ticket 190?

1 What is the task?
Describe the task in your own words. Then list any questions that you may have. How can you find answers to your questions?
Sample answer: I need to determine the probability of a customer holding ticket 190 given that the customer is helped by Naveen. What two events are occurring and how do they relate to the formula for conditional probability? I can read through the problem again to identify what event B will occur given that event A has already occurred.

2 How will you approach the task? What have you learned that you can use to help you complete the task?
Sample answer: I will find P(A), the probability that the number on the ticket is even, then I will find P(A and B), the probability that the ticket is both 190 and even. I will use the formula for conditional probability to find the solution.

3 What is your solution?
There are _16_ available tickets.
The sample space from event A contains 8 outcomes. From least to greatest, these outcomes are: (_180_, _182_, _184_, _186_, _188_, _190_, _192_, _194_).
So, $P(A) = \frac{8}{16}$ or $\frac{1}{2}$.
The sample space for P(A and B) contains 1 outcome: (_190_).
So, $P(A \text{ and } B) = \frac{1}{16}$.

$P(B|A) = \frac{P(A \text{ and } B)}{P(A)}$ Formula for conditional probability

$= \frac{1}{8}$ Simplify.

4 How can you know that your solution is reasonable?
✏️ **Write About It!** Write an argument that can be used to defend your solution.
Sample answer: This situation can be represented with a Venn diagram. There are only eight even numbers in the sample space, and only one out of these numbers is 190. Therefore, the $P(B|A) = \frac{1}{8}$.

Check

SCHOOL A high school has a total of 1700 students, with 450 seniors. Of the 1700 students, 1550 are taking a math class, 280 of which are seniors. If a student is chosen at random, what is the probability that he or she is taking a math class, given that the student is a senior? Write your answer as a fraction or as a percent expressed to the nearest tenth.
$\frac{28}{45}$ or 62.2%

Your Notes

🌐 **Go Online**
to practice what you've learned in Lessons 12-2 and 12-5 through 12-7.

🌐 **Go Online**
You can complete an Extra Example online.

Interactive Presentation

Conditional Probability

🌐 GROCERY SHOPPING There are currently 16 customers in line at the deli counter, each holding a numbered ticket from 179 to 194. Naveen will help customers holding tickets with even numbers, and Ellie will help customers holding tickets with odd numbers. If a customer is helped by Naveen, what is the probability that the customer is holding ticket 190?

Apply Example 1

DRAG

Students will drag what they know and what they need to find in order to plan their solution process.

TAP
Students tap to move through the solution process.

CHECK

Students complete the Check online to determine whether they are ready to move on.

🌐 **Apply Example 1** Conditional Probability

📝 Teaching the Mathematical Practices

1 Check Answers Mathematically proficient students continually ask themselves, "Does this make sense?" Point out that in this example, students need to check their answer. Point out that they should ask themselves whether their answer makes sense and whether they have answered the problem question.

Recommended Use
Have students work in pairs or small groups. You may wish to present the task, or have a volunteer read it aloud. Then allow students the time to make sure they understand the task, think of possible strategies, and work to solve the problem.

Encourage Productive Struggle
As students work, monitor their progress. Instead of instructing them on a particular strategy, encourage them to use their own strategies to solve the problem and to evaluate their progress along the way. They may or may not find that they need to change direction or try out several strategies.

Signs of Non-Productive Struggle
If students show signs of non-productive struggle, such as feeling overwhelmed, frustrated, or disengaged, intervene to encourage them to think of alternate approaches to the problem. Some sample questions are shown.

- Define Conditional Probability.
- How many even number tickets are given out?

📝 Write About It!
Have students share their responses with another pair/group of students or the entire class. Have them clearly state or describe the mathematical reasoning they can use to defend their solution.

Common Error
Remind students that the vertical symbol that represents conditional probability is not a division operation symbol.

Exit Ticket

Recommended Use
At the end of class, go online to display the Exit Ticket prompt and ask students to respond using a separate piece of paper. Have students hand you their responses as they leave the room.

Alternate Use
At the end of class, go online to display the Exit Ticket prompt and ask students to respond verbally or by using a mini-whiteboard. Have students hold up their whiteboards so that you can see all student responses. Tap to reveal the answer when most or all students have completed the Exit Ticket.

Practice and Homework

Suggested Assignments

Use the table below to select appropriate exercises.

DOK	Topic	Exercises
1, 2	exercises that mirror the examples	1–4
2	exercises that use a variety of skills from this lesson	5–11
3	exercises that emphasize higher-order and critical-thinking skills	12–14

ASSESS AND DIFFERENTIATE

 Use the data from the **Checks** to determine whether to provide resources for extension, remediation, or intervention.

IF students score 90% or more on the Checks, **BL**
THEN assign:

- Practice, Exercises 1–11 odd, 12–14
- Extension: Probability and Tic-Tac-Toe
- **◎ ALEKS·** Probability of Independent and Dependent Events

---

IF students score 66%–89% on the Checks, **OL**
THEN assign:

- Practice, Exercises 1–13 odd
- Remediation, Review Resources: Probability of Compound Events
- Personal Tutors
- Extra Example 1
- **◎ ALEKS·** Finding Probabilities of Independent and Dependent Events

---

IF students score 65% or less on the Checks, **AL**
THEN assign:

- Practice, Exercises 1–3 odd
- Remediation, Review Resources: Probability of Compound Events
- *Quick Review Math Handbook*: Conditional Probability
- **◎ ALEKS·** Finding Probabilities of Independent and Dependent Events

---

Answers

10b. No; P(chips) = 0.5 and P(chips | hamburger) = 0.8. Because these two probabilities are not the same, the events are dependent.

10c. 28%; P(drink | hot dog) = 0.8 and P(hot dog) = 0.35. Because $P(\text{drink} \mid \text{hot dog}) = \dfrac{P(\text{drink and hot dog})}{P(\text{hot dog})}$, P(drink and hot dog) = P(drink | hot dog) · P(hot dog) = (0.8)(0.35) = 0.28.

Name _____ Period _____ Date _____

Practice

◎ Go Online You can complete your homework online.

Example 1

1. **CLUBS** The Spanish Club is having a potluck lunch where each student brings in a cultural dish. The 10 students randomly draw cards numbered with consecutive integers from 1 to 10. Students who draw odd numbers will bring main dishes. Students who draw even numbers will bring desserts. If Cynthia is bringing a dessert, what is the probability that she drew the number 10? $\frac{1}{5}$ or 20%

2. A card is randomly drawn from a standard deck of 52 cards. What is the probability that the card is a king of diamonds, given that the card drawn is a king? $\frac{1}{4}$

3. **GAME** In a game, a spinner with the 7 colors of the rainbow is spun. Find the probability that the color spun is blue, given the color is one of the three primary colors: red, yellow, or blue. $\frac{1}{3}$

4. Fifteen cards numbered 1–15 are placed in a hat. What is the probability that the card has a multiple of 3 on it, given that the card picked is an odd number? $\frac{3}{8}$

Mixed Exercises

5. A blue marble is selected at random from a bag of 3 red and 9 blue marbles and not replaced. What is the probability that a second marble selected will be blue? $\frac{8}{11}$ or about 73%

6. A die is rolled. If the number rolled is less than 5, what is the probability that it is the number 2? $\frac{1}{4}$ or about 25%

7. If two dice are rolled, what is the probability that the sum of the faces is 4, given that the first die rolled is odd? $\frac{1}{9}$ or about 11%

8. A spinner numbered 1 through 12 is spun. Find the probability that the number spun is an 11 given that the number spun was an odd number. $\frac{1}{6}$ or about 17%

9. If two dice are rolled, what is the probability that the sum of the faces is 8, given that the first die rolled is even? $\frac{1}{6}$ or about 17%

10. **PICNIC** A school picnic offers students hamburgers, hot dogs, chips, and a drink.

    a. At the picnic, 60% of the students order a hamburger and 48% of the students order a hamburger and chips. What is the conditional probability that a student who orders a hamburger also orders chips? 0.8 or 80%

    b. If 50% of the students ordered chips, are the events of ordering a hamburger and ordering chips independent? Explain. See margin.

    c. If 80% of the students who ordered a hot dog also ordered a drink and 35% of all the students ordered a hot dog, find the probability that a student at the picnic orders a hot dog and drink. Explain. See margin.

Lesson 12-7 · Conditional Probability **761**

1 CONCEPTUAL UNDERSTANDING   2 FLUENCY | 3 APPLICATION

11. The Venn diagram shows students' favorite places to study, the library (L) or home (H).

a. A total of 60 students responded to the survey. Determine the number of students who replied that they study neither at the library nor at home. **6 students**

b. What is the probability that if a student selected the library, he or she selected the library and at home? Explain.

$P(H|L) = \frac{1}{3}$; $P(L) = \frac{3}{10}$ and $P(H \text{ and } L) = \frac{1}{10}$. So, $P(H|L) = \frac{P(H \text{ and } L)}{P(L)} = \frac{\frac{1}{10}}{\frac{3}{10}}$ or $\frac{1}{3}$.

c. A student says that selecting the library and selecting at home are independent events. Do you agree? Explain.

No; sample answer: If $P(H|L)$ is the same as $P(H)$ or $P(L|H)$ is the same as $P(L)$, then H and L are independent. Because $P(H|L)$ is $\frac{1}{3}$ and $P(H)$ is $\frac{7}{10}$, H and L are not independent.

🧠 **Higher-Order Thinking Skills**

12. WRITE Let A represent the event of owning a house and let B represent the event of owning a car. Are these events independent or dependent? How do you think $P(A|B)$ compares to $P(B|A)$? Explain your reasoning. Sample answer: I expect the probability of someone having a car, given that they have a house, to be higher than the probability of someone having a car. This would mean that $P(\text{car} \mid \text{house}) \neq P(\text{car})$, so the events would have to be dependent. I think that there is a higher probability of someone owning a car if they already own a house as compared to owning a house if they already own a car because many people can afford a car but not a house. This means that $P(B|A) > P(A|B)$.

13. PERSEVERE Of all the students at North High School, 25% are enrolled in Algebra and 20% are enrolled in Algebra and Health.

a. If a student is enrolled in Algebra, find the probability that the student is enrolled in Health as well. 80%; $P(Algebra) = 0.25$ and $P(Algebra \text{ and } Health) = 0.2$,

so $P(Health|Algebra) = \frac{P(Algebra \text{ and } Health)}{P(Algebra)} = \frac{0.2}{0.25} = 0.8$.

b. If 50% of the students are being enrolled in Health, are being enrolled in Algebra and being enrolled in Health independent events? Explain. No; $P(Health|Algebra) = 0.8$ and $P(Health) = 0.5$. Because the two probabilities are not equal, the two events are dependent.

c. Of all the students, 20% are enrolled in Accounting and 5% are enrolled in Accounting and Spanish. If being enrolled in Accounting and being enrolled in Spanish are independent events, what percent of students are enrolled in Spanish? Explain. 25%; $P(Accounting) = 0.2$ and $P(Accounting \text{ and } Spanish) = 0.05$,

so $P(Spanish|Accounting) = \frac{P(Accounting \text{ and } Spanish)}{P(Accounting)} = \frac{0.05}{0.2} = 0.25$. Because the events are

independent, $P(Spanish|Accounting) = P(Spanish) = 0.25$.

14. ANALYZE In a standard deck of playing cards, the face-value cards are the cards numbered 2–10. Two cards are to be randomly drawn without replacing the first card. Find the probability of drawing two face-value cards and the conditional probability that exactly one of those cards is a 4. Explain.

$\frac{630}{1326}$, $\frac{64}{315}$. The total number of combinations of 2 cards is $_{52}C_2 = 1326$. There are 36 face-value cards so the total number of combinations of 2 face-value cards is $_{36}C_2 = 630$. So, the probability of drawing two face-value cards is $\frac{630}{1326}$. There are four cards with a 4 on them and 32 other face-value cards left, so the number of combinations with exactly one 4 is $4 \cdot {}_{32}C_1 = 4 \cdot 32 = 128$. The probability is $\frac{128}{630}$ or $\frac{64}{315}$.

Two-Way Frequency Tables

LESSON GOAL

Students decide if events are independent and approximate conditional probabilities using two-way frequency tables.

1 LAUNCH

Launch the lesson with a **Warm Up** and an introduction.

2 EXPLORE AND DEVELOP

Explore: Two-Way Frequency Tables

Develop:

Independent Events in Frequency Tables
- Frequency and Relative Frequency Tables
- Independence and Relative Frequency
- Conditional Probability with Two-Way Frequency Tables

You may want your students to complete the **Checks** online.

3 REFLECT AND PRACTICE

Exit Ticket

Practice

DIFFERENTIATE

View reports of student progress on the **Checks** after each example.

Resources	AL	OL	BL	ELL
Remediation: Two-Way Tables	●	●		●
Extension: Graphical Representations of Relative Frequencies		●	●	●

Language Development Handbook

Assign page 90 of the *Language Development Handbook* to help your students build mathematical language related to two-way frequency tables.

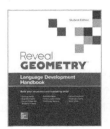

ELL You can use the tips and suggestions on page T90 of the handbook to support students who are building English proficiency.

Suggested Pacing

90 min	**1 day**
45 min	**2 days**

Focus

Domain: Statistics & Probability

Standards for Mathematical Content:

S.CP.4 Construct and interpret two-way frequency tables of data when two categories are associated with each object being classified. Use the two-way table as a sample space to decide if events are independent and to approximate conditional probabilities.

S.CP.6 Find the conditional probability of *A* given *B* as the fraction of *B*'s outcomes that also belong to *A*, and interpret the answer in terms of the model.

Standards for Mathematical Practice:

2 Reason abstractly and quantitatively.

4 Model with mathematics.

Coherence

Vertical Alignment

Previous
Students solved probability problems involving conditional probability.
S.CP.3, S.CP.5

Now
Students use two-way frequency tables in probability situations.
S.CP.4, S.CP.6

Rigor

The Three Pillars of Rigor

1 CONCEPTUAL UNDERSTANDING	2 FLUENCY	3 APPLICATION

Conceptual Bridge In this lesson, students expand on understanding of two-way frequency tables (from Algebra 1) and build fluency by using frequencies to approximate conditional probabilities. They apply their understanding of two-way frequency tables and conditional probability by solving real-world problems.

Mathematical Background

A two-way frequency table, or contingency table, is used to show the frequencies of data from a survey or experiment classified according to two variables, with the rows indicating one variable and the columns indicating the other.

Interactive Presentation

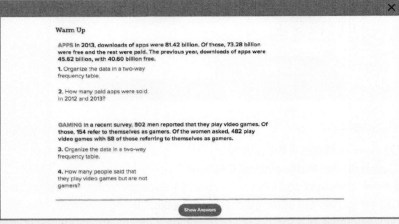

Warm Up

APPS In 2013, downloads of apps were 81.42 billion. Of those, 73.28 billion were free and the rest were paid. The previous year, downloads of apps were 45.62 billion, with 40.60 billion free.

1. Organize the data in a two-way frequency table.

2. How many paid apps were sold in 2012 and 2013?

GAMING In a recent survey, 502 men reported that they play video games. Of those, 154 refer to themselves as gamers. Of the women asked, 482 play video games with 58 of those referring to themselves as gamers.

3. Organize the data in a two-way frequency table.

4. How many people said that they play video games but are not gamers?

Show Answers

Warm Up

3. (Chart below)

Video Game Use			
Year	Players	Gamers	Total
Men	348	154	502
Women	424	58	482
Total	772	212	984

4. 772

Launch the Lesson

Companies often rely on the feedback of focus groups as they develop and market products. A focus group is a type of qualitative research where people are asked for their opinions on a product, concept, service, or other idea. As the members of the group openly discuss their opinions, the researcher records the information.

Suppose a company wants to get feedback on their new logo design. The researcher might want to analyze the reactions of previous customers and noncustomers. She might also want to analyze comments from those who prefer the old logo and those who prefer the new logo. Placing the data into a two-way frequency table allows for easy comparisons between these two variables.

Launch the Lesson

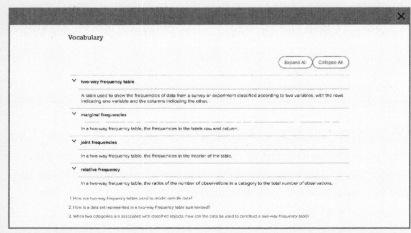

Vocabulary

Expand All   Collapse All

⌄ **two-way frequency table**

A table used to show the frequencies of data from a survey or experiment classified according to two variables, with the rows indicating one variable and the columns indicating the other.

⌄ **marginal frequencies**

In a two-way frequency table, the frequencies in the totals row and column.

⌄ **joint frequencies**

In a two-way frequency table, the frequencies in the interior of the table.

⌄ **relative frequency**

In a two-way frequency table, the ratios of the number of observations in a category to the total number of observations.

1. How are two-way frequency tables used to model real-life data?
2. How is a data set represented in a two-way frequency table summarized?
3. When two categories are associated with classified objects, how can the data be used to construct a two-way frequency table?

Today's Vocabulary

Warm Up

Prerequisite Skills

The Warm Up exercises address the following prerequisite skill for this lesson:

- using two-way tables

Answers

1. (Chart below)

Downloaded Apps (billions)			
Year	Free	Paid	Total
2012	40.60	5.02	45.62
2013	73.28	8.14	81.42
Total	113.88	13.16	127.04

2. 13.16 billion

Launch the Lesson

MP Teaching the Mathematical Practices

> **4 Apply Mathematics** In this Launch the Lesson, students can see a real-world application of two-way frequency tables.

Go Online to find additional teaching notes and questions to promote classroom discourse.

Today's Standards

Tell students that they will be addressing these content and practice standards in this lesson. You may wish to have a student volunteer read aloud *How can I meet these standards?* and *How can I use these practices?* and connect these to the standards.

See the Interactive Presentation for I Can statements that align with the standards covered in this lesson.

Today's Vocabulary

Tell students that they will be using these vocabulary terms in this lesson. You can expand each row if you wish to share the definitions. Then, discuss the questions below with the class.

Explore Two-Way Frequency Tables

Objective
Students use their understanding of probability to solve problems in a two-way frequency table.

Ideas for Use
Recommended Use Present the Inquiry Question, or have a student volunteer read it aloud. Have students work in pairs to complete the Explore activity on their devices. Pairs should discuss each of the questions. Monitor student progress during the activity. Upon completion of the Explore activity, have student volunteers share their responses to the Inquiry Question.

What if my students don't have devices? You may choose to project the activity on a whiteboard. A printable worksheet for each Explore is available online. You may choose to print the worksheet so that individuals or pairs of students can use it to record their observations.

Summary of the Activity
Students will complete guiding exercises throughout the Explore activity. They will proceed through a series of questions and activities related to calculating probabilities of events using a two-way frequency table. Then, students will answer the Inquiry Question.

 Go Online to find additional teaching notes and sample answers for the guiding exercises.

(continued on the next page)

Interactive Presentation

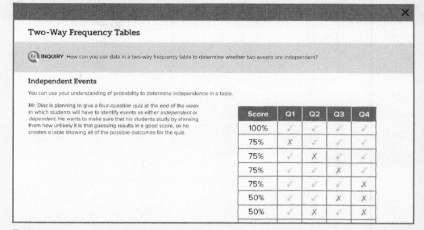

Explore

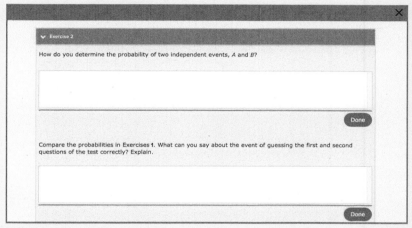

Explore

TYPE

$a|$ Students complete the calculations to complete the two-way frequency table.

Interactive Presentation

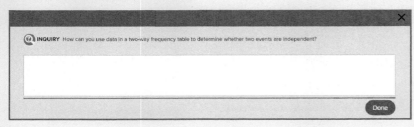

INQUIRY How can you use data in a two-way frequency table to determine whether two events are independent?

×

Done

Explore

TYPE

Students will respond to the Inquiry Question and can view a sample answer.

Explore Two-Way Frequency Tables (*continued*)

Teaching the Mathematical Practices

6 Communicate Precisely Encourage students to routinely write or explain their solution methods. Point out that they should use clear definitions when they discuss their solutions with others.

7 Look for a Pattern Help students to see the pattern in this Explore.

Questions

Have students complete the Explore activity.

Ask:

- Are the events guessing on the second question and guessing on the third question independent? Sample answer: Yes, the probabilities are the same if you multiply the probabilities for each event and if you look in the table.

- What other events' independence could you determine from the second table? Sample answer: You could determine if the events of randomly selecting a girl who studied less than 2 hours is independent.

Inquiry

How can you use data in a two-way frequency table to determine whether two events are independent? Sample answer: I can compare the product of the probabilities of the two events with the probability of the two events occurring to determine independence in events.

Go Online to find additional teaching notes and sample answers for the guiding exercises.

Learn Independent Events in Frequency Tables

Objective

Students construct and interpret two-way frequency tables and use them to determine whether events are independent.

 Teaching the Mathematical Practices

7 Use Structure Help students to explore the structure of two-way frequency tables in this Learn.

Things to Remember

Point out to students that the "marginal frequencies" represent the values in the right and bottom "margin" of the table, along the outer edges of the table. Remind them that "joint frequencies" represent the combination of two values, which is why they are in the interior of the table. This will help them to remember the distinction between these two frequencies.

Common Misconception

Students may believe that calculating the bottom rightmost "Total" cell involves adding all of the other values in the table, forgetting that they need to only add the "Total" column or row (marginal frequencies). Remind them that they can check this value by adding the joint frequencies, without the "Total" row or column, to be sure the sum reaches the final total.

 Go Online

- Find additional teaching notes.
- View performance reports of the Checks.
- Assign or present an Extra Example.

S.CP.4, S.CP.6

Lesson 12-8

Two-Way Frequency Tables

Explore Two-Way Frequency Tables

Online Activity Use the tables to complete the Explore.

INQUIRY How can you use data in a two-way frequency table to determine whether two events are independent?

Learn Independent Events in Frequency Tables

A **two-way frequency table**, or **contingency table**, is used to show the frequencies of data from a survey or experiment classified according to two variables, with the rows indicating one variable and the columns indicating the other.

The two-way frequency table shows the results of a survey of 220 men and women about the time of day that they shower. The frequencies reported in the *Totals* row and *Totals* column are called **marginal frequencies**, with the bottom rightmost cell reporting the total number of observations. Marginal frequencies allow you to analyze with respect to one variable. For example, the marginal frequencies in the right column separate the data by gender.

Two-Way Frequency Table

	Shower in the Morning	Shower in the Evening	Totals
Women	98	37	135
Men	23	62	85
Totals	121	99	220

The frequencies reported in the interior of the table are called **joint frequencies**. These show the frequencies of all possible combinations of the categories for the first variable with the categories for the second variable.

A **relative frequency** is the ratio of the number of observations in a category to the total number of observations. When survey results are classified according to variables, you may want to decide whether these variables are independent of each other. Variable A is considered independent of variable B if $P(A \text{ and } B) = P(A) \cdot P(B)$.

Two-Way Relative Frequency Table

	Shower in the Morning	Shower in the Evening	Totals
Women	$\frac{98}{220}$	$\frac{37}{220}$	$\frac{135}{220}$
Men	$\frac{23}{220}$	$\frac{62}{220}$	$\frac{85}{220}$
Totals	$\frac{121}{220}$	$\frac{99}{220}$	$\frac{220}{220}$

Today's Goals
- Construct and interpret two-way frequency tables and use them to determine whether events are independent.

Today's Vocabulary
two-way frequency table
marginal frequencies
joint frequencies
relative frequency

Interactive Presentation

Independent Events in Frequency Tables

A **two-way frequency table**, or contingency table, is used to show the frequencies of data from a survey or experiment classified according to two variables, with the rows indicating one variable and the columns indicating the other.

The two-way frequency table shows the results of a survey of 220 men and women about the time of day that they shower. The frequencies reported in the *Totals* row and *Totals* column are called **marginal frequencies**, with the bottom rightmost cell reporting the total number of observations. Marginal frequencies allow you to analyze with respect to one variable. For example, the marginal frequencies in the right column separate the data by gender.

Two-Way Frequency Table

	Shower in the Morning	Shower in the Evening	Totals
Women	98	37	135
Men	23	62	85
Totals	121	99	220

Learn

Your Notes

Example 1 Frequency and Relative Frequency Tables

BREAKFAST Francesca asks a random sample of 140 upperclassmen at her high school whether they prefer eating breakfast at home or at school. She finds that 55 juniors and 23 seniors prefer eating breakfast at home before school, while 12 juniors and 50 seniors prefer eating breakfast at school.

Part A Organize the responses in a two-way frequency table.

Identify the variables. The students surveyed can be classified according to *class* and *preference*. Because the survey included only upperclassmen, the variable *class* has two categories: senior or __junior__. The variable *preference* also has two categories: *prefers eating breakfast at home* and *prefers eating breakfast at school*.

Create a two-way frequency table. Let the rows of the table represent *class* and the columns represent *preference*. Then fill in the cells of the table with the information given.

Add a Totals row and a Totals column to your table and fill in these cells with the correct sums.

	Breakfast at Home	Breakfast at School	Totals
Senior	23	50	73
Junior	55	12	67
Totals	78	62	140

Part B Construct a relative frequency table.

To complete a relative frequency table for these data, start by dividing the frequency reported in each cell by the total number of respondents, 140. Then, write each fraction as a percent rounded to the nearest tenth.

	Breakfast at Home	Breakfast at School	Totals
Senior	$\frac{23}{140} = 16.4\%$	$\frac{50}{140} = 35.7\%$	$\frac{73}{140} = 52.1\%$
Junior	$\frac{55}{140} = 39.3\%$	$\frac{12}{140} = 8.6\%$	$\frac{67}{140} = 47.9\%$
Totals	$\frac{78}{140} = 55.7\%$	$\frac{62}{140} = 44.3\%$	$\frac{140}{140} = 100\%$

Think About It!
What is the probability that a surveyed student is a junior who prefers eating breakfast at home?

39.3%

Go Online You can complete an Extra Example online.

764 Module 12 · Probability

Example 1 Frequency and Relative Frequency Tables

Teaching the Mathematical Practices

2 Make Sense of Quantities Mathematically proficient students need to be able to make sense of quantities and their relationships. In this example, notice the relationship between the problem variables and the dependency of events.

Questions for Mathematical Discourse

AL In a relative frequency table, what frequency always goes in the bottom right cell of the table? 100%

OL What is the relative frequency of seniors who prefer eating breakfast at school? 35.7%

BL If there are a total of 600 upperclassmen at Francesca's school, about how many of them would you expect to be seniors who prefer eating breakfast at home? about 98

Interactive Presentation

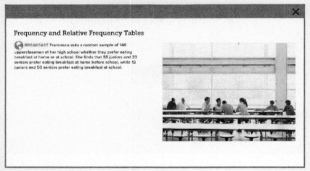

Frequency and Relative Frequency Tables

BREAKFAST Francesca asks a random sample of 140 upperclassmen at her high school whether they prefer eating breakfast at home or at school. She finds that 55 juniors and 23 seniors prefer eating breakfast at home before school, while 12 juniors and 50 seniors prefer eating breakfast at school.

Example 1

TAP

Students move through the steps to construct a two-way frequency table and a relative frequency table.

TYPE

a|

Students complete the calculations to construct a relative frequency table.

Example 2 Independence and Relative Frequency

Teaching the Mathematical Practices

4 Apply Mathematics In this example, students apply what they have learned about two-way frequency tables to solving a real-world problem.

Questions for Mathematical Discourse

AL How many college freshmen told Anaud they prefer EDM? 100

OL How do you calculate the expected joint relative frequencies of high school seniors who prefer hip-hop? Sample answer: Multiply 13.8% by 51.7%. 0.138 · 0.517 ≈ 0.071, which is 7.1%.

BL Why would the variables be dependent if the expected and actual joint relative frequencies were different? Sample answer: The expected joint relative frequencies are predicting the behavior of one variable using the results for the other variable. If that prediction doesn't match the actual values, it means that there is some extra influence between the two variables, which represents a dependent relationship.

Example 2 Independence and Relative Frequency

MUSIC Anaud polls 240 of his friends on social media about what grade they are in and whether they prefer electronic dance music (EDM) or hip-hop. He posts the results of the survey in the table.

	EDM	Hip-Hop	Totals
College Freshman	100	107	207
High School Senior	16	17	33
Totals	116	124	240

Use the table to determine whether a respondent's musical preference is independent of his or her grade level.

In a two-way frequency table, you can test for the independence of two variables by comparing the joint relative frequencies with the products of the corresponding marginal relative frequencies.

Divide each reported frequency by 240 to convert the frequency table to a relative frequency table. Enter each fraction as a percent rounded to the nearest tenth. Complete the table.

	EDM	Hip-Hop	Totals
College Freshman	$\frac{100}{240} = 41.7$ %	$\frac{107}{240} = 44.6$ %	$\frac{207}{240} = 86.3$ %
High School Senior	$\frac{16}{240} = 6.7$ %	$\frac{17}{240} = 7.1$ %	$\frac{33}{240} = 13.8$ %
Totals	$\frac{116}{240} = 48.3$ %	$\frac{124}{240} = 51.7$ %	$\frac{240}{240} = 100$%

Calculate the expected joint relative frequencies if the two variables were independent. Then compare them to the actual relative frequencies.

For example, if 86.3% of respondents were college freshmen and 48.3% of respondents prefer EDM, then one would expect that 86.3% · 48.3% or about 41.7% of respondents are college freshmen who prefer EDM. The table below shows the expected joint relative frequencies.

	EDM	Hip-Hop	Totals
College Freshman	41.7%	44.6%	86.3%
High School Senior	6.7%	7.1%	13.8%
Totals	48.3%	51.7%	100%

Comparing the two tables, the expected and actual joint relative frequencies are the same. Therefore, the musical preferences for these respondents are independent of grade level.

Go Online You can complete an Extra Example online.

Interactive Presentation

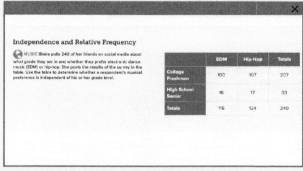

Independence and Relative Frequency

MUSIC Blaire polls 240 of her friends on social media about what grade they are in and whether they prefer electronic dance music (EDM) or hip-hop. She posts the results of the survey in the table. Use the table to determine whether a respondent's musical preference is independent of his or her grade level.

	EDM	Hip-Hop	Totals
College Freshman	100	107	207
High School Senior	16	17	33
Totals	116	124	240

Example 2

TYPE

Students complete the calculations to construct a relative frequency table.

CHECK

Students complete the Check online to determine whether they are ready to move on.

| 1 CONCEPTUAL UNDERSTANDING | 2 FLUENCY | 3 APPLICATION |

Check

SCHOOL Immediately after a physics test, the entire class sits together at lunch and discusses how long each of them studied and how many questions they guessed on. The table shows the responses from the classmates.

	Guessed on < 5 Problems	Guessed on > 5 Problems	Totals
Studied 4 Hours or Less	9	3	12
Studied More Than 4 Hours	12	4	16
Totals	21	7	28

True or False: For these classmates, guessing on more than 5 problems on the physics test is independent of studying 4 hours or less. __False__

⊕ Example 3 Conditional Probability with Two-Way Frequency Tables

You can use joint and marginal relative frequencies to approximate conditional probabilities.

MEMES Abu posts a question to an online forum about the originality of posts to the site. Of the 55 respondents who have posted viral memes, 27 photos and 15 videos were not original content, while 3 photos and 10 videos were original content.

Part A Construct a relative frequency table of the data. Round each percent to the nearest tenth.

	Not Original Content	Original Content	Totals
Video	27.3%	18.2%	45.6 %
Photo	49.1 %	5.5 %	54.6 %
Totals	76.4 %	23.6 %	100%

Part B Find the probability that a viral meme on the forum is not original content given that is it a photo.

The probability that a meme is not original content given that it is a photo is the conditional probability P(not original content|photo).

$$P(\text{not original content|photo}) = \frac{P(\text{not original content and photo})}{P(\text{photo})}$$

$$\approx \frac{0.491}{0.546} \text{ or } 89.9 \%$$

So the probability that a viral meme on the forum is not original content given that it is a photo is 89.9%.

🔗 **Go Online** You can complete an Extra Example online.

Copyright © McGraw-Hill Education

💭 **Think About It!**
Why do we divide by 0.546 when finding the conditional probability in the example?

Sample answer: 0.546 represents $P(A)$, or the probability that a viral meme selected at random is a photo. Divide by $P(A$ and $B)$ by $P(A)$ to find the conditional probability.

Interactive Presentation

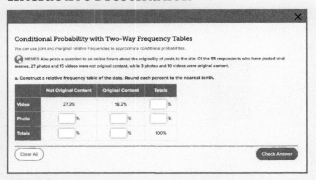

Conditional Probability with Two-Way Frequency Tables

You can use joint and marginal relative frequencies to approximate conditional probabilities.

⊕ MEMES Abu posts a question to an online forum about the originality of posts to the site. Of the 55 respondents who have posted viral memes, 27 photos and 15 videos were not original content, while 3 photos and 10 videos were original content.

a. Construct a relative frequency table of the data. Round each percent to the nearest tenth.

	Not Original Content	Original Content	Totals
Video	27.3%	18.2%	%
Photo	%	%	%
Totals	%	%	100%

Clear All   Check Answer

Example 3

TYPE

Students complete the calculations to find conditional probability with two-way frequency tables.

CHECK

Students complete the Check online to determine whether they are ready to move on.

⊕ Example 3 Conditional Probability with Two-Way Frequency Tables

ⓂⓅ Teaching the Mathematical Practices

4 Apply Mathematics In this example, students apply what they have learned about conditional probabilities to solving a real-world problem.

Questions for Mathematical Discourse

AL How do you calculate the relative frequency of 27.3% in the top left cell? Sample answer: 15 videos were not original content, out of a total of 55 respondents. $\frac{15}{55} = 27.3\%$

OL What is the probability that a random viral meme on the forum is an original photo? $\frac{3}{55}$

BL What is the probability that a meme is original content given that it is a photo? Show your work. Sample answer: P(original content|photo) $= \frac{P(\text{original content and photo})}{P(\text{photo})} \approx \frac{0.055}{0.545}$ or 10.1%

Common Error

Prompt students to investigate the sums of the rows and columns of relative frequencies. Calculate the total for the photo row directly from the original data and note that it does not exactly match the sum of relative frequencies in that row. Encourage students to recognize that rounding with percentages may result in total percentage sums that are not exactly equal to 100%.

Exit Ticket

Recommended Use

At the end of class, go online to display the Exit Ticket prompt and ask students to respond using a separate piece of paper. Have students hand you their responses as they leave the room.

Alternate Use

At the end of class, go online to display the Exit Ticket prompt and ask students to respond verbally or by using a mini-whiteboard. Have students hold up their whiteboards so that you can see all student responses. Tap to reveal the answer when most or all students have completed the Exit Ticket.

Practice and Homework

Suggested Assignments

Use the table below to select appropriate exercises.

DOK	Topic	Exercises
1, 2	exercises that mirror the examples	1–4
2	exercises that use a variety of skills from this lesson	5–8
3	exercises that emphasize higher-order and critical-thinking skills	9–10

ASSESS AND DIFFERENTIATE

📊 Use the data from the **Checks** to determine whether to provide resources for extension, remediation, or intervention.

IF students score 90% or more on the Checks,   `BL`
THEN assign:

- Practice, Exercises 1–7 odd, 9–10
- Extension: Graphical Representations of Relative Frequencies
- 🅐 ALEKS° Two-Way Tables

IF students score 66%–89% on the Checks,   `OL`
THEN assign:

- Practice, Exercises 1–9 odd
- Remediation, Review Resources: Two-Way Tables
- Personal Tutors
- Extra Examples 1–3
- 🅐 ALEKS° Two-Way Tables

IF students score 65% or less on the Checks,   `AL`
THEN assign:

- Practice, Exercises 1–3 odd
- Remediation, Review Resources: Two-Way Tables
- *Quick Review Math Handbook*: Two-Way Frequency Tables
- 🅐 ALEKS° Two-Way Tables

Name _____ Period _____ Date _____

Practice

🌐 **Go Online** You can complete your homework online.

Example 1

1. **VEHICLES** One hundred people are surveyed about the type of vehicle they drive. The survey finds that 15 males and 40 females drive SUVs, while 35 males and 10 females drive trucks.

   a. Organize the responses in a two-way frequency table.

	SUV	Truck	Totals
Male	15	35	50
Female	40	10	50
Totals	55	45	100

   b. Construct a relative frequency table.

	SUV	Truck	Totals
Male	$\frac{15}{100} = 15\%$	$\frac{35}{100} = 35\%$	$\frac{50}{100} = 50\%$
Female	$\frac{40}{100} = 40\%$	$\frac{10}{100} = 10\%$	$\frac{50}{100} = 50\%$
Totals	$\frac{55}{100} = 55\%$	$\frac{45}{100} = 45\%$	$\frac{100}{100} = 100\%$

2. **SOCIAL MEDIA** One hundred students are asked whether or not they have social media accounts. The survey finds that 25 males and 35 females have social media accounts, while 25 males and 15 females do not have social media accounts.

   a. Organize the responses in a two-way frequency table.

	Social Media	No Social Media	Totals
Male	25	25	50
Female	35	15	50
Totals	60	40	100

   b. Construct a relative frequency table.

	Social Media	No Social Media	Totals
Male	25%	25%	50%
Female	35%	15%	50%
Totals	60%	40%	100%

Example 2

3. **COLLEGE** A ride-sharing company surveys 2000 of its customers who are college students. The survey asks the following two questions about the previous academic year:

   - Are you attending college in or out of state?
   - Did you visit home more than four times this school year?

   The survey finds that of the 1260 students who attend an in-state college, 928 visited home more than four times and 332 visited home four or less times. Of the 740 students who attend an out-of-state college, 118 visited home more than four times and 622 visited home four or less times.

   a. Organize the responses in a two-way frequency table. *See margin.*

   b. Construct a relative frequency table. Enter each fraction as a percent rounded to the nearest tenth, if necessary. *See margin.*

   c. Suppose you let event A represent whether the students attend an in-state or an out-of-state college, and event B represent whether the students visit home more than four times or visit home four or fewer times. Use the table to determine whether the number of visits home is independent or dependent on whether the student is attending college at an in-state or out-of-state institution. Justify your response. *Sample answer: 63% of the college students surveyed are attending an in-state college. 52.3% of the college students surveyed visited home more than 4 times. It would be expected that 63% · 52.3%, or about 33% would be in-state students that visited home more than 4 times. Because $P(A$ and $B) \neq P(A) \cdot P(B)$, or 33% ≠ 46.4%, the events are dependent.*

Example 3

4. **TICKETS** A movie theater is keeping track of the last 800 tickets it sold to two different movies. Of the 578 adult tickets sold, 136 of them were for the animated film and 442 were for the documentary film. Of the 222 student tickets sold, 181 of them were for the animated film and 41 were for the documentary film.

   a. Complete the two-way frequency table shown.

	Adult	Student	Totals
Animated	136	181	317
Documentary	442	41	483
Totals	578	222	800

   b. Construct a relative frequency table of your completed two-way frequency table. Round each percent to the nearest tenth, as necessary.

	Adult	Student	Totals
Animated	$\frac{136}{800} = 17\%$	$\frac{181}{800} = 22.6\%$	$\frac{317}{800} = 39.6\%$
Documentary	$\frac{442}{800} = 55.3\%$	$\frac{41}{800} = 5.1\%$	$\frac{483}{800} = 60.4\%$
Totals	$\frac{578}{800} = 72.3\%$	$\frac{222}{800} = 27.8\%$	$\frac{800}{800} = 100\%$

   c. Find the probability that a ticket sold is an adult ticket given that it is a documentary ticket. Show your work by writing the formula that you used to perform the calculation. *91.6%;*

   $$P(\text{adult}|\text{documentary}) = \frac{P(\text{adult and documentary})}{P(\text{documentary})}$$
   $$\approx \frac{0.553}{0.604} \text{ or } 91.6\%$$

Name _____ Period _____ Date _____

Mixed Exercises

5. **SCHOOL** The two-way frequency table compares data about students in a class who completed or did not complete homework and those who passed or did not pass an exam. How many students completed their homework and passed the exam? Identify whether marginal or joint frequencies are used.

	Completed Homework	Did Not Complete Homework	Totals
Passed Exam	18	2	20
Did Not Pass Exam	4	2	6
Totals	22	4	26

18; joint frequency

6. **MOVIES** Raquel surveys 160 people to determine if they prefer drama or comedy movies. The relative frequency table shows the data collected from the survey. Determine whether gender is independent of movie type preference. Explain your reasoning.

	Drama	Comedy	Totals
Male	12.5%	25%	37.5%
Female	46.9%	15.6%	62.5%
Totals	59.4%	40.6%	100%

Sample answer: Find the expected joint frequencies. Male and Drama = (37.5%)(59.4%) = 22.3%; Male and Comedy = (37.5%)(40.6%) = 15.2%; Female and Drama = (62.5%)(59.4%) = 37.1%; Female and Comedy = (62.5%)(40.6%) = 25.4%. Because the expected and actual joint relative frequencies are not the same, gender is not independent of movie type.

7. **TECHNOLOGY** For a business report on technology use, Darnell asks a random sample of 72 shoppers whether they own a smart phone and whether they own a tablet computer. His survey shows that out of 51 shoppers who own smart phones, 9 of them also own a tablet, while out of 21 shoppers who do not own smart phones, 15 of them do not own tablets either. Find the conditional probability that a shopper has a tablet, given that he or she has a smart phone. Justify your reasoning.

17.7%; $P(\text{has a tablet} \mid \text{has a smart phone}) = \frac{P(\text{has a tablet and has a smart phone})}{P(\text{has a smart phone})} \approx \frac{0.125}{0.708}$ or 17.7%

8. **CONSTRUCT ARGUMENTS** Paz asks a random sample of seniors at her high school whether they own a car and whether they have a job. The results of the survey are shown in the two-way relative frequency table. Paz says the conditional probability that a student has a job given that he or she has a car is 46.7%. Do you agree? Justify your argument.

	Has a Job	Does Not Have a Job	Totals
Has a Car	21.9%	12.5%	34.4%
Does Not Have a Car	25%	40.6%	65.6%
Totals	46.9%	53.1%	100%

No; sample answer: Paz found the conditional probability that a student has a car, given they have a job: $P(\text{has a car} \mid \text{has a job}) = \frac{P(\text{has a car and has a job})}{P(\text{has a job})} \approx \frac{0.219}{0.469}$ or 46.7%. The correct answer is $P(\text{has a job} \mid \text{has a car}) = \frac{P(\text{has a job and has a car})}{P(\text{has a car})} \approx \frac{0.219}{0.344}$ or 63.7%.

🖐 **Higher-Order Thinking Skills**

9. **PERSEVERE** Suppose an exit poll held outside a voting area on the day of an election produced these results.

Age and Gender	Votes for Candidate A	Votes for Candidate B
18–30 Male	19	32
18–30 Female	31	18
31–45 Male	51	12
31–45 Female	43	20
46–60 Male	42	35
46–60 Female	20	42
60+ Male	45	21
60+ Female	27	18

a. Which events are mutually exclusive? voting for candidate A or B and being within a particular age/gender category

b. Find the probability that a male between the ages of 46 and 60 would vote for Candidate A. 55%

c. Find the probability that a female would vote for Candidate A. 55%

d. Find the probability that someone who voted for Candidate B was a female and age 18–30. 9%

e. According to the data, on which demographic(s) does Candidate A need to focus campaign efforts? Sample answer: males age 18–30 and females age 46–60

f. According to the data, on which demographic(s) does Candidate B need to focus campaign efforts? Sample answer: females age 18–30, males and females age 31–45, and anyone over 60

10. **ANALYZE** A market research firm asks a random sample of 240 adults and students at a movie theater whether they would rather see a new summer blockbuster in 2-D or 3-D. The survey shows that 64 adults and 108 students prefer 3-D, while 42 adults and 26 students prefer 2-D.

a. Organize the responses into a two-way frequency table. See margin.

b. Convert the table from part a into a two-way relative frequency table. Round to the nearest tenth of a percent. Out of every 10 people surveyed, about how many would prefer to see the movie in 3-D? Explain. See margin.

c. Find the probability that a person surveyed prefers seeing the movie in 3-D, given that he or she is an adult. Write the formula that you used to perform the calculation.
60.4%; $P(\text{prefers 3-D} \mid \text{adult}) = \frac{P(\text{prefers 3-D and adult})}{P(\text{adult})} \approx \frac{0.267}{0.442}$ or 60.4%.

d. An analyst at the firm claims that the probability that a person surveyed is a student given that he or she does not prefer to see the movie in 3-D is 10.8%. Do you agree? Justify your answer. No; sample answer: The analyst used the relative frequency instead of finding the conditional probability; the probability would be $P(\text{student} \mid \text{prefers 2-D}) = \frac{P(\text{student and prefers 2-D})}{P(\text{prefers 2-D})} \approx \frac{0.108}{0.283}$ or 38.2%.

e. Is a preference for 2-D or 3-D movies independent of age? Explain your reasoning.
No; sample answer: If 44.2% of the responders are adult and 28.3% of the responders prefer 2-D, then the expected frequency for adults who prefer 2-D would be 44.2% · 28.3% or about 12.5%; Because the expected and actual joint relative frequencies for these respondents are not equal, movie preference is not independent of age.

Answers

3a.

	More Than 4	4 or Fewer	Totals
In state	928	332	1260
Out of state	118	622	740
Totals	1046	954	2000

3b.

	More Than 4	4 or Fewer	Totals
In state	$\frac{928}{2000} = 46.4\%$	$\frac{332}{2000} = 16.6\%$	$\frac{1260}{2000} = 63\%$
Out of state	$\frac{118}{2000} = 5.9\%$	$\frac{622}{2000} = 31.1\%$	$\frac{740}{2000} = 37\%$
Totals	$\frac{1046}{2000} = 52.3\%$	$\frac{954}{2000} = 47.7\%$	$\frac{2000}{2000} = 100\%$

10a.

Age	Prefers 2-D	Prefers 3-D	Totals
Adult	42	64	106
Student	26	108	134
Totals	68	172	240

10b.

Age	Prefers 2-D	Prefers 3-D	Totals
Adult	17.5%	26.7%	44.2%
Student	10.8%	45%	55.8%
Totals	28.3%	71.7%	100%

7; Sample answer: The total relative frequency for Prefers 3-D is 71.7%, which is about 7 out of 10 people surveyed.

Review

Rate Yourself! 👎 👌 👍

Have students return to the Module Opener to rate their understanding of the concepts presented in this module. They should see that their knowledge and skills have increased. After completing the chart, have them respond to the prompts in their *Interactive Student Edition* and share their responses with a partner.

℮ Answering the Essential Question

Before answering the Essential Question, have students review their answers to the Essential Question Follow-Up questions found throughout the module.

- How can we predict the outcomes of events?
- How can geometry be used to make predictions?
- How can we quantify predictions?
- How can the probabilities of independent and dependent events be used to make predictions?

Then have them write their answer to the Essential Question in the space provided.

DINAH ZIKE FOLDABLES

ELL A completed Foldable for this module should include the key concepts related to Probability.

LS **LearnSmart** Use LearnSmart as part of your test preparation plan to measure student topic retention. You can create a student assignment in LearnSmart for additional practice on these topics for **Applications of Probability.**

- Understand independence and conditional probability and use them to interpret data
- Use the rules of probability to compute probabilities of compound events in a uniform probability model
- Use probability to evaluate outcomes of decisions

℮ Essential Question
How can you use measurements to find probabilities?

Sample answer: You can find the number of favorable outcomes for an experiment and also find the total number of possible outcomes for an experiment and then find probabilities using a ratio. That ratio can be used to predict how many times a certain event may occur.

Module Summary

Lessons 12-1 through 12-3
Probability of Simple Events
- The number of possible outcomes in a sample space can be found by multiplying the number of possible outcomes from each stage or event.
- For the probability of the intersection of two or more events, find the ratio of the number of outcomes in both events to the total number of possible outcomes.
- When two events A and B occur, the union of A and B is the set of all outcomes in the sample space of event A combined with all outcomes in the sample space of event B.
- If region A contains a region B and a point E in region A is chosen at random, then the probability that point E is in region B is $\frac{\text{area of region } B}{\text{area of region } A}$.

Lesson 12-4
Permutations and Combinations
- The number of distinguishable permutations of n objects in which one object is repeated r_1 times, another is repeated r_2 times, and so on, is $\frac{n!}{r_1! r_2! \cdot \ldots \cdot r_k!}$.
- The number of permutations of n distinct objects taken r at a time is denoted by $_nP_r$ and given by $_nP_r = \frac{n!}{(n-r)!}$.
- The number of combinations of n distinct objects taken r at a time is denoted by $_nC_r$ and is given by $_nC_r = \frac{n!}{(n-r)! r!}$.

Lessons 12-5 through 12-7
Probability of Compound Events
- If two events A and B are independent, the $P(A \text{ and } B) = P(A) \cdot P(B)$.
- If two events A and B are dependent, then $P(A \text{ and } B) = P(A) \cdot P(B \mid A)$.
- If two events A or B are mutually exclusive, then $P(A \text{ or } B) = P(A) + P(B)$.
- If two events A or B are not mutually exclusive, then $P(A \text{ or } B) = P(A) + P(B) - P(A \text{ and } B)$.
- The conditional probability of B given A is $P(B \mid A) = \frac{P(A \text{ and } B)}{P(A)}$, where $P(A) \neq 0$.

Lesson 12-8
Frequency Tables
- The frequencies in the Totals row and Totals column are marginal frequencies.
- The frequencies in the interior of the table are joint frequencies.
- A relative frequency is the ratio of the number of observations in a category to the total number of observations.

Study Organizer

Foldables
Use your Foldable to review this module. Working with a partner can be helpful. Ask for clarification of concepts as needed.

Test Practice

1. MULTIPLE CHOICE Two dice are tossed. Which is the sample space of the event that the sum of the outcomes is 5? (Lesson 12-1)

Ⓐ {(5, 5)}

Ⓑ {(1, 4), (2, 3)}

Ⓒ {(1, 4), (2, 3), (3, 2), (4, 1)}

Ⓓ {(1, 5), (2, 5), (3, 5), (4, 5), (5, 5)}

2. OPEN RESPONSE A restaurant has a special deal where you can build your own meal from certain selections in the menu. The number of selections available in each category is shown in the table.

Item	Number of Choices
Drink	12
Appetizer	7
Main Entrée	8
Side Dishes	14
Dessert	9

If a person selects one of each item, how many different meals can be ordered? (Lesson 12-1)

84,672

3. MULTIPLE CHOICE An integer between 1 and 12 is generated using a random number generator. Let A be the event of generating a multiple of 4, and let B be the event of generating a factor of 12. Which of the following represents A ∩ B? (Lesson 12-2)

Ⓐ {4, 12}

Ⓑ {4, 8, 12}

Ⓒ {1, 2, 3, 4, 6, 12}

Ⓓ {1, 2, 3, 4, 6, 8, 12}

4. OPEN RESPONSE Jenell's birthday is in May. Let W be the event that his birthday lands on a weekend. Let P be the event that his birthday is a prime number.

What is W ∩ P? (Lesson 12-2)

May						
Sun	Mon	Tues	Wed	Thurs	Fri	Sat
	1	2	3	4	5	6
7	8	9	10	11	12	13
14	15	16	17	18	19	20
21	22	23	24	25	26	27
28	29	30	31			

{7, 13}

5. MULTIPLE CHOICE Point J will be placed randomly on $\overline{AD}$.

What is the probability that point J is on $\overline{AC}$ to the nearest percent? (Lesson 12-3)

Ⓐ 14%

Ⓑ 77%

Ⓒ 64%

Ⓓ 86%

Review and Assessment Options

The following online review and assessment resources are available for you to assign to your students. These resources include technology-enhanced questions that are auto-scored, as well as essay questions.

Review Resources

Put It All Together: Lessons 12–2 and 12–5 through 12–7
Vocabulary Activity
Module Review

Assessment Resources

Vocabulary Test
AL Module Test Form B
OL Module Test Form A
BL Module Test Form C
Performance Task*

*The module-level performance task is available online as a printable document. A scoring rubric is included.

Test Practice

You can use these pages to help your students review module content and prepare for online assessments. Exercises 1–16 mirror the types of questions your students will see on online assessments.

Question Type	Description	Exercise(s)
Multiple Choice	Students select one correct answer.	1, 3, 5, 6, 7, 12, 14, 15
Multi-Select	Multiple answers may be correct. Students must select all correct answers.	11
Table Item	Students complete a table by entering in the correct values.	9
Open Response	Students construct their own response in the area provided.	2, 4, 8, 10, 13, 16

To ensure that students understand the standards, check students' success on individual exercises.

Standard(s)	Lesson(s)	Exercise(s)
S.CP.1	12-1, 12-2	1, 2, 3, 4
S.CP.2	12-5	9, 10
S.CP.3	12-7	13, 14, 16
S.CP.4	12-8	15
S.CP.5	12-7	13, 14, 16
S.CP.6	12-8	15
S.CP.7	12-6	11, 12
S.CP.8	12-5	9, 10
S.CP.9	12-4	7, 8
S.MD.6	12-3	5, 6
S.MD.7	12-3	5, 6

---

6. MULTIPLE CHOICE Josefina is at a carnival trying to win a prize. She must toss a bean bag in the hole to win.

12 in.

12 in.

3 in.

What is the probability that when tossed randomly, the bean bag lands in the hole? Assume that the bean bag lands on the board. (Lesson 12-3)

Ⓐ 4.9%

Ⓑ 7.065%

Ⓒ 19.625%

Ⓓ 28.26%

7. MULTIPLE CHOICE If three points are randomly chosen from those named on hexagon *ABCDEF*, what is the probability that they all lie on the same line segment? (Lesson 12-4)

E H D
G   I
F   C
L   J
A K B

Ⓐ $\frac{1}{1320}$

Ⓑ $\frac{1}{220}$

Ⓒ $\frac{1}{216}$

Ⓓ $\frac{3}{220}$

8. OPEN RESPONSE The numbers 0–39 are used to create a locker combination. Show how to determine the probability that the combination is 20-21-22. (Lesson 12-4)

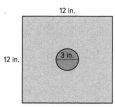

$$_{40}P_3 = \frac{40!}{(40-3)!} = \frac{40!}{37!} = \frac{40 \times 39 \times 38 \times 37!}{37!}$$
$$= 40 \times 39 \times 38 = 59,280 \text{ outcomes}$$
So, the probablity is $\frac{1}{59,280}$.

9. TABLE ITEM Identify each situation as *independent* or *dependent* events. (Lesson 12-5)

Situation	Independent	Dependent
Two dice are tossed.	X	
Two marbles are selected from a bag.		X
Two students are chosen as the captains of a team.		X
A coin is tossed and a card is chosen.	X	
Three books are selected from the library.		X
One student from each class is chosen to collect papers.	X	

10. OPEN RESPONSE The table shows the books of several different genres available to read on Imelda's bookshelf.

Genre	Number of Books
Action	8
Mystery	5
Romance	2
Science fiction	12
Horror	3

Imelda selects two different books. What is the probability, as a fraction, that Imelda selects two mysteries? (Lesson 12-5)

$\frac{2}{87}$

11. MULTI-SELECT Suppose a die is tossed once. Which of these events are mutually exclusive? Select all that apply. (Lesson 12-6)

Ⓐ Landing on a 4 or a 5

Ⓑ Landing on a 2 or an even

Ⓒ Landing on a 2 or a prime

Ⓓ Landing on 4 or an odd

Ⓔ Landing on an odd or a prime

12. MULTIPLE CHOICE A group of college students was surveyed about their browser use. The results are shown on the circle graph.

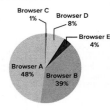

What is the probability that a student selected randomly will use either Browser A or Browser D? (Lesson 12-6)

Ⓐ $\frac{47}{100}$

Ⓑ $\frac{12}{25}$

Ⓒ $\frac{14}{25}$

Ⓓ $\frac{87}{100}$

13. OPEN RESPONSE Two dice have been tossed. What is the probability of tossing a sum of 8 given that at least one die landed on an odd number? (Lesson 12-7)

$\frac{2}{27}$

14. MULTIPLE CHOICE In a recent survey, 1650 students were asked what they are studying. Of the 1650 students, 948 students are learning Spanish. 426 students are studying physics, 378 of whom are also learning Spanish.

If a student is chosen at random, what is the probability that he or she is studying physics, given the student is studying Spanish? (Lesson 12-7)

Ⓐ 57.5%

Ⓑ 52.9%

Ⓒ 39.9%

Ⓓ 25.8%

15. MULTIPLE CHOICE The table shows the results of a survey asking whether the respondent preferred to use the Internet on a phone or laptop.

	Phone	Laptop	Total
12–29 years old	85	21	106
30+ years old	124	87	211
Total	209	108	317

What is the probability that a participant is 30+ years old given that they prefer a laptop to use the Internet? (Lesson 12-8)

Ⓐ 27.4%

Ⓑ 41.2%

Ⓒ 59.3%

Ⓓ 80.6%

16. OPEN RESPONSE Booker asks 29 students from his math class and 21 different students from his science class when they typically start working on their homework. Of the students, 18 from math class and 8 from science class respond that they do their homework as soon as they return home from school, and 11 from math class and 13 from science class respond that they start working on homework after dinner. What is the probability, as a percent to the nearest tenth, that a student waits to start homework until after dinner, given that they are in Booker's math class? (Lesson 12-7)

37.9%

Selected Answers

Module 7

Quick Check

1. 150 **3.** 1

Lesson 7-1

1. $m\angle Q = 121°$; $m\angle R = 58°$; $m\angle S = 123°$; $m\angle T = 58°$ **3.** $m\angle A = 90°$; $m\angle B = 90°$; $m\angle C = 128°$; $m\angle D = 74°$; $m\angle E = 158°$
5. 135° **7.** 128.6° **9.** 10 **11.** 18 **13.** 6
15. 37 **17.** 44 **19.** 72° **21.** 60° **23.** 40°
25. 51.4°; 128.6° **27.** 25.7°; 154.3° **29.** 30
31. 186°; 137°; 40°; 54°; 123° **33.** 360°
35. Consider the sum of the measures of the exterior angles N for an n-gon. N = sum of measures of linear pairs − sum of measures of interior angles

$$= 180n − 180(n − 2)$$
$$= 180n − 180n + 360$$
$$= 360$$

So, the sum of the exterior angle measures is 360° for any convex polygon. **37.** 15 **39.** 360° **41.** Liang; by the Polygon Exterior Angles Sum Theorem, the sum of the measures of any convex polygon is 360.

43. 8; Sample answer:

Interior angles sum = $(5 − 2) \cdot 180$ or 540°
Twice this sum is 2(540) or 1080°. A polygon with this interior angles sum is the solution to $(n − 2) \cdot 180 = 1080$. So, $n = 8$.

45. Always; sample answer. By the Polygon Exterior Angles Sum Theorem, $m\angle QPR = 60°$ and $m\angle QRP = 60°$. Because the sum of the interior angle measures of a triangle is 180°, the measure of $\angle PQR = 180 − m\angle QPR − m\angle QRP = 180 − 60 − 60 = 60°$. So, $\triangle PQR$ is an equilateral triangle.

Lesson 7-2

1. 52° **3.** 5 **5.** $x°$
7. Proof:

Statements (Reasons)
1. *WXTV* and *YZTV* are parallelograms. (Given)
2. $\overline{WX} \cong \overline{VT}$, $\overline{VT} \cong \overline{YZ}$ (Opp. sides of a parallelogram are ≅.)
3. $\overline{WX} \cong \overline{YZ}$ (Transitive Property of Congruence)

9. $x = 5$, $y = 17$ **11.** $x = 58$, $y = 63.5$
13. 203.32 m; 2125 m²
15. Proof:

Statements (Reasons)
1. ▱*PQRS* (Given)
2. Draw auxiliary segment *PR*. (Diagonal of *PQRS*)
3. $\overline{PQ} \parallel \overline{SR}$, $\overline{PS} \parallel \overline{QR}$ (Opp. sides of a parallelogram are ∥.)
4. $\angle QPR \cong \angle SRP$, $\angle SPR \cong \angle QRP$ (Alt. Interior Angles Thm.)
5. $\overline{PR} \cong \overline{PR}$ (Reflexive Property of ≅)
6. $\triangle QPR \cong \triangle SRP$ (ASA)
7. $\overline{PQ} \cong \overline{RS}$, $\overline{QR} \cong \overline{SP}$ (CPCTC)

Selected Answers

17. Proof:

Statements (Reasons)

1. ▱*GKLM* (Given)
2. $\overline{GK} \parallel \overline{ML}$, $\overline{GM} \parallel \overline{KL}$ (Opp. sides of a parallelogram are ∥.)
3. ∠*G* and ∠*K* are supplementary.
∠*K* and ∠*L* are supplementary.
∠*L* and ∠*M* are supplementary.
∠*M* and ∠*G* are supplementary.
(Consecutive Int. ∠s Thm.)

19. 3 **21.** 131° **23.** 29° **25a.** $JP = \sqrt{13}$, $LP = \sqrt{13}$, $MP = \sqrt{34}$, $KP = \sqrt{34}$; because $JP = LP$ and $MP = KP$, the diagonals bisect each other. **25b.** No; $JP + LP \neq MP + KP$. **25c.** No; sample answer: The slope of $\overline{JK} = 0$, and the slope of $\overline{JM} = 2$. The slopes are not negative reciprocals of each other, so the consecutive sides are not perpendicular. **27.** 7 **29.** Sample answer: In a parallelogram, the opp. sides and ∠s are ≅. Two consecutive ∠s in a ▱ are supplementary. If one angle of a ▱ is right, then all the angles are right. The diagonals of a parallelogram bisect each other. **31.** $m\angle 1 = 116°$, $m\angle 10 = 115°$; Sample answer: $m\angle 8 = 64°$ because alternate interior angles are congruent. ∠1 is supplementary to ∠8 because consecutive angles in a parallelogram are supplementary, so $m\angle 1$ is 116°. ∠10 is supplementary to the 65°-angle because consecutive angles in a parallelogram are supplementary, so $m\angle 10 = 180° - 65°$ or 115°.

Lesson 7-3

1. Yes; a pair of opposite sides are parallel and congruent. **3.** No; none of the tests for parallelograms are fulfilled. **5.** Yes; the diagonals bisect each other. **7.** $x = 20$; $y = 45$ **9.** $x = -6$; $y = 23$

11. Yes; sample answer: Use the Slope Formula.

$$m = \frac{y_2 - y_1}{x_2 - x_1}$$

slope of $\overline{AD} = \frac{3 - 0}{-2 - (-3)} = \frac{3}{1} = 3$

slope of $\overline{BC} = \frac{2 - (-1)}{3 - 2} = \frac{3}{1} = 3$

slope of $\overline{AB} = \frac{2 - 3}{3 - (-2)} = -\frac{1}{5}$

slope of $\overline{CD} = \frac{-1 - 0}{2 - (-3)} = -\frac{1}{5}$

Because opposite sides have the same slope, $\overline{AB} \parallel \overline{CD}$ and $\overline{AD} \parallel \overline{BC}$. Therefore, *ABCD* is a parallelogram by definition.

13. Yes; $SR = ZT$ and the slopes of $\overline{SR}$ and $\overline{ZT}$ are equal, so one pair of opposite sides is parallel and congruent.

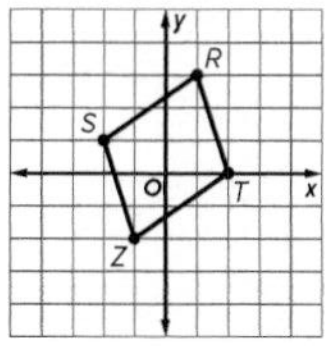

15. No; slope $\overline{XY} = -\frac{3}{5}$ and slope of $\overline{WZ} = -\frac{1}{3}$, so opposite sides are not parallel.

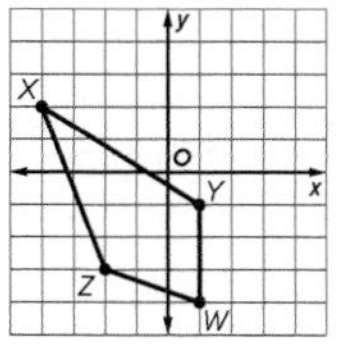

17. Given: *ABCD* is a parallelogram. ∠*A* is a right angle.
Prove: ∠*B*, ∠*C*, and ∠*D* are right angles.

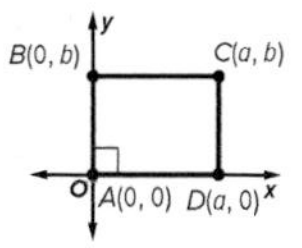

Proof:

slope of $\overline{AD} = \frac{0 - 0}{a - 0} = 0$

slope of $\overline{BC} = \frac{b - b}{a - 0} = 0$

slope of $\overline{AB}$ is undefined

slope of $\overline{CD}$ is undefined

Therefore, $\overline{AB} \perp \overline{BC}$, $\overline{BC} \perp \overline{CD}$, and $\overline{AB} \parallel \overline{CD}$. So, ∠*B*, ∠*C*, and ∠*D* are right angles.

19. Proof:

Statements (Reasons)

1. $\overline{PR}$ bisects $\overline{TQ}$; $\overline{TQ}$ bisects $\overline{PR}$. (Given)
2. $\overline{PV} \cong \overline{VR}$, $\overline{TV} \cong \overline{VQ}$ (Def. of bisector)
3. ∠*PVT* ≅ ∠*RVQ*, ∠*TVR* ≅ ∠*QVP* (Vertical Angles Thm.)
4. △*PVT* ≅ △*RVQ*, △*TVR* ≅ △*QVP* (SAS)
5. $\overline{PQ} \cong \overline{RT}$, $\overline{PT} \cong \overline{RQ}$ (CPCTC)
6. *PQRT* is a parallelogram. (If both pairs of opp. sides are ≅, then quad. is a ▱.)

21. (4, −1), (0, 3), or (−4, −5) **23.** −4 **25.** 28 cm **27.** Yes; sample answer: The lengths of the opposite sides are congruent. When the coordinate plane is placed over the map, the street lamps align perfectly with the points on the grid.
29. No; sample answer: Madison and Angela have to be the same distance from the center and Nikia and Shelby have to be the same distance from the center, but Nikia and Shelby's distance from the center does not have to be equal to Madison and Angela's distance.

31. Given: *RSTV* is a quadrilateral. *A*, *B*, *C*, and *D* are midpoints of sides $\overline{RS}$, $\overline{ST}$, $\overline{TV}$, and $\overline{VR}$, respectively.

Prove: *ABCD* is a parallelogram.

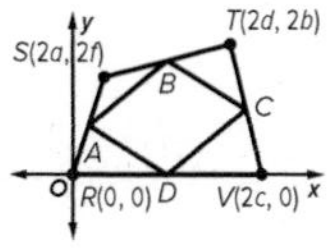

Proof:

Place quadrilateral *RSTV* on the coordinate plane and label the coordinates as shown. By the Midpoint Formula, the coordinates of *A*, *B*, *C*, and *D* are:

$A\left(\frac{2a}{2}, \frac{2f}{2}\right) = (a, f)$;

$B\left(\frac{2d + 2a}{2}, \frac{2f + 2b}{2}\right) = (d + a, f + b)$;

$C\left(\frac{2d + 2c}{2}, \frac{2b}{2}\right) = (d + c, b)$; and $D\left(\frac{2c}{2}, \frac{0}{2}\right) = (c, 0)$.

Find the slopes of $\overline{AB}$ and $\overline{DC}$.

slope of $\overline{AB} = \frac{(f + b) - f}{(d + a) - a} = \frac{b}{d}$

slope of $\overline{DC} = \frac{0 - b}{c - (d + c)} = \frac{-b}{-d} = \frac{b}{d}$

The slopes of $\overline{AB}$ and $\overline{DC}$ are the same, so the segments are parallel. Use the Distance Formula to find *AB* and *DC*.

$AB = \sqrt{(d + a - a)^2 + (f + b - f)^2} = \sqrt{d^2 + b^2}$

$DC = \sqrt{(d + c - c)^2 + (b - 0)^2} = \sqrt{d^2 + b^2}$

Thus, $AB = DC$ and $\overline{AB} \cong \overline{DC}$. Therefore, *ABCD* is a parallelogram because if one pair of opposite sides of a quadrilateral are both parallel and congruent, then the quadrilateral is a parallelogram.

33. Sample answer: The theorems are converses of each other. The hypothesis of Theorem 7.3 is *a quadrilateral is a parallelogram*, and the hypothesis of Theorem 7.9 is *both pairs of opposite sides of a quadrilateral are congruent*. The conclusion of Theorem 7.3 is *opposite sides are congruent*, and the conclusion of Theorem 7.9 is *the quadrilateral is a parallelogram*.
35. (−3, 1) and (−2, −2)

Lesson 7-4

1. 2 ft **3.** 50° **5.** 39 ft **7.** 52° **9.** $x = 7$
11. 77° **13.** 180°
15. Proof:

Statements (Reasons)

1. *ABCD* is a rectangle. (Given)
2. *ABCD* is a parallelogram. (Def. of rectangle)
3. $\overline{AD} \cong \overline{BC}$ (Opp. sides of a parallelogram are ≅.)
4. $\overline{DC} \cong \overline{DC}$ (Reflexive Property of ≅)
5. $\overline{AC} \cong \overline{BD}$ (Diag. of a rectangle are ≅.)
6. △*ADC* ≅ △*BCD* (SSS)

17. Yes; sample answer: Opposite sides are parallel and consecutive sides are perpendicular.

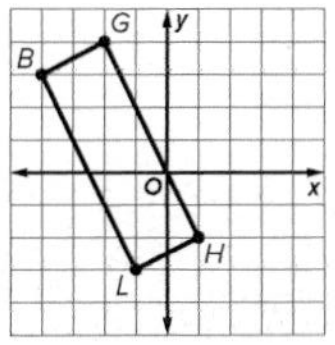

19. No; sample answer: Consecutive sides are not perpendicular.

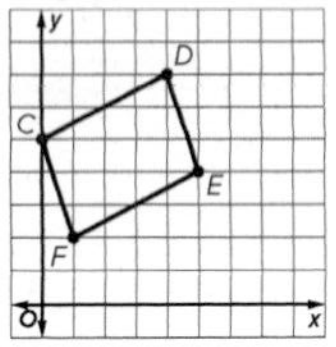

21. Yes; sample answer: Both pairs of opposite sides are congruent and diagonals are congruent.

23. Proof:

Statements (Reasons)

1. *ABCD* is a rectangle. (Given)
2. $\overline{AD} \cong \overline{BC}$ (If a quad. is a ▱, its opp. sides are ≅.)
3. $\overline{DC} \cong \overline{DC}$ (Reflexive Property of ≅)
4. ∠*ADC* and ∠*BCD* are rt. angles. (Def. of rectangle)
5. ∠*ADC* ≅ ∠*BCD* (All rt. angles are ≅.)
6. △*ADC* ≅ △*BCD* (SAS)
7. $\overline{AC} \cong \overline{BD}$ (CPCTC)

25. No; sample answer: If you only know that opposite sides are congruent and parallel, then the most that you can conclude is that the plot is a parallelogram.

27. Sample answer: Because $\overline{RP} \perp \overline{PQ}$ and $\overline{SQ} \perp \overline{PQ}$, $m\angle P = m\angle Q = 90°$. Lines that are perpendicular to the same line are parallel, so $\overline{RP} \parallel \overline{SQ}$. The same compass setting was used to locate points *R* and *S*, so $\overline{RP} \cong \overline{SQ}$. If one pair of opposite sides of a quadrilateral is both parallel and congruent, then the quadrilateral is a parallelogram. A parallelogram with right angles is a rectangle. Thus, *PRSQ* is a rectangle.

29. 5 **31.** They should be equal. **33.** (−6, 3)

35. *x* = 6; *y* = −10 **37.** Sample answer: All rectangles are parallelograms because, by definition, both pairs of opposite sides are parallel. Parallelograms with right angles are rectangles, so some parallelograms are rectangles, but others with nonright angles are not.

39. Yes; sample answer: By Theorem 7.6, if a parallelogram has one right angle, then it has four right angles. Therefore, a parallelogram with one right angle must be a rectangle.

Lesson 7-5

1. 60° **3.** 24 **5.** 32° **7.** 10 **9.** 21

11. Proof:

Statements (Reasons)

1. *ACDH* and *BCDF* are parallelograms; $\overline{BF} \cong \overline{AB}$. (Given)
2. $\overline{BF} \cong \overline{CD}, \overline{CD} \cong \overline{AH}$ (If a quad. is a ▱, then its opp. sides are ≅.)
3. $\overline{BF} \cong \overline{AH}$ (Transitive Property of ≅)
4. $\overline{BC} \cong \overline{FD}, \overline{AC} \cong \overline{HD}$ (If a quad. is a ▱, then its opp. sides are ≅.)
5. *BC* = *FD*, *AC* = *HD* (Def. of ≅ segments)
6. *AC* = *AB* + *BC*, *HD* = *HF* + *FD* (Seg. Add. Post.)
7. *AB* + *BC* = *HF* + *FD* (Substitution)
8. *AB* + *FD* = *HF* + *FD* (Substitution)
9. *AB* = *HF* (Subtraction Property of =)
10. $\overline{AB} \cong \overline{HF}$ (Def. of ≅ segments)
11. *ABFH* is a parallelogram. (If both pairs of opp. sides of a quad. are ≅, then the quad. is a ▱.)
12. *ABFH* is a rhombus. (If two consecutive sides of a ▱ are ≅, then the ▱ is a rhombus.)

13. Proof:

Statements (Reasons)

1. $\overline{WZ} \parallel \overline{XY}, \overline{WX} \parallel \overline{ZY}, \overline{WX} \cong \overline{XY}$ (Given)
2. *WXYZ* is a parallelogram. (Both pairs of opposite sides are parallel.)
3. *WXYZ* is a rhombus. (If one pair of consecutive sides of a parallelogram are congruent, then the parallelogram is a rhombus.)

---

15. Sample answer: Because consecutive sides are congruent, the garden is a rhombus. Jorge needs to know if the diagonals of the garden are congruent to determine whether it is a square. **17.** Parallelogram, rectangle, rhombus, square; the four sides are congruent and consecutive sides are perpendicular.

19. Parallelogram, rhombus; all sides are congruent and the diagonals are perpendicular, but not congruent. **21.** Parallelogram, rhombus, rectangle, square; all sides are congruent and the diagonals are perpendicular and congruent.

23. 55 **25.** 38.9 **27.** 6 **29.** 90°

31. Proof:

Statements (Reasons)

1. *ABCD* is a rhombus. (Given)
2. *ABCD* is a parallelogram. (Def. of rhombus)
3. ∠*DAB* ≅ ∠*DCB*, ∠*ABC* ≅ ∠*ADC* (If a quad. is a ▱, its opp. ∠s are ≅.)
4. $\overline{AB} \cong \overline{BC} \cong \overline{CD} \cong \overline{AD}$ (Def. of rhombus)
5. △*DAB* ≅ △*DCB*, △*ABC* ≅ △*ADC* (SAS)
6. ∠8 ≅ ∠7, ∠3 ≅ ∠4, ∠1 ≅ ∠2, ∠5 ≅ ∠6 (CPCTC)
7. $\overline{AC}$ bisects ∠*DAB* and ∠*DCB*. $\overline{BD}$ bisects ∠*ABC* and ∠*ADC*. (Def. of angle bisector)

33. Proof:

Statements (Reasons)

1. *RSTU* is a parallelogram; $\overline{RS} \cong \overline{ST}$. (Given)
2. $\overline{RS} \cong \overline{UT}, \overline{RU} \cong \overline{ST}$ (If a quad. is a ▱, its opp. sides are ≅.)
3. $\overline{RS} \cong \overline{RU}$ (Transitive Property of ≅)
4. *RSTU* is a rhombus. (Def. of rhombus)

35. The figure consists of 15 congruent rhombi.

37. square

39.

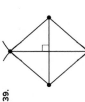

Sample answer: The diagonals bisect each other, so the quadrilateral is a parallelogram. Because the diagonals of the parallelogram are perpendicular to each other, the parallelogram is a rhombus. **41.** right triangles

43. Parallelogram: Opposite sides of a parallelogram are parallel and congruent. Opposite angles of a parallelogram are congruent. The diagonals of a parallelogram bisect each other and each diagonal separates a parallelogram into two congruent triangles.

Rectangle: A rectangle has all the properties of a parallelogram. A rectangle has four right angles. The diagonals of a rectangle are congruent.

Rhombus: A rhombus has all the properties of a parallelogram. All sides of a rhombus are congruent. The diagonals of a rhombus are perpendicular and bisect the angles of the rhombus.

Square: A square has all of the properties of a parallelogram. A square has all the properties of a rectangle. A square has all of the properties of a rhombus. **45.** True; sample answer: A rectangle is a quadrilateral with four right angles and a square is both a rectangle and a rhombus, so a square is always a rectangle.

Converse: If a quadrilateral is a rectangle, then it is a square. False; sample answer: A rectangle is a quadrilateral with four right angles. It is not necessarily a rhombus, so it is not necessarily a square.

Inverse: If a quadrilateral is not a square, then it is not a rectangle. False; sample answer: A quadrilateral that has four right angles and two pairs of congruent sides is not a square, but it is a rectangle.

Contrapositive: If a quadrilateral is not a rectangle, then it is not a square. True; sample answer: If a quadrilateral is not a rectangle, it is also not a square by definition.

Lesson 7-6

1a. Proof:

Statements (Reasons)

1. *WXYZ* is an isosceles trapezoid. (Given)
2. $\overline{WZ} \cong \overline{XY}$ (Def. of isosceles trapezoid)
3. *WZ* = *XY* (Def. of congruent segments)

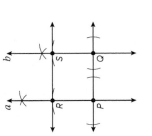

4. $4x + 5 = 5x - 3$ (Substitution)

5. $5 = x - 3$ (Subtraction Prop. of Equality)

6. $8 = x$ (Addition Prop. of Equality)

7. $x = 8$ (Symmetric Prop. of Equality)

1b. 74° **1c.** 110 in. **3.** 112°

5a. $\overline{AD} \parallel \overline{BC}$, but $\overline{AB} \nparallel \overline{CD}$. **5b.** yes; $AB = 5$ and $CD = 5$

7. 11 **9.** 13 **11.** $(-3, -0.5)$ and $(2, 2)$

13. 101° **15a.** $\sqrt{65}$ **15b.** 42.2

17. 15 **19.** 100° **21.** 17.5 ft

23. Proof:

Statements (Reasons)

1. $TUVW$ is a trapezoid; $\angle W \cong \angle V$. (Given)
2. Draw auxiliary line $\overline{UX} \parallel \overline{TW}$. (Parallel Postulate)
3. $\angle UXV \cong \angle W$ (Corresponding Angles Thm.)
4. $\angle UXV \cong \angle V$ (Transitive Property of $\cong$)
5. $\overline{UX} \cong \overline{UV}$ (Converse of Isosceles Triangle Thm.)
6. $\overline{TU} \parallel \overline{WV}$ (Def. of a trapezoid)
7. $TUXW$ is a parallelogram. (Def. of parallelogram)
8. $\overline{TW} \cong \overline{UX}$ (If a quad. is a ▱, its opp. sides are $\cong$.)
9. $\overline{TW} \cong \overline{UV}$ (Transitive Property of $\cong$)
10. Trapezoid $TUVW$ is isosceles. (Def. of isosceles trapezoid)

25. Proof: It is given that $LMNP$ is a kite. By the definition of kite, $\overline{LM} \cong \overline{LP}$ and $\overline{MN} \cong \overline{PN}$. By the Reflexive Property of Congruence, $\overline{LN} \cong \overline{LN}$. Therefore, $\triangle LMN \cong \triangle LPN$ by SSS. $\angle M \cong \angle P$ by CPCTC. If both pairs of opposite angles of a quadrilateral are congruent, then the quadrilateral is a parallelogram. So, if $\angle MLP \cong \angle MNP$, then $LMNP$ is a parallelogram. It is given that $LMNP$ is a kite. Therefore, $\angle MLP \ncong \angle MNP$.

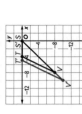

27. Sample answer: $y = 3$, $y = 1$, $y = x$, $y = -x + 10$; The intersection points of the four lines are $A(1, 1)$, $B(3, 3)$, $C(7, 3)$, and $D(9, 1)$. The slope of $\overline{AD}$ is 0, and the slope of $\overline{BC}$ is 0. Therefore, $\overline{AD} \parallel \overline{BC}$. The slope of $\overline{AB}$ is 1, and the slope of $\overline{CD}$ is -1. So, $\overline{AB} \nparallel \overline{CD}$. $AB = 2\sqrt{2}$, and $CD = 2\sqrt{2}$. Therefore, by definition, $ABCD$ is an isosceles trapezoid.

29. Belinda; sample answer: Because $ABCD$ is a kite, $m\angle D = m\angle B$. So, $m\angle A + m\angle B + m\angle C + m\angle D = 360°$, or $m\angle A + 100 + 45 + 100 = 360°$. Therefore, $m\angle A = 115°$.

31. Sample answer: A quadrilateral must have exactly one pair of sides parallel to be a trapezoid. If the legs are congruent, then the trapezoid is an isosceles trapezoid. If a quadrilateral has exactly two pairs of consecutive congruent sides with the opposite sides not congruent, the quadrilateral is a kite. A trapezoid and a kite both have four sides. In a trapezoid and isosceles trapezoid, both have exactly one pair of parallel sides.

33. Never; sample answer: Exactly two pairs of adjacent sides are congruent.

Module 7 Review

1. C **3.** C **5.** $m\angle Q = 108°$ and $m\angle R = 72°$

7.

Quadrilateral	Parallelogram?	
	Yes	No
A		X
B	X	
C	X	
D		X

9. A **11.** A

13.

Shape	Can be created?	
	Yes	No
Kite		X
Parallelogram	X	
Rectangle	X	
Rhombus	X	
Square	X	
Trapezoid		X

15. A, B, C, E **17.** B

15.

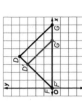

Module 8

Quick Check

1. $\frac{1}{4}$ **3.** $\frac{3}{5}$ **5.** $\frac{4}{5}$ **7.** 40 in.

Lesson 8-1

1. enlargement; 3 **3.** reduction; $\frac{2}{3}$

5. 50%; The perimeter of the updated blueprint will be 26 units.

7. $S'(0, 0)$, $T'(-5, 0)$, $V(-10, -10)$

9. $D'(3, 3)$, $F'(0, 0)$, $G'(6, 0)$

11. 1.5

13.

17. $\frac{2}{3}$ **19.** enlargement; 2

21.

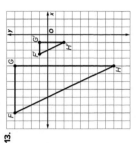

23a. $\frac{b}{a}$; Sample answer: The coordinates of P' are (ka, kb).

The slope of $\overleftrightarrow{PP'}$ is $\frac{kb - b}{ka - a} = \frac{b(k - 1)}{a(k - 1)} = \frac{b}{a}$.

23b. Sample answer: If P lies on the y-axis, then its image P' will also lie on the y-axis. In this case, $\overleftrightarrow{PP'}$ will be vertical, and the slope will be undefined.

25. $y = 4x - 3$

27a. Always; sample answer: Points remain invariant under the dilation.

27b. Always; sample answer: Because the rotation is centered at B, point B will always remain invariant under the rotation.

27c. Sometimes; sample answer: If one of the vertices is on the x-axis, then that point will remain invariant under reflection. If two vertices are on the x-axis, then the two vertices located on the x-axis will remain invariant under reflection.

27d. Never; sample answer: When a figure is translated, all points move an equal distance. Therefore, no points can remain invariant under translation.

27e. Sometimes; sample answer: If one of the vertices of the triangle is located at the origin, then that vertex would remain invariant under the dilation. If none of the points of $\triangle XYZ$ are located at the origin, then no points will remain invariant under the dilation.

29. Sample answer: Translations, reflections, and rotations produce congruent figures because the sides and angles of the preimage are congruent to the corresponding sides and angles of the image.

Lesson 8-2

1. $\angle A \cong \angle W$, $\angle B \cong \angle X$, $\angle C \cong \angle Y$, $\angle D \cong \angle Z$, $\frac{AB}{WX} = \frac{BC}{XY} = \frac{CD}{YZ} = \frac{AD}{WZ}$

3. $\angle F \cong \angle J$, $\angle G \cong \angle K$, $\angle H \cong \angle L$, $\frac{FG}{JK} = \frac{GH}{KL} = \frac{FH}{JL}$

5. $\angle A \cong \angle F$, $\angle B \cong \angle G$, $\angle C \cong \angle H$, $\angle D \cong \angle J$, $\frac{AB}{FG} = \frac{BC}{GH} = \frac{CD}{HJ} = \frac{AD}{FJ}$

7. no; $\angle W \not\cong \angle M$ **9.** no; $\frac{MN}{GH} \neq \frac{NP}{HJ}$ **11.** 3

13. 5   **15.** 8.5 km   **17.** 18.9

19. $x = 63$, $y = 32$ **21.** Because $\triangle DEF \sim \triangle DEF$, $\frac{AB}{DE} = \frac{BC}{EF} = \frac{AC}{DF}$. So, $\frac{AB}{DE} = \frac{BC}{EF} = \frac{AC}{DF} = \frac{m}{n}$. By the Multiplication Property of Equality, $AB = DE\left(\frac{m}{n}\right)$, $BC = EF\left(\frac{m}{n}\right)$, and $AC = DF\left(\frac{m}{n}\right)$. Using substitution, the perimeter of $\triangle ABC = DE\left(\frac{m}{n}\right) + EF\left(\frac{m}{n}\right) + DF\left(\frac{m}{n}\right) = \frac{m}{n}(DE + EF + DF)$. The ratio of the perimeters is $\frac{\text{Perimeter of } \triangle ABC}{\text{Perimeter of } \triangle DEF} = \frac{\left(\frac{m}{n}\right)(DE + EF + DF)}{DE + EF + DF} = \frac{m}{n}$.   **23.** $\frac{3}{2}$

25. Yes; the ratio of the longer dimensions of the rinks is $\frac{20}{17}$, and the ratio of the smaller dimensions of the rinks is $\frac{20}{17}$.   **27.** 4

29. Sample answer: $\frac{4}{3} \neq \frac{4}{10}$;

[4 cm × 3 cm rectangle]   [10 cm × 4 cm rectangle]

31. Sample answer: The figures could be described as congruent if they are the same size and shape, similar if their corresponding angles are congruent and their corresponding sides are proportional, and equal if they are the same figure, or none of those.

Lesson 8-3

1. Yes; $\triangle FGH \sim \triangle JHK$ by AA Similarity.

3. No; the triangles would be similar by AA Similarity if $\overline{AB} \parallel \overline{DF}$.   **5.** Yes; the triangles are similar by AA Similarity.   **7.** 135 ft

9. $\triangle ABC \sim \triangle DBE$; 16   **11.** $\triangle DEF \sim \triangle GEH$; 9

13. Sample answer: $m\angle ADB = 108°$, so $m\angle DBA = 36°$ because base angles of an isosceles triangle are congruent. Thus, $m\angle ABC = 72°$. Similarly, $m\angle DCB = 36°$ and $m\angle ACB = 72°$. So, $m\angle BEC = 72°$ and $m\angle BAC = 36°$. Therefore, $\triangle ABC$ and $\triangle BCE$ are similar.

15. Yes; sample answer: The triangles are similar. It is given that $\overline{KM} \perp \overline{JL}$ and $\overline{JK} \perp \overline{KL}$. $\angle JKL \cong \angle JMK$ because they are both right angles. By the Reflexive Property of Congruence, we know $\angle J \cong \angle J$. Therefore, by the AA Similarity Postulate, we can conclude that $\triangle JKL \sim \triangle JMK$.

Lesson 8-4

1. Yes; $\triangle RST \sim \triangle WSX$ (or $\triangle XSW$) by SAS Similarity   **3.** Yes; $\triangle STU \sim \triangle JPM$ by SAS Similarity   **5.** $\triangle HIJ \sim \triangle KLI$; 5

7. $\triangle RST \sim \triangle UVW$; 11.25   **9.** 5 ft   **11.** 202.2 in.

13. Sample answer: $m\angle TSU = m\angle QSR$ because they are vertical angles. $\frac{ST}{SQ}$ is proportional to $\frac{SU}{SR}$. Therefore, $\triangle STU$ and $\triangle SQR$ are similar by the SAS Similarity Theorem.

15. Sample answer: The AA Similarity Postulate, SSS Similarity Theorem, and SAS Similarity Theorem are all tests that can be used to determine whether two triangles are similar. The AA Similarity Postulate is used when two pairs of congruent angles of two triangles are given. The SSS Similarity Theorem is used when the corresponding proportional side lengths of two triangles are given. The SAS Similarity Theorem is used when two corresponding proportional side lengths and the included angle of two triangles are given.   **17.** 6

29. Sample answer: By Corollary 8.1, $\frac{a}{b} = \frac{c}{d}$.

Lesson 8-5

1. 6   **3.** yes; $\frac{PN}{NM} = \frac{QR}{RM} = \frac{1}{2}$
5. 50   **7.** 1.135   **9.** 1.12 km   **11.** $x = 6$, $y = 6.5$
13. 15   **15.** 8   **17.** 12 ft
19. Because $\frac{AD}{DB} = \frac{AE}{EC}$, an equivalent proportion is $\frac{DB}{AD} = \frac{EC}{AE}$. Add 1 to each side of the proportion as follows: $\frac{DB}{AD} + \frac{AD}{AD} = \frac{EC}{AE} + \frac{AE}{AE}$. Therefore, $\frac{DB + AD}{AD} = \frac{EC + AE}{AE}$. By the Segment Addition Postulate, this is equivalent to $\frac{AB}{AD} = \frac{AC}{AE}$. Because $\frac{AB}{AD} = \frac{AC}{AE}$ and $\angle A \cong \angle A$ by the Reflexive Property of Congruence, $\triangle ADE \sim \triangle ABC$ by the SAS Similarity Theorem. Therefore, $\angle ADE \cong \angle ABC$ because they are corresponding angles of similar triangles; so $\overline{DE} \parallel \overline{BC}$, because if corresponding angles are congruent, then the lines are parallel.

21. Proof: We are given that $\overline{AE} \parallel \overline{BF} \parallel \overline{CG}$. Draw $\overline{AG}$ so that $\overline{AG}$ intersects $\overline{BF}$ at D.

In $\triangle ACG$, $\overline{CG} \parallel \overline{BD}$. By the Triangle Proportionality Theorem, $\frac{BC}{AB} = \frac{AD}{DG}$. In $\triangle AGE$, $\overline{AE} \parallel \overline{DF}$. By the Triangle Proportionality Theorem, $\frac{AD}{DG} = \frac{EF}{FG}$. Therefore, by the Transitive Property, $\frac{AB}{BC} = \frac{EF}{FG}$.

23. 39 cm; Sample answer: Because J, K, and L are midpoints of their respective sides, $JK = \frac{1}{2}QR$, $KL = \frac{1}{2}PQ$, and $JL = \frac{1}{2}PR$ by the Triangle Midsegment Theorem. So $JK + KL + JL = \frac{1}{2}(QR + PQ + PR) = \frac{1}{2}(78) = 39$.

25a. $ST = 8$ $UV = 4$ $WX = 2$

25b. Based on the pattern, the length of the midsegment of $\triangle WXR = 1$.

27. Always; sample answer: FH is a midsegment. Let $BC = x$, then $FH = \frac{1}{2}x$. $FHCB$ is a trapezoid, so $DE = \frac{1}{2}(BC + FH) = \frac{1}{2}\left(x + \frac{1}{2}x\right) = \frac{1}{2}x + \frac{1}{4}x = \frac{3}{4}x$. Therefore, $DE = \frac{3}{4}BC$.

Lesson 8-6

1. 16.5   **3.** 11   **5.** 8.4   **7.** 7 yd
9. 8.4   **11.** 5.3 cm
13. Proof:

Statements (Reasons)
1. $\triangle ABC \sim \triangle RST$, $\overline{AD}$ is a median of $\triangle ABC$ and $\overline{RU}$ is a median of $\triangle RST$. (Given)
2. $CD = DB$, $TU = US$ (Definition of median)
3. $\frac{AB}{RS} = \frac{CB}{TS}$ (Definition of similar triangles)
4. $CB = CD + DB$, $TS = TU + US$ (Segment Addition Postulate)
5. $\frac{AB}{RS} = \frac{CD + DB}{TU + US}$ (Substitution)
6. $\frac{AB}{RS} = \frac{DB + DB}{US + US} = \frac{2(DB)}{2(US)}$ (Substitution)
7. $\frac{AB}{RS} = \frac{DB}{US}$ (Substitution)
8. $\angle B \cong \angle S$ (Definition of similar triangles)
9. $\triangle ABD \sim \triangle RSU$ (SAS Similarity)
10. $\frac{AD}{RU} = \frac{DB}{RS}$ (Definition of similar triangles)

15. Chun; sample answer: By the Angle Bisector Theorem, the correct proportion is $\frac{5}{8} = \frac{15}{x}$.

17. $PS = 18.4$, $RS = 24$

Module 8 Review

1. D   3. $A'(4, 3.2)$, $B'(8, 6.4)$, and $C'(16, 0)$

5. $\angle A \cong \angle F$, $\angle B \cong \angle G$, $\angle C \cong \angle H$, $\angle D \cong \angle E$

$\dfrac{AB}{FG} = \dfrac{BC}{GH} = \dfrac{CD}{HE} = \dfrac{DA}{EF}$

$\dfrac{9}{12} = \dfrac{6}{8} = \dfrac{12}{16}$

$\dfrac{3}{4} = \dfrac{3}{4} = \dfrac{3}{4} = \dfrac{3}{4}$

Therefore, quadrilateral $ABCD \sim$ quadrilateral $FGHE$.

7. C   9. C   11. B

13.

Sides	Lengths			
	1.6	2.0	2.4	3.6
$\overline{AB}$	X			
$\overline{BD}$				X
$\overline{BC}$			X	

15. 8   17. A

Module 9

Quick Check

1. $x = 18$ 3. 10   5. 14   7. 17

Lesson 9-1

1. $\sqrt{24}$ or $2\sqrt{6} \approx 4.9$ 3. 10   5. $\sqrt{51} \approx 7.1$

7. $\triangle ACB \sim \triangle BCD \sim \triangle ABD$

9. $\triangle EGF \sim \triangle GHF \sim \triangle EHG$

11. $x = \sqrt{184}$ or $2\sqrt{46} \approx 13.6$; $y = \sqrt{248}$ or $2\sqrt{62} \approx 15.7$; $z = \sqrt{713} \approx 26.7$

13. $x = 4.5$; $y = \sqrt{13} \approx 3.6$; $z = 6.5$

15. 7.2 ft
Sample answer:

Statue — 12 ft, 9 ft, x, 15 ft

17. 2.88 mi

19. Proof: It is given that $\triangle ADC$ is a right triangle and $\overline{DB}$ is an altitude of $\triangle ADC$. $\angle ADC$ is a right angle by the definition of a right triangle. Therefore, $\triangle ADB \sim \triangle DCB$, because if the altitude is drawn from the vertex of the right angle to the hypotenuse of a right triangle, then the two triangles formed are similar to the given triangle and to each other. So, $\dfrac{AB}{DB} = \dfrac{DB}{CB}$ by the definition of similar triangles.

21. $x = 5.2$; $y = 6.8$; $z = 11.1$

23. Sample answer: 9 and 4, 8 and 8; For two whole numbers to result in a whole-number geometric mean, their product must be a perfect square.

25a. Never; sample answer: The geometric mean of two consecutive integers is $\sqrt{x(x + 1)}$, and the average of two consecutive integers is $\dfrac{x + (x + 1)}{2}$. If you set the two expressions equal to each other, the equation has no solution.

25b. Always; sample answer: Because $\sqrt{ab}$ is equal to $\sqrt{a} \cdot \sqrt{b}$, the geometric mean for two perfect squares will always be the product of two positive integers, which is a positive integer.

25c. Sometimes; sample answer: When the product of two integers is a perfect square, the geometric mean will be a positive integer.

Lesson 9-2

1. $\sqrt{18}$ or $3\sqrt{2} \approx 4.2$ 3. 60   5. $\sqrt{1345} \approx 36.7$

7. 15   9. 100   11. 6   13. about 4.6 feet high

15. Yes; right; sample answer: The measures of the sides would be $XY = \sqrt{8} \approx 2.83$, $YZ = \sqrt{2} \approx 1.41$, and $XZ = \sqrt{10} \approx 3.16$. Because $2.83 + 1.41 > 3.16$, $2.83 + 3.16 > 1.41$, and $1.41 + 3.16 > 2.83$, the side lengths can form a triangle. Because $(\sqrt{8})^2 + (\sqrt{2})^2 = (\sqrt{10})^2$, we know that the triangle is a right triangle.

17. Yes; obtuse; sample answer: The measures of the sides would be $XY = 5$, $YZ = 2$, and $XZ = \sqrt{41} \approx 6.40$. Because $5 + 2 > 6.40$, $5 + 6.40 > 2$, and $2 + 6.40 > 5$, the side lengths can form a triangle. Because $5^2 + 2^2 < (\sqrt{41})^2$, we know that the triangle is an obtuse triangle.

19. 30 ft   21. yes, right; $(\sqrt{12})^2 = (\sqrt{8})^2 + 2^2$

23. Proof:

Statements (Reasons)

1. In $\triangle DEF$, $f^2 < d^2 + e^2$ where f is the length of the longest side. In $\triangle LMN$, $\angle M$ is a right angle. (Given)
2. $d^2 + e^2 = x^2$ (Pythagorean Thm.)
3. $f^2 < x^2$ (Substitution)
4. $f < x$ (Take the positive square root.)
5. $m\angle M = 90°$ (Def. of right angle)
6. $m\angle F < m\angle M$ (Conv. of the Hinge Thm.)
7. $m\angle F < 90°$ (Substitution)
8. $\angle F$ is an acute angle. (Def. of acute angle)
9. $m\angle D < m\angle F$, $m\angle E < m\angle F$ (If one side of a $\triangle$ is longer than another side, then the $\angle$ opp. the longer side has a greater measure than the $\angle$ opp. the shorter side.)
10. $m\angle D < 90°$, $m\angle E < 90°$ (Transitive Prop. of Inequality)
11. $\triangle DEF$ is an acute triangle. (Def. of acute $\triangle$)

25. 2129   27. $P = 36$ units; $A = 60$ units^2

29. 15   31a. Because the height of the tree is 20 m, $JL = 20 - x$. By the Pythagorean Theorem, $16^2 + x^2 = (20 - x)^2$.

31b. $16^2 + x^2 = (20 - x)^2$, so $256 + x^2 = 400 - 40x + x^2$. Subtracting x^2 from both sides gives $256 = 400 - 40x$. Therefore, $-144 = -40x$. Dividing both sides by -40 gives $3.6 = x$. The stump of the tree is 3.6 meters tall. 33. 10 35. $\frac{1}{2}$

37. 12.04 miles

43. Sample answer: Incommensurable magnitudes are magnitudes of the same kind that do not have a common unit of measure. Irrational numbers were invented to describe geometric relationships, such as ratios of incommensurable magnitudes that cannot be described using rational numbers. For example, to express the measures of the sides of a square with an area of 2 square units, the irrational number $\sqrt{2}$ is needed.

Lesson 9-3

1.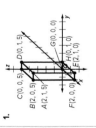

3.

5.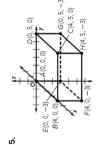

7. $\sqrt{29}$ 9. $\sqrt{46}$ 11. 20.2 mi 13. $(1, -1, -2)$
15. $\left(4, \frac{7}{2}, \frac{17}{2}\right)$ 17. $\left(5, 4, \frac{19}{2}\right)$
19. $PQ = \sqrt{36}$ or 6; $(-3, -1, 1)$
21. $FG = \sqrt{10}$; $\left(\frac{3}{10}, \frac{3}{2}, \frac{2}{5}\right)$
23. $BC = \sqrt{39}$; $\left(-\frac{\sqrt{5}}{2}, 3, 3\sqrt{2}\right)$
25. Proof: Points $A(x_1, y_1, z_1)$ and $B(x_2, y_2, z_2)$ are given. It is also given that M is the midpoint of $\overline{AB}$. To find the coordinates of point M, you

39a. Sample answer: $a^2 + b^2 = (m^2 - n^2)^2 + (2mn)^2 = m^4 - 2m^2n^2 + n^4 + 4m^2n^2 = m^4 + 2m^2n^2 + n^4$ and $c^2 = (m^2 + n^2)^2 = m^4 + 2m^2n^2 + n^4$. This means that $a^2 + b^2 = c^2$, so a, b, and c do form the sides of a right triangle by the Converse of the Pythagorean Theorem.

39b.

m	n	a	b	c
2	1	3	4	5
3	1	8	6	10
3	2	5	12	13
4	1	15	8	17
4	2	12	16	20
4	3	7	24	25
5	1	24	10	26

39c. Sample answer: Take $m = 24$ and $n = 7$ to get $a = 527$, $b = 336$, and $c = 625$.

41.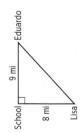

Right; sample answer: If you double or halve the side lengths, all three sides of the new triangles are proportional to the sides of the original triangle. Using the Side-Side-Side Similarity Theorem, you know that both of the new triangles are similar to the original triangle, so they are both right.

must find the coordinates of a point that is $\frac{1}{2}$ of the distance from point A to point B in three-dimensional space. The difference between the x-, y-, and z-coordinates of points A and B are $x_2 - x_1$, $y_2 - y_1$, and $z_2 - z_1$, respectively. Because point M is halfway between points A and B, the distances between the x-, y-, and z-coordinates of points A and M are $\frac{1}{2}(x_2 - x_1)$, $\frac{1}{2}(y_2 - y_1)$, and $\frac{1}{2}(z_2 - z_1)$, respectively. To find the coordinates of point M, add the fractional distances to the coordinates of point A.

coordinates of point $M =$
$$\left(x_1 + \tfrac{1}{2}(x_2 - x_1), y_1 + \tfrac{1}{2}(y_2 - y_1), z_1 + \tfrac{1}{2}(z_2 - z_1)\right) =$$
$$\left(\frac{2x_1 + x_2 - x_1}{2}, \frac{2y_1 + y_2 - y_1}{2}, \frac{2z_1 + z_2 - z_1}{2}\right) =$$
$$\left(\frac{x_1 + x_2}{2}, \frac{y_1 + y_2}{2}, \frac{z_1 + z_2}{2}\right)$$

27. Teion; sample answer: Camilla made a mistake when substituting the value for y_r.
29. $2\sqrt{19}$

Lesson 9-4

1. $7\sqrt{2}$ 3. $6\sqrt{2}$ 5. 10 7. $18\sqrt{2}$ 9. $25\sqrt{2}$
11. 2 13. $5\sqrt{2}$ 15. $2\sqrt{2}$ 17. 16 19. $x = 8$;
$y = 16$ 21. $x = \frac{15\sqrt{3}}{2}$, $y = \frac{15}{2}$ 23. $x = 24\sqrt{3}$;
$y = 48$ 25. 20 ft 27. No; sample answer: The height of the frame is only 10 centimeters, and the height of the certificate is about 10.4 centimeters. So, the certificate will not fit.
29. $6\sqrt{2}$ yd or about 8.49 yd 31a. x feet
31b. $\sqrt{3}$ ft 31c. 20.5 ft 33. $x = \frac{13\sqrt{2}}{2}$, $y = 45$
35. $x = 3$; $y = 1$ 37. $x = 6\sqrt{3}$; $y = 3$
39. Proof: A $45°$-$45°$-$90°$ triangle with a leg of length ℓ and a hypotenuse of length h is given. Because the measure of each acute angle in the triangle is $45°$ by the definition of congruent angles, the angles are congruent. Therefore, by the Converse of the Isosceles Triangle Theorem, the legs of the triangle are congruent. Because the legs are congruent, the measure of each leg is ℓ. By the Pythagorean Theorem, $\ell^2 + \ell^2 = h^2$. This equation simplifies to $2\ell^2 = h^2$. Take the positive square root of each side to get

$\sqrt{2\ell^2} = \sqrt{h^2}$. So, $\ell\sqrt{2} = h$. By the Symmetric Property of Equality, $h = \ell\sqrt{2}$.
41. $(6, 9)$

43. $RS \approx 5.464$ ft; $ST \approx 9.464$ ft; $RT \approx 10.928$ ft
45. 59.8 47. Carmen; sample answer: Because the three angles of the larger triangle are congruent, it is an equilateral triangle and the right triangles formed by the altitude are $30°$-$60°$-$90°$ triangles. The hypotenuse is 6, so the shorter leg is 3 and the longer leg x is $3\sqrt{3}$.
49. Sample answer:

Let ℓ represent the length.
$\ell^2 + w^2 = (2w)^2$; $\ell^2 = 3w^2$; $\ell = w\sqrt{3}$

Lesson 9-5

1. $\sin L = \frac{5}{13} \approx 0.38$; $\cos L = \frac{12}{13} \approx 0.92$; $\tan L = \frac{5}{12} \approx 0.42$; $\sin M = \frac{12}{13} \approx 0.92$; $\cos M = \frac{5}{13} \approx 0.38$; $\tan M = \frac{12}{5} = 2.4$
3. $\sin R = \frac{8}{17} \approx 0.47$; $\cos R = \frac{15}{17} \approx 0.88$; $\tan R = \frac{8}{15} \approx 0.53$; $\sin S = \frac{15}{17} \approx 0.88$; $\cos S = \frac{8}{17} \approx 0.47$; $\tan S = \frac{15}{8} \approx 1.88$
5. $\frac{1}{2}$; 0.5 7. $\frac{1}{2}$; 0.5 9. $\frac{\sqrt{3}}{3}$; 0.58 11. 22.55
13. 24.15 15. 15.5 ft 17. 33.6° 19. 35.5°
21. 67.0° 23. $WX = 15.1$; $XZ = 9.8$; $m\angle W = 33°$
25. $RT = 3.7$; $ST = 5.9$; $m\angle R = 58°$
27. $NQ = 25.5$; $MQ = 18.0$; $m\angle N = 45°$
29. 56.3° 31. 28.52 cm; 23.39 cm²
33a. $\cos 26°$ or $\sin 64°$ 33b. $\cos 64°$ or $\sin 26°$ 33c. $\tan 64°$ 35. Sample answer: The sine of an angle equals the cosine of its complement. So, $\sin \beta = \cos \alpha = 0.7660$. Similarly, $\cos \beta = \sin \alpha = 0.6428$. 37. $x = 9.2$; $y = 11.7$ 39. Yes, they are both correct; sample answer: Because $27 + 63 = 90$, the sine of 27° is the same ratio as the cosine of 63°.
41. Yes; sample answer: Because the values of sine and cosine are both calculated by

dividing one of the legs of a right triangle by the hypotenuse, and the hypotenuse is always the longest side of a right triangle, the values will always be less than 1. You will always be dividing the smaller number by the larger number.

43. Sample answer: To find the measure of an acute angle of a right triangle, you can find the ratio of the leg opposite the angle to the hypotenuse and use a calculator to find the inverse sine of the ratio; you can find the ratio of the leg adjacent to the angle to the hypotenuse and use a calculator to find the inverse cosine of the ratio; or you can find the ratio of the leg opposite the angle to the leg adjacent to the angle and use a calculator to find the inverse tangent of the ratio.

Lesson 9-6

1. 64 m   **3.** about 21 ft   **5.** about 35°
7. 14.8°   **9.** 10 feet tall   **11.** 19 ft
13. 62.3 units²   **15.** 71.5 units²   **17.** 10.0 ft²
19. 32.9 cm²   **21.** 106.4 ft²   **23a.** Sample answer: Because the horizontal distance between the hiker and the park ranger is known, I can use the 32° angle of depression to estimate the distance that the backpack fell.
23b. 71 ft   **25.** 12.2°   **27.** 4.8 cm²   **29.** 9.1 ft²
31. 22.4 ft²   **33.** Sample answer: What is the relationship between the angle of elevation and the angle of depression?   **35.** 7.8

Lesson 9-7

1. x ≈ 102.1   **3.** x ≈ 22.9   **5.** x ≈ 4.1
7. x ≈ 22.8   **9.** x ≈ 15.1   **11.** x ≈ 2.0
13. 6.2 mi   **15.** two solutions; m∠B ≈ 64°, m∠C ≈ 66°, c ≈ 40.4; m∠B ≈ 116°, m∠C ≈ 14°, c ≈ 11.0   **17.** one solution; m∠B ≈ 34°, m∠C ≈ 21°, c ≈ 9.6   **19.** one solution; m∠B = 90°, m∠C = 60°, c ≈ 3.5   **21.** one solution; m∠B ≈ 34°, m∠C ≈ 108°, c ≈ 15.4
23. one solution; m∠B ≈ 35°, m∠C ≈ 12°, c ≈ 2.6   **25.** one solution; m∠B ≈ 31°, m∠C ≈ 40°, c ≈ 16.4   **27a.** Definition of sine
27b. Multiplication Property   **27c.** Substitution
27d. Division Property   **29.** 24.3   **31a.** 402 m

31b. 676 m   **33.** 119.4° or 16.6°

35. 2; b sin A = 16 sin 55° or about 13.1; Because ∠A is acute, 14 < 16, and 14 > 13.1, the measures define 2 triangles.   **37.** 2; b sin A = 25 sin 39° or about 15.7; Because ∠A is acute, 22 < 25, and 22 > 15.7, the measures define 2 triangles.

39. 1; Because ∠A is acute and a = b = 10, the measures define 1 triangle.

41. 0; b sin A = 17 sin 52° or about 13.4; Because ∠A is acute and 13 < 13.4, the measures define 0 triangles.

43. 2; b sin A = 15 sin 33° or about 8.2; Because ∠A is acute, 10 < 15, and 10 > 8.2, the measures define 2 triangles.

45. Cameron; sample answer: ∠R is acute and r > t, so there is one solution.

47a. m∠B ≈ 70°, m∠C ≈ 68°, c ≈ 20.9
47b. m∠B ≈ 110°, m∠C ≈ 28°, c ≈ 10.4
49a. Sample answer: a = 22, b = 25, m∠A = 70°   **49b.** Sample answer: a = 25, b = 22, m∠A = 95°   **49c.** Sample answer: a = 22, b = 30, m∠A = 43°

Lesson 9-8

1. x ≈ 29.9   **3.** x ≈ 74   **5.** x ≈ 20   **7.** 69°
9. m∠A ≈ 41°, m∠C ≈ 54°, b ≈ 6.1   **11.** c ≈ 12.8, m∠A ≈ 67°, m∠B ≈ 33°   **13.** m∠N = 42°, n ≈ 35.8, m ≈ 24.3   **15.** Law of Sines; m∠B = 142°, a ≈ 21.0, b ≈ 67.8   **17.** Law of Sines; m∠B ≈ 33°, m∠C ≈ 110°, c ≈ 31.2   **19a.** about 11.3 yd   **19b.** about 40.9°   **21.** 5.6   **23.** Sample answer: When solving a right triangle, you can use the Pythagorean Theorem to find missing side lengths and trigonometric ratios to find missing side lengths or angle measures. To solve any triangle, you can use the Law of Sines or the Law of Cosines, depending on what measures you are given.

Module 9 Review

1. A   **3.** A, D   **5.** Multiplication Property of Equality; Distributive Property   **7.** $\frac{9}{2}\sqrt{5}$
9. 8.7 feet   **11.** $\frac{\sqrt{2}}{2}$ **13.** 45 ft   **15.** 5.4   **17.** D

Module 10

Quick Check

1. 8 in.   **3.** −2.4, 1.6   **5.** −1.8, 2.2

Lesson 10-1

1. ⊙O   **3.** $\overline{AB}$ and $\overline{CD}$ **5.** $\overline{PA}$, $\overline{PB}$, and $\overline{PC}$
7. $\overline{AB}$ **9.** 9 mm   **11.** Yes; all diameters of the same circle are congruent.   **13.** 9.5 m
15. 13 in.; 81.68 in.   **17.** 12.73 in.; 6.37 in.
19. 4.97 m; 2.49 m   **21.** 25.31 yd; 12.65 yd
23. 0.5   **25.** 6   **27.** 4.25 in.; 26.70 in.
29. 199.90 m; 99.95 m   **31.** 1.14x cm; 5.57x cm
33. congruent   **35.** neither   **37.** 9√2 π in.
39. 11π yd   **41.** 2π cm   **43.** Sample answer: The face of the clock in Elizabeth Tower in London, England, has a circumference of 72.26 feet.   **45.** chord   **47a.** 0.796 m
47b. 0.398 m   **49.** 24 units   **51.** Sample answer: First apply the translation (x, y)→(x − 3, y − 4) to ⊙D. The dilation should have a scale factor of 3 and be centered at (−1, −1). The translation and dilation are similarity transformations, so ⊙D is similar to ⊙E.

Lesson 10-2

1. 80   **3.** 138   **5.** minor arc; 50°   **7.** major arc; 210°   **9.** semicircle; 180°   **11.** 108°
13. 180°   **15.** 50°   **17.** 130°   **19.** 320°
21. 2.09 yd   **23.** 12.57 ft   **25.** 13.09 in.
27. $\frac{\pi}{4}$ radians   **29.** $\frac{\pi}{2}$ radians   **31.** $\frac{5\pi}{4}$ radians
33. 270°   **35.** 150°   **37.** 15°   **39.** 2.79 in.
41. 5.24 in.   **43.** 98.4°   **45a.** 62.83 in.
45b. 7.85 in.   **45c.** 57.3°
47. Proof:

Statements (Reasons)

1. ∠BAC ≅ ∠DAE (Given)

2. m∠BAC ≅ m∠DAE (Def. of congruent angles)

3. m$\overarc{BAC}$ = m$\overarc{BC}$ and m$\overarc{DAE}$ = m$\overarc{DE}$ (Def. of arc measure)

4. m$\overarc{BC}$ = m$\overarc{DE}$ (Substitution)

5. $\overarc{BC}$ ≅ $\overarc{DE}$ (Def. of congruent arcs)

---

49. 150°   **51.** 52   **53.** 128

55a. 10π or about 31.4 ft   **55b.** Sample answer: She can find the circumference of the entire circle and then use the arc measure to find the appropriate fraction of the circle. If the radius of the circle is r and the measure of the arc is x, then the arc length is $\frac{x}{360}$ · 2πr.
57. Never; sample answer: Obtuse angles intersect arcs that measure between 90° and 180°.

59. Selena; sample answer: The circles are not congruent because they do not have congruent radii. So, the arcs are not congruent.

61. Sample answer:

63. m$\overarc{LM}$ = 150°; m$\overarc{MN}$ = 90°; m$\overarc{NL}$ = 120°

Lesson 10-3

1. 148   **3.** 82   **5.** 7   **7.** 2   **9.** 13   **11.** 5
13. 45   **15.** 4.47   **17.** 7   **19.** Sample answer: Draw two chords on the arc and find the perpendicular bisector of each chord. The perpendicular bisectors will intersect at the center of the original circle. Then use a compass and the radius to draw the circle for the original size plate.

21. Proof:

Statements (Reasons)

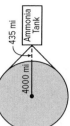

1. $\overline{FG}$ and $\overline{JH}$ are equidistant from center L. (Given)
2. $\overline{LX} \cong \overline{LY}$ (Definition of equidistant)
3. $\overline{LG} \cong \overline{LH}$ (All radii of a circle are congruent.)
4. $\overline{LX} \perp \overline{FG}, \overline{LY} \perp \overline{JH}$ (Definition of equidistant)
5. $\angle LXG$ and $\angle LYH$ are right angles. (Definition of perpendicular lines)
6. $\triangle XGL \cong \triangle YHL$ (HL)
7. $\overline{XG} \cong \overline{YH}$ (CPCTC)
8. $XG = YH$ (Definition of congruent segments)
9. $2(XG) = 2(YH)$ (Multiplication Property of Equality)
10. $\overline{LX}$ bisects $\overline{FG}; \overline{LY}$ bisects $\overline{JH}$ ($\overline{LX}$ and $\overline{LY}$ are contained in radii. A radius perpendicular to a chord bisects the chord.)
11. $FG = 2(XG); JH = 2(YH)$ (Definition of segment bisector)
12. $FG = JH$ (Substitution)
13. $\overline{FG} \cong \overline{JH}$ (Definition of congruent segments)

23. Sample answer: Neil can draw a line perpendicular to the chord he just drew through the mark he made. If the midpoint of the first chord is also the midpoint of the second line, it is a diameter.

25. Sample answer:

$BC = 4$ cm and
$AD = 2$ cm;
Because $\overline{AD}$ is perpendicular to $\overline{BC}$, $\overline{AD}$ bisects $\overline{BC}$, and $BD = 2$.

The Pythagorean Theorem can be used to find the length of the radius $\overline{AB}$.

$AB^2 = AD^2 + BD^2$
$\quad = 2^2 + 2^2$
$\quad = 8$
$AB = 2\sqrt{2}$ or about 2.83 cm

Lesson 10-4

1. 72° **3.** 226° **5.** 81° **7.** 17° **9.** 43°

---

11. Proof: It is given that $m\angle T = \frac{1}{2}m\angle S$. This means that $m\angle S = 2m\angle T$. By the Inscribed Angle Theorem, $m\angle S = \frac{1}{2}m\widehat{TUR}$ and $m\angle T = \frac{1}{2}m\widehat{URS}$. By Substitution, $\frac{1}{2}m\widehat{TUR} = 2\left(\frac{1}{2}m\widehat{URS}\right)$. Multiplying each side of the equation by 2 results in $m\widehat{TUR} = 2m\widehat{URS}$.

13. 39 **15.** 16 **17.** 58° **19.** 69° **21.** 105°
23. 72° **25a.** 22.5 **25b.** 23; 90° **25c.** Yes; sample answer: Because my estimate for the value of x is close to the exact value and $\angle J$ appears to be a right angle, my answer is reasonable. **27.** 82° **29.** 158° **31.** 65°
33. Proof: By arc addition and the definitions of arc measure and the sum of central angles, $m\widehat{EFG} + m\widehat{EDG} = 360°$. By Theorem 10.7, $m\angle D = \frac{1}{2}m\widehat{EFG}$ and $m\angle F = \frac{1}{2}m\widehat{EDG}$. So, $m\angle D + m\angle F = \frac{1}{2}m\widehat{EFG} + \frac{1}{2}m\widehat{EDG}$ or $\frac{1}{2}(m\widehat{EFG} + m\widehat{EDG})$. By substitution, $m\angle D + m\angle F = \frac{1}{2}(360)$ or 180°. By the definition of supplementary angles, $\angle D$ and $\angle F$ are supplementary. Because the sum of the measures of the interior angles of a quadrilateral is 360°, $m\angle D + m\angle F + m\angle E + m\angle G = 360°$. By substitution, 180° + $m\angle E + m\angle G = 360°$. By the Subtraction Property of Equality, $m\angle E + m\angle G = 180°$. Therefore, $\angle E$ and $\angle G$ are supplementary by the definition of supplementary angles.

35. Proof: Because $PQRS$ is inscribed in a circle, $\angle Q$ is supplementary to $\angle S$ because they are opposite angles. Because $\angle Q \cong \angle S$, $\angle Q$ and $\angle S$ must be right angles. So, $\angle Q$ intercepts $\widehat{PSR}$, $m\angle Q = 90°$ and $m\widehat{PSR} = 180°$ by the Inscribed Angle Theorem. This means that $\widehat{PSR}$ is a semicircle, so $\overline{PR}$ must be a diameter. **37.** 72°
39. $m\angle SRU = 80°; x = 12$ **41.** Always; sample answer: Rectangles have right angles at each vertex, therefore each pair of opposite angles will be supplementary and inscribed in a circle.
43. Sometimes; sample answer: A rhombus can be inscribed in a circle as long as it is a square. Because the opposite angles of rhombi that are not squares are not supplementary, they cannot be inscribed in a circle.

45. $\frac{\pi}{2}$

---

47. Sample answer:
$m\widehat{EHG} = m\widehat{HGF} = m\widehat{GFE} = m\widehat{FEH} = 180°$

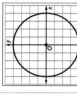

49. Never; sample answer: $\widehat{PR}$ is a minor arc, so $m\widehat{PR} < 180°$. By the Inscribed Angle Theorem, $m\angle PQR < 90°$. **51.** Always; sample answer: Each angle of the triangle measures 60°, so each intercepted arc measures 120°.

Lesson 10-5

1. 4 **3.** 3 **5.** yes; $9^2 + 40^2 = 41^2$ **7.** no; $20^2 + 21^2 \neq 28^2$ **9.** 25 **11.** 20 **13.** 8 **15.** 4
17. 72 in. **19.** 48° **21.** 80 **23.** 24 **25.** 4; 64
27a. 9.5 in. **27b.** 34 in.
29. Proof:

Statements (Reasons)

1. $\overline{RQ}$ is tangent to $\odot P$ at Q; $\overline{RT}$ is tangent to $\odot P$ at T. (Given)
2. $\overline{PQ} \perp \overline{RQ}, \overline{PT} \perp \overline{RT}$ (A tangent is $\perp$ to the radius drawn to the point of tangency.)
3. $\angle Q$ and $\angle T$ are rt. angles. ($\perp$ segments form right angles.)
4. $m\angle Q = 90°, m\angle T = 90°$ (Def. of right angle)
5. $PQRT$ is a quadrilateral. (Def. of quadrilateral)
6. $m\angle P + m\angle Q + m\angle R + m\angle T = 360°$ (Polygon Interior Angles Sum Thm.)
7. $m\angle P + 90° + m\angle R + 90° = 360°$ (Substitution)
8. $m\angle P + m\angle R + 180° = 360°$ (Substitution)
9. $m\angle P + m\angle R = 180°$ (Subtraction Property of Equality)

31a. 5; 2; 10 **31b.** 68
33. 8.06 **35.** spoke 10 **37.** 1916 mi;

39. Figure B; because one of the sides of the quadrilateral is not tangent to the circle, the quadrilateral is not circumscribed about the circle.

41. By Theorem 10.12, if two segments from the same exterior point are tangent to a circle, then they are congruent. So, $\overline{XY} \cong \overline{XZ}$ and $\overline{XZ} \cong \overline{XW}$. Thus, $\overline{XY} \cong \overline{XZ} \cong \overline{XW}$.

Lesson 10-6

1. 42.5° **3.** 62° **5.** 53° **7.** 84° **9.** 148°
11. 99° **13.** 40° **15.** 264° **17.** 128° **19.** 9
21. 19 **23.** Sample answer: Find the difference of the two intercepted arcs and divide by 2.
25. 32

Lesson 10-7

1. $x^2 + y^2 = 64$ **3.** $(x - 3)^2 + (y - 2)^2 = 4$
5. $(x - 3)^2 + (y + 4)^2 = 16$
7. $(x + 4)^2 + (y + 1)^2 = 20$
9. $(0, 0); r = 4$

11. (0, 0); $r = 2$

13. $(x − 2)^2 + (y − 4)^2 = 45$
15. (0, 3), (−2.4, −1.8) **17.** (−3, −4), (1, 10)
19. $(x − 3)^2 + y^2 = 25$ **21.** Disagree; sample answer: Completing the square shows that the equation can be written as $x^2 + 4x + 4 + y^2 − 10y + 25 = k + 29$ or $(x + 2)^2 + (y − 5)^2 = k + 29$. The radius of the circle is $\sqrt{k + 29}$, and this expression results in a positive radius only when $k + 29 > 0$. So, the equation represents a circle only if $k > −29$.

23. $(x − 4)^2 + (y − 3)^2 = 4$ **27.** $(x − 3)^2 + (y + 2)^2 = 4$
25. 18 mi

Module 10 Review

1. D **3.** $\frac{4\pi}{3}$, 3; Sample answer: I used the constant of proportionality $\frac{\pi}{180}$ multiplied by 240 to find the measure in radians.
5. Sample answer: Use a compass to construct a circle with center C. Place point P on the circle. Keeping the same compass setting that was used to construct circle C, place the point of the compass on P and construct an arc through the circle. Label the point of intersection Q. Without changing the compass setting, place the compass point on Q and intersect the circle again labeling the new point R. Repeat this step for points S, T, and U. Use a straightedge to connect each point to the next consecutive point. The result is a regular hexagon. **7.** C
9. $m\widehat{LM} = 96°$, $m\angle JMK = 39°$
11. B **13.** $(x − 1)^2 + (y − 7)^2 = 225$; yes
15. $y = \frac{1}{12}(x − 4)^2 + 2$

Lesson 10-8

1. $y = \frac{1}{12}x^2$ **3.** $y = −\frac{1}{20}x^2$ **5.** $y = \frac{1}{16}x^2$
7. $y = \frac{1}{32}(x − 1)^2 − 1$ **9a.** $y = \frac{1}{100}(x − 100)^2 + 30$
9b. 126.49 km **11.** (−1, 1), (2, 4)
13. (−2, −12), (0, 0) **15.** $x = \frac{1}{10}y^2$ **17.** $x = −\frac{5}{18}y^2$
19. Sample answer: Because the directrix is vertical, the parabola must open left or right. The focus is $\left(−\frac{3}{4}, 0\right)$, which is to the left of the directrix, so the parabola opens to the left.
21. Never; sample answer: Because the vertex is a point on the parabola, it is always equidistant from the focus and directrix.

Module 11

Quick Check

1. $x = 5$ **3.** 9.2 **5.** 3

Lesson 11-1

1. 108 m² **3.** 19.1 ft² **5.** 288.7 mm² **7.** 61.3 m²
9. 350 ft² **11.** 137.5 ft² **13a.** 13.5 ft²
13b. $94.50 **15.** 10.6 cm, 31.7 cm **17.** 4 m
19. 10 ft **21.** 6 m; 24 m **23.** 480 m²
25. 389.7 ft² **27.** 24 units² **29.** Sample answer: Using the area formula for the given figure, you can substitute the known area and all the other known dimensions into the formula. Use algebraic properties to solve for the missing dimension. **31.** Pieces 3 and 4 are the largest. The area of the top of the cake is 30 square inches. **33.** 8 in²
35. Always; sample answer: If the areas are equal, the perimeter of the nonrectangular parallelogram will always be greater because the length of the side that is not perpendicular to the height forms a right triangle with the height. The height is a leg of the triangle and the side of the parallelogram is the hypotenuse of the triangle. Because the hypotenuse is always the longest side of a right triangle, the non-perpendicular side of the parallelogram is always greater than the height. The bases of the quadrilaterals must be the same because the areas and the heights are the same. Because the bases are the same and the height of the rectangles is also the length of a side, the perimeter of the parallelogram will always be greater. **37.** 7.2 **39.** Sometimes; sample answer: If the areas are equal, it means that the products of the diagonals are equal. The only time that the perimeters will be equal is when the diagonals are also equal, or when the two rhombi are congruent.

Lesson 11-2

1. Sample answer: center: point Z, radius: $\overline{ZY}$, apothem: $\overline{ZO}$, central angle: $\angle YZR$, 45°
3. 277 mm² **5.** 124.7 ft²

7. 181.0 ft² **9.** 198 cm² **11.** 49.5 cm²
13. 31.2 in² **15.** 128.1 ft²
17. Sample answer:

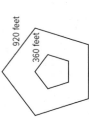

19. 52.0 in² **21a.** Sample answer: Floor area = $(7.5)(2.2) + (3.5)(4.2 − 2.2) + \frac{1}{2}(7.5 − 3.5 − 2.0)(4.2 − 2.2) = 25.5$ m², $\frac{x}{1.0\text{ L}} = \frac{25.5 \text{ m}^2}{4.5 \text{ m}^2}$, so $x = \frac{25.5 \text{ m}^2}{4.5 \text{ m}^2} \cdot (1.0\text{ L}) \approx 5.7$ L.
21b. Sample answer: Perimeter = $7.5 + 2.2 + 2.0 + 2.8 + 3.5 + 4.2 = 22.2$ m. Area to be painted (ignoring door and windows) = $(22.2)(2.6) = 57.72$ m², $\frac{x}{1.0\text{ L}} = \frac{57.72 \text{ m}^2}{7.5 \text{ m}^2}$, so $x = \frac{57.72 \text{ m}^2}{7.5 \text{ m}^2} \approx 7.7$ L. **21c.** Sample answer: Miguel may need to adjust the estimate because I did not account for the area taken up by doors and windows. So, the original estimate is too high.
23a. Sample answer:

920 feet
360 feet

23b. 1,233,238.2 ft² **25.** 754.4 in²
27. 591,377.6 ft² **29.** 6.9 cm² **31.** 3.87 cm²
33. Chenglei; sample answer: The measure of each angle of a regular hexagon is 120°, so the segments from the center of each vertex form 60°-angles. The triangles formed by the segments from the center to each vertex are equilateral, so each side of the hexagon is 11 in. The perimeter of the hexagon is 66 in. Using technology, the length of the apothem is about 9.5 in. Substituting the values into the formula for the area of a regular polygon and simplifying, the area is about 313.5 in².

Left page (SA20)

35. Sample answer:

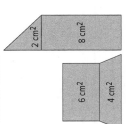

6 cm² 8 cm² 4 cm² 2 cm²

37. Sample answer: You can decompose the figure into shapes of which you know the area formulas. Then, you can add all of the areas to find the total area of the figure.

Lesson 11-3

1. 153.9 m² **3.** 346.4 m² **5a.** 12.6 in²
5b. about $5.21 **7.** 10.9 mm **9.** 6.0 in.
11. 15.0 in. **13.** 1.8 m² **15.** 331.3 m²
17. 2520 cm² **19.** 1625 mm² **21.** 882 m²
23a. 176.7 ft² **23b.** 173.6 ft² **25.** 88.4 cm²
27. Sample answer: The area of the circle is 36π. The area of the hexagon is $A = \frac{1}{2}aP$. Because a regular hexagon can be divided into six equilateral triangles, use the 30°-60°-90° triangle ratios to find a and the length of one side of the hexagon. So, $a = 3\sqrt{3}$ in., each side is 6 in., and $P = 36$ in. By substitution, the area of the hexagon is 93.5 in². The area of the shaded region is 36π − 93.5 ≈ 19.6 in². **29.** 64 in² **31a.** red: 102.6 ft²; purple: 94.2 ft²; green: 84.8 ft²
31b. The largest sector was neither the one with the largest radius nor the one with the largest central angle. We can conclude that both factors affect the area of the sector. **31c.** purple: 2.5 stars per square foot; green: 1.8 stars per square foot **31d.** 2 × 1.8 = 3.6; 3.6(area of the red sector) ≈ 370 stars **33.** 30.1 cm² **35.** Sample answer: You can find the shaded area of the circle by subtracting x from 360 and using the resulting measure in the formula for the area of a sector. You could also find the shaded area by finding the area of the entire circle, finding the area of the unshaded sector using the formula for the area of a sector,

and subtracting the area of the un-shaded sector from the area of the entire circle. The first method is more efficient. It requires less steps, is faster, and there is a lower probability for error.
37. Sample answer: A ≈ 9.42 cm²

2 cm

270°

Lesson 11-4

1. L = 528 yd²; S = 768 yd² **3.** L = 138 cm²; S = 378 cm² **5.** L = 324 cm²; S = 394.2 cm²
7. L ≈ 377.0 in²; S ≈ 603.2 in² **9.** L ≈ 226.2 yd²; S ≈ 282.7 yd² **11.** L ≈ 603.2 in²;
S ≈ 1005.3 in² **13a.** 12x² **13b.** 768 ft²
15a. 3x² **15b.** 243 ft² **17.** S ≈ 615.8 in²
19. S ≈ 289.5 mm² **21.** 49πx⁴
23. S ≈ 301.6 cm² **25.** 156.3 ft²
27. 8.6 m **29.** L ≈ 996.0 in²;
S ≈ 1686.0 in² **31.** L ≈ 34.7 cm²; S ≈ 43.8 cm²
33a. S = 12.6 cm² **33b.** S = 128 ft²
35. 825 cm² **37.** 1885.0 in² **39a.** Sample answer: I drew a figure showing all of the surfaces of the sofa, using simple geometric figures with the dimensions labeled. To find the total surface area, I can find and add the areas of the simple figures.

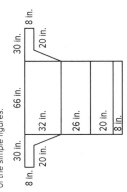

8 in.   66 in.   30 in.   8 in.
30 in.   32 in.   30 in.   20 in.
20 in.   26 in.
                20 in.
                8 in.

39b. Sample answer: Area = (66)(8 + 20 + 26 + 32) + 2(30)(8) + 2[½(30 − 20)(32 − 8)] = 6396 in²; I did not include the base in my calculation. **41.** No; sample answer: The slant height of the cone is $\frac{2\sqrt{\pi}}{\pi}$ or about 1:13 times

Right page (SA21)

greater than the slant height of the square pyramid. **43.** Sample answer: To find the surface area of any solid figure, find the area of the base (or bases) and add the area of the lateral faces of the figure. The lateral bases of a rectangular prism are rectangles. Because the bases of a cylinder are circles, the lateral face of a cylinder is a rectangle.
45. $\frac{\sqrt{3}}{2}\ell^2 + 3\ell h$; Sample answer: The area of an equilateral triangle with side length ℓ is $\frac{\sqrt{3}}{4}\ell^2$, and the perimeter of the triangle is 3ℓ. So, the total surface area is $\frac{\sqrt{3}}{2}\ell^2 + 3\ell h$.

Lesson 11-5

1. The square pyramid has 2 planes of symmetry. One plane of symmetry is perpendicular to the base of the pyramid and passes through the vertex. Another plane of symmetry is perpendicular to the base of the pyramid, perpendicular to the first plane of symmetry, and passes through the vertex.
3. The triangular prism has 1 plane of symmetry. The plane of symmetry is parallel to the base of the prism and passes through the center of the prism. **5.** triangle **7.** triangle **9.** cylinder with a cylinder removed from the middle
11. cone **13.** yes **15.** yes **17.** yes
19. rectangle **21.** Sample answer: Reshan could have rotated the semicircle around a horizontal axis. **23.** Sample answer: ice cream cone

25a. yes

25b. yes

25c. yes

25d. yes

25e. yes

25f. no
27. trapezoid

29a. sphere; any cut **29b.** cylinder; cut parallel to base **29c.** cone; cut parallel to base
31. Equilateral triangular pyramid; sample answer: Because the figure has axis symmetry of order 3, the base has to be an equilateral triangle. Because it does not have plane symmetry, you know that it is a pyramid instead of a prism. Therefore, the figure must be an equilateral triangular pyramid. **33.** Sample answer: The cross section is a triangle. There are six different ways to slice the pyramid so that two equal parts are formed because the figure has six planes of symmetry. In each case, the cross section is an isosceles triangle. Only the side lengths of the triangles change.
35. False; sample answer: If a plane has a slope different than the slant height of the pyramid and intersects a lateral face of the pyramid, then the cross section is a trapezoid.

Lesson 11-6

1. 2304 cm³ **3.** 90 m³ **5.** 2928.0 cm³
7. 1224 cm³ **9.** 66.7 ft³ **11.** 55.1 in³
13a. $5.25x³ + 3x²$ **13b.** 54 in³
15a. $\frac{3\sqrt{3}}{4}x³$ **15b.** 162.4 in³ **17.** 25 ft³
19. 301.1 in³ **21.** 14,508 in³ **23.** 156 cm³
25. 900,000 ft³ **27a.** 1024 ft³ **27b.** 432 ft³
27c. 592 ft³ **27d.** about 26,640 pounds
29a. Sample answer: He can find the volume of the contents of each box by multiplying the length times the width times 2 less than the height of the box and then multiply by the mass per cubic centimeter of the contents.
29b. baking soda: volume = 8 · 4 · 10 = 320 cm³, weight = 320 · 2.2 = 704 grams; corn flakes: volume = 30 · 6 · 33 = 5940 cm³, weight = 5940 · 0.12 = 712.8 grams

31a. $V = \frac{1}{3} \cdot 2^2 \cdot 3 = 4$; the volume is 4 in³, and the price per cubic inch is $0.50.
31b. Sample answer: Doubling the length and the width multiplies the volume by 4. He would need to multiply the price by 4 and charge $8.00 for the larger box. **31c.** Sample answer: base has sides of 3 inches, and the height is 2.5 inches; $V = \frac{1}{3} \cdot 3^2 \cdot 2.5 = 7.5$; the volume is 7.5 in³. **33.** Francisco; sample answer: Valerie incorrectly used $4\sqrt{3}$ as the length of one side of the triangular base. Francisco used a different approach, but his solution is correct.
35. Sample answer: Because the volume of a pyramid is one-third the volume of the same prism, 3 of the pentagonal pyramids would fit in a prism of the same height.

Lesson 11-7

1. 2035.8 in³ **3a.** $4\pi x^3 - 8\pi x^2$ mm³
5a. 10,053.1 mm³ **5a.** $3\pi x^3 + 4\pi x^2$ ft³
5b. 3676 ft³ **7a.** $\frac{1}{3}\pi(2x)^2(5x - 5)$ cubic units
7b. 3769.9 m³ **9.** 5.03 in³ **11.** 33.5 in³
13a. $\frac{4}{3}\pi(4x)^3$ cubic units **13b.** 2681 cm³
15a. $\frac{4}{3}\pi(5x - 0.5)^3$ cubic units **15b.** 1.8 yd³
17. 1102.7 m³ **19.** 1043 in³ **21.** $2\pi r^3 + \frac{2\pi r^2}{3} + \frac{\pi r^3}{3}$ or $3\pi r^3$ cubic units **23.** 1210.6 mm³
25. 60.63 ft³ **27a.** About 382 in³; sample answer: The cube root of 729 is 9, so the side length of the cube of wood is 9 inches. The largest sphere that could be carved has a radius of 4.5 inches. So, $V = \frac{4}{3}\pi(4.5)^3$ or about 382 in³. **27b.** Yes; sample answer: The radius of the sphere is exactly one half the length of the side of the cube. If the cube has a side length s, then the volume of the sphere is $\frac{4}{3}\pi\left(\frac{s}{2}\right)^3 = \frac{4}{3}\pi \frac{s^3}{8} = \frac{s^3\pi}{6} = s^3 \frac{\pi}{6}$. Therefore, the volume of a sphere that shares a diameter with the side of a cube is always $\frac{\pi}{6}$ times the volume of the cube.
29. Sample answer: I would find the volume of the original container. Then, I would substitute that volume and the 8-inch height in the volume formula and solve for r, 3.4 inches.

31. Sample answer:

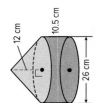

33. Sometimes; sample answer: The statement is true if the base area of the cone is 3 times as great as the base area of the prism. For example, if the base of the prism has an area of 10 square units, then its volume is $10h$ cubic units. So, the cone must have a base area of 30 square units so that its volume is $\frac{1}{3}(30)h$ or $10h$ cubic units. **35.** True; sample answer: A cone of radius r and height $4r$ has the same volume, $\frac{4}{3}\pi r^3$, as a sphere with radius r.

Lesson 11-8

1. 320 m² **3.** 1843.2 m² **5.** $\frac{1}{3}$ 7 m **7.** $\sqrt{\frac{7}{16}}$; 4.5 in. **9.** 27.8 in² **11.** 5 in² **13.** small: 108 cm³; large: 256 cm³ **15.** small: 98.2 cm³; large: 785.4 cm³ **17.** 36 cm **19.** 27 : 64
21. 313 pieces of cake
23. Proof: We are given rectangular prisms with a scale factor of $a : b$. By the definition of similar solids, $\frac{f}{t} = \frac{g}{u} = \frac{h}{v} = \frac{a}{b}$, so $t = r\cdot\frac{b}{a}$, $u = g\cdot\frac{b}{a}$, and $v = h\cdot\frac{b}{a}$.
Then, $\dfrac{\text{surface area of smaller prism}}{\text{surface area of larger prism}} =$

$$\frac{2fg + 2fh + 2gh}{2tu + 2tv + 2uv}$$

By substitution, the right side of the equation becomes

$$\frac{2fg + 2fh + 2gh}{2\left(f\cdot\frac{b}{a}\right)\left(g\cdot\frac{b}{a}\right) + 2\left(f\cdot\frac{b}{a}\right)\left(h\cdot\frac{b}{a}\right) + 2\left(g\cdot\frac{b}{a}\right)\left(h\cdot\frac{b}{a}\right)}.$$

Simplify this fraction to get

$$\frac{2fg + 2fh + 2gh}{2fg\cdot\frac{b^2}{a^2} + 2fh\cdot\frac{b^2}{a^2} + 2gh\cdot\frac{b^2}{a^2}}.$$

By using the Distributive Property, this becomes

$$\frac{2fg + 2fh + 2gh}{(2fg + 2fh + 2gh)\cdot\frac{b^2}{a^2}} = \frac{a^2}{b^2}.$$

Also, the ratio of the volume is $\dfrac{\text{volume of smaller prism}}{\text{volume of larger prism}} = \dfrac{fgh}{tuv}$. Using the definition of similar solids, we can rewrite the right side of the equation above as $\dfrac{\left(r\cdot\frac{b}{a}\right)\left(g\cdot\frac{b}{a}\right)\left(h\cdot\frac{b}{a}\right)}{fgh}$.

After multiplying, this becomes $\dfrac{fgh\cdot\frac{b^3}{a^3}}{fgh}$, which simplifies to $\dfrac{a^3}{b^3}$. Thus, the surface areas have a ratio of $a^2 : b^2$, and the volumes have a ratio of $a^3 : b^3$.
25a. 2 in.
25b. No; sample answer: The larger sculpture has an apothem of about 8.5 inches. This means that the octagonal shape of the larger sculpture is about 17 inches across. This is greater than the diameter of the box. **27.** Sample answer: As the diameter increases, the volume increases by the cube of the ratio of the diameters. For example, from size Small to Medium, the ratio of the diameters is $\left(\frac{4.5}{3}\right)^3$ or 1.5. The volume of the Medium is $4.5\pi(1.5)^3$ or 15.1875π.

Size	Diameter (cm)	Volume (cm³)
Small	3	4.5π
Medium	4.5	15.1875π
Large	6.75	51.2578125π

29. Neither; sample answer: To find the area of the enlarged circle, you can multiply the radius by the scale factor and substitute it into the area formula, or you can multiply the area formula by the scale factor squared.
The formula for the area of the enlargement is $A = \pi(kr)^2$ or $A = k^2r^2$. **31.** Sample answer: Because the ratio of the areas should be 4 : 1, the ratio of the lengths of the sides will be $\sqrt{4} : \sqrt{1}$ or 2 : 1. Thus, a 0.5-inch by 1-inch rectangle and a 1-inch by 2-inch rectangle are similar, and the ratio of their areas is 4 : 1.

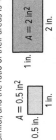

33. 8 : 135; Sample answer: The volume of Cylinder C is 8 times the volume of Cylinder A, and the volume of Cylinder D is 27 times the volume of Cylinder B. If the original ratio of

volumes was $1x : 5x$, the new ratio is $8x : 135x$. So, the ratio of volumes is 8 : 135.

Lesson 11-9

1. ≈ 14,290.0 people/mi²
3. ≈ 13,525.6 people/mi² **5.** 24
7a. 0.512 oz/in³ **7b.** 62,500 in³ **7c.** 8000
9. 41.67 people/mi² **11.** No; sample answer: Because the load will weigh 42,411.6 pounds, which exceeds the limit of 34,000 pounds, it will not meet the weight restrictions.
13. Pentagonal prism; the pentagonal prism would only allow for 105.4 cubic inches per plant. **15.** False; Block B has a density of 0.79 g/cm³, and Block A has a density of 0.66 g/cm³. So, Block B has a greater density.

Module 11 Review

1. C **3.** C **5.** A, B, E, F **7.** A **9.** B, D, E, F
11. $\dfrac{x^2(x + 2)}{3}$ **13.** 101 in³ **15.** 244 cm³ **17.** D

Module 12

Quick Check

1. $\frac{5}{6}$ or 83% **3.** $\frac{1}{6}$ or 17% **5.** $\frac{1}{5}$ or 20%
7. $\frac{11}{20}$ or 55%

Lesson 12-1

1. $S = \{H, T\}$ **3a.** $S = \{1, 2, 3, 4, 5, 6, 7, 8, 9, 10, 11, 12\}$ **3b.** S(even number) = {2, 4, 6, 8, 10, 12}
5. BB, BW, WB, WW

	Blue Pants	White Pants
Blue Shirts	B, B	B, W
White Shirts	W, B	W, W

7. finite, S = {yellow, blue, green, red}
9. infinite; continuous
11. 28,800 **13.** 360 **15.** 1296 **17a.** 4
17b. 12 **17c.** 16 **19.** 2592
21. Sample answer: 6 different ways

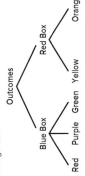

23. 12 **25a.** 5 **25b.** 18
27. $P = n^k$. Sample answer: The total number of possible outcomes is the product of the number of outcomes for each of the stages 1 through k. Because there are k stages, you are multiplying n by itself k times which is n^k.
29. Sample answer: In an experiment, you choose between a blue box and a red box. You then remove a ball from the box that you chose without looking into the box. The blue box contains a red ball, a purple ball, and a green

ball. The red box contains a yellow ball and an orange ball.

Outcomes

Blue Box — Red, Purple, Green, Yellow
Red Box — Yellow, Orange

31. Never; sample answer: The sample space is the set of all possible outcomes. An outcome cannot fall outside the sample space. A failure occurs when the outcome is in the sample space, but is not a favorable outcome.

Lesson 12-2

1. $A \cap B = \{6\}$ **3a.** 4, 10 **3b.** 4, 8, 12 **3c.** 4
5. $\frac{1}{52}$ or 1.92% **7a.** A, E, O, U **7b.** J
7c. A, E, O, U, J **9a.** 5, 10, 15, 20
9b. 1, 2, 3, 4, 5, 6, 7, 8, 9, 10, 11
9c. 1, 2, 3, 4, 5, 6, 7, 8, 9, 10, 11, 15, 20
11. $\frac{39}{52}$ or $\frac{3}{4}$ or 0.75 **13.** $\frac{240}{250}$ or 0.96
15. $\frac{10}{100}$ or $\frac{1}{10}$ or 0.10 **17.** $\frac{13}{20}$ or 0.65
19a. {Amy, Alex} **19b.** P(one musical) = $1 - P(\text{both}) = 1 - \frac{2}{9} = \frac{7}{9}$ or about 0.78
21. 0.275
23.

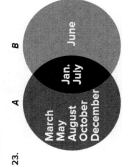

25. Sometimes; sample answer: While it is usually the case that the union of two sets will consist of more elements than their intersection, there are exceptions. For example, let A be the days of the week that end in *day*, and let B be the days of the week that begin with the letters F, M, S, T, or W. Because the two sets have the same list of items, their intersection and union will also be this same list.

Lesson 12-3

1. $\frac{1}{5}$, 0.2, or 20% **3.** $\frac{1}{2}$, 0.5, or 50%
5. $\frac{5}{12}$ = $0.41\overline{6}$ or about 42% **7.** $\frac{1}{3}$ = $0.\overline{3}$ or about 33%
9. $\frac{49}{100}$, 0.49, or 49%
11. approximately 0.054 or about 5%
13. $\frac{1}{9}$ = $0.\overline{1}$ or about 11%
15. $\frac{1}{9}$ = $0.\overline{1}$ or about 11%
17. $\frac{2}{9}$ = $0.\overline{2}$ or about 22%
19. $\frac{7}{12}$ = $0.58\overline{3}$ or about 58%
21. Sample answer: spinner landing on yellow
23. Sample answer: a point between 10 and 20
25. $\frac{\pi}{4} \approx 0.79$ or about 79%
27. $\frac{1}{3}$, $0.3\overline{3}$, or about 33%
29a. 0.842 **29b.** 0.205 **31.** 14.3%
33. No; sample answer: Athletic events should not be considered random because there are other factors involved such as pressure and ability that have an impact on the success of the event.
35. Sample answer: The probability of a randomly chosen point lying in the shaded region of the square on the left is found by subtracting the area of the unshaded square from the area of the larger square and finding the ratio of the difference of the areas to the area of the larger square. The probability is $1^2 - 0.75^2$ or 43.75%. The probability of a randomly chosen point lying in the shaded region of the square on the right is the ratio of the area of the shaded square to the area of the larger square, which is $\frac{0.4375}{1}$ or 43.75%. Therefore, the probability of a randomly chosen point lying in the shaded area of either square is the same.

Lesson 12-4

1. $\frac{1}{66}$ **3.** $\frac{1}{2450}$ **5.** $\frac{1}{420}$
7a. $\frac{1}{35}$ **7b.** $\frac{1}{210}$ **9.** $\frac{1}{1140}$ **11.** $\frac{1}{252}$
13. $\frac{1}{495}$ **15.** $\frac{1}{20}$ **17a.** 10 **17b.** $\frac{1}{10}$ **19.** $\frac{1}{38,760}$

21a. $\frac{1}{30}$; Sample answer: There are 6 possible coupons for the first customer, 5 possible for the second customer, and so forth, so the total number of possible outcomes is 6! = 720. If the first customer gets the 10% coupon and the second customer gets the 25% coupon, then there are 4! = 24 ways the remaining four customers can get coupons so the total number of favorable outcomes is 24. The probability is $\frac{\text{number of favorable outcomes}}{\text{number of possible outcomes}}$ = $\frac{24}{720} = \frac{1}{30}$.
21b. ${}_6C_2 = 15$ **23.** $\frac{1}{15,120}$
25. $\frac{13}{261}$
27. Sample answer: Both permutations and combinations are used to find the number of possible arrangements of a group of objects. The order of the objects is important in permutations, but not in combinations.
29. Sample answer:
$$r! \cdot {}_nC_r = r! \cdot \frac{n!}{(n - r)!r!}$$
$$= \frac{n!r!}{(n - r)!r!}$$
$$= \frac{n!}{(n - r)!}$$
$$= {}_nP_r$$

${}_nC_r$ and ${}_nP_r$ differ by the factor $r!$ because there are always $r!$ ways to order the groups that are selected. Therefore, there are $r!$ permutations of each combination.

Lesson 12-5

1. $\frac{1}{6}$ or about 17% **3.** $\frac{1}{12}$ or about 8%
5. $\frac{6}{25}$ or 24%
7. Dependent; sample answer: Because the first ace drawn was not replaced, the probability of drawing the second card is affected.
9. Independent; sample answer: These two rolls have no bearing on each other.
11. $\frac{25}{2652}$ or about 1%
13. $\frac{1}{16}$ or about 6.25%
15. $\frac{11}{850}$ or about 1.29% **17.** 0.43

Left Page (SA26)

19. Yes; sample answer: The probability of selecting a defective chip from Box A is $\frac{1}{25}$. Because $\frac{1}{625} = \frac{1}{25} \cdot \frac{1}{25}$, $P(A \text{ and } B) = P(A) \cdot P(B)$ and the events are independent.

21.

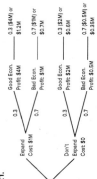

0.3 Good Econ. Profit $4M — 0.3 ($4M) or $12M
Expand Cost $1M
0.7 Bad Econ. Profit $1M — 0.7 ($1M) or $0.7M
0.3 Good Econ. Profit $2M — 0.3 ($2M) or $0.6M
Don't Expand Cost $0
0.7 Bad Econ. Profit $0.5M — 0.7 ($0.5M) or $0.35M

23. $\frac{1}{2704}$; Sample answer: The card is replaced, so the events are independent; the probability of each picking the queen of spades is $\frac{1}{52}$, so the probability of them both picking it is $\frac{1}{52} \cdot \frac{1}{52} = \frac{1}{2704}$.

25a. The first branch of the tree should be the first serve, while the second set of branches should be the second serve. The second serve only occurs when the first serve is a fault.

25b. A double fault is back-to-back faults, or $P(F, F)$, which equals 0.18 or 18%.

27. Sample answer: In order for the events to be independent, two things must be true: 1) the chance that a person is left-handed is the same as the chance that a person is left-handed given that the person's parent is left-handed and 2) the chance that a person's parent is left-handed is the same as the chance that a person's parent is left-handed given that the person is left-handed.

29. A and B are independent events.

Lesson 12-6

1. Not mutually exclusive; sample answer: These events are not mutually exclusive because a 6 is also an even number.

3. $\frac{1}{2}$ or 0.50 **5.** 0.65 **7.** $\frac{1}{13}$ or 7.7%

9. $\frac{3}{13}$ or 23.1% **11.** $\frac{4}{13}$ or about 31%

13. $\frac{4}{13}$ or about 31% **15.** 0.30 **17.** $\frac{3}{4}$ or 75%

19. $\frac{739}{750}$ or about 98.5% **21.** 56% **23.** 0.6

25. 0.074; Sample answer: There are three outcomes in which the values of two or more of the dice are less than or equal to 4 and one outcome where the values of all three of the dice are less than or equal to 4. You have to find the probability of each of the four scenarios and add them together.

27. Not mutually exclusive; sample answer: Because squares are rectangles, but rectangles are not necessarily squares, a quadrilateral can be both a square and a rectangle, and a quadrilateral can be a rectangle but not a square.

29. Not mutually exclusive; sample answer: A natural number is also a complex number.

Lesson 12-7

1. $\frac{1}{5}$ or 20% **3.** $\frac{1}{3}$ **5.** $\frac{8}{11}$ or about 73%

7. $\frac{1}{9}$ or about 11% **9.** $\frac{1}{6}$ or about 17%

11a. 6 students

11b. $P(H|L) = \frac{1}{3}$; $P(L) = \frac{3}{10}$ and $P(H \text{ and } L) = \frac{1}{10}$.

So, $P(H|L) = \frac{P(H \text{ and } L)}{P(L)} = \frac{\frac{1}{10}}{\frac{3}{10}}$ or $\frac{1}{3}$.

11c. No; sample answer: If $P(H|L)$ is the same as $P(H)$ or $P(L|H)$ is the same as $P(L)$, then H and L are independent. Because $P(H|L)$ is $\frac{1}{3}$ and $P(H)$ is $\frac{7}{10}$, H and L are not independent.

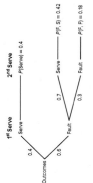

1st Serve / 2nd Serve
P(Serve) = 0.4
0.4 Serve
0.6 Fault
0.7 Serve P(F, S) = 0.42
0.3 Fault P(F, F) = 0.18
Outcomes

Right Page (SA27)

13a. 80%; $P(Algebra) = 0.25$ and $P(Algebra$ and $Health) = 0.2$, so $P(Health|Algebra) = \frac{P(Algebra \text{ and } Health)}{P(Algebra)} = \frac{0.2}{0.25} = 0.8$.

13b. No; $P(Health|Algebra) = 0.8$ and $P(Health) = 0.5$. Because the two probabilities are not equal, the two events are dependent.

13c. 25%; $P(Accounting) = 0.2$ and $P(Accounting$ and $Spanish) = 0.05$, so $P(Spanish|Accounting) = \frac{P(Accounting \text{ and } Spanish)}{P(Accounting)} = \frac{0.05}{0.2} = 0.25$. Because the events are independent, $P(Spanish|Accounting) = P(Spanish) = 0.25$.

Lesson 12-8

1a.

	SUV	Truck	Totals
Male	15	35	50
Female	40	10	50
Totals	55	45	100

1b.

	SUV	Truck	Totals
Male	$\frac{15}{100} = 15\%$	$\frac{35}{100} = 35\%$	$\frac{50}{100} = 50\%$
Female	$\frac{40}{100} = 40\%$	$\frac{10}{100} = 10\%$	$\frac{50}{100} = 50\%$
Totals	$\frac{55}{100} = 55\%$	$\frac{45}{100} = 45\%$	$\frac{100}{100} = 100\%$

3a.

	More Than 4	4 or Fewer	Totals
In State	928	332	1260
Out of State	118	622	740
Totals	1046	954	2000

3b.

	More Than 4	4 or Fewer	Totals
In State	$\frac{928}{2000} = 46.4\%$	$\frac{332}{2000} = 16.6\%$	$\frac{1260}{2000} = 63\%$
Out of State	$\frac{118}{2000} = 5.9\%$	$\frac{622}{2000} = 31.1\%$	$\frac{740}{2000} = 37\%$
Totals	$\frac{1046}{2000} = 52.3\%$	$\frac{954}{2000} = 47.7\%$	$\frac{2000}{2000} = 100\%$

3c. Sample answer: 63% of the college students surveyed are attending an in-state college. 52.3% of the college students surveyed visited home more than 4 times. It would be expected that $63\% \cdot 52.3\%$, or about 33% would be in-state students that visited home more than 4 times. Because $P(A$ and $B) \neq P(A) \cdot P(B)$, or 33% ≠ 46.4%, the events are dependent.

5. 18; joint frequency

7. 17.7%; $P(\text{has a tablet | has a smart phone}) = \frac{P(\text{has a tablet and has a smart phone})}{P(\text{has a smart phone})} \approx \frac{0.125}{0.708}$ or 17.7%

9a. voting for candidate A or B and being within a particular age/gender category

9b. 55% **9c.** 55% **9d.** 9%

9e. Sample answer: males age 18–30 and females age 46–60

9f. Sample answer: females age 18–30, males and females age 31–45, and anyone over 60

Module 12 Review

1. C **3.** A **5.** D **7.** D

9.

Situation	Independent	Dependent
Two dice are tossed.	X	
Two marbles are selected from a bag.		X
Two students are chosen as the captains of a team.		X
A coin is tossed and a card is chosen.	X	
Three books are selected from the library.		X
One student from each class is chosen to collect papers.	X	

11. A, D **13.** $\frac{2}{27}$ **15.** D

Glossary

English	Español
	A
30°-60°-90° triangle **(Lesson 9-4)** A right triangle with two acute angles that measure 30° and 60°.	triángulo 30°-60°-90° Un triángulo rectángulo con dos ángulos agudos que miden 30° y 60°.
45°-45°-90° triangle **(Lesson 9-4)** A right triangle with two acute angles that measure 45°.	triángulo 45°-45°-90° Un triángulo rectángulo con dos ángulos agudos que miden 45°.
accuracy **(Lesson 2-7)** The nearness of a measurement to the true value of the measure.	exactitud La proximidad de una medida al valor verdadero de la medida.
adjacent angles **(Lesson 2-1)** Two angles that lie in the same plane and have a common vertex and a common side but have no common interior points.	ángulos adyacentes Dos ángulos que se encuentran en el mismo plano y tienen un vértice común y un lado común, pero no tienen puntos comunes en el interior.
adjacent arcs **(Lesson 10-2)** Arcs in a circle that have exactly one point in common.	arcos adyacentes Arcos en un círculo que tienen un solo punto en común.
alternate exterior angles **(Lesson 3-7)** When two lines are cut by a transversal, nonadjacent exterior angles that lie on opposite sides of the transversal.	ángulos alternos externos Cuando dos líneas cortadas por un ángulo transversal, no adyacente exterior que se encuentran en lados opuestos de la transversal.
alternate interior angles **(Lesson 3-7)** When two lines are cut by a transversal, nonadjacent interior angles that lie on opposite sides of the transversal.	ángulos alternos internos Cuando dos líneas cortadas por un ángulo transversal, no adyacente interior que se encuentran en lados opuestos de la transversal.
altitude of a parallelogram **(Lesson 11-1)** A perpendicular segment between any two parallel bases.	altitud de un paralelogramo Un segmento perpendicular entre dos bases paralelas.
altitude of a prism or cylinder **(Lesson 11-4)** A segment perpendicular to the bases that joins the planes of the bases.	altitud de un prisma o cilindro Un segmento perpendicular a las bases que une los planos de las bases.
altitude of a pyramid or cone **(Lesson 11-4)** A segment perpendicular to the base that has the vertex as one endpoint and a point in the plane of the base as the other endpoint.	altitud de una pirámide o cono Un segmento perpendicular a la base que tiene el vértice como un punto final y un punto en el plano de la base como el otro punto final.
altitude of a triangle **(Lesson 6-3)** A segment from a vertex of the triangle to the line containing the opposite side and perpendicular to that side.	altitud de triángulo Un segmento de un vértice del triángulo a la línea que contiene el lado opuesto y perpendicular a ese lado.

A

ambiguous case (Lesson 9-7) When two different triangles could be created or described using the given information.
caso ambiguo Cuando dos triángulos diferentes pueden ser creados o descritos usando la información dada.

analytic geometry (Lesson 1-1) The study of geometry that uses the coordinate system.
geometría analítica El estudio de la geometría que utiliza el sistema de coordenadas.

angle (Lesson 2-1) The intersection of two noncollinear rays at a common endpoint.
ángulo La intersección de dos rayos no colineales en un extremo común.

angle bisector (Lesson 2-1) A ray or segment that divides an angle into two congruent angles.
bisectriz de un ángulo Un rayo o segmento que divide un ángulo en dos ángulos congruentes.

angle of depression (Lesson 9-6) The angle formed by a horizontal line and an observer's line of sight to an object below the horizontal line.
ángulo de depresión El ángulo formado por una línea horizontal y la línea de visión de un observador a un objeto por debajo de la línea horizontal.

angle of elevation (Lesson 9-6) The angle formed by a horizontal line and an observer's line of sight to an object above the horizontal line.
ángulo de elevación El ángulo formado por una línea horizontal y la línea de visión de un observador a un objeto por encima de la línea horizontal.

angle of rotation (Lesson 2-4) The angle through which a figure rotates.
ángulo de rotación El ángulo a través del cual gira una figura.

apothem (Lesson 11-2) A perpendicular segment between the center of a regular polygon and a side of the polygon or the length of that line segment.
apotema Un segmento perpendicular entre el centro de un polígono regular y un lado del polígono o la longitud de ese segmento de línea.

approximate error (Lesson 2-7) The positive difference between an actual measurement and an approximate or estimated measurement.
error aproximado La diferencia positiva entre una medida real y una medida aproximada o estimada.

arc (Lesson 10-2) Part of a circle that is defined by two endpoints.
arco Parte de un círculo que se define por dos puntos finales.

arc length (Lesson 10-2) The distance between the endpoints of an arc measured along the arc in linear units.
longitud de arco La distancia entre los extremos de un arco medido a lo largo del arco en unidades lineales.

area (Lesson 2-3) The number of square units needed to cover a surface.
área El número de unidades cuadradas para cubrir una superficie.

auxiliary line (Lesson 5-1) An extra line or segment drawn in a figure to help analyze geometric relationships.
línea auxiliar Una línea o segmento extra dibujado en una figura para ayudar a analizar las relaciones geométricas.

axiom (Lesson 1-1) A statement that is accepted as true without proof.
axioma Una declaración que se acepta como verdadera sin prueba.

axiomatic system (Lesson 1-1) A set of axioms from which theorems can be derived.
sistema axiomático Un conjunto de axiomas de los cuales se pueden derivar teoremas.

axis symmetry (Lesson 11-5) If a figure can be mapped onto itself by a rotation between 0° and 360° in a line.
eje simetría Si una figura puede ser asignada sobre sí misma por una rotación entre 0° y 360° en una línea.

B

base angles of a trapezoid (Lesson 7-6) The two angles formed by the bases and legs of a trapezoid.
ángulos de base de un trapecio Los dos ángulos formados por las bases y patas de un trapecio.

base angles of an isosceles triangle (Lesson 5-6) The two angles formed by the base and the congruent sides of an isosceles triangle.
ángulo de la base de un triángulo isósceles Los dos ángulos formados por la base y los lados congruentes de un triángulo isósceles.

base edge (Lesson 11-4) The intersection of a lateral face and a base in a solid figure.
arista de la base La intersección de una cara lateral y una base en una figura sólida.

base of a parallelogram (Lesson 11-1) Any side of a parallelogram.
base de un paralelogramo Cualquier lado de un paralelogramo.

base of a pyramid or cone (Lesson 2-5) The face of the solid opposite the vertex of the solid.
base de una pirámide o cono La cara del sólido opuesta al vértice del sólido.

bases of a prism or cylinder (Lesson 2-5) The two parallel congruent faces of the solid.
bases de un prisma o cilindro Las dos caras congruentes paralelas de la figura sólida.

bases of a trapezoid (Lesson 7-6) The parallel sides in a trapezoid.
bases de un trapecio Los lados paralelos en un trapecio.

betweenness of points (Lesson 1-3) Point C is between A and B if and only if A, B, and C are collinear and $AC + CB = AB$.
intermediación de puntos El punto C está entre A y B si y sólo si A, B, y C son colineales y $AC + CB = AB$.

biconditional statement (Lesson 3-2) The conjunction of a conditional and its converse.
declaración bicondicional La conjunción de un condicional y su inverso.

bisect (Lesson 1-7) To separate a line segment into two congruent segments.
bisecar Separar un segmento de línea en dos segmentos congruentes.

C

center of a circle (Lesson 10-1) The point from which all points on a circle are the same distance.
centro de un círculo El punto desde el cual todos los puntos de un círculo están a la misma distancia.

center of dilation (Lesson 8-1) The center point from which dilations are performed.
centro de dilatación Punto fijo en torno al cual se realizan las homotecias.

center of a regular polygon (Lesson 11-2) The center of the circle circumscribed about a regular polygon.
centro de un polígono regular El centro del círculo circunscrito alrededor de un polígono regular.

center of rotation (Lesson 2-4) The fixed point about which a figure rotates.
centro de rotación El punto fijo sobre el que gira una figura.

center of symmetry (Lesson 4-6) A point in which a figure can be rotated onto itself.
centro de la simetría Un punto en el que una figura se puede girar sobre sí misma.

central angle of a circle (Lesson 10-2) An angle with a vertex at the center of a circle and sides that are radii.
ángulo central de un círculo Un ángulo con un vértice en el centro de un círculo y los lados son radios.

central angle of a regular polygon (Lesson 11-2) An angle with its vertex at the center of a regular polygon and sides that pass through consecutive vertices of the polygon.
ángulo central de un polígono regular Un ángulo con su vértice en el centro de un polígono regular y lados que pasan a través de vértices consecutivos del polígono.

centroid (Lesson 6-3) The point of concurrency of the medians of a triangle.
baricentro El punto de intersección de las medianas de un triángulo.

chord of a circle or sphere (Lessons 10-1, 11-4) A segment with endpoints on the circle or sphere.
cuerda de un círculo o esfera Un segmento con extremos en el círculo o esfera.

circle (Lesson 10-1) The set of all points in a plane that are the same distance from a given point called the center.
círculo El conjunto de todos los puntos en un plano que están a la misma distancia de un punto dado llamado centro.

circumcenter (Lesson 6-1) The point of concurrency of the perpendicular bisectors of the sides of a triangle.
circuncentro El punto de concurrencia de las bisectrices perpendiculares de los lados de un triángulo.

circumference (Lesson 2-3) The distance around a circle.
circunferencia La distancia alrededor de un círculo.

circumscribed angle (Lesson 10-5) An angle with sides that are tangent to a circle.
ángulo circunscrito Un ángulo con lados que son tangentes a un círculo.

circumscribed polygon (Lesson 10-5) A polygon with vertices outside the circle and sides that are tangent to the circle.
polígono circunscrito Un polígono con vértices fuera del círculo y lados que son tangentes al círculo.

collinear (Lesson 1-2) Lying on the same line.
colineal Acostado en la misma línea.

combination (Lesson 12-4) A selection of objects in which order is not important.
combinación Una selección de objetos en los que el orden no es importante.

common tangent (Lesson 10-5) A line or segment that is tangent to two circles in the same plane.
tangente común Una línea o segmento que es tangente a dos círculos en el mismo plano.

complement of A (Lesson 12-2) All of the outcomes in the sample space that are not included as outcomes of event A.
complemento de A Todos los resultados en el espacio muestral que no se incluyen como resultados del evento A.

complementary angles (Lesson 2-2) Two angles with measures that have a sum of 90°.
ángulos complementarios Dos ángulos con medidas que tienen una suma de 90°.

component form (Lesson 2-4) A vector written as $\langle x, y\rangle$, which describes the vector in terms of its horizontal component x and vertical component y.
forma de componente Un vector escrito como $\langle x, y\rangle$, que describe el vector en términos de su componente horizontal x y componente vertical y.

composite figure (Lesson 11-2) A figure that can be separated into regions that are basic figures, such as triangles, rectangles, trapezoids, and circles.
figura compuesta Una figura que se puede separar en regiones que son figuras básicas, tales como triángulos, rectángulos, trapezoides, y círculos.

composite solid (Lesson 11-4) A three-dimensional figure that is composed of simpler solids.
solido compuesta Una figura tridimensional que se compone de figuras más simples.

composition of transformations (Lesson 4-4) When a transformation is applied to a figure and then another transformation is applied to its image.
composición de transformaciones Cuando una transformación se aplica a una figura y luego se aplica otra transformación a su imagen.

compound event (Lesson 12-5) Two or more simple events.
evento compuesto Dos o más eventos simples.

compound statement (Lesson 3-2) Two or more statements joined by the word *and* or *or*.
enunciado compuesto Dos o más declaraciones unidas por la palabra *y* o *o*.

concave polygon (Lesson 2-3) A polygon with one or more interior angles with measures greater than 180°.
polígono cóncavo Un polígono con uno o más ángulos interiores con medidas superiores a 180°.

concentric circles (Lesson 10-1) Coplanar circles that have the same center.
círculos concéntricos Círculos coplanarios que tienen el mismo centro.

conclusion (Lesson 3-2) The statement that immediately follows the word *then* in a conditional.
conclusión La declaración que inmediatamente sigue la palabra *entonces* en un condicional.

concurrent lines (Lesson 6-1) Three or more lines that intersect at a common point.
líneas concurrentes Tres o más líneas que se intersecan en un punto común.

conditional probability (Lesson 12-7) The probability that an event will occur given that another event has already occurred.
probabilidad condicional La probabilidad de que un evento ocurra dado que otro evento ya ha ocurrido.

conditional statement (Lesson 3-2) A compound statement that consists of a premise, or hypothesis, and a conclusion, which is false only when its premise is true and its conclusion is false.
enunciado condicional Una declaración compuesta que consiste en una premisa, o hipótesis, y una conclusión, que es falsa solo cuando su premisa es verdadera y su conclusión es falsa.

cone (Lesson 2-5) A solid figure with a circular base connected by a curved surface to a single vertex.
cono Una figura sólida con una base circular conectada por una superficie curvada a un solo vértice.

congruent (Lesson 1-3) Having the same size and shape.
congruente Tener el mismo tamaño y forma.

congruent angles (Lesson 2-1) Two angles that have the same measure.
ángulos congruentes Dos ángulos que tienen la misma medida.

congruent arcs (Lesson 10-2) Arcs in the same or congruent circles that have the same measure.
arcos congruentes Arcos en los mismos círculos o congruentes que tienen la misma medida.

congruent polygons (Lesson 5-2) All of the parts of one polygon are congruent to the corresponding parts or matching parts of another polygon.
polígonos congruentes Todas las partes de un polígono son congruentes con las partes correspondientes o partes coincidentes de otro polígono.

congruent segments (Lesson 1-3) Line segments that are the same length.
segmentos congruentes Línea segmentos que son la misma longitud.

congruent solids (Lesson 11-8) Solid figures that have exactly the same shape, size, and a scale factor of 1:1.
sólidos congruentes Figuras sólidas que tienen exactamente la misma forma, tamaño y un factor de escala de 1:1.

conic sections (Lesson 11-5) Cross sections of a right circular cone.
secciones cónicas Secciones transversales de un cono circular derecho.

conjecture (Lesson 3-1) An educated guess based on known information and specific examples.
conjetura Una suposición educada basada en información conocida y ejemplos específicos.

conjunction (Lesson 3-2) A compound statement using the word *and*.
conjunción Una declaración compuesta usando la palabra y.

consecutive interior angles (Lesson 3-7) When two lines are cut by a transversal, interior angles that lie on the same side of the transversal.
ángulos internos consecutivos Cuando dos líneas se cortan por un ángulo transversal, interior que se encuentran en el mismo lado de la transversal.

constructions (Lesson 1-3) Methods of creating figures without the use of measuring tools.
construcciones Métodos de creación de figuras sin el uso de herramientas de medición.

contrapositive (Lesson 3-2) A statement formed by negating both the hypothesis and the conclusion of the converse of a conditional.
antítesis Una afirmación formada negando tanto la hipótesis como la conclusión del inverso del condicional.

converse (Lesson 3-2) A statement formed by exchanging the hypothesis and conclusion of a conditional statement.
recíproco Una declaración formada por el intercambio de la hipótesis y la conclusión de la declaración condicional.

convex polygon (Lesson 2-3) A polygon with all interior angles measuring less than 180°.
polígono convexo Un polígono con todos los ángulos interiores que miden menos de 180°.

coordinate proofs (Lesson 5-7) Proofs that use figures in the coordinate plane and algebra to prove geometric concepts.
pruebas de coordenadas Pruebas que utilizan figuras en el plano de coordenadas y álgebra para probar conceptos geométricos.

coplanar (Lesson 1-2) Lying in the same plane.
coplanar Acostado en el mismo plano.

corollary (Lesson 5-1) A theorem with a proof that follows as a direct result of another theorem.
corolario Un teorema con una prueba que sigue como un resultado directo de otro teorema.

corresponding angles (Lesson 3-7) When two lines are cut by a transversal, angles that lie on the same side of transversal and on the same side of the two lines.
ángulos correspondientes Cuando dos líneas se cortan transversalmente, los ángulos que se encuentran en el mismo lado de una transversal y en el mismo lado de las dos líneas.

corresponding parts (Lesson 5-2) Corresponding angles and corresponding sides of two polygons.
partes correspondientes Ángulos correspondientes y lados correspondientes.

cosine (Lesson 9-5) The ratio of the length of the leg adjacent to an angle to the length of the hypotenuse.
coseno Relación entre la longitud de la pierna adyacente a un ángulo y la longitud de la hipotenusa.

counterexample (Lesson 3-1) An example that contradicts the conjecture showing that the conjecture is not always true.
contraejemplo Un ejemplo que contradice la conjetura que muestra que la conjetura no siempre es cierta.

cross section (Lesson 11-5) The intersection of a solid and a plane.
sección transversal Intersección de un sólido con un plano.

cylinder (Lesson 2-5) A solid figure with two congruent and parallel circular bases connected by a curved surface.
cilindro Una figura sólida con dos bases circulares congruentes y paralelas conectadas por una superficie curvada.

D

decomposition (Lesson 11-1) Separating a figure into two or more nonoverlapping parts.
descomposición Separar una figura en dos o más partes que no se solapan.

deductive argument (Lesson 3-4) An argument that guarantees the truth of the conclusion provided that its premises are true.
argumento deductivo Un argumento que garantiza la verdad de la conclusión siempre que sus premisas sean verdaderas.

deductive reasoning (Lesson 3-3) The process of reaching a specific valid conclusion based on general facts, rules, definitions, or properties.
razonamiento deductivo El proceso de alcanzar una conclusión válida específica basada en hechos generales, reglas, definiciones, o propiedades.

defined term (Lesson 1-1) A term that has a definition and can be explained.
término definido Un término que tiene una definición y se puede explicar.

definitions (Lesson 1-1) An explanation that assigns properties to a mathematical object.
definiciones Una explicación que asigna propiedades a un objeto matemático.

degree (Lesson 10-2) $\frac{1}{360}$ of the circular rotation about a point.
grado $\frac{1}{360}$ de la rotación circular alrededor de un punto.

density (Lesson 11-9) A measure of the quantity of some physical property per unit of length, area, or volume.
densidad Una medida de la cantidad de alguna propiedad física por unidad de longitud, área o volumen.

dependent events (Lesson 12-5) Two or more events in which the outcome of one event affects the outcome of the other events.
eventos dependientes Dos o más eventos en que el resultado de un evento afecta el resultado de los otros eventos.

diagonal (Lesson 7-1) A segment that connects any two nonconsecutive vertices within a polygon.
diagonal Un segmento que conecta cualquier dos vértices no consecutivos dentro de un polígono.

E

diameter of a circle or sphere (Lessons 10-1, 11-4) A chord that passes through the center of a circle or sphere.

dilation (Lesson 8-1) A nonrigid motion that enlarges or reduces a geometric figure.

directed line segment (Lesson 1-5) A line segment with an initial endpoint and a terminal endpoint.

directrix (Lesson 10-8) An exterior line perpendicular to the line containing the foci of a curve.

disjunction (Lesson 3-2) A compound statement using the word or.

distance (Lesson 1-4) The length of the line segment between two points.

E

edge of a polyhedron (Lesson 2-5) A line segment where the faces of the polyhedron intersect.

enlargement (Lesson 8-1) A dilation with a scale factor greater than 1.

equiangular polygon (Lesson 2-3) A polygon with all angles congruent.

equidistant (Lesson 1-7) A point is equidistant from other points if it is the same distance from them.

equidistant lines (Lesson 3-10) Two lines for which the distance between the two lines, measured along a perpendicular line or segment to the two lines, is always the same.

equilateral polygon (Lesson 2-3) A polygon with all sides congruent.

event (Lesson 12-1) A subset of the sample space.

experiment (Lesson 12-1) A situation involving chance.

exterior of an angle (Lesson 2-1) The area outside of the two rays of an angle.

exterior angle of a triangle (Lesson 5-1) An angle formed by one side of the triangle and the extension of an adjacent side.

diámetro de un círculo o esfera Un acorde que pasa por el centro de un círculo o esfera.

dilatación Un movimiento no rígido que agranda o reduce una figura geométrica.

segmento de línea dirigido Un segmento de línea con un punto final inicial y un punto final terminal.

directriz Una línea exterior perpendicular a la línea que contiene los focos de una curva.

disyunción Una declaración compuesta usando la palabra o.

distancia La longitud del segmento de línea entre dos puntos.

E

arista de un poliedro Un segmento de línea donde las caras del poliedro se cruzan.

ampliación Una dilatación con un factor de escala mayor que 1.

polígono equiangular Un polígono con todos los ángulos congruentes.

equidistante Un punto es equidistante de otros puntos si está a la misma distancia de ellos.

líneas equidistantes Dos líneas para las cuales la distancia entre las dos líneas, medida a lo largo de una línea o segmento perpendicular a las dos líneas, es siempre la misma.

polígono equilátero Un polígono con todos los lados congruentes.

evento Un subconjunto del espacio de muestra.

experimento Una situación de riesgo.

exterior de un ángulo El área fuera de los dos rayos de un ángulo.

ángulo exterior de un triángulo Un ángulo formado por un lado del triángulo y la extensión de un lado adyacente.

---

exterior angles (Lesson 3-7) When two lines are cut by a transversal, any of the four angles that lie outside the region between the two intersected lines.

F

face of a polyhedron (Lesson 2-5) A flat surface of a polyhedron.

factorial of n (Lesson 12-4) The product of the positive integers less than or equal to n.

finite sample space (Lesson 12-1) A sample space that contains a countable number of outcomes.

flow proof (Lesson 3-4) A proof that uses boxes and arrows to show the logical progression of an argument.

focus (Lesson 10-8) A point inside a parabola having the property that the distances from any point on the parabola to them and to a fixed line have a constant ratio for any points on the parabola.

fractional distance (Lesson 1-5) An intermediary point some fraction of the length of a line segment.

G

geometric mean (Lesson 9-1) The nth root, where n is the number of elements in a set of numbers, of the product of the numbers.

geometric model (Lesson 2-3) A geometric figure that represents a real-life object.

geometric probability (Lesson 12-3) Probability that involves a geometric measure such as length or area.

glide reflection (Lesson 4-4) The composition of a translation followed by a reflection in a line parallel to the translation vector.

ángulos externos Cuando dos líneas son cortadas por una transversal, cualquiera de los cuatro ángulos que se encuentran fuera de la región entre las dos líneas intersectadas.

F

cara de un poliedro Superficie plana de un poliedro.

factorial de n El producto de los enteros positivos inferiores o iguales a n.

espacio de muestra finito Un espacio de muestra que contiene un número contable de resultados.

demostración de flujo Una prueba que usa cajas y flechas para mostrar la progresión lógica de un argumento.

foco Un punto dentro de una parábola que tiene la propiedad de que las distancias desde cualquier punto de la parábola a ellos ya una línea fija tienen una relación constante para cualquier punto de la parábola.

distancia fraccionaria Un punto intermediario de alguna fracción de la longitud de un segmento de línea.

G

media geométrica La enésima raíz, donde n es el número de elementos de un conjunto de números, del producto de los números.

modelo geométrico Una figura geométrica que representa un objeto de la vida real.

probabilidad geométrica Probabilidad que implica una medida geométrica como longitud o área.

reflexión del deslizamiento La composición de una traducción seguida de una reflexión en una línea paralela al vector de traslación.

H

height of a parallelogram (Lesson 11-1) The length of an altitude of the parallelogram.

altura de un paralelogramo La longitud de la altitud del paralelogramo.

height of a solid (Lesson 11-4) The length of the altitude of a solid figure.

altura de un sólido La longitud de la altitud de una figura sólida.

height of a trapezoid (Lesson 11-1) The perpendicular distance between the bases of a trapezoid.

altura de un trapecio La distancia perpendicular entre las bases de un trapecio.

hypothesis (Lesson 3-2) The statement that immediately follows the word *if* in a conditional.

hipótesis La declaración que sigue inmediatamente a la palabra *si* en un condicional.

I

if-then statement (Lesson 3-2) A compound statement of the form *if p, then q,* where *p* and *q* are statements.

enunciado si-entonces Enunciado compuesto de la forma *si p, entonces q,* donde *p* y *q* son enunciados.

image (Lesson 2-4) The new figure in a transformation.

imagen La nueva figura en una transformación.

incenter (Lesson 6-2) The point of concurrency of the angle bisectors of a triangle.

incentro El punto de intersección de las bisectrices interiors de un triángulo.

included angle (Lesson 5-3) The interior angle formed by two adjacent sides of a triangle.

ángulo incluido El ángulo interior formado por dos lados adyacentes de un triángulo.

included side (Lesson 5-4) The side of a triangle between two angles.

lado incluido El lado de un triángulo entre dos ángulos.

independent events (Lesson 12-5) Two or more events in which the outcome of one event does not affect the outcome of the other events.

eventos independientes Dos o más eventos en los que el resultado de un evento no afecta el resultado de los otros eventos.

indirect measurement (Lesson 9-6) Using similar figures and proportions to measure an object.

medición indirecta Usando figuras y proporciones similares para medir un objeto.

indirect proof (Lesson 6-5) One assumes that the statement to be proven is false and then uses logical reasoning to deduce that a statement contradicts a postulate, theorem, or one of the assumptions.

demostración indirecta Se supone que la afirmación a ser probada es falsa y luego utiliza el razonamiento lógico para deducir que una afirmación contradice un postulado, teorema o uno de los supuestos.

indirect reasoning (Lesson 6-5) Reasoning that eliminates all possible conclusions but one so that the one remaining conclusion must be true.

razonamiento indirecto Razonamiento que elimina todas las posibles conclusiones, pero una de manera que la conclusión que queda una debe ser verdad.

inductive reasoning (Lesson 3-1) The process of reaching a conclusion based on a pattern of examples.

razonamiento inductive El proceso de llegar a una conclusión basada en un patrón de ejemplos.

informal proof (Lesson 3-4) A paragraph that explains why the conjecture for a given situation is true.

prueba informal Un párrafo que explica por qué la conjetura para una situación dada es verdadera.

inscribed angle (Lesson 10-4) An angle with its vertex on a circle and sides that contain chords of the circle.

ángulo inscrito Un ángulo con su vértice en un círculo y lados que contienen acordes del círculo.

inscribed polygon (Lesson 10-4) A polygon inside a circle in which all of the vertices of the polygon lie on the circle.

polígono inscrito Un polígono dentro de un círculo en el que todos los vértices del polígono se encuentran en el círculo.

intercepted arc (Lesson 10-4) The part of a circle that lies between the two lines intersecting it.

arco intersecado La parte de un círculo que se encuentra entre las dos líneas que se cruzan.

interior of an angle (Lesson 2-1) The area between the two rays of an angle.

interior de un ángulo El área entre los dos rayos de un ángulo.

interior angle of a triangle (Lesson 5-1) An angle at the vertex of a triangle.

ángulo interior de un triángulo Un ángulo en el vértice de un triángulo.

interior angles (Lesson 3-7) When two lines are cut by a transversal, any of the four angles that lie inside the region between the two intersected lines.

ángulos interiores Cuando dos líneas son cortadas por una transversal, cualquiera de los cuatro ángulos que se encuentran dentro de la región entre las dos líneas intersectadas.

intersection (Lesson 1-2) A set of points common to two or more geometric figures.

intersección Un conjunto de puntos communes a dos o más figuras geométricas.

intersection of A and B (Lesson 12-2) The set of all outcomes in the sample space of event A that are also in the sample space of event B.

intersección de A y B El conjunto de todos los resultados en el espacio muestral del evento A que también se encuentran en el espacio muestral del evento B.

inverse (Lesson 3-2) A statement formed by negating both the hypothesis and conclusion of a conditional statement.

inverso Una declaración formada negando tanto la hipótesis como la conclusión de la declaración condicional.

inverse cosine (Lesson 9-5) The ratio of the length of the hypotenuse to the length of the leg adjacent to an angle.

inverso del coseno Relación de la longitud de la hipotenusa con la longitud de la pierna adyacente a un ángulo.

inverse sine (Lesson 9-5) The ratio of the length of the hypotenuse to the length of the leg opposite the angle.

inverso del seno Relación de la longitud de la hipotenusa con la longitud de la pierna opuesta a un ángulo.

inverse tangent (Lesson 9-5) The ratio of the length of the leg adjacent to an angle to the length of the leg opposite the angle.

inverso del tangente Relación de la longitud de la pierna adyacente a un ángulo con la longitud de la pierna opuesta a un ángulo.

isosceles trapezoid (Lesson 7-6) A quadrilateral in which two sides are parallel and the legs are congruent.

trapecio isósceles Un cuadrilátero en el que dos lados son paralelos y las patas son congruentes.

isosceles triangle (Lesson 5-6) A triangle with at least two sides congruent.

triángulo isósceles Un triángulo con al menos dos lados congruentes.

J

joint frequencies (Lesson 12-8) In a two-way frequency table, the frequencies in the interior of the table.
frecuencias articulares En una tabla de frecuencia bidireccional, las frecuencias en el interior de la tabla.

K

kite (Lesson 7-6) A convex quadrilateral with exactly two distinct pairs of adjacent congruent sides.
cometa Un cuadrilátero convexo con exactamente dos pares distintos de lados congruentes adyacentes.

L

lateral area (Lesson 11-4) The sum of the areas of the lateral faces of the figure.
área lateral La suma de las áreas de las caras laterales de la figura.

lateral edges (Lesson 11-4) The intersection of two lateral faces.
aristas laterales La intersección de dos caras laterales.

lateral faces (Lesson 11-4) The faces that join the bases of a solid.
caras laterales Las caras que unen las bases de un sólido.

lateral surface of a cone (Lesson 11-4) The curved surface that joins the base of a cone to the vertex.
superficie lateral de un cono La superficie curvada que une la base de un cono con el vértice.

lateral surface of a cylinder (Lesson 11-4) The curved surface that joins the bases of a cylinder.
superficie lateral de un cilindro La superficie curvada que une las bases de un cilindro.

legs of an isosceles triangle (Lesson 5-6) The two congruent sides of an isosceles triangle.
patas de un triángulo isósceles Los dos lados congruentes de un triángulo isósceles.

legs of a trapezoid (Lesson 7-6) The nonparallel sides in a trapezoid.
patas de un trapecio Los lados no paralelos en un trapezoide.

line (Lesson 1-2) A line is made up of points, has no thickness or width, and extends indefinitely in both directions.
línea Una línea está formada por puntos, no tiene espesor ni anchura, y se extiende indefinidamente en ambas direcciones.

line of reflection (Lesson 2-4) A line midway between a preimage and an image.
línea de reflexión Una línea a medio camino entre una preimagen y una imagen.

line of symmetry (Lesson 4-6) An imaginary line that separates a figure into two congruent parts.
línea de simetría Una línea imaginaria que separa una figura en dos partes congruentes.

line segment (Lesson 1-3) A measurable part of a line that consists of two points, called endpoints, and all of the points between them.
segmento de línea Una parte medible de una línea que consta de dos puntos, llamados extremos, y todos los puntos entre ellos.

line symmetry (Lesson 4-6) Each half of a figure matches the other half exactly.
simetría de línea Cada mitad de una figura coincide exactamente con la otra mitad.

linear pair (Lesson 2-1) A pair of adjacent angles with noncommon sides that are opposite rays.
par lineal Un par de ángulos adyacentes con lados no comunes que son rayos opuestos.

logically equivalent (Lesson 3-2) Statements with the same truth value.
lógicamente equivalentes Declaraciones con el mismo valor de verdad.

M

magnitude (Lesson 4-2) The length of a vector from the initial point to the terminal point.
magnitud La longitud de un vector desde el punto inicial hasta el punto terminal.

magnitude of symmetry (Lesson 4-6) The smallest angle through which a figure can be rotated so that it maps onto itself.
magnitud de la simetría El ángulo más pequeño a través del cual una figura se puede girar para que se cargue sobre sí mismo.

major arc (Lesson 10-2) An arc with measure greater than 180°.
arco mayor Un arco con una medida superior a 180°.

marginal frequencies (Lesson 12-8) In a two-way frequency table, the frequencies in the totals row and column.
frecuencias marginales En una tabla de frecuencias de dos vías, las frecuencias en los totales de fila y columna.

median of a triangle (Lesson 6-3) A line segment with endpoints that are a vertex of the triangle and the midpoint of the side opposite the vertex.
mediana de un triángulo Un segmento de línea con extremos que son un vértice del triángulo y el punto medio del lado opuesto al vértice.

midpoint (Lesson 1-7) The point on a line segment halfway between the endpoints of the segment.
punto medio El punto en un segmento de línea a medio camino entre los extremos del segmento.

midsegment of a trapezoid (Lesson 7-6) The segment that connects the midpoints of the legs of a trapezoid.
segment medio de un trapecio El segmento que conecta los puntos medios de las patas de un trapecio.

midsegment of triangle (Lesson 8-5) The segment that connects the midpoints of the legs of a triangle.
segment medio de un triángulo El segmento que conecta los puntos medios de las patas de un triángulo.

minor arc (Lesson 10-2) An arc with measure less than 180°.
arco menor Un arco con una medida inferior a 180°.

mutually exclusive (Lesson 12-6) Events that cannot occur at the same time.
mutuamente exclusivos Eventos que no pueden ocurrir al mismo tiempo.

N

negation (Lesson 3-2) A statement that has the opposite meaning, as well as the opposite truth value, of an original statement.
negación Una declaración que tiene el significado opuesto, así como el valor de verdad opuesto, de una declaración original.

net (Lesson 2-6) A two-dimensional figure that forms the surfaces of a three-dimensional object when folded.
red Una figura bidimensional que forma las superficies de un objeto tridimensional cuando se dobla.

nonrigid motion (Lesson 8-1) A transformation that changes the dimensions of a given figure.
movimiento no rígida Una transformación que cambia las dimensiones de una figura dada.

O

octant (Lesson 9-3) One of the eight divisions of three-dimensional space.
octante Una de las ocho divisiones del espacio tridimensional.

opposite rays (Lesson 2-1) Two collinear rays with a common endpoint.
rayos opuestos Dos rayos colineales con un punto final común.

order of symmetry (Lesson 4-6) The number of times a figure maps onto itself.
orden de la simetría El número de veces que una figura se asigna a sí misma.

ordered triple (Lesson 9-3) Three numbers given in a specific order used to locate points in space.
triple ordenado Tres números dados en un orden específico usado para localizar puntos en el espacio.

orthocenter (Lesson 6-3) The point of concurrency of the altitudes of a triangle.
ortocentro El punto de concurrencia de las altitudes de un triángulo.

orthographic drawing (Lesson 2-6) The two-dimensional views of the top, left, front, and right sides of an object.
dibujo ortográfico Las vistas bidimensionales de los lados superior, izquierdo, frontal y derecho de un objeto.

outcome (Lesson 12-1) The result of a single performance or trial of an experiment.
resultado El resultado de un solo rendimiento o ensayo de un experimento.

P

parabola (Lesson 10-8) A curved shape that results when a cone is cut at an angle by a plane that intersects the base.
parábola Forma curvada que resulta cuando un cono es cortado en un ángulo por un plano que interseca la base.

paragraph proof (Lesson 3-4) A paragraph that explains why the conjecture for a given situation is true.
prueba de párrafo Un párrafo que explica por qué la conjetura para una situación dada es verdadera.

parallel lines (Lesson 3-7) Coplanar lines that do not intersect.
líneas paralelas Líneas coplanares que no se intersecan.

parallel planes (Lesson 3-7) Planes that do not intersect.
planos paralelos Planos que no se intersecan.

parallelogram (Lesson 7-2) A quadrilateral with both pairs of opposite sides parallel.
paralelogramo Un cuadrilátero con ambos pares de lados opuestos paralelos.

perimeter (Lesson 2-3) The sum of the lengths of the sides of a polygon.
perímetro La suma de las longitudes de los lados de un polígono.

permutation (Lesson 12-4) An arrangement of objects in which order is important.
permutación Un arreglo de objetos en el que el orden es importante.

perpendicular (Lesson 2-2) Intersecting at right angles.
perpendicular Intersección en ángulo recto.

perpendicular bisector (Lesson 6-1) Any line, segment, or ray that passes through the midpoint of a segment and is perpendicular to that segment.
mediatriz Cualquier línea, segmento o rayo que pasa por el punto medio de un segmento y es perpendicular a ese segmento.

pi (Lesson 10-1) The ratio $\frac{\text{circumference}}{\text{diameter}}$.
pi Relación $\frac{\text{circunferencia}}{\text{diámetro}}$

plane (Lesson 1-2) A flat surface made up of points that has no depth and extends indefinitely in all directions.
plano Una superficie plana compuesta de puntos que no tiene profundidad y se extiende indefinidamente en todas las direcciones.

plane symmetry (Lesson 11-5) When a plane intersects a three-dimensional figure so one half is the reflected image of the other half.
simetría plana Cuando un plano cruza una figura tridimensional, una mitad es la imagen reflejada de la otra mitad.

Platonic solid (Lesson 2-5) One of five regular polyhedra.
sólido platónico Uno de cinco poliedros regulares.

point (Lesson 1-2) A location with no size, only position.
punto Una ubicación sin tamaño, solo posición.

point of concurrency (Lesson 6-1) The point of intersection of concurrent lines.
punto de concurrencia El punto de intersección de líneas concurrentes.

point of symmetry (Lesson 4-6) The point about which a figure is rotated.
punto de simetría El punto sobre el que se gira una figura.

point of tangency (Lesson 10-5) For a line that intersects a circle in one point, the point at which they intersect.
punto de tangencia Para una línea que cruza un círculo en un punto, el punto en el que se cruzan.

point symmetry (Lesson 4-6) A figure or graph has this when a figure is rotated 180° about a point and maps exactly onto the other part.
simetría de punto Una figura o gráfica tiene esto cuando una figura se gira 180° alrededor de un punto y se mapea exactamente sobre la otra parte.

polygon (Lesson 2-3) A closed plane figure with at least three straight sides.
polígono Una figura plana cerrada con al menos tres lados rectos.

polyhedron (Lesson 2-5) A closed three-dimensional figure made up of flat polygonal regions.
poliedros Una figura tridimensional cerrada formada por regiones poligonales planas.

postulate (Lesson 1-1) A statement that is accepted as true without proof.
postulado Una declaración que se acepta como verdadera sin prueba.

precision (Lesson 2-7) The repeatability, or reproducibility, of a measurement.
precisión La repetibilidad, o reproducibilidad, de una medida.

preimage (Lesson 2-4) The original figure in a transformation.
preimagen La figura original en una transformación.

principle of superposition (Lesson 5-2) Two figures are congruent if and only if there is a rigid motion or series of rigid motions that maps one figure exactly onto the other.
principio de superposición Dos figuras son congruentes si y sólo si hay un movimiento rígido o una serie de movimientos rígidos que traza una figura exactamente sobre la otra.

G16

prism (Lesson 2-5) A polyhedron with two parallel congruent bases connected by parallelogram faces.

proof (Lesson 3-4) A logical argument in which each statement is supported by a statement that is accepted as true.

proof by contradiction (Lesson 6-5) One assumes that the statement to be proven is false and then uses logical reasoning to deduce that a statement contradicts a postulate, theorem, or one of the assumptions.

pyramid (Lesson 2-5) A polyhedron with a polygonal base and three or more triangular faces that meet at a common vertex.

Pythagorean triple (Lesson 9-2) A set of three nonzero whole numbers that make the Pythagorean Theorem true.

R

radian (Lesson 10-2) A unit of angular measurement equal to $\frac{180°}{\pi}$ or about 57.296°.

radius of a circle or sphere (Lessons 10-1, 11-4) A line segment from the center to a point on a circle or sphere.

radius of a regular polygon (Lesson 11-2) The radius of the circle circumscribed about a regular polygon.

ray (Lesson 2-1) Part of a line that starts at a point and extends to infinity.

rectangle (Lesson 7-4) A parallelogram with four right angles.

reduction (Lesson 8-1) A dilation with a scale factor between 0 and 1.

reflection (Lesson 2-4) A function in which the preimage is reflected in the line of reflection.

regular polygon (Lesson 2-3) A convex polygon that is both equilateral and equiangular.

regular polyhedron (Lesson 2-5) A polyhedron in which all of its faces are regular congruent polygons and all of the edges are congruent.

---

prisma Un poliedro con dos bases congruentes paralelas conectadas por caras de paralelogramo.

prueba Un argumento lógico en el que cada sentencia está respaldada por una sentencia aceptada como verdadera.

prueba por contradicción Se supone que la afirmación a ser probada es falsa y luego utiliza el razonamiento lógico para deducir que una afirmación contradice un postulado, teorema o uno de los supuestos.

pirámide Poliedro con una base poligonal y tres o más caras triangulares que se encuentran en un vértice común.

triplete Pitágorico Un conjunto de tres números enteros distintos de cero que hacen que el Teorema de Pitágoras sea verdadero.

radián Una unidad de medida angular igual o $\frac{180°}{\pi}$ alrededor de 57.296°.

radio de un círculo o esfera Un segmento de línea desde el centro hasta un punto en un círculo o esfera.

radio de un polígono regular El radio del círculo circunscrito alrededor de un polígono regular.

rayo Parte de una línea que comienza en un punto y se extiende hasta el infinito.

rectángulo Un paralelogramo con cuatro ángulos rectos.

reducción Una dilatación con un factor de escala entre 0 y 1.

reflexión Función en la que la preimagen se refleja en la línea de reflexión.

polígono regular Un polígono convexo que es a la vez equilátero y equiangular.

poliedro regular Un poliedro en el que todas sus caras son polígonos congruentes regulares y todos los bordes son congruentes.

G17

regular pyramid (Lesson 11-4) A pyramid with a base that is a regular polygon.

regular tessellation (Lesson 4-5) A tessellation formed by only one type of regular polygon.

relative frequency (Lesson 12-8) In a two-way frequency table, the ratios of the number of observations in a category to the total number of observations.

remote interior angles (Lesson 5-1) Interior angles of a triangle that are not adjacent to an exterior angle.

rhombus (Lesson 7-5) A parallelogram with all four sides congruent.

rigid motion (Lesson 2-4) A transformation that preserves distance and angle measure.

rotation (Lesson 2-4) A function that moves every point of a preimage through a specified angle and direction about a fixed point.

rotational symmetry (Lesson 4-6) A figure can be rotated less than 360° about a point so that the image and the preimage are indistinguishable.

S

sample space (Lesson 12-1) The set of all possible outcomes.

scale factor of a dilation (Lesson 8-1) The ratio of a length on an image to a corresponding length on the preimage.

secant (Lesson 10-6) Any line or ray that intersects a circle in exactly two points.

sector (Lesson 11-3) A region of a circle bounded by a central angle and its intercepted arc.

segment bisector (Lesson 1-7) Any segment, line, plane, or point that intersects a line segment at its midpoint.

semicircle (Lesson 10-2) An arc that measures exactly 180°.

---

pirámide regular Una pirámide con una base que es un polígono regular.

teselado regular Un teselado formado por un solo tipo de polígono regular.

frecuencia relativa En una tabla de frecuencia bidireccional, las relaciones entre el número de observaciones en una categoría y el número total de observaciones.

ángulos internos no adyacentes Ángulos interiores de un triángulo que no están adyacentes a un ángulo exterior.

rombo Un paralelogramo con los cuatro lados congruentes.

movimiento rígido Una transformación que preserva la distancia y la medida del ángulo.

rotación Función que mueve cada punto de una preimagen a través de un ángulo y una dirección especificados alrededor de un punto fijo.

simetría rotacional Una figura puede girar menos de 360° alrededor de un punto para que la imagen y la preimagen sean indistinguibles.

espacio muestral El conjunto de todos los resultados posibles.

factor de escala de una dilatación Relación de una longitud en una imagen con una longitud correspondiente en la preimagen.

secante Cualquier línea o rayo que cruce un círculo en exactamente dos puntos.

sector Una región de un círculo delimitada por un ángulo central y su arco interceptado.

bisectriz del segmento Cualquier segmento, línea, plano o punto que interseca un segmento de línea en su punto medio.

semicírculo Un arco que mide exactamente 180°.

semiregular tessellation (Lesson 4-5) A tessellation formed by two or more regular polygons.

teselado semirregular Un teselado formado por dos o más polígonos regulares.

sides of an angle (Lesson 2-1) The rays that form an angle.

lados de un ángulo Los rayos que forman un ángulo.

significant figures (Lesson 2-8) The digits of a number that are used to express a measure to an appropriate degree of accuracy.

dígitos significantes Los dígitos de un número que se utilizan para expresar una medida con un grado apropiado de precisión.

similar polygons (Lesson 8-2) Two figures are similar polygons if one can be obtained from the other by a dilation or a dilation with one or more rigid motions.

polígonos similares Dos figuras son polígonos similares si uno puede ser obtenido del otro por una dilatación o una dilatación con uno o más movimientos rígidos.

similar solids (Lesson 11-8) Solid figures with the same shape but not necessarily the same size.

sólidos similares Figuras sólidas con la misma forma pero no necesariamente del mismo tamaño.

similar triangles (Lesson 8-3) Triangles in which all of the corresponding angles are congruent and all of the corresponding sides are proportional.

triángulos similares Triángulos en los cuales todos los ángulos correspondientes son congruentes y todos los lados correspondientes son proporcionales.

similarity ratio (Lesson 8-2) The scale factor between two similar polygons.

relación de similitud El factor de escala entre dos polígonos similares.

similarity transformation (Lesson 8-2) A transformation composed of a dilation or a dilation and one or more rigid motions.

transformación de similitud Una transformación compuesto por una dilatación o una dilatación y uno o más movimientos rígidos.

sine (Lesson 9-5) The ratio of the length of the leg opposite an angle to the length of the hypotenuse.

seno La relación entre la longitud de la pierna opuesta a un ángulo y la longitud de la hipotenusa.

skew lines (Lesson 3-7) Noncoplanar lines that do not intersect.

líneas alabeadas Líneas no coplanares que no se cruzan.

slant height of a pyramid or right cone (Lesson 11-4) The length of a segment with one endpoint on the base edge of the figure and the other at the vertex.

altura inclinada de una pirámide o cono derecho La longitud de un segmento con un punto final en el borde base de la figura y el otro en el vértice.

slope (Lesson 3-8) The ratio of the change in the y-coordinates (rise) to the corresponding change in the x-coordinates (run) as you move from one point to another along a line.

pendiente La relación entre el cambio en las coordenadas y (subida) y el cambio correspondiente en las coordenadas x (ejecución) a medida que se mueve de un punto a otro a lo largo de una línea.

slope criteria (Lesson 3-8) Outlines a method for proving the relationship between lines based on a comparison of the slopes of the lines.

criterios de pendiente Describe un método para probar la relación entre líneas basado en una comparación de las pendientes de las líneas.

solid of revolution (Lesson 11-5) A solid figure obtained by rotating a shape around an axis.

sólido de revolución Una figura sólida obtenida girando una forma alrededor de un eje.

solving a triangle (Lesson 9-5) When you are given measurements to find the unknown angle and side measures of a triangle.

resolver un triángulo Cuando se le dan mediciones para encontrar el ángulo desconocido y las medidas laterales de un triángulo.

space (Lesson 1-2) A boundless three-dimensional set of all points.

espacio Un conjunto tridimensional ilimitado de todos los puntos.

sphere (Lesson 2-5) A set of all points in space equidistant from a given point called the center of the sphere.

esfera Un conjunto de todos los puntos del espacio equidistantes de un punto dado llamado centro de la esfera.

square (Lesson 7-5) A parallelogram with all four sides and all four angles congruent.

cuadrado Un paralelogramo con los cuatro lados y los cuatro ángulos congruentes.

statement (Lesson 3-2) Any sentence that is either true or false, but not both.

enunciado Cualquier oración que sea verdadera o falsa, pero no ambas.

straight angle (Lesson 2-1) An angle that measures 180°.

ángulo recto Un ángulo que mide 180°.

supplementary angles (Lesson 2-2) Two angles with measures that have a sum of 180°.

ángulos suplementarios Dos ángulos con medidas que tienen una suma de 180°.

surface area (Lesson 2-5) The sum of the areas of all faces and side surfaces of a three-dimensional figure.

área de superficie La suma de las áreas de todas las caras y superficies laterales de una figura tridimensional.

symmetry (Lesson 4-6) A figure has this if there exists a rigid motion—reflection, translation, rotation, or glide reflection—that maps the figure onto itself.

simetría Una figura tiene esto si existe un movimiento rígido–reflexión, una traducción, una rotación o una reflexión de deslizamiento rígida–que mapea la figura sobre sí misma.

synthetic geometry (Lesson 1-1) The study of geometric figures without the use of coordinates.

geometría sintética El estudio de figuras geométricas sin el uso de coordenadas.

T

tangent (Lesson 9-5) The ratio of the length of the leg opposite an angle to the length of the leg adjacent to the angle.

tangente La relación entre la longitud de la pata opuesta a un ángulo y la longitud de la pata adyacente al ángulo.

tangent to a circle (Lesson 10-5) A line or segment in the plane of a circle that intersects the circle in exactly one point and does not contain any points in the interior of the circle.

tangente a un círculo Una línea o segmento en el plano de un círculo que interseca el círculo en exactamente un punto y no contiene ningún punto en el interior del círculo.

tangent to a sphere (Lesson 11-4) A line that intersects the sphere in exactly one point.

tangente a una esfera Una línea que interseca la esfera exactamente en un punto.

tessellation (Lesson 4-5) A repeating pattern of one or more figures that covers a plane with no overlapping or empty spaces.

teselado Patrón repetitivo de una o más figuras que cubre un plano sin espacios superpuestos o vacíos.

theorem (Lesson 1-1) A statement that can be proven true using undefined terms, definitions, and postulates.

teorema Una afirmación o conjetura que se puede probar verdad utilizando términos, definiciones y postulados indefinidos.

transformation (Lesson 2-4) A function that takes points in the plane as inputs and gives other points as outputs.

transformación Función que toma puntos en el plano como entradas y da otros puntos como salidas.

translation (Lesson 2-4) A function in which all of the points of a figure move the same distance in the same direction.

traslación Función en la que todos los puntos de una figura se mueven en la misma dirección.

translation vector (Lesson 2-4) A directed line segment that describes both the magnitude and direction of the slide if the magnitude is the length of the vector from its initial point to its terminal point.

vector de traslación Un segmento de línea dirigido que describe tanto la magnitud como la dirección de la diapositiva si la magnitud es la longitud del vector desde su punto inicial hasta su punto terminal.

transversal (Lesson 3-7) A line that intersects two or more lines in a plane at different points.

transversal Una línea que interseca dos o más líneas en un plano en diferentes puntos.

trapezoid (Lesson 7-6) A quadrilateral with exactly one pair of parallel sides.

trapecio Un cuadrilátero con exactamente un par de lados paralelos.

trigonometric ratio (Lesson 9-5) A ratio of the lengths of two sides of a right triangle.

relación trigonométrica Una relación de las longitudes de dos lados de un triángulo rectángulo.

trigonometry (Lesson 9-5) The study of the relationships between the sides and angles of triangles.

trigonometría El estudio de las relaciones entre los lados y los ángulos de los triángulos.

truth value (Lesson 3-2) The truth or falsity of a statement.

valor de verdad La verdad o la falsedad de una declaración.

two-column proof (Lesson 3-4) A proof that contains statements and reasons organized in a two-column format.

prueba de dos columnas Una prueba que contiene declaraciones y razones organizadas en un formato de dos columnas.

two-way frequency table (Lesson 12-8) A table used to show the frequencies of data from a survey or experiment classified according to two variables, with the rows indicating one variable and the columns indicating the other.

tabla de frecuencia bidireccional Una tabla utilizada para mostrar las frecuencias de datos de una encuesta o experimento clasificados de acuerdo a dos variables, con las filas indicando una variable y las columnas que indican la otra.

U

undefined terms (Lesson 1-1) Words that are not formally explained by means of more basic words and concepts.

términos indefinidos Palabras que no se explican formalmente mediante palabras y conceptos más básicos.

uniform tessellation (Lesson 4-5) A tessellation that contains the same arrangement of shapes and angles at each vertex.

teselado uniforme Un teselado que contiene la misma disposición de formas y ángulos en cada vértice.

union of A and B (Lesson 12-2) The set of all outcomes in the sample space of event A combined with all outcomes in the sample space of event B.

unión de A y B El conjunto de todos los resultados en el espacio muestral del evento A combinado con todos los resultados en el espacio muestral del evento B.

V

valid argument (Lesson 3-3) An argument is valid if it is impossible for all of the premises, or supporting statements, of the argument to be true and its conclusion false.

argumento válido Un argumento es válido si es imposible que todas las premisas o argumentos de apoyo del argumento sean verdaderos y su conclusión sea falsa.

vertex of an angle (Lesson 2-1) The common endpoint of the two rays that form an angle.

vértice de un ángulo El punto final común de los dos rayos que forman un ángulo.

vertex angle of an isosceles triangle (Lesson 5-6) The angle between the sides that are the legs of an isosceles triangle.

ángulo del vértice de un triángulo isósceles El ángulo entre los lados que son las patas de un triángulo isósceles.

vertex of a polyhedron (Lesson 2-5) The intersection of three edges of a polyhedron.

vértice de un polígono La intersección de tres bordes de un poliedro.

vertical angles (Lesson 2-1) Two nonadjacent angles formed by two intersecting lines.

ángulos verticales Dos ángulos no adyacentes formados por dos líneas de intersección.

volume (Lesson 2-5) The measure of the amount of space enclosed by a three-dimensional figure.

volumen La medida de la cantidad de espacio encerrada por una figura tridimensional.

Index

A

C

D

INDEX

E

ELL Support
every What Will You Learn, second page
Language Development Support, every
Lesson Teacher a page
see Differentiate, Activities

Essential Question, 1, 63, 151, 247, 287, 347, 403, 459, 505, 567, 627, 709
Essential Question Follow-Up, 11, 27, 35, 44, 59, 65, 78, 88, 137, 147, 154, 161, 173, 183, 201, 209, 225, 243, 264, 270, 276, 283, 297, 321, 335, 343, 357, 384, 387, 399, 421, 437, 445, 455, 462, 469, 501, 515, 541, 558, 563, 593, 609, 616, 623, 647, 665, 673, 705, 712, 728, 735, 751, 771

Explore, Explore and Develop, pages c-h

F

Foldables®, 1, 59, 63, 147, 151, 243, 247, 283, 287, 343, 347, 399, 403, 455, 459, 501, 505, 563, 567, 623, 627, 705, 709, 771

Formative Assessment Math Probe, 1b, 63b, 151b, 247b, 287b, 347b, 403b, 459b, 505b, 567b, 627b, 709b

G

Growth Mindset, *see Mindset Matters*

I

Inquiry, *see Explore*

Create, See *Practice* in the lessons
cross sections, 665
cylinders, 107

D

decision making, See the digital lesson Expand 12-3
decomposition, 629
deductive
arguments, 181
reasoning, 171
defined terms, 3
definitions, 3
degrees, 577
densities, 699
based on area, 699
based on volume, 701
diagonals, 405
of a rectangle, 429
of a rhombus, 437
diameters
of circles, 569
of spheres, 663, 684
dilations, 461
directrix, 619
disjunctions, 161
distances, 27

E

edges of polyhedron, 107
Estimation, 38, 144, 149, 236, 320, 337, 338, 341, 354, 446, 514, 547, 571, 598, 653, 714
enlargements, 461
equidistant, 49
events, 711
compound, 743
dependent, 745
independent, 743
intersections of two, 719
mutually exclusive, 751
union of two, 719
experiments, 711

F

faces of polyhedra, 107
factorials of *n*, 735
fair, See the digital lesson Expand 12-3

Find the Error, 10, 18, 48, 84, 105, 106, 116, 128, 146, 170, 188, 196, 224, 232, 242, 252, 260, 268, 282, 304, 312, 320, 324, 332, 356, 372, 412, 436, 444, 454, 494, 500, 512, 524, 532, 540, 548, 556, 586, 618, 638, 646, 654, 680, 690, 698, 726, 742, 758
foci, 619
formulas
Circumference Formula, 569
Diameter Formula, 569
Distance Formula in Space, 523
Distance Formula on a Number Line, 27
Distance Formula on the Coordinate Plane, 29
Midpoint Formula in Space, 523
Midpoint Formula on a Number Line, 49
Midpoint Formula on the Coordinate Plane, 51
Radius Formula, 569
Section Formula on a Number Line, 37
Section Formula on the Coordinate Plane, 44
fractional distances, 35
frequencies
joint, 763
marginal, 763
relative, 763
Fundamental Counting Principle, 713

G

geometric
means, 507
models, 88
probability, 727
glide reflections, 261

H

heights
of parallelograms, 629
of solids, 655, 657
of trapezoids, 630
Hypotenuse-Angle Congruence (HA), 321
Hypotenuse-Leg Congruence (HL), 321
hypothesis, 162

I

image, 95
incenters, 359
included
angles, 307
sides, 313
indirect
measurement, 541
reasoning, 381
inscribed
angle, 593
polygon, 595
intersections, 13
inverses, 162
cosine, 535
sine, 535
tangent, 535
isometry, 95

K

kites, 449

L

lateral areas
of regular pyramids, 657
of right cones, 657
of right cylinders, 655
of right prisms, 655
lateral faces, 655
Laws
of Cosines, 557
of Sines, 549
Leg-Angle Congruence (LA), 321
Leg-Leg Congruence (LL), 321
legs
of a trapezoid, 445
of an isosceles triangle, 325
line segments, 19
directed, 35
linear pairs, 69
lines, 11
auxiliary, 326
concurrent, 350
equidistant, 237
parallel, 207
perpendicular, 76–77
of reflection, 95
skew, 207
logically equivalent, 162

Index   **IN3**

Copyright © McGraw-Hill Education

M

P

R

S

Teaching the Mathematical Practices
every Lesson Teacher b page
every Explore
every Explore and Develop

Test Practice, 60–62, 148–150, 244–246, 284–286, 344–346, 400–402, 456–458, 502–504, 564–566, 624–626, 706–708, 772–774

V

Vertical Alignment, every page a

Vocabulary, 2, 3b, 11b, 19b, 27b, 35b, 49b, 64, 65b, 75b, 85b, 95b, 107b, 117b, 129b, 137b, 152, 153b, 161b, 171b, 179b, 207b, 215b, 233b, 248, 253b, 261b, 269b, 275b, 288, 289b, 297b, 305b, 313b, 325b, 333b, 348, 349b, 357b, 365b, 381b, 404, 405b, 413b, 429b, 437b, 445b, 460, 461b, 469b, 477b, 487b, 506, 507b, 513b, 521b, 525b, 533b, 541b, 549b, 568, 569b, 577b, 593b, 601b, 609b, 619b, 628, 629b, 639b, 647b, 655b, 665b, 691b, 699b, 710, 711b, 719b, 727b, 735b, 743b, 751b, 759b, 763b

---